P9-DGV-124

An anthology of articles on loudspeakers from the pages of the Journal of the Audio Engineering Society

Vol. 1–Vol. 25
(1953-1977)

2nd Edition

Library of Congress Catalog Card No. 80-53465. Selections from Volumes 1 through 25, 1953–1977. First printing October 1978; second printing October 1980

preface

The history of loudspeakers is now well into its second century and the development of really effective practical devices has already been underway for more than fifty years. The importance of the loudspeaker in the emergence of the entertainment industry can scarcely be overestimated for, without it, none of the popular media such as radio, television and film could exist in their present form and the development of the phonograph would have taken an altogether different course.

The main impetus to the commercial growth and wider application of high quality loudspeakers began after the end of the Second World War. Development was encouraged by improvements in disc recording and by the advent of VHF broadcasting which reduced the limitations on both bandwidth and dynamic range. Both media were also greatly influenced by the introduction of magnetic tape recording which made the long playing record a commercial possibility and subsequently reduced the dependence of broadcasting on live performances. These developments influenced loudspeaker development as the need arose to keep pace with improvements in the quality of programme sources.

Before World War II, the majority of loudspeakers were characterised by limited bandwidth—usually restricted to a frequency range of 70 to 7,000 Hz—large physical dimensions arising from a need for high sensitivity to operate satisfactorily with available tube amplifiers (average continuous power 10-15 watts) and irregular amplitude-frequency response. During the decade 1945-1955 attention was concentrated mainly on extending bandwidth by about one octave at each end of the range, i.e. 35 to 15,000 Hz.

With these objectives satisfactorily accomplished, high quality loudspeakers still remained large enough, and some would say ugly enough, to cause resistance to their introduction in domestic settings. This state of affairs altered rapidly towards the end of the Fifties due to the introduction of so-called air suspension speakers which traded sensitivity against internal air volume. By this means it was possible to reduce the overall bulk of loudspeakers to about one quarter of their former size. These developments were given quite considerable encouragement by the advent of commercial stereo disc records, and by the end of the 1955-65 decade the majority of domestic loudspeakers were less than two cubic feet in volume, with low sensitivity and correspondingly wide bandwidth. At this time (1965) high-fidelity was still a rarified hobbyist pursuit, but there quickly followed what can only be described as an explosion of interest in domestic sound reproduction, and just as quickly it became big business on a world-wide scale.

The focusing of attention and the availability of funds for research inevitably led to the development of even better loudspeakers. This period has so far been marked by the introduction of new diaphragm materials, better constructional methods for enclosures and studies for improving the integration of sound in multi-way speaker systems. Along with these developments have come radically new methods of measurement and evaluation made possible by advances in digital computer technology and associated industries. These new techniques are not only more accurate but are also considerably faster and therefore more convenient than conventional methods of measurement.

Throughout this period, beginning with the formation of AES in 1948, the Journal of the Audio Engineering Society has published more than 160 papers on loudspeakers. The collection of papers presented here has been selected from those which are considered to be of significance, either because they mark an important stage in the development of loudspeaker technology or because they contribute to the understanding and the history of the subject. Recognising that much of significance has appeared outside the pages of the Society's journal, we have also included a list of references to other important published work. The publication of this anthology, together with the list of related reading at the end of this volume, represents a fitting monument to all those whose endeavors have advanced the art and science of sound reproduction to its present state.

Raymond E. Cooke
Maidstone, Kent, England

October 1978

contents

PART I: 1953 THROUGH 1969

PART II: 1970 TO 1978

PART II: 1970 TO 1978 (Cont.)

1953 through 1969

AUDIO
A
ES

Design Factors in Horn-Type Speakers

Daniel J. Plach
Jensen Manufacturing Company, Chicago, Illinois

Maximum efficiency in a horn unit can be achieved only if a conjugate match exists between driver and horn. This match is possible only if the unloaded resonance of the driver is greater than horn cutoff frequency. Since the throat resistance of a finite horn at cutoff is a small fraction of its asymptotic value, the point of reactance annulling is chosen at this frequency.

The use of hyperbolic-exponential horns makes possible practically any desired resistance or reactance characteristic near cutoff. The hyperbolic-exponential horn allows much more uniform transmission down nearer to cutoff than is possible with the exponential type.

THE ADVANTAGES of horns have been known since the early days of the acoustic art when the conical horn found extensive use in the radiation of sound. In 1919 Webster indicated the superiority of the exponential horn over the conical type. Subsequent investigation of generalized plane-wave infinite horn theory has led to the development of a family of hyperbolic exponential horns that have more desirable characteristics than the exponential type. This family of horns has been patented by the Jensen Manufacturing Company, and projectors using these flares are currently marketed under the trade name of Hypex.[1,2]

The general expansion of this family of horns is given by the equation

$$A_x = A_t \left(\cosh \frac{x}{x_0} + T \sinh \frac{x}{x_0} \right)^2$$

The T in this equation determines the family to which the horn belongs. If T is made equal to zero, the expansion is that of a hyperbolic cosine and has the form

$$A_x = A_t \cosh^2 \left(\frac{x}{x_0} \right)$$

For a T equal to 1, the familiar exponential horn results:

$$A_x = A_t \, e^{2x/x_0}$$

If T is set equal to infinity, the conical horn is obtained, given by the relationship

$$A_x = A_t \left(1 + \frac{x}{x_0} \right)^2$$

These horns may be classified as falling into two groups, the hyperbolic cosine or "cosh horn," where T includes values between zero and 1, and the hyperbolic sine or "sinh horns," where T includes values between 1 and infinity. The expansion of the cosh horn can be put in the form

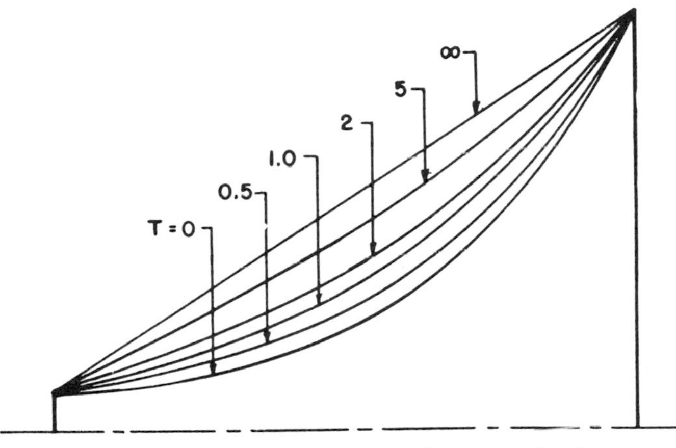

FIG. 1. Flare comparison of hyperbolic-exponential horns.

$$A_x = \frac{A_t \cosh^2 \left(\frac{x}{x_0} + a \right)}{\cosh^2 a}$$

$$T = \tanh a$$

$$\cosh a = (1 - T^2)^{-1/2}$$

For the sinh horn, the following relationships apply:

$$A_x = \frac{A_t \sinh^2 \left(\frac{x}{x_0} + a \right)}{\sinh^2 a}$$

$$T = \coth a$$

$$\sinh a = (T^2 - 1)^{-1/2}$$

Figure 1 is a comparison of horns of various T values having the same terminal dimensions. It will be noted that horns with smaller T values are characterized by smaller slopes near the throat, the T equal zero horn having zero slope at the throat. For a given cutoff frequency and throat size the horns with smaller T values expand more slowly and therefore require a somewhat greater length to achieve a given mouth size.

The throat impedance of an infinite horn may be repre-

---

[1] V. Salmon, U.S. Pat. 2,338,262.
[2] V. Salmon, Hypex Horns, *Electronics,* 14, 39 (July, 1941).

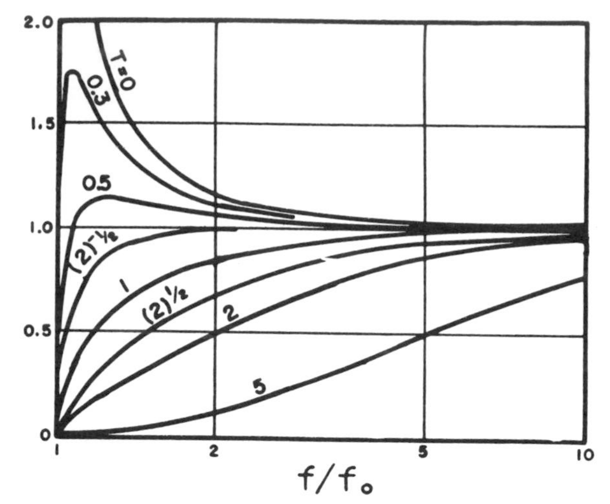

FIG. 2. Throat resistance characteristics for horns of various T values.

sented by an inductance shunted by a resistance. The impedance presented to a driver by a horn is

$$Z_h = 267 \frac{A_d^2}{A_t} \left[\frac{\left(1 - \frac{1}{u^2}\right)^{1/2} + jT/u}{1 - \left(\frac{1 - T^2}{u^2}\right)} \right]$$

It will be noted that as u approaches infinity the asymptotic resistance presented to the driver is independent of the value of T and approaches $267(A_d^2/A_t)$ mechanical ohms and the reactive component T/u approaches zero. Near cutoff, where u has values near unity, the throat impedance is dependent on the parameter T. A normalized plot of throat resistance as a function of frequency with T as a parameter is shown in Fig. 2. If the driver unit is operated under constant-velocity conditions, these curves also indicate the relative acoustic output. By the choice of the parameter T practically any desired characteristic near cutoff may be obtained. Variation of mouth resistance can be partially compensated by the use of a hyperbolic-exponential horn having the appropriate throat resistance rise near cutoff.

Although resistance considerations will generally dictate the particular value of T to be used, the reactance characteristics may be an important factor in some cases. A plot of normalized reactance of a horn is given in Fig. 3. It is seen that small values of T result in a higher reactive component at cutoff, the reactance being $1/T$ times the reactance of an exponential horn. The reactance, however, is seen to drop more rapidly above cutoff for smaller T values. For a horn having a T of zero there is no reactive component above cutoff.

The preceding discussion applied to the characteristics of infinite horns. In practice a horn has a finite length and mouth area, so deviation from the characteristics of the infinite horn is to be expected. Since a horn is essentially a tapered acoustic transmission line, it must be properly terminated in order to avoid reflections which would cause large variations of the throat resistance above and below its asymptotic value, with consequent irregularities in radiated power. If a horn is expanded until its circumference is equal to or greater than a wavelength at the lowest frequency to be passed, the effects of reflections are minimized. This condition is satisfied when

$$D_m \geqq \frac{4{,}300}{f}$$

An equivalent expression on an area basis yields

$$A_m \geqq \frac{1.45 \times 10^7}{f^2}$$

These figures apply for operation in free space. When radiation occurs into smaller solid angles, the required area can be reduced. Figure 4 is a plot of required mouth size against frequency for various modes of operation. Curve A would be applicable to any units designed for operation in free space. Operation of lf horns at the intersection of a wall and floor reduces the area requirement by a factor of 4, as shown in curve B. For corner operation the area can be reduced by a factor of 8 as compared to free space, and curve C applies. When the horn is operated under matched conditions, the area may be further reduced as the driver then becomes relatively insensitive to fairly large impedance variations.

At this point we will consider the behavior of a horn when coupled to a driver unit. Figure 5 represents the equivalent circuit of this system.

To obtain maximum power transfer between a driver and horn requires that the driver impedance be a conjugate of the impedance of the horn. If this condition is satisfied,

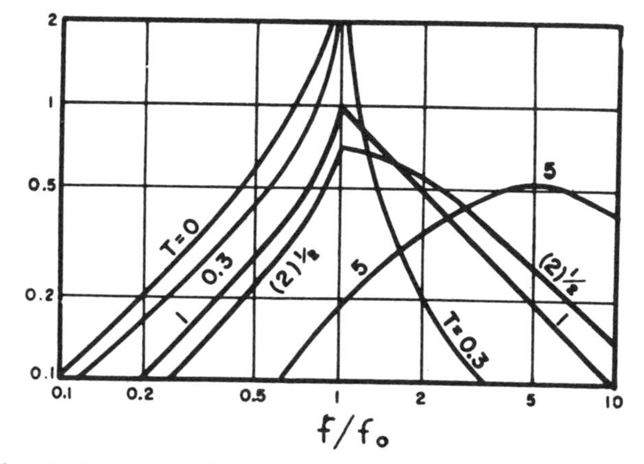

FIG. 3. Frequency dependence of throat reactance for horns of various T values.

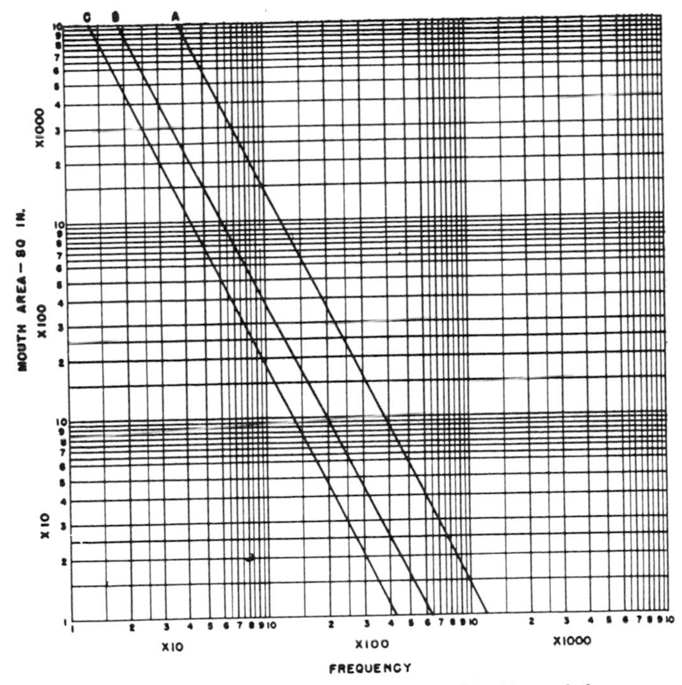

FIG. 4. Minimum horn mouth size as a function of frequency: A, operation in free space; B, intersection of two planes; C, operation in a corner.

the resistive components are equal and the reactive components are equal but of opposite sign and therefore cancel out. In the direct radiator type of speaker the moving system impedance is normally much higher than that of the air load, and this ideal condition of a conjugate match is approached only at resonance. This mismatch accounts for the relatively low efficiency of the direct radiator type of speaker.

The driver can be considered as a generator having an internal impedance:

$$Z_d = \frac{(Bl)^2}{R_g + R_c} + j\left(\omega M_d - \frac{S_d}{\omega}\right)$$

The mechanical impedance of a driver is resistive only at its resonant frequency and is highly reactive at any other frequency. If the cutoff frequency of the horn is placed below the unloaded resonance of a driver, the horn reactance is positive and increasing with decreasing frequency while the driver reactance is negative and also increasing with decreasing frequency. Thus it is possible to make the net mechanical reactance between horn cutoff and driver resonance close to zero. The cutoff frequency is generally chosen as the point where the net mechanical reactance is zero, since in the finite horn the mechanical resistance at and below cutoff is not zero but has a finite value which is a small fraction of the asymptotic value. This expedient leads to a large efficiency improvement at and near cutoff.

The effective reactance of a driver at the cutoff frequency may be put in the form

$$X_d = \omega_0 M_d \left[1 - \left(\frac{f_r}{f_0}\right)^2\right]$$

and the reactance of the horn at cutoff is

$$X_h = \frac{\omega_0 \, 42.7 \, A_d^2}{T \, f_0 \, A_t}$$

If these two expressions are equated, the condition for reactance annulling at cutoff is obtained. Solving for the product $M_d f_0 A_t$, we obtain

$$M_d \, f_0 \, A_t = \frac{42.7 \, A_d^2}{T\left[1 - \left(\frac{f_r}{f_0}\right)^2\right]}$$

Since the throat size is based on considerations of efficiency, electrical impedance, and in some cases permissible throat distortion, and the mass and the effective diaphragm area for a given driver are fixed, the variables in the preceding equation are f_0, f_r, and T. Figure 6 is a plot of the product of $M_d f_0 A_t$ against the ratio f_r/f_0, with T as a parameter. Since f_0 is chosen to satisfy lf performance requirements, the product $M_d f_0 A_t$ is determined, from which may be obtained the required ratio of f_r/f_0 and, therefore, the resonant frequency f_r for a given value of T. This figure is based on a 15-in. speaker. For a speaker of any other area A, multiply the value of $M_d f_0 A_t$ obtained from this chart by $(A/125)^2$.

Where the radiation from one side of the driver is utilized, the value of f_r can be adjusted by varying the volume of the cavity enclosing the nonradiating side. The cavity places a stiffness in series with the suspension system, and its value may be calculated from

$$S_c = \frac{2.26 \times 10^6 \, D_d^4}{V}$$

The required cavity size may be obtained experimentally by adjusting the cavity volume until an impedance maximum occurs at the cutoff frequency. For this application a linear speaker of low resonance is used, and since the resonant frequency is increased appreciably by the cavity the controlling reactance becomes that of the cavity. This results in reduced distortion owing to the suspension system nonlinearities.

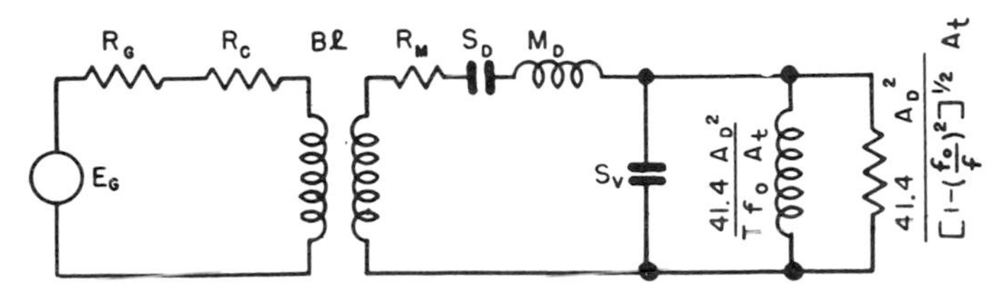

FIG. 5. Equivalent circuit of horn-type speaker.

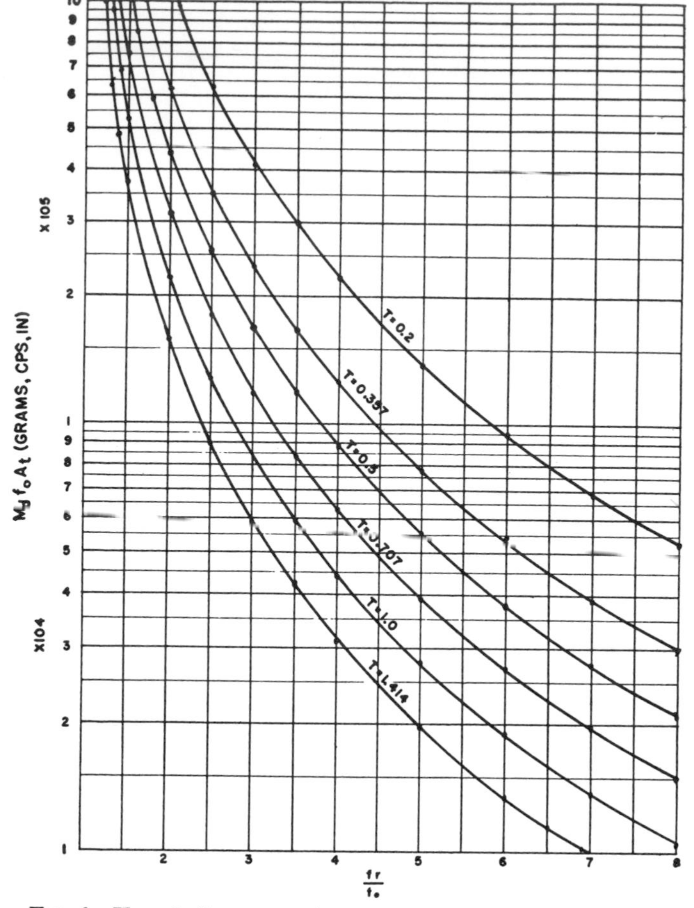

FIG. 6. Hyperbolic-exponential horn reactance annulling conditions.

This type of horn arrangement is capable of yielding the highest possible lf efficiency, since a conjugate match is possible between horn cutoff frequency and driver resonance. The disadvantage of this arrangement in lf corner horns is the rapid attenuation and response roughness that occur at frequencies above a few hundred cycles, necessitating a very low crossover frequency.

With enclosures that combine horn back-loading with front radiation maximum efficiency cannot generally be achieved, since the speakers used in this application have a relatively low resonant frequency which may be close to cutoff, making a conjugate match impossible. Improved efficiency may be achieved by designing around a woofer with a relatively high resonance or by treating the cone annulus with a stiffening lacquer to raise the resonance.

EFFICIENCY

A knowledge of the efficiency characteristics of a horn unit is important. If the driver constants and the nature of the terminating impedance are known, the efficiency may be calculated. The efficiency may also be determined by measurement of the driver impedance in its horn enclosure, in vacuum, and in its blocked state for every frequency where information is required.

The energy efficiency, sometimes referred to as the initial efficiency, is defined as the ratio of acoustic power output to electrical power input and is given by

$$\eta_e = \frac{(Bl)^2 R_h \times 10^{-9}}{R_c\,(R_m + R_h)^2 + (R_m + R_h)\,(Bl)^2 \times 10^{-9}}$$

The energy efficiencies for a properly designed horn unit may exceed values of 80%. Since the impedance of a unit is not constant, cognizance must be taken of its ability to draw power from a source. The energy efficiency multiplied by the loss due to impedance mismatch is the actual measure of horn performance. This type of efficiency is designated as the absolute efficiency and is the ratio of acoustical power output to the maximum power available from a matched source, given by the expression

$$\eta_a = \frac{\dfrac{4 R_g R_h (Bl)^2 \times 10^{-9}}{(R_m + R_h)^2 + (\omega M_d)^2}}{\left[R_g + R_c + \dfrac{(Bl)^2 \times 10^{-9}\,(R_m + R_h)}{(R_m + R_h)^2 + (\omega M_d)^2}\right]^2 + X_e^2}$$

where X_e includes the motional reactance and voice coil reactance. The efficiency as determined in this manner may be appreciably less than the energy efficiency. For a properly designed horn unit the reactive component is small compared to total mechanical resistance, and the losses above cutoff are negligible compared to total resistance. The expression may then be simplified to

$$\eta_a = \frac{4R_g\,(Bl)^2 \times 10^{-9}}{R_h \left[R_g + R_c + \dfrac{(Bl)^2 \times 10^{-9}}{R_h}\right]^2}$$

Differentiation of η with respect to $(Bl)^2/R_h$ yields the condition for maximum efficiency given by

$$\frac{(Bl)^2 \times 10^{-9}}{R_h} = R_g + R_c$$

Since R_h varies with frequency, the matching requirement is generally satisfied somewhat above cutoff where the load presented by the horn is close to the ultimate value. The required throat area is then given by

$$A_t = \frac{267\,A_d^2\,(R_g + R_c)}{(Bl)^2 \times 10^{-9}}$$

If this condition is satisfied, the efficiency is relatively independent of throat impedance variations, since an increase in resistance by four times or a reduction by the same factor results in a loss of less than 2 db.

In some cases the distortion characteristics must be considered in choosing the throat size. The pressure-volume characteristic can be considered linear only for small pressure changes. Large pressure changes result in the production of second-harmonic distortion. In a horn this distortion increases as the observed frequency is increased above cutoff. To maintain the throat distortion under 1% at any frequency requires that

$$\frac{P_a}{A_t}\left(\frac{f}{f_0}\right)^2 \leq 450$$

where P_a is the acoustical power output in watts, A_t is the throat area in square inches, and f is the frequency at which the measurement is made. Generally this condition can be readily satisfied for tweeter or woofer horn units.

HIGH-FREQUENCY PERFORMANCE

The mass of the moving system, sound chamber, and voice coil inductance form a low-pass filter. If the sound chamber were absent, the equivalent circuit would consist of the blocked speaker impedance in series with the combination of motional capacity in parallel with the load resistance. This would form a half-filter section, the cutoff being given by

$$f_1 = \frac{(Bl) \times 10^{-9}}{2\pi\ (M_d L_c)^{1/2}}$$

Above cutoff the motional resistance becomes small and the efficiency is given by the relationship

$$\eta_a = \frac{4R_g R_h\ (Bl)^2 \times 10^{-9}}{\omega^2\ M_d^2\ (R_g + R_c)^2 + [\omega^2\ M_d\ L_c - (Bl)^2]^2 \times 10^{-9}}$$

At frequencies where the term $\omega^4 M_d^2 L_c^2$ predominates, the slope of the efficiency characteristic becomes asymptotic to 12 db per octave.

Most horn units have a sound chamber associated with them. The chamber volume combined with the moving system mass and voice coil inductance form a low-pass T section on the electrical side, as shown in Fig. 7.

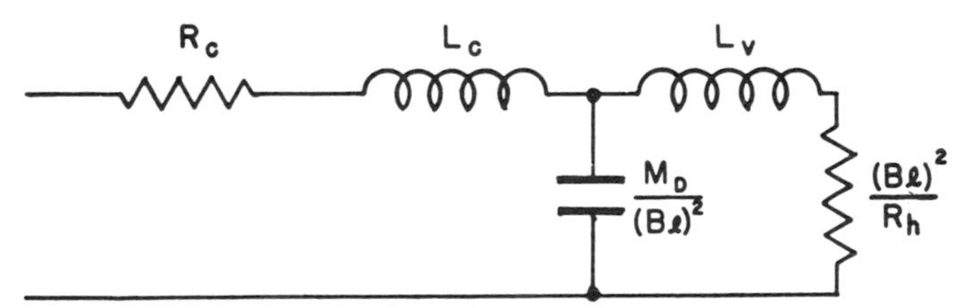

FIG. 7. Equivalent circuit of horn-type speaker at high frequencies.

The effect of adding a sound chamber of the proper size is to multiply the theoretical cutoff by a factor of the square root of 2 for a given moving system mass, or, conversely, the moving system mass may be doubled for the same cutoff frequency. The mass of the moving system appears as a shunt capacity having a value

$$C_m = \frac{M_d}{(Bl)^2 \times 10^{-9}}$$

The air chamber appears as an inductive reactance on the electrical side and is given by

$$L_v = \frac{(Bl)^2}{S_v} = \frac{4.42 \times 10^{-16}\, V\, (Bl)^2}{D_d^4}$$

If the chamber possesses circular symmetry, the value of the inductance is

$$L_v = \frac{3.47 \times 10^{-16}\, h\ (Bl)^2}{D_d^2}$$

If the horn unit is designed on a filter basis, the value of the chamber clearance is adjusted so that the preceding expression equals the voice coil inductance. This choice of h may not always be feasible, since this clearance in tweeters may depend on the maximum excursion that is to be handled at low frequencies. Also, at high frequencies the voice coil inductance is not constant because of core losses. This effectively places a shunt resistance across the voice coil which tends to reduce the inductance. Whereas the chamber extends the cutoff by 1.4 times the value in the absence of the chamber, the slope of the efficiency characteristic is 18 db per octave instead of 12 db above cutoff.

From the foregoing it can be realized that it is difficult to achieve a wide pass band in a single horn unit. The diaphragm excursion varies inversely with frequency so that relatively large chamber clearances are required combined with rugged moving systems to reproduce the lower frequencies, whereas light moving systems and small clearances are required to obtain good efficiency at high frequencies. Thus the requirements of lf power handling capacity are incompatible with the hf requirements. This is one of the factors which has led to the use of multiple horns, each covering a part of the spectrum, when performance to the limits of audibility is required.

SYMBOLS

x = distance from throat, inches
x_0 = cutoff parameter = $2{,}155/f_0$
f_0 = horn cutoff frequency
A_x = horn area at distance x
A_m = mouth area, square inches
A_t = throat area, square inches
A_d = effective diaphragm area, square inches
D_d = effective diaphragm diameter, inches
D_m = mouth diameter, inches
T = flare parameter
Z_h = horn impedance as seen by driver
R_h = resistive component of horn impedance
X_h = reactive component of horn impedance
Z_d = driver mechanical impedance
X_d = driver mechanical reactance
u = frequency ratio, f/f_0
M_d = moving system mass, grams
S_c = cavity stiffness
S_d = suspension system stiffness
S_v = throat air chamber stiffness
R_m = mechanical loss resistance
R_c = voice coil resistance
L_c = voice coil inductance
B = flux density, gauss
l = conductor length, centimeters
η = efficiency
f_r = unloaded driver resonant frequency
V = throat air chamber volume, cubic inches
h = diaphragm-chamber clearance, inches

Recent Developments in Direct-Radiator High-Fidelity Loudspeakers

HARRY F. OLSON, JOHN PRESTON, and EVERETT G. MAY
RCA Laboratories, Princeton, New Jersey

Three high-fidelity loudspeakers have been developed and commercialized. These include 8-, 12-, and 15-in. units. The characteristics of these loudspeakers are uniform response over a wide frequency range combined with broad directivity, low nonlinear distortion, and faithful transient response. Cabinets and other loading systems for these loudspeakers have also been developed.

INTRODUCTION

THE ALMOST universal use of the dynamic direct-radiator loudspeaker in small- and medium-scale sound reproduction is due to the following characteristics:[1] a simple vibrating system; a wide variety of design possibilities; a rugged mechanism; inherently low-cost construction; and relatively small space requirements. For these reasons it is possible to develop and build direct-radiator loudspeakers which will satisfy almost any requirement of response, distortion, and directivity. The gamut of applications include the very small loudspeakers found in personal radio receivers, the low- and medium-cost loudspeakers for a wide variety of applications in radio and television receivers, phonographs, and sound systems, and the high-quality loudspeakers used in all types of high-fidelity systems. The inherent fundamental design flexibility of the vibrating system of the direct-radiator loudspeaker provides a wide range of research possibilities in the development of new and improved systems. It is the purpose of this paper to describe some recent developments in direct-radiator loudspeaker systems.

FIG. 2. RCA 12-in. loudspeaker, Type SL12.

FIG. 1. RCA 8-in. loudspeaker, Type SL8.

DIRECT-RADIATOR LOUDSPEAKER MECHANISMS

The three loudspeaker mechanisms shown in Figs. 1, 2, and 3, designated as SL8, SL12 and LC1A, have been developed for high-fidelity applications. These are, respectively, 8-, 12-, and 15-in. loudspeaker mechanisms. The SL8 and SL12 are single-cone units; the LC1A is a duo-cone unit. This section will describe some of the developments incorporated in these loudspeakers which contribute to improved performance.

Of all the performance characteristics of a loudspeaker, the response-frequency characteristic is the most useful and important because it conveys the most information. A uniform response-frequency characteristic was obtained in these loudspeakers by employing a particular shape of

[1] H. F. Olson, *Elements of Acoustical Engineering*, D. Van Nostrand Company, 2nd ed., New York, 1947.

Fig. 3. RCA 15-in duo-cone loudspeaker, Type LC1A.

curvilinear cone, a special pulp for the material of the cone, and a damping ring in the outside suspension of the cone. The material and shape of the cone were determined from tests made to obtain a smooth response-frequency characteristic and a broad directivity pattern. The internal damping in the pulp of the cone plays an important role in determining the form of the response-frequency characteristic. The configuration of the cone influences the high-frequency response and the directivity of the cone.

After the shape and material of the cone had been determined, it was found that additional damping was required in the suspension system to smooth out the response.

The outside suspension of the cone consists of a corrugated disk which provides a flexible connecting means between the cone and the fixed support, as shown in Fig. 4A. The normal mode of vibration of the cone and suspension is shown in Fig. 4B. The maximum excursions of each part of the suspension and cone are shown by the dotted lines. It will be seen that the amplitude falls off gradually in the suspension from the edge of the cone to the fixed outside edge. Unfortunately, a suspension does not behave in this manner throughout the frequency range but breaks into resonance in the midfrequency range. The amplitude of the suspension may be greater than that of the cone, as shown in Fig. 4C. The vibration of the suspension may be in phase with the cone, as shown in Fig. 4C, and out of phase, as shown in Fig. 4D. The in- and out-of-phase vibration of the suspension with respect to the cone will produce a corresponding peak and a dip in the response-frequency characteristic.

In the past, the procedure has been to coat the suspension with some highly viscous material, thereby providing damping which reduces the amplitude at resonance. In this way, the response is smooth and free from the peak and the dip. The objection to the use of viscous substances is that these materials tend to dry out, with the result that the damping efficiency is lost. The vibration can be controlled and the deleterious effects of any resonance reduced to a negligible amount by means of a special rubber damping ring,[2] as shown in Fig. 5. The curve of Fig. 6, taken without the damping ring, can be compared with that of Fig. 7 taken with the damping ring. It will be seen that the response-frequency characteristic without the damping ring exhibits a peak and a dip at 800 and 1100 cps, respectively.

In the direct-radiator loudspeaker the sound vibrations start at the voice coil, flow out in the cone, and then into the suspension system. In the low-frequency range the phase shift, in degrees, along the cone is relatively small, and the cone behaves essentially as a piston. However, in the high-frequency range the phase difference between the voice coil and suspension may be several radians. In this frequency range it is important that the wave that travels into the suspension system be absorbed and not reflected back. The latter condition would lead to standing waves, which would produce a ragged response-frequency characteristic. The

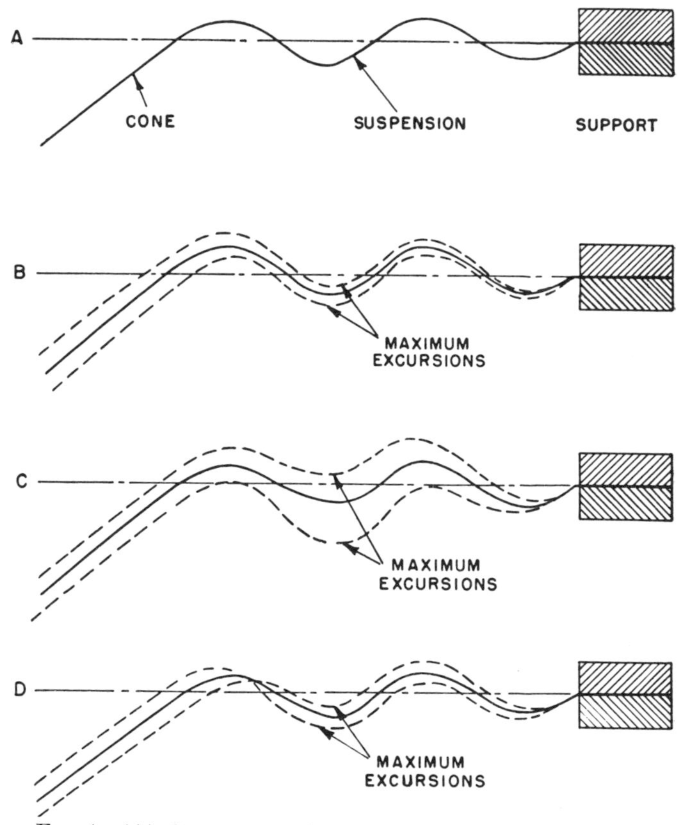

Fig. 4. (A) Outer suspension system for the cone of a direct-radiator loudspeaker. (B) Normal vibration of the suspension. (C) Resonant vibration of the suspension in phase with the cone. (D) Resonant vibration of the suspension out of phase with the cone.

[2] H. F. Olson and J. Preston, *Radio and Television News,* **51**, No. 2, p. 69 (1954).

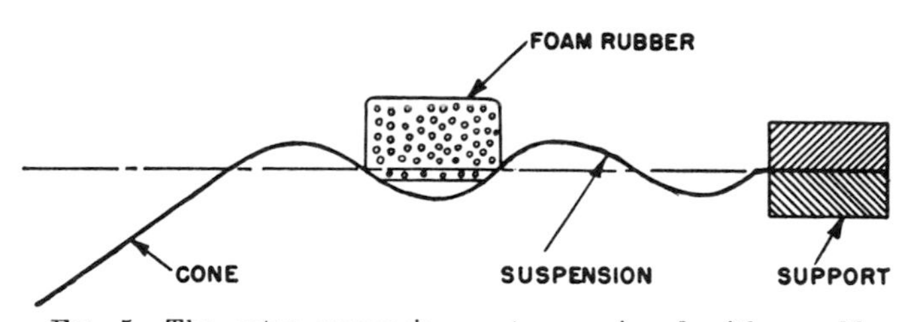

FIG. 5. The outer suspension system equipped with a rubber damper.

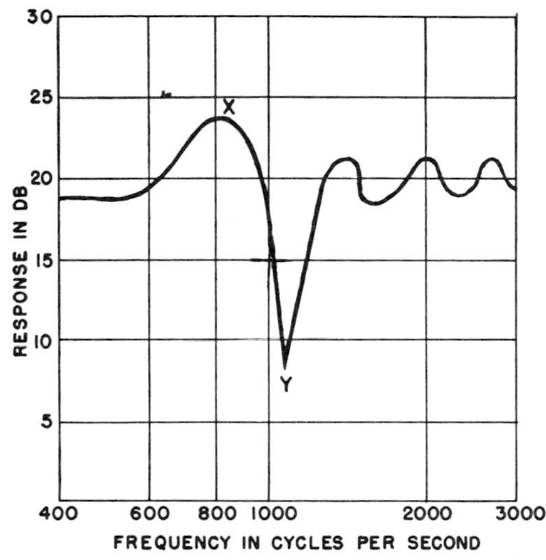

FIG. 6. Midfrequency response-frequency characteristic for a direct-radiator loudspeaker with a conventional suspension system.

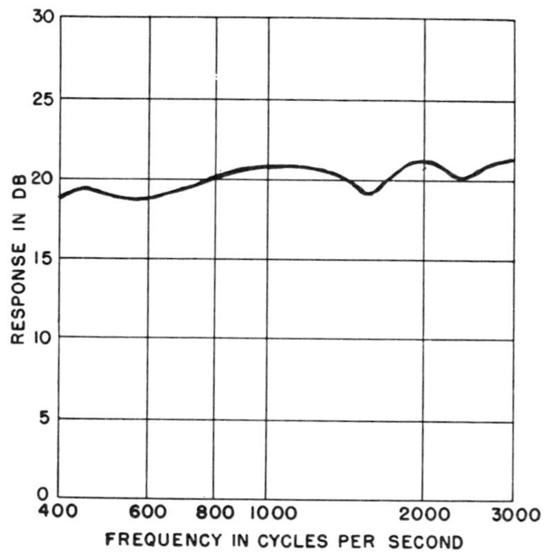

FIG. 7. Midfrequency response-frequency characteristic of a direct-radiator loudspeaker with a suspension system equipped with a rubber damper.

rubber damping ring serves as a suitable acoustical termination, thereby absorbing the vibrations which flow into the suspension system. The response-frequency characteristics without and with the rubber damping ring are shown in Figs. 8 and 9, respectively. It will be seen that response is smoother with the rubber damping ring.

The directivity pattern of a direct-radiator loudspeaker is a function of the ratio of the effective radiating dimensions of the cone to the wavelength, the velocity of sound in the material of the cone, and the geometrical configuration of the cone. Thus, there are three parameters that establish the directional characteristic of a direct-radiator loudspeaker. The part that these parameters play will now be discussed.

Figure 10 illustrates the roles that the shape and material of the cone play in determining the directivity pattern. The cone angle in Fig. 10A is 90 degrees. The velocity of wave propagation, V_C, in the cone is 1.4 times the velocity of wave propagation, V_A, in air. Under these conditions, the cone emits practically a plane wave front in the high-frequency region, which is manifested as a very narrow directivity pattern. The directivity pattern can be broadened by using a

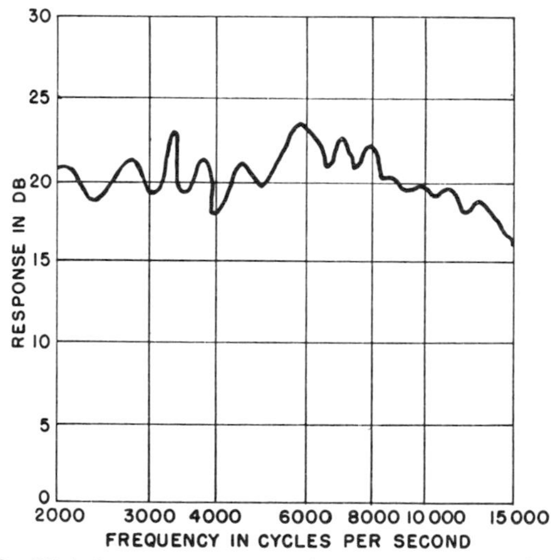

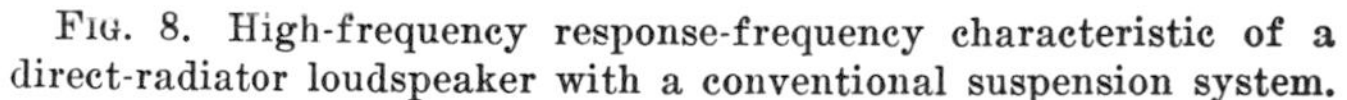

FIG. 8. High-frequency response-frequency characteristic of a direct-radiator loudspeaker with a conventional suspension system.

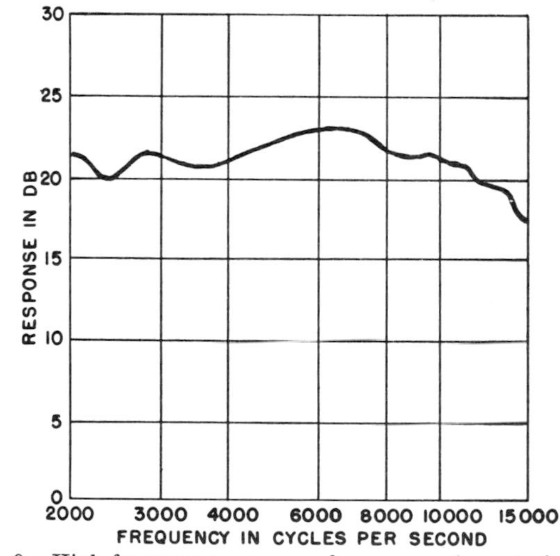

FIG. 9. High-frequency response-frequency characteristic of a direct-radiator loudspeaker with a suspension system equipped with a rubber damper.

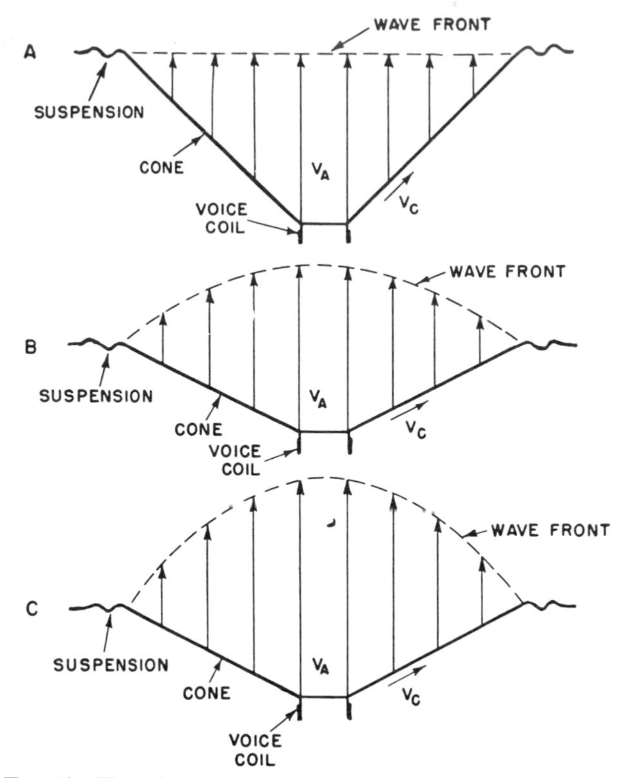

FIG. 10. Wave fronts emitted by various cones. (A) Cone angle of 90 degrees. (B) Cone angle of 135 degrees. (C) Cone angle of 135 degrees, with a slower propagation velocity in the cone.

cone with a wider angle. The cone angle in Fig. 10B is 135 degrees. The velocity of wave propagation in the cone of Fig. 10B is the same as in Fig. 10A. The emitted wave front is convex, and, as the radius of curvature of the wave front decreases, the directivity pattern becomes broader. Therefore, the directivity pattern of the cone of Fig. 10B will be broader than that of the cone of Fig. 10A. The radius of curvature of the wave front can be decreased further by reducing the velocity of wave propagation in the cone. In Fig. 10C, the velocity of wave propagation, V_C, in the cone is equal to the velocity of sound propagation, V_A, in air. The radius of curvature is reduced, and, as a result, the directivity pattern is broadened.

The shape and material of the cone in these loudspeakers have been determined from these principles. These loudspeakers provide directivity patterns as broad and uniform as possible and still retain uniform response, low distortion, and adequate power-handling capacity.

In a two-unit loudspeaker, employing a large cone for the reproduction of sound in the low-frequency range and a small cone for the reproduction of sound in the high-frequency range, a uniform directivity pattern can be obtained over the entire audio-frequency range. This is because the ratio of wavelength to linear dimensions can be employed in addition to the expedients used in the cones of the loudspeakers shown in Figs. 1 and 2. This is illustrated in Fig. 11, in which the directivity patterns of 15-in. and 2½-in. loudspeakers are compared for a 6:1 ratio of frequency, that is, for a constant ratio of diameter to wavelength. Figure 11 shows that the directivity pattern of a 15-in. loudspeaker at 200 to 1000 cps corresponds to that of a 2½-in. loudspeaker at 1200 and 6000 cps. These relationships were used in designing the two units of the speaker of Fig. 3.

In addition, in this loudspeaker, the small cones which are attached to the wide-angle cone reduce the velocity of wave propagation in the large cone. This broadens the directivity pattern of the low-frequency cone. In the high-frequency range, the conical domes attached to the surface of the low-

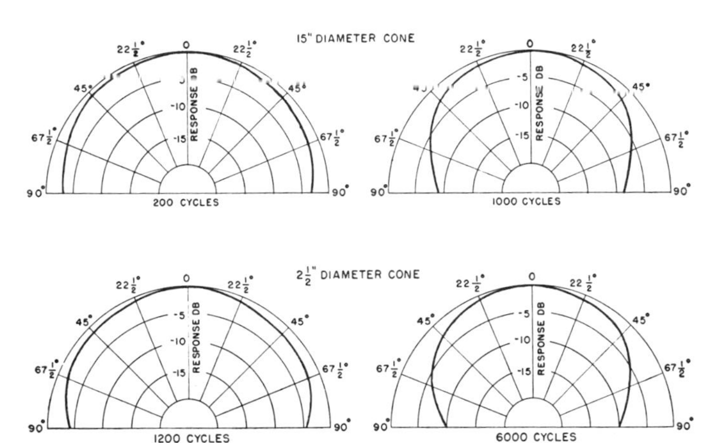

FIG. 11. Directional characteristics of 15-in. and 2½-in. loudspeakers.

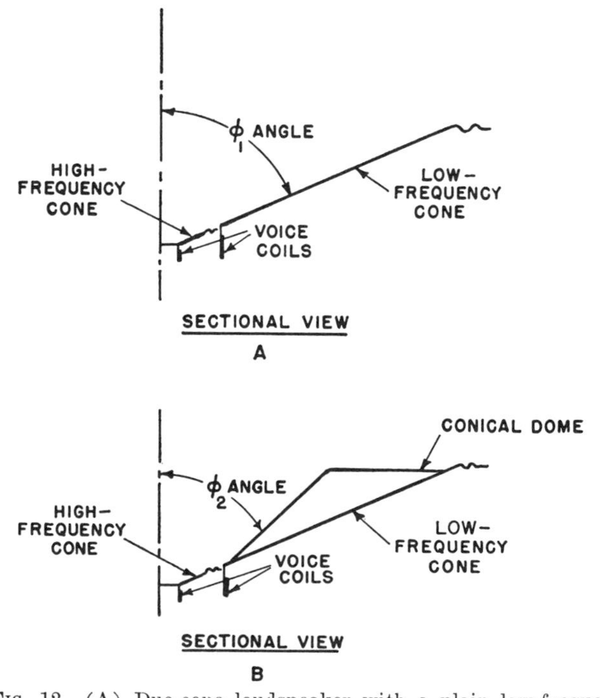

FIG. 12. (A) Duo-cone loudspeaker with a plain low-frequency cone. (B) Duo-cone loudspeaker with domes attached to the low-frequency cone.

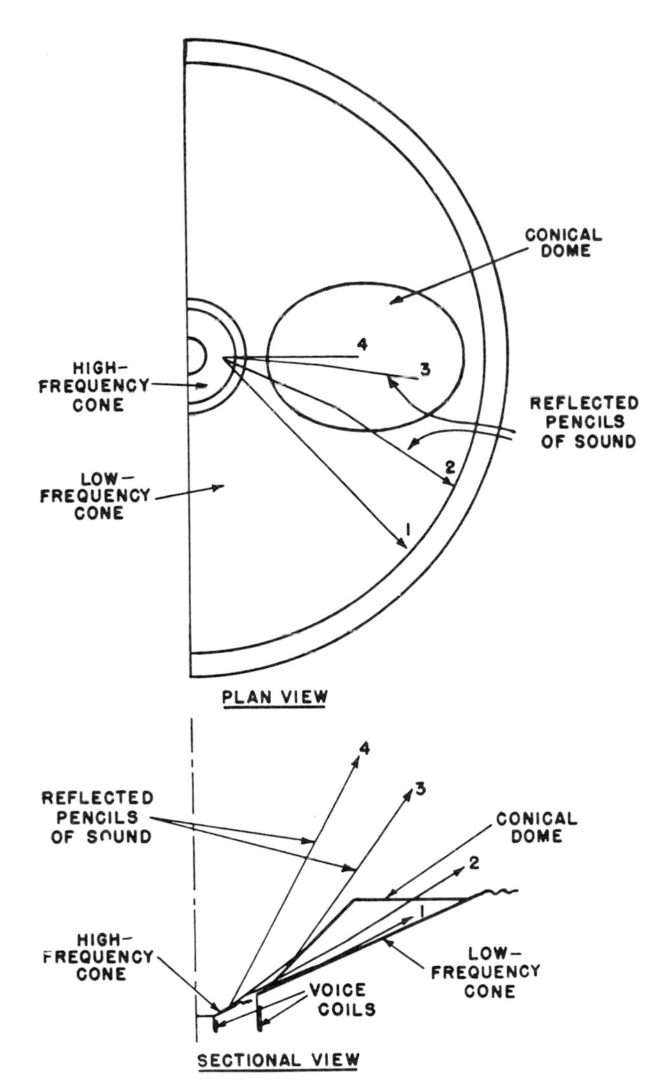

FIG. 13. Diffuse reflections of the sound emitted by the high-frequency cone by the domes attached to the low-frequency cone.

frequency cone improve the performance in three ways: by decreasing the angle into which the high-frequency cone feeds, thereby increasing the output of the high-frequency cone; by diffusely reflecting some of the sound emitted by the high-frequency cone, thereby eliminating discrete reflections; and by diffracting some of the sound emitted by the high-frequency cone, thereby broadening the directivity pattern.

The angles into which the high-frequency cone feeds, without and with the conical domes applied to the low-frequency cone, are designated as ϕ_1 and ϕ_2, respectively, in Fig. 12A and 12B. Since ϕ_2 is smaller than ϕ_1, the acoustic radiation load on the cone is greater with the conical domes than without them. When the acoustic radiation load on a direct-radiator loudspeaker is increased, the sound power output is increased. Thus, it will be seen that the conical domes increase the high-frequency sound radiated by the high-frequency cone. In other words, the high-frequency efficiency is improved.

Some of the sound emitted by the high-frequency cone is diffusely reflected by the conical domes, as shown in Fig. 13. Without the domes, there would be many similar reflections which would lead to reinforcements and cancellations with the direct radiation. The result would be corresponding peaks and dips in the response of the high-frequency cone. With the domes, the symmetry of the low-frequency cone is upset and there are many reflections in different directions and of different path lengths. The reflections, therefore, cancel out, and the net result is a smooth response-frequency characteristic.

Some of the sound emitted by the high-frequency cone is diffracted by the conical domes, as shown in Fig. 14. By diffraction is meant the bending of the sound around an obstacle. The pencils of sound designated 1 and 2 in Fig. 14 are diffracted. The pencils of sound designated 3 to 7 in-

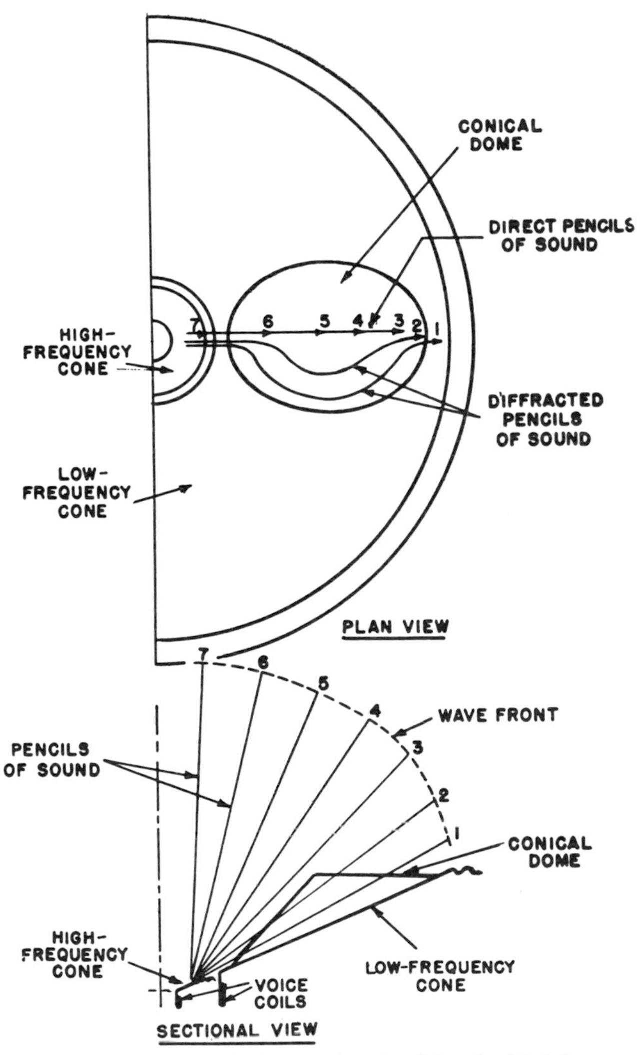

FIG. 14. Diffraction of the sound emitted by the high-frequency cone by the domes attached to the low-frequency cone.

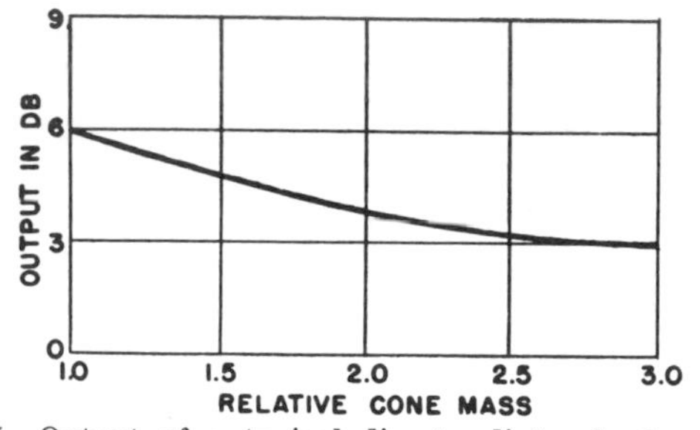

FIG. 15. Output of a typical direct-radiator loudspeaker as a function of the mass of the cone.

clusive are radiated directly into space from the high-frequency cone. It will be seen that the effect of the diffracted sound is to decrease the curvature of the wave front in the direction of 1, 2, and 3. As a result, the directivity pattern is broadened.

In the frequency region above 10,000 cps, small deflectors are used to broaden the directivity pattern of the small cone to conform with the directivity pattern of the remainder of the frequency range.

One of the effects of nonlinearity in the elements of the vibrating system of a loudspeaker is the production of harmonics and subharmonics. Nonlinearity in a cone occurs when the force *vs* displacement characteristic deviates from a straight line. In a lightweight cone, this deviation occurs at a relatively small input.

The reason for the use of a lightweight cone is to obtain greater sensitivity. However, the increased sensitivity is obtained at the expense of greater nonlinear distortion. The relative output of a typical direct-radiator loudspeaker as a function of the weight of the cone is shown in Fig. 15. In this example, the weight of the permanent magnet was kept constant. However, the mass of the voice coil and the dimensions of the air gap were selected to obtain the maximum output. The sound output for a certain value of nonlinear distortion as a function of the weight of the cone is shown in Fig. 16. Figures 15 and 16 show that high sensitivity and low distortion are not compatible. In order to obtain low nonlinear distortion, a relatively heavy cone must be used. In the loudspeakers shown in Figs. 1, 2, and 3, heavy cones are employed in order to obtain a low value of nonlinear distortion.

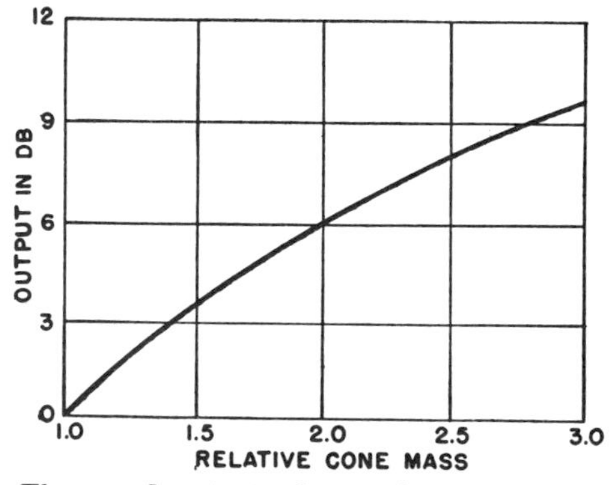

FIG. 16. The sound output of a typical direct-radiator loudspeaker, for a certain value of nonlinear distortion, as a function of the mass of the cone.

For home and other small-room sound reproduction, high sensitivity[3] is not a requirement because the power available from the amplifier is more than adequate to obtain satisfactory sound levels. For example, the loudspeakers described in this paper will deliver a sound level of 80 db in the average living room for an input of 0.05 watt. Most amplifiers used in high-fidelity radio receivers and phonographs have an output of at least 5 watts. A 5-watt input to these loudspeakers will produce a sound level of 100 db in the average living room. This is the peak level of a full symphony orchestra, in the best seat in an orchestral hall. Furthermore, the loudspeaker with the heavier cone and lower sensitivity, when used with conventional amplifiers, will actually deliver more sound power before it overloads than a loudspeaker with a lightweight cone.

One of the common methods for testing the transient response of a loudspeaker is by observing the response to a tone burst. A tone burst is a single-frequency, sine-wave signal of short duration, having a rectangular envelope. The duration of the signal may vary from 50 to 500 msec, depending on the frequency. The rectangular envelope characteristic means that a tone burst consists of a signal of practically instantaneous rise and decay periods. A deviation from the rectangular envelope depicts the transient response of the loudspeaker. The maintenance of a rectangular envelope, that is, the almost instantaneous rise and decay of the tone burst, is a very severe test. Therefore, any loudspeaker passing this test will handle any transients encountered in speech and music without distortion. It is possible to correlate the shape of the response-frequency characteristic with the form of the envelope of the tone burst. For example, if there is a peak in the response-frequency characteristic, as for example at point X in Fig. 6, some time will be required for the output to build up to the steady-state value after the electrical input has been applied, and some time will be required for the output to decay after the electrical input has been stopped. This is illustrated in A of Fig. 17. If there is a dip in the response-frequency characteristic, as for example at point Y of Fig. 6, there will be a rapid build-up in the output after the electrical input has been applied; then this is followed by a very low, steady-state value, and then another rapid rise in the output when the electrical input has been stopped. This is illustrated in B of Fig. 17. From the foregoing it will be seen that the growth and decay characteristics of speech and music will

[3] H. F. Olson and A. R. Morgan, *Radio and Television News,* **44**, No. 5, p. 54 (1950).

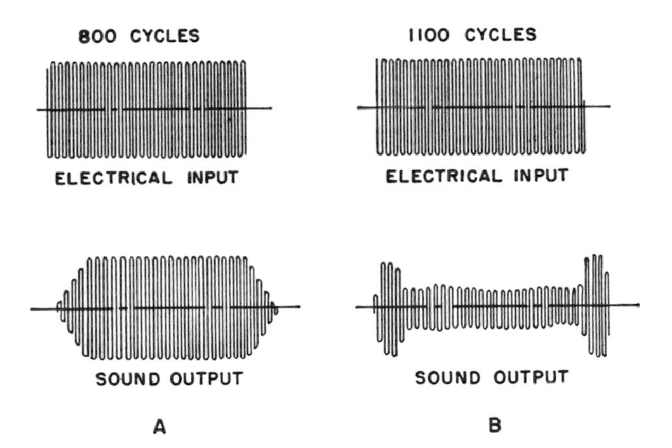

FIG. 17. The transient response of the loudspeaker having response-frequency characteristic depicted in Fig. 6: (A) at 800 cps; (B) at 1100 cps.

not be reproduced unless the system exhibits good response to transients. The tone-burst tests of these loudspeakers have shown that the shape of the tone burst is faithfully reproduced throughout the frequency range of the loudspeakers. Therefore, these loudspeakers will reproduce the growth and decay characteristics of speech and music.

DIRECT-RADIATOR LOUDSPEAKER CABINETS[4,5]

Direct-radiator loudspeakers for high-fidelity sound reproduction are usually mounted in some type of enclosure. Four parameters involving the cabinet influence the performance of the loudspeaker mechanism, namely, the internal acoustical impedance of the cabinet, the external coupling to the cabinet exclusive of the loudspeaker mechanism, the mounting of the loudspeaker mechanism, and the shape or configuration of the outside of the cabinet. A study has been made involving these parameters which has resulted in some new developments in wide-range loudspeaker cabinets.

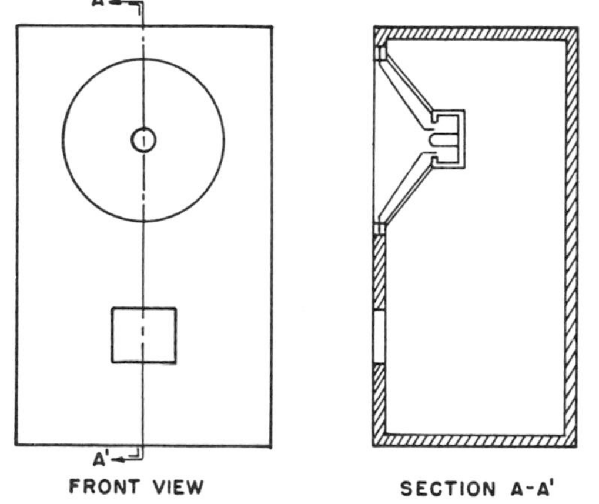

FIG. 18. A phase-inverter cabinet equipped with a port.

[4] H. F. Olson, *Audio Eng.*, **35**, No. 11, p. 34 (1951).
[5] H. F. Olson, *Radio and Television News*, **45**, No. 5, p. 53 (1951).

It is the purpose of this section to describe these developments.

Drone Cone Phase Inverter

The phase-inverter or bass-reflex cabinet consists of an enclosed cabinet equipped with a port as shown in Fig. 18. A study of this system has shown that the particle velocity is not uniform, with respect either to phase or to amplitude, over the area of the port. The result is a loss in energy due to phase shift and viscous friction. Another problem in the ported cabinet is the difficulty of providing a port of large cross-sectional area so that the particle velocity in the port will be relatively low. The appropriate inertance in the port can be obtained with a large cross-sectional area if the length of the port is increased by the required amount. When this is done, the port becomes very long; and, as a result, the losses due to viscosity are very large. Thus, it will be seen that a simple port in the phase-inverter or bass-reflex cabinet is not a satisfactory system from the standpoint of maximum performance. These objectionable features can be overcome by means of an undriven cone termed a drone cone instead of the port as shown in Fig. 19. In this

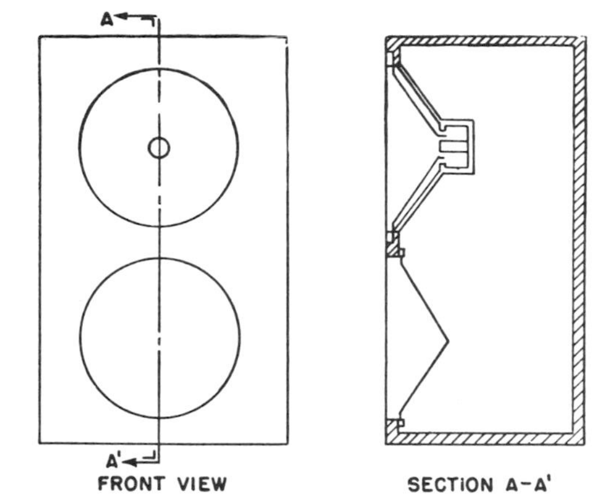

FIG. 19. A phase-inverter cabinet equipped with a drone cone.

system the port area of the drone cone can be made the same as that of the active cone. The phase and amplitude of the particle velocity are the same over the entire area of the drone cone. Furthermore, the particle velocity is relatively low because the area of the drone cone is large compared to a port. As a result, the losses are lower in the drone cone phase inverter.

A typical response-frequency characteristic of the drone cone phase inverter is shown in Fig. 20. Two response-frequency characteristics of the same loudspeaker in the same cabinet but with two different ports are also shown in Fig. 20. In one case, the frequency range of the port is the same as the drone cone, but the output obtained with the port is lower. In the other case, the output of the port is the same

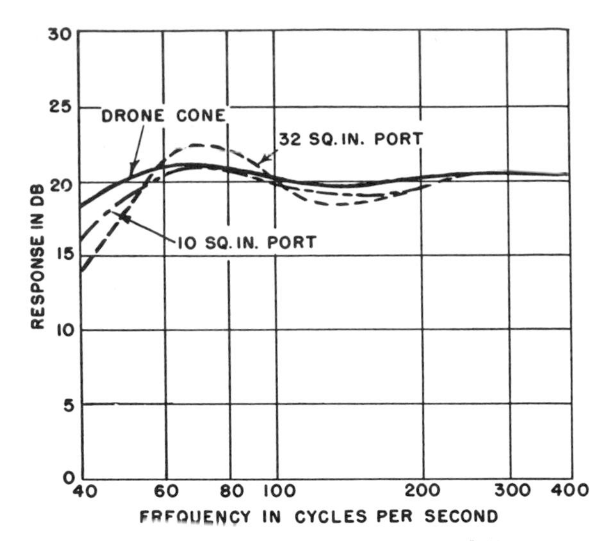

Fig. 20. Response-frequency characteristics of the LC1A loud speaker in various phase-inverter cabinets.

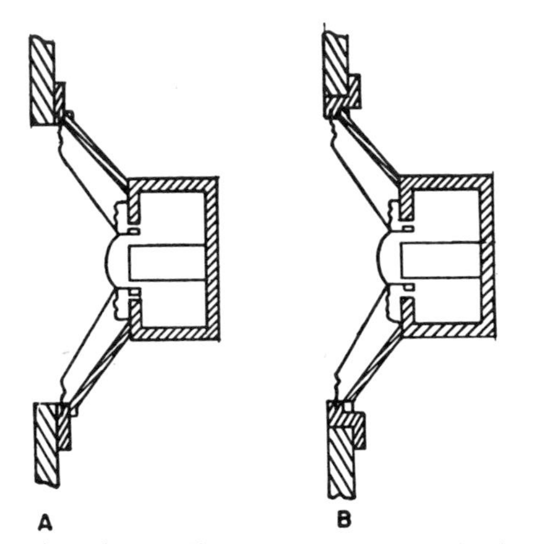

Fig. 21. (A) Direct-radiator loudspeaker mechanism mounted in the conventional manner. (B) Direct-radiator loudspeaker mechanism mounted flush with the front of the cabinet wall.

as that of the drone cone, but the frequency range obtained with the port is narrower. To summarize, these curves show that a wider frequency range with greater output can be obtained with the drone cone type of phase inverter as compared to the port type, the reason being that the losses in the drone cone are less than in the port.

Mechanism Mounting Arrangement[6]

The mounting arrangement of the loudspeaker mechanism in the front wall of the cabinet influences the response owing to the resonances of the air cavity in front of the mechanism. In addition, variations in the response are produced by reflections and diffractions from the circular boundary of this cavity. The standard mounting arrangement for loudspeaker mechanisms which has been used for years is shown in Fig. 21A. Reference to Fig. 21A, indicates that the cabinet wall forms a cavity in front of the loudspeaker. The resonances and antiresonances of this cavity, as well as reflections and diffractions at this wall edge, introduce variations in the response-frequency characteristic as shown in Fig. 22. These variations in response can be reduced by the improved loudspeaker mounting arrangement shown in Fig. 21B. It will be seen that the cavity in front of the loudspeaker mechanism has been materially reduced. The reflecting edge of the cutout in the cabinet wall has been completely eliminated. The abruptness of the edge has also been reduced, which mitigates the diffraction effects due to this edge. The response-frequency characteristic of a loudspeaker mechanism mounted as shown in Fig. 21B is shown

[6] H. F. Olson, *Radio and Television News,* **45**, No. 5, p. 53 (1951).

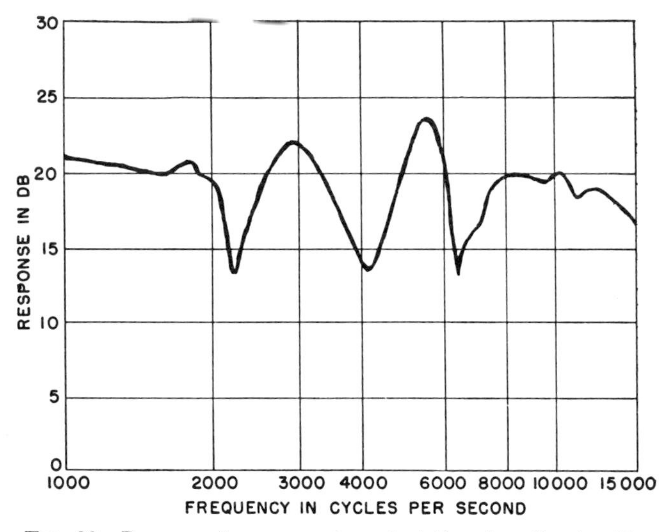

Fig. 22. Response-frequency characteristic of a direct-radiator loudspeaker mechanism mounted as shown in Fig. 21A.

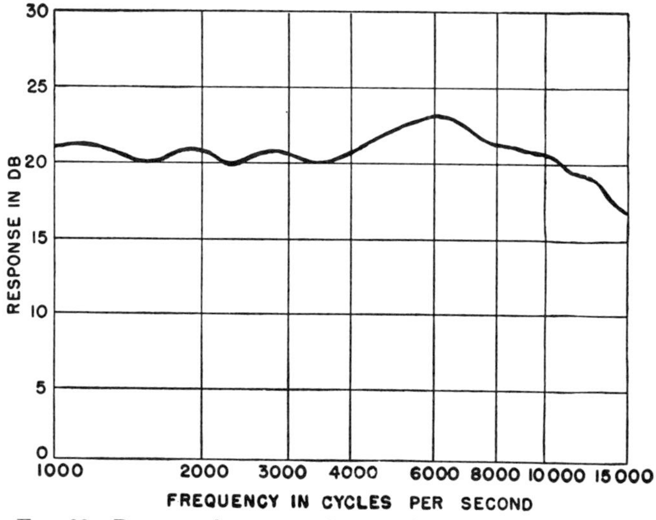

Fig. 23. Response-frequency characteristic of a direct-radiator loudspeaker mechanism mounted as shown in Fig. 21B.

in Fig. 23. Comparison of the response-frequency characteristics of Figs. 22 and 23 will reveal that a considerable improvement in response can be obtained with the mounting arrangement shown in Fig. 21B.

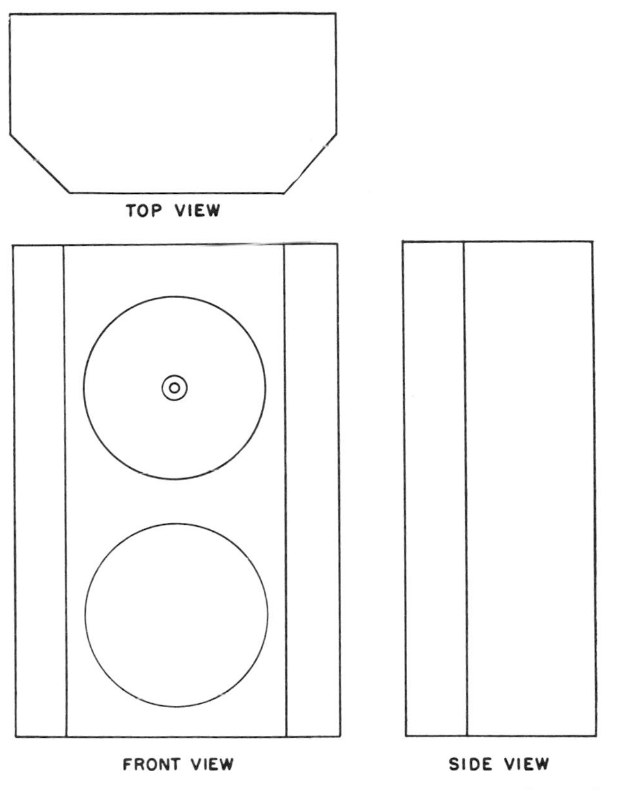

FIG. 24. A cabinet designed to eliminate the deleterious effects of diffraction on the response-frequency characteristics.

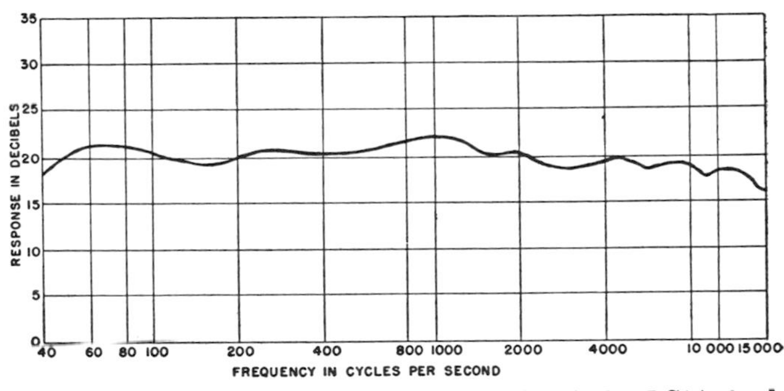
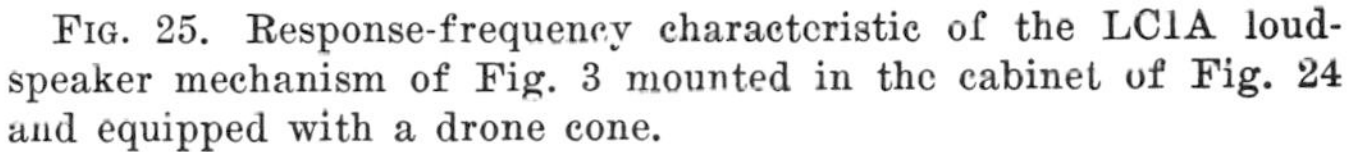

FIG. 25. Response-frequency characteristic of the LC1A loudspeaker mechanism of Fig. 3 mounted in the cabinet of Fig. 24 and equipped with a drone cone.

Cabinet Configuration[7]

The outside configuration of the cabinet influences the response, owing to diffraction effects produced by the sharp discontinuities introduced by the edges of the cabinet. As a result of a study of the shape of the outside of the cabinet, a cabinet has been developed in which the deleterious effects of diffraction have been reduced to a practical value. The cabinet which has been evolved is shown in Fig. 24. It will be seen that the sharp front edges of a standard rectangular parallelopiped type of cabinet, which would set up diffracted waves, have been eliminated. As a result, the variations in the response due to diffraction effects have been reduced to a negligible amount.

The response-frequency characteristic of the LC1A loudspeaker mechanism mounted in the cabinet of Fig. 24, which incorporates all the improved features, is shown in Fig. 25.

---

[7] H. F. Olson, *Audio Eng.*, **35**, No. 11, p. 34 (1951).

Correlation of Transient Measurements on Loudspeakers with Listening Tests*

MURLAN S. CORRINGTON†
Radio Corporation of America, Camden, New Jersey

The transient distortion of a loudspeaker may be measured by intermittently applying sine-wave bursts, consisting of four or sixteen cycles each, to the speaker. Each burst starts with the wave going through zero degrees and ceases, after the desired number of cycles has been counted off, with the wave once again crossing the zero axis. Each burst is followed by an "off" period whose duration is equal to that of the burst; the burst is then repeated. A microphone situated in front of the loudspeaker is gated to measure the sound "hangover" during the "off" period. A curve is then drawn of this transient hangover as a function of frequency. The correlation of the curve thus obtained with listening tests is discussed.

INTRODUCTION

WHEN a pianist strikes a note on the piano, the hammer hits the string and the string suddenly starts to vibrate and produces sound. At the end of the note, the damper suddenly stops the string and the sound ends abruptly. If this note is reproduced by a loudspeaker, the loudspeaker must start suddenly, produce the required sound, and then immediately stop. If the loudspeaker continues to produce its own characteristic sound after the note is ended, this undesired output probably will not be harmonically related to the next note and disagreeable distortion will result.

Since many sounds start and stop abruptly, it is evident that an important test of a loudspeaker is to observe the manner in which it builds up a sound when a tone is applied, and the way it stops emitting sound when the driving force is removed.

TONE-BURST EQUIPMENT

One test seems to come closer to giving a true measure of this transient response to suddenly-applied tones than any other.[1,2] In this test, sine-wave bursts are applied intermittently to the loudspeaker. A computer circuit turns the burst on at the precise instant when the sine wave goes through zero, counts off a predetermined number of cycles (four or sixteen) and then turns the burst off just as the wave is going through zero. The wave is left turned off for a prescribed number of cycles (usually the same as the "on" period) and then turned on again, and the sequence repeated.

Each burst of tone is applied to the voice coil of the loudspeaker. The sound developed by the loudspeaker, during the time when driving force is turned off, is picked up by a microphone, rectified, and used to drive automatic curve-drawing equipment. From the data thus obtained a curve is then plotted of the transient "hangover" as a function of frequency; this latter curve is compared with the steady-state sound-pressure curve.

A block diagram of the transient recorder is shown by Fig. 1. An audio oscillator generates continuous sine waves of the desired frequency. An electronic computing circuit opens the gate at the instant when a particular sine wave is going through zero degrees, counts off a given number of cycles (four or sixteen), and then closes the gate for an interval whose duration is equal to that of the "on" period. The continuous stream of tone bursts is amplified and applied to the loudspeaker in an anechoic chamber.

The microphone situated in front of the loudspeaker picks up the transient sound output of the loudspeaker. The gate following the microphone amplifier is permitted to remain open during the interval when the driving force is turned off, allowing for the time the sound is delayed in going from the loudspeaker to the microphone. The output from the gate is the sound output delivered by the loudspeaker *after* removal of the driving force; this sound output is the tran-

* Presented at the Sixth Annual Convention of the Audio Engineering Society, New York, October 14-16, 1954.
† RCA Victor Television Division.
[1] Murlan S. Corrington, "Transient Testing of Loudspeakers," *Audio Eng.*, 34, No. 8, pp. 9-13 (August, 1950). This article contains an extensive bibliography.
[2] Franz Brunner, "Untersuchungen an Lautsprechern," *Oesterreichische Zeitschift für Telegraphen-, Telephon-, Funk- und Fernsehtechnik,* 8, Nos. ½, 1-7 (1954).

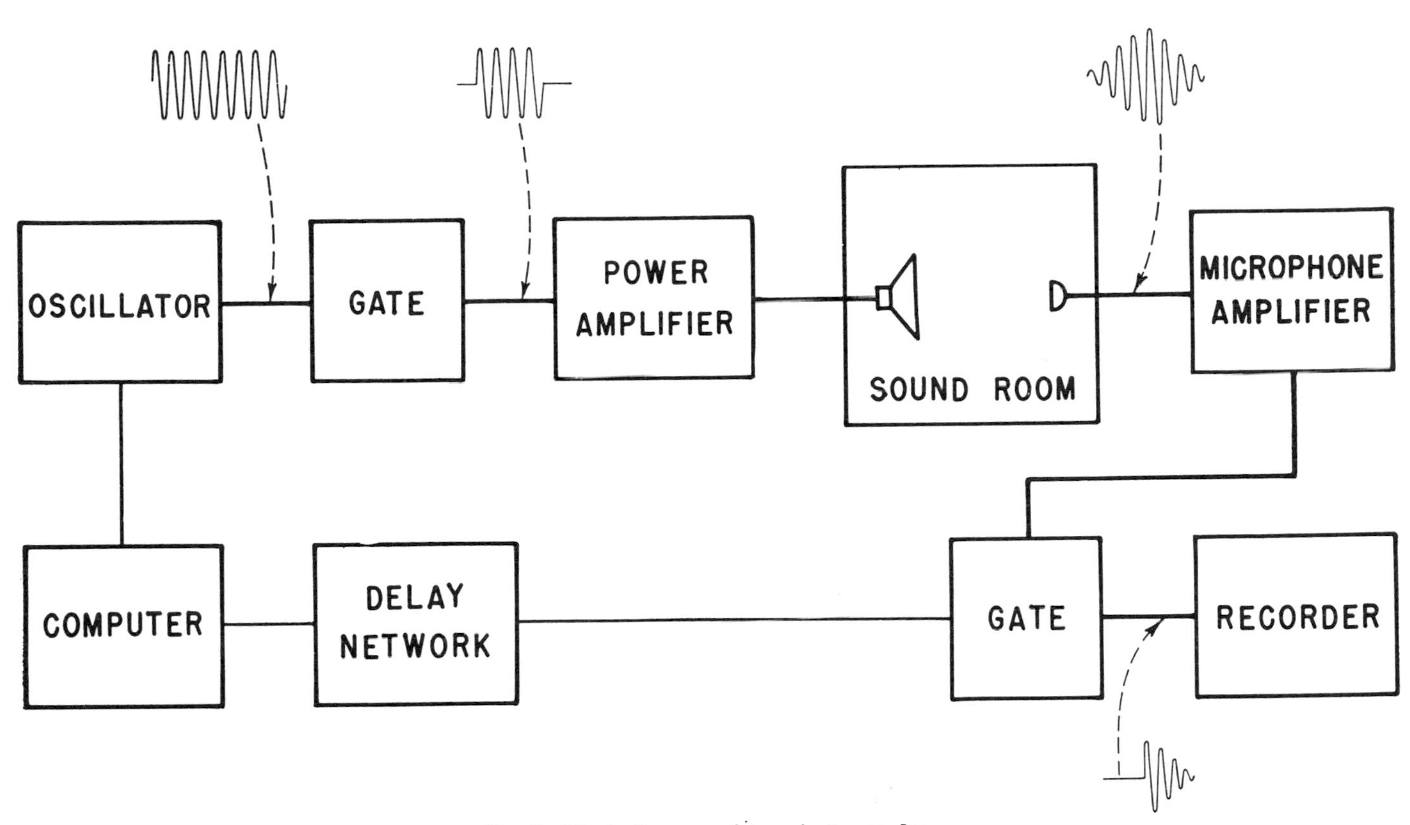

Fig. 1. Block diagram of transient recorder.

sient "hangover." This gated output is rectified, averaged, and applied to the recorder to produce a graph of the transient hangover at each frequency. The circuit details of this equipment are described in a paper by Kidd.[3]

COMPARISON WITH STEADY-STATE RESPONSE

To provide a steady-state response curve at the proper level for direct comparison with the graph of the transient response, gating is applied, *not* to the loudspeaker, but to the recorder so that the latter receives a signal 50% of the time. This gives a curve 6 db below the curve obtained if the recorder is not gated, and thus is comparable with the transient curve obtained when the recorder is turned off during the "on" period of the tone burst. Experience shows that the error introduced by the gating process is never more than one-half decibel at any frequency.

The transient response is usually drawn in two parts. Below 200 cps the tone burst consists of four complete cycles of the sine wave and above 200 cps, sixteen complete cycles are used. This 200-cycle changeover frequency is not critical, but was chosen so that it would fall in between the fundamental low-frequency resonance point and the region of cone "breakup."

[3] Marshall C. Kidd, "Tone-Burst Generator Checks A-F Transients," *Electronics*, **25**, 132-135 (July, 1952).

SOME EXPERIMENTAL RESULTS

The oscillograms of Fig. 2 show the transient response to a burst of tone for an 8-in. loudspeaker and a 12-in. loudspeaker, respectively, each at the low-frequency resonant point.

The upper curve is the current input to the voice coil. It is slightly distorted because of the limited low-frequency bandwidth of the amplifier. The next curve is the sound-pressure output as measured with a microphone. The bottom curve shows the transient distortion; it represents the sound output delivered by the loudspeaker after the driving force has been removed from the voice coil. This rectified output is applied to the curve-drawing equipment.

The curves of Fig. 3 are for the 8-in. loudspeaker at 900 and 3300 cps. Sixteen cycles of the tones are used in each burst. The 900-cps transient is caused by the rim resonance[4] and is down 15 db from the gated steady-state response. The 3300-cps transient hangover lasts longer and is caused by cone breakup. It is down 16 db from the sound-pressure curve.

The 8-in. loudspeaker has a small magnet and relatively low flux density in the air gap. The transient hangover is

[4] Murlan S. Corrington and Marshall C. Kidd, "Amplitude and Phase Measurements on Loudspeaker Cones," *Proc. I.R.E.*, **39**, No. 9, pp. 1021-1026 (September, 1951).

nearly as great as the main response. The 12-in. loudspeaker has a large ring magnet and some acoustical damping. The transient hangover at low frequencies is quite small. Compared with the steady-state response, it is about 18 db down.

The curves of Fig. 4 show the steady-state sound-pressure output, the transient distortion, and impedance curves for the 8-in. loudspeaker of Figs. 2 and 3. The fundamental resonance at 90 cps is easily seen in all three curves.

The rim resonance[4] occurs at 900 cps and is shown as point *A*. The rim is in violent oscillation and gives a sharp peak in the sound-pressure curve and a large transient. At 1000 cps, the rim is out of phase with respect to the rest of the cone and cancellation of the sound output occurs.

The cone has a series of resonances above 2000 cps. The curves show that even though the speaker has a fairly smooth sound-pressure curve above 2000 cps, there are many peaks in the transient response. For the resonances at 2300 cps and at 3300 cps, shown as points *B* and *C*, the sound-pressure peaks are only 1.5 db high, but there are very sharp peaks in the transient.

This loudspeaker has a boom in the bass and is somewhat disagreeable on speech and piano music. The extreme highs are missing. When this speaker is used for complex orchestral music, there are times when the high frequencies sound disagreeable momentarily. This apparently occurs when the transient peaks are excited.

8-INCH LOUDSPEAKER F=90 CPS

12-INCH LOUDSPEAKER F=50 CPS

ELECTRICAL INPUT

ACOUSTIC OUTPUT

TRANSIENT DISTORTION

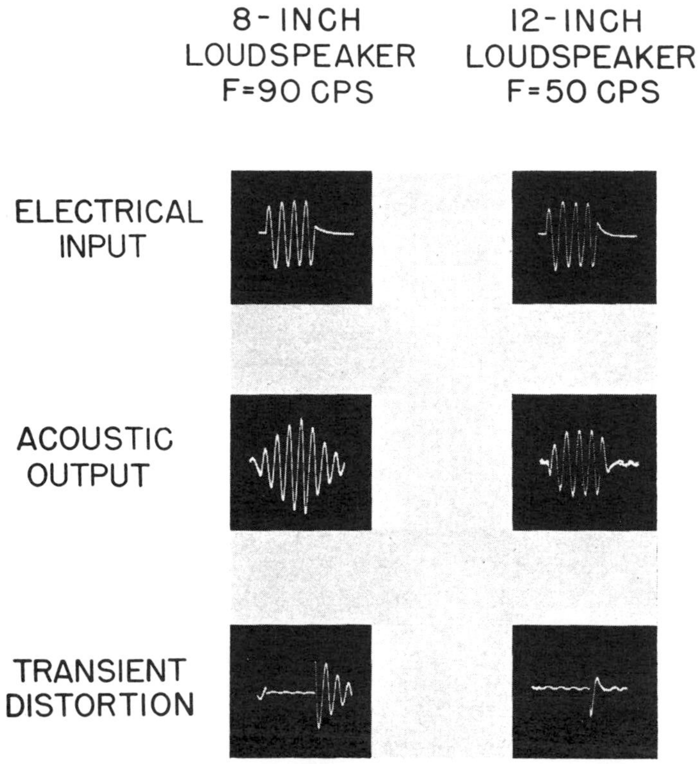

FIG. 2. Transient distortion for 8- and 12-in. loudspeakers.

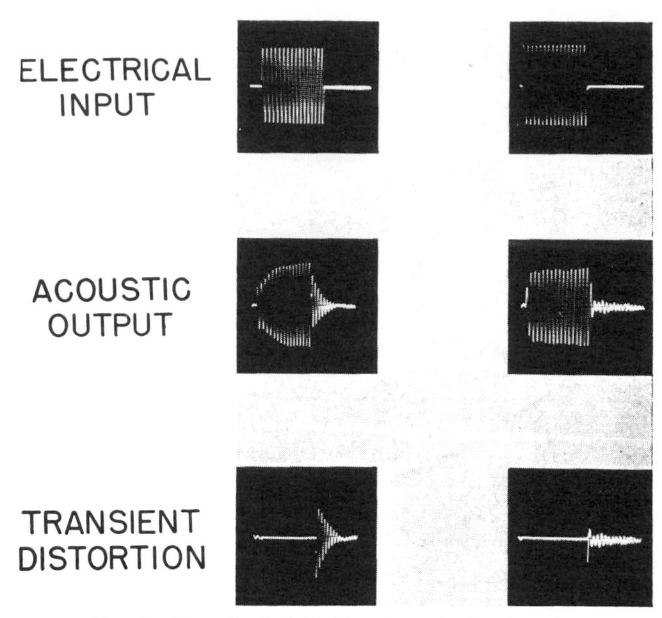

FIG. 3. Transient distortion for 8-in. loudspeaker.

The curves of Fig. 5 are for an 8-in. loudspeaker in a small open-back metal cabinet similar to that used with some communications receivers. The frequencies below 150 cps have been "rolled off" to avoid boom on male speech. These sound-pressure and transient curves are much more complex because of the combined effects of the metal cabinet and various diffractions. The four-cycle sequence tone burst has been continued to 420 cps for comparison. The

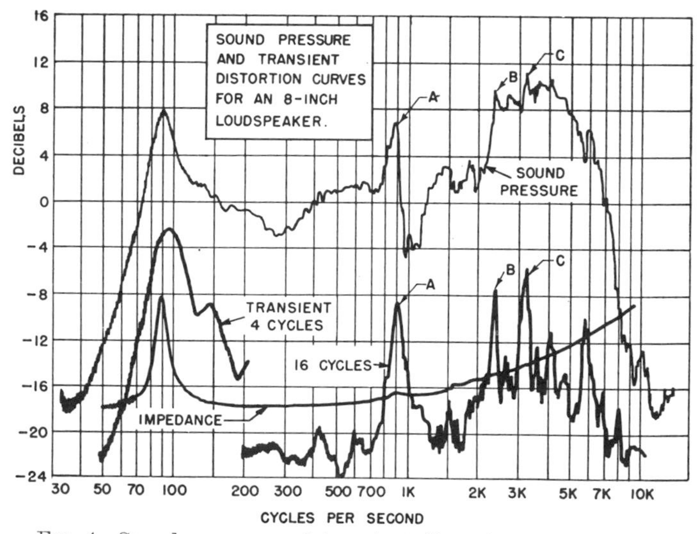

FIG. 4. Sound-pressure and transient distortion curves for 8-in. loudspeaker.

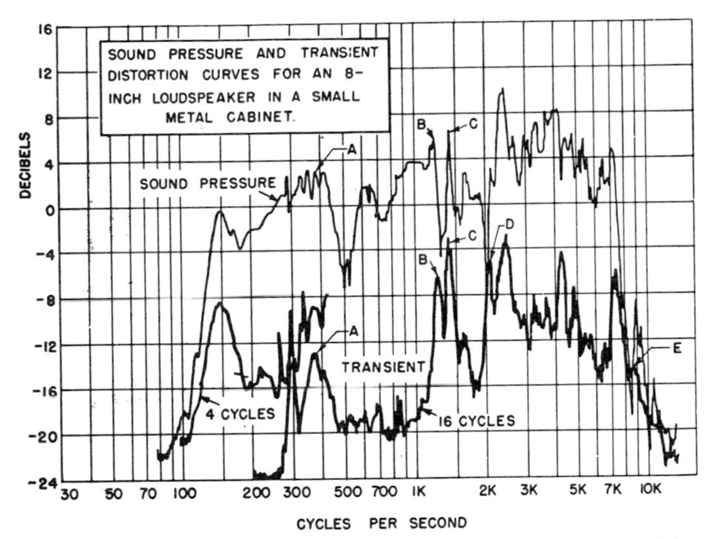

FIG. 5. Sound-pressure and transient distortion curves for 8-in. loudspeaker.

bad transient at 380 cps, shown as point *A,* is due to the open back. This peak would not be expected from the sound-pressure curve.

The bad transients at points *B* and *C* are in the region of maximum harmonic content of the singing voice and produce disagreeable distortion, especially if the singer has a strong vibrato.

At point *D,* the transient hangover is equal to the direct response; the loudspeaker puts out as much sound when it is turned off as it does when it is on. There are several bad transients at higher frequencies due to cone breakup. The one at point *E* is especially interesting. Here, too, the loudspeaker puts out more sound when it is turned off than when it is on.

This effect can be explained as follows: When the sine wave is suddenly applied to the system, it shock-excites the system and causes it to "ring" at its natural frequencies, which are near the applied frequency. If this transient "ringing" is of the right phase to cancel out the applied frequency for an appreciable time, the sound output will be reduced during the interval when the tone burst is being applied. When the driving force is removed, there is no longer any cancellation and the output, due to the transient ringing, is greater than when the tone burst is on.

It is fairly easy to find loudspeakers that put out more sound when they are turned off than when they are on. Imagine what this would do to a piano concerto, since the ringing frequencies are unlikely to be harmonially related to the applied frequency.

The loudspeaker of Fig. 5 is quite disagreeable on music; it has no "lows" and will not reproduce a singing voice properly. It is an inexpensive speaker suitable for intelligible reproduction of speech only.

The curves of Fig. 6 are for a 12-in. extended-range loudspeaker that is widely sold as part of a moderate priced high-fidelity receiver. The gradual rise in the high end is compensated electrically to give a fairly flat response. There is more transient distortion in the low end than would be obtained if a bigger magnet and higher flux density in the gap were used. Cone breakup begins at 6000 cps. For an inexpensive loudspeaker this is a very good curve.

This speaker system has a wide range, a pleasing tone quality, and is widely accepted by the public. Some people, however, may object to the bass output of this loudspeaker as not being as "clear" as that of some units.

A small folded horn, such as that used in the more expensive dual units, or for small theater work, exhibits the response of Fig. 7. The crossover frequency is usually 800

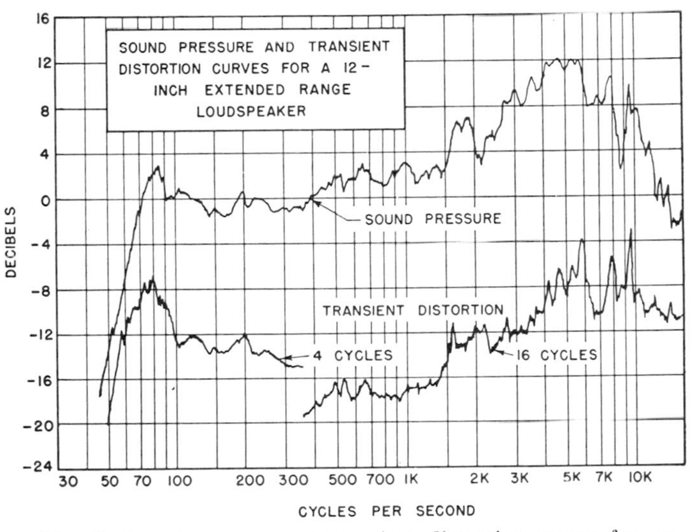

FIG. 6. Sound-pressure and transient distortion curves for extended-range loudspeaker.

or 1000 cps. This unit is characterized by unusually low transient distortion up to 5000 cps. The system is usually "rolled off" above this frequency. The diaphragm starts to "break up" above 5000 cps. The transient distortion is at least 20 db down from 800 to 5000 cps. This folded horn reproduces the speaking and singing voice very well and is very good on symphonic music. It will not distort, even at high output levels.

The smoothest curve we have been able to obtain in our laboratory is shown by Fig. 8. It is an 18 × 18 in.-square electrostatic unit similar to that developed by A. A. Janszen‡ at Harvard University. The moving element is 0.8

‡ Mr. Janszen now heads the Janszen Laboratory, 1 Gray Street, Cambridge 38, Massachusetts. A paper by Mr. Janszen, entitled, "An Electrostatic Loudspeaker Development," will appear in a subsequent issue of the JOURNAL.

mil of pliofilm with a graphite coating. Both curves are quite smooth and individual resonances are negligible. This speaker operates with 3000 volts bias and several hundred volts of signal. Below 700 cps, the stretched wires of the back electrode add some distortion. The transient distortion is down 18 db or more from 700 to 13,000 cps. This speaker, when used with a woofer, gives what we regard as unusually "clean" reproduction of voice and all musical instruments. We have often used it as a standard for listening tests.

The microphone used to obtain these curves was the RCA KB2C bantam velocity unit. Since this microphone gave transient curves with no repeating peaks for different speakers, it was felt that transient distortion introduced by the microphone was very low. It has been found that other microphones whose sound-pressure frequency response is flat within 1 db show transient response characteristics

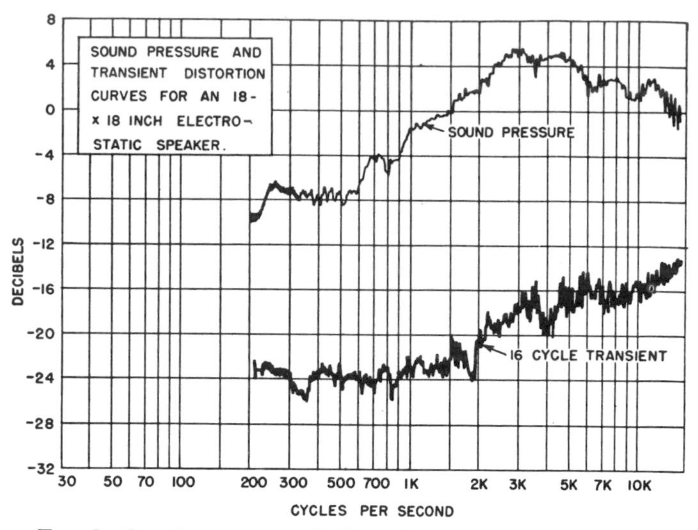

FIG. 8. Sound-pressure and distortion curves for electrostatic speaker.

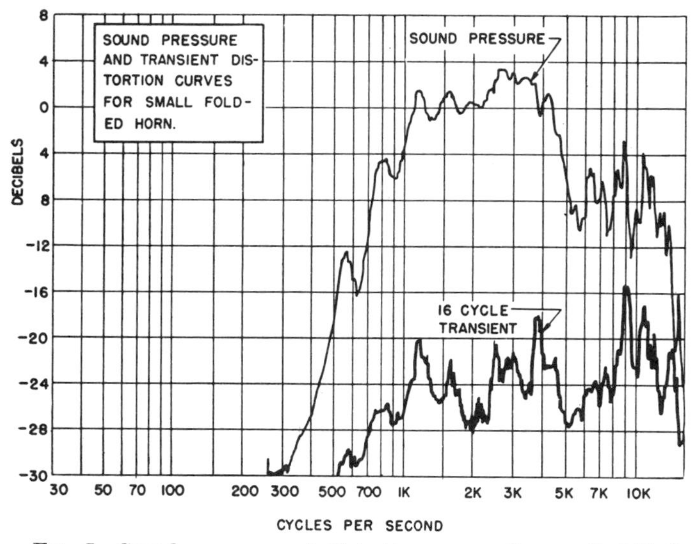

FIG. 7. Sound-pressure and distortion curves for small folded horn.

which are much worse. Abrupt discontinuities in microphone response, even though small, make some microphones unsuitable for the type of studies described in this paper.

CONCLUSIONS

Equipment has been developed to record the transient distortion of any audio amplifier, loudspeaker, or enclosure at all audio frequencies. A burst of tone consisting of four or sixteen successive cycles of a sine wave is applied to the system with the duration of the "off" period equal to that of the burst. The sound emitted when the driving force is turned off is recorded as a function of frequency. It is thus possible to give a numerical value for the transient distortion. Any speaker or sound system with less than 10 or 12% (18 to 20 db down) distortion over the useful range will be comparable to the best available.

This information supplements the steady-state sound-pressure measurements. We have never found any system with low transient distortion that did not also have a smooth sound-pressure curve; on the other hand, we have measured systems with fairly sharp and small peaks in the sound-pressure response that produced objectionable transient distortion.

There is very good correlation between transient distortion and subjective listening tests. Whenever there are peaks in the transient distortion, one can be sure that the listening tests will reveal unpleasant distortion, even though the sound-pressure curve is quite smooth. The transient test will not show small amounts of distortion in the amplifier; the latter should therefore be checked separately. It is a test of the loudspeaker only.

The effect of enclosure resonances and of diffraction effects is to produce transient ringing which coincides with the peaks in the sound-pressure curve.

Extensive measurements show that for a high-quality audio system the sound-pressure curve must be smooth and properly shaped, and that the transient distortion should be down at least 18 db throughout the range. One can then be fairly certain that the system will pass very careful listening tests.

ACKNOWLEDGMENT

The author wishes to acknowledge the help of Marshall C. Kidd in building the equipment and making the measurements for the study described in this paper.

An Electrostatic Loudspeaker Development*

ARTHUR A. JANSZEN
The Janszen Laboratory, Cambridge, Massachusetts

The idea of bringing electromechanical forces of transduction to bear directly on the transmitting medium spurred many pre-high-fidelity experimenters to extensive attempts to harness the electrostatic mechanism of transduction to the design of loudspeakers. Early attempts were not notably successful, either in this country or abroad. The advent of new materials and techniques and the growing awareness of, and demand for, fidelity in the reproduction of recorded music and other program material have provided both the incentive and the means for a renewal of effort. One of the results of this effort is the Janszen electrostatic loudspeaker, which is designed for use with two-way systems. High efficiency is obtained over a wide frequency range, which extends from below 1000 cps to above 20 kc. The membrane used in its building-block elements is so light that, over most of its frequency range, it functions as an imaginary boundary in the air. The axial pressure response, therefore, is extremely smooth. The unit operates from the 8-ohm or 16-ohm output of any amplifier, and contains its own bias supply. Maximum power output is 0.5 acoustic watt.

IT IS WELL KNOWN that although condenser-type microphones have been in extensive use for the last 30 years, condenser or electrostatic loudspeakers have not enjoyed a comparable popularity. The literature and the files of the U. S. and other patent offices, notably the British and the German, give evidence of much interest and activity in electrostatic devices for the reproduction of sound, especially during the 1920's. Nevertheless, it seems that only two electrostatic loudspeakers were ever sold in significant quantities: In this country, it was the Kyle condenser loudspeaker, which was incorporated in the Peerless radio around 1930; the second electrostatic loudspeaker was produced commercially in Germany.

About 1930, the electrodynamic loudspeaker made its debut. The electrostatics, being less viable creatures—afflicted with unwanted discharges and other ailments that apparently were not remediable at the time—were driven off the market by the more rugged and efficient dynamic speakers. A long hiatus followed, during which little interest was shown in electrostatic actuation for loudspeakers, if a lack of material in the literature and in the patent files is any indication. Only recently—since about 1950—have electrostatic loudspeakers begun to appear on the market again. These are in the form of structures that seem to be based, in general, on designs that can be found in patents issued in the twenties and early thirties.

* Presented at the Sixth Annual Convention of the Audio Engineering Society, New York, October 14–16, 1954.

It might be asked, Why did they reappear? The answer seems to be that high-fidelity listeners demand effective reproduction of the very high frequencies which are to be found in many of our present-day phonograph and tape recordings. Electrostatic loudspeakers are effective in reproducing these very high frequencies because they can be designed in such a way that a uniform actuating force is applied over essentially the entire area of a flexible vibrating element, which can be made extremely light. Flexural rigidity is not required as it is when the driving force is applied over only a *portion* of the vibrating element.

Early attempts to incorporate into commercial units the advantages inherent in electrostatic drives were frustrated by a variety of difficulties. Chief among these were susceptibility to electrical breakdown, low efficiency, rapid oxidation of unstable structural materials (caused by the generation of ozone), and the difficulty of obtaining manageable membrane materials thin enough to be classified as *really* thin membranes. The recent appearance of new materials, such as polyester plastics, and of new techniques has encouraged further efforts to overcome these earlier difficulties. New concepts of design have evolved, also, directed toward the full realization of the potentialities of electrostatic loudspeakers in commercially practical packages.

The electrostatic loudspeaker design described in this paper was developed at the Janszen Laboratory, Cambridge, Massachusetts, and is based on work done at the Acoustics Research Laboratory, Harvard University.

Figure 1 shows the loudspeaker, which consists of four

building-block elements arranged in a horizontal array.

FIG. 1. The Janszen electrostatic loudspeaker.

The frequency response of the speaker extends from below 1000 cps to above 20 kc, making it suitable for use in two-way systems. The choice of frequency response represents a compromise, but not a difficult one. Woofer-sized dynamic loudspeakers can be built to operate as pistons below 1000 cps, in that portion of the audio spectrum where the design of electrostatic loudspeakers with adequate acoustic power output-per-unit-area presents engineering difficulties not easily overcome. The difficulties encountered in the use of cones for the reproduction of frequencies above 1000 cps are well known. It was considered essential that the electrostatic loudspeaker—if it were to represent a useful advance in

FIG. 2. A single building-block element of the electrostatic loudspeaker.

high-fidelity reproduction—be able to take over from the low-frequency dynamic elements above 1000 cps.

Figure 2 shows a single unit of the present design.[1] Four such units are built into the assembly of Fig. 1. Figure 3

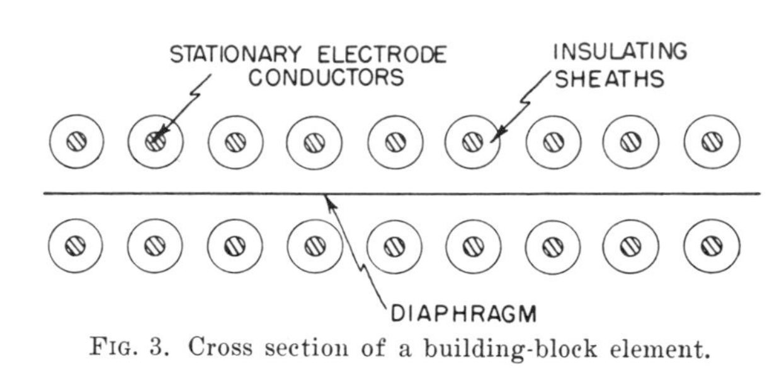

FIG. 3. Cross section of a building-block element.

gives the unit in cross section. Sheathed conductors are situated in two parallel planes and are supported by two plastic moldings in a push-pull arrangement, with a centrally-located diaphragm supported by the same plastic moldings.

There are several possible methods of obtaining bias and signal voltages for the generation of actuating forces. Figure 4 illustrates one method—a conventional push-pull system—in which the bias voltage is applied between the conducting material of the diaphragm and the center tap of the transformer supplying the signal voltages to the stationary electrodes.

Figure 5 shows the axial pressure response of a single

STATIONARY ELECTRODE CONDUCTORS
BIAS SUPPLY
TO POWER AMPLIFIER
DIAPHRAGM
STEP-UP TRANSFORMER

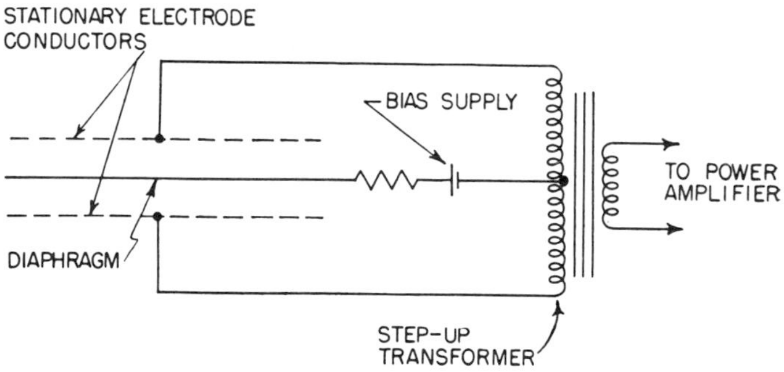

FIG. 4. Electrical hookup of a building-block element.

modular element for a constant-voltage signal. The very unconventional 6-db-per-octave rise in axial pressure over most of the frequency range results from the fact that the

[1] A. A. Janszen, U. S. Patent No. 2,631,196 (issued March 10, 1953).

driving force, being proportional to the signal voltage—which is kept constant—is acting against a resistive impedance which is the resistive component of the radiation impedance. The constant diaphragm velocity that results from the constant force acting against a constant resistive impedance gives rise to a constant energy output. Since the diaphragm behaves like a true piston, moving with the same amplitude and in the same phase over its entire area, the directivity pattern sharpens up at a predictable rate, and the axial pressure characteristic rises at the rate of 6 db per octave. The surface density of the diaphragm is so low as to make its mass reactance small in comparison with the resistive component of the radiation impedance over most of the frequency range. In short, the diaphragm behaves as if it had neither stiffness nor mass, or as if it were not there at all. The 6-db-per-octave rise in response contrasts with the gradual rolloff in energy output that generally characterizes dynamic or other mass-loaded loudspeakers in which the driving force is kept constant.

At first glance, this unconventional response curve would seem to require rolloff equalization to make it conform more nearly to the typical response curve of dynamic loudspeakers. Listening tests, however, indicate that this is not necessary. The following explanation is offered for consideration.

Since "flatness" of response in the entire recording and playback system is generally the goal in high fidelity, it is implied that the individual acoustic pressure components contributed at the microphone by each one of the instruments being recorded are to be duplicated at the ears of the listeners. This is not strictly true, of course, but it is probably about as good an approximation to a valid general statement as can be made when standards are as flexible as they are today in the art of high fidelity. With such completely "flat" systems, the desired effect is approximated with mass-loaded loudspeakers only if the listeners' ears are situated on

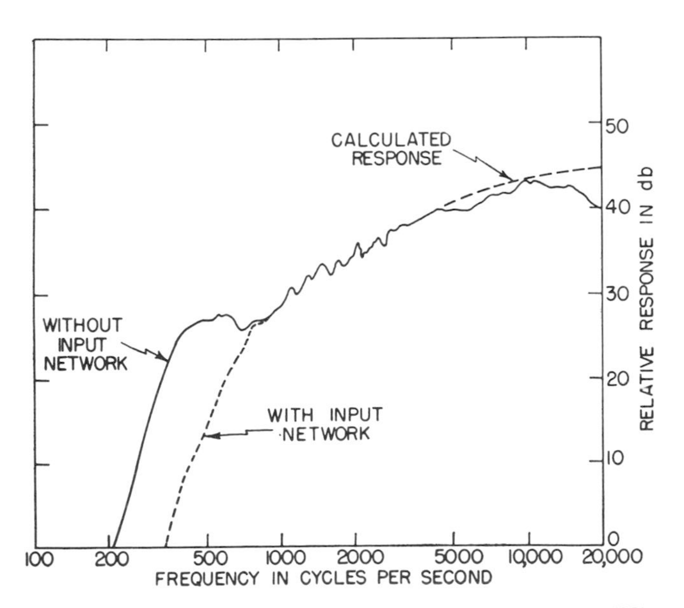

Fig. 5. Axial acoustic pressure response of a single building-block element, for constant-voltage input.

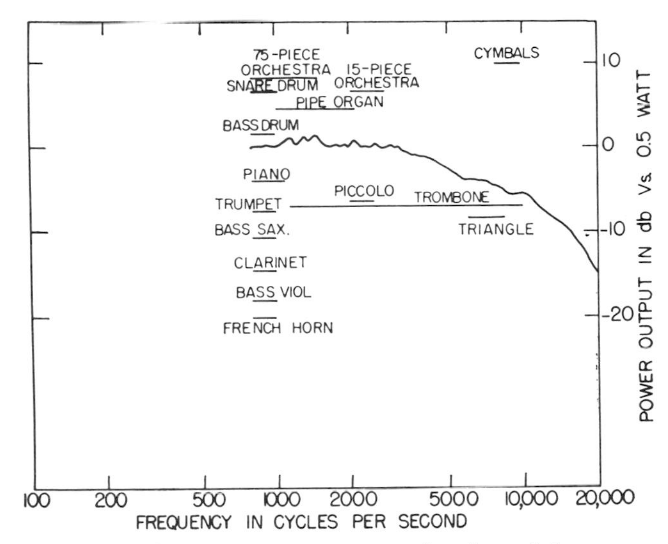

Fig. 6. Maximum power output as a function of frequency of an array of four electrostatic building-block elements (with constant-voltage input).

the axes of the loudspeakers in rooms in which there are no reflections. Of course, not much listening is done under such conditions. In live rooms, reflections cause sound diffusion, and horns and lenses are used to improve this diffusion. Under conditions in which diffusion is complete at all frequencies, the acoustic pressure will fall off 6 db per octave in the case of a mass-loaded loudspeaker, unless electrical compensation is introduced, and will not represent an approach to the pressures recorded by the microphone. On the other hand, the electrostatic loudspeaker, used at the end of a "flat" system, will provide a constant pressure over most of its frequency range when the diffusion is complete. Although conditions in which all frequencies are completely diffused are probably as atypical as conditions in which there is no diffusion, it is probably true that most rooms are more alive than dead. If this is true, then it is probably also true that the electrostatic loudspeaker more nearly recreates, with a "flat" system, the pressures recorded by the microphone.

The maximum power output of four building-block elements in parallel is approximately 0.5 watt, or 0.125-watt-per-modular element. This can be obtained over the range from 1000 cps to 3 kc. Above 3 kc, the maximum power output falls off gradually and smoothly. Figure 6 shows the maximum power output as a function of frequency. It also shows the approximate peak power output of a number of instruments and orchestras and the frequencies within the spectrum of the modular elements at which these peaks occur (according to the data published by Sivian, Dunn, and White[2]) to aid in assessing the power-handling capabilities of the present design. The magnitude of the calculated values of peak power output, calculated by assuming a uniform distribution of pressure over a sphere, for each instrument, are, of course, probably very inaccurate for many, if not all, instruments. They are shown only for the purpose of a rough comparison.

The assembly of Fig. 1 comprises four building-block elements, an ac-operated bias voltage supply, a crossover network, and a matching network. In normal operation, its two input terminals are connected in shunt with the woofer section of a two-way system.

[2] L. J. Sivian, H. K. Dunn, and S. D. White, "Absolute Amplitudes and Spectra of Certain Musical Instruments and Orchestras," *J. Acoust. Soc. Amer.*, **2**, 330 (January 1931).

The Isophase Loudspeaker*

THEODORE LINDENBERG†
Pickering & Company, Inc., Oceanside, New York

The author describes a push-pull electrostatic loudspeaker, featuring large diaphragm area, which makes possible low-velocity sound propagation per unit area.

THE DEVELOPMENT of an electrostatic speaker was undertaken with a definite objective—to overcome certain basic disadvantages of the electromagnetic cone speaker, particularly in the propagation of acoustic energy at the upper end of the audio spectrum. The cone speaker, driven by a voice coil which is attached near the center of the diaphragm, fails, as is known, to act as a piston at the middle and high frequencies. The universal occurrence of breakup in cones used at the higher frequencies means that the voice coil does not actually control the diaphragm motion, and we have the familiar lack of correspondence between electrical input and acoustic output.

After experimenting with small models of an electrostatic speaker, we were so impressed with the low distortion, the greatly improved frequency and transient response, the generally "sweet" sound, that we decided to go "all out" in making an electrostatic speaker that would cover as much of the spectrum as possible. While the particular design to be described and demonstrated here should not be considered a perfect transducer, we feel that the improved reproduction within the operating range has abundantly rewarded us for our efforts to date.

THE ELECTROSTATIC SPEAKER

Now let us consider the basic characteristics of an electrostatic speaker: it has a diaphragm which is driven equally at every point on its surface. We find that the very troublesome phenomenon of breakup is eliminated, and with it go the distortions of phase differences, etc., that are inescapable with a diaphragm every part of which does not move as a unit.

Because of the configuration of the electrostatic speaker, the diaphragm can be made essentially massless, i.e., the mass can be made extremely small compared to the air load on the speaker. Our observation is that this gives the speaker unparalleled high-frequency and transient response; the response is basically peakless throughout the operating range.

The push-pull electrostatic transducer, moreover, is essentially linear: it is free from waveform distortion, producing neither even nor odd harmonics. This welcome characteristic of the push-pull electrostatic design has been thoroughly investigated both experimentally and theoretically by F. V. Hunt of Harvard.[1]

WAYS OF MAKING ELECTROSTATIC SPEAKERS

There are several ways of constructing an electrostatic speaker. Two of the most important are

1. Stretching the diaphragm between supports around its periphery, and leaving an airgap between the diaphragm and the two electrodes.

2. Using an "inert diaphragm," which is supported by a great multiplicity of tiny suspension elements, disposed across the entire surface of the electrodes and acting as spacing elements to hold the diaphragm in the center between the electrodes as shown in Fig. 1.

Our speaker is of this second type. The diaphragm is a sheet of plastic material on which has been deposited a very thin conductive layer. The diaphragm is supported by a multiplicity of small elastic elements which secure it but allow it to move in obedience to the signal modulation.

The electrodes on each side of the diaphragm must be

* Presented before the New York Section of the Audio Engineering Society, January 11, 1956.
† Chief Design Engineer.

[1] Frederick V. Hunt, *Electroacoustics,* John Wiley and Sons, Inc., New York (1954).

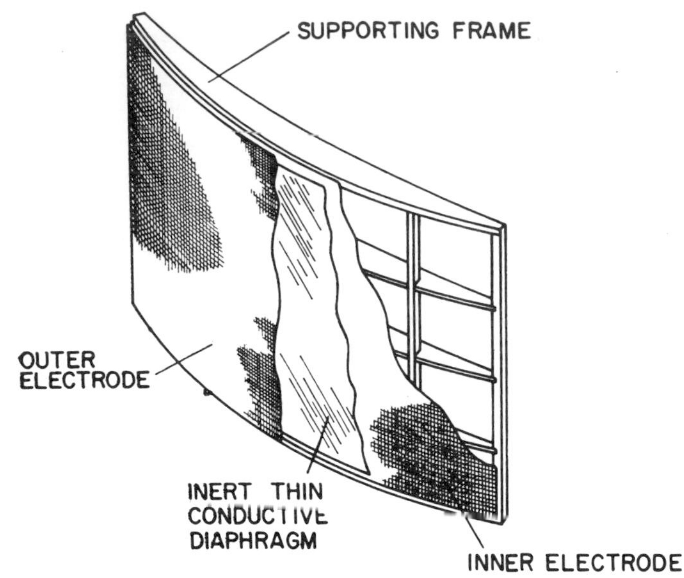

Fig. 1. Constructional aspects of the Isophase push-pull electrostatic speaker. Control of the radius of curvature in the horizontal plane and of the vertical height of the speaker afford control of the sound-dispersion pattern.

acoustically transparent in order to avoid pressure effects from the trapped air, as well as to allow the acoustic energy to move away from the diaphragm.

This construction enables us to make a transducer of any size we wish. The performance per unit area remains the same regardless of the overall area of the diaphragm; the transducer can, in a sense, be turned out like carpet, subject, of course, to limitations of space, cost, etc. Incidentally, we call the working element of the speaker "the sandwich."

FORM OF THE SPEAKER

As Fig. 1 indicates, the speaker is made as a plane surface curved in the horizontal plane: it is a section of a cylinder. As is well known, a surface which is large with respect to the wavelength becomes increasingly directional as a propagator of high frequencies. A surface as large as that of the diaphragm of our speaker sends a large proportion of the high-frequency energy out at right angles to the plane of the surface. By curving the plane in the horizontal direction, we get even dispersion of "highs," all the way out to the end of the reproduced spectrum, over a horizontal angle of 55°.

Since the diaphragm is a flat plane in the vertical direction, the vertical pattern is essentially of a uniform thickness equal to the vertical dimension of the speaker. Thus by controlling the radius of curvature in the horizontal plane and the vertical height of the speaker, it is possible to control the sound-dispersion pattern to the exact requirements of the listening area.

FREQUENCY LIMITS

Since the device is designed to couple directly, in effect, with the air resistance, the mass of the diaphragm, as already mentioned, can be neglected. The velocity of the diaphragm is directly proportional to the electrostatic force applied, except as affected by the stiffness of the suspension. In our speaker, the constants are such that the response is essentially linear to well beyond the limits of hearing. The only clue we have noted thus far as to the limit of response at the high end is a rise and apparent resonance in the impedance curve which may be observed at 35 kc. Pressure-response measurements, using the best available calibrated microphones with constant voltage applied, indicate flat acoustic response to well beyond the human range of hearing.

The factors which limit frequency response at the low end are

1. The maximum linear amplitude of diaphragm motion, as set by the electrode spacing and stiffness of the suspension.

2. The increased power needed to overcome the stiffness of the suspension and maintain sound pressure at low frequencies, with the diaphragm area large enough to move a volume of air adequate for this purpose. (See Fig. 2.)

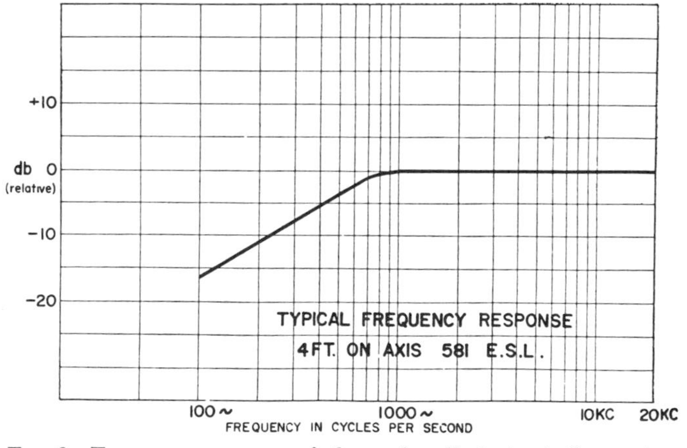

Fig. 2. Frequenc response of the push-pull electrostatic speaker.

EFFICIENCY

For years, most of us have regarded the electrostatic speaker as a device of essentially very low efficiency. This viewpoint is even found in some of the standard reference works. However, our development work seems to throw a somewhat different light on this topic, particularly in relation to extended-range, direct-radiator cone speakers. Our objective, in the present design, was to match—if we could—the efficiencies of the higher-grade woofers with which our electrostatic speaker was intended to be mated. The data

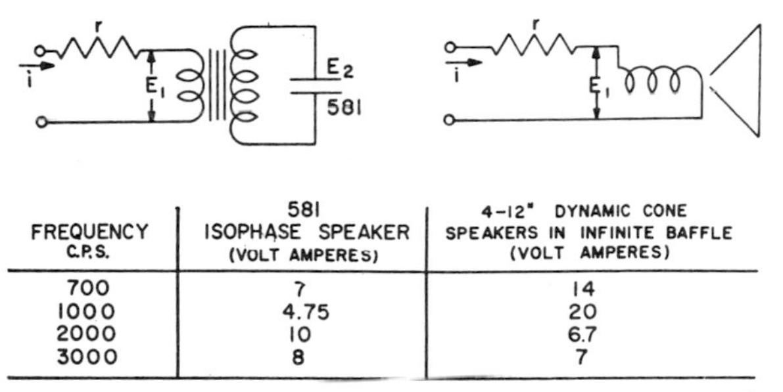

FREQUENCY C.P.S.	581 ISOPHASE SPEAKER (VOLT AMPERES)	4-12" DYNAMIC CONE SPEAKERS IN INFINITE BAFFLE (VOLT AMPERES)
700	7	14
1000	4.75	20
2000	10	6.7
3000	8	7

FIG. 3. Chart showing the relative power required to produce a sound pressure of 3.3 dynes per sq cm at a distance of 4 ft on axis.

in Fig. 3, we feel, indicate that we have been quite successful in this regard. The electrostatic speaker, we are convinced, can "hold up its end" efficiency-wise; nevertheless, we are by no means near the theoretical limits of efficiency yet—not by a good margin!

POWER LIMITS

The maximum power output, with a speaker of any given diaphragm area, is determined by the maximum strength of the electrostatic field that can be produced between the diaphragm and the electrodes. (The ionization of the air is the event encountered at the top limit.) The maximum electrostatic field is the sum of the field produced by the polarizing voltage and that of the peak signal voltage which is superimposed on the field. In this speaker, the polarizing potential is set at 1000 volts dc, and the maximum ac signal for which the speaker is designed is 1000 volts rms. As shown in Fig. 4, with the push-pull connection the signal is split between the two sides of the speaker, so that the peak potential applied between the diaphragm and either electrode is about 1700 volts.

DRIVING THE SPEAKER

An electrostatic speaker is, of course, nothing but a capacitor. The present speaker represents a capacitance of about 0.0025 mfd from electrode to electrode. Thus the impedance which the speaker presents to the output terminals of an amplifier falls off at a constant 6-db-per-octave rate with increasing frequency. This makes it almost impossible—with conventional amplifiers—to maintain constant voltage across the speaker at high power levels, because of the matter of voltage regulation. If the matching transformer is designed for efficient transfer of power to the speaker at the upper end of the audio band, insufficient voltage will be available to operate the speaker at the middle frequencies.

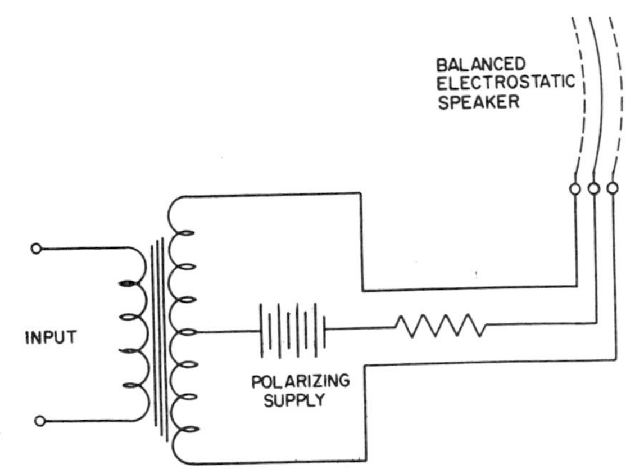

FIG. 4. The application of polarizing and signal voltages to the electrostatic speaker. The peak potential applied between the diaphragm and either electrode at any instant is about 1700 volts.

However, the distribution of energy in typical program material, as is well known, falls off above about 2500 cps at 6 db per octave. Advantage is taken of this typical energy-distribution characteristic in the RIAA[2] disc-recording curve to permit pre-emphasis of the high end of recording, with corresponding attenuation of the high end during playback, for the purpose of improving the signal-to-noise ratio. Thus the applied sound energy falls off at 6 db per octave at the high end.

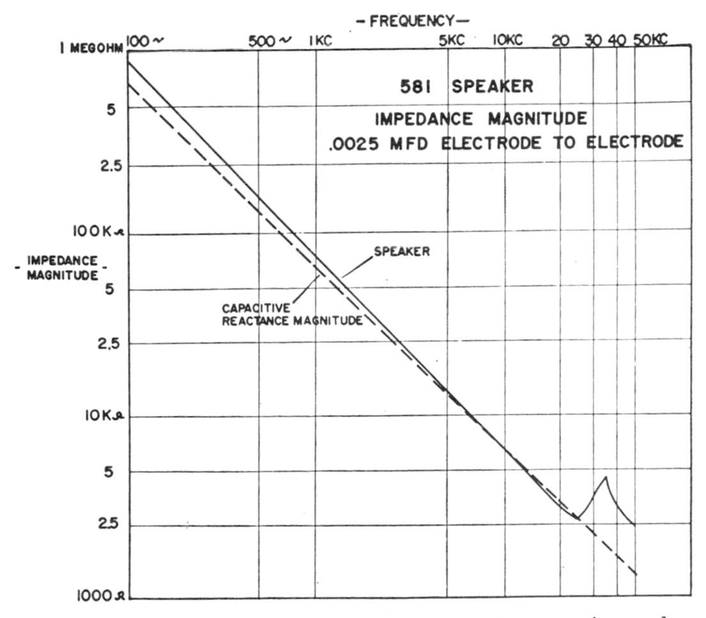

FIG. 5. The variation of impedance in the electrostatic speaker with frequency.

The impedance of the electrostatic speaker also falls off at 6 db per octave (Fig. 5), so that the current through the speaker—with typical program material—is maintained constant. This means that, since power is equal to voltage $\times$ current, the power requirement at the high end drops at about 3 db per octave.

[2] Recording Industry Association of America.

FIG. 6. The large model. This electrostatic speaker is designed to cover the spectrum from 400 cps up.

This makes it possible to couple the speaker to the amplifier for the best energy transfer in the neighborhood of 3000 cps, and insures that program material above this frequency will not overload the amplifier.

POWER REQUIREMENT

Taking into account the energy distribution referred to above and the diaphragm area and other characteristics of the present speaker, the maximum power requirement will occur in the neighborhood of 3000 cps. If we use the figures previously shown for the voltage drive and acoustic output of the speaker, we can calculate that the speaker draws a maximum of 44 watts at its full rated capacity. The power required to drive a given electrostatic speaker design to full rated capacity increases in direct relation to the area of the diaphragm. (See Fig. 5.)

AVAILABLE SPEAKERS AND ADAPTER UNIT

In addition to the large electrostatic speaker thus far discussed, shown in final form in Fig. 6, there is also a *smaller* model, shown in Fig. 7. The large model is designed to cover the spectrum from 400 cps up, and the smaller one from 1000 cps up. With each speaker an adapter unit (Fig. 8) is supplied which performs the following functions:

1. Provides the polarizing voltage.

FIG. 7. The smaller model, designed to cover the spectrum from 1000 cps up.

2. Supplies a dividing network to divide the frequency spectrum between the electrostatic speaker and the woofer to be used with it.
3. Matches the electrostatic speaker to the amplifier.
4. Provides a control for balancing the output of the woofer and the tweeter.

The adapter is connected to the 16-ohm output of any typical high-fidelity amplifier. The woofer and the electrostatic speaker are connected to the adapter. The two speakers are balanced by means of the control on the adapter.

The electrostatic speaker is designed to stand on or near the woofer. It should be placed away from the wall, with each end of the unit at least 6 in. from the wall, if a corner is used.

FIG. 8. The adapter unit supplied with the Isophase electrostatic speakers. The unit provides polarizing voltage and matches the speaker to the amplifier. Incorporated, too, are a dividing network and a manual control for balancing the output of woofer and tweeter.

The Corona Wind Loudspeaker*

GERALD SHIRLEY†

Televex Co., Yonkers, N. Y.

The discovery in England of a method of controlling the wind produced by a corona discharge provides the basis for a new loudspeaker design having no moving parts and offering other potential advantages over conventional speakers. The inventor of the Corona Wind Loudspeaker is Dr. David M. Tombs.‡

The author first describes the construction of a corona triode in which a ring mounted coaxially about one electrode and given suitable potentials is found to control the discharge and hence the magnitude of the wind. Characteristic curves indicating triode-like behavior for various electrode spacings are presented.

By applying an af voltage to the ring, a sound source results. An early experimental model of such a loudspeaker is described and illustrated, together with its observed frequency response. Comparisons with the Ionophone and the electrostatic loudspeaker are made, which indicate its potential superiority in wide range reproduction. The author discusses the acoustical and electrical problems that arise in the construction of a practical loudspeaker, and concludes with details of the research and development program necessary for its commercial realization.

BACKGROUND

UNTIL RECENTLY corona has been regarded almost universally as an undesirable phenomenon, and such studies of it as have been made were usually undertaken with a view to suppressing it. Most engineers in the communications field are aware that it is a source of hf noise and interference, and that countermeasures are regularly applied to aircraft and high voltage power lines. In the latter case the need to control power losses is a primary concern.

Since so little is known about corona on the positive side, it was necessary to make some rather fundamental tests and observations of the phenomenon, and in particular on the wind that accompanies a corona discharge. A convenient method of observing the properties of these winds—direction, strength and pattern—consists of injecting a smoke stream at low velocity into the corona field.

Starting with the simplest case, a pair of electrodes, one of which was sharply pointed and the other blunt, it was found that only the sharp electrode produces a wind. Further, the wind is stronger when the needle (i.e., the sharp electrode) has a positive potential on it than when it bears a negative sign.

In order to control this wind, it was thought that a smooth ring mounted coaxially around the needle might provide a valve action in the same manner as the grid in a triode vacuum tube. It was found that the corona current could be controlled by changing the potential on the ring, and was also affected by the diameter of the ring as well as by its position with respect to the tip of the needle. In order to measure these several parameters so that the "plate characteristics" of the corona triode could be graphed, special laboratory apparatus with micrometer controls and a series of rings of different diameters was constructed. This apparatus is shown in Fig. 1.§ The triode section is on the left. (The two long needles on the right side were used to measure and plot the resistance characteristics of corona diodes, which could be used as 'loads' for corona triodes. These diode characteristics are shown in Fig. 2.) The E_g–I_p–E_p characteristics of the corona triode for several varying geometries are shown in Figs. 3 and 4. The very interesting similarity of these curves to the plate curves for certain triode vacuum tubes is immediately apparent.

In this form—i.e., with one sharp and one dull electrode plus a ring or grid—the corona triode can act as a "uni-

* Paper presented before the June 12, 1956 meeting of the New York Section of the Audio Engineering Society.

† President.

‡ D. M. Tombs, *Nature*, **176**, 923 (1955).

§ Figures 1 to 5 have been furnished through courtesy of Dr. Tombs.

FIG. 1. Laboratory model of the corona triode. The needle and ring-like grid is seen at the left, with the blunt electrode at the center. Grids of various sizes are shown in the foreground.

directional" loudspeaker if an audio signal is applied between grid and the sharp electrode. This is shown diagrammatically in Fig. 5a. The sound output can be described as "modulated dc." In other words, there is a steady (dc, uni-directional) wind accompanying the (ac) sound.

If two sharp electrodes are used in constructing the triode, two opposed winds are created, the positive wind being the stronger of the two, and also having a narrower "beam" as shown by the smoke patterns. By suitable positioning of the grid (and adjustment of its voltage) with respect to the positive needle, it is possible to balance the two winds so that with no signal present there is no "net" wind. This is shown diagrammatically in Fig. 5b.

The amount of sound produced by a single corona triode is very faint, and in order to get sufficient volume a large number of them must be operated in parallel. The first stacked triode speaker which was built utilizes 144 pairs of needles spaced one-half inch apart, giving an outside dimension of $6'' \times 6''$, or one-quarter square foot. This is shown in Fig. 6. The grid was constructed in the form of a screen made up of interlaced wires spaced one-half inch apart. Thus there is a square hole for each pair of needles, and when properly aligned the axes of the needle pairs intersect the centers of the square holes. The supporting structures for the grid and needle matrices shown in the photograph are not the original ones but were hastily improvised by the author, since Dr. Tombs was able to bring only the grid and matrices when he came to the U. S. A. Because of the time element it was not possible to construct a highly accurate structure with guide rails or other similar means to ensure exact mechanical parallelism at all settings, and adjustments have to be made by looking and listening.

The amount of sound produced by this first crude model is still rather small, though it can be reported that AES members sitting in the back row during the demonstration given by the author (June 12, 1956) at a New York Section meeting of the Society in a fairly large room were able to hear what was being reproduced fairly well. It is obvious that a commercially acceptable Corona Wind Loudspeaker (hereafter referred to as CWLS) will have to be considerably larger. Dr. Tombs estimates that four or five square feet may produce adequate volume for home use, though for hi-fi enthusiasts the figure would probably have to be increased. Obviously, too, the ultimate size will be affected not only by the acoustic power output requirements but also by the ultimate efficiency of the device. It is believed that this is one of several factors which can be improved by further research.

CHARACTERISTICS OF THE CORONA WIND LOUDSPEAKER

To any audio engineer, and particularly to any loudspeaker designer, the most significant thing about the CWLS is the absence of any moving parts. Actually this is not the first transducer to convert electrical energy directly into sound. Several years ago the French inventor Klein

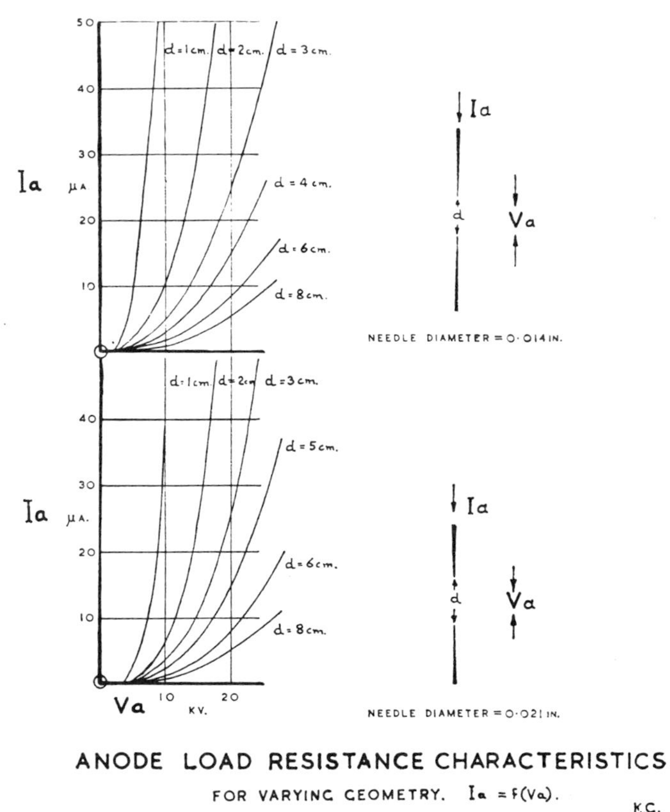

FIG. 2. Corona diode characteristics. The corona current I_a depends upon the electrode potential difference V_a, and the separation d. The effect of the needle diameter, 14 mils (above) and 21 mils (below), is not apparent until d is less than 2 cm.

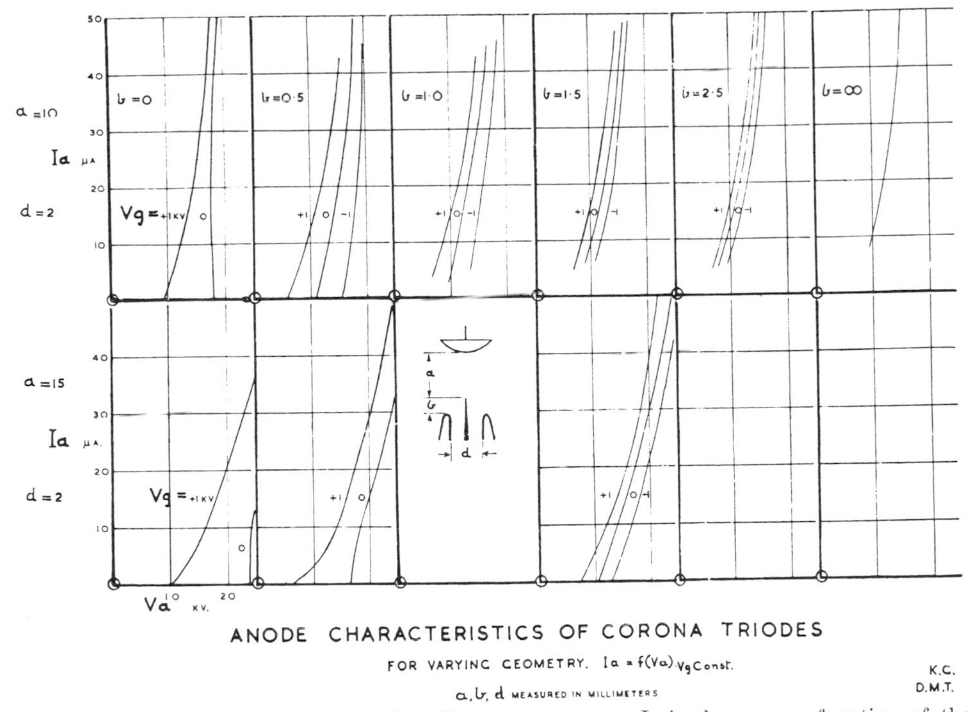

FIG. 3. Corona triode characteristics. The corona current I_a is shown as a function of the electrode potential difference V_a for various electrode spacings and three different grid voltages. At the top, the needle-to-blunt electrode spacing, a, is held at 10 mm, but the needle tip-to-grid distance, b, is varied. Below, a has been increased to 15 mm. In both cases, the needle remains 1 mm away from the grid.

demonstrated his Ionophone[1] which also has no moving parts. On theoretical grounds, at least, the CWLS appears to have certain important advantages over the Ionophone, not the least of which is its wide range, whereas the Ionophone is evidently limited to tweeter applications. Other comparisons which can be made are:

1) the Ionophone is a point source of sound (and a very small point at that) whereas the CWLS is an extended source;
2) the Ionophone functions as a power diode, whereas the CWLS is apparently a triode device, which is more efficient than a diode.

In comparing the CWLS to electrostatic speakers the following points can be made:

1) both are extended rather than point sources of sound, and both are adaptable to push-pull operation;
2) the CWLS can reproduce a wider frequency range, and should be able to create a greater amplitude of air motion at any frequency, both of these advantages deriving from the absence of any diaphragm. (The excursion of the diaphragm in an electrostatic speaker is severely limited);
3) for electrostatic speakers actual watts of audio power are required (to drive an essentially capacitive load) as well as polarizing voltages (these voltages, however, are not high enough to cause ionization).

The requirements for the CWLS, to be discussed in detail further on in this paper, will be seen to be quite different.

Having made these brief comparisons, the discussion will now revert to the characteristics of the CWLS itself, the first of which is its frequency response. The CWLS appears to be capable of covering the entire audio spectrum from zero on up. The very fact that it can produce a wind is prima facie evidence of its low frequency capabilities. However, actual measurements in the range from zero to 20 cycles will present some interesting problems. First of all, to provide an ultra-low frequency signal it is necessary to use a beat-frequency oscillator, since conventional audio oscillators normally extend down to only 20 cycles. Secondly, a microphone which responds all the way down to zero, and is accurately calibrated, is not easily come by—if indeed it exists at all. Subjective judgments are not likely to be of much help considering that the crossover point between hearing and feeling is in the vicinity of 20 cycles. Perhaps a more promising approach would be the observation of the movement of a flame (as from a candle) held in front of the CWLS. This method has been used

1 S. Klein, *Comptes Rendues,* **222,** 1282 (1946), **233,** 143 (1951), *L'Onde Electrique,* **32,** 314 (1952).

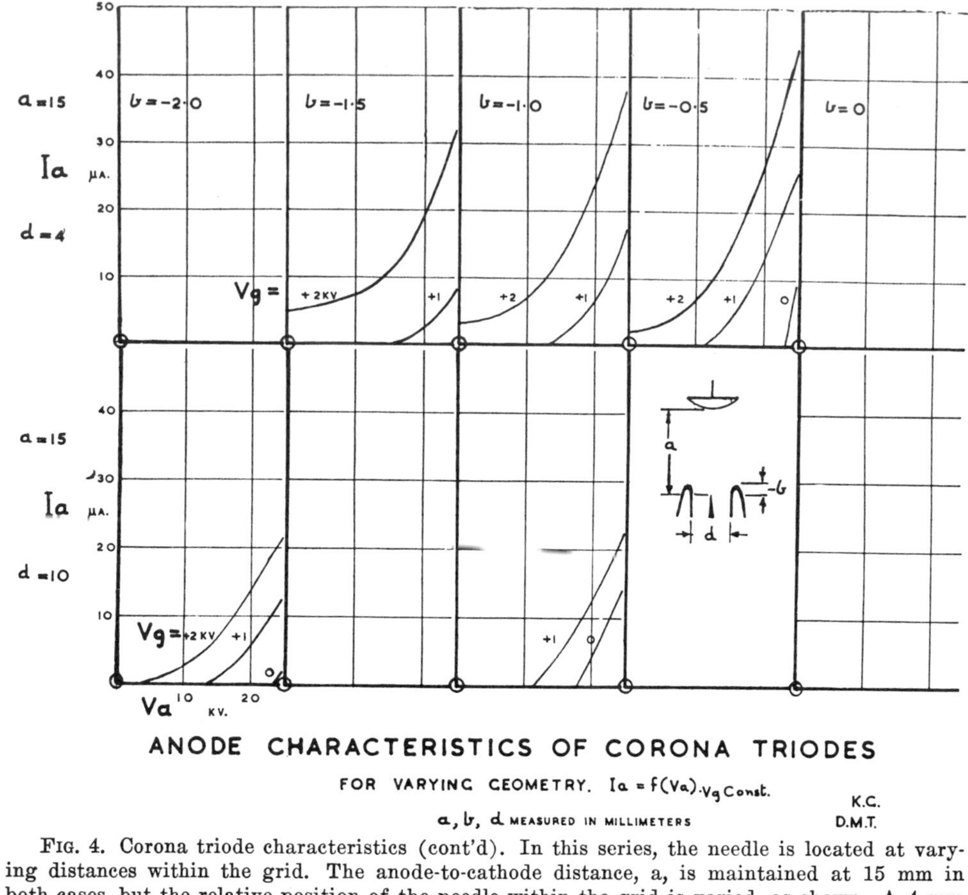

FIG. 4. Corona triode characteristics (cont'd). In this series, the needle is located at varying distances within the grid. The anode-to-cathode distance, a, is maintained at 15 mm in both cases, but the relative position of the needle within the grid is varied, as shown. A 4 mm ring is used in the series at the top, and a 10 mm ring below.

by Dr. Tombs to demonstrate the response at around four or five cycles. It seems likely that a fair degree of accuracy could be achieved in measuring the amplitude of a flame movement by using a specially constructed sighting—or optical projection—device.

The upper limit of frequency response of the CWLS would appear on theoretical grounds to be well up in the ultrasonic region, depending in large measure on the recombination time of an ionized gas. It therefore seems reasonable to anticipate that response to a minimum of 20 kc will be readily obtained.

Due to the absence of moving mechanical parts (and associated suspensions) the overall response curve is in general much smoother than that obtained from a typical cone-type speaker. In Fig. 7 there is shown a curve taken on the first model. The measurements were made with a calibrated microphone over the range shown. This is obviously not yet a "flat" response, and indeed it would have been surprising if perfection had been obtained on the first try. Even so, this curve represents a deviation from flat response of only 3.5 db, assuming a reference frequency of 1500 cycles. The dip at 8000 cycles, which is the only pronounced irregularity in the curve, is apparently related to the physical spacing between the tips of the two sets of needles and corresponds to a half-wavelength at the indicated frequency. Since the spacing can be varied, the position of the dip can be moved up or down, though it is unlikely that this would be the decisive factor in establishing an optimum spacing. More important, it is believed that there are several approaches which could succeed in minimizing the amplitude of the dip, if not in eliminating it completely.

The CWLS is not immune from the degradation of low frequency performance which results from cancellation effects between front and back radiation. In other words baffling is necessary. Depending on the application and the desired low-end response, either a bass reflex or an infinite baffle type enclosure could be used.

No measurements have been made on the polar dispersion pattern as a function of frequency. Theoretically the CWLS should show an increasing tendency towards beaming as the frequency is increased, and subjective judgments based on listening to an audio oscillator indicate that this is so. (In this respect the CWLS is similar to electrostatic

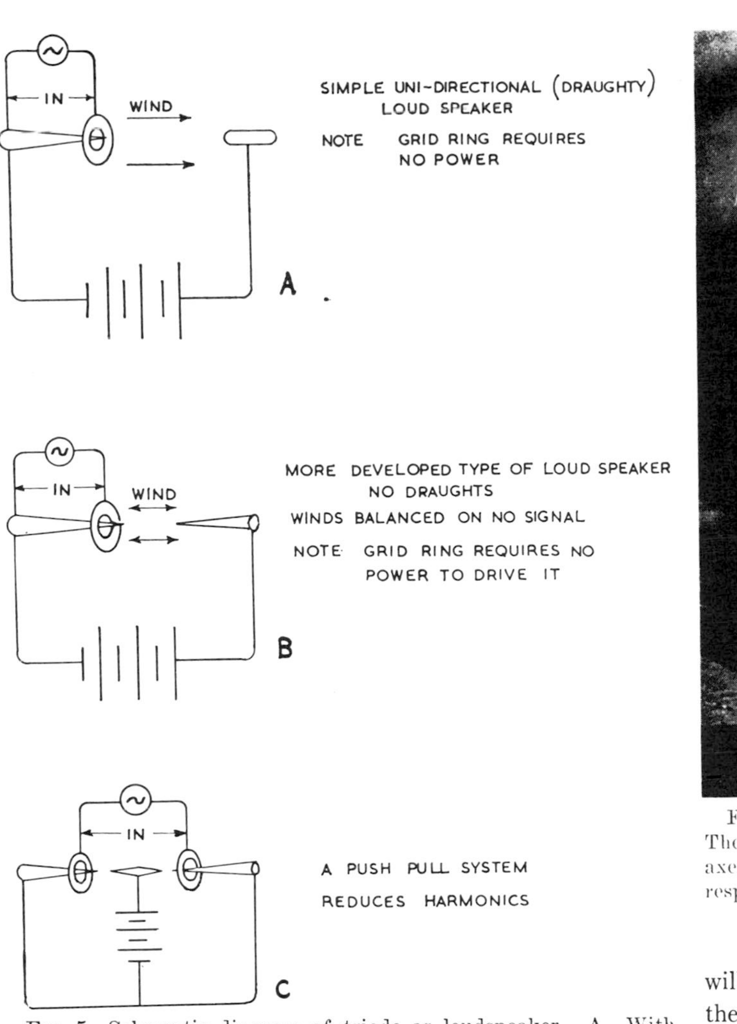

FIG. 5. Schematic diagram of triode as loudspeaker. A. With the polarities shown, an audio signal applied to the grid produces a wind in the anode direction. B. Replacing the blunt anode with a needle causes winds in both directions. C. Push-pull arrangement.

FIG. 6. Experimental form of loudspeaker as an extended source. The grid is a screen with square holes, one-half inch wide. The axes of each electrode pair pass through the center of the corresponding hole.

speakers.) In production models uniform sound dispersion through any desired angle could be obtained by constructing the needle matrices and grids in a curved section rather than in a flat plane. Since these members have to be made rigid anyway, it is thought that there should be no great difficulties in constructing the speaker with a curved cross-section. Alternatively it could be made in narrow planar segments joined together so as to approximate a curved section of any desired arc. Inasmuch as satisfactory vertical dispersion patterns are (evidently) obtained in electrostatic speakers without curving them in two planes, the chances are that double curvature would not be necessary in the CWLS either.

Measurements on distortion have not yet been undertaken. These will be part of the program of research and development on the CWLS, one of whose aims, of course, will be to chart all the relationships between distortion and the various electrical and mechanical parameters. With the first model which is in the author's possession, some distortion is definitely audible, and seems to vary with the mechanical "settings" of the matrices and grid (which are

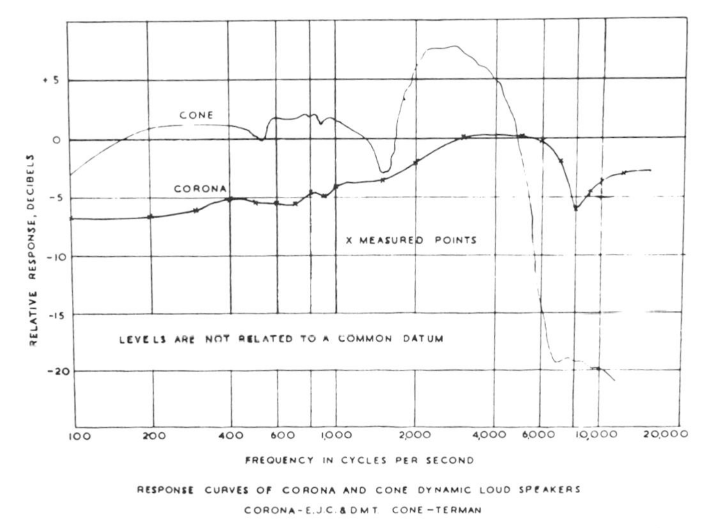

FIG. 7. Frequency response of the experimental loudspeaker. The dip at 8 kc results when the electrode separation is $\lambda/2$ of the applied signal (see text).

not highly accurate, as previously explained), and also on the amount of drive voltage fed into it. The CWLS can be overdriven like any other transducer (despite the absence of a diaphragm), and in playing around with the small model there is always the desire to crank up the volume in order to hear it better. It is interesting to speculate on whether the CWLS may not be inherently less susceptible to intermodulation distortion by virtue of its weightless "invisible diaphragm."

Still on the subject of distortion, a very important point to consider is that the configuration which has been discussed thus far is single-ended—both the speaker and the driver amplifier. It is very easy to construct the CWLS in a symmetrical, push-pull form, one version of which is shown schematically in Fig. 5c. Dr. Tombs has since constructed a push-pull model and reports that the performance is definitely superior to that of the first (single ended) model. It is driven by a push-pull amplifier with negative feedback over the output (driver) stage only. The possibility of applying *over-all* feedback—with all of its well-known benefits—is one that will naturally occur to most readers, and there are several methods whereby this could be accomplished.

Measurements on the acoustic output of the first model show that for minimum audible distortion a figure of about 0.1 mw/sq. cm. is attained, and it is believed that this is roughly comparable to the output of electrostatic speakers. The electrical power input (dc) is about 50 mw/sq. cm. at 12 kv. A quick calculation shows that the efficiency is quite low, but as mentioned earlier, this factor may be susceptible of improvement. Whether such improvement would be nominal or considerable only time and further research will tell. Direct comparisons of efficiency with cone-type speakers are not completely relevant, since with these the lowest level of efficiency which can be tolerated is in part dictated by the economics of providing sufficient watts of audio power to drive them. This is not a desideratum in the case of the CWLS, since only an audio *voltage* is required to drive it, regardless of its physical size and acoustic output. There remains, of course, the economics of the high voltage supply for the corona field, and from this standpoint it is obvious that the goal of improved efficiency will have a priority second only to the goals of linear response and elimination of all distortion.

It is frequently asked whether the background hiss of the corona discharge is objectionably audible. No quantitative measurements have been made, but those who have heard the first model would generally agree that with proper adjustment the hiss is practically inaudible. Starr[2] has shown that radio interference and acoustic hiss can be greatly reduced by using a slender needle. Though the needles used to construct the first model are of small diameter, it is by no means certain that they represent an optimum selection from the viewpoint of hiss-suppression. At close settings of the needle matrices it is necessary that all the tips of each set of needles lie exactly in a plane, and that the two planes be exactly parallel to each other. If this condition is not met, then as the matrices are brought closer together whichever pair of needles has the smallest inter-tip spacing will pass a higher than average corona current and this will be accompanied by audible hissing. As the matrices are moved still closer, at some point arc-over will occur as the dielectric strength of the air is exceeded. In a darkened room one can see the corona discharge, which takes the form of a tiny blue glow at the tip of each needle.

[2] E. C. Starr, A.I.E.E. Technical Paper 40-118 (May 1940).

DRIVE REQUIREMENTS FOR THE CWLS

The required amplitude of the audio driving voltage is in the neighborhood of one to two kv peak to peak. At first glance this may seem like a serious and costly obstacle, but in reality it is quite simple to achieve, inasmuch as a high voltage supply (at least 8 kv) is already required for the corona field. The only other elements needed are a suitable voltage amplifier tube and a load resistor. There are currently available special purpose tubes such as the 6BK4 and 6BD4A originally designed for regulator use in high voltage power supplies, which perform very satisfactorily in this application. These tubes draw very little current and have an amplification factor of 2000. Thus it is necessary to apply only a few volts to the grid in order to get the required 1 to 2 kv swing at the plate which is directly coupled to the grid of the CWLS. The circuit employed in the experimental model is given in Fig. 8.

POWER REQUIREMENTS

The power requirements for the corona field vary proportionately with the number of needle pairs and in inverse ratio to the distance between the opposed tips. The effect of increasing or decreasing the spacing between (adjacent) needles is not yet known. The amount of current drawn is also influenced by the mechanical configuration of the grid structure, its position relative to the needles, and the voltage on it. According to Dr. Tombs' measurements on the first model, each needle pair passes "some tens of microamperes" of current. No precise figure can be given, of course, without defining all the electrical and mechanical conditions.

The minimum voltage required is one that will cause a corona discharge, and maintain it with an adequate margin of reserve to overcome any conditions which might tend to "quench" it. The maximum—tolerable—voltage will be defined by considerations of efficiency, performance, cost, hiss, safety, and so on. There is evidently a wide range

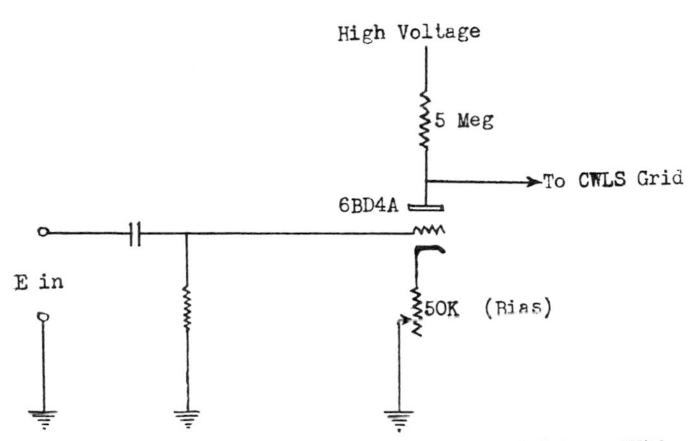

FIG. 8. Schematic diagram of high voltage af driver. With a voltage gain of about 60 db, and an anode supply voltage of from 10 to 20 kv, an audio signal of 1 to 2 kv appears at the anode.

of usable voltages, and one of the goals of the R and D program will be to determine the optimum value.

NON-ACOUSTIC OUTPUTS OF CORONA TRIODES

As an electronic amplifier, the corona triode has a voltage gain of about 3. No especially useful application comes to mind for this, and any suggestions would be welcome. Someone has pointed out that a corona triode—or several in cascade—could be used to obtain the high driving voltage required for a CWLS. This is an intriguing idea, but is probably doing it "the hard way".

The other non-acoustic output of corona triodes is ozone and nitrous oxide, which are by-products of the corona discharge. This will have to be studied carefully to determine whether it presents a health hazard.

RESEARCH AND DEVELOPMENT PROGRAM FOR THE CORONA WIND LOUDSPEAKER

A program of research and development aimed at bringing the CWLS to a point where it can be commercially produced could logically start with a careful investigation of the corona wind phenomenon itself. There are certain fundamental questions whose answers might well save time during later phases of the program. For example: What actually causes the winds? Is the relationship between wind velocity or volume and corona current linear? A search of the literature might uncover earlier studies which could reveal useful information, but it is thought likely that the bulk of references will concern various (usually harmful) effects of corona and methods of suppressing it. In the present instance the goal is to encourage corona—not to discourage it.

The first phase of the R and D program will undoubtedly consider the CWLS only as a wind producing mechanism (corona diode), and will be concerned with investigating and measuring the effects of the various mechanical and electrical parameters on efficiency and hiss. Efficiency would be defined, of course, as the ratio of wind out to power in.

On the mechanical side the starting point of the investigation would be the electrodes themselves. The effects of varying the length, diameter, including angle, and tip radius will all have to be individually determined. It would probably be unwise to start out with any preconceived notions as to what the effects are going to be. In fact, it should not even be assumed that a needle shape is necessarily the best for electrode use. Other shapes and configurations should also be tested. For example, one could try thin-wall tubing of various diameters, down to hypodermic needle sizes, and with various treatments of the emitting ends, such as bevelling (to get a fine edge) or flaring.

On the electrical side, it will be necessary to determine the relationship between power in and wind out, and also whether it makes any difference if the power consists of high voltage at low current or vice versa. Of course, the voltage always has to be high enough to start and maintain the corona discharge, but from that point on there is quite a range.

Dr. Tombs has made an interesting suggestion concerning the possibility of making the tips of the needles radioactive. Ionization should thereby be aided, but whether this would increase the efficiency could only be determined by actual tests.

Not only are the velocity and volume of wind important but also its direction. Dr. Tombs' smoke experiments have shown that positive winds are more tightly 'beamed' (forward) than negative winds. The latter have an umbrella shape. Presumably a negative wind would yield less acoustic output, when modulated, than a positive one. It is possible that by suitably manipulating the dimensions and geometry of a negative electrode its wind could be made more nearly coaxial. (But it is not a foregone conclusion that this would be desirable.) Another interesting possibility is that of somehow turning the negative wind around so that it aids instead of opposes the positive wind.

During the corona diode stage of the R and D program it might be well to get started on a study of the effects of varying humidity levels. Offhand it would seem that a high humidity level might aid the flow of corona current, thus setting a limit to how close the opposed electrode tips could be. In other words, mechanical and electrical specifications might have to be chosen so that arc-over would not occur during periods of abnormally high humidity. If this limitation were found to exact too great a penalty on efficiency (during periods of normal or low humidity), then it might be worthwhile to incorporate a compensating circuit using a humidity-sensing transducer which would automatically adjust the voltage level in reference to the humidity level.

When all the facts are in on the corona diode as a wind producer, the next phase will concern itself with corona triodes. The first subject for consideration is the grid structure. The size and shape of the openings, the width of the walls, the thickness of the structure—all these will have to be individually varied to determine their effects (if any) on efficiency, frequency response and distortion. Tests should also be made with finer mesh grids to see if they offer any advantages over structures which have one hole for each pair of electrodes.

The positioning of the grid with respect to the electrodes is already known to have a significant effect on the operating characteristics, and accurate measurements to chart these relationships will be an important step. Not only does the position of the grid have an effect but also the electrical operating point—i.e., the no-signal dc voltage. If an analogy to vacuum tube operation is valid (and it certainly seems possible on the basis of the triode characteristics), then it may be possible to obtain various types of operation—i.e., Class A, Class AB^{1}, Class AB^{2}, and so on. This could be of significance in later work on the push-pull versions.

Another mechanical variable is the spacing between adjacent electrodes, and this brings up an interesting point. Though the CWLS does not have any moving parts there is a strong temptation to postulate an invisible diaphragm; this leads to some questions as to the physical properties of this diaphragm. Specifically, how porous is it? And does the porosity vary with frequency? The relationship between porosity and efficiency must be fairly obvious. It may turn out that an electrode spacing which yields maximum efficiency at low frequencies (long wavelengths) results in an intolerable attenuation of high frequencies. If such a condition is in fact found to exist, then several solutions are available, the most obvious one being a compromise spacing. Still on the subject of porosity, it may be pertinent to ask whether a negative wind may not be less porous than a positive wind. The reason for this could be that the winds from each electrode in a negative field blow not only forward but also sideways towards the other electrodes. This could perhaps have the effect of making the invisible diaphragm more impervious—i.e., less porous, hence more efficient.

When the analysis of the CWLS as a single-ended transducer is complete, and the effects of every single variable on the operating characteristics (and on each other) are thoroughly understood and measured, then the next phase —push-pull operation—can be started.

However, before too large an expenditure of time and money is made on the development of the CWLS as an air-operated device, it might be well to determine whether its production of ozone actually constitutes a health problem, and if so whether it can be overcome. If it cannot, then the CWLS will be developed for operation in an inert gas, such as argon. In this case the speaker would be mounted in an infinite baffle type of enclosure, but instead of the usual solid front panel (for mounting the speaker) there would be a thin plastic membrane, such as Mylar. (Actually both the speaker and membrane could be set in a short distance from the front edge of the cabinet so that a grill cloth could be attached in front.) In order that the usual drawbacks of diaphragms and elastic suspensions may be avoided, the membrane would probably not be fastened under tension, but would rather be loose and floppy, serving chiefly as a separator between the gas inside and the air outside. While at first glance gas operation might seem to be an undesirable complication, nevertheless it may offer some unsuspected advantages such as better efficiency, lower distortion, etc. One known advantage is that there would be no problem of metal corrosion, which does exist with air operation. The ozone and nitrous oxide which result from corona discharges in air have a corrosive effect on certain metals. Dr. Tombs has suggested that it may be possible to neutralize these chemical compounds by providing a "sacrifice" material within the speaker enclosure which the compounds could attack. (The analogy to sacrificial magnesium anodes used in water tanks and on ship hulls comes to mind.) The electrodes, or their emitting tips, could be made of stainless steel or some other corrosion-resistant metal. The grids and support structures could be made of less expensive metal and protected by a coat of suitable plastic (such as du Pont Hypalon).

In experimenting with push-pull configurations different combinations of electrodes—positive, negative, sharp, blunt —can be tried, as well as various classes of operation (Class A, Class AB^{1}, etc.). As mentioned earlier, it may be worthwhile to try to turn the negative winds around so that they aid their respective positive winds. In this way each half of the speaker would produce one wind instead of a pair, and this might improve certain of the operating characteristics.

With push-pull operation, excitation of the corona field by rf power (instead of dc) may be feasible, and this presents a number of interesting possibilities which should be looked into. (The analogy to high frequency bias in tape recording comes to mind, though it may not be a valid analogy.)

Still on the subject of power supplies, the subject of regulation is one that would probably be started on during the earlier single-ended phase of the program and would of course continue on through into the push-pull phase. Since the cost of power supplies bears a direct relation to the degree of built-in regulation, it is clear that one of the goals of the program will be to find a combination of mechanical and electrical parameters which will yield optimum acoustic performance and at the same time require as little regulation as possible in the power supply.

The last important project will be the development of an over-all feedback system so that any residual distortion or irregularity in the response curve will be eliminated, or at least reduced to insignificant proportions. This boils down to finding a suitable transducer to sample the acoustic output and provide a corresponding voltage which can be fed back into the driver amplifier. A microphone comes to mind immediately, of course, but it must be remembered that ordinary microphones are neither wide-ranged (compared to the CWLS) nor particularly flat. It might be possible to make a very simple condenser type of microphone at low cost which would be incorporated right in the speaker.

In summary, one can fairly say that the complete R and D program for the CWLS will represent a rather extensive undertaking. However, there appear to be good reasons for believing that the final results should fully justify the costs of the program.

Note Added in Proof

After completing this paper, the author sent a copy to Dr. Tombs for his comments. In his reply, Dr. Tombs calls attention to an error in the description of the corona wind:

"It is obvious that I have not made myself clear about the shape of the negative corona wind. This is not umbrella-shaped in the absence of a positive wind. Positive and negative winds separately are similar in shape, the positive being rather stronger than the negative, and it is the interaction of these two blowing simultaneously which appears to give the umbrella shape in the proximity of the negative electrode."

He also comments on the drive requirements and the efficiency comparisons:

" . . . I suggest . . . that you should mention that only very small power is required to drive the Corona Loudspeaker, the power being primarily to make good the losses in . . . the way . . . the driving power of the grid of a valve . . . has to make good the losses . . . It might be worthwhile pointing out that the efficiency of ordinary loudspeakers is very low and the power required to drive them is not a measure of the acoustic power generated. The CWLS requires negligible power. The loudspeaker is in fact a control device like a valve, in which the power is supplied by the polarizing high voltage source."

EDITOR'S NOTE: Additional photographs and description of the CWLS may be found in the recent paper: D. M. Tombs, E. J. Chatterton, and K. Galpin, *Electronics,* **30**, No. 7, p. 198 (July 1, 1957).

Problems of Bass Reproduction in Loudspeakers*

E. M. Villchur

Acoustic Research, Inc., Cambridge, Massachusetts

The special problems of speaker bass performance: harmonic distortion, frequency range, and uniformity of response (an index of transient response) are discussed, and approaches to their solution are made.

The special problems associated with speaker bass reproduction have to do with harmonic distortion, uniformity of frequency response (an index of transient response), and frequency range. Such a statement could be made about many other elements of a sound reproducing system, and applied to other portions of the frequency spectrum, but the problems to be discussed here are peculiar both to speakers in general and particularly to their reproduction of the low-frequency range.

We can probably best establish a background for these problems and their current modes of solution by considering the case of a speaker mounted in an infinite baffle, that is, facing its audience through a hole in a large wall.

That frequency whose wavelength is equal to about ⅔ the diameter of the cone is called the frequency of ultimate air-load resistance. Above this frequency the air-load resistance (which, for a given cone velocity, tells us how much acoustic energy will be accepted by the air from the speaker) remains essentially constant. Below this frequency, however, the air-load resistance decreases by a factor of 4 for each lower octave—the cone progressively loses some of its "bite."[1] Thus, if we are to maintain constant acoustic output from our speaker below the frequency of ultimate air-load resistance—approximately 800 cps for a 12-in. speaker—the cone velocity must double with each lower octave, and the cone excursion must *quadruple* with each lower octave.

Current dynamic speakers are mass-controlled over the bass range (above their mounted resonant frequency), unless they are over- or under-damped, and the requirement for doubling of cone velocity with each lower octave is automatically fulfilled, at least in theory. It is the second listed requirement, that of increasing voice-coil travel by a factor of four for each halving of the frequency, which constitutes the core of the problem of bass reproduction in speakers. Large excursions introduce values of bass harmonic distortion which would be indignantly rejected as unacceptable in the case of any other component, and they make the problem of producing fundamental energy at extreme low frequencies very difficult. A recent report[2] by a consumer testing organization, the Audio League, indicated that speakers with anything less than 30% distortion in acoustical output, at 30 cps and at moderate power, were few in number. Distortion ratings for amplifiers are often carried to the second decimal place; speaker distortion ratings are conspicuous by their rarity.

There are three basic approaches to providing the large air displacements needed. These are as follows:

(1) Horn loading the diaphragm. The effective radiating area of the diaphragm may be increased to that of the horn's mouth, and a given acoustic output will be associated with a much smaller excursion of the actual mechanical diaphragm. Horn loading also brings with it its own special problems. The rate of flare must be gradual enough to keep the cutoff frequency low; the mouth area must be large enough to minimize the impedance discontinuity between the horn and the room, and the attendant standing-wave resonances. These requirements add up to a large structure. The volume of this structure may, however, be reduced by using the walls of the room as an extension of the horn flare, as in the well-known Klipsch design.

(2) Use of an acoustical resonator in mesh with the mechanical resonant system of the speaker. The speaker diaphragm is made to radiate through an acoustical resonator, normally tuned to the same frequency as, and anti-resonant to, the speaker itself. In the bass-reflex system the rear of

* Presented September 28, 1956 at the Eighth Annual Convention of the Audio Engineering Society, New York.

[1] J. G. Frayne and H. Wolfe, *Elements of Sound Recording* (John Wiley and Sons, New York, 1949), Chap. 30.

[2] The Audio League Report, Vol. 1, No. 9, October, 1955.

the speaker communicates with the room through a Helmholtz resonator; in other systems, such as the RJ and the Kelton, the front of the diaphragm faces into the resonator; and in the acoustical labyrinth type, the rear of the cone faces an air column. When the resonator is correctly tuned and damped in relation to the speaker used, it, like the horn, enables the system to radiate a given acoustical bass power with smaller diaphragm excursions. It also brings its own special problems into the picture; unless the acoustical resonator is properly damped, it will introduce ringing and exaggeration of part of the bass range.

(3) Use of a baffled direct-radiator with a moving system capable of executing the required large excursions. This involves either wall mounting or a large, rigid cabinet, unless the acoustic suspension system referred to later is employed. The present paper will concentrate on the direct-radiator approach, since the author's own experience has yielded the most success in this direction.

The burden placed on the speaker mechanism at bass frequencies is by far the greatest in a direct-radiator system. This burden is not, however, impractically large, as is sometimes believed. For example, the center-to-peak excursion required of a 10-in.-diam rigid piston (representing a nominal 12-in. speaker) at 30 cps, for an acoustical power output of 0.2 w, is reported by Massa[3] to be 0.58 in. This is for the case of radiation into a solid angle of 180 deg. If we consider the far more typical situation of radiation into 90 deg (speaker mounted at the junction of floor and wall, for example), the radiated power at this frequency, for the same excursion, is doubled, and with the speaker radiating from a three-sided corner the power is increased by a factor of four. A 12-in. direct-radiator, mounted in a solid angle of 45 deg, can thus radiate slightly less than 0.2 acoustical watt at 30 cps with half-inch, peak-to-peak excursions. This power will create an over-all intensity level of about 97 db in a 3000-cu-ft living room of typical reverberation characteristics; at very low frequencies 0.2 w will create an even higher intensity level due to increased reverberation time.

In comparing the performance described above with that of a horn-loaded system, it must be remembered that 30 cps is well below the cutoff frequency of commercial horns. The horn has largely ceased to load the driver in the 30-cps region.

The practicality of excursions of the order of ½ in. may be demonstrated visually with a Strobotac, microphone, and oscilloscope. The microphone and oscilloscope serve to monitor the linearity of the acoustic output of the speaker, while the Strobotac is tuned a cycle or two off frequency from the speaker, so that the cone excursions appear as a slow "breathing."

Such large excursion requirements, in addition to increasing the problem of bass harmonic distortion, influence performance in other ways. When the speaker moving system, for one reason or another, is unwilling to provide the necessary excursions in a linear manner, the amplitude of the fundamental output is reduced, and the range of bass response suffers. An input test signal of 30 cps may produce a loud sound from the speaker but little actual 30-cps output.

The third problem referred to, uniformity of frequency response, is associated with resonance and damping, but the practical nature of the problem changes with the type of speaker system used. In direct-radiators the electromechanical system of the speaker itself is primarily involved. In horn and resonant systems it is the acoustical system that is of primary importance.

The above general discussion is based on some fairly simple mathematical relationships, which we may now describe. The acoustical power output of a speaker can be represented by the familiar I^2R term, where I is the diaphragm velocity and R the air-load resistance reflected into the speaker mechanical system. We know that R will be reduced by 4 for each octave below the frequency of ultimate air-load resistance. The diaphragm velocity I must then double with each lower octave to keep the I^2R term constant in value. If we now take into consideration the inverse relationship between frequency and excursion (with velocity held constant), it will be seen that the diaphragm excursion must quadruple when the frequency is halved to keep I^2R the same.

Just as current through an electrical circuit whose impedance is predominantly inductive will, for a given applied voltage, be doubled for each lower octave (ignoring resistive elements in the circuit), so velocity in a mechanical system whose predominant impedance is mass will, for a given applied force, be doubled for each lower octave. Below resonance, however, the speaker mechanical system is no longer mass-controlled. If it were resistance-controlled, velocity would remain constant, and output would be attenuated at the rate of 6 db/octave due to the continuing drop in air-load resistance. In fact, it is compliance-controlled—the predominant impedance is that of the elastic restoring force of the system—and bass output is therefore attenuated at the rate of 12 db/octave.

The transient response of an electrical circuit with both reactive and resistive components may be described quantitatively, and the same expressions apply to the speaker mechanical system. Transient response refers to the performance of the system during the attack and decay portions of the sound. In discussing bass transient response we are concerned primarily with the decay; attack frequencies are reproduced by whatever unit handles the higher frequency sound components and may not even involve the woofer at all.

The tendency of a system to ring is described by its Q. A high Q system shows a response peak at its resonant fre-

[3] Frank Massa, *Acoustic Design Charts,* The Blakiston Company, 1942, Chart 61, p. 127.

quency and exhibits hangover—it continues to oscillate after the stimulus is removed. A system with a Q of about one has the flattest response curve, and does not ring appreciably. Values of Q lower than one are also indicative of a condition of no-ringing, but response in the region of resonance is attenuated. The well-known family of universal Q curves illustrates these relationships exactly.[4]

In resonant-type enclosures, and especially in horns, the mechanical Q of the speaker itself is liable to be of relatively minor significance, as the resistance elements in the speaker mechanism are swamped by acoustical resistance terms. In direct-radiators the speaker's mechanical Q assumes primary importance.

THE ACOUSTIC SUSPENSION SYSTEM

The general nature of the problem has been discussed briefly. We may now consider in further detail one particular solution—that offered by the acoustic suspension system (specifically, by the Acoustic Research model AR-1 speaker system).

Bass harmonic distortion in speakers derives primarily from the nonlinearity associated with large excursions. This nonlinearity is, in turn, primarily a function of two things: (1) decrease of magnetic flux around the voice-coil when the coil is in its extreme positions, and (2) nonlinear increase of elastic restraint imposed by the mechanical cone suspensions.

The first of these difficulties can be met by making the voice-coil longer than the gap, so that the same amount of copper is always immersed in the field within a given range of excursion. Since part of the voice-coil then becomes inactive, there is a definite sacrifice in efficiency. In the case of the AR-1 woofer, the total voice-coil overhang is half an inch; that is, the voice-coil is half an inch longer than the gap.

The second (and normally more serious) difficulty has been the target of the efforts of speaker design engineers for some twenty-five years. The acoustic suspension approach cuts rather than unties the Gordian knot.

The mechanical suspensions of a loudspeaker serve two functions. They must center the voice-coil in the gap so that it does not rub, and they must provide an elastic restoring force to the moving system. This elastic restoring force, in conjunction with the moving mass, determines the mechanical bass resonant frequency. With too little restoring force the bass resonant frequency becomes lower than it should be for that particular speaker, and the bass excursions increase to values within the nonlinear range. Other things being equal, we would like the resonant frequency to be as low as possible, but the lowest resonant frequency that we can afford for a given power rating must be selected on the basis of the allowable linear excursion which a particular

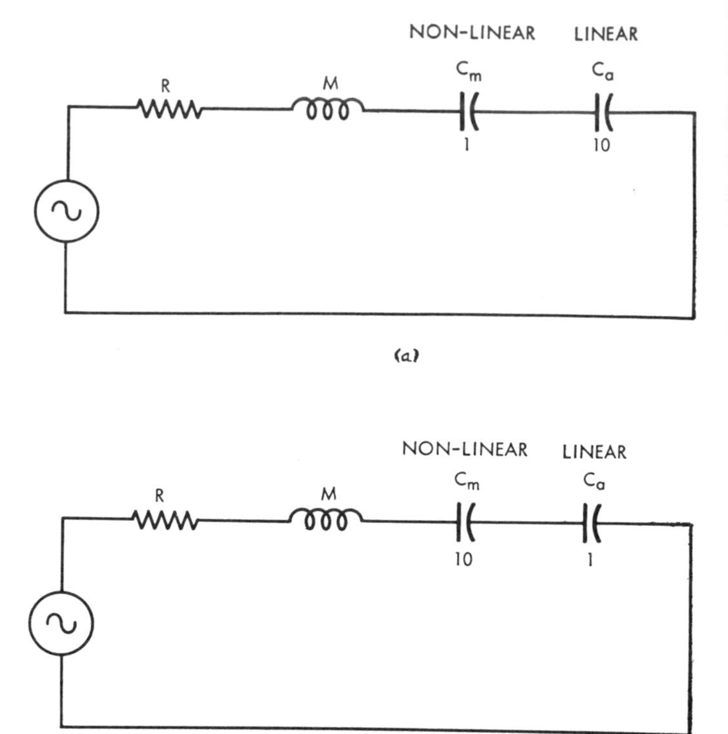

FIG. 1. (a) Simplified electrical analogy to the mechanical system of a conventional direct-radiator speaker using a large, totally enclosed cabinet. The acoustic stiffness reactance of the air in the cabinet, X_{C_A}, is small compared to X_{C_M}, the mechanical stiffness reactance of the speaker suspensions. (b) Electrical analogy to the mechanical system of the acoustic suspension speaker. The mechanical stiffness of the speaker suspensions is small compared to the acoustic stiffness of the air in the cabinet. Here C_M and C_A are interchanged in value compared to Fig. 1(a), and the controlling stiffness is the linear C_A rather than the nonlinear C_M.

speaker will provide. It may be noted at this point that the worse the mechanico-acoustic coupling of the speaker system, the greater the excursions required for a given acoustical power, and the higher the safe resonant frequency is liable to be. Thus, speakers with small cone diameters are properly designed with higher resonant frequencies, and speaker systems which employ bass acoustical loading other than direct can afford lower resonant frequencies.

The AR-1 acoustic suspension woofer was designed, in terms of allowable excursion and power handling capability,

FIG. 2. Acoustic suspension low-frequency speaker system, plus separately housed tweeter (Acoustic Research model AR-1).

[4] Leo L. Beranek, *Acoustics* (McGraw-Hill Book Company, Inc., New York, 1954), p. 226.

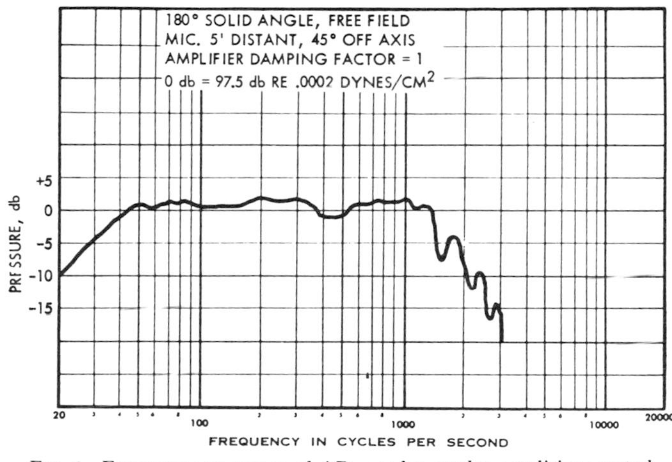

FIG. 3. Frequency response of AR woofer, under conditions noted.

for a resonant frequency of about 43 cps. The normal approach to designing a direct-radiator, once this parameter has been determined, would be to provide spider and rim suspensions with an elastic restoring force such that in conjunction with the moving mass the resonance of the mechanical system would be 43 cps. The speaker would then be mounted in a wall or in an enclosure of such large dimensions that the acoustic stiffness of the air enclosed behind the cone would not add any appreciable elastic restoring force to the system and would not raise its resonant frequency.

The acoustic spspension system uses a different approach; the speaker suspensions are designed with only a very small part of their usual elastic stiffness, and the speaker mechanism has a subsonic resonant frequency. It should be clear from the previous discussion that the AR woofer by itself is a "crippled" unit, unsuitable for conventional direct-radiator mounting. When this speaker is mounted in a small, acoustically sealed enclosure, however,

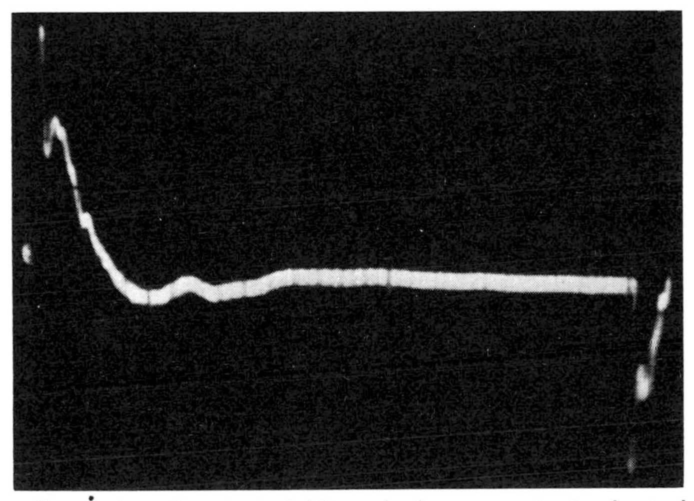
FIG. 4. Acoustic output of AR woofer in response to step front of 20-cps square wave. Same test conditions as for Fig. 3.

the elastic restoring force of the sealed-in air replaces the decimated mechanical stiffness of the speaker suspensions. The volume of the enclosure is adjusted to provide a final resonant frequency of that value for which the speaker was designed, that is, 43 cps. The cabinet is unusually rigid, and is filled, rather than lined, with sound absorbent material, but these features are not fundamental to the design concept.

The substitution of acoustical for mechanical elasticity virtually replaces a nonlinear element by an almost ideally linear one, within the range of compressions and rarefactions involved. The result is a radical decrease in bass harmonic distortion, particularly at the extreme low frequencies. The bass response of the speaker system conforms accurately to the theoretical curve that can be expected of an ideal direct-radiator with a given resonant frequency in its final mounting. The only advantage of the acoustic suspension system with respect to bass response lies in the absence of the influence of nonlinear mechanical suspensions to impede the large excursions required at low frequencies.

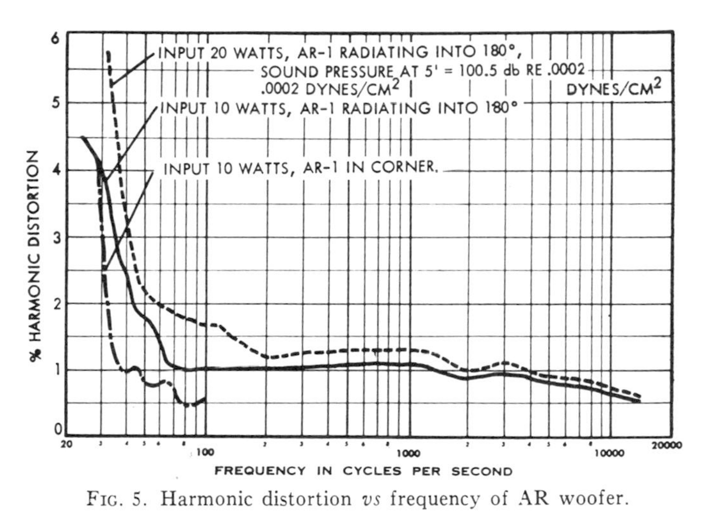

FIG. 5. Harmonic distortion *vs* frequency of AR woofer.

Figure 1(a) is a simplified electrical analogy to the mechanical system of a direct-radiator speaker in a large "infinite baffle" type enclosure. The compliance of the enclosed air C_A is very large in relation to C_M, the mechanical compliance of the speaker suspensions, so that the cabinet does not significantly raise the resonant frequency of the system. The controlling stiffness reactance is therefore mechanical. Figure 1(b) is the electrical analogy to the acoustic suspension system. It may be seen that the only apparent difference is quantitative. The relative values of C_A and C_M are interchanged, and the controlling stiffness reactance is that of the air in the cabinet.

In spite of the traditionally conceived relationship between the size of a speaker installation and bass performance, the acoustic suspension speaker system is subject to all the advantages and disadvantages of an infinite baffle

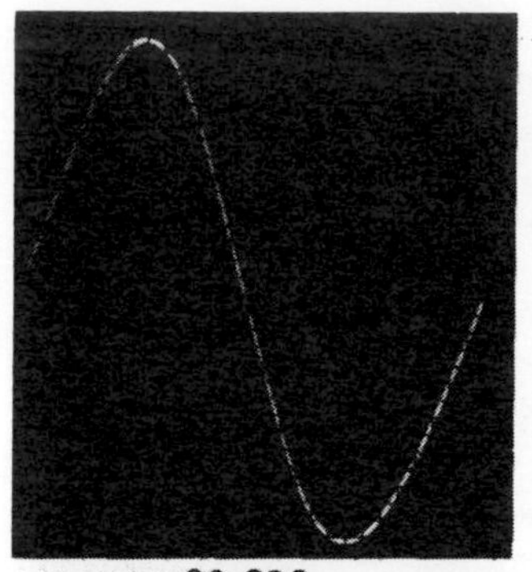

60 CPS

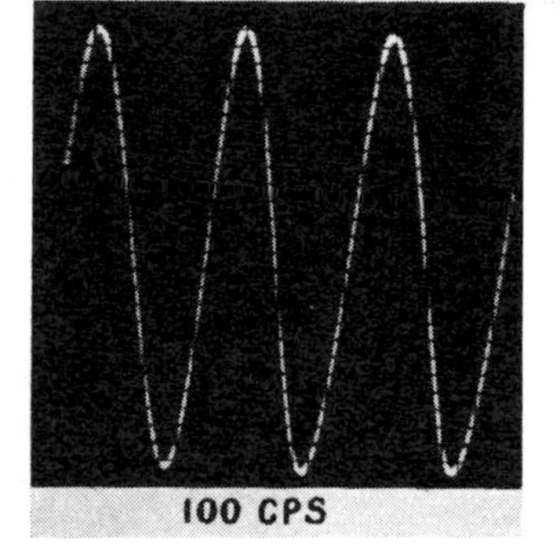

FIG. 6. Oscilloscope photographs of acoustic output of AR woofer at 32, 60, and 100 cps. Input power (to rated impedance) 10 w; acoustical pressure at 5 ft, 97.5 db *re* 0.0002 dyne/cm^2; mounted in 3-sided corner of room.

system, with two important differences—the increased excursion linearity and the large reduction in optimum cabinet size, the latter turning up as an extra dividend. Other than the above, the design problems of an acoustic suspension system are precisely those of a speaker in an infinite baffle or large totally enclosed cabinet. Figure 2 illustrates the enclosure and the woofer of the AR-1, plus a tweeter which is separately housed in the box at the right.

Figure 3 shows the frequency response of a recent unselected production model of an AR-1 woofer, as measured in an open field with the system radiating into a solid angle of 180 deg (sunk into the earth, the cabinet face flush with the surface of the ground). Details of the conditions of measurement have been published elsewhere.[5]

The oscilloscope photograph of Fig. 4 illustrates the bass transient response; it plots the acoustic output of the speaker following stimulation by the step wave front of a 20-cps square wave under the same measurement conditions.

Figure 5 gives information on the harmonic distortion *vs* frequency of the AR woofer, and Fig. 6 consists of oscilloscope photographs of the acoustic output of the AR woofer at 32, 60, and 100 cps. These photographs were taken with the speaker mounted more favorably than under open field conditions—in the corner of a room. The input electrical power was 10 w, the acoustical pressure at the 5-ft distant microphone was 97.5 db *re* 0.0002 dyne/cm^2.

The grossest deficiencies that exist in current sound reproducing systems include those due to poor low-frequency performance in loudspeakers. High harmonic distortion and peaked response (which implies ringing on transients) are tolerated. At the same time this is the subject about which the least quantitative data are available, a condition which the writer feels is in urgent need of correction.

---

[5] E. M. Villchur, "Commercial Acoustic Suspension Speaker," *Audio*, July, 1955.

Application of Negative Impedance Amplifiers to Loudspeaker Systems*

R. E. WERNER and R. M. CARRELL
Radio Corporation of America, Camden, N. J.

Successful application of negative damping factors to loudspeakers is not so difficult a task as one would infer from the literature of recent years. Foremost in importance are the cancellation of voice-coil inductance as well as resistance, equalization for low-frequency radiation characteristics; and utilization of infinite baffle rather than a reflex or horn type. When satisfactory attention is granted these factors, substantial improvement in loudspeaker performance is almost certain. In a typical application of a negative impedance amplifier, resonant hangover is eliminated, the nonlinear distortion halved, and the low-frequency response leveled and extended about an octave.

INTRODUCTION

IT IS well known that the output impedance of an amplifier affects the performance of a moving-coil loudspeaker to which it is connected. However, comparatively little attention has been given to the behavior of loudspeakers when driven by negative impedance sources.

GENERAL EFFECTS OF OUTPUT IMPEDANCE

The performance of a loudspeaker in the frequency range where cone breakup occurs is more or less beyond the control of the driving amplifier. At frequencies below about 1000 cps, however, the sound pressure is directly determined by the motion of the voice-coil. Just as the mechanical load on an electric motor is reflected as a change in electrical load on the power line, so are the mechanical characteristics of a loudspeaker reflected into the electrical circuit. Thus it should be (and is) possible to utilize the changes in electrical impedance to control the electrical signal to compensate for undesirable changes in mechanical impedance.

Referring all of the low-frequency mechanical and acoustical characteristics of the loudspeaker to the electrical circuit results in the equivalent circuit of Fig. 1. Here it is seen that the cone suspension and box compliance combine to form a single inductance. Since the cone suspension is non-linear, this non-linearity is reflected in the inductance. This inductance is in parallel with the capacitance which represents the reflected mass of the cone. These elements resonate to give the familiar rise of impedance at resonance. If it were possible to connect a very low impedance generator across these elements, the cone resonance would be eliminated. Furthermore, since the compliance is short-circuited, the non-linear distortion is reduced. Unfortunately, the voice-coil impedance isolates these components from the speaker terminals, so that to achieve these effects we must effectively eliminate the voice-coil impedance. An amplifier whose output is negative can accomplish just that. Whether or not the results are as desired is dependent upon factors which, to be identified, require more than a cursory examination of the equivalent circuit.

LOW-FREQUENCY RESPONSE

The basic factor in the low-frequency response of a loudspeaker is the radiation resistance of the cone, which increases with the square of the frequency, that is, at a rate of 12 db/octave. If the velocity of the cone were independent of frequency, as it is when it is heavily damped, it can be shown that the sound pressure in front of the speaker will rise 6 db/octave with increasing frequency. In the ordinary loudspeaker uniform low-frequency response is obtained by making the cone resonant at a low frequency. Above the resonant frequency, the cone is mass-controlled and its velocity falls 6 db/octave with increasing frequency, compensating for the rising radiation resistance of the cone, and resulting in uniform sound pressure output. Fig. 2 illustrates the influence of the radiation resistance on the response of a loudspeaker.

If the loudspeaker cone is heavily damped by any means, its velocity will tend to become independent of frequency and the low-frequency response will fall off with a 6 db/octave

* Received October 7, 1957. Delivered before the Ninth Annual Convention of the Audio Engineering Society, October 12, 1957.

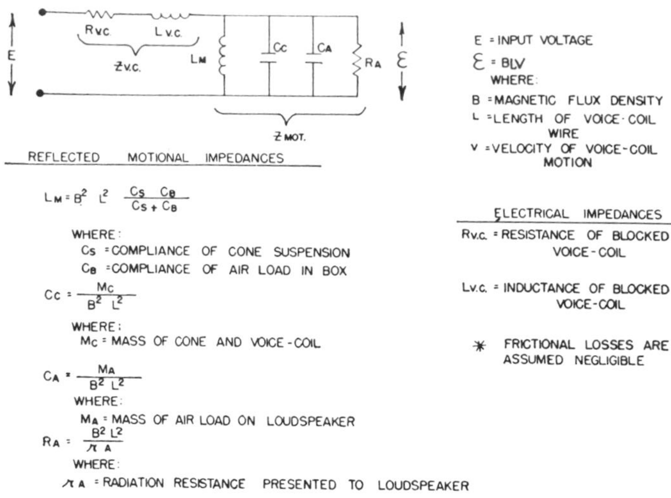

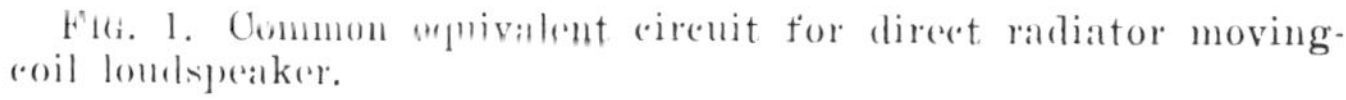

Fig. 1. Common equivalent circuit for direct radiator moving-coil loudspeaker.

slope. This must be compensated for by equalization in the amplifier. If the damping is accomplished by means of acoustical or mechanical damping, the damping constitutes a power sink and the amplifier must deliver substantially greater power output at low frequencies. If the damping is accomplished by electrical means, then the amplifier need not supply added power down to the resonant frequency of the loudspeaker. If the compensation is carried beyond the speaker resonance, then additional power will be required. Curves 1 and 2 of Fig. 3 indicate the output requirements of a negative impedance amplifier at low frequencies.

HIGH FREQUENCIES

In the high-frequency range, the voice-coil serves mainly to excite the cone and exercises little control over its vibration. Therefore there is little that can be done electrically (other than simple equalization) to compensate for deficiencies in the high-frequency performance.

Unless the negative impedance amplifier is properly designed for the speaker with which it is used, the interaction of the speaker and amplifier may seriously upset the overall frequency response curve.

If the amplifier is designed to exhibit only a negative output resistance sufficient to nearly cancel the voice-coil resistance, the voice-coil inductance will remain in series with the parallel resonant circuit which constitutes the motional impedance of the cone. This voice-coil inductance will resonant with the capacitance of the motional impedance at a frequency of a few hundred cps. The resonance can be quite pronounced, since the resistance in the circuit is nearly cancelled out.

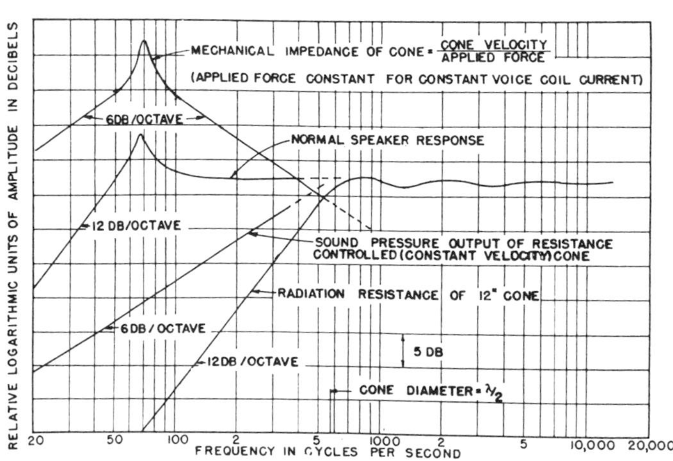

Fig. 2. Impedance and radiation characteristics of a hypothetical 12" loudspeaker cone in an infinite flat baffle.

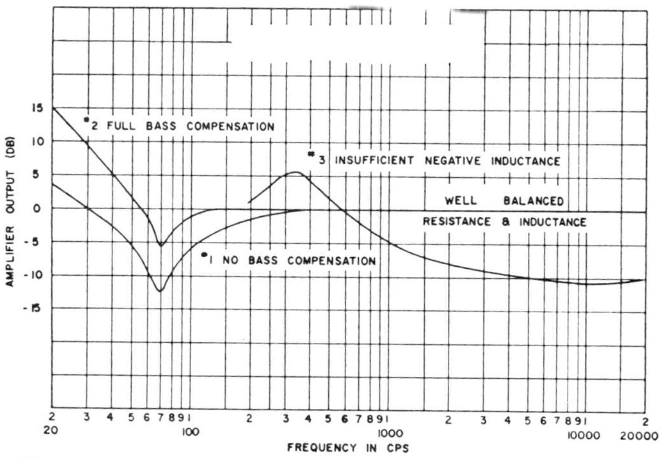

Fig. 3. Response of negative impedance amplifier at loudspeaker terminals.

It is necessary, then, that the inductance, as well as the resistance, of the voice-coil be cancelled out. This is simple enough in principle. Accomplishing this is another matter, since the voice-coil is surrounded by the iron magnet structure with its hysteresis and eddy-current losses. This results in a rather impure inductance, whose impedance may not rise at 6 db/octave.

If the actual impedance characteristic of the speaker is not matched by the negative output impedance of the amplifier, the overall high frequency response characteristic may resemble curve 3 of Fig. 3.

These effects become more pronounced as the impedance of the voice-coil is more nearly cancelled out.

A neglect of the voice-coil inductance may account for some of the disappointment which has attended the use of negative output impedance amplifiers. Certainly, the use of a large negative resistance alone will degrade the performance of the speaker rather than improve it.

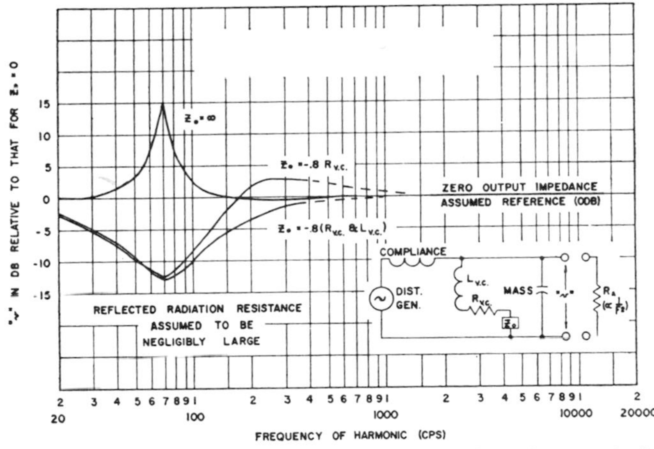

FIG. 4. Effect of output impedance on distortion of cone velocity relative to distortion for zero output impedance.

TRANSIENT RESPONSE

In general the discussion on frequency response is applicable to transient response problems. If the voice-coil impedance is shorted out, the resonant mechanical circuits are effectively shorted out. Here too it is important that the voice-coil inductance be substantially cancelled since its Q is increased if only the voice-coil resistance is reduced, and its resonance with the moving mass can occur at a frequency only slightly higher than the original speaker resonance. This new resonance may be more offensive than the natural cone resonance which is suppressed.

DISTORTION

There are two major sources of distortion in a loudspeaker, the non-linear distribution of the air-gap flux and the non-linearity of the cone suspension. Of these, the cone suspension is the more important. When the electrical impedance of the voice-coil is cancelled out by the amplifier, the cone is driven by a very low reflected mechanical impedance and the distortion is greatly reduced.

If the voice-coil resistance alone is cancelled out, we have seen that the cone will resonate at some point above the normal resonant frequency. If the cone is driven at some subharmonic of this new resonance, any non-linearity of the cone will be emphasized, resulting in an actual increase of distortion over what it would have been if the output impedance were zero. This is illustrated in Fig. 4, for a hypothetical speaker. These emphasized distortion components lie at a comparatively high frequency, where the ear is more sensitive than in the region of the cone resonance and where the radiation efficiency of the speaker is greater.

If the inductance is suitably cancelled, the loudspeaker distortion is reduced over a wide range of frequencies.

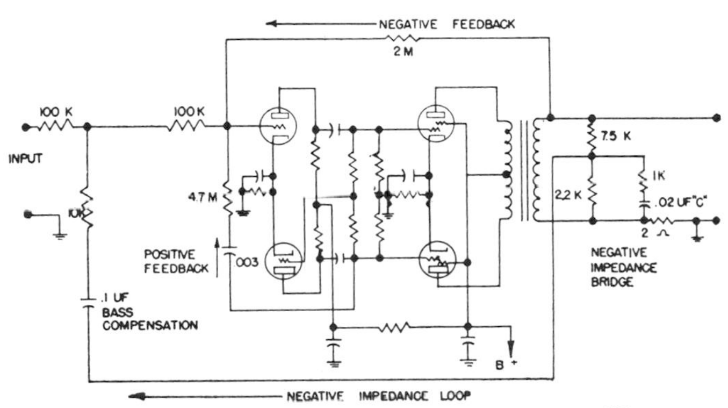

FIG. 5. Practical negative output impedance amplifier.

A NEGATIVE IMPEDANCE SYSTEM

A practical negative output impedance amplifier circuit is shown in Fig. 5. Negative voltage and positive current feedback are mixed at the output and fed through a common feedback loop. This arrangement is very stable and provides effective control of the output impedance to the extremes of the audio spectrum. Bass boost to compensate for the low frequency radiation characteristics is accomplished in the feedback loop without reducing the efficiency of the negative impedance circuit in the frequency range of interest. Internal positive and negative feedback are employed to produce a basic amplifier of high gain and very low distortion.[1] The .02 μf capacitor "C" produces the negative inductance and also adds treble boost to compensate for the approximation of the correct inductance.

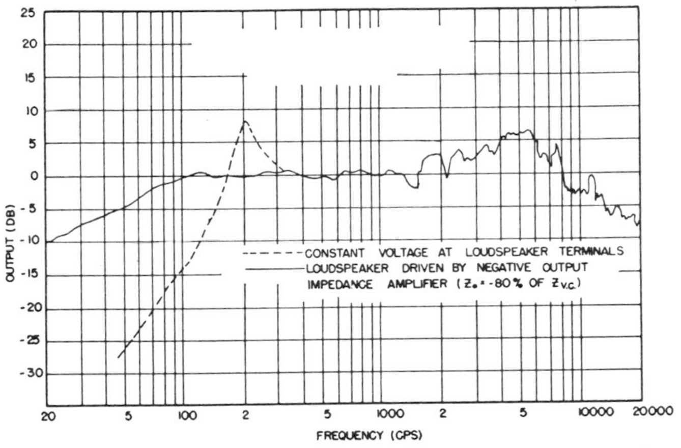

FIG. 6. Response-frequency characteristic on axis. *RCA SL-12* loudspeaker in ½ cu ft box.

MEASUREMENTS

An inexpensive amplifier was constructed using a circuit similar to Fig. 5 but without the internal positive and negative feedback circuits aforementioned. The output impedance was adjusted to cancel approximately 80% of the voice-coil impedance of a 12″ loudspeaker mounted in a ½ cubic foot box. Sufficient bass compensation was provided

[1] John M. Miller, Jr., *Electronics*, **23**, 106-109 (March 1950).

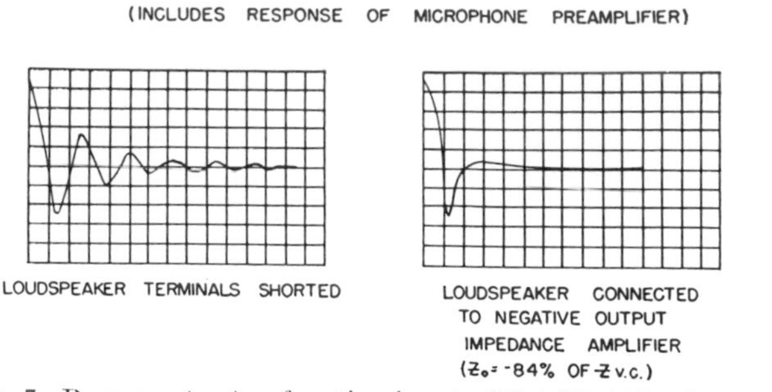

Fig. 7. Response to step function input. *RCA SL-12* loudspeaker in ½ cu ft box.

to extend the response about an octave and a half. The frequency response of the system is shown in Fig. 6 along with the response (dashed line) of the speaker when driven by a constant voltage. Fig. 7 shows the effect on transient response ("hangover") when the negative impedance amplifier is used. To measure distortion, a deluxe amplifier was used incorporating the aforementioned internal positive and negative feedback. Fig. 8 shows the effect of the output impedance upon the distortion at 40 cps when the speaker was mounted in a large (3 cubic foot) box. It is apparent that non-linear flux density is a minor menace since the distortion reaches a minimum at 100% cancellation of the voice-coil impedance.

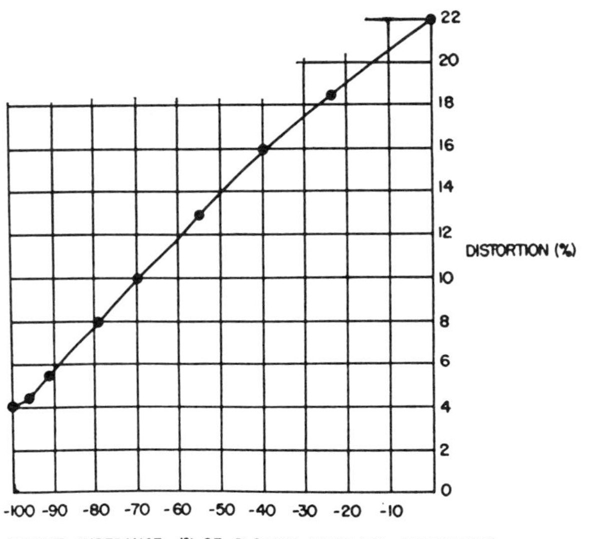

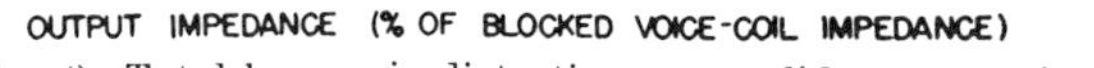

Fig. 8. Total harmonic distortion *vs* amplifier output impedance. Four watts at 40 cps into *RCA SL-12* loudspeaker in 3 cu ft box.

We have seen that a negative impedance amplifier can produce a useful improvement in loudspeaker performance. The improvement in response is most pronounced where the enclosure volume is small. The procedures given here will produce the improvement in low-frequency response which is also sought by the use of resonated enclosures and horns. The negative impedance amplifier should be used only with speakers mounted in infinite baffles. With the speaker performance rigidly controlled by the amplifier, acoustical anti-resonators and semi-horn enclosures have little effect on the cone motion and their own resonances may become considerably exaggerated.

CONCLUSIONS

Close study of the equivalent circuit of a loudspeaker has led to the conclusion that previous measurements of negative impedance loudspeaker systems limited to negative *resistance* amplifiers produce pessimistically misleading results. The study further discloses that suitable cancellation of the voice-coil inductance and compensation for radiation characteristics should prove the worth of a negative impedance speaker system. Careful laboratory measurements support this theory in full.[2]

[2] Results of additional measurements on negative impedance-speaker systems have been published. See R. E. Werner, *J. Acoust. Soc. Am.*, **29**, 335-340 (1957).

THE AUTHORS

Mr. Werner received his A.B. degree in electrical engineering from Cornell, in 1950. After graduation, he served for three years with the Navy, engaged in electronics. He joined RCA in 1953, to engage in development and design of commercial microphones and other transducers. His original work in the field of negative impedance amplifiers dates from 1949; a paper on that subject was delivered at the Second International Congress on Acoustics in 1956. His works have been published in the *Journal of the Acoustical Society of America*, in the *Journal of the Audio Engineering Society*, and in *Broadcast News*. He is a member of the Acoustical Society of America and of the Audio Engineering Society.

Mr. Carrel graduated from Iowa State College. Joining RCA after graduation, he worked on the development and design of military communications systems, military and commercial microphones, acoustic instrumentation and electromechanical speech-multiplexing devices. He has presented papers at the meetings of the Acoustical Society of America and the Second International Congress on Acoustics. His writings have appeared in *Broadcast News*, the *RCA Engineer* and in our own *Journal*. He is a member of the Institute of Radio Engineers and of the Acoustical Society of America.

Performance of Enclosures for Low Resonance High Compliance Loudspeakers*

JAMES F. NOVAK†

Jensen Manufacturing Company, Chicago 38, Illinois

A generalized theory on the design and performance of vented loudspeaker enclosures, including the special case of the pressure-tight closed box, is presented. It is experimentally shown that excellent response, high output, and low distortion can be realized to very low frequencies.

A method is described for the design of small enclosures utilizing super-low resonance, high-compliance loudspeakers.

Inherent interrelationships of the speaker-amplifier system Q, efficiency, and response balance are shown, with application to commercial design.

INTRODUCTION

THE SUBJECT OF enclosure design for direct-radiator loudspeakers has received much attention in recent years. There is no other subject so controversial, perhaps as a result of a general lack of understanding of the basic principles of operation of enclosures. The current trend is toward smaller enclosures, lower speaker resonances and better performance claims. Trade journals tell of "all new enclosures," "revolutionary concepts" and "totally new principles of acoustics" when in reality there is a close identity with enclosure systems described long ago in well-known classics on acoustics. Actually there has been no basically new type of enclosure developed in this decade, although much worthwhile effort has been devoted to refinement and improvement of existing basic types.

The objectives of this paper are to select one of the currently popular enclosures, analyze its low frequency behavior, discuss its limitations and find a means of improving its performance.

The pressure-tight closed box using a high compliance, low frequency speaker was selected for two reasons: (1) the design is based on sound engineering principles, and (2) the ever increasing popularity of this enclosure may alone have justified the expenditure of the time.

THE PRESSURE-TIGHT CLOSED BOX

In order to proceed intelligently, it is necessary to define certain design criteria for low frequency reproduction. A slight problem arises here because all loudspeaker and enclosure designs must at the final stages of development be based on subjective judgments by people as to what constitutes "good quality." Because of this, it is not possible to be too specific in defining the design criteria. A reasonable amount of research into this problem disclosed that most listeners preferred a flat response to frequencies as low as about 40 cps. They also preferred speaker systems with low harmonic distortion and little or no transient distortion. Low efficiency speaker systems were generally frowned upon because in most cases this meant forced obsolescence of existing amplifiers.

It will be shown later that it will be necessary to sacrifice overall efficiency in order to extend the low frequency response. It now remains to determine the maximum allowable efficiency loss. That a maximum limit on efficiency loss must be established becomes apparent when one considers:

1) the amplifier economics;
2) the necessity for adequate reserve power to handle peaks without overload;
3) the deterioration of amplifier characteristics with time.

This last factor is tied in closely with the second.

Observations have shown that VU meter readings of one watt or so are about as high as reached in normal home listening. It should be possible, therefore, to justify a loss of 4 to 5 db of efficiency before noticing distortion on peaks from a good 10 to 12 watt amplifier. A loss of 10 db would be too excessive for a 10 to 12 watt amplifier as there would then be no reserve to handle peaks.

From the evidence just stated it is possible to set up the design criteria.

1) The response must be flat to as low a frequency as possible.

* Received December 29, 1958. Delivered before the Tenth Annual Convention of the Audio Engineering Society, New York, October 3, 1958.

† Senior Design Engineer

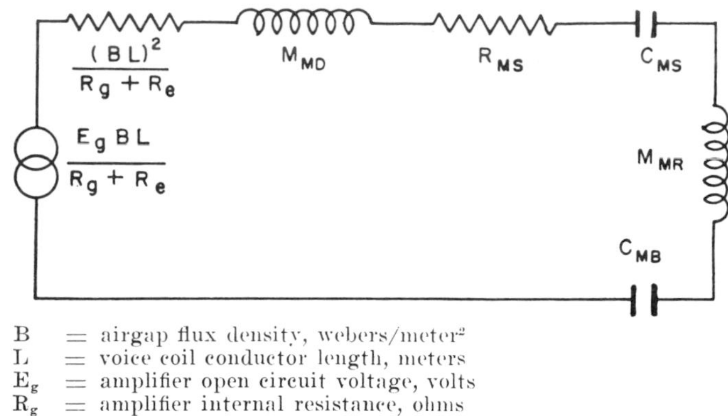

B = airgap flux density, webers/meter^2
L = voice coil conductor length, meters
E_g = amplifier open circuit voltage, volts
R_g = amplifier internal resistance, ohms
R_e = voice coil resistance, ohms
R_{MS} = mechanical resistance of suspension, mks mechanical ohms
M_{MD} = diaphragm and voice coil mass, kilograms
M_{MR} = total air load mass, kilograms
C_{MS} = total mechanical compliance of the suspension, meters/newton
C_{MR} = total mechanical compliance of the enclosure volume, meters/newton
ω_0 = $2\pi f_0$, resonant frequency in radians/second

FIG. 1. Mechanical equivalent circuit for the closed-box speaker system.

2) The total harmonic distortion must be as low as possible.
3) There must be no transient hangover.
4) The efficiency must be great enough to permit the use of a 10 to 12 watt amplifier.

The first design criterion, the extension of response to as low a frequency as possible, ordinarily would mean that the value of enclosure compliance would be made as large as possible so that the suspension compliance determined the resonant frequency. Because the small box precludes this approach, the speaker compliance is made as large as practicable. The enclosure compliance then determines the resonant frequency. Although it is not possible to obtain a resonant frequency much lower than about 65 cps in this manner, the distortion characteristics are somewhat improved as a result of the good linearity of the enclosure compliance.

The resonant frequency can be lowered an additional 10 to 15 per cent by completely filling the box with loosely packed fiberglass, kapok or cellufoam.[1] The resonant frequency decreases because the compressions become isothermal. This means that the velocity of sound decreases from about 344 m/sec to 291 m/sec. A 1 to 2 db loss in efficiency results, however, because the resistive component of box impedance is increased.

The mechanical equivalent circuit, Fig. 1, and equations of motion of the closed-box speaker system are well known. The steady-state solution yields the equation describing amplitude which when multiplied by the angular frequency and effective speaker area becomes the equation for volume velocity. Once volume velocity is known, it is a simple matter to obtain the sound pressure output.

The plot of amplitude *vs* frequency, Fig. 2, reveals that the amplitude increases many times in the region of resonance and below when Q becomes greater than 0.5.

Suspension non-linearities play an important part in determining the amount of total harmonic distortion at large amplitudes even though the box compliance supplies the major part of the restoring force. The result of a non-linear suspension is the production of odd-order harmonics with the third harmonic being predominant. Because the amplitude of a direct radiator speaker is inversely proportional to frequency squared below the region of ultimate radiation resistance, greatest distortion will occur at the low frequencies[2].

Figure 3 is a plot of the sound pressure response of a closed box speaker system. Note that a Q of 0.5 corresponding to critical damping and best transient response does not give the flattest output down to the lowest frequency possible. For flat response, Q should approximately

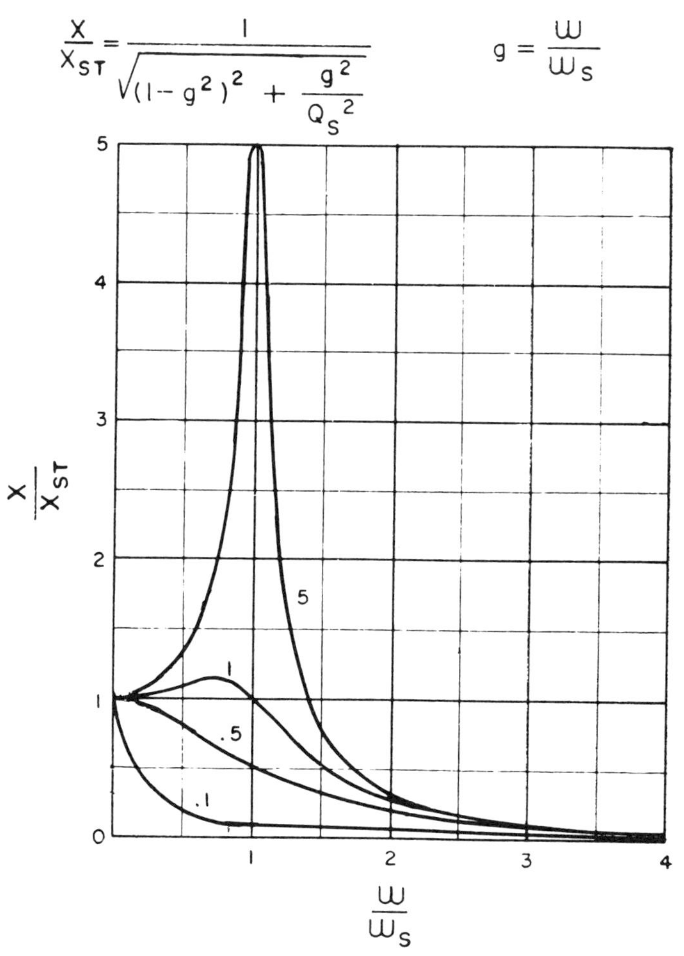

FIG. 2. Amplitude *vs* frequency response of the closed-box.

[1] L. L. Beranek, *Acoustics,* (McGraw-Hill Book Co., New York, 1954), p. 220.

[2] H. F. Olson, *Acoustical Engineering* (D. Van Nostrand Co., Inc., Princeton, 1957), p. 186.

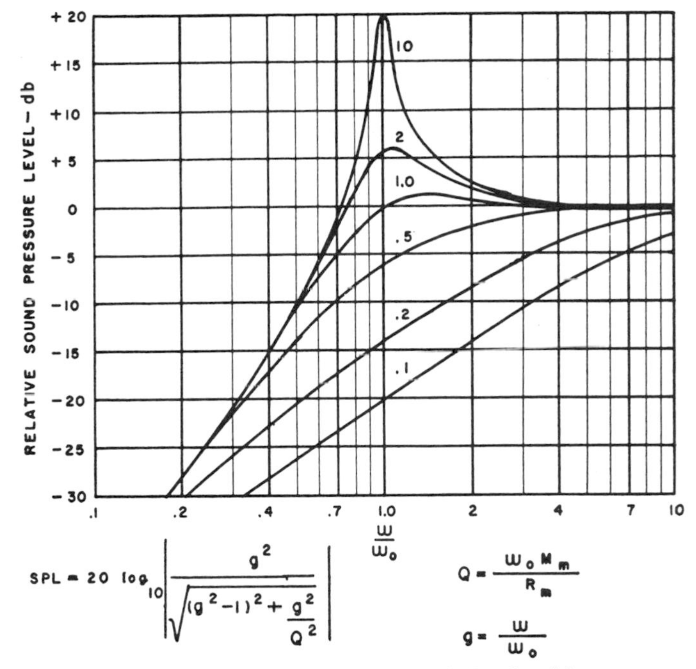

Fig. 3. Sound pressure response of the closed-box.

equal unity. This conflicts with the first and third design criteria.

The only factor determining the transient response and low frequency performance is the amount of damping. The damping can be changed by proper choice of amplifier damping factor or by adjustment of the flux density in the magnetic circuit. The popular belief that a large value of air stiffness in a small closed box increases speaker damping is erroneous. Damping is a function of resistances in the system.

The factor exerting the greatest influence on Q (damping) and low frequency output is the product of magnetic field strength and voice coil conductor length commonly known as the *Bl* product. Decreasing the *Bl* product will actually increase efficiency in the region of resonance but an efficiency loss results at frequencies above resonance. It now becomes apparent that the pressure-tight closed box cannot fulfill adequately all four design criteria. It will be necessary to compromise transient response and overall efficiency because increases in Q are usually achieved by an increase in moving system mass, a decrease in *Bl* product, or both.

THE VENTED ENCLOSURE

A review of other known speaker enclosures suggested that the vented enclosure when used with a high compliance speaker could produce a sound pressure response at least as good as that of the completely closed box and with certain advantages.

A search of the literature pertaining to vented enclosure design revealed that although equivalent circuits and equations for calculating Helmholtz resonance and location of the three critical frequencies were thoroughly developed, apparently no method has been published for calculating the response shape. Beranek describes a method for obtaining the relative sound pressure level at the three critical frequencies.[3] But the critical frequencies become widely separated when the box is small, and because the speaker system operates as a simple doublet at the lowest critical frequency, it is no longer possible to describe adequately the response shape because useful output occurs at only two of the three points: the middle and upper critical frequencies.

The mechanical equivalent circuit of the vented enclosure, Fig. 4, can be solved with the methods used for the closed box case. An exact solution becomes extremely complex because of the mutual coupling between the speaker and vent and the presence of resistance in both meshes. The vent resistance, however, can be ignored because the Q of the vent mesh is usually 20 to 40 times greater than the speaker mesh Q. The effects of mutual coupling can also be ignored since gains are insignificant when the two piston areas are very much different.[4]

The error resulting from these simplifications becomes significant only for large enclosures and then only in the region of speaker resonance when the vent Q is less than 10.

A vent in the closed box adds a second degree of freedom to the system causing a redistribution of the resonant frequency and damping of the speaker. The original speaker resonance is replaced by two new resonances, one near the

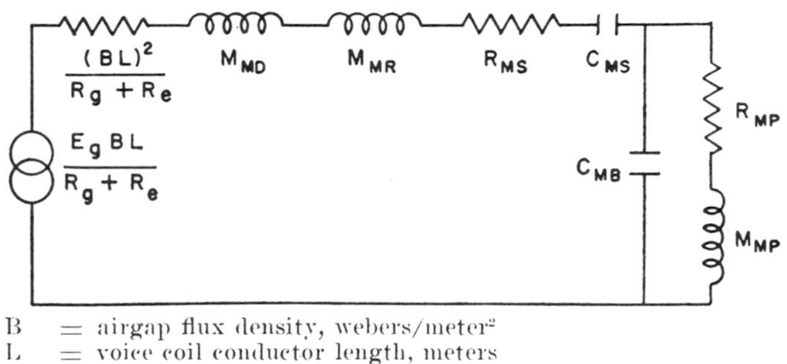

B = airgap flux density, webers/meter^2
L = voice coil conductor length, meters
E_g = amplifier open circuit voltage, volts
R_g = amplifier internal resistance, ohms
R_e = voice coil resistance, ohms
R_{MS} = mechanical resistance of suspension, mks mechanical ohms
M_{MD} = diaphragm and voice coil mass, kilograms
M_{MR} = total air load mass, kilograms
C_{MS} = total mechanical compliance of the suspension, meters/newton
C_{MB} = total mechanical compliance of the enclosure volume, meters/newton
ω_0 = $2\pi f_0$, resonant frequency in radians/second
M_{MP} = total vent air mass, kilograms
R_{MP} = total port resistance, mks mechanical ohms

Fig. 4. Mechanical equivalent circuit for the vented enclosure.

---

[3] L. L. Beranek, *Acoustics* (McGraw-Hill Book Co., New York, 1954), pp. 241-258.

[4] S. J. Klapman, "Interaction Impedance of a System of Circular Pistons", *J. Acous. Soc. Am.*, 11, 289 (1940).

closed box resonance and one substantially below the speaker resonance. Damping at these two resonances is greater than for the closed box case.[5]

The vent acts as an acoustical mass which resonates with the compliance of the enclosure volume at a particular frequency. The equivalent circuit indicates that if the enclosure is tuned to the speaker resonance, the impedance becomes a maximum and is resistive at this frequency so that speaker amplitude should be greatly reduced. Maximizing the equation for sound pressure output with respect to enclosure resonance reveals that enclosure resonance must indeed be equal to speaker resonance for maximum overall output to the lowest possible frequency. This condition of tuning will be assumed for the remainder of this paper although it may be desirable to tune the enclosure to a higher frequency if increased output is desired in the region of the upper critical frequency. The sound pressure output of the system now becomes a function of two variables, the speaker Q and the ratio of enclosure stiffness to speaker suspension stiffness. This ratio can be thought of as a coefficient of coupling between the speaker and port meshes.

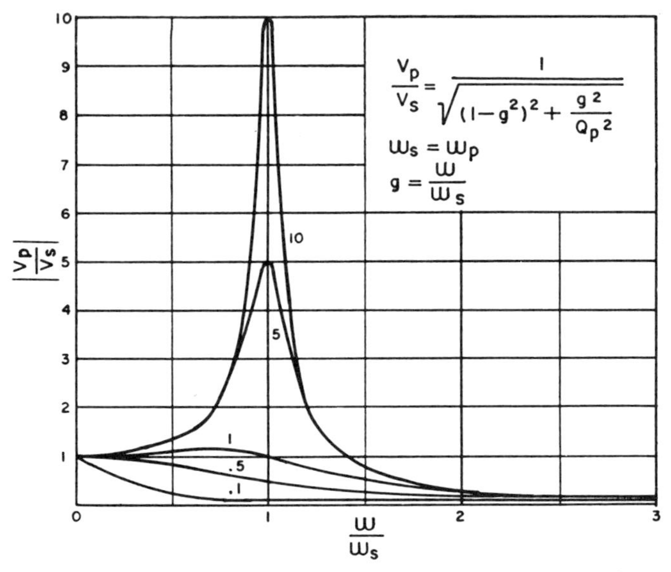

FIG. 5. Ratio of vent velocity to speaker diaphragm velocity as a function of vent Q.

Low frequency output is increased and the low frequency cutoff is lowered when the stiffness ratio is decreased. Although output varies directly with speaker Q as in the closed box case it will be shown that a Q of less than 0.5 will give a flat response whereas the closed box requires a Q of approximately unity.

Figure 5, a plot of the ratio of vent velocity to speaker diaphragm velocity, shows that for normal vent Q's (greater than 10) the acoustic power radiated from the vent predominates over that radiated from the speaker diaphragm

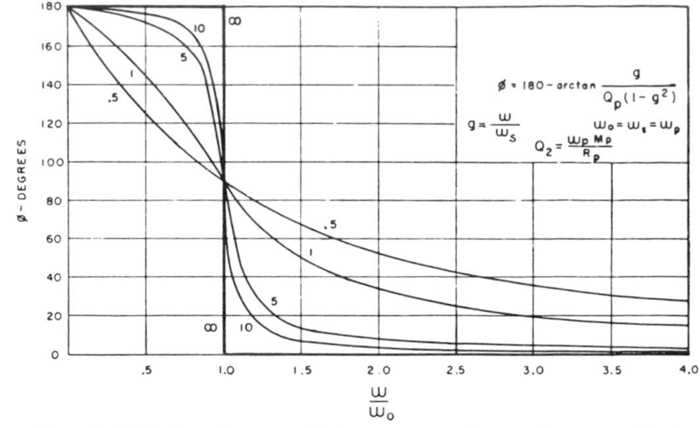

FIG. 6. Relative phase angle between speaker and port radiation as a function of vent Q.

for about ½ octave above and below speaker resonance. It is observed, however, that total radiation decreases rapidly below speaker resonance. This occurs because at frequencies below speaker resonance the volume velocity in the vent becomes out of phase with the speaker diaphragm volume velocity.

Figure 6 is a plot of the relative phase angle between vent and speaker diaphragm volume velocity. Although vent and diaphragm radiation are in quadrature at speaker resonance for all values of vent Q, the transition to out-of-phase or in-phase operation is very rapid when the vent Q is greater than 5.

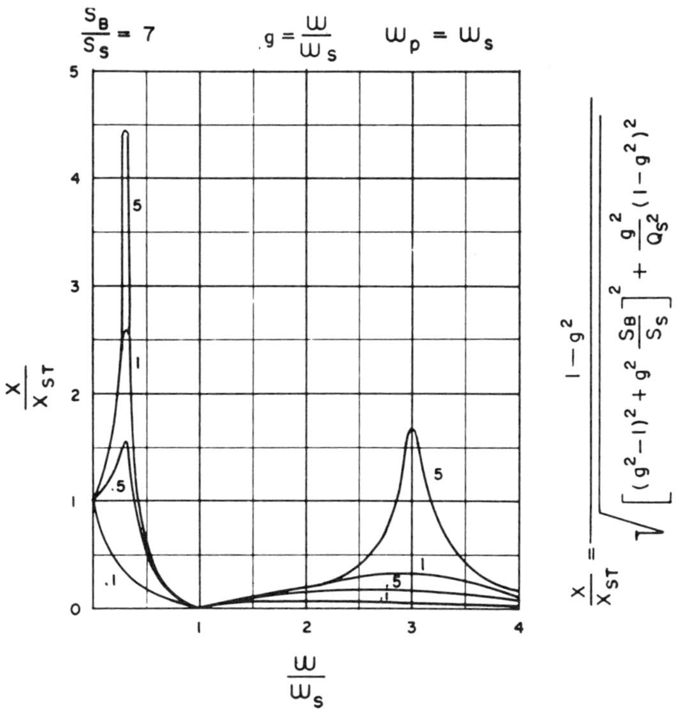

FIG. 7. Excursion of the direct radiator in the vented enclosure, stiffness ratio = 7, as a function of speaker Q.

[5] J. B. Crandall, *"Theory of Vibrating Systems and Sound"* (D. Van Nostrand Co., Inc., Princeton, 1926), pp. 62-63, 2nd edition.

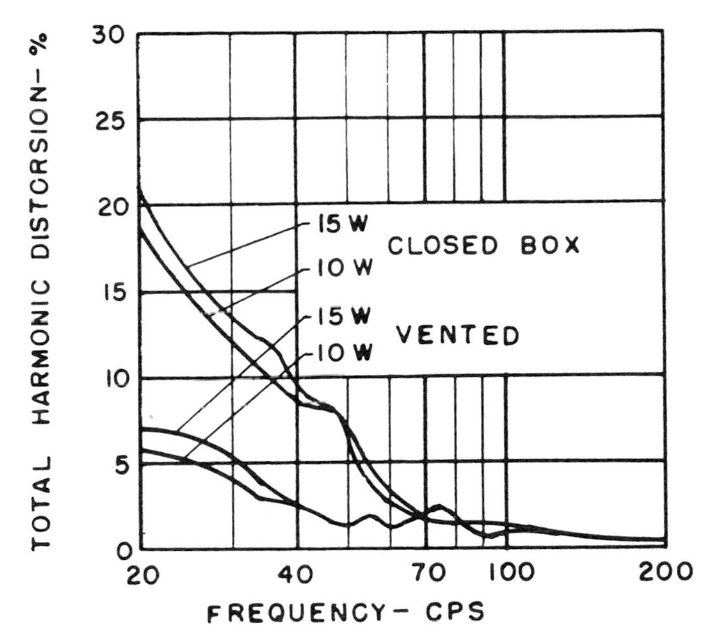

FIG. 8. Distortion characteristics of the closed-box *vs* the vented enclosure for 10 and 15 watt input to speaker.

The gradual phase shift occurring when the vent Q is less than 0.5 may lead to the erroneous conclusion that low values of vent Q can lower the low-frequency cutoff. An extension of low-frequency cutoff cannot occur because vent power output diminishes rapidly as Q becomes equal to or less than unity (see Fig. 5). The performance then approaches the closed box performance. This is predicted by the equations of motion which reduce to those of a closed box when either the vent Q or the area is allowed to approach zero.

The diaphragm amplitude becomes a minimum at speaker resonance as opposed to the maximum which occurs in the closed box. Figure 7 shows the amplitude variations of a

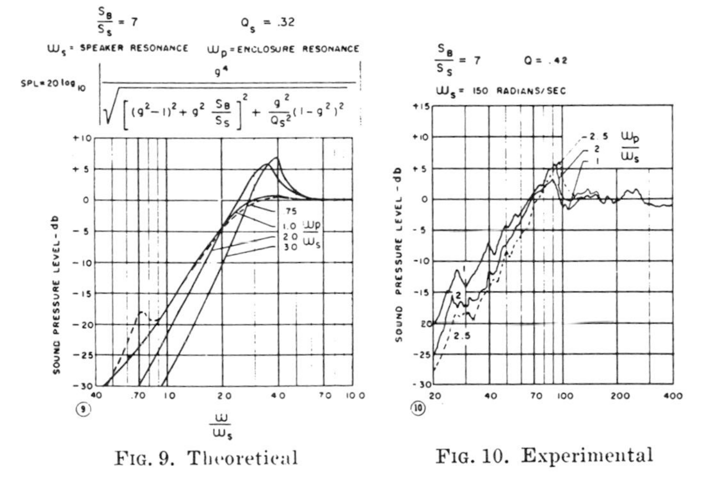

FIG. 9. Theoretical

FIG. 10. Experimental

Relative sound pressure level response of the direct radiator in a vented enclosure as a function of enclosure tuning.

speaker diaphragm in a vented enclosure for a stiffness ratio of 7, as a function of speaker Q. A stiffness ratio of 7 corresponds to a 12″ high-compliance speaker in an enclosure volume of about 2.25 cu ft. The diaphragm amplitude remains very uniform down to speaker resonance for critically damped or overdamped speaker operation. Because the vent mesh consists of linear elements, the harmonic and intermodulation distortion are greatly reduced.[6]

Figure 8 shows the distortion characteristics of a 2.25 cu ft closed *vs* vented box speaker system. The speaker used in these measurements was a *Jensen P12-NF* high-compliance woofer operating with a Q of 0.5.

Figure 9 illustrates the dependence of flat response on proper enclosure tuning. Figure 10 is the experimental data verifying the theoretical data of Figure 9. Figures 11, 12, and 13 show the theoretical sound pressure response of the vented enclosure with stiffness ratios of 1, 3 and 7 respectively, as a function of speaker Q. The experimental

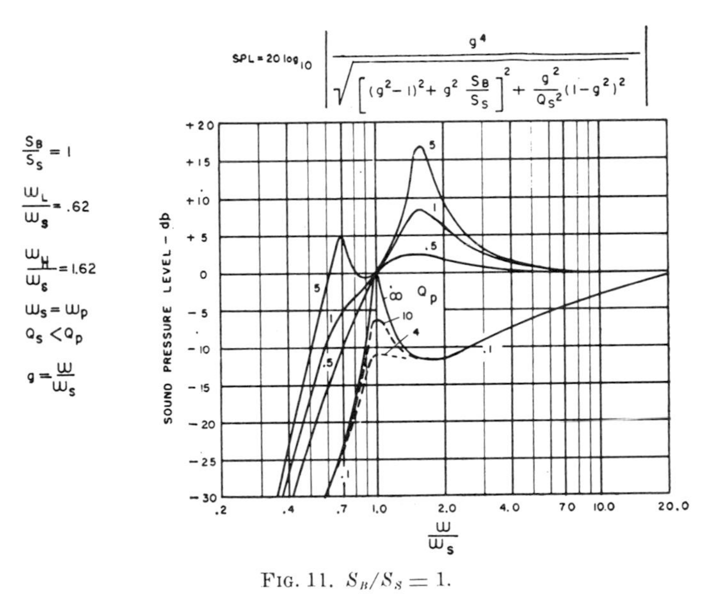

FIG. 11. $S_B/S_S = 1$.

data in Fig. 14 verify the theoretical data of Fig. 13 and substantiate the validity of the theoretical equations. These response curves certainly demonstrate that a large box still outperforms a small box. An important result of these data is that flat response is in all cases obtained with a speaker Q of less than 0.5. The data also show that the acoustic output from small enclosures is only slightly improved by venting. Consider the case of a stiffness ratio of 7 and assume a speaker resonant frequency of 20 cps.

Figure 13 shows that flat response is maintained to 54 cps for a speaker Q of .32 with the 10 db down point occurring at 28 cps. The same stiffness ratio applied to a closed box would increase the speaker resonance to 60 cps. Figure 3

[6] H. S. Knowles, "Loudspeakers and Room Acoustics", *Radio Engineers Handbook* (McGraw-Hill Book Co., New York, 1950), pp. 760-761.

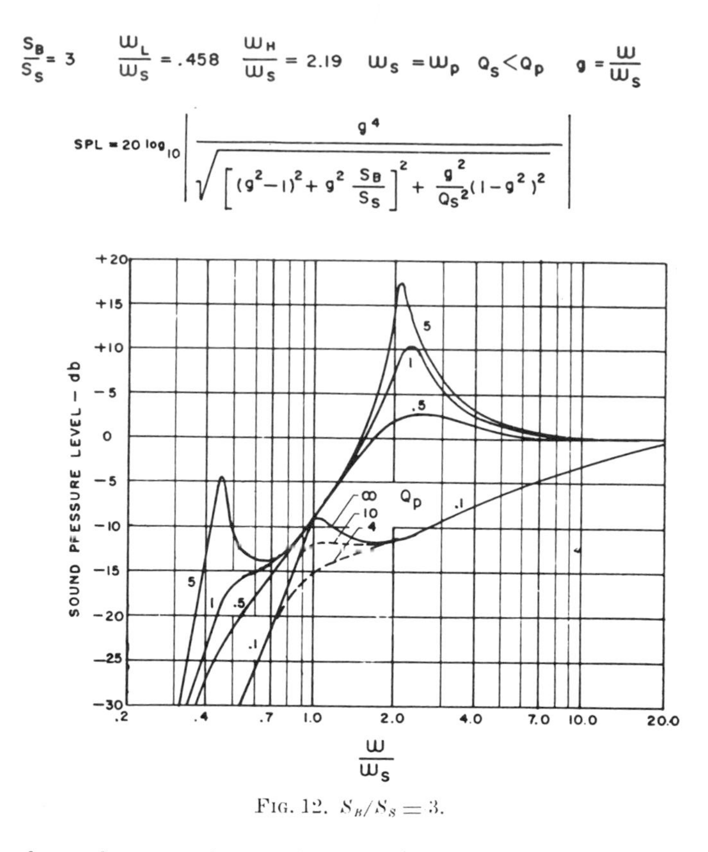

FIG. 12. $S_B/S_S = 3$.

shows that a speaker Q of 1 will give flat response to 60 cps with the 10 db down point occurring at 32 cps. The increase in output from 28 to 60 cps in the vented enclosure is barely 1 db. The transient response, harmonic and intermodulation distortion are, however, greatly improved. In cases where the enclosure volume can be more generous, venting offers considerable gains in output.

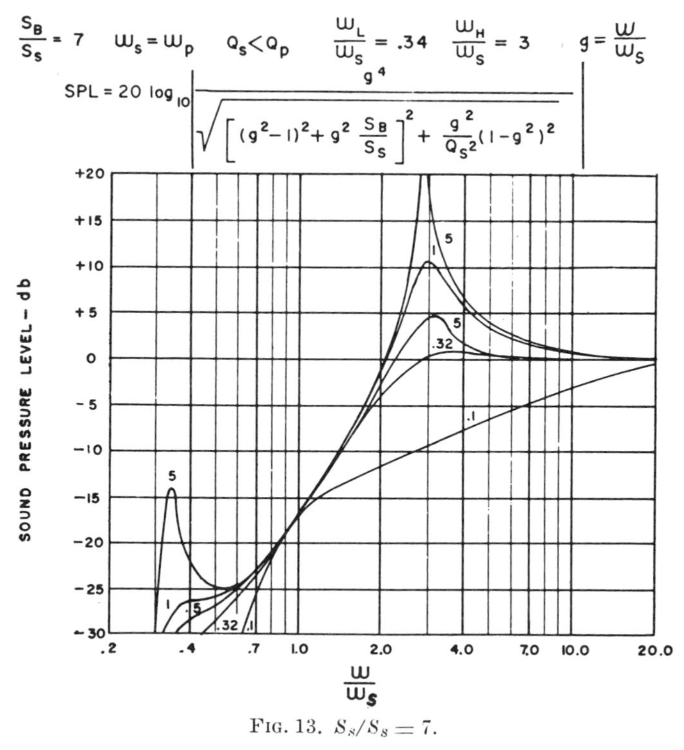

FIG. 13. $S_B/S_S = 7$.

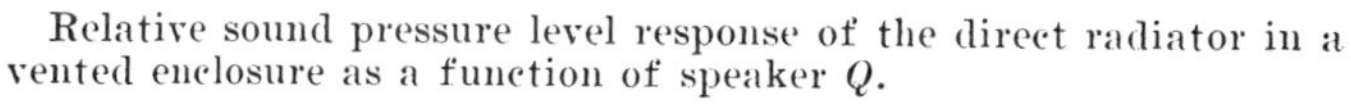
Relative sound pressure level response of the direct radiator in a vented enclosure as a function of speaker Q.

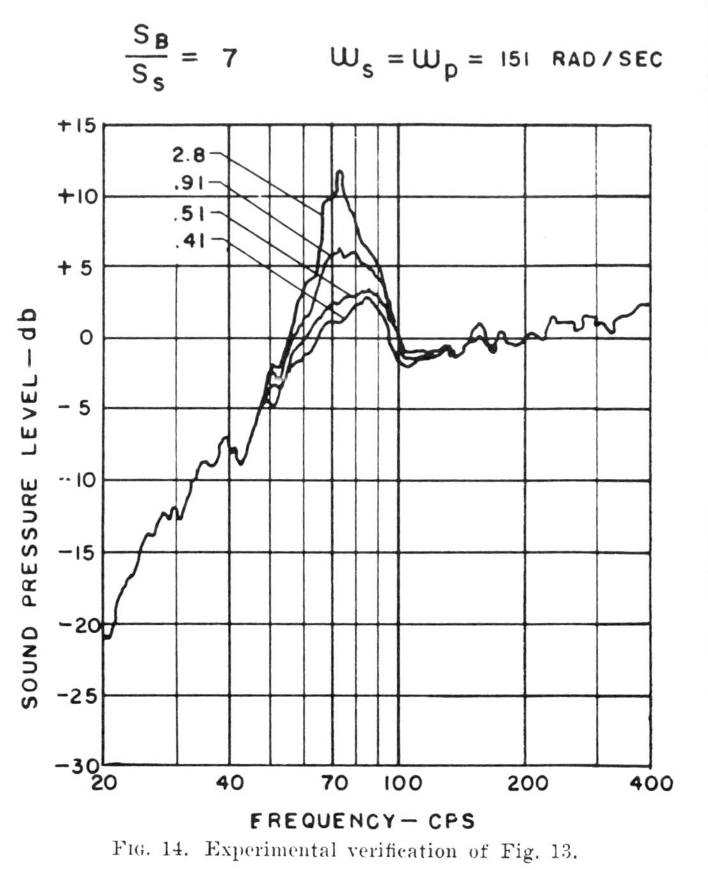

FIG. 14. Experimental verification of Fig. 13.

CONCLUSIONS

Many considerations lead to the conclusion that a vented enclosure can do everything the closed box can do, and with certain advantages. But honest comparison of the two must include all factors, not just those favoring one system.

Important points against venting which could result in poor performance if proper consideration is not given them are:

1) Drop in output below the resonant frequency is 18 db/octave compared to 12 db/octave for the closed box. It is commonly thought that the transient effects resulting from a cut-off as sharp as 18 db/octave can be bothersome.

2) Very small enclosure volume coupled with a very low speaker resonant frequency may require a vent so small as to be ineffective because of excessive viscous losses in the vent. The operation is then about the same as that of the closed box. In extreme cases of this sort, rectification has been observed in the air flow through the vent. This caused a displacement in

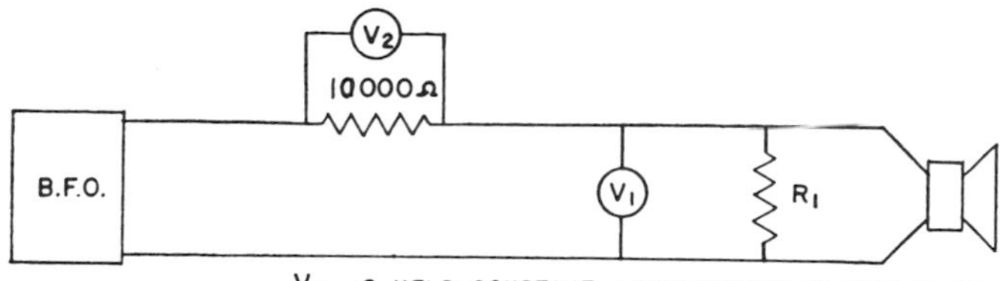

(1) RESONANT FREQUENCY

VARY OSCILLATOR FREQUENCY UNTIL V_1 IS MAXIMUM.

(2) LOADED Q

(A) OPEN CIRCUIT R_1. OBTAIN SHAPE OF VELOCITY CURVE BY PLOTTING AGAINST FREQUENCY THE QUANTITY

$$e = V_1 - \frac{R_{VC} V_2}{10000} \qquad Q_1 = \frac{f}{\Delta f}$$

(B) INSERT R_1 (ABOUT 80 OHMS). PLOT NEW VELOCITY CURVE

$$Q_2 = \frac{f}{\Delta f}$$

(C) DETERMINE MECHANICAL RESISTANCE, R_M, FROM

$$R_M = (R_1 + R_{VC})\left(\frac{Q_1}{Q_2} - 1\right)$$

(D) LOADED Q IS GIVEN BY

$$Q_L = \frac{R_g + R_{VC}}{R_g + R_{VC} + R_M} Q_1$$

$$Q_L = \frac{R_{VC}}{R_{VC} + R_M} Q_1 \quad \text{IF} \quad R_g \ll R_{VC}$$

R_{VC} = VOICE COIL RESISTANCE – OHMS

R_g = GENERATOR INTERNAL RESISTANCE – OHMS

GENERATOR INTERNAL RESISTANCE CAN BE OBTAINED FROM

$$\text{DB REGULATION} = 20 \log_{10} \frac{R_g + R_L}{R_L}$$

R_L = LOAD RESISTANCE – OHMS

FIG. 15. Experimental procedure for the determination of speaker Q.

the dynamic center of diaphragm amplitude. The resulting distortion was greater than for the closed box.

3) Mistuning or incorrect speaker Q can exaggerate the output in the vicinity of the upper critical frequency. This can cause an aggravated booming sound generally too high in frequency to give even a good impression of false bass.

The optimum system goal as defined by the four design criteria must overcome these limitations. This can be accomplished in the following manner:

The speaker resonant frequency must be low enough that the 18 db/octave slope occurs below 20 cps. Subjective listening tests did not indicate the presence of any troublesome transients. An acceptable resonant frequency would be between 20 and 30 cps.

The vent must have small enough resistance so that the volume velocity is not impeded seriously. Volume velocity will be independent of vent area so long as viscous losses are minimized. If the vent area becomes too small, a larger area with a duct must be used.

The amplifier must have a damping factor sufficient to maintain at least critical damping in the speaker mesh. Speaker Q's ranging from 0.3 to 0.4 give best results.

The limitations being disposed of by proper design, the vented enclosure has definite and important advantages over the closed box. All exist in the octave or octave and one-half in the region of speaker resonance. They stem from the one characteristic differentiating the vented enclosure from the closed box—better diaphragm loading in the region where the box is an active element.

The vent relieves the diaphragm of much of the necessity to move. The reduced diaphragm amplitude is not at the expense of sound output because the vent also assumes the task of radiation of sound energy. The advantages of the vented enclosure are

1) lower harmonic distortion because the linear vent operation and reduced diaphragm amplitude minimize the effects of speaker non-linearities;
2) reduced intermodulation distortion because of reduced diaphragm amplitude;
3) improved transient response because the speaker is at least critically damped;
4) greater acoustic output for a given amount of distortion;
5) less of the deliberate efficiency loss for purposes of response levelling is required because the speaker must be operated at a lower Q.

The Q can be decreased by increasing the speaker efficiency. It has been found that the efficiency averages at least 3 db better, for equivalent response trend, than would have been allowable with the closed box system.

The author believes that in spite of its simple appearance the design of a vented enclosure is sufficiently difficult that it should not be attempted by the layman unless he is exceptionally well informed and has adequate test facilities.

APPENDIX

A piston whose diameter is less than $\lambda/3$ is essentially nondirectional at low frequencies. It can, therefore, be approximated by a hemisphere whose rms volume velocity, U_c, is equal to the product of voice coil velocity, v_c and effective speaker cone area, A_d:

$$U_c = v_c A_d$$

The magnitude of rms sound pressure at a distance r (in the far field) from the speaker is[7]

$$|p| = \frac{U_c f \rho}{r}. \tag{1}$$

The equations describing sound pressure response of the closed and vented enclosure can be obtained from the equations of motion for the two systems by substituting for volume velocity in Eq. 1.

Closed Box

The equation of motion obtained from Fig. 1 is

$$(-M_m\omega^2 + S_m + jR_m\omega)\,x = F \tag{2}$$

[7] L. L. Beranek, *op. cit.*, p. 188.

Eq. 2 is solved for x. The equation describing the amplitude, x, becomes

$$x = \frac{x_{ST}}{\sqrt{(1-g^2)^2 + \dfrac{g^2}{Q_S^2}}}. \qquad (3)$$

The expression for voice coil velocity, v_S, is obtained by multiplying (3) by the angular frequency:

$$v_S = \omega x. \qquad (4)$$

Volume velocity is obtained by multiplying (4) by the effective speaker cone area.

$$U_S = A_d \omega x. \qquad (5)$$

The sound pressure level is obtained by substituting (5) into (1),

$$p = \frac{A_d \omega x_{ST} f \rho}{r\sqrt{(1-g^2)^2 + \dfrac{g^2}{Q_S^2}}}. \qquad (6)$$

A reference volume velocity is defined by

$$U_{ref} = \frac{x_{ST}\omega A_d}{g^2}. \qquad (7)$$

This is the actual volume velocity above resonance under the special condition that the expression under the radical in (3) is proportional to g^4, *i.e.*, the diaphragm is completely mass controlled:

$$(g^2-1)^2 >> \frac{g^2}{Q_S^2}.$$

A reference sound pressure is defined for low frequencies by substituting (7) into (1),

$$p_{ref} = \frac{x_{ST}\omega A_d f \rho}{g^2 r}. \qquad (8)$$

An expression for relative sound pressure level in db is obtained by taking the ratio of (6) to (8),

$$\text{S.P.L.} = 20 \log \left| \frac{g^2}{\sqrt{(g^2-1)^2 + \dfrac{g^2}{Q_S^2}}} \right| \qquad (9)$$

Vented Enclosure

The equations of motion obtained from Fig. 4 are

$$\left. \begin{aligned} (-M_S\omega^2 + S_S + S_B + jR_S\omega)\,x_S - S_B x_p &= F \\ -S_B x_S + (-M_p\omega^2 + S_B + jR_p\omega)\,x_p &= 0 \end{aligned} \right\} \qquad (10)$$

Eq. 10 is solved for x_S and x_p.

Amplitude

In order to simplify the expressions, Q_p is assumed to equal infinity. The resulting error is very small because the typical vent mesh Q is 20 to 40 times greater than the speaker mesh Q. The speaker and vent amplitudes become respectively

$$x_S = \frac{x_{ST}(h^2-g^2)}{\sqrt{\left[(g^2-1)(g^2-h^2) - g^2\dfrac{S_B}{S_S}\right]^2 + g^2\left[\dfrac{h^2-g^2}{Q_S}\right]^2}}. \qquad (11)$$

and

$$x_p = \frac{x_{ST}h^2}{\sqrt{\left[(g^2-1)(g^2-h^2) - g^2\dfrac{S_B}{S_S}\right]^2 + g^2\left[\dfrac{h^2-g^2}{Q_S}\right]^2}}. \qquad (12)$$

The volume velocities are obtained exactly as in the closed box case,

$$U_S = A_d \omega x_S, \qquad (13)$$

$$-U_p = -A_d \omega x_p. \qquad (14)$$

The total sound pressure is obtained by substituting (13) and (14) into (1) and adding the two pressures. A negative sign is used for U_p because, except for the phase shift introduced in the vent mesh, the radiation from the back of the speaker cone is 180° out of phase with the front radiation. Using the concept of reference sound pressure, the relative sound pressure level in db is

$$\text{S.P.L.} = \left|\frac{p_S - p_p}{p_{ref}}\right| =$$

$$20 \log \left| \frac{g^4}{\sqrt{\left[(g^2-1)(g^2-h^2) - g^2\dfrac{S_B}{S_S}\right]^2 + g^2\left[\dfrac{h^2-g^2}{Q_S}\right]^2}} \right|. \qquad (15)$$

This allows the calculation of response for any condition of tuning.

Maximizing (15) with respect to enclosure tuning shows that maximum output at speaker resonance is obtained when the enclosure is tuned to speaker resonance, *i.e.*, $h = 1$. The expression for relative sound pressure level becomes

$$\text{S.P.L.} = 20 \log \left| \frac{g^4}{\sqrt{\left[(g^2-1)^2 - g^2\dfrac{S_B}{S_S}\right]^2 + \dfrac{g^2}{Q_S^2}(1-g^2)^2}} \right|. \qquad (16)$$

Designing the Enclosure

The enclosure volume should be based on the maximum amount of space available. The object is to get the lowest possible value of S_B/S_S. It is necessary to know only two factors, S_B/S_S and Q_S, in order to calculate the response.

Determination of S_B/S_S

1) Measure free air speaker resonance. Denote this by f_1.

2) Install speaker in the *unvented* enclosure and measure resonance again. Denote this by f_2.

3) The stiffness ratio is given by $S_B/S_S \doteq (f_2/f_1)^2 - 1$.

Determination of Speaker Q

Q_S is determined from the velocity curve as described in Fig. 15. The width, Δf cps, is measured between the points of the curve on either side of the resonance peak where the voltage is 3 db down (0.707) from the maximum voltage.

The area of the vent is obtained from

$$f_r = 2155 \sqrt{\frac{A_p}{V_B(t + .96\sqrt{A_p})}}. \qquad (17)$$

The enclosure should be tuned to the resonant frequency of the speaker. It is permissible to tune to a higher frequency if increased output is desired in the region of the upper critical frequency. In some cases, the output in the region of the upper critical frequency may tend to peak up. Peaking can be minimized by increasing the damping on the speaker by increasing amplifier damping factor. A negative damping factor may have to be used in some instances. If the damping factor cannot be changed, the enclosure should be tuned lower than speaker resonance. While this will reduce the peak, it will also result in some losses in output lower in frequency.

Since the vent behaves as a simple source at low frequencies, the amount of power radiated is independent of the vent area for any given volume velocity. It is permissible, therefore, to use any value of vent area so long as the desired enclosure resonance is obtained.

The use of resistive loading over the vent or the use of a series of small holes distributed over a large area (another way of adding resistive loading) is generally not recommended. An important reason for using a vented enclosure is that the loudspeaker produces far less distortion in the octave above speaker resonance than would be the case if the box were closed. Adding resistance to the vent will reduce the power radiated and will increase the speaker diaphragm amplitude and distortion. The vent area should not be allowed to be less than about 4 in^2. If (17) indicates an area less than this value, the area should be increased arbitrarily and a duct (installed behind the vent) used to properly tune the enclosure. The expression for resonance now becomes

$$f_r = 2155 \sqrt{\frac{A_p}{(V_B - V_D)\,(l_d + .96\sqrt{A_p})}}. \qquad (18)$$

The enclosure should be lined with a two-inch thickness of fiberglass on at least three sides to eliminate any normal modes.

The approximate location of the upper and lower critical frequencies is obtained from

$$f_{L,H} = (.707)\,f_S \sqrt{2 + \frac{S_B}{S_S} \pm \sqrt{4\frac{S_B}{S_S} + \left[\frac{S_B}{S_S}\right]^2}} \qquad (19)$$

The response shape can be calculated from either (15) or (16) depending on whether or not the enclosure is tuned to speaker resonance. The calculations can become rather tedious but unfortunately there is no short cut.

TABLE OF SYMBOLS

A_d = effective speaker diaphragm area, [m^2]
A_p = area of vent, [in^2]
B = air gap flux density, [webers/m^2]
E_g = input voltage to voice coil, [volts]
f, f_L, f_H, f_r = input frequency, lower critical frequency, upper critical frequency, enclosure resonant frequency, [sec^{-1}]
$F = \frac{Bl\,E_g}{R_g + R_e}$ = driving force, [newton]
$g = \frac{\omega}{\omega_S}$ = forced frequency ratio
$h = \frac{\omega_P}{\omega_S}$ = tuned frequency ratio
l_d = duct length, [in]
l = voice coil conductor length, [m]
M_m = total speaker moving system mass, [kg]
M_p = air mass of vent, [kg]
ω_L = lower critical frequency, [sec^{-1}]
ω_H = upper critical frequency, [sec^{-1}]
ω_0 = system resonant frequency, [sec^{-1}]
$\omega, \omega_S, \omega_P$ = input frequency, speaker resonant frequency, enclosure resonant frequency, [sec^{-1}]
p, p_S, p_p = complex rms sound pressure, complex rms sound pressure from speaker diaphragm, complex rms sound pressure from vent, [newton/m^2]
$Q_S = \frac{\omega_S M_m}{R_m}$ = speaker mesh Q
$Q_p = \frac{\omega_P M_p}{R_p}$ = port mesh Q
R_m = total mechanical resistance in speaker mesh, [mks mech ohm]
R_p = total mechanical resistance in vent mesh, [mks mech ohm]
ρ = density of air, [kg/m^3]
R_g = amplifier internal resistance, [ohm]
r = average distance of observation point from diaphragm and/or port, [m]
R_E = voice coil resistance, [ohm]
S_S = speaker suspension stiffness, [newton/m]
S_B = stiffness of enclosure volume, [newton/m]
t = vent wall thickness, [in]
U, U_S, U_p = complex rms volume, velocity, complex rms volume velocity of speaker diaphragm, complex rms volume velocity of vent, [m^3/sec]
v_S = speaker diaphragm velocity, [m/sec]
v_p = vent velocity, [m/sec]
x, x_S, x_p = amplitude, diaphragm amplitude, vent amplitude, [m]
$x_{ST} = \frac{F}{S_S}$ = static deflection, [m]
V_B = volume of enclosure, [in^3]
V_D = volume of duct, [in^3]

JOURNAL REPRINT

The following paper is reprinted from the November 1958 issue of the *Proceedings of the Institution of Electrical Engineers,* by kind permission of the Institution and its Editor. In view of the other loudspeaker papers appearing in this issue the Editor has felt that a survey paper of this nature would be welcomed, particularly since many of our members will not have had access to it.

A SURVEY OF PERFORMANCE CRITERIA AND DESIGN CONSIDERATIONS FOR HIGH-QUALITY MONITORING LOUDSPEAKERS

By D. E. L. SHORTER, B.Sc.(Eng.), Associate Member.

SUMMARY

Loudspeakers used for monitoring purposes in broadcasting and recording studios are dèsigned to give the nearest practicable approach to realistic reproduction. The paper discusses the various criteria which can be applied to the performance of such loudspeakers, together with the relationship between the measured free-field characteristics and the response as subjectively assessed in the working environment.

While the degree of realism achieved in sound reproduction can only be judged aurally, even subjective assessments can be misleading unless carried out under controlled conditions and with clearly defined terms of reference; the precautions necessary in such tests are discussed.

Some of the less obvious design considerations are reviewed and illustrated by examples.

(1) INTRODUCTION

(1.1) Functions of a Monitoring Loudspeaker

Broadcasting and recording organizations use high-quality loudspeakers to assess the aesthetic and technical merits of the programme material which they originate and to guide them in the control of such variables as the placing of artistes and microphones in the studio. It is sometimes suggested that monitoring of this kind should be carried out with loudspeakers of mediocre quality, such as are used by the majority of the public, the implication being that the programme material ought to be modified as necessary to offset the shortcomings of these instruments. In fact, the various types of low-grade sound-reproducer, while having certain features in common, differ so much in many respects that attempts to compensate for the characteristics of one lead to unnecessarily poor reproduction with another. Moreover, the occasional presence of fault conditions, to which every system is liable, is most noticeable with high-grade reproducing equipment, and it is clearly undesirable that the existence of technical faults should become apparent to even a minority of listeners while remaining unobserved by the operating staff. Finally, if progress in the science of sound transmission is to continue, the technical equipment concerned in originating the programme should have a higher standard of performance than that employed in reproducing it, since the former can be replaced only at long intervals while the latter is more frequently renewed and can more easily be kept up to date. It is therefore customary for loudspeaker systems employed for monitoring purposes to be made as free as possible from technical defects. There must be, however, a limit to the degree of elaboration to which it is proper to go; for example, the use of two or more separate loudspeakers to give a pseudo-stereophonic effect would be completely unrealistic at the present time. Moreover, even a broadcasting or recording organization must limit the size and cost of its listening equipment. In practice, a monitoring loudspeaker is intended to represent the best product of its kind which could be used by a member of the listening public, assuming an outlay comparable with that of the high-quality radio-receiving and record-reproducing equipment required to do justice to it.

Mr. Shorter is with the British Broadcasting Corporation.

(1.2) Scope of Paper

Although considerable literature on various aspects of loudspeaker design exists, the fundamental question of the requirements to be met by the finished article is less fully documented. A large part of this survey is therefore devoted to the various performance criteria, subjective as well as objective, which have from time to time been proposed. Various means of meeting present-day requirements are also discussed. It should be emphasized, however, that at present no clear-cut solution is possible. It is not the function of the paper to add to the already long list of publications advocating particular methods of achieving the desired result; the examples cited are intended solely to illustrate some modern trends of development and to show the limitations, as well as the possibilities, of particular lines of approach.

(2) CRITERIA OF LOUDSPEAKER PERFORMANCE

(2.1) Terms of Reference

It is assumed that the ideal to be aimed at in sound reproduction is realism, i.e. that the sound pressures produced at the observer's ears should at any moment be equal to those which would obtain if either the original source of sound were brought into the listening room, or the observer were transported to some designated spot in the vicinity of the sound source. It should, however, be appreciated that, while the first condition might conceivably be produced if the geometry of the reproducing system bore some relation to that of the original sound source, the second, which is the one required for the majority of programme items, is fundamentally impossible to achieve—at all events, by a single loudspeaker.* It would require that the sound reaching the listener's ears from every direction should be related to the acoustic properties of the studio or concert hall but not to those of the room in which the loudspeaker is placed. The characteristics of a loudspeaker required to give the nearest approach, from an observer's point of view, to this impossible ideal depend upon subjective factors and cannot yet be prescribed from first principles. Fortunately, every broadcasting or recording organization employs a number of operating staff, whose daily activities involve listening alternately in studios and monitoring rooms and making critical comparisons between the sounds heard in the two places. Such observers are probably the best available judges of realism, and since their function constitutes them a species of consumers' representative, it seems reasonable to regard them as the final arbiters.

(2.2) Difficulties of Objective Assessment

Since the product of loudspeaker reproduction cannot be objectively defined, all that can be done is to specify those

* Stereophonic or pseudo-stereophonic systems are excluded from this discussion.

characteristics of the vibrating and radiating system which are thought to be relevant to the final result. Few of these characteristics can be varied independently of the others, while some of them cannot be accurately reproduced in nominally identical specimens. As a result, deductions regarding the influence of the various factors on the subjective end-product are often very uncertain, and any advance in making meaningful measurements is a slow process of trial and error. The position could be improved by more frequent publication of experimental results by those able to produce significant data, so that a body of experience could be built up. A greater degree of standardization in methods of measuring and expressing the performance of loudspeakers is, however, desirable; in this connection, attention may be drawn to the British Standard[1] of 1954 dealing with this subject.

The significance of the various measurable characteristics will now be discussed.

(2.3) Effects of Environment and Directional Characteristics

For the purpose of this discussion the term 'loudspeaker' includes the complete radiating system, comprising one or more vibrating diaphragms and some form of baffle or enclosure. It is a 3-dimensional device which is invariably small compared with the longest wavelength of sound to be radiated and large compared with the smallest. Its directional properties therefore vary widely with frequency; i.e. its frequency response varies widely with the direction of radiation. In general, loudspeakers are used indoors, so that much of the sound reaching the listener arrives indirectly, after having been radiated in various directions and reflected from the boundaries of the room, being further modified in the process through the variation of reflection coefficient with frequency. By some process not fully understood, the listener is able without conscious effort to integrate all the resulting stimuli into a single impression. It is clear, therefore, that any attempt to predict from the free-field characteristics of a loudspeaker the frequency response as it appears to the listener must take into account the radiation in various directions. For simple cases, where the relationship between the frequency characteristics for various angles of radiation is fixed, empirical rules, based on subjective assessment, have been formulated. Thus, McMillan and West[2] adopted the mean spherical response as a criterion; they described a loudspeaker, having a 7 in diameter cone, in which the mean spherical response* was held constant with frequency by making the axial frequency characteristic rise by about $2\frac{1}{2}$ dB per octave. This principle is not, however, universally applicable, and experience with loudspeakers covering frequencies up to 10 kc/s or above suggests that, if a single quantity representing 'effective' response is to be found at all, it will lie somewhere between the axial and mean spherical response. Such a quantity could be obtained by carrying out a modified spherical integration at each of a number of frequencies, taking zones concentric with the loudspeaker axis, and applying some weighting function which would give the front response more prominence. The measurement could be economically undertaken by using the normal equipment for tracing directivity patterns with the addition of a suitable signal-integrating device.[3]

Deduction of the effective frequency response of a loudspeaker from its free-space characteristics usually involves the tacit assumptions that complete diffusion of sound energy exists, and that the reaction of the reflected sound upon the loudspeaker, as manifested by changes in the acoustic impedance presented to the latter, may be neglected. These assumptions become invalid at wavelengths comparable with the dimensions of the room; where these dimensions are small, the sound level below 100 c/s is difficult to predict, and it may be desirable to adjust the low-frequency characteristics of the loudspeaker to suit local conditions. It should also be pointed out that most monitoring loudspeakers are required to operate in a variety of positions, so that devices such as corner horns, which can only function at particular places in the room, are unsuitable for general use.

So far, the question of directional characteristics has been considered only in relation to the apparent frequency response of the loudspeaker/room combination. However, the final result as assessed by the listener also includes the apparent size and position of the sound source; this attribute of a loudspeaker cannot be directly specified, but is likewise a function of the directivity pattern. Single-cone loudspeakers of conventional construction become increasingly directional with increasing frequency, and in rooms of average reverberation time give the impression of a clearly localized small source of sound. Less directional loudspeakers produce more reverberant sound in the listening room and give a more spacious effect; and with a nearly omnidirectional system the source appears to be distributed over a wide area. It by no means follows, however, that omnidirectional radiation at all frequencies represents the ideal condition. From subjective experiments with loudspeakers of widely differing directional characteristics, Kaufmann[4] recently concluded that the preferred form of polar distribution was that of the original source of sound. Further subjective studies are now required to decide on the best compromise for all purposes.

* The term 'mean spherical response' in acoustics relates to the total acoustic power output from a sound source and is analogous to the term 'mean spherical candle power' used in optics.

(2.4) Significance of Broad Trends in Response

(2.4.1) General.

Because of the irregular nature of loudspeaker frequency characteristics, which commonly exhibit local fluctuations of ± 5 dB or more about the mean, the effects of smaller deviations in the broad trend of the response, such as would be considered significant in other parts of the transmission chain, are often underrated. Changes of ± 2 dB or less in the general trend or in the relative level of certain critical frequency bands can be detected in whatever part of the transmission chain they occur; for example, two frequency characteristics, each within ± 2 dB of uniformity but one increasing slowly and the other decreasing slowly throughout the range, give distinctly different subjective effects. It is therefore convenient to consider the broad trends in the response of the system, averaged over a series of frequency bands by the use of wide-range warble tones or bands of noise; in dealing with derived quantities such as the mid-band sensitivity or the mean spherical response, such an approach may in any case be necessary on practical grounds. For instrumental reasons, the accuracy with which the details of a frequency response curve can be delineated is often little better than ± 2 dB. However, many of the errors to which this type of measurement is subject are absent for a noise-band test, in which results can usually be repeated to better than $\frac{1}{2}$ dB; such tests are of practical value for routine maintenance, since valid comparisons between loudspeakers of the same type can be made in a 'live' room.

(2.4.2) Significance of Specific Frequency Bands.

Experience with loudspeakers of known characteristics, supplemented by experiments on raising or lowering the response in specific regions by means of band-pass or band-stop circuits, enables the subjective effect of an excess or deficiency to be predicted. Many of the conclusions to be drawn from such experience are too well known to require recapitulation; two, however, are worth mentioning because of their bearing on design.

If a progressive decline in response with increasing frequency

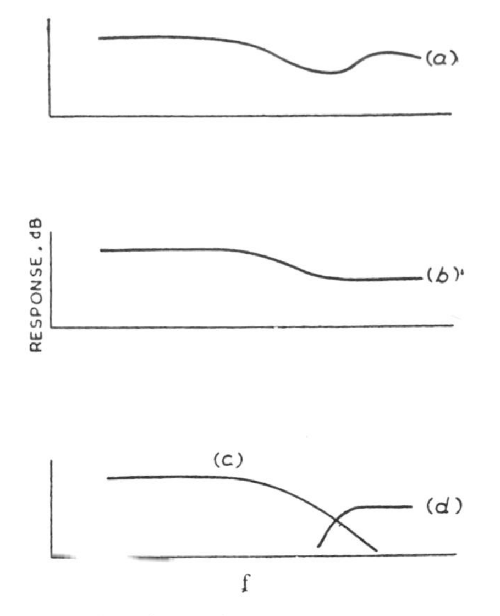

Fig. 1.—Typical defects in upper-frequency response.

is followed by an increase, giving the type of characteristic illustrated in curve (*a*) of Fig. 1, the upper frequency range will be heard to stand out in unnatural relief, even though the response may nowhere rise above the mid-band level. It should be noted that this form of frequency characteristic modifies the spectrum of the reproduced sound in a way not experienced when listening to natural sounds. Progressive attenuation with increasing frequency is an everyday occurrence—it is experienced, for example, when listening to sound which has travelled round a corner—but, apart from isolated cases of specular reflection, selective reinforcement of the upper frequency range does not appear in nature. Even a shelving characteristic, such as that shown in curve (*b*) of Fig. 1, can give the effect of a 'disembodied' high-frequency output, a result which could be explained on the assumption that the energy spectrum is subjectively analysed into a continuously falling curve (*c*) of Fig. 1, with the addition of a secondary curve, (*d*). The above remarks naturally apply to some extent to the sound radiated in all directions and it seems to be a safe rule that the ear, in integrating the characteristics for the various angles of radiation, will take in the most well-defined—which in practice means the worst—features of each. Unfortunately, the off-axis frequency characteristics of wide-range multi-radiator loudspeakers are particularly likely to be of the humped or shelving type shown in curves (*a*) and (*b*), even though the axial characteristic may be flat.

The second observation concerns the critical nature of the frequency band in the region 2–4 kc/s, the level of which, relative to the remainder of the spectrum, has a pronounced effect upon the apparent auditory perspective. Deficiency in this band gives a distant impression; slight excess gives a forward quality, sometimes referred to as 'presence'. The tonal quality associated with extreme deficiency or excess in this region ranges from hollow, or distant, to hard or metallic.* This complete gamut of effects can often be passed through with a change in level of plus or minus a few decibels in the band concerned. With most cone radiators designed to cover the lower-frequency range the response in the 2–4 kc/s region is difficult to control and often varies widely in manufacture. To obtain consistent performance in production, therefore, it is desirable in multi-unit loudspeaker systems, first, that the first cross-over frequency should not be higher than 2 kc/s, and secondly, that means should be provided for adjusting, in steps not greater than 2 dB, the relative levels of the signals applied to the high- and low-frequency units to compensate for production variations in sensitivity.

* Such expressions as these may seem out of place in a technical context. They are, however, typical of the terms in which the end product of a sound-reproduction system is described by the observer, and when employed by individuals known to be capable of consistent judgment must be treated with respect.

(2.4.3) **Overall Slope of Response Characteristics.**

It is often tacitly assumed that, for the highest degree of realism in sound reproduction by a single loudspeaker, the axial response, the mean spherical response or some intermediate quantity ought to be held constant with frequency. This assumption is not always supported by subjective judgment. Observers who with one type of loudspeaker prefer an axial response rising slightly with increasing frequency may demand with another type that the axial characteristic, and hence all other characteristics, should fall. The desire for a reduced high-frequency output is often expressed when the frequency response curve in the upper part of the range is not smooth; in other cases, the varying preferences may be connected with the directional characteristics. Again, with loudspeakers of conventional directional properties, a uniform axial frequency response is necessarily accompanied by a considerable increase in total sound output at the lower frequencies; this increase is seldom regarded as excessive and is sometimes felt to be insufficient. The demand for an overemphasized low-frequency response may be partly accounted for by the apparent weakening of the lower-frequency components which is observed when a sound is reproduced at a level below that of the original. However, in view of the complexity of the factors on which the illusion of reality depends, varying preferences such as those referred to need occasion no surprise and it seems unprofitable to be dogmatic on the subject. The only firm conclusion which can safely be drawn is that with wide-range loudspeakers of conventional directional characteristics a flat axial response may be acceptable but a flat mean-spherical response is intolerable.

(2.5) **Frequency-Response Irregularity and Related Criteria**

(2.5.1) **General.**

So far, attention has been concentrated on broad trends in the frequency characteristics such as would remain after averaging the response over bands of, say, ½–1 octave. Performance criteria based on such a smoothing process represent a minimum requirement. Clearly, the response within each band should vary as smoothly as possible with frequency; the permissible degree of fluctuation has, however, always been open to doubt. Much of the published work on this subject is concerned with the relationship between the frequency response of the system and the time response as shown by the reproduction of transient signals; it will therefore be convenient to survey these two subjects together, along with the closely connected subject of phase distortion.

Most of the detailed studies of frequency characteristics have treated the loudspeaker as a minimum-phase-shift device; in such a case, supplementary measurements of phase shift or transient response could be undertaken for convenience but would in principle be unnecessary. The practical limitations imposed by the minimum-phase-shift assumption will be discussed later.

(2.5.2) **Transient Response.**

The direct observation of transient phenomena in loudspeakers has been the subject of a number of publications. Early investigations were carried out by McLachlan and Sowter, using a unit-step signal, and in 1937 Helmbold,[5] using an interrupted tone, was able to demonstrate the relationship between build-up time and steady-state frequency response.

Some years ago the author suggested[6] that, since correlation between subjective quality and frequency-response irregularity was still unsatisfactory, the interrupted-tone testing method should be extended to the later stages of the transient, the form of which can in simple cases be related to the smaller fluctuations in the frequency characteristic. Attention was concentrated on the decay transient, the envelope of which had been found at particular frequencies to take the form approximately represented in Fig. 2(*a*). The slowly decaying tail presumably represents the sound output from some resonant element having relatively little damping; this sound can thus be regarded as having been diluted by the main sound output in the ratio $A_0' : A_0$, which, in conjunction with the two decay factors Δ_1 and Δ_2, serves as a useful quantitative index to the transient behaviour of the system. At the cost of some instrumental complication, the data obtained from oscillograms can be presented as a function of the frequency of the interrupted tone. To this end the cycle of interruption is repeated at short intervals while the frequency is slowly varied and the envelope amplitude A_1, appearing at time t_1 after the start of the decay, is plotted; the same process, repeated for times t_2, t_3, etc., gives a family of curves, of the form shown in Fig. 2(*b*), which exhibit peaks at the various frequencies of resonance. This presentation can be used even where the decays are not exponential. The information shown in Fig. 2(*b*) can also be presented as a 3-dimensional model representing amplitude, frequency and time; Fig. 2(*c*) shows such a model constructed from experimental data.

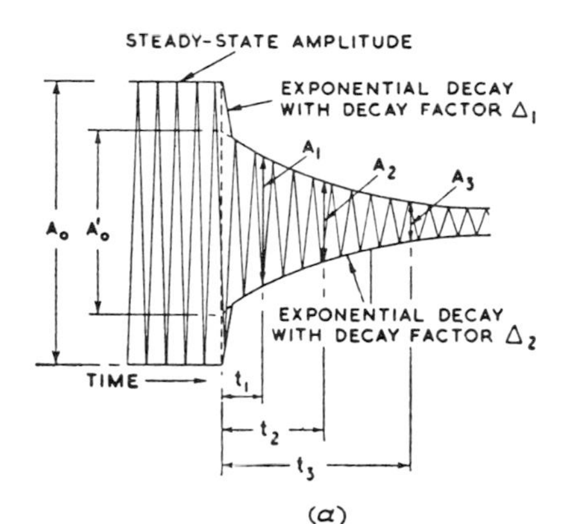

(*a*)

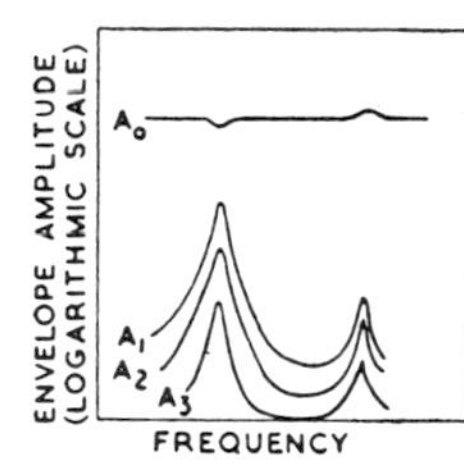

(*b*)

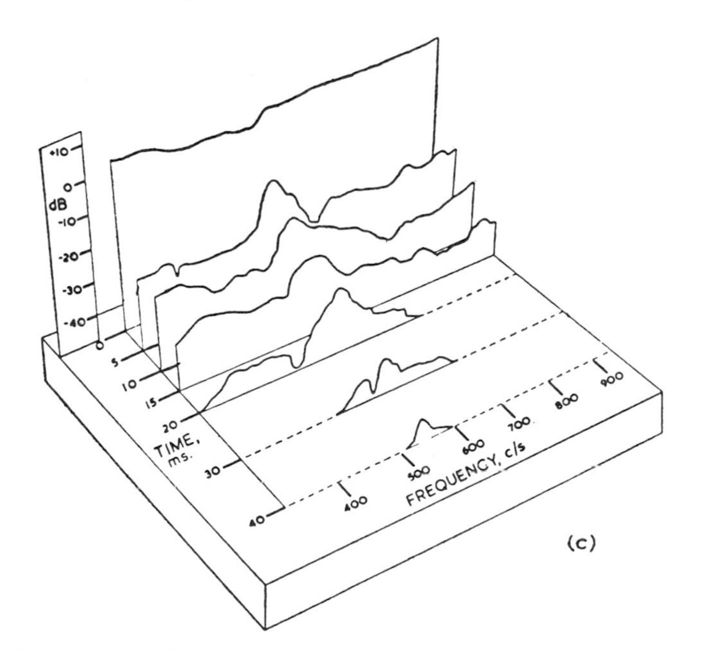

(c)

Fig. 2.—Methods of representing response of multiple resonant system to interrupted tone.

(*a*) As a function of time.
(*b*) As a function of time and frequency.
(*c*) As a 3-dimensional model in time and frequency.

Following the same approach, Corrington,[7] in the United States, showed experimentally the connection between various modes of cone resonance, the associated transient phenomena observed with an interrupted tone signal and the corresponding fluctuations in the frequency characteristic, many of which, in the examples given, were less than 1 dB in extent. As a sequel to this work, an ingenious electronic device was designed[8] to interrupt the test tone at intervals corresponding to a prescribed number of cycles and to record, as a function of frequency, the mean sound output registered during the nominally silent periods. From the results, it was suggested[8, 9] as a criterion that the mean sound pressure during the first 16 cycles of the decay transient should not exceed some 12% of the steady-state pressure at the same frequency.

In contrast to the methods just described is the work of Hentsch[10] and Seemann,[11] in Switzerland, on the influence of irregularities in the frequency characteristic. Seemann proposed some empirical rules, based on subjective experiments with interrupted tone passed through various resonant circuits and filters and presented to the observers by high-quality earphones; he concluded that, *inter alia*, irregularities in frequency response up to ± 2 dB are imperceptible.

The various lines of approach outlined above have more in common than may at first appear. Consider a case in which irregularities of ± 2 dB, i.e. approximately $\pm 25\%$ about the mean response curve, are caused by the presence in the loudspeaker system of a series of subsidiary resonant elements, the maximum output from each element being 25% of the mean output and either in phase or in antiphase with it.[6] The tail of the transient will then start its decay with an amplitude A_0' which is 0·25 of the mean steady-state sound pressure in the frequency region concerned. Let it now be assumed, for example, that the final rate of decay is 1 dB/millisec ($\Delta_2 = 115$)—a figure which lies roughly in the middle of the range encountered in practice and within one order of the extreme values—and that $\Delta_1 \gg \Delta_2$; it is then readily shown that at 1 kc/s the average level of the transient tail taken over the first 16 cycles is $0{\cdot}48A_0'$ or 0·12 of the mean steady-state pressure. In the example given, therefore, the frequency response which just satisfies Seemann's criterion of ± 2 dB is associated with a form of transient which just meets the 12% requirement laid down by Corrington.

(2.5.3) Effect of Non-Minimum-Phase-Shift Condition.

In all the work described in the last Section, frequency-response irregularity and transient distortion existed simultaneously and no attempt was made in the experiments to introduce the one without the other. In any system to which the minimum-phase-shift condition does not apply, the two attributes can, of course, be independent of each other, but little information is available on the subjective effect of varying them separately. Hentsch,[10] however, described some tests carried out with a series of all-pass networks, which allowed phase shifts to be introduced into the transmission chain without alteration of the frequency characteristic; the networks gave a maximum group delay, i.e. rate of change of phase with frequency, up to 35 millisec at 524 c/s but very little delay at other frequencies. Interrupted tone at 524 c/s was passed through the delay networks and presented to the observers through high-quality headphones; the smallest perceptible group delay time was found to be of the order of 10 millisec. Tests were also carried out with a simple resonant circuit tuned to a frequency of 524 c/s; a circuit of this kind, having a time-constant of about 2 millisec, was found to have the same—just perceptible—subjective effect as the all-pass system with a group delay of 10 millisec. These results illustrate the limitations of transient-response measurement when minimum-phase-shift conditions cannot be assumed. In such circumstances, however, the steady-state response/frequency characteristic is equally inadequate as an index of performance unless supplemented by the corresponding phase/frequency characteristic.

(2.5.4) **Phase Distortion.**

Many cases occur in practice in which a loudspeaker imposes on the reproduced sound a strong characteristic coloration, although the frequency response curve in the region concerned is smooth and level or has been made so by electrical equalization. These loudspeakers presumably cannot be regarded as minimum-phase-shift devices, and consideration of their phase distortion is indicated. Measurement of phase distortion in loudspeakers has hitherto received little attention, probably because of the instrumental difficulties involved, though Ewaskio and Mawardi[12] have published some group-delay/frequency characteristics for single- and double-unit loudspeakers, together with the corresponding amplitude-response/frequency characteristics. Measurements of this kind may ultimately provide the solution in otherwise intractable cases, but much further work will be necessary before the practical value of this approach can be properly assessed.

(2.5.5) **Effect of Interference.**

In the foregoing discussion it is tacitly assumed that sound from the various parts of the radiating surface reaches the measuring point by paths of nearly equal length so that interference effects are negligible. To achieve such a condition, even on the axis of a small diaphragm, is less simple than might be expected. Even though the radiation from the rear of the diaphragm is completely suppressed, interference can be caused by reflection at the discontinuity formed by the edges of the enclosure. This effect, first demonstrated by Nichols[13] and Olson,[14] may extend throughout the audio-frequency range; it can be minimized by mounting the radiating unit asymmetrically and by rounding or chamfering the front edges of the enclosure.

A difficult situation arises when the loudspeaker consists of several units. Where each unit covers a different band of frequencies, interference is confined to the cross-over region. If, however, two or more units are used to cover the same band—a growing practice in loudspeakers intended to give wide-angle radiation at high frequencies—the effect will extend over a wider band and it may be impossible to find any point equidistant from all the radiating surfaces at which to measure the response.

As long as interference effects in free space vary with the position at which the pressure measurement is taken and do not affect the average response of the loudspeaker over a wide band, they fall into the same category as interference effects produced by reflections in a live listening room and may be relatively harmless. Some method of measurement which would automatically discount irregularities in the frequency characteristics arising from interference, while retaining enough information about irregularities arising from other causes, is therefore desirable. Meanwhile, it may be necessary, in investigating the performance of a multi-unit loudspeaker, to test each unit separately, if necessary in another enclosure.

(2.6) Non-Linearity

(2.6.1) **General.**

The effects of non-linearity in loudspeakers differ from those occurring in most other parts of a sound transmission system in the manner in which they vary with the frequency of the signal. Apart from a gradual increase in distortion towards the lower end of the working frequency range, pronounced non-linearity often appears in a series of very narrow bands,[15] so that measurements are laborious and the results are particularly difficult to interpret for a complex signal waveform. It is therefore not surprising that the literature on the subject is concerned more with the description of methods of distortion measurement, illustrated by results for particular cases, than with systematic investigations to discover the maximum permissible values. With some forms of distortion it would probably be easier, as well as more profitable, to remove the cause by appropriate design than to discover rules for assessing the effect. More information on the mechanism of the various forms of distortion in loudspeakers is therefore required; to obtain this information various refinements of measuring techniques may be necessary.

Measurements of non-linearity in loudspeakers at discrete frequencies are of limited value unless these frequencies are chosen by ear, using a gliding-tone signal. Ideally, distortion should be measured as a continuous function of frequency, and this can be done by heterodyne methods or by switching filters.

(2.6.2) **Application of Harmonic and Intermodulation-Distortion Tests.**

In single-tone distortion testing, it is advisable to measure the individual harmonics, since loudspeakers are prone to a type of non-linearity[16] which is more offensive to the ear than the total harmonic content would suggest. Such distortion can arise when some vibrating element, e.g. the cone surround, is in resonance and reaches the limit of its excursion while the rest of the moving system is still operating linearly.

Fig. 3 shows an example of a harmonic-distortion measurement on a loudspeaker made by means of a gliding-tone heterodyne analyser. The signal at the input of the associated amplifier was held constant with frequency at such a value as to produce at 400 c/s and at 4 ft 6 in distance an axial sound pressure of 10 dyn/mc^2 r.m.s. (94 dB above the reference level, 2×10^{-4} dyn/cm^2). Fig. 3 shows the fundamental and harmonics up to the sixth in their correct relative positions on a decibel scale. The degree of distortion shown at the highest and lowest frequencies is not reached in practice, since the spectrum of normal programme material falls at the extremes of the frequency band,[17, 18] To cover all conditions it would be possible to repeat the distortion measurements at a series of different input levels. A less laborious alternative would have been deliberately to reduce the applied signal at high and low frequencies according to some law based on the spectrum of the programme; to this end it would be helpful if agreement on a standard law of attenuation could be reached.

Harmonic-distortion tests cannot be extended to the upper end of the audio-frequency range, since many of the distortion products then fall outside the pass-band of the loudspeaker or measuring equipment; this limitation is not serious unless the

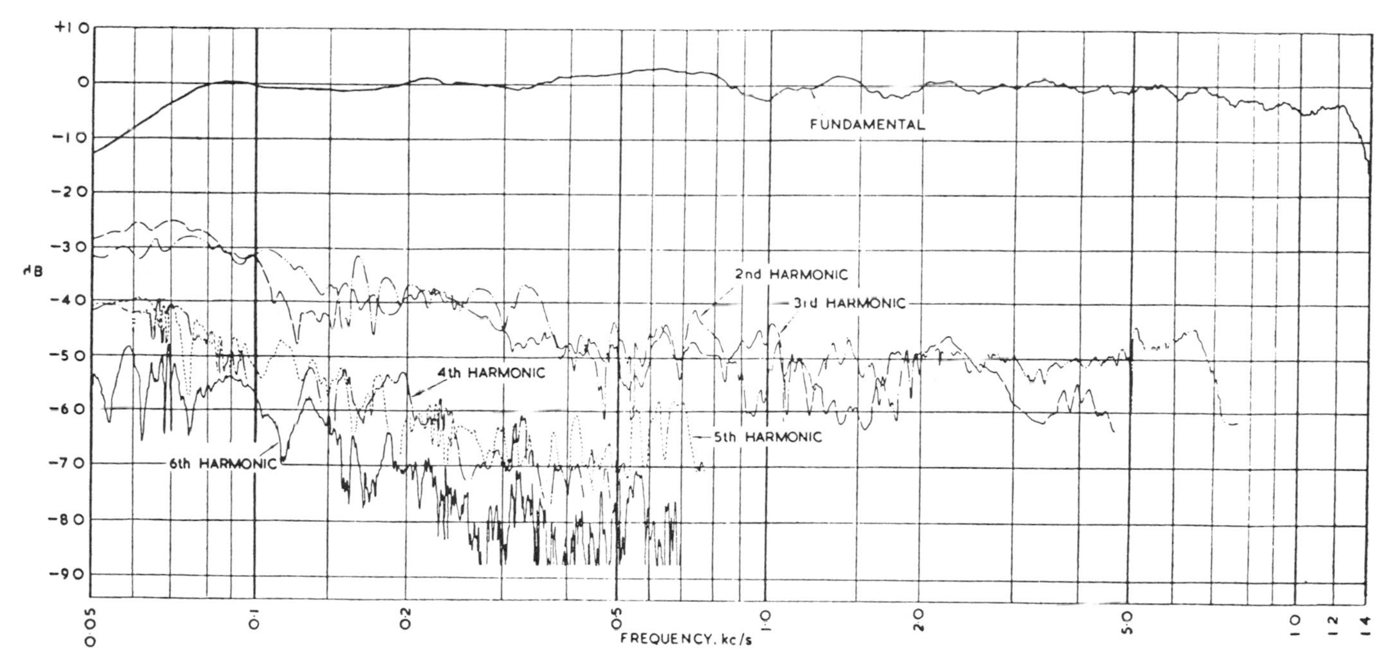

Fig. 3.—Fundamental and harmonics in output of loudspeaker excited with gliding tone.

distortion produced by the loudspeaker or its associated amplifier increases at higher frequencies. Where it is important to test the linearity of the system up to the limit of the audio-frequency band, an intermodulation test with two gliding tones, of frequencies f_1 and f_2 ($f_2 > f_1$) and a constant difference $f_2 - f_1$, may be applied. Fig. 4 shows the results of such a test on the loudspeaker of the last example. The amplitude of each tone was $1/\sqrt{2}$ of the amplitude of the single tone in the harmonic measurement and $f_2 - f_1$ was 120 c/s. The curves show the relative levels of the fundamental signals and the intermodulation products having frequencies $f_2 - f_1$, $2f_1 - f_2$, $3f_1 - 2f_2$ and $4f_1 - 3f_2$. It will be seen that in tests of this kind it is insufficient to take the difference frequency alone; on the other hand, the measurement of one or two of the higher-order products will probably give all the information that is required.

In a more common form of intermodulation test, two tones widely separated in frequency are applied; the amplitude of the higher-frequency tone is generally made about one-quarter that of the lower-frequency signal[1] and the distortion is assessed in terms of the degree of modulation of the former by the latter. This type of measurement is primarily intended to indicate non-linearity at frequency f_1, the signal of frequency f_2 being regarded as a pilot tone, the precise frequency and amplitude of which are unimportant, and which in itself creates no distortion products. The method has the great advantage that the acoustic measurement can be confined to a small range of frequencies in the middle of the audio-frequency band. In an alternative scheme proposed by Ingerslev[19] the two applied signals are of equal amplitude and the level of the intermodulation products is plotted as a function of f_2, f_1 remaining fixed. The results of such a measurement must, however, depend on the degree of non-linearity existing at both f_1 and f_2, and a number of tests would be necessary to identify the various sources of distortion.

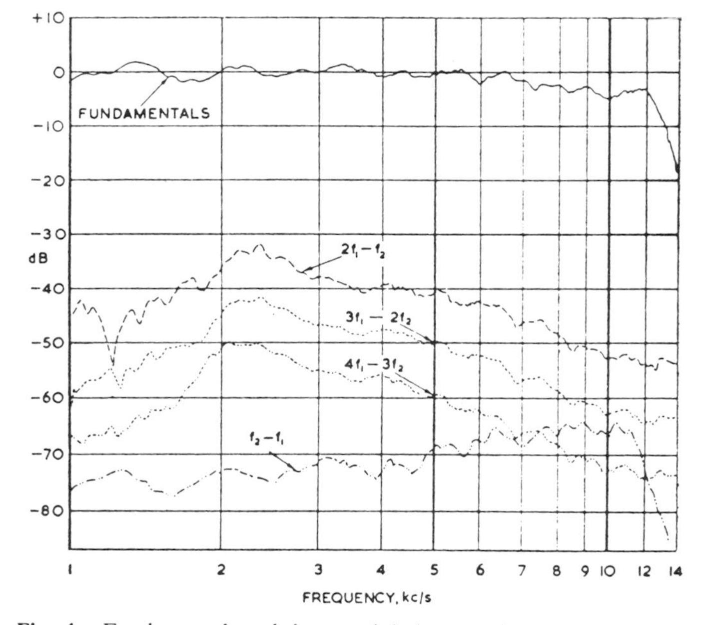

Fig. 4.—Fundamental and intermodulation products in output of loudspeaker excited with two gliding tones of equal amplitude having a constant frequency difference.

(2.7) Methods of Subjective Assessment

(2.7.1) General.

The subjective assessment of loudspeaker performance might appear to be a simple and straightforward operation and was once so regarded. It was common practice to judge loudspeakers by their reproduction of a variety of transmitted programme material without reference to the original sound; sometimes the criterion of the 'most pleasing sound' was adopted. However, when the standard of reproduction advanced to the point where some slight semblance of realism was possible, this somewhat naïve approach had to be abandoned, for the order of merit was found to vary with the type of programme material, the studio acoustics, the microphone placing, and with other factors such as the position of the different loudspeakers in the listening room. Further experience showed that, by systematic listening tests carried out under more carefully controlled conditions, the effects of irrelevant factors could be largely eliminated and the risk of a wrong judgment, i.e. one which would later have to be revised after a period of service, much reduced.

(2.7.2) **Noise Tests.**

Many of the salient features of loudspeaker response can be very quickly appreciated subjectively by applying to the input a continuous-spectrum random-noise voltage. To avoid aural fatigue and to render the test more sensitive, it is advantageous for this and other subjective assessments to place a second loudspeaker beside the one under consideration and to switch back and forth between the two; by contrast, the individual peculiarities of both loudspeakers will then become evident. This test will usually disclose differences even between nominally identical loudspeakers.

(2.7.3) **Speech Tests.**

The realistic, as distinct from the merely intelligible, reproduction of speech is particularly difficult to achieve; the transmission of a voice which is familiar to the observers is a stringent test for a loudspeaker. Male voices are the most suitable, as they reveal various defects common in the 250–1 000 c/s band. The speech should be transmitted from a non-reverberant room or from the open air, for it is not the function of a loudspeaker to compensate for peculiarities in the acoustics of studios. It is not permissible to reduce the amount of transmitted reverberation by bringing the microphone close to the talker's mouth; speech picked up at distances less than 12 in has an unnatural character, particularly at high frequencies, which cannot be compensated by electrical equalization.

For these and the remaining subjective tests, the loudspeakers to be compared should be concealed from the observers to prevent identification.

(2.7.4) **Music Tests.**

The final test consists of a comparison between live and reproduced music, the listening point being established as near as possible to the studio or concert hall so that the observers may pass freely between the two. Such freedom of movement is possible only during rehearsals, and observers must note the tonal quality being produced in the studio *at the time*, since musicians often reserve their fullest efforts for the final performance. Good sound insulation between studio and listening room is important, especially at the extremely low frequencies, at which an attenuation of at least 35 dB is essential.

The quality of reproduction obtained will naturally depend on the disposition of the performers and of the microphones in the studio—technically known as the 'balance' of the transmission. It is important, however, that defects in the loudspeaker should not be unwittingly compensated by an alteration in balance; for the purpose of the test, therefore, the instruments of the orchestra should be arranged to give an acceptable result as heard in the studio, and a single microphone, so placed as to avoid over-emphasis of any one instrument, should be used. It is true that in certain types of programme more than one microphone is frequently employed; with dance bands, to take an extreme example, a separate microphone may be provided for each group of instruments, and by this means effects can be produced which are not audible to a listener in the studio. Programme material of this type is, however, inadmissible when an unambiguous comparison between original and reproduced sound has to be made.

In studios and concert halls having good sound diffusion—a condition which can be verified by direct listening—the microphone placing is not highly critical.[20] For a particular orchestral layout, however, there is usually a preferred position, and this position in itself gives an additional check on loudspeaker performance. The better types of loudspeaker, while each departing in a different way from the ideal and so giving an appreciably different version of the transmitted sound, have in practice so much in common that the best microphone position for any one of them is nearly the same. On the other hand, a loudspeaker having some peculiarity in response, which, for example, throws into prominence one type of orchestral instrument, may require for best results a different microphone position or even a different orchestral layout.

All that has been said on the subject of optimum microphone placing applies equally to the directional characteristics of the microphone required to give the best overall effect. Differences in performance between high-quality microphones having the same nominal directional characteristics are too small to affect the order of preference between different loudspeakers.

(3) DESIGN CONSIDERATIONS

(3.1) Electrical Equalization

The loudspeaker designer's task could frequently be eased by modifying the frequency characteristics of the preceding amplifier chain. This expedient, often employed in one form or another in the design of radio receivers, introduces some obvious instrumental complications when applied to an independent loudspeaker, but has important advantages where an exceptionally high and consistent standard of performance is required. It may even be practicable to introduce corrective circuits between the final amplifier and the loudspeaker proper, due regard being paid to the power-handling capacity of the system.

A notable example of electrical equalization of loudspeaker characteristics is furnished by the 'omnidirectional' radiating system produced by Harz and Kösters[21] in Germany for broadcast monitoring purposes; in this type of loudspeaker, the associated power amplifier is preceded by a separate low-power equalization amplifier, incorporating both low- and high-frequency pre-emphasis circuits, together with as many as six other networks designed to correct specific features in the frequency characteristics.

Electrical compensation for low-damped resonances in a loudspeaker is impracticable, if only because of the difficulty in maintaining long-term stability of the mechanical system. Electrical control of general trends in the frequency characteristics or of the response within a broad band is, however, perfectly feasible; it allows adjustments to be made to offset production variations in the electro-acoustic transducers or to compensate for differences between the acoustic conditions in individual listening rooms.

(3.2) Division of Frequency Range

In the design of wide-range loudspeakers it is usual either to provide a separate unit for the higher end of the audio-frequency band or to employ a single unit, equipped with an auxiliary diaphragm in the form of a concentric dome or cone driven from the common speech coil, to give the same effect. The change-over from the low-frequency to the high-frequency radiating system should preferably take place at a frequency at which the former is not appreciably directional. If this requirement is not met, a state of affairs arises which is represented, in simplified form, in Fig. 5. Assume that a low- and a high-frequency unit, each having uniform axial response, are mounted on a common axis and fed through a cross-over network in such a way that the combined axial response ($\theta = 0$) is likewise uniform. If, at the cross-over frequency f_{co}, the low-frequency radiator is appreciably directional, the frequency characteristics at angles θ_1, θ_2, etc., will exhibit a depression in the region just below f_{co}. This effect could be largely avoided if the frequency range were divided into three bands, using diaphragms of progressively smaller diameters; for most purposes, however, this solution is uneconomic, not only because of the extra

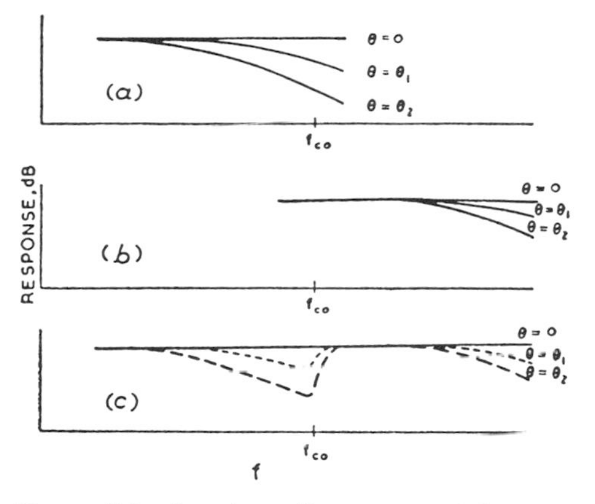

Fig. 5.—Two-unit loudspeaker: effect on overall frequency characteristics of change in directional properties at cross-over.

(*a*) Frequency response of low-frequency unit.
(*b*) Frequency response of high-frequency unit.
(*c*) Combined frequency response.

radiating system, but also because of the additional cross-over networks and the extra setting-up adjustments required in production.

(3.3) General Properties of Cone Radiators

Although cone loudspeakers have been in common use for more than 30 years, the amount of systematic research carried out on their performance is surprisingly small and their design is still, to a large extent, a matter of trial and error. The behaviour of the diaphragm is not readily amenable to mathematical treatment, the difficulty of analysis being aggravated by the various departures from the simple conical form which in course of time have been empirically introduced. Experimental studies are hampered by the high price of the tools required to form the diaphragm; it may cost several hundred pounds to discover the effect of a minor change in profile.

The diaphragm of a cone loudspeaker is a complex vibratory system capable of motion in various regimes. The quality of sound produced by it is not always predictable from the frequency/response characteristics, even in the region below 1 kc/s where these may be relatively smooth. In particular, an objectionable type of coloration in the lower-middle-frequency range seems to be characteristic of a large number of units of less than 10 in cone diameter. The effect is usually associated with the presence of low-damped radial modes; however, attempts to simulate the subjective result electrically by the introduction of single tuned circuits having a comparable decrement have not been successful, and it may be that, as in the study of reverberation phenomena, a combination of modes is involved. Until this difficulty is overcome, it may be necessary in high-quality loudspeakers to employ diaphragms having areas much greater than those dictated by considerations of power-handling capacity.

(3.4) Alternative Radiating Systems for High Frequencies

The most economical form of direct radiator for the upper frequency band is undoubtedly a smaller version of the cone unit used for the low-frequency range, employing a pulp or plastic diaphragm. However, with the relatively small radiating area required, other forms of construction become possible. Small horn-type units, having coil-driven or ribbon-type diaphragms, have been extensively used; while horn radiators have been demonstrated[22] in which the diaphragm was replaced by a modulated high-frequency glow discharge taking place in a quartz tube. In recent years, there has been a revival of the electrostatic radiator for high frequencies, though not all of these units have been in the high-quality class. Finally, a form of direct radiator has been developed which is similar in structure to the moving-coil elements commonly used in conjunction with horns. Fig. 6 shows the construction of a commercial unit of

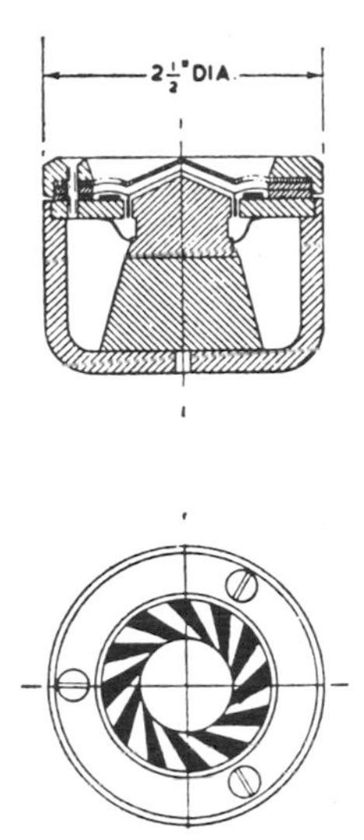

Fig. 6.—Example of modern direct-radiator high-frequency unit.

this type; the diaphragm, of plastic-impregnated fabric, moves as a whole at frequencies up to at least 10 kc/s. Because of its small dimensions the unit is less directional at high frequencies than a conventional cone or single horn radiator.

Other things being equal, the usefulness of a high-frequency radiator is limited by the acoustic power which it can produce without distortion or damage, and this usually diminishes rapidly with decreasing frequency. Direct radiating units which are small enough not to be unduly directional are generally suitable only for frequencies above 1·5 kc/s, while some are unusable below 3 kc/s. Moving-coil-driven horn systems offer some improvement in this respect and allow a nominal cross-over frequency which usually lies between 1 and 2 kc/s.

Attempts have been made to produce a radiating system substantially omnidirectional even at high audio frequencies. The best-known example of such a design is the loudspeaker of Harz and Kösters previously referred to.[21] Here the frequency range above 400 c/s is radiated by 12 small cone units mounted on the faces of a dodecahedral structure, thus giving an approximation to a spherical radiator. Fig. 7 shows an external view of the omnidirectional assembly placed a short distance away from the associated low-frequency unit, which is mounted, with axis vertical, in the top of its enclosure. In a later version[23] of the loudspeaker the number of high-frequency units has been increased to 32.

The design of such omnidirectional assemblies is hampered by the lack of suitable cone units. Few commercial units small enough for the purpose have the wide frequency range, smooth frequency response and freedom from non-linear distortion which experience shows to be necessary in high-quality loudspeakers of the conventional type, and there is no evidence that the special directional characteristics allow the normal requirements to be relaxed.

The effect of an omnidirectional loudspeaker can be partly simulated by directing the radiation from a conventional unit towards a corner of the listening room and relying on the scattering of the sound by multiple reflection; the results, however, depend so much on local conditions that the method is not universally applicable.

Fig. 7.—Omnidirectional loudspeaker using 12 high-frequency units.

(3.5) Factors influencing Low-Frequency Response

(3.5.1) Enclosure.

With the exception of the large-area electrostatic loudspeaker referred to in Section 5, every direct-radiator loudspeaker designed to operate to the lower limit of the audio-frequency range includes some kind of baffle or enclosure designed to prevent destructive interference by sound radiated from the rear of the diaphragm.

During the past decade, a considerable amount of literature on the design of such enclosures has appeared and many ingenious devices for reducing the volume required for a given performance have been described. Unfortunately, most of the publications concerned are largely theoretical or descriptive in character and seldom include any results of acoustic response measurements to support the claims made. The basic form of enclosure employed with wide-range loudspeakers has remained unchanged for some 20 years. In some arrangements the space at the rear of the diaphragm is completely closed; most designs, however, employ the well-known phase-inverting device due to Thuras,[24] whereby sound escapes at low frequencies through an auxiliary aperture or vent in aiding phase and thus increases the low-frequency range of the loudspeaker by half an octave or more. The effectiveness of this arrangement depends, however, on the relationship between the mechanical impedance presented by the cone and the acoustic load imposed on it by the enclosure. With enclosures of small volume the requirements can best be met when the area of the cone is likewise small; where it is necessary, for the reasons indicated in Section 3.3, to employ large cones in conjunction with small enclosures, the introduction of a vent may be useless or even detrimental to performance.

Except in very large enclosures, there is no difficulty in making the walls stiff enough to prevent any appreciable transmission of sound at frequencies below 100 c/s. At higher frequencies, a certain minimum mass of material per unit wall area is required to give adequate attenuation; further increasing the mass by increasing wall thickness, however, does not give a proportionate advantage unless the material exhibits sufficient internal damping at the various resonance frequencies.

A useful comparative test of materials can be carried out by constructing experimental enclosures without the normal sound outlets, setting up sound pressures by an internal sound source—a heavy-duty 'pressure' unit of the kind employed to operate cinema-type horn loudspeakers is suitable—and measuring, as a function of frequency, the pressures produced at some external point. Fig. 8 shows curves obtained by this method, the current in the speech coil of the pressure unit being the same in each case. Curve (*a*) relates to a bare enclosure constructed of $\frac{3}{8}$ in plywood, and curve (*b*) to the same enclosure after the addition of an internal layer of $\frac{3}{8}$ in soft building board firmly bonded to the wood. The increase in mass produced by the addition of the building board is only about 11% and the principal reason for the reduced sound transmission is the increased damping of the flexural modes. Measurements of this kind, while purely empirical in character, can lead not only to improved performance of the loudspeaker as a whole, but to appreciable saving in weight, an important factor in transportable equipment.

(3.5.2) Electro-Mechanical Efficiency.

The electro-mechanical efficiency of most early moving-coil loudspeakers was relatively low and the motional impedance was often negligible. This position has been greatly changed in recent years, largely by the introduction of improved magnetic materials. The high electro-mechanical efficiency obtained with many modern units presents, however, another design problem, for the motional impedance at low frequencies rises to high values and may reduce the current entering the speech coil below the value required for uniform frequency response; the effect is most marked when the loudspeaker is fed from an amplifier of low output impedance. At frequencies for which the motional impedance is high, any increase in flux density beyond a certain point will actually *reduce* the motion of the speech coil and hence the acoustic response of the system, the increase in electro-mechanical efficiency being more than offset by the reduction in power transfer from amplifier to loudspeaker. The situation can be eased by the use of a vented enclosure designed to present an appropriate acoustic impedance to the diaphragm. However, if the volume of the enclosure is restricted, the loading may be effective only over a narrow band.

One solution to this problem is to apply to the signal entering the associated amplifier such low-frequency pre-emphasis as will produce the desired overall frequency response. To obtain the maximum undistorted power output from the amplifier/loudspeaker combination, the amplifier must then be designed for a load intermediate between the low-frequency and mid-band impedance of the loudspeaker. Alternatively, it may be possible to obtain a better overall result at comparable total cost by reducing the flux density of the loudspeaker field and increasing the amplifier power.

The use of loudspeaker units having high electro-mechanical efficiency has been advocated on account of the heavy damping of the mechanical system at low frequencies which results when the electrical terminals are connected to a circuit of low resistance; to increase the damping even further, amplifiers with a negative output resistance have been employed to nullify part of the speech-coil resistance. It is often suggested that the damping of the fundamental resonance ought to be as high as possible

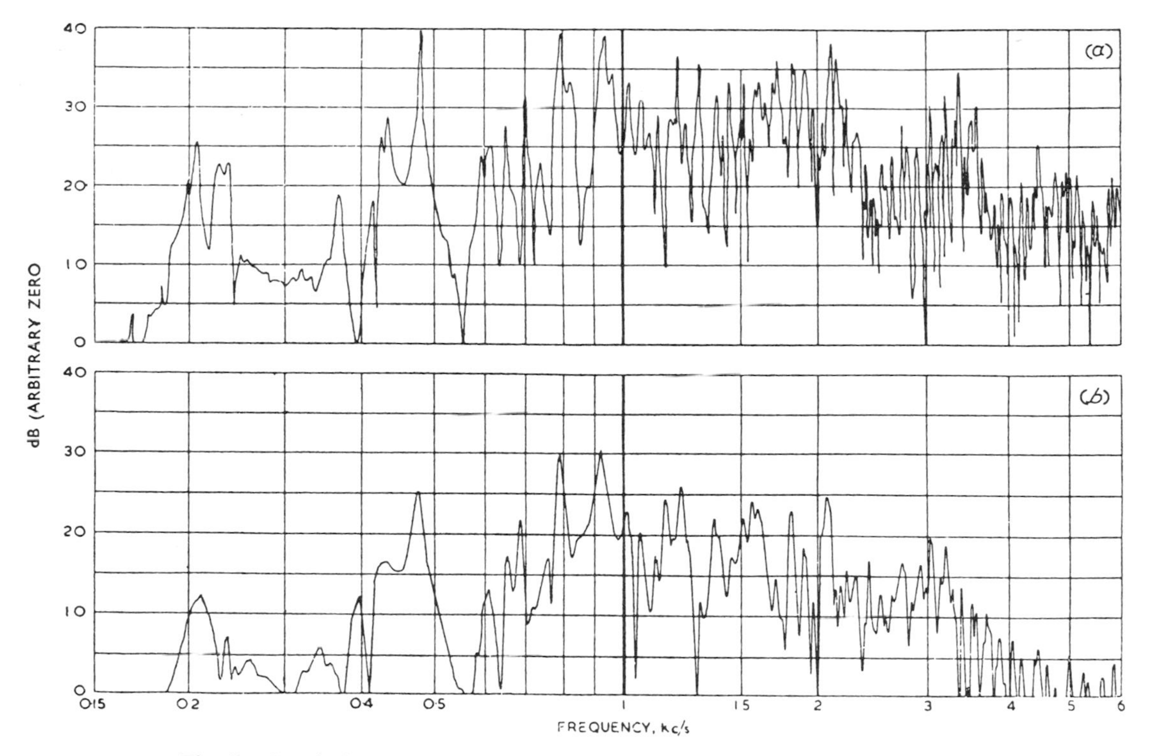

Fig. 8.—Level of sound transmitted through walls of plywood loudspeaker enclosure.
(*a*) Bare. (*b*) With damping introduced by lining of building board.

and certainly above the critical value, which corresponds to a Q-factor of 0·5. The necessity for such a high degree of damping does not appear to have been demonstrated by subjective investigation, and is all the more difficult to appreciate when it is considered that the associated enclosure, if vented, will have a low-frequency resonance of its own with a Q-factor of 3 or more.

(4) EXAMPLES OF CURRENT DESIGN

(4.1) General

To illustrate some of the points discussed in Sections 2 and 3, two types of monitoring loudspeaker recently developed by the B.B.C. will now be briefly described. One of these, referred to as loudspeaker A, is designed to meet the requirements for studio monitoring; the other loudspeaker, B, forms part of the portable equipment designed for use on outside broadcasts. Both employ similar high- and low-frequency units, so that a comparison of their performance enables the influence of other factors to be studied.

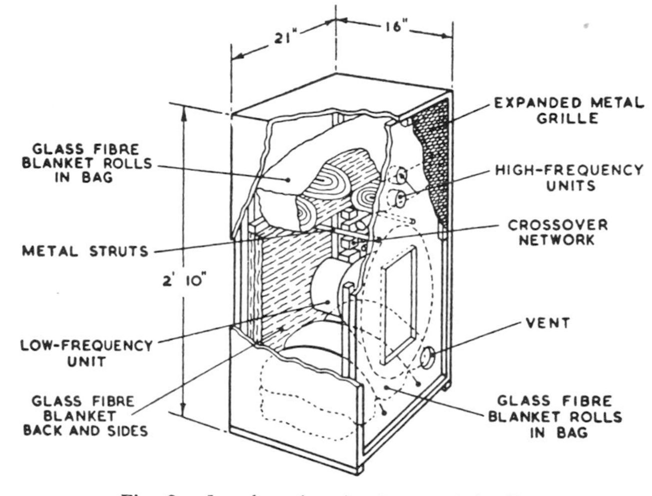

Fig. 9.—Loudspeaker A: structural details.

(4.2) Construction of Loudspeaker A

Fig. 9 shows the construction of loudspeaker A; the enclosure is of $\frac{3}{4}$ in veneered chipboard, reinforced by metal struts to restrict the vibration of the rear panel. The internal volume of the enclosure is 4·7 ft^3; a small vent resonating with the volume at about 50 c/s gives a slight increase in low-frequency output.

The low-frequency unit used is a 15 in commercial type which has an axial frequency range extending to about 4 kc/s, and which has been found to be relatively free from the coloration effect referred to in Section 3.3. Fig. 10 shows the constant-voltage frequency characteristics of the l.f. unit alone taken on the axis and at 45° to the axis in the horizontal plane. The curves of Fig. 10(*a*) relate to an enclosure similar to that of Fig. 9 but having a circular opening 12$\frac{1}{2}$ in in diameter; above 500 c/s the system is appreciably directional. By restricting the sound outlet to a vertical slot—a device due to Chapman and Trier[25]—the axial response at the upper end of the range is slightly lowered and the response at oblique angles in the horizontal plane is raised, as shown in Fig. 10(*b*), thus helping to redress the balance. The optimum slot width—in this case 7$\frac{1}{2}$ in—depends upon the geometry of the cone but is not critical.

Commercial high-frequency units of the type shown in Fig. 6 are used, two of them to increase the power-handling capacity of the system. Low- and high-frequency units are mounted in a vertical line as shown in Fig. 9; under normal listening conditions the separation between sound sources is not noticeable to observers listening at distances over 4 ft.

Both high- and low-frequency units have been tested with interrupted-tone input in the manner described in Section 2.5.2 and found to be free from any prominent low-damped resonances.

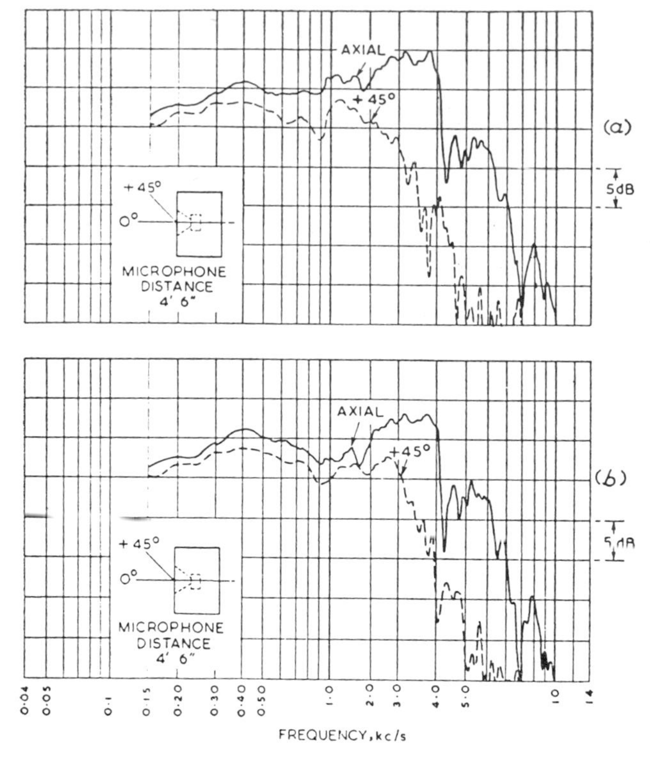

Fig. 10.—Constant-voltage response of 15 in low-frequency unit, measured on axis and at 45° in horizontal plane.

(*a*) With 12½ in diameter baffle aperture.
b With 7½ in wide vertical slot aperture.

The sound pressures produced on the axis by these units are made equal at 1·45 kc/s, though this is not the frequency at which equal power inputs are supplied to the two. In designing the cross-over network, the form of which is shown in Fig. 11, account had to be taken of the motional impedance of the h.f. unit at the lower end of its range. It was found that the requirements could most easily be met by parallel-connected high- and low-pass filters working independently of one another; with modern low-output-impedance amplifiers, interaction between the two filters is negligible and a constant-resistance cross-over network is unnecessary. On grounds of economy, inductors wound on laminated gapped nickel-iron cores are used instead of the usual air-cored coils; by designing for low flux density, intermodulation effects arising in the iron core are made smaller than those produced by the loudspeaker units themselves. The combined choke and auto-transformer T_1 is tapped to allow initial adjustment of the signal level applied to the h.f. units; to avoid any change of frequency characteristic with tap adjustment, alternative capacitors C_1, C_2 and C_3 are provided.

The resistor R_1, shunted by the inductor L_2, is introduced in series with the speech coil of the l.f. unit to correct, at the cost of a certain amount of mid-band loss, for the positive slope in the axial frequency response which would otherwise occur between 100 c/s and 1 kc/s; this feature of the characteristic represents the combined effects of loss at low frequencies due to motional impedance and gain at high frequencies due to increased directivity. The rejector circuit L_3C_6 is employed to reduce the output of the low-frequency unit in the 2·2 kc/s region, thereby avoiding some interference effects which would otherwise appear

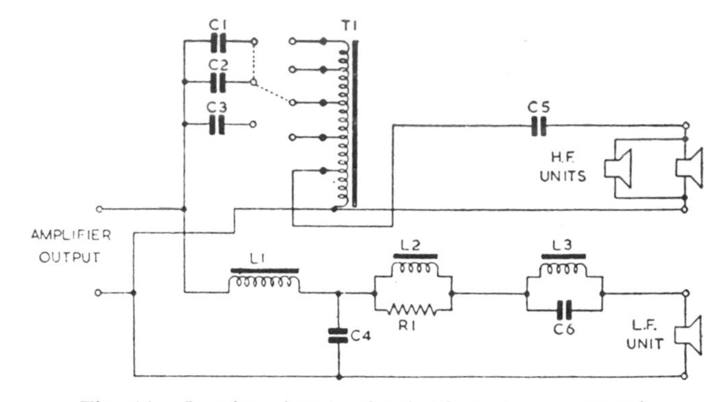

Fig. 11.—Loudspeaker A: circuit of cross-over network.

in the cross-over region. Provision for adjusting the shape of the frequency characteristics above 3 kc/s and below 150 c/s is made in an electrical network introduced into the circuit ahead of the associated power amplifier.

(4.3) Construction of Loudspeaker B

Loudspeaker B, shown in Fig. 12, is an adaptation of the basic design of loudspeaker A and employs similar low- and high-frequency units; it illustrates some of the compromises which may be necessary in special cases.

Because of the restrictions placed on the size and weight of portable equipment, the internal volume of the enclosure used for loudspeaker B is only 2·8 ft^3; with a 15 in cone unit the performance of the loudspeaker at low frequencies is better without a vent. Because of the reduced dimensions of the enclosure, a slightly lighter wall construction than with loudspeaker A is permissible, and the combination of ⅜ in plywood lined with an equal thickness of soft building board (see Section 3.5.1) is used. Electrical equalization is again employed to control the axial frequency characteristics, but in this instance all the networks involved are introduced after the associated amplifier and form part of the loudspeaker. In spite of the loss of

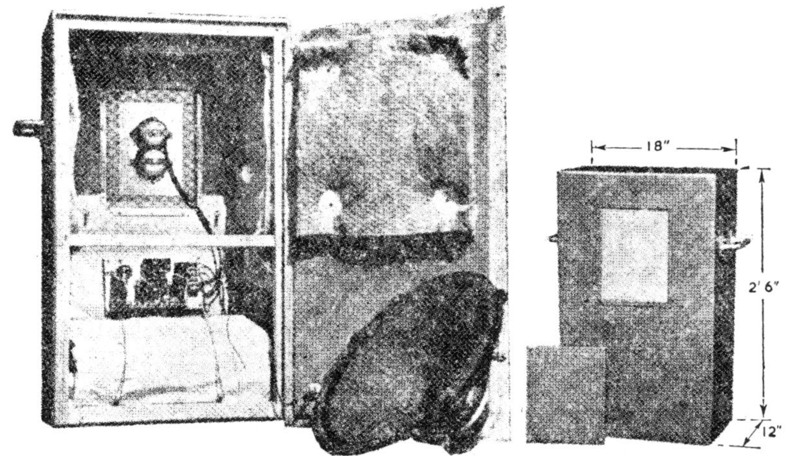

Fig. 12.—Loudspeaker B: internal and external views.

efficiency thus occasioned, adequate sound level can be produced by the use of a power amplifier rated at 15 watts output.

At outside broadcasts the space available for technical equipment is often very limited and the listener may be very close to the loudspeaker; it is therefore essential that the low- and high-frequency radiating systems should be as nearly as possible coaxial. The two h.f. units of loudspeaker B are accordingly

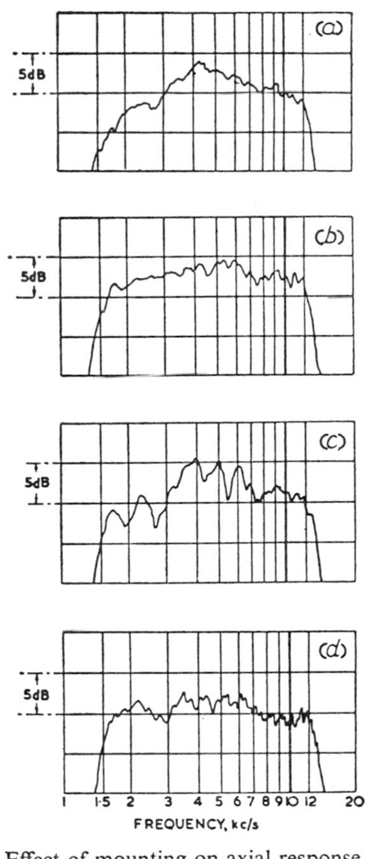

Fig. 13.—Effect of mounting on axial response of a pair of high-frequency units.

(*a*) Free space.
(*b*) Large baffle.
(*c*) Baffle with slot $7\frac{1}{2}$ in × 10 in.
(*d*) As (*c*) but with perforated baffle plate.

mounted within the cone of the l.f. unit, on a partially perforated metal plate. This plate (see Fig. 12) acts as a baffle in the upper part of the range while offering little obstruction to sound from the l.f. unit. The advantage of providing some form of baffle for the h.f. units is evident from Fig. 13; the curves show the frequency response obtained on the axis mid-way between the two units mounted (*a*) in free space, (*b*) in a large baffle, (*c*) in the $7\frac{1}{2}$ in × 10 in opening in front of the cone, and (*d*) as in (*c*) but with the perforated plate. It should be noted that these curves include the effect of the internal cross-over and corrective networks.

(4.4) Frequency Characteristics of Loudspeakers A and B

Fig. 14 shows the overall frequency response of loudspeaker A with its associated amplifier, measured at various angles in the horizontal and vertical planes and for two different settings of the l.f. response adjustment. At frequencies above 150 c/s measurements were made with the loudspeaker in a non-reverberant room having a working space 15 ft × 10 ft 8 in × 7 ft 4 in high; the response at lower frequencies was obtained in the open air with the loudspeaker mounted on a tower 55 ft high. The mean spherical response and the directivity index, both measured in half-octave bands, are also given. As an illustration of the observations made in Section 2.4.3, it may be noted that, at the listening levels usual in studio monitoring practice,[26] the l.f. response of curve (i) is sometimes regarded as insufficient, while in certain rooms that of curve (ii) is not found excessive.

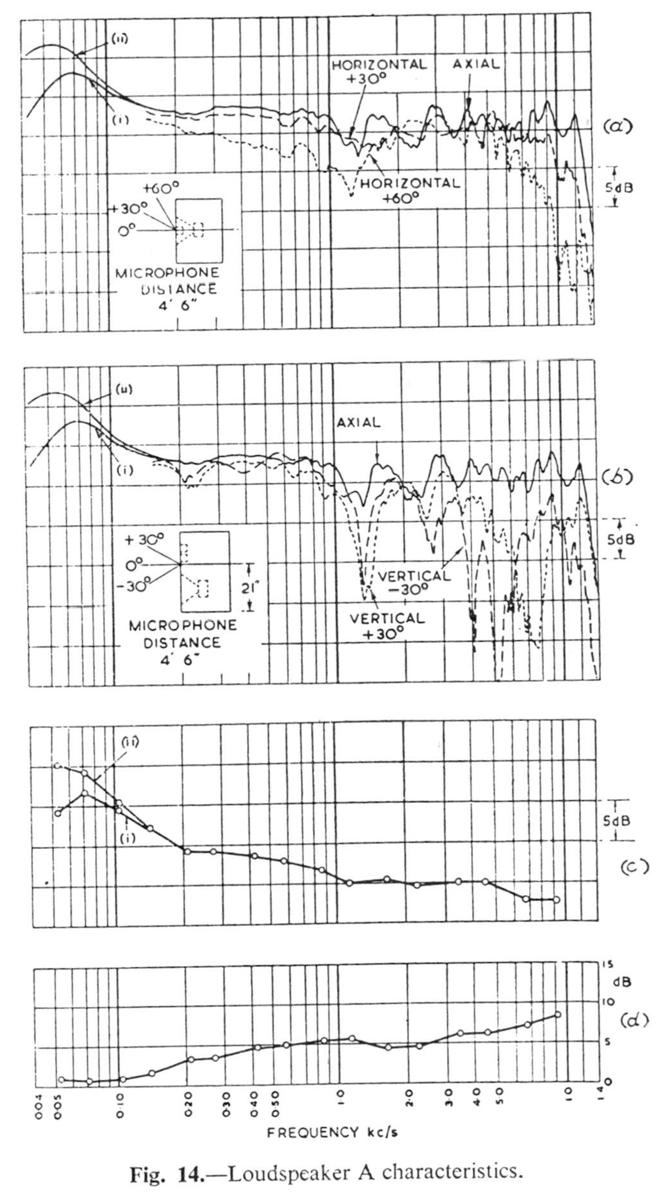

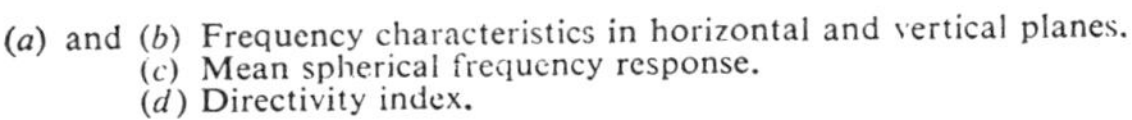

Fig. 14.—Loudspeaker A characteristics.

(*a*) and (*b*) Frequency characteristics in horizontal and vertical planes.
(*c*) Mean spherical frequency response.
(*d*) Directivity index.

Fig. 15 shows the frequency/response curves of loudspeaker B, together with the mean spherical response and directivity, again averaged over half-octave bands.

The differences between the directional properties shown in Figs. 14 and 15 are mainly attributable to the difference in geometry of the two systems and in particular to the form of the sound outlet for the l.f. unit of loudspeaker B. It should be noted in comparing the curves that for measurement purposes loudspeaker A has been assigned an arbitrary axis passing between the low- and high-frequency systems.

Figs. 14 and 15 illustrate the difficulty of describing the various attributes of a loudspeaker without either emphasizing irrelevant detail or losing important information through over-simplification. For example, the disposition of the h.f. units in loudspeaker B allows the observer to listen at close range without becoming aware of more than one sound source; there is, however, little in the curves to suggest that loudspeaker A is different in this respect. Again, the difference in directional properties

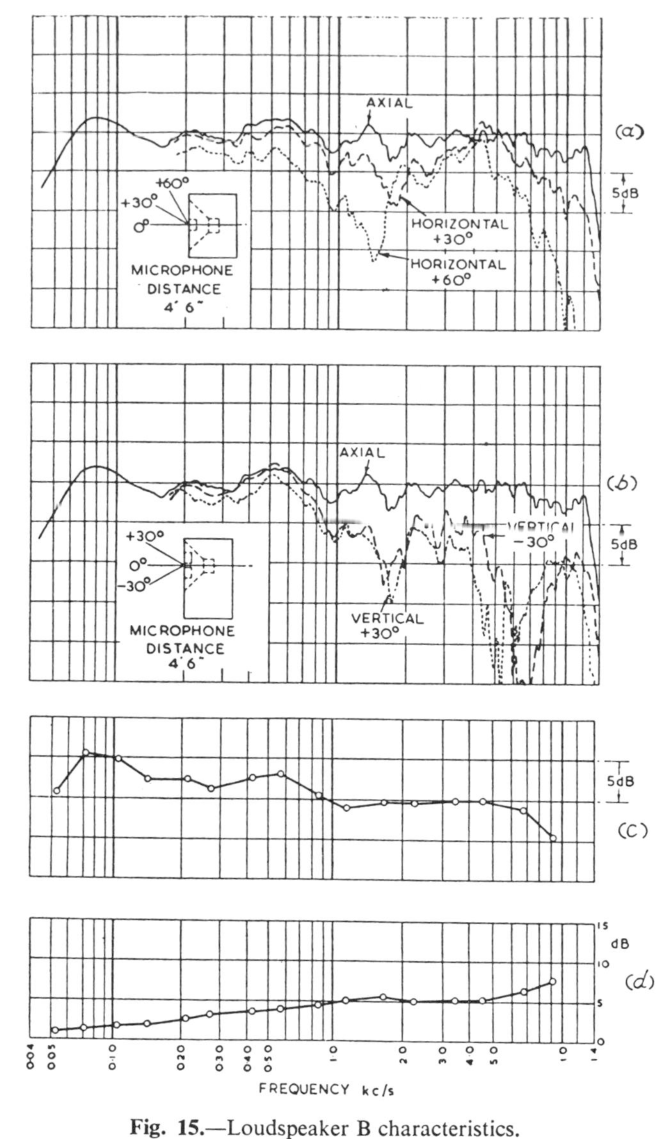

Fig. 15.—Loudspeaker B characteristics.

(*a*) and (*b*) Frequency characteristics in horizontal and vertical planes.
(*c*) Mean spherical frequency response.
(*d*) Directivity index.

of the two loudspeakers, as shown by the spacing of the response curves taken at various angles, is not apparent in the directivity or mean spherical response characteristics, and it would clearly have been misleading to take the latter as the sole criterion of frequency response.

Although the results of the change in directional properties of the loudspeaker at cross-over are not in either case serious, the effects referred to in Section 3.2 are present to some extent in both A and B. The change of régime at cross-over is accompanied by a change in the slope of curves (*d*) of Figs. 14 and 15; for reasons partly connected with the action of the perforated baffle plate, the effective cross-over frequency in loudspeaker B is somewhat higher than in loudspeaker A, the axial sound pressures produced by the high- and low-frequency units being equal at 1·6 kc/s.

The data on harmonics and intermodulation distortion, given as examples in Section 2.6.2, Figs. 4 and 5, relate to loudspeaker B. The difference at low frequencies between the shape of the frequency/response curve for the fundamental and that shown in Fig. 15 arises mainly from residual reflections from the walls of the non-reverberant room in which the distortion measurements were carried out; the separation between fundamental and harmonics below 100 c/s is, in fact, somewhat greater than that indicated.

(5) FUTURE TRENDS IN DESIGN

Apart from any radical change in the operating principles of loudspeakers, many of the refinements introduced during the next few years are likely to be concerned with directional properties.

Because of the pleasantly 'spacious' subjective effects to be obtained by wide-angle distribution of sound, commercial receivers incorporating two or more supplementary loudspeaker units mounted in different faces of the enclosure[27] have recently been produced. This practice, were it to become widespread, might lead the users of monitoring loudspeakers to call for a corresponding refinement, though it is not suggested that an omnidirectional system such as that referred to in Section 3.4 should necessarily be adopted.

While the potential applications of stereophonic transmission to broadcasting are limited, the development of stereophonic recording is proceeding rapidly and will probably create a demand for monitoring loudspeakers having special polar characteristics. Some workers[28] in this field have advocated the use of directional loudspeakers to reduce the variation in the position of the apparent sound source with the position of the observers. However, since the required directional characteristics cannot be maintained throughout the audio-frequency range, other designers[29] prefer to aim at a uniform response over the widest possible angle in the horizontal plane.

Perhaps the most notable development in recent years is the design of electrostatic loudspeakers covering the complete audio-frequency range,[30] instead of being confined, as hitherto, to the region above 1 kc/s. Loudspeakers of this type have been produced during the last few years but have only recently become generally available in this country; little detailed information has so far been published on their construction and performance. The two principal factors which have stimulated their development are the production of plastics suitable for the manufacture of diaphragms having a sufficiently low mass and stiffness, and the realization of the fact, demonstrated by Hunt[31] in America, that the non-linear distortion can be greatly reduced by keeping the polarizing charge, as distinct from the polarizing voltage, constant.

To produce the required sound level without exceeding the linear limits of the electrostatic system, diaphragms of large area have to be employed. In order to avoid unwanted directional effects, the radiating surface may be subdivided so that only a small portion is operative at high frequencies; even so, the directional pattern at the upper end of the audio-frequency range may be narrower, at least in one plane, than that of some conventional loudspeakers.

Probably the most striking feature of the full-range electrostatic loudspeaker is that the usual enclosure may be dispensed with and sound from both surfaces of the diaphragm allowed to radiate into the room; the resulting loss in output at low frequencies through back-to-front interference can be corrected by an internal network. At low frequencies, where the wavelength is large compared with the dimensions of the diaphragm, the unit may be regarded as a doublet source. The directional characteristic is then of figure-of-eight form, and the proportion of reverberant to direct sound received by the listener will therefore be less than with a conventional loudspeaker; there is, however, insufficient evidence to show whether this characteristic of the system is conducive to realism in reproduction.

Fig. 16 shows an external view of a commercial full-range

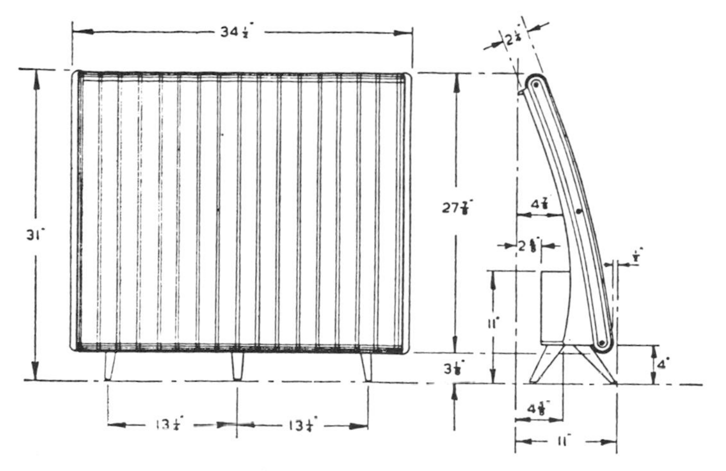

Fig. 16.—Full-range electrostatic loudspeaker.

electrostatic loudspeaker; the unit incorporates a rectifier for providing the polarizing voltage and a matching transformer to enable the loudspeaker to operate from a low-impedance circuit. Whatever the merits or shortcomings of these loudspeakers as a class, it seems likely that their cost may eventually be below that of a moving-coil loudspeaker system of comparable performance.

(6) CONCLUSIONS

In the paper an attempt has been made to bring together, on the one hand, the essentials of the art as they appear in the literature on design and measured performance, and on the other, the accumulated experience, mostly unpublished, of those users of loudspeakers who are in a position to compare the original and reproduced sound.

It will be seen that one of the greatest single obstacles to further progress is the difficulty of formulating in sufficient detail the requirements to be met. The characteristics of the ideal loudspeaker, often regarded as self-evident, are found on closer examination to be indefinable in objective terms. However, as long as the user remains consistent in his demands, there seems no reason why subjective studies should not ultimately yield a set of workable criteria for the guidance of designers.

(7) ACKNOWLEDGMENTS

The author wishes to acknowledge the contributions made to the material of the paper by other members of the B.B.C. Research Department and, in particular, the work of Mr. T. Somerville on subjective assessment of quality, together with that of Messrs. H. D. Harwood and J. R. Chew on the design of loudspeakers and measuring equipment. His thanks are also due to the Acoustical Manufacturing Co. Ltd., the General Electric Co. Ltd., the Institut für Rundfunktechnik G.m.b.H., Hamburg, and the Plessey Company Limited, for supplying technical information and illustrations.

The paper is published by kind permission of the Chief Engineer, British Broadcasting Corporation.

(8) REFERENCES

(1) 'Recommendations for Ascertaining and Expressing the Performance of Loudspeakers by Objective Measurements', British Standard 2498: 1954.

(2) McMillan, D., and West, W.: 'The Design of a Loudspeaker', *Journal I.E.E.*, 1940, **86**, p. 432.

(3) Gee, A., and Shorter, D. E. L.: 'An Automatic Integrator for Determining the Mean Spherical Response of Loudspeakers and Microphones', B.B.C. Engineering Division Monograph No. 8.

(4) Kaufmann, G.: 'Beitrag zur subjektiven Beurteilung von Musikwiedergaben mittels Lautsprecherkombinationen', *Technische Hausmitteilungen des N.W.D.R.*, 1956, **8**, No. 5/6, p. 93.

(5) Helmbold, J. G.: 'Oszillographische Untersuchungen von Einschwingvorgängen bei Lautsprechern', *Akustische Zeitschrift*, 1937, **2**, p. 256.

(6) Shorter, D. E. L.: 'Loudspeaker Transient Response: Its Measurement and Graphical Representation', *B.B.C. Quarterly*, 1946, **1**, p. 121.

(7) Corrington, M. S.: 'Transient Testing of Loudspeakers', *Audio Engineering*, 1950, **34**, p. 9.

(8) Kidd, Marshal C.: 'Tone Burst Generator Checks A–F Transients', *Electronics*, 1952, **25**, No. 7, p. 132.

(9) Corrington, M. S.: 'Correlation of Transient Measurements on Loudspeakers with Listening Tests'. Paper presented at the Annual Convention of the Audio Engineering Society, October 16, 1954.

(10) Hentsch, J.-C.: 'La fidelité des haut-parleurs dans la reproduction des phenomènes transitoires', *Technische Mitteilungen PTT*, 1951, No. 6, p. 201.

(11) Seemann, E.: 'Beurteilung der Einschwingverzerrungen von Lautsprechern an Hand der Frequenzgänge', *ibid.*, 1952, No. 4, p. 121.

(12) Ewaskio, C. A., and Mawardi, O. K.: 'Electroacoustic Phase Shift in Loudspeakers', *Journal of the Acoustical Society of America*, 1950, **22**, p. 444.

(13) Nichols, R. H.: 'Effects of Finite Baffles on Response of Source with Back Enclosed', *ibid.*, 1946, **18**, p. 151.

(14) Olson, H. F.: 'Direct Radiator Loudspeaker Enclosures', *Audio Engineering*, November, 1951, **35**, p. 34.

(15) Brittain, F. H.: 'The Appraisement of Loudspeakers', *G.E.C. Journal*, 1936, **7**, p. 266.

(16) Shorter, D. E. L.: 'The Influence of High Order Products in Non-Linear Distortion', *Electronic Engineering*, 1950, **22**, p. 152.

(17) Sivian, L. J., Dunn, H. K., and White, S. D.: 'Absolute Amplitudes and Spectra of Certain Musical Instruments and Orchestras', *Journal of the Acoustical Society of America*, 1931, **2**, p. 330.

(18) Belger, D.: 'Untersuchungen über den maximalen Amplitudengehalt der Modulation bei hohen Frequenzen', *Technische Hausmitteilungen des N.W.D.R.*, 1955, **7**, No. 7/8, p. 151.

(19) Ingerslev, F.: 'Measurement of Non-Linear Distortions in Loudspeakers', *Proceedings of the First I.C.A. Congress on Electro-Acoustics*, 1953, p. 74.

(20) Somerville, T.: 'Monitoring Sound Broadcasting Programmes', *Wireless World*, 1956, **62**, p. 228.

(21) Harz, H., and Kösters, H.: 'Ein neuer Gesichtspunkt für die Entwicklung von Lautsprechern?' *Technische Hausmitteilungen des N.W.D.R.*, 1951, **3**, p. 205.

(22) Klein, S.: 'The Ionophone', *Onde Électrique*, 1952, **32**, p. 314.

(23) Enkel, F.: 'Neue hochwertige Abhöranlage für Regieräume', *Elektronische Rundschau*, 1957, **11**, No. 2, p. 51.

(24) Thuras, A. L.: British Patent No. 1869178: 1930.

(25) Chapman, R., and Trier, R. H.: British Patent No. 659063: 1947.

(26) Somerville, T., and Brownless, S. F.: 'Listeners' sound-level Preferences', *B.B.C. Quarterly*, 1949, **3**, p. 11.

(27) KUHL, W., and ZOSEL, J. M.: 'Untersuchungen zur Pseudo-stereophonie und Sterephonie mit Kugellautsprechern und "Raumklang"—Geraten', *Akustische Beihefte*, 1956, No. 2, p. 474.

(28) BRITTAIN, F. H., and LEAKEY, D. M.: 'Two-Channel Stereophonic Sound Systems', *Wireless World*, 1956, **62**, pp. 206 and 331.

(29) CLARK, H. A. M., DUTTON, G. F., and VANDERLYN, P. B.: 'The "Stereosonic" Recording and Reproducing System', *Proceedings I.E.E.*, Paper No. 2332 R, February, 1957 (**104** B, p. 417).

(30) WALKER, P. J.: 'Wide-range Electrostatic Loudspeakers', *Wireless World*, 1955, **61**, pp. 208, 265 and 381.

(31) HUNT, F. V.: 'Electroacoustics', Harvard Monographs in Applied Science No. 5 (Harvard University Press), pp. 188 *et seq*.

DISCUSSION BEFORE THE RADIO AND TELECOMMUNICATION SECTION, 23RD APRIL, 1958

Dr. G. F. Dutton: The loudspeaker is the last in a varied collection of components in the chain connecting the original sound with the reproduced sound in the studio or listening room. Consequently it has to bear the blame for most shortcomings of the system. The more one improves the performance of the loudspeaker with regard to the frequency range the more critical will be the conditions for showing up high-frequency buzzes, clicks, etc.; and they are all blamed on to the loudspeaker. It is necessary to convince people that these noises are not in the loudspeaker but are in their various components. The only distortion that I have not heard blamed on the loudspeaker is 'wow' and 'flutter'.

I do not agree entirely with the statement in the Summary that the purpose of the broadcasting or recording engineers is to give an approximate approach to a realistic reproduction. It depends on what the sounds are intended to be and what is meant by 'realistic'. The microphone is often placed very close to the instruments to be recorded, in a position much closer than could be normally assumed by a member of the audience, and perhaps closer than a normal person would tolerate. On the other hand, the broadcasting people might prefer to use microphones further away and even over the top of the orchestra—again these are positions not normally assumed by the audience. Therefore, the interpretation of a realistic sound is somewhat difficult.

In the gramophone recording industry we have had this problem of loudspeaker design for monitors for some time. We have been trying to decide whether the characteristics for the standard monitoring loudspeaker should represent the average commercial loudspeaker or should have some ideal smooth characteristic, such as that indicated by the author. We have come to the conclusion that a smooth characteristic up to 12 or 15 kc/s on ~~the axis of~~ a reasonably good spherical radiation characteristic is the one to aim for. No particular fashion has been set for having a high rise in the region of 3 or 4 kc/s, which is very common to most loudspeakers of the lower price range. This is, perhaps, hard to fight in practice because the brighter loudspeakers with the rise at about 3 or 4 kc/s usually play popular recordings very nicely, while the more extended and flattering frequency characteristic tends to show up any distortion in the brass section, and you have to be very careful to judge whether this is real or originates in the system.

I agree with the author that wide-band noise tests can be very useful in quickly assessing the difference between two loudspeakers, and we use these tests for comparing the test monitoring loudspeaker with the standard that we have set ourselves. Very small differences in characteristic can easily be detected by this test.

In Section 3 there is a reference to equalization. I agree that equalization in the loudspeaker amplifier is essential in order to cover adequately a large frequency range, and I consider that this compensation can only be made if the resonances to be corrected are not too sharp. If they are too sharp, of course, the reliability of the compensation is in doubt.

After a great deal of impartial listening, I have come to the conclusion that direct-radiator cone loudspeakers are preferable to the horn-driven types. The reason for this is not quite clear. It is probably due to a number of small reasons rather than one particular one. For instance, directivity is probably very important.

The author refers to the coloration that can occur owing to the break-up of the cone into radial modes. I think we have overcome that trouble by using elliptically-shaped cones.

The monitoring loudspeaker that we have designed and are using in our studios has a cabinet 4 ft high, and the rear baffle for the low-frequency unit is totally enclosed with a volume of $3\frac{1}{4}$ ft^3. The high-frequency unit is exactly similar to the one described by the author. It is fitted directly above the cone loudspeaker, and is completely enclosed so that no inter-modulation can exist between the low- and high-frequency units. The power amplifier is placed in the lower compartment. There are three correcting networks applied to the unit. The bass correction starts at about 800 c/s and rises to 40 c/s and is of the order of 6 dB at 40 c/s. The high-frequency correction occurs at about 7 kc/s, and there is a rise at about 11 kc/s.

The elliptical unit is placed with the long axis vertical in order to improve the radiation pattern in the horizontal plane. That unit, with its corrective network, can be within $\pm 1\frac{1}{2}$ dB from 40 c/s to 12 kc/s.

An important point that should be discussed in relation to monitoring loudspeakers is the replay level. Most engineers and 'hi-fi' enthusiasts seem to play loudspeakers at a level much higher than they should be played, or at least higher than the average person for whom the records are made or for whom broadcasts are intended would play them. But the whole balance can be misjudged by playing at too high a level. Whether or not the level should be as high as the original sound is questionable, but the full effect of an orchestra on the *fortes* cannot be obtained unless the level is up to its full original value.

Mr. G. A. Briggs: I agree with the author about the doublet effect with the full-range electrostatic loudspeaker. We have had some experience with a moving-coil doublet system. It is perfectly true that a doublet excites less room resonance than a direct radiator, but this makes it more selective, and the performance is therefore very much affected by its position in the room. The doublet effect can be reduced by placing one edge of the loudspeaker against a wall, or by putting the loudspeaker itself near a corner. It is essential to try various locations in any room, and this latitude seems to make the doublet a popular proposition, whether with a moving-coil or an electrostatic loudspeaker.

With regard to magnets and damping factors, the author very wisely draws attention to the loss of bass response with high-flux-density magnet systems driven by amplifiers with very low output resistance, and suggests as a possible solution the use of smaller magnets and larger amplifiers. I do not agree with this idea for domestic use. A high-flux-density loudspeaker sounds brighter and cleaner than a low-flux-density model.

I submit that the root of the trouble lies in our absurd obsession with high damping factors and constant voltages. Tests show that a damping factor of 15 produces a drop in output of about 3 dB at 40 c/s in a 10 in loudspeaker with a 10-kilogauss magnet; but the drop is 10 dB with a 14-kilogauss magnet. Why should a resistance of 1 ohm be connected in parallel with a high-quality 15-ohm loudspeaker? Why do we not have amplifiers with variable damping factor, using a mixture of voltage and current feedback as produced in America? A preset control could be adjusted to suit the loudspeaker and the room.

Mr. P. J. Walker: A number of attempts have been made in the past to lay down a series of objective tests for loudspeakers which will be meaningful in comparing performance. Their interpretation is based solely on past experience of comparing objective tests with subjective assessment.

It seems relevant to point out that interpretation experience gained on one type of transducer may give misleading results when applied to an entirely different type of transducer.

It is now possible to make electrostatic loudspeakers with low mechanical impedance as opposed to the high mechanical impedance of the moving coil. The change from free field conditions to room conditions will differ in the two cases.

The importance of local response irregularities is dependent upon whether these are due to interference or resonance effects. Here again, a change of transducer type profoundly alters the relationship between the two causes. Similar remarks apply to the shape of distortion curves and some other physical properties.

The confidence with which we can compare overall performance from objective tests varies directly with the physical similarity of the loudspeakers to be compared.

Mr. F. H. Brittain: I entirely agree with Dr. Dutton that the axial response curve should be as flat as possible, and certainly not worse than 5 dB down at a frequency of 10 kc/s and 30° off axis. In my opinion it is never permissible to maintain a good mean spherical response by having a rising response on the listening axis. It does not occur in nature and will not be tolerated.

When examining a frequency-response curve, it must be remembered that shape plays a great part in the appeal to the eye. Shape is best obliterated by taking the mean output over a number of bands of frequencies.

The author suggests that male speech is useful for listening tests, but female speech should also be included because it utilizes different frequencies. In both cases it must be ensured that pressure-gradient microphones are not used nearer than 6 ft to the person speaking.

With regard to Section 3, it often happens that a high-frequency unit is used in conjunction with a 'cross-over' network which effectively disconnects it from the amplifier. In these circumstances, the diaphragm of the h.f. unit is probably undamped at its main resonance and may develop excessive movement from the local sound pressure falling on it, or because it is partially driven electrically. It is then desirable to provide some damping in the form of a series-tuned circuit connected across the h.f. unit.

Mr. J. K. Webb: The author mentions the full-range electrostatic loudspeaker, a commercial model of which has recently become available. I heard this demonstrated recently in direct comparison with a well-known make of large corner horn assembly and did not find that it bore much relation to what I had come to regard as 'hi-fi', whereas the corner horn did. One of my acquaintances, shocked at my verdict, has since persuaded me to read the maker's accompanying pamphlet from which it appears that my judgment is coloured by the fact that I am not musical! While this is reminiscent of the fairy story about the emperor's clothes, it does illustrate the difficulty in assessing performance criteria which are found, as the author says, to be indefinable in objective terms. It would seem, however, that users are now to be persuaded to change their demands and adopt different criteria than heretofore. How, then, does the author suggest that designers should seek guidance?

Mr. P. P. Eckersley: In connection with the demonstration did the author assume a 'perfect' microphone? It is often the case that, when designing a microphone, the designer judges it by a 'perfect' loudspeaker, and when another is designing a loudspeaker he judges it by a 'perfect' microphone. In the case of the demonstration, what was the 'perfect' microphone, what was the 'perfect' recording system and what was the 'perfect' amplifier? I have been told that to do real justice to 'hi-fi' loudspeakers the amplifier ought to have a flat response up to about 100 kc/s, otherwise there will be transient distortion. Is this idea viable? Was such an amplifier used in connection with the demonstration?

On the question of measurement, is the microphone assumed to be 'perfect'? Since the microphone must have a finite size, will it not set up standing waves between the loudspeaker and itself, thus vitiating the results, or is some method used to vary the distance while integrating the energy?

THE AUTHOR'S REPLY TO THE ABOVE DISCUSSION

Mr. D. E. L. Shorter (*in reply*): Dr. Dutton's difficulty in accepting 'realism' as an ideal is understandable in view of the varying interpretations placed on that much overworked word. Realism, as an attribute of a sound-reproducing system, has too often come to be associated with the unpleasant sounds which result when the design of the loudspeaker is based on over-simplified ideas of technical correctness; as used in the paper, however, the term refers solely to the extent to which a listener could imagine himself to be in the presence of the performer, irrespective of the means by which the illusion is produced. It is true that microphones are often located in positions which would not be acceptable for direct listening. This placing does not necessarily represent a departure from realism; it is an artifice employed, in the interests of realism, to compensate for unavoidable shortcomings of the system—in particular for the deficiencies inherent in a monaural transmission. There are certainly cases in which the compensation process has been carried further in an attempt to improve on nature; however, I do not think that arbitrary factors introduced in this way ought to be regarded as permanent features of the transmission system.

In reply to Mr. Webb, it seems reasonable that the designer of monitoring loudspeakers should be guided by the judgment of those individuals who are best qualified by experience to assess the degree of realism achieved. It so happens that most of these individuals belong to the category which could be described as musical; I would not, however, suggest that musical knowledge is in itself necessary to enable an observer to judge the degree to which a reproduced sound resembles the original.

Mr. Briggs's proposed method of electrical equalization by varying the output impedance of the loudspeaker amplifier is less flexible in its application than the use of corrective networks earlier in the chain, and does not overcome the difficulty of transferring power at low frequencies to a load impedance far in excess of the optimum value. Whichever procedure is adopted, however, there is a strong case for treating the amplifier for design purposes as part of the loudspeaker.

Corner Speaker Placement*

PAUL W. KLIPSCH

Klipsch and Associates, Hope, Arkansas

That superior sound quality is afforded by corner speaker placement has been recognized for more than thirty years. Measurements and listening tests were conducted with both monophonic and stereophonic reproducing equipment to compare the performance of speakers designed for use away from a corner and for corner installation. Measurable and audible advantages accrue with corner placement of either speaker, with the greater improvement being shown by a speaker of proper design. The advantages are more easily observed for stereophonic than for monophonic reproduction.

PART ONE: MONOPHONIC SOUND REPRODUCTION

Introduction

THE ORIGIN of the idea that there is an advantage to corner speaker placement may be as old as loudspeakers themselves. At any rate, patents on corner speakers date back to 1925.[1]

In the following investigation, a non-corner speaker with 6.7 cubic feet enclosure was tested out of and in a corner. With corner placement the bass response was improved more than 20 db. Listening tests confirmed the evidence of the measurement and indicated a further improvement when a speaker designed for corner installation was observed.

The reasons for improved sound quality are obvious: the smaller treble radiation angle required to cover a room area is one; the mirror image effect of the walls, increasing the radiation resistance, is another; a third is the fact that most well designed speakers offer a 90-degree radiation angle, and only from a corner can this radiation cover the entire room.

No information has been discovered giving the quantitative advantages of corner placement.

Experiment

An experiment was set up using a 6.7 cubic foot box with a 3-way drive system including a heavy-magnet 15-inch woofer motor. This unit will be referred to simply as "the box."

This box was placed on an open legged bench about 14 inches high and about 4 feet from each wall at a corner. The drive unit was about 4 feet from the floor. This was to deny benefit of wall and floor reflections. Two microphones were set up, one in the center of the room, and the other in the middle of the half of the room where the speaker was located. See Fig. 1.

A response pressure curve was run and plotted as Curve 1 in Fig. 2. Peaks and dips were sought, and no attempt to smooth by moving the microphones was attempted. The two microphones were averaged by rectifying and then adding. Indicated sound was held constant by varying speaker input, the input level being read off a calibrated potential divider between the oscillator and amplifier.

Oscillographic examination of the output of each microphone before rectification was used to detect harmonic distortion.

The microphones were calibrated by pistonphone and were down 0.5 db at 30 c relative to 300.

A considerable peak-to-trough ratio is normally to be expected from this sort of measurement. Some troughs in the response curve could have been raised by moving one or both microphones. The standing wave pattern was ignored, however, for the concern is with the relative performance of a given speaker in a given room, the independent variable being the location in the room. Outdoor response curves are more valuable for determining intrinsic speaker performance; here the problem is to evaluate the advantages of different locations of a given speaker.

The speaker was then set on the floor over the same spot in the room. The microphones were not moved. The pressure response is Curve 2 of Fig. 2.

Finally the speaker was moved into the corner and the response is Curve 3 of Fig. 2.

For the purpose of these tests, various microphone placements were contemplated. Experience indicated that the extreme bass range could be favored by microphone placement in a far corner or in close proximity to the speaker. Several microphone locations were tried with the oscillator swept quickly through the pertinent spectrum, and the two-

* Received April 24, 1958. Revised copy received July 18 and September 17, 1958.

[1] M. Weil, U. S. Patent 1,820,996 issued 1931, filed 1925; and Sandeman, U. S. Patent 1,984,550 issued 1934, filed 1931.

microphone placement chosen was the one giving the lowest peak-to-trough ratio for all three speaker locations.

Movement of the speaker from one test to another was only about 5 feet, or 1/4 wavelength at 50 c, not enough to affect the measurements materially—say more than 3 or 4 db. The closer speaker-to-microphone spacing of Locations 1 and 2 would favor the bass for these locations, compared to Location 3. The listening tests qualitatively corroborated the measurements, the differences being gross enough to discern without the refinement of an "A-B test."

Taking the speaker down off its perch improved the response at 50 c more than 20 db. On legs, the speaker cutoff should be considered to be 65 c. On the floor the response at 50 c is 10 db down from its peak at 65 c.

In the corner, however, the useful range extends to 38 c. The improvement in response at 40 c is 9 db, which represents an 8-fold increase in efficiency.

In each step toward better placement, the peak-to-trough ratio in the usable spectrum was reduced, and the distortion was reduced by a large amount.

While the major aspect may be thought to be the improved and extended bass, the reduced distortion is far more important. Less noticeable on the curves is the reduced peak-to-trough ratio (the lowered effect of standing waves in the room) but this effect is actually of considerable importance. More about this will be given in the section **Listening Tests.**

All these benefits are achieved for a non-corner-type speaker merely by placing the speaker in a corner, in spite of the fact that the speaker was deliberately chosen as a non-corner type.

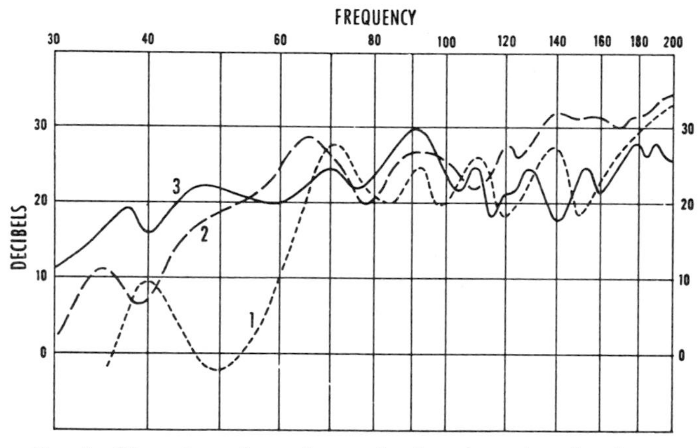

FIG. 1. Plan view of speaker and microphone location in tests. Speaker location 1, as shown, was on a 14-in. high bench to deny benefit of the mirror image formed by the floor. Speaker location 2 was at the same plan location but on the floor to couple the actual speaker with its mirror image. Location 3 was on the floor in the corner to couple the actual speaker to all its mirror images.

Microphones were 6½ feet apart, located as shown; their outputs were rectified and then added to produce an averaging effect and to reduce standing wave effects.

Distortion, indicated by the cathode ray scope, was large below 70 c for the conditions of Curve 1, considerably below 60 c for conditions of Curve 2, and slightly below 35 c for conditions of Curve 3.

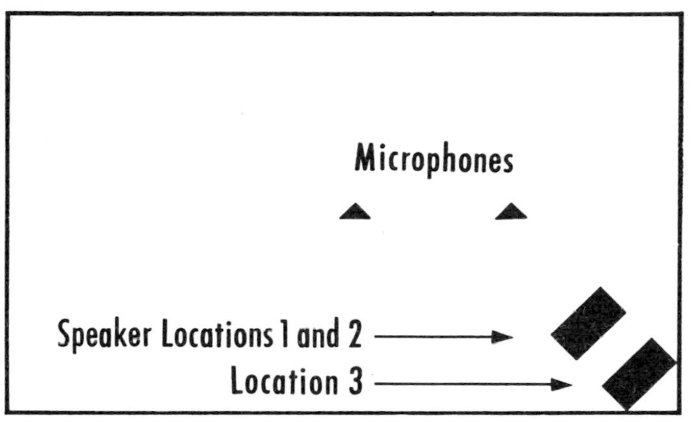

FIG. 2. Response Curves 1, 2 and 3 correspond to the speaker locations 1, 2 and 3 in Fig. 1.

The advantages of corner placement are:

- reduced distortion due to better loading;
- increased bass range for a given size of speaker system;
- increased bass range for a given size of room, or increased effective size of the room;[2]
- smoother response—less peaking in the second octave.

In addition to benefits in the bass range, other benefits derive from corner placement:

- the available radiation angle of high-frequency system covers the whole room area (most speakers of good quality offer a 90-degree radiation angle);
- better ratio of direct to reverberant sound; longer travel of a wave before it strikes a reflecting surface;[3]
- better appearance due to smaller size for a stated performance.

The above observations are applicable both to monophonic and stereophonic reproduction.

All these advantages appear as a result of corner placement of any speaker, but of course a maximization of all the advantages is obtained by using a speaker type designed for corner operation.

Listening Tests

The curves and objective data ignore frequencies above 200 c, which are not particularly affected by corner placement except as it affects room coverage with a given radiation angle.

For a listening test, however, the middle and upper ranges are all important, so a three-way drive system was used.

The box was subjected to a listening test in the various locations. An A-B test was not necessary to reveal the superiority of the floor location compared to the location on legs. Moving from floor to corner afforded as great a listen-

---

[2] Paul W. Klipsch, "Room Dimensions for Optimum Listening and the Half-Room Principle," *Trans. IRE, PGA,* **AU-6**, 1 (January-February, 1958).

[3] *Ibid.*

ing difference as did moving from bench to floor, especially where heavy bass comprised a considerable part of the program material.

Finally a comparison was made between the box and a corner-horn back-loading system of the same front panel size, the same drive system, and some 22 per cent less occupied space.[4]

The advantage of the unit designed for corner application was immediately evident. The improvement in bass over that reproduced by the box was almost as great as the improvement afforded by moving the box from the floor to the corner.

Conclusion

These experiments should illustrate the fact that good acoustical design takes maximum advantage of the mirror images produced by the floor and walls, and that the maximum benefits are derived when the mirror surfaces are proximate to the prime source. This excludes styling which involves legs or risers which separate a speaker's radiating area by even as little as half a foot from the floor; it dictates structure which places the radiation surfaces as close to the walls and floor as possible.

PART TWO: STEREOPHONIC SOUND REPRODUCTION

Introduction

A SERIES of experiments was undertaken to determine preferred speaker separation for two-channel stereophonic sound reproduction.

First an outdoor experiment discloses that an angle as small as 9 degrees suffices to make the stereo effect discernible, and desirable angles are of the order of 30 to 40 degrees for most observers.

Indoors, the angles must increase to nearly 30 degrees to afford a detectable stereo effect, and to 50 degrees or more to be desirable.

A narrow margin of listener preference was found for wide speaker spacing compared to narrow spacing in two-channel arrays. A preponderance of preference was shown for corner placement. Three-channel stereo with wide spacing was preferred over all other arrays tried.

Experiment One

In an outdoor environment, what minimum stereo angle is required that the stereo effect be observed, and what is the preferred angle?

Two small speakers were placed 8 feet apart against a wall, about 2 feet above the ground, outdoors.[5] Program material was a high quality recording of a symphonic band. Observers were asked to explore the median line between speakers, and indicate: (1) the preferred distance from the speakers, and (2) the maximum distance at which they could detect the stereo effect.

Experience indoors indicated an *a priori* estimate that the minimum stereo angle would be about 25 or 30 degrees. The following results were observed:

		Preferred Angle (in degrees)	Minimum Angle (in degrees)
	Max.	70	16
5 Men	Aver.	45	13
	Min.	28	11
	Max.	33	14
3 Women	Aver.	26	12
	Min.	19	9
Average, Men and Women		37	12

The average minimum angle was 12 degrees instead of the expected 25 degrees or more. A more detailed experiment might well bring this angle considerably below 12 degrees. Note, however, this is *outdoors* and the same experiment conducted indoors produced data which put the minimum angle much larger. This is as would be expected; room reverberation masked the direct sound and a listener had to subtend a larger angle to detect the stereo effect. Another factor involved was that the ambient noise level was extremely low compared to an average city dwelling.

But the results remain: preferred listening subtended angle, 37 degrees; minimum 12 degrees, for outdoor stereo (average figures).

Experiment Two

Indoors, what are the preferred and minimum angles?

In a room 16 by 25 feet, one pair of speakers was set up 7 feet apart, and another identical pair at about 14 feet.

The array was disposed along the wall at one end of the room. The row of speakers was about 2 feet from the 16-foot wall and the end speakers were about 1 foot from the long walls. The spacing from the walls was to avoid any benefit from the improved bass range due to corner effects. It was desired to find the preference for the narrow or the wide spacing, not whether the improved bass range afforded by the corner would induce a preference.

The inside pair was fed from one stereo-pair of amplifiers, the outside pair from another stereo-pair of amplifiers, and the volumes were carefully adjusted to be the same. Switching was between the tape preamplifiers and the stereo-pair of power amplifiers.

[4] While the box had a volume of 6.7 cubic feet (about 7.0 cubic feet outside), its chargeable space included 3 cubic feet of unused space behind it. Thus the total space taken up in the corner was approximately 10 cubic feet. The corner horn used for comparison requires only 7.8 cubic feet of space.

[5] Small for portability, and to determine various configurations. Speakers were 3-way with the "K-ORTHO-12-A" drive system, with a peak-to-trough ratio less than 10 db from 150 to 21,000 c. Mid-range and tweeter were of the horn-loaded type to minimize distortion.

The listener was first seated at a distance of 15 feet on a median line between the speakers, and asked to indicate a preference.

The results:

Preference for narrow spacing	1
Indecisive, but generally favoring narrow spacing	2
Indecisive, but generally favoring wide spacing	3
Preferred wide spacing	1
Changed opinion from preference of narrow to preference of wide spacing	1

This is almost a standoff. Note the subtended angles here are 50 degrees and 27 degrees for the wide and narrow spacings.

The angular values found are consistent with those which a concert listener would observe in, say, the 5th to the 10th row; the orchestra might be spread out 45 feet (typically) and the observer would sit in a distance range of 20 feet (front row), 45 feet (more or less ideal) and 90 feet in the back of the balcony. A larger auditorium would be likely to have a wider stage. Expressed in degrees, the optimum listening stereo angle in the auditorium would range from over 90 degrees down to perhaps 45 degrees depending on the preference for front row or far balcony.

Next with the same speaker configuration, the observers were asked to "explore" the end of the room away from the speakers (about 22 feet) and indicate if they could detect the stereo effect.

Only one observer could detect the stereo effect at a distance of 24 feet with the 7-foot spacing, but all could with 14-foot spacing.

Experiment Three

What is the effect of using one speaker in the corner?

The widely spaced experiment was repeated with one change: one small speaker was removed and a large full-bass-range corner horn speaker substituted. The spacing increased to 15 feet, but the stereo geometry seemed to condense in that the angle seemed to become less rather than greater, yet the stereo effect was still discernible at the far end of the room. Also the "two-peephole effect" of the array using small speakers was brought to attention by its disappearance when using a large corner speaker. The placement in the corner seems to aid in completing a curtain of sound. This is believed to be due to the simpler mirror image system pertaining to the corner type speaker.

Most narrow-spaced stereo systems are also narrow band, in that the speakers are too small to exhibit an extended bass response. With an added bass range plus the added reverberation due to such added bass, it is a considered opinion that a wider speaker spacing would be highly desirable if not absolutely necessary. The larger effective radiating surface of the full-range corner speaker more nearly simulates the original sound spatially as well as tonally and therefore approaches a stereophonic effect. The smaller point source speakers tend to focus the sound into two discrete points; large corner speakers offer a closer approach to a curtain of sound, while still focusing individual entities in the mass of original sound.

Experiment Four

For non-corner speakers, is the long or short wall of an oblong room preferred?

A near-corner array on the short wall of the room (the 14-foot spacing of Experiment 2) was compared with a similar array on the long wall of the room, with about 24-foot spacing. Again the small speakers were employed. The preference for the 14-foot spacing on the short wall of the room ranged from mild to positive with only a couple of observers favoring the long wall placement.

This would appear to temper my earlier conclusions.[6] The fact that on some types of music some listeners perceive an impression of a "hole in the middle" is not to be overlooked. The "hole in the middle" effect is less likely to be noticed when the speakers are placed in the corners at the narrow end of the room.[7]

Experiment Five

This is not a formal experiment set up in a laboratory, but is a collection of this writer's observations made over the period since the fall of 1956 when the idea was evolved of three-channel stereo derived from two-track source material.[8]

A very informal comparison was made between two-channel stereo using two corner speakers on the 16-foot wall, and three-channel using two corner speakers on the 25-foot wall plus a third speaker in the middle of the 25-foot wall.

A great many demonstrations were made in which the middle speaker could be readily cut in and out of circuit. Here the preference was overwhelmingly for the three-channel with the long-wall spacing.

One situation with two-channel stereo on wide corner

---

[6] Paul W. Klipsch, "Experiences in Stereophony," *Audio,* **39**, 16 (1955); and

Paul W. Plipsch, "Making Stereophonic Tapes," *Hi-Fi Music at Home,* **2**, 54 (1955).

[7] A configuration suggested in the sheet accompanying RCA-Victor stereo tapes.

[8] Paul W. Klipsch, "Stereophonic Sound with Two Tracks, Three Channels by Means of a Phantom Circuit," *J. Audio Eng. Soc.,* **6**, 118 (1958).

Also popular digests by the same author: "Two-Track, Three-Channel Stereo," *Audiocraft,* **2**, 26 (1957); and "Phantom Channel," *Audiocraft,* **3**, 37 (1958).

Note that this does not require three sound tracks, but recovers a third channel from two sound tracks. This depends on the fact that if two microphones are properly spaced relative to each other and to the plane of the sound source, their combined output is that of a third microphone in the middle. This middle microphone—the microphone that wasn't there—can be recovered and reproduced by combination of the two accessible sound tracks. All stereo recordings so far played over this writer's two-track three-channel system have displayed the focusing effect of the derived center channel.

spacing which is objectionable to some listeners is the reproduction of a soloist or an intimate group like a string quartet. The three-channel stereo restores such a group to its intimate dimensions, even with arrays subtending more than a 60-degree angle.

CONCLUSION

The following advantages of corner speaker placement pertain particularly to stereo:

Better stereo area coverage due to radiation angle being fully utilized,

Better stereo separation and larger stereo area,

Better focus of all events between flanks; better reproduction of stereo geometry,

Full vantage of the derived third channel which (properly used) offers precise focus and sharp definition of all sonic events between extreme flanks.

All these advantages appear as a result of corner placement of any speaker, but of course a maximization of all the advantages is possible by using a speaker type designed for corner operation.

Genuine stereophonic sound reproduction may be regarded as a close approach to recapturing the original spatial effect or "geometry," just as "high fidelity" aims to recapture the original tonal effects or "tonality." These cannot be achieved by merely pin-pointing the two halves of a musical group.

The more nearly genuine stereo is a more difficult and expensive thing to achieve. The end result should be a curtain of sound, not just a couple of peepholes.

The more sophisticated system will require larger and more expensive speakers, and will render a larger part of the room available for listening; a given sound will not be pin-pointed at the tweeter opening of a particular speaker but ideally will appear at some point or space in a curtain of sound between the speakers.

When one graduates to the more sophisticated stereo system, several opportunities open up; corner speaker placement becomes possible with all the advantages incident thereto; the third stereo channel becomes worthwhile. The results in listening are:

(1) a more nearly continuous curtain of sound;
(2) a larger effective area of sound curtain;
(3) a more accurate geometric delineation—as an extreme case, a string quartet will occupy a small central part of the sound curtain even with flanking corner speakers 25 to 50 feet apart;
(4) a simulation of the original sound and environment, including the ability of the members of the audience to change location over a wide area while the sound remains natural both in tonality and geometry.

Analysis of the Effects of Nonlinear Elements Upon the Performance of a Back-Enclosed, Direct Radiator Loudspeaker Mechanism*

HARRY F. OLSON
RCA Laboratories, Princeton, New Jersey

A theoretical analysis of the nonlinear suspension and the nonlinear compliance of the air in the cabinet of a loudspeaker has been carried out. The results of the analysis have been applied to the development of a back-enclosed, direct radiator loudspeaker with low distortion. The use of the accordion direct radiator loudspeaker mechanism in a back-enclosed cabinet provides a loudspeaker with low nonlinear distortion and wide frequency range in a relatively small enclosure.

INTRODUCTION

THE general trend in some types of direct radiator loudspeakers is a reduction in size. As a consequence, there is a corresponding increase in the amplitude of the cone of the loudspeaker because for the same acoustic output the amplitude of the cone increases inversely as the area of the cone. Many apparently peculiar activities are manifested by the loudspeaker when the amplitude of the vibration of the cone is large. These phenomena are due to the nonlinear characteristics of the suspension system of the cone. For the past two decades considerable attention has been given to alleviation of the undesirable effects which occur as the result of the nonlinear characteristics of the cone suspension system of a direct radiator loudspeaker. The deleterious effects of a nonlinear suspension system, manifested as nonlinear distortion, become more pronounced in the low frequency range where the mechanical impedance due to the compliance of the suspension system becomes the controlling mechanical impedance. One of the expedients employed to reduce the undesirable effects of the nonlinear suspension system is to introduce a linear mechanical impedance as the controlling element. As a specific example, more than two decades ago a direct radiator loudspeaker was developed in which the controlling mechanical impedance in the low frequency range is the air in the completely enclosed cabinet. In this connection, the compliance due to the air in the cabinet is also a nonlinear element. However, as the analysis in this report will show, for normal operation the compliance due to the air in the cabinet is essentially invariant. Complete analysis[1] of the performance of a back-enclosed, direct radiator loudspeaker with linear elements has been carried out. Studies[2] of the action of the nonlinear elements in a direct radiator loudspeaker have also been made. Some of the developments in direct radiator loudspeakers indicate that an extension of the nonlinear investigations are in order. For example, during the past few years there has been increasing interest in small size loudspeakers, particularly of the back enclosed type. When these loudspeakers are operated in the region of large sound power outputs, the relatively small elements are subjected to high stress conditions. As a consequence, some of the mechanical elements display considerable deviation from linearity. In this connection, the main elements which exhibit nonlinear characteristics are the cone suspension and the air in the cabinet. Accordingly, the purpose of this paper is to analyze the performance of the nonlinear suspension and the nonlinear stiffness of the air in the cabinet in the back-enclosed, direct radiator loudspeaker and to describe a direct radiator loudspeaker in which the air in the cabinet is the controlling mechanical impedance in the low frequency range.

GENERAL CONSIDERATIONS

A direct radiator loudspeaker mechanism with the back of the cone completely enclosed by the cabinet is shown in Fig. 1. From the mechanical circuit of the vibrating system of Fig. 1, the velocity of the cone is given by

$$dx/dt = f_M/z_{MT} = f_M/[r_{MS} + r_{MA} + j\omega\,(m_C + m_A) + (1/j\omega)\,(1/C_{MS} + 1/C_{MB})] \quad (1)$$

where dx/dt = velocity of the cone, in centimeters per second, f_M = driving force, in dynes, z_{MT} = total mechanical impedance at point f_M, in mechanical ohms, r_{MS} = mechanical resistance of the suspension system, in mechanical ohms, r_{MA} = mechanical radiation resistance, in mechanical ohms,

[1] H. F. Olson, *Acoustical Engineering* (D. Van Nostrand Co., New York, 1957).
[2] H. F. Olson, *J. Acoust. Soc. Am.* **16**, 1 (1944).

* Presented at 1960 Fall Convention of the Audio Engineering Society in New York and at 1961 Spring Convention in Los Angeles.

m_C = mass of the cone and voice coil, in grams, m_A = mass of the air load on the cone, in grams, C_{MS} = compliance of the suspension system, in dynes per centimeter, C_{MB} = compliance of the air volume of the cabinet, in dynes per centimeter, $\omega = 2\pi f$, and f = frequency, in cycles per second.

The driving force is given by

$$f_M = Bli \qquad (2)$$

where B = flux density in the air gap, in gausses, l = length of the voice coil conductor, in centimeters, and i = current in the voice coil, in abamperes.

From the electrical circuit of Fig. 1, the current in the voice coil is given by

$$i = e_G/(r_{EG} + r_{EC} + j\omega L + z_{EM}) \qquad (3)$$

where e_G = electromotive force of the electrical generator, in abvolts, r_{EG} = electrical resistance of the generator, in abohms, r_{EC} = damped electrical resistance of the voice coil, in abohms, L = damped inductance of the voice coil, in abhenries, $z_{EM} = (Bl)^2/z_T$ = electrical impedance due to the mechanical system, and z_T = mechanical impedance at f_M of the mechanical circuit of Fig. 1, in mechanical ohms.

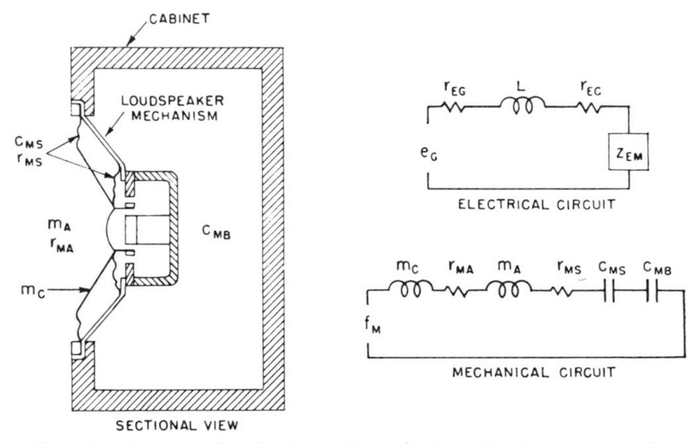

FIG. 1. Cross-sectional view of a single-coil, single-cone, direct radiator, dynamic loudspeaker mechanism mounted in a closed-back cabinet. In the voice coil circuit: e_G = the internal voltage of the generator; r_{EG} = the internal electrical resistance of the generator; r_{EC} and L = the electrical resistance and inductance of the voice coil; z_{EM} = the motional electrical impedance. In the mechanical circuit: m_C = the mass of the cone and voice coil; C_{MS} = the compliance of the suspension system; r_{MS} = the mechanical resistance of the suspension system; m_A = the mass of the air load; r_{MA} = the mechanical resistance of the air load; C_{MB} = the compliance of the cabinet; f_M = the mechanomotive force of the voice coil.

From the standpoint of this report there are two nonlinear elements in the mechanical circuit, namely, the compliance C_{MS} of the suspension system and the compliance C_{MB} due to the air in the cabinet. The effect of the nonlinearity of these elements will be considered in the sections which follow.

NONLINEAR SUSPENSION SYSTEM

The force displacement characteristic of a typical direct radiator loudspeaker cone suspension system is shown in Fig. 2. An examination of the characteristics of Fig. 2 shows that for small displacements the suspension system is linear. However, for large amplitudes the suspension is nonlinear.

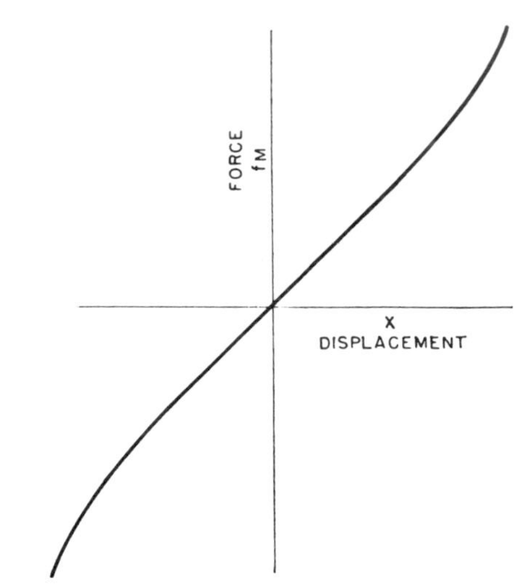

FIG. 2. Force displacement characteristics of the suspension system of a direct radiator loudspeaker.

The force deflection charcteristic of the loudspeaker cone suspension system of Fig. 2 may be approximately represented by the suspension

$$f_M = f(x) = \alpha x + \beta x^3 \qquad (4)$$

where f_M = force, in dynes, x = displacement, in centimeters, α = constant > 0, and β = constant > 0.

The compliance of the suspension system is

$$C_{MS} = x/f_M = 1/(\alpha + \beta x^2). \qquad (5)$$

The differential equation of the vibrating system of Fig. 3 is

$$m\,(d^2x/dt^2) + r_M\,(dx/dt) + x/C_{MB} = F \cos \omega t \qquad (6)$$

where x = displacement of the cone, in centimeters, dx/dt =

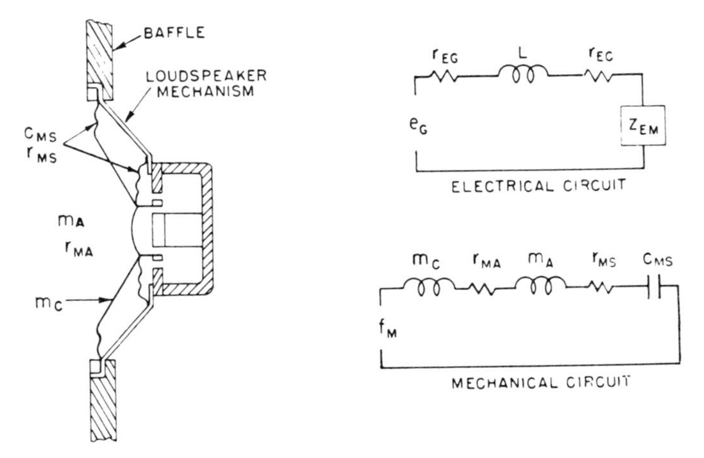

FIG. 3. Cross-sectional view of a single-coil, single-cone, direct radiator, dynamic loudspeaker mechanism mounted in a baffle. In the voice coil circuit: e_G = the internal voltage of the generator; r_{EG} = the internal electrical resistance of the generator; r_{EC} and L = the electrical resistance and inductance of the voice coil; z_{EM} = the motional electrical impedance. In the mechanical circuit: m_C = the mass of the cone and voice coil; C_{MS} = the compliance of the suspension system; r_{MS} = the mechanical resistance of the suspension system; m_A = the mass of the air load; r_{MA} = the mechanical resistance of the air load; f_M = the mechanomotive force in the voice coil.

velocity of the cone, in centimeters per second, d^2x/dt^2 = acceleration of the cone, in centimeters per second per second, $m = m_C + m_A$, m_C = mass of the cone, in grams, m_A = mass of the air load, in grams, $r_M = r_{MS} + r_{MA}$, r_{MS} = mechanical resistance of the suspension system, in mechanical ohms, r_{MA} = mechanical radiation resistance, in mechanical ohms, C_{MS} = compliance of the suspension system, in centimeters per dyne, $F = Bli$, F = force, in dynes, B = flux density, in gausses, l = length of the voice coil conductor, in centimeters, i = current in the voice coil, in abamperes, $\omega = 2\pi f$, f = frequency, in cycles per second, and t = time, in seconds.

Substituting for C_{MS} from Eq. (5) in Eq. (6), the differential equation becomes

$$m\,(d^2x/dt^2) + r_M\,(dx/dt) + \alpha x + \beta x^3 = F \cos \omega t. \quad (7)$$

Since the mechanical resistance, r_M, is quite small compared to the mechanical reactance, save over a very narrow frequency range near the resonant frequency, Eq. (7) can be written as follows:

$$m\,(d^2x/dt^2) + \alpha x + \beta x^3 = F \cos \omega t. \quad (8)$$

A number of investigators[3,4] have obtained an approximate solution of this differential equation.

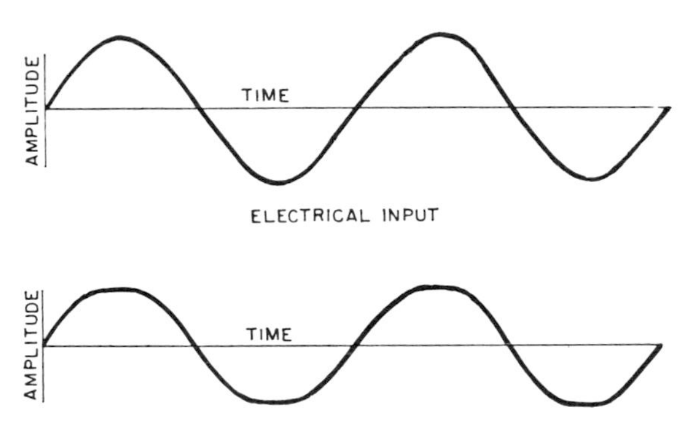

FIG. 4. The wave shapes of the electrical input and the sound pressure output of a loudspeaker with a nonlinear suspension system.

If β is considered to be small, the relation

$$\omega^2 = \alpha/m + \tfrac{3}{4}\,\beta A^2/m - F/A_m \quad (9)$$

between the arbitrary amplitude A and ω may be obtained.

An approximate solution of the differential equation (8) for unit mass is

$$x = A \cos \omega t + 1/32 \quad (10)$$
$$[\beta A^3/(\alpha x + \tfrac{3}{4}\,\beta A^2 - F/A)] \cos 3\,\omega t.$$

As expected, the nonlinear distortion is manifested as the introduction of a third harmonic term. The wave form of the sound output for large amplitudes is shown in Fig. 4.

[3] K. O. Friedricks and J. J. Stoker, *Quarterly of Applied Math.* **1**, 97 (1943).
[4] Cunningham, *Nonlinear Analysis* (McGraw-Hill Book Co., New York, 1958).

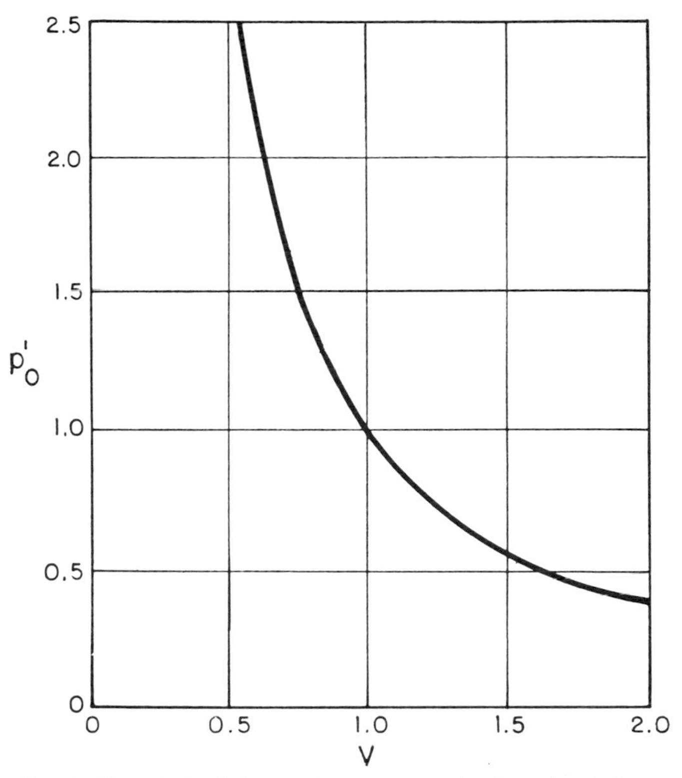

FIG. 5. The relation between the pressure and volume in air for an adiabatic process. p'_0 = absolute pressure; $p'_0 = 1$, the normal atmospheric pressure.

NONLINEAR STIFFNESS OF THE AIR IN THE CABINET VOLUME

The relation between the pressure and the volume in air for an adiabatic process is given by

$$p'_0 = C/V^\gamma \quad (11)$$

wher p'_0 = absolute pressure, in dynes, C = constant, V = volume, in cubic centimeters, and γ = ratio of specific heats, 1.4 for air.

The normalized characteristic of p'_0 as a function of V is shown in Fig. 5. An examination of the characteristics of Fig. 5 shows that the relationship between the pressure and volume is not linear.

The air in the loudspeaker cabinet is compressed and expanded by the excursion of the cone in vibration. A schematic diagram illustrating the compression and expansion of the air in a cylindrical chamber by the motion of the piston is shown in Fig. 6.

The range of amplitudes and pressures shown in Fig. 6 are far in excess of those found in actual conditions. The relationship between the pressure and the displacement of the piston over the range shown by the graph may be approximately expressed as

$$p = \eta' x + \kappa' x^2 \quad (12)$$

where p = excess pressure or sound pressure, in dynes per square centimeter, x = displacement of the piston, in centimeters, η' = constant > 0, and κ' = constant > 0.

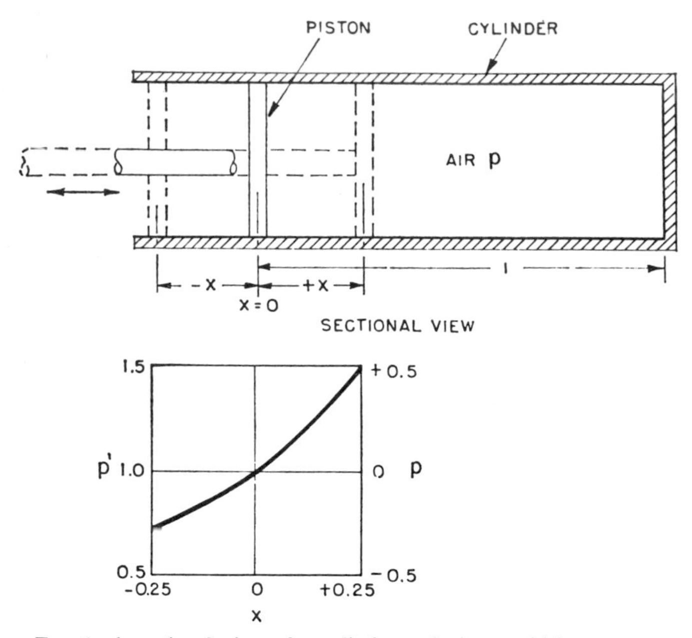

Fig. 6. A sectional view of a cylinder and piston which compresses and expands the air above and below the normal atmospheric pressure and a graph showing the relation between the pressure in the cylinder and the displacement of the piston. p'_o = absolute pressure; p'_o = 1, the normal atmospheric pressure; p = sound pressure.

The force exerted on the piston by the air in the cabinet is

$$f_M = pS \tag{13}$$

where f_M = force, in dynes, and S = area of the cone, in square centimeters.

Let $\eta = \eta' S$ and $\kappa' = \kappa' S$. Then equation (12) becomes

$$f_M = \eta x + \kappa x^2. \tag{14}$$

The compliance of the air in the cabinet is

$$C_M = 1/(\eta + \kappa x). \tag{15}$$

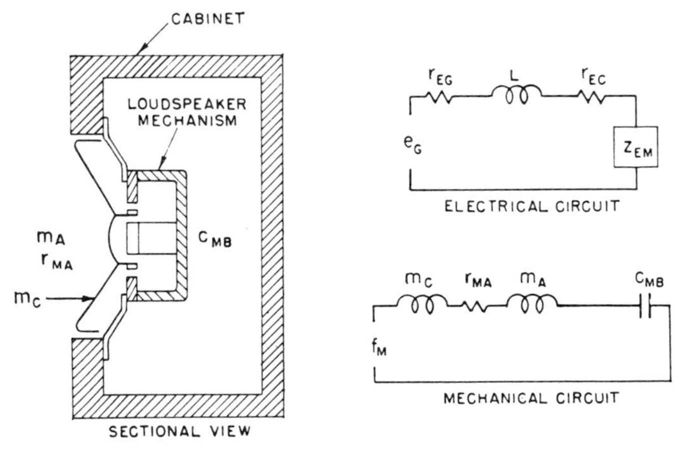

Fig. 7. Cross-sectional view of a single-coil, single-cone, direct radiator, dynamic loudspeaker mechanism mounted in a closed-back cabinet. In the voice coil circuit: e_G = the internal voltage of the generator; r_{EG} = the internal electrical resistance of the generator; r_{EC} and L = the electrical resistance and inductance of the voice coil; z_{EM} = the motional electrical impedance. In the mechanical circuit: m_C = the mass of the cone and voice coil; m_A = the mass of the air load; r_{MA} = the mechanical resistance of the air load; C_{MB} = the compliance of the cabinet; f_M = the mechanomotive force in voice coil.

A direct radiator loudspeaker in which the suspension system has been eliminated for the purpose of these considerations is shown in Fig. 7. In the idealized system of Fig. 7, the leakage of air through the slit between the cone and the cabinet is considered to be negligible. The differential equation for the vibrating system of Fig. 7 is

$$m\,(d^2x/dt^2) + r_{MS}\,(dx/dt) + x/C_{MB} = F \cos \omega t \tag{16}$$

where x = displacement of the cone, in centimeters, dx/dt = velocity of the cone, in centimeters per second, d^2x/dt^2 = acceleration of the cone, in centimeters per second per second, $m = m_C + m_A$, m_C = mass of the cone, in grams, m_A = mass of the air load, in grams, r_{MS} = mechanical resistance of the air load, in mechanical ohms, C_{MB} = compliance of the air in the cabinet, in centimeters per dyne, $F = Bli$, F = force, in dynes, B = flux density, in gausses, l = length of the voice coil conductor, in centimeters, i = current in the voice coil, in abamperes, $\omega = 2\pi f$, f = frequency, in cycles per second, and t = time, in seconds.

Substituting the value of the compliance C_{MB} from Eq. (15) in Eq. (16), the differential equation becomes

$$m\,(d^2x/dt^2) + r_{MS}\,(dx/dt) + \eta x + \kappa x^2 = F \cos \omega t. \tag{17}$$

Since the mechanical resistance, r_{MS}, is quite small compared to the mechanical reactance, save over a very narrow frequency range near the resonant frequency, Eq. (17) may be written

$$m\,(d^2x/dt^2) + \eta x + \kappa x^2 = F \cos \omega t. \tag{18}$$

If κ is considered to be small, the relation

$$\omega^2 = (\eta/m) - (F/Bm) \tag{19}$$

between the arbitrary amplitude B and ω may be obtained.

An approximate solution of the differential equation for unit mass is

$$x = B \cos \omega t + 1/8\,[\kappa B^2/(\eta - F/B)] \cos 2\,\omega t. \tag{20}$$

As would be expected, Eq. (20) contains the fundamental and second harmonic term. Figure 8 shows the wave form for the output of the loudspeaker for very large amplitudes.

The measured sound pressure for full power output, in the

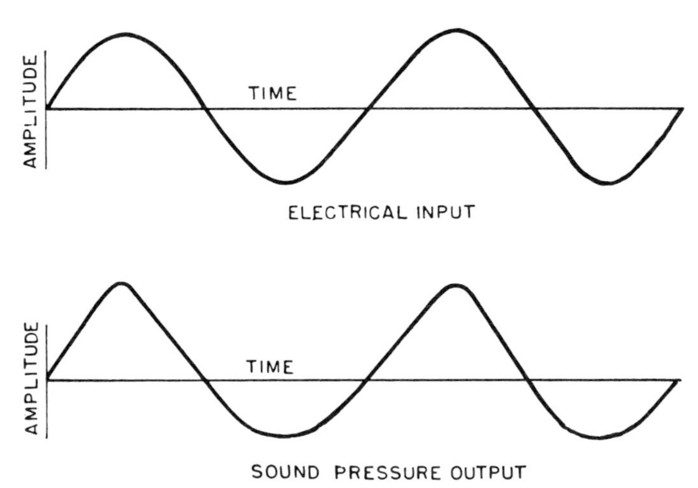

Fig. 8. The wave shapes of the electrical input and the sound pressure output of the back-enclosed loudspeaker of Fig. 7.

cabinet of the back-enclosed loudspeaker to be described in the next section, is 2000 dynes. The second harmonic term under these conditions is of the order of 0.3 percent.

CONSIDERATIONS IN THE DESIGN OF A BACK-ENCLOSED, DIRECT RADIATOR LOUDSPEAKER WITH LOW NONLINEAR DISTORTION AND WIDE FREQUENCY RANGE

The analysis of the distortion introduced by the nonlinear suspension and the nonlinear stiffness of the air in the cabinet of a back-enclosed direct radiator loudspeaker shows that the distortion introduced by the nonlinear stiffness of the air in the cabinet is relatively small. On the other hand, the nonlinear distortion introduced by the conventional suspension is relatively large. A consideration of the mechanical circuit of Fig. 1 and of Eq. (1) shows that the compliances, C_{MS} and C_{MB}, are the important elements in determining the response in the low frequency range. Furthermore, since the nonlinear distortion introduced by the compliance due to air in the cabinet is small, the distortion will be reduced by making the compliance of the suspension large compared to the compliance due to the air in the cabinet. For example, referring to Eq. (1), distortion introduced by compliance of the suspension is determined by the ratio

$$D = [C_{MB}/(C_{MB} + C_{MS})]\ 100 \qquad (21)$$

where D = nonlinear distortion introduced by the suspension system, in percent, C_{MS} = compliance of the suspension, in dynes per centimeter, and C_{MB} = compliance of the air in the cabinet, in dynes per centimeter.

Equation (21) shows that the nonlinear distortion introduced by the suspension will be reduced by making the compliance due to the air in the cabinet the controlling element.

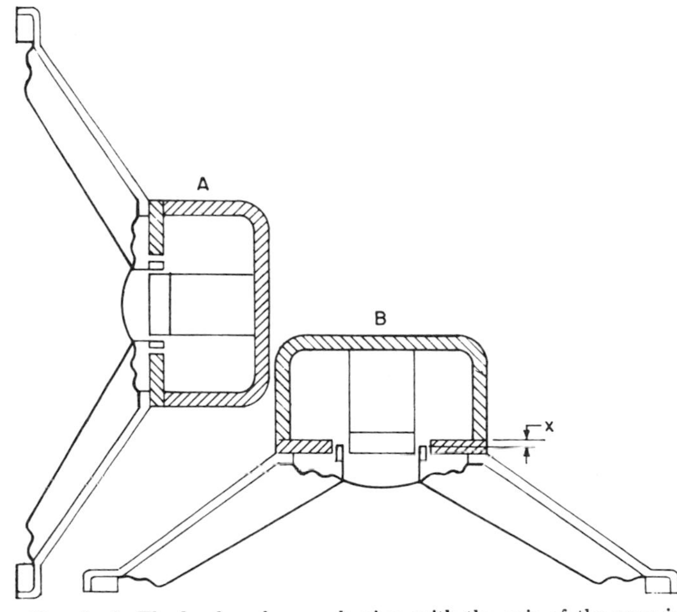

FIG. 9. A. The loudspeaker mechanism with the axis of the cone in a horizontal direction. B. The loudspeaker mechanism with the axis of the cone in a vertical direction and the deflection x of the cone and voice coil due to the force of gravity.

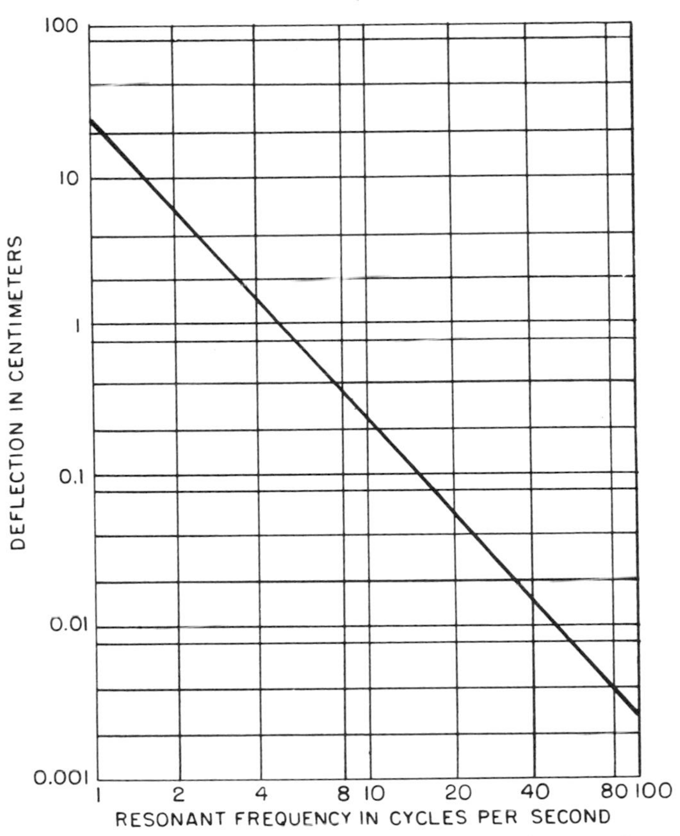

FIG. 10. The deflection of the cone and voice coil due to a change in the axis of the cone from a horizontal to a vertical direction as a function of the resonant frequency.

Nevertheless, the nonlinear distortion due to the suspension cannot be completely eliminated by this expedient while still retaining a practical suspension system. For example, if the compliance, C_{MS}, is made very large, the suspension will be very limp and voice coil will not remain centered in air gap.

The change in position of the voice coil by a variation of the angular orientation of the mechanism can be deduced as follows. The resonant frequency of the loudspeaker mechanism is given by

$$(2\pi f_R)^2 = 1/(m_C C_{MS}) \qquad (22)$$

where f_R = resonant frequency, in cycles per second. The deflection[5] of cone and coil due to application of a force is

$$x = f_M C_{MS} \qquad (23)$$

where f_M = force, in dynes, and x = deflection, in centimeters.

When the axis of the cone is horizontal as shown in Fig. 9A, there will be no gravitational force acting to displace the cone. However, if the axis of the cone is vertical as shown in Fig. 9B, the cone and voice coil will be deflected by a

[5] H. F. Olson, *Dynamical Analogies* (D. Van Nostrand Company, New York, 1959).

force due to gravity given by

$$f_M = 980\, m_C. \qquad (24)$$

From Eqs. (22), (23), and (24), the deflection of the cone and coil due to a change of the axis of the cone from a horizontal to a vertical position, in terms of the resonant frequency, will be

$$x = 25/f_R^2. \qquad (25)$$

The deflection as a function of the resonant frequency is depicted in Fig. 10.

An examination of Fig. 10 shows that there is a limit to the amount that the resonant frequency can be lowered and still retain a system in which the voice coil will remain centered in the air gap. A practical consideration of the stability requirements of the cone and coil shows that the compliance of the suspension C_{MS} cannot be made sufficiently large compared to C_{MB} that the distortion due to the suspension can be neglected (Eq. 21). Therefore, the suspension should be designed to provide as linear operation as possible. A suspension in which the linearity has been improved over that of a conventional suspension will be described next.

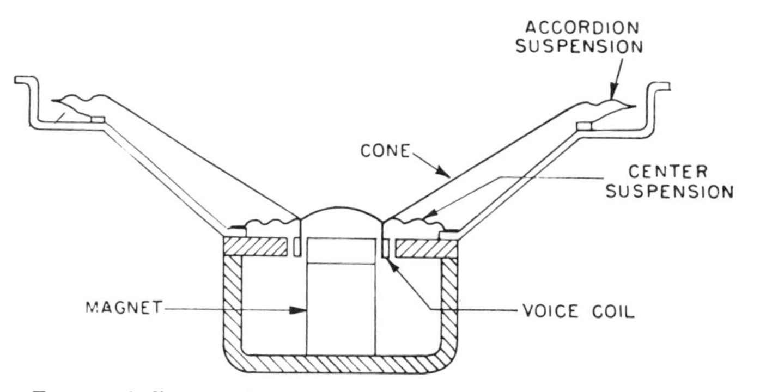

Fig. 11. A direct radiator loudspeaker mechanism with an accordion edge suspension.

ACCORDION-EDGE LOUDSPEAKER MECHANISM

The preceding considerations have shown that the distortion due to a nonlinear suspension system in a back-enclosed, direct radiator loudspeaker may be quite large even when the compliance due to the air in the cabinet is small compared to the compliance of the suspension. Therefore, the suspension should be made as linear as possible. The linearity of the suspension has been improved by the development of the accordion-edge suspension. A sectional view of a direct radiator loudspeaker with an accordion edge suspension is shown in Fig. 11. The actions of the accordion suspension system and the conventional suspension system are shown in Fig. 12. In the case of the accordion suspension the outer edge of the suspension is not constrained by the support in an axial direction as in the case of the conventional suspension system (the axial motion of the outer edge of the accordion suspension is illustrated in Fig. 12). Furthermore, the double suspension of the accordion edge doubles the axial length of the suspension system. The result of removing the axial constraint and doubling the axial length is that

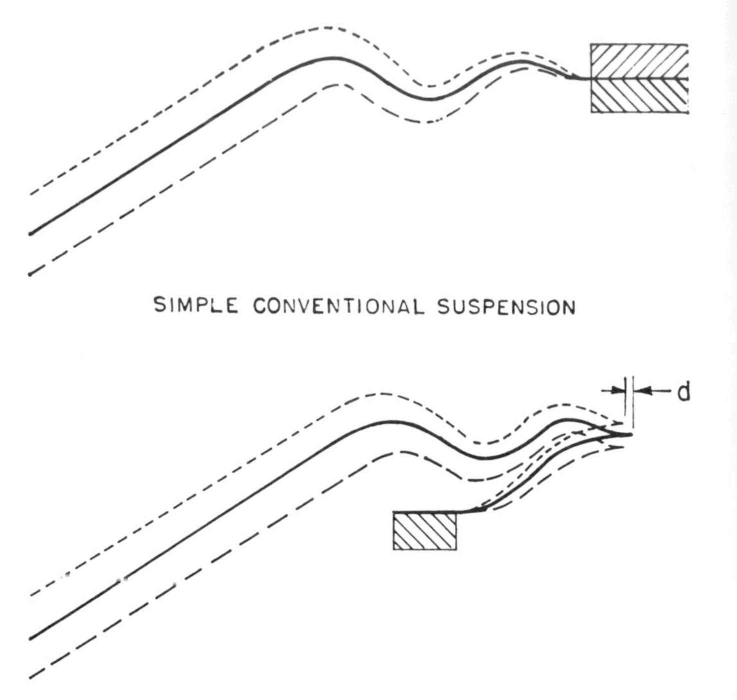

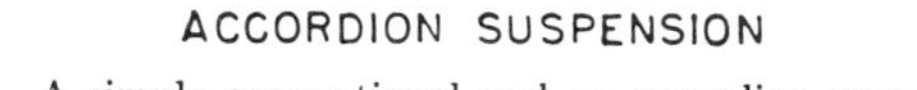

Fig. 12. A simple conventional and an accordion suspension.

the accordion suspension is linear over a wider excursion range than the conventional suspension. As a consequence, for full amplitude operation, the distortion due to the nonlinearity of the accordion suspension is about one-third that of a conventional suspension system.

Fig. 13. RCA Duplex Accordion Loudspeaker Mechanism, MI-12435-C.

BACK-ENCLOSED, ACCORDION-EDGE LOUDSPEAKER[6,7]

The original RCA Accordion Loudspeaker Mechanism commercialized two decades ago was the first low resonant loudspeaker designed to operate in a back-enclosed cabinet in which the compliance of the air in the cabinet is a fraction of the compliance of the cone suspension. The main application of the RCA Accordion Edge Loudspeaker has been in the field of sound systems for offices, schools, hospitals and factories. The loudspeaker has been sold in large quantities for these applications for more than twenty years and is still today one of the outstanding loudspeakers.

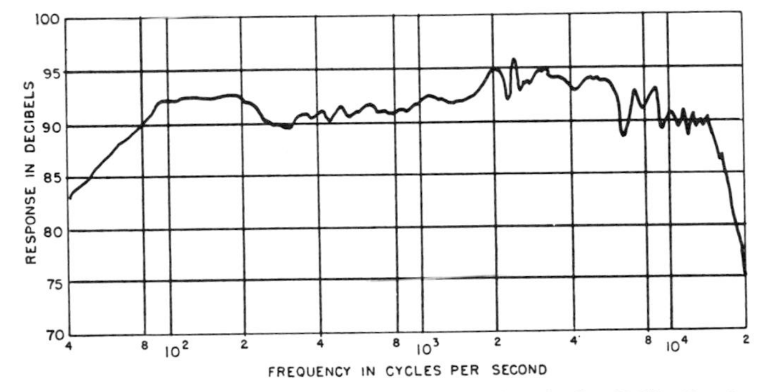

FIG. 14. Response frequency characteristic of the RCA Duplex Accordion Loudspeaker Mechanism mounted in a completely enclosed cabinet of one-half cubic foot. The response frequency characteristic depicts the sound pressure output at four feet for one watt input. Note: 92 db = 8 dynes per square centimeter.

The performance of the RCA Accordion Edge Loudspeaker Mechanism has been continuously improved by the application of new developments and techniques in the gen-

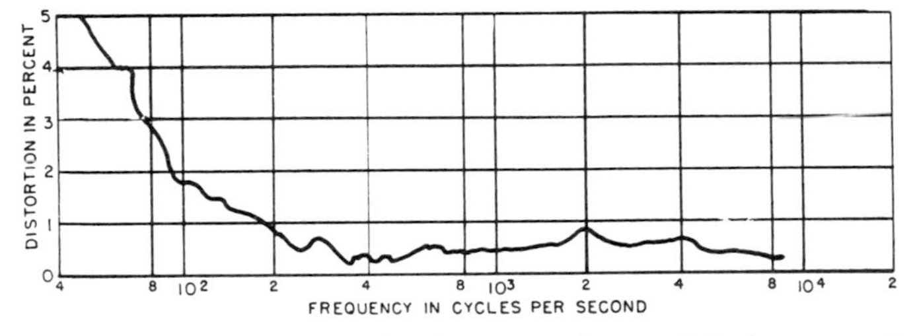

FIG. 15. Nonlinear distortion frequency characteristic for one watt input of the RCA Duplex Accordion Loudspeaker Mechanism mounted in a completely enclosed cabinet of one-half cubic foot.

eral loudspeaker field. For example, the latest model is the RCA Duplex Accordion Loudspeaker Mechanism, MI-12435-C, shown in Fig. 13. In this loudspeaker the high frequency range has been increased by the addition of a small cone in the center, sometimes termed a "wisser." The diameter of the main cone is 5 in. and the diameter of the wisser cone is 2 in. The flux density in the air gap is 9800 gauss. The diameter of the voice coil is ¾ in. The resonant frequency of the loudspeaker in free space is 60 cps. The compliance of the suspension is 10^{-6} cm/d. The compliance of the air in the one-half foot cabinet for this loudspeaker is 6×10^{-7} cm/d. Therefore, the resonant frequency in the cabinet having a volume of one-half cubic foot is 100 cps. The response frequency characteristic of the loudspeaker in a cabinet of one-half cubic foot is shown in Fig. 14. Uniform response is maintained over a frequency range of 70 to 15,000 cps. As a matter of fact, the low frequency response is down only 6 db at 50 cps. The sound pressure output at a distance of 4 ft for one watt input is 92 db or 8 d/cm^2. The nonlinear distortion for one watt input is shown in Fig. 15. The wide frequency range, high sensitivity, and low distortion, (see Figs. 14 and 15), are outstanding and remarkable for a loudspeaker of such small size.

[6] H. F. Olson, *Proc. Radio Club Am.* 18, No. 1 (January, 1941).

[7] H. F. Olson and J. Preston, U. S. Patent No. 2,490,466. Filed July 19, 1944; issued December 6, 1949.

THE AUTHOR

Harry F. Olson received the B.S., M.S., Ph.D., and E.E. degrees from the University of Iowa, and an Honorary D.Sc. degree from Iowa Wesleyan College. He has been affiliated with the Research Department of Radio Corporation of America, the Engineering Department of RCA Photophone, the Research Division of RCA Manufacturing Company, and RCA Laboratories. He is Director of the Acoustical and Electromechanical Laboratory of the RCA Laboratories.

Dr. Olson is a past president of the Acoustical Society of America and past chairman of the Administrative Committee of the IRE Professional Group on Audio.

He holds more than 82 U. S. Patents. He is the author of 75 papers and the books, "Elements of Acoustical Engineering," "Acoustical Engineering," "Dynamical Analogies," and "Musical Engineering."

Dr. Olson has received the following honors: the Modern Pioneer Award of the National Association of Manufacturers, the John H. Potts Medal of the Audio Engineering Society, the Samuel L. Warner Medal of the Society of Motion Picture and Television Engineers, the John Scott Medal of the City of Philadelphia, and the Achievement Award of the Professional Group on Audio of the Institute of Radio Engineers.

Dr. Olson is a member of Tau Beta Pi, Sigma Xi, and the National Academy of Sciences. He is a Fellow of the Society of Motion Picture and Television Engineers, the American Physical Society, the Institute of Radio Engineers, and the Acoustical Society of America, and an honorary member of the Audio Engineering Society.

On the Transient Response of Ideal Crossover Networks*

J. ROBERT ASHLEY

Sperry Electronic Tube Division, Sperry Rand Corporation, Gainesville, Florida

---

THIS investigation is an attempt to explain a difference in the sound quality of a system employing crossover networks that can be either 6 db per octave or 12 db per octave filters. To insure proper termination of the network and proper driving impedance for the loudspeakers, separate power amplifiers are used to drive the high and low frequency loudspeakers. Thus, the problems of the crossover network are separated from those of the loudspeakers and the crossover network can be considered to be operating under ideal conditions.

The first filter considered is a 6 db per octave filter as shown in Fig. 1. This network has a response equivalent to

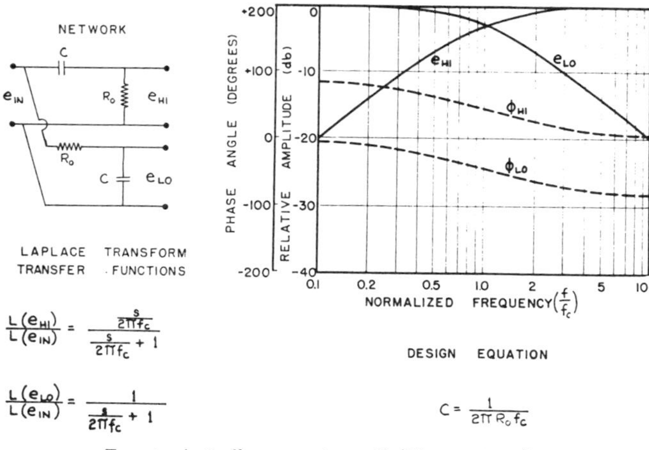

FIG. 1. A 6 db per octave dividing network.

that of a constant-resistance-type dividing network using one capacitor and one inductor.[1]

From a loudspeaker design standpoint, a 12 db per octave crossover network considerably eases the requirements on the speakers, especially the high frequency speaker, if it is a horn type. A simple 12 db per octave network can be formed by cascading two of the 6 db per octave networks. If the capacitors of the second section are one tenth the size of those in the first section and the resistors of the second section are ten times those of the first section, the network will have a damping factor of 1.05 which is within 5% of that which would be achieved with cathode followers between two identical sections.

Most "electronic crossover networks" use a filter network which is less than critically damped. Damping factors in the range .5 to .7 will cause only small overshoot to a square wave response and will improve the frequency response of the separate filter sections. A particularly important network of this class is the 12 db per octave constant-resistance frequency-dividing network.[2] As shown by the transfer function given in Fig. 2, this network has .707 critical damp-

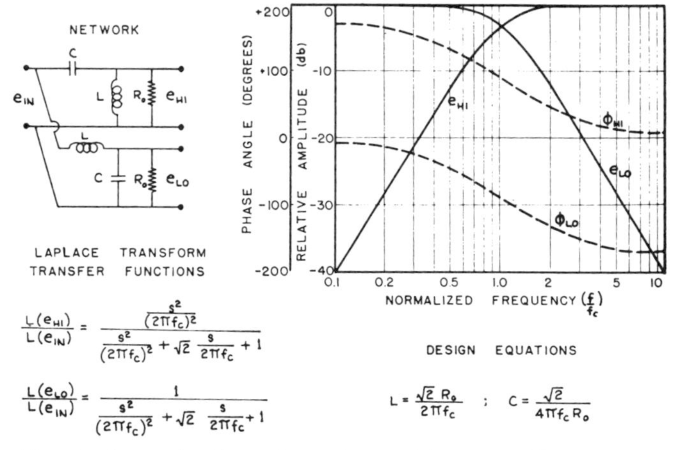

FIG. 2. An under-damped constant-resistance 12 db per octave dividing network.

ing and a very well behaved frequency response for each channel.

It is the opinion of the author that neither 12 db per octave network sounds as pleasing as the 6 db per octave network. An investigation of the transient response was chosen because an analog computer was available and the transient curves are easier to obtain than the frequency response. None of the calculations are so difficult that they could not be accomplished by well known analytic methods.

To restrict the range of this study, several assumptions were made: 1. The network is built with "perfect" components. 2. The network is not loaded by the amplifier which follows. 3. The amplifier-speaker combinations have zero

---

* Presented October 10, 1961 at the Thirteenth Annual Convention of the Audio Engineering Society, New York.

[1] F. E. Terman, *Radio Engineers' Handbook* (McGraw-Hill Book Company, New York, 1943), Fig. 117 (c).

[2] Terman, *op. cit.*, Fig. 117 (d).

phase shift and flat frequency response through the crossover region. 4. The listener is equidistant from both speakers. These are quite similar assumptions to those used by Boegli in his frequency response study of the same problem.[3]

With these assumptions, the total sound wave reaching the listener can be obtained by simply adding the output of the two filter networks. To obtain the transfer function relating the total response to the input, it is only necessary to add the transfer functions for the individual networks.

For the 6 db per octave networks the result of this addition is:

$$\pounds(e_T)/\pounds(e_{IN}) = [(s/2\pi f_c) + 1]/[(s/2\pi f_c) + 1] = 1 \quad (1)$$

where e_T is a voltage proportional to the total sound wave reaching the listener. Thus, if the speakers meet the previous assumptions, the crossover network will give perfect division of the spectrum.

The result for the cascaded RC 12 db per octave network is not this ideal:

$$\pounds(e_T)/\pounds(e_{IN}) = \{[s^2/(2\pi f_c)^2] + 1\}/\{[s^2/(2\pi f_c)^2] + [2.1\ (s/2\pi f_c)] + 1\} \quad (2)$$

Similarly, the result for the under-damped 12 db per octave network such as a constant resistance dividing network is not ideal:

$$\pounds(e_T)/\pounds(e_{IN}) = \{[s^2/2\pi f_c)^2] + 1\}/\{[s^2/(2\pi f_c)^2] + [\sqrt{2}\ (s/2\pi f_c)] + 1\}. \quad (3)$$

To evaluate this response, the square wave response of the under-damped network was studied with an analog computer. Figure 3 shows a typical result. The blunted leading edge for the low frequency channel is expected, just as the sharp leading edge and drooping response on the top of the wave is expected of the high channel. It is the combined response that is not as desired. Hopefully, the combined response would be a replica of the square wave input, but this is not the case for the under-damped 12 db per octave network.

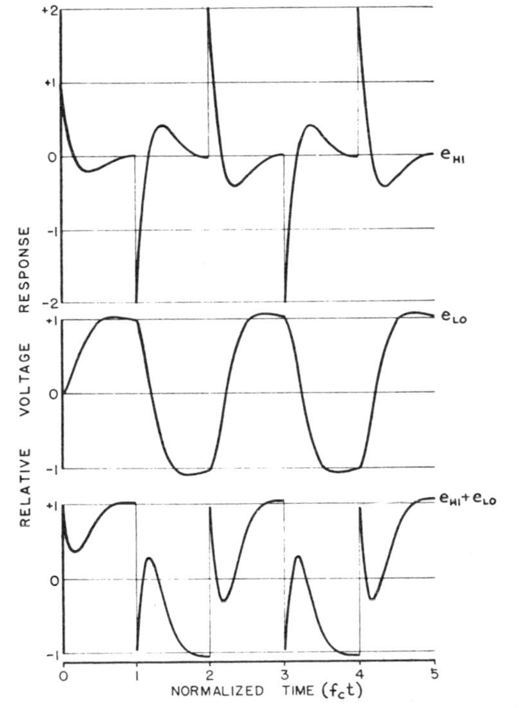

FIG. 3. Square wave response of the under-damped network shown in Fig. 2.

If buffer amplifiers are used between a crossover network and the transducers, the constant resistance property of the network is of little value. The network can be operated at a moderate level with a relatively low impedance driver stage (such as a cathode follower) and an impedance variation of the network will cause no trouble. With this freedom, it is possible to choose unequal design frequencies for each of the filters. Mathematically this does not lead to a perfect frequency division property, but it is worth performing the experiment with the computer to see if non-equal design frequencies will give an output which closely approximates the input.

Figure 4 is the computed result for several cases. Even with a two octave overlap of the design crossover frequencies, the transient response is not a good approximation of the input. To go further would not improve the response appreciably and the requirement on the speakers would exceed the range required for the mathematically perfect 6 db per octave network.

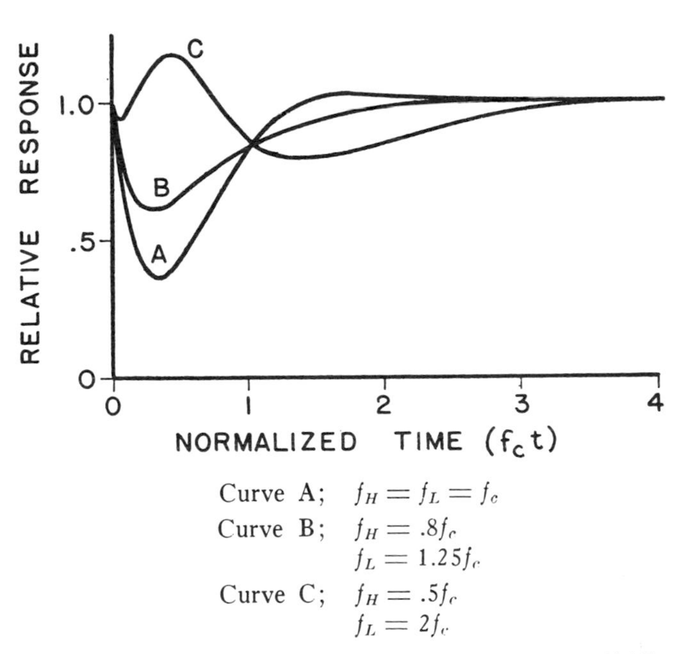

Curve A; $f_H = f_L = f_c$
Curve B; $f_H = .8f_c$, $f_L = 1.25f_c$
Curve C; $f_H = .5f_c$, $f_L = 2f_c$

FIG. 4. Total transient response of a 0.7 critically damped dividing network with non-equal crossover frequencies.

The fundamental reason why the transient response is not perfect for the 12 db per octave network is that the numerator of the total transfer function, Eq. (3), does not have a $\sqrt{2}\ (s/2\pi f_c)$ term. To obtain a total transfer function which does have this "missing middle term," a modification of the filter circuit is required.

[3] Charles P. Boegli, *Audio* 40, (Nov., 1956).

It is easily shown that a series R-L-C circuit has a transfer function with a denominator such as the transfer functions of Eqs. (2) and (3). By taking the output across the inductor, a high pass filter results. Taking the output across the capacitor results in a low pass filter. The voltage across the resistor is the voltage required to form the "missing middle term" in the transfer function.

One way to build an improved crossover network is to use a single R-L-C circuit as shown in Fig. 5. The fact that the combined transfer function

$$\frac{\pounds(e_T)}{\pounds(e_{IN})} = \frac{s^2/(2\pi f_c)^2}{[s^2/(2\pi f_c)^2]+[2\zeta\,(s/2\pi f_c)]+1} + \frac{[2\zeta\,(s/2\pi f_c)]+1}{[s^2/(2\pi f_c)^2]+[2\zeta\,(s/2\pi f_c)]+1} \qquad (5)$$

where $f_c = 1/[2\pi\,(LC)^{1/2}]$ and $\zeta = (R/2)\,(C/L)^{1/2}$ yields perfect frequency and transient response is an obvious consequence of Kirchhoff's Voltage Law. This network has the further advantage of not requiring two matched sets of filter network components. Imperfections in the components will slightly change the crossover frequency and the damping factor, but the very nature of the filter will cause any errors in one channel to be compensated for in the other channel. A 10% change in either the crossover frequency or the damping factor will not result in a noticeable difference in the sound of the system; thus non-precision components will yield excellent results.

The network of Fig. 5 is difficult to use because the center

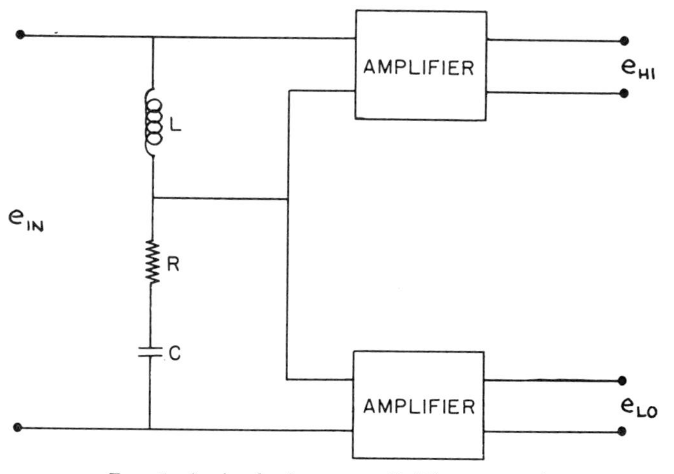

FIG. 5. A simple frequency-dividing network.

terminal is common to both amplifiers instead of being one of the end terminals. Either a transformer coupled drive or some form of differential amplifier for one of the channels would be required. The computer simulation of these networks suggests a simple and practical way to build an ideal crossover network. The basic technique is illustrated in Fig. 6. A cascaded RC network can be substituted if the use of an inductor is undesirable.

This is not the only possible configuration of this type;

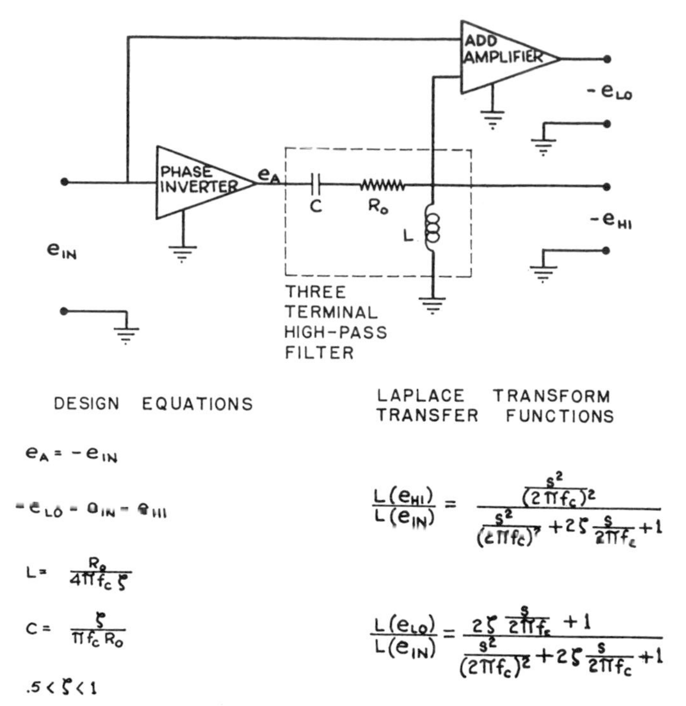

FIG. 6. An electronic frequency-dividing network with ideal transient response.

but it does have several advantages in regard to requirements on the following amplifier and speaker. The reason for using a high-pass filter instead of a similar arrangement using a low-pass filter is that any failure of a component in the filter network will not completely stop the filter action in the high channel. Since the high frequency range transducer is easier to damage by applied signals outside the rated frequency range, this is a safety feature of the network. Also, inserting the "missing middle term" increases the power handling requirement of one of the amplifier speaker combinations in the first octave of the stop band. The low frequency amplifier and transducer is usually better able to supply this additional power. Therefore, the "missing middle term" has been put into the low frequency channel rather than the high frequency channel, and the frequency response of the network is shown in Fig. 7. By tapping R_o, the "missing middle term" can be divided between the two channels in any desired proportion.

The extension to stereo systems is shown in Fig. 8. It will be noticed that three amplifiers and only one low frequency speaker are required. Inserting the "missing middle term" into the low frequency channel provides a signal somewhat similar to the mixed signal supplied to a three-speaker, two-channel conventional system to eliminate the "hole in the middle."

The phase inverter and the addition amplifier stages can be easily implemented by the use of the analog computer "operational amplifier" philosophy. For this application, a single high-mu triode amplifier stage driving a cathode follower makes an excellent operational amplifier. The net-

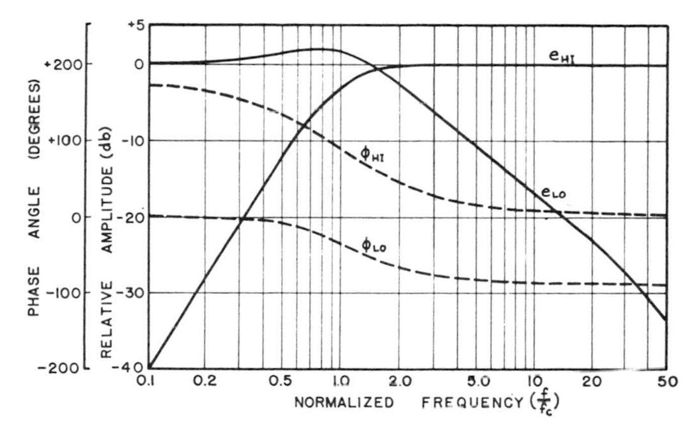

Fig. 7. Frequency and transient response of the electronic frequency-dividing network shown in Fig. 6.

work of resistors used to make this amplifier a unity-gain, phase inverting addition circuit is essentially a high inverse feedback system. Thus, the low impedance of the cathode follower is reduced by a factor of about 1/50 for a typical dual triode. Such an amplifier is a good driver for a filter network which can have wide variations in impedance over the audio spectrum.

The simple circuit used for the demonstration filter is given in Fig. 9. This amplifier has been designed to use a

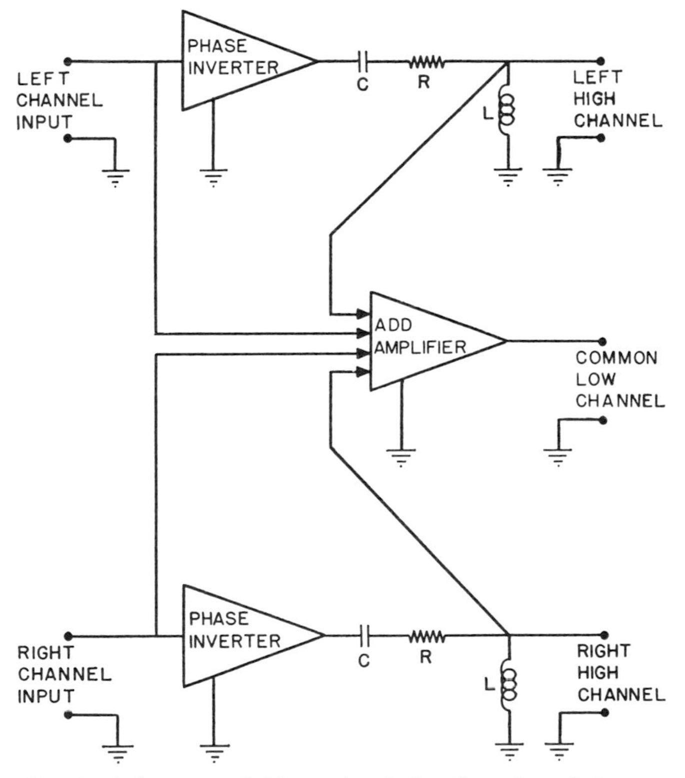

Fig. 8. A frequency-dividing network for three-channel stereo.

minimum number of components and to use as few component values as possible. The amplifier is easily capable of several volts output, and the large amount of inverse feedback in the phase inverting or addition circuit reduces distortion to a quite negligible amount. This type of filter network works at a level appropriate for insertion between the usual preamplifier and power amplifier.

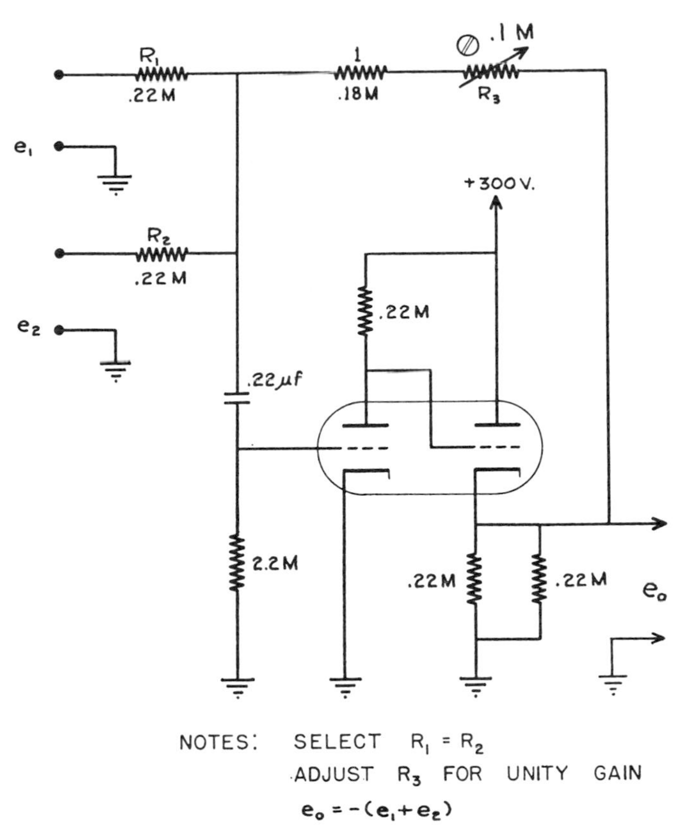

Fig. 9. The computer-type adding and inverting circuit for audio-frequency-dividing networks.

The support of the Sperry Electronic Tube Division in the preparation and presentation of this paper is gratefully acknowledged. The use of the analog computer facilities of the Sperry Microwave Electronics Company is also acknowledged.

THE AUTHOR

J. Robert Ashley was born in Kansas City, Missouri, in 1927. In 1946 and 1947, he studied and taught at the Navy Electronics School on Treasure Island, California. After receiving the BSEE degree from the University of Kansas in 1952, Mr. Ashley worked on megawatt klystrons at the Sperry Gyroscope Company. He returned to the University of Kansas to teach electrical engineering, and in 1956, he received the MSEE degree. The same year Mr. Ashley joined the Sperry Electronic Tube Division as a project engineer. His work includes the development of klystron oscillators, equipment design for grid modulated klystron amplifiers, and analog computation of electron beam trajectories.

Mr. Ashley is a member of the Audio Engineering Society, a senior member of the Institute of Radio Engineers and belongs to several fraternities. He has two patents pending.

Loudspeaker Enclosure Walls*

PETER W. TAPPAN

Warwick Manufacturing Corporation, Chicago, Illinois

While it is traditional to use thick wooden enclosure walls, thick or heavy walls are not always necessary for high quality. Acoustical requirements, typical wall behavior, and the effects on system performance of various wall properties are discussed.

INTRODUCTION

FOR as long as the cone-type loudspeaker has been in existence, it has been traditional to house it in a wooden cabinet in applications where sound quality has been an important consideration. Even today, virtually every high-fidelity loudspeaker system employs an all-wooden cabinet, and virtually every hi-fi expert advises the do-it-yourselfer to make his enclosure out of plywood at least three quarters of an inch thick, although some go so far as to advocate brick or concrete.

In view of the widespread use of high-quality loudspeaker systems, the high cost of wood, and the vast amount of research that has been done to improve and reduce the cost of audio systems, it is surprising that so few attempts to improve enclosure walls have been reported in the literature. Rather, the nearly universal recommendation of thick wooden walls seems to have propagated itself by tradition.

After all, the general purpose of enclosure walls is to prevent the sound radiated by the back of the loudspeaker from escaping in an uncontrolled manner into the room where it can interfere with that from the front of the loudspeaker; and when it is considered that all this sound is being generated by a thin paper cone, it seems illogical that it should require ¾ in. plywood to stop it.

On the basis of these considerations, it was deemed that research on enclosure wall materials and structures might be valuable, and a study was instigated. In the bulk of the paper, the acoustical requirements and behavior of enclosure walls and the factors affecting wall adequacy will be discussed. It will be shown that thick wooden walls are not always necessary. The results of tests on various kinds of panels and experiments on several actual loudspeaker systems will also be described.

ACOUSTICAL REQUIREMENTS OF ENCLOSURE WALLS

The basic function of the walls of a loudspeaker enclosure is to prevent the transmission of sound through them. In a closed-box system, fulfillment of this function completely contains the sound pressure generated by the rear of the loudspeaker or loudspeakers, so that this sound cannot interfere with that radiated by the front of the loudspeaker. In a bass reflex system, the walls should prevent the escape of rear radiation except through the port, and the port and enclosure sizes are selected so that this rear radiation is caused to aid the front radiation at low frequencies above the system cutoff. In an open-baffle system, the walls should prevent the rear radiation from joining the front radiation until it has traversed a relatively long path, to prevent destructive interference within the useful frequency range of the system. In a horn system, too, the walls should prevent passage of sound through them, so that all the sound may be guided along the horn and emerge from its mouth.

Of course, in reality there is no such thing as a perfectly immovable wall; and, therefore, no such thing as a perfectly soundproof wall. Fortunately, however, the walls need not be perfectly soundproof; the thing that matters is that the sound intensity at the listener should not be audibly altered by transmission of sound through the enclosure walls. For a very high-fidelity system, a good steady-state criterion might be that the wall transmission should change the sound level at the listener by less than one db, within the useful frequency range of the system.

Another requirement of great importance is that the walls should not cause "hangover," or audible sound radiation after the loudspeaker cone has ceased moving. Sound pressures generated by a loudspeaker within an enclosure cause the walls to vibrate, and the vibrating walls radiate sound into the listening room. This is the mechanism of wall transmission. If the walls continue to vibrate for a long time after the loudspeaker cone has ceased moving, then hangover will be produced. Hangover imparts a ringing or "barrel" characteristic to the reproduced sound and is very unpleasant. It is important, therefore, that wall vibration should be adequately damped so that it decays rapidly after the exciting force has ceased. A simple test for adequate wall damping is to rap on the walls with the knuckles. An insufficiently damped wall will ring, whereas a well damped wall will produce a "dead" thump. Objectionable wall

* Presented October 10, 1961 at the Thirteenth Annual Fall Convention of the Audio Engineering Society, New York.

hangover is not usually produced by wooden walls. Although wall mobility and damping are interrelated, it is possible to have a hangover-free system with an unsatisfactory steady-state system frequency response (flat paper walls); and, conversely, a system with a satisfactory steady-state frequency response but objectionable hangover (eighth-inch steel walls).

ACOUSTICAL BEHAVIOR OF ENCLOSURE WALLS

A typical enclosure wall is a uniform flat panel clamped at the edges. It has a fundamental resonant mode at some frequency, and an infinite number of higher-order modes at higher frequencies. The frequencies of these modes are not harmonically related, in general.

When the loudspeaker emits a note, it causes the air pressure within the enclosure to vary in accordance with the motion of the loudspeaker cone. This pressure variation acts on the enclosure walls and causes them to vibrate at the same frequency or frequencies as are being emitted by the loudspeaker. When the emitted frequency is below that of the fundamental wall resonance, it is the stiffness of the wall that determines how much it will vibrate. The wall must therefore be adequately stiff if loss of low-frequency response is to be avoided. Most normal-sized conventional walls are satisfactory in this respect, event when made of quarter-inch plywood or eighth-inch hardboard.

The effect of the wall mobility on the system response may be understood more clearly by considering an equivalent circuit of the system. For example, an equivalent acoustical circuit of the impedance type for a loudspeaker in a small closed box, with one wall of the box having a non-negligible mobility, is shown in Fig. 1. In this circuit P_s

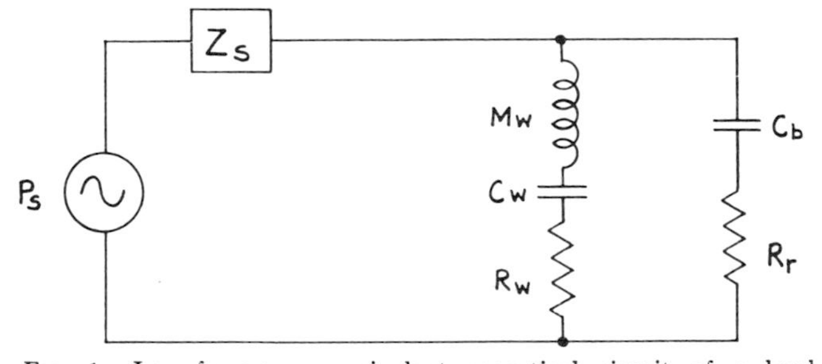

Fig. 1. Low-frequency equivalent acoustical circuit of a loudspeaker in a small closed box with one incompletely rigid wall.

is the acoustic pressure equivalent of the applied electrical signal; Z_s is the acoustic impedance equivalent of the loudspeaker (Z_s consists of the acoustic resistance equivalent of the electromagnetic damping; the acoustic resistance of the diaphragm suspension system; the acoustic mass reactance of the voice coil, spider, cone and air that moves with the cone; and the stiffness reactance of the diaphragm suspension system, all in series); C_b is the acoustic compliance of the air confined within the box; R_r is the acoustic radiation resistance of the air load on the front of the cone and the box wall (the resistance through which acoustic power is radiated from the system); M_w is the equivalent inertance or acoustic mass of the wall and air load thereon; C_w is the equivalent acoustic compliance of the wall; and R_w is the equivalent acoustic resistance of the wall due to damping in the wall structure. (If the acoustic impedances of the other walls were to be included in the circuit, they would be placed in parallel with that of the first.) This circuit is approximately valid only in the frequency region where all system dimensions are small compared to a wavelength and the cone moves as a rigid piston, and only below and in the vicinity of the fundamental wall resonant frequency (where the wall mass, stiffness, and resistance may be treated as lumped constants).

Below the resonance of the wall mass M_w with the wall compliance C_w, C_w becomes the predominating factor in the wall impedance. If we wish to obtain good low-frequency response, the shunting effect of the wall impedance across R_r and C_b must be kept small. Since the reactance of the acoustic compliance C_b of the air in the box is normally much larger than the radiation resistance R_r, the requirement for good low-frequency response is that C_w should be small compared to C_b. Of course, in reality, all the walls must be taken into account, and the sum of their compliances must be small compared to the compliance of the air in the box. There is little point in making C_w less than one-tenth of C_b, as far as low-frequency response is concerned, because a further increase in wall stiffness would boost the response less than one db.

When the emitted frequency is equal to that of the fundamental resonance, the restraining negative acoustic reactance of the wall stiffness is canceled out by the positive reactance of the wall mass; and the only factor inhibiting wall vibration is the internal friction or damping of the wall. The wall vibration is at its maximum in the vicinity of this frequency, with consequent greatest effect on the system response. In a closed-box or bass reflex system, when the resonance occurs at a frequency where the enclosure dimensions are small compared to the sound wavelength in air, the effect on the system response is to reduce the sound output at frequencies just below and at resonance, and increase the output at frequencies slightly above resonance. Thus, if the response curve were flat in the absence of the resonance, in its vicinity the resonance would cause the curve to assume the shape of an *S* turned on its side.

Again, this effect may be understood more clearly by considering an equivalent circuit. In Fig. 1, when the wall is at resonance, its shunting effect across C_b and R_r is a maximum; and the volume velocity through the radiation resistance R_r is therefore reduced, creating a dip in the system response. If the wall damping R_w were sufficient, the shunting effect would be negligible.

The equivalent mass of a normal wall is so great that above the wall resonant frequency the wall reactance rises very rapidly. Slightly above the wall resonant frequency, therefore, this reactance resonates with C_b; and the volume velocity through R_r is thereby increased, creating a peak in the response. Again, if the wall damping were sufficient, the increase would be negligible.

Similar behavior occurs at some of the higher resonant frequencies, but several factors cause the effects of these resonances to be less severe than those of the fundamental. One of these factors is the decreased effective radiating area. In the fundamental mode, all parts of the wall are moving in the same direction at the same time. In higher-order modes, different parts of the wall are moving in opposite directions. A cancellation of sound radiation from these oppositely moving surfaces occurs, provided that their dimensions are small compared to a wavelength, so that the net radiation decreases. For example, in one mode the wall may "break up" into three roughly equal moving areas, adjacent areas moving in opposite directions. The net panel motion is thus virtually that of only one-third of the total area. In some modes there is very little net radiation. Also, it is more difficult for the pressure variations within the enclosure to excite these higher-order modes, because parts of the wall are bucking the pressure. Another factor is that the higher-order modes are more easily damped.[1,2] An overall result of these factors is that above the first few resonant frequencies, it is essentially the wall mass that determines how much sound it will transmit. Conventional enclosure walls have more than adequate mass to prevent deleterious transmission in this frequency region. Factors of absorption within the enclosure and radiation directivity, which will be discussed later, also contribute to reduced interference at the higher wall resonances.

Thus, even the flimsiest conventional wood or hardboard walls are adequate in the stiffness-controlled low-frequency region and in the mass-controlled high-frequency region. It is only in the vicinity of the first few resonances that conventional walls can give trouble, the fundamental resonance being the worst offender. If the wall vibration is sufficiently small near the fundamental resonance, it is virtually certain to be more than sufficiently small at the higher resonances. The acoustical problem in enclosure wall design is therefore essentially that of insuring sufficiently small wall vibration near the fundamental resonance. As a general rule, this means that the absorption within the enclosure, the wall damping, and the fundamental resonant frequency of the wall must all be sufficiently high. This statement will be amplified in the following sections.

FACTORS AFFECTING WALL ADEQUACY

Internal Absorption

When an enclosure contains a lining, partition, or filling of a sound-absorbing material such as fiberglass blanket, cellulose fiber blanket, creped cellulose wadding, or shredded tissue paper, this material absorbs some of the sound radiated by the back of the loudspeaker; and therefore less sound strikes the enclosure walls than if this material were absent. The walls consequently vibrate less and radiate less sound into the room. Depending on various factors, the wall radiation at its fundamental resonance may be decreased by two db or more. Although the usual improvement is not large, it will help. Moreover, the absorption serves the important function of preventing response irregularities caused by reflection of sound from the walls back to the loudspeaker, and its use wherever possible is therefore recommended even when wall transmission is not a problem. Figure 2 shows the low-frequency response of a

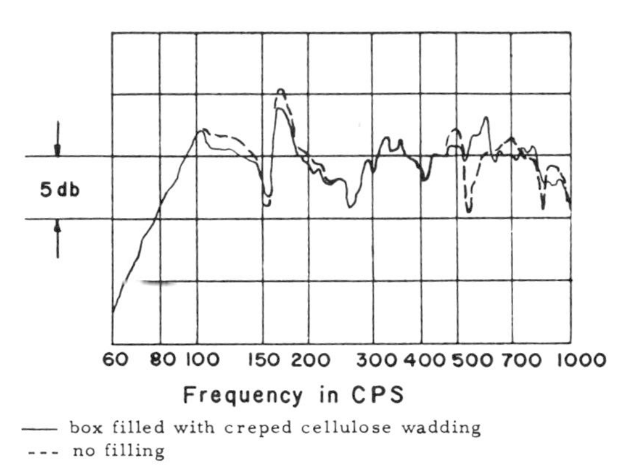

FIG. 2. Frequency response of a closed-box system with rigid walls except for one ¼-inch plywood wall.

loudspeaker in a closed box with adequately rigid walls except for one 12 in. × 18 in. panel of quarter-inch plywood. The fundamental resonance of this panel caused roughly a five db dip at 155 cps followed by a peak of similar magnitude at 170 cps. It can be seen that loosely filling the enclosure with creped cellulose wadding tempered the dip by about half a db and sliced a db off the peak. A greater improvement would be expected with a larger enclosure or a higher resonant frequency, because the absorption would be greater.

Absorbing material is most effective when it is not too close to a rigid boundary. For this reason, a loose filling or a partition is preferable to a lining. For the same effectiveness, a partition will require less material than a lining. At first glance, it might seem that a lining would serve the additional function of damping the walls. Most good absorbing materials, however, are too light to affect any significant wall damping, unless backed by a stiff or heavy septum so that the material is squeezed when the wall vibrates. The septum must be perforated in order to preserve the absorption of the lining. An absorbent partition should be positioned to intercept sound from the back of the loudspeaker and should preferably not be parallel to any of the walls. If the enclosure is filled with absorbing material, care must be taken that the filling cannot touch the loudspeaker cone.

Damping

An increase in wall damping will reduce vibration near the wall resonant frequencies. It is therefore desirable to use a wall material that has reasonably high inherent damp-

[1] Paul H. Geiger, *Noise Reduction Manual* (Engineering Research Institute, University of Michigan, 1955), p. 66.

[2] T. Mariner and F. G. Dochat, "How to Reduce Noise in Sheet-Metal Enclosures with Flexural Damping Materials," *Machine Design* (April 19, 1956).

ing. A rough idea of the damping of any material may be gained by holding a panel of it loosely and striking it with the knuckles. Panels with little damping will ring audibly. A few examples of materials with poor, fair, and good damping are given below:

Poor	Fair	Good
Steel	Wood	Asphalt felt
Aluminum	Hardboard	Rubber
Glass	Lead	Mastic

When it is necessary or expedient to use a thin wall of a poorly damped material, it is possible to improve the damping by bonding to the wall a layer of well damped material such as asphalt felt. The amount of such material necessary to achieve the desired improvement must be determined by experiment. It is usually unnecessary to cover the entire wall, but in most cases at least 25% of the area should be covered if the material is to be fully effective. The damping material should be centered on the wall for maximum effect. For a given damping material, doubling the thickness increases the damping rate by a factor of three.[3]

With walls having fair inherent damping such as wood or hardboard, on the other hand, lining with a highly damped material is not usually the best solution unless the wall is very thin. The reason for this is that an inordinate amount of damping material would be required to effect a significant improvement with a heavy wall.

Unfortunately, most well-damped materials are too soft and limp to be practicable as walls by themselves.

Figure 3 shows the effect on low-frequency response of a

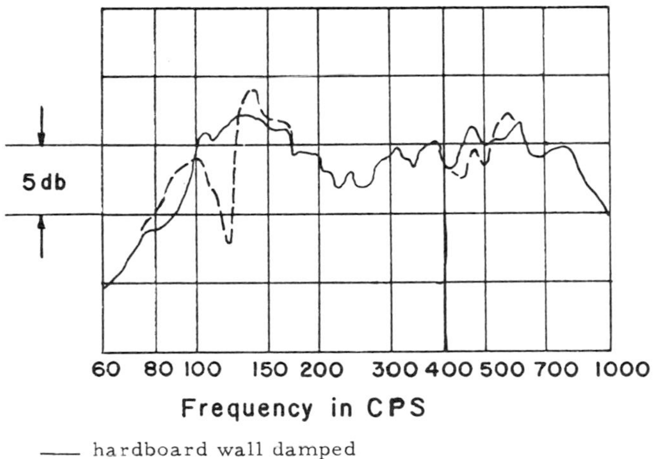

FIG. 3. Frequency response of a closed-box system with rigid walls except for one 1/8-inch tempered hardboard wall.

loudspeaker in a closed box with adequately rigid walls except for one 12 in. × 18 in. panel of eighth-inch tempered hardboard, resulting from the addition of a lining of eighth-inch pebbled asphalt felt roofing to the hardboard panel. It is evident that the additional damping radically improved the system performance.

As mentioned previously, in addition to its influence on steady-state response, the wall damping also affects the transient response. The plywood and hardboard panel resonances evident in Figs. 2 and 3 produce rather nasty fluctuations in the steady-state response, but it was found that they caused negligible hangover. To learn how much hangover might be produced by metal enclosures and how much damping would be required to render it inaudible, an experiment was performed with three metal-walled closed-box systems housing identical 12 in. loudspeakers. The enclosures were approximately 23 in. × 21 in. × 21 in. and were constructed of steel about 0.035 in. thick. No absorbing material was used in any of the cabinets. One cabinet was left unlined, one was completely lined with ninety-pound asphalt felt cemented to the metal, and one with 5/32 in. corrugated cardboard cemented in place. Frequency-response measurements in front of and above the systems revealed only minor differences, consisting primarily in shifts in the wall resonances due to the different stiffnesses and masses of the linings. Listening tests were then made, and it was found that the unlined system did suffer from objectionable hangover. This hangover or metallic ringing was evident with percussive or rapidly decaying sounds such as certain kinds of drums, the male speaking voice, and especially with the explosive sound created by flicking a phonograph stylus with the finger. The hangover was not evident with either of the lined systems, showing that the linings used provided sufficient damping to eliminate audible hangover. In fact, the felt-lined system did not sound appreciably better or worse than the corrugated-cardboard-lined system. However, although it was not apparent when listening to music or voice reproduction, the asphalt felt is a more effective deadener than the corrugated cardboard, as revealed by rapping the knuckles against the walls.

Resonant Frequencies

When a wall resonance is adversely affecting the system response, the performance will generally be improved by increasing the resonant frequency. This may be accomplished by using a wall material with a higher stiffness-to-weight ratio, by changing the shape of the wall, by increasing the wall thickness, or by bracing the wall. The increased resonant frequencies are beneficial for three reasons. One is that most methods of increasing resonant frequency also increase the wall damping. For example, bracing a wall or increasing its thickness raises the acoustic resistance of the wall as well as its stiffness. The second reason is that the absorption of any absorbent filling, partition, or lining in the enclosure increases with frequency in the low-frequency region. Thus as frequency is raised, more sound radiated by the back of the speaker is absorbed, and consequently less strikes the walls. The third reason is that flat sources radiate sound more directionally as frequency is increased. A simple flat sound source emitting a wavelength that is long, compared to the dimensions of the source, radiates

[3] *Ibid.*

essentially uniformly in all directions. As the emitted frequency increases and the wavelength grows short compared to the dimensions of the source, the radiation concentrates into a narrow beam perpendicular to the plane of the source. Thus, at low frequencies, a loudspeaker in a closed-box enclosure is essentially an omnidirectional radiator. If one of the enclosure walls has a low-frequency resonance, permitting sound radiation from the wall at frequencies near this resonance, this radiation will interfere with that from the front of the loudspeaker, changing the system frequency response at any listening position. If, on the other hand, the first wall resonance occurs at a sufficiently high frequency, both the wall and the loudspeaker will be directional radiators. The loudspeaker will radiate primarily in the forward direction, and the wall will radiate in whatever direction it is facing. If it is not facing in the same direction as the loudspeaker, the interference between the two sources will be greatly reduced, compared to that at low frequencies. Further, since radiation from the back of the loudspeaker will also be directional, the side and front walls will receive less sound that at low frequencies provided that the enclosure contains some absorbing material.

Examples of the improvement achieved through increased wall resonant frequency are shown in Figs. 4 and 5. These response curves are of a closed-box system with adequately rigid walls except for one 12 in. × 18 in. test panel. In Fig. 4 this panel was eighth-inch corrugated cardboard. A wooden brace across the middle of the long dimension is seen to smooth the response considerably. A brace across the other dimension would have been even better. In Fig. 5 it is apparent that adequacy is achieved by increasing the thickness of a quarter-inch plywood panel to half an inch.

Although it is desirable for all the enclosure walls to have high fundamental resonant frequencies, it is also desirable that these frequencies should be staggered. That is, if possible, no two walls should have the same fundamental resonant frequency. If they do, both will have maximum transmission at the same frequency; and the effect on the system response will be considerably worse than if the resonances were different. The resonances of two walls may be made different by making them different sizes. Obviously, a cube is a poor choice of shape for an enclosure because all six walls are then the same size. With a rectangular enclosure, it is recommended that the height, width, and depth differ from each other by at least twenty per cent whenever possible. Even when this is done, opposite pairs of walls are the same size. With the front and back walls, this does not matter because the resonance of the front wall is usually changed by mounting the loudspeaker on it. The side walls and the top and bottom walls may be given different resonances by making them different thicknesses or of different materials or by bracing one better than the other.

In the rest of this section, the effects of various parameters on wall resonant frequencies will be discussed.

Wall Thickness.—Theoretically, the resonant frequencies of a homogeneous flat wall are proportional to the thickness.[4,5] In practice this relation will hold approximately but not exactly, because of edge and surface effects and material differences. For example, the fundamental resonant frequency of a 12 in. × 18 in. panel of quarter-inch fir plywood clamped at the edges was measured to be 155 cps, while that of a half-inch panel was 295 cps.

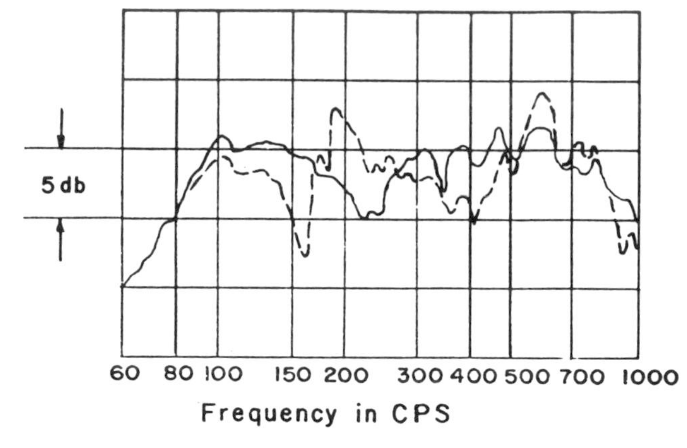

FIG. 4. Frequency response of a closed-box system with rigid walls except for one ⅛-inch corrugated cardboard wall.

Incidentally, a double wall of two identical panels adjacent to each other is not usually as good as a single panel of the same thickness as the pair, because although the damping of the former may be greater by virtue of friction between the adjacent surfaces, the stiffness of the thick single panel is considerably greater than that of the pair. Of course, such a pair is usually considerably better than one of the pair alone.

Wall Area.—For a given wall shape, structure, material, and thickness, the wall resonant frequencies are theoretically

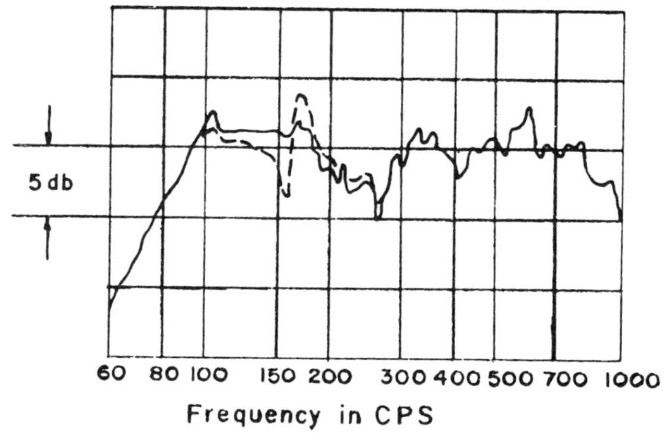

FIG. 5. Frequency response of a closed-box system with rigid walls except for one thin plywood wall.

[4] S. Timoshenko, *Vibration Problems in Engineering* (D. Van Nostrand Co., Inc., Princeton, N. J., 1955), third edition, p. 446.
[5] J. N. Macduff and R. P. Felgar, "Vibration Design Charts," *Am. Soc. Mech. Engrs. Paper No.* 56-A-75, p. 1 (July, 1956).

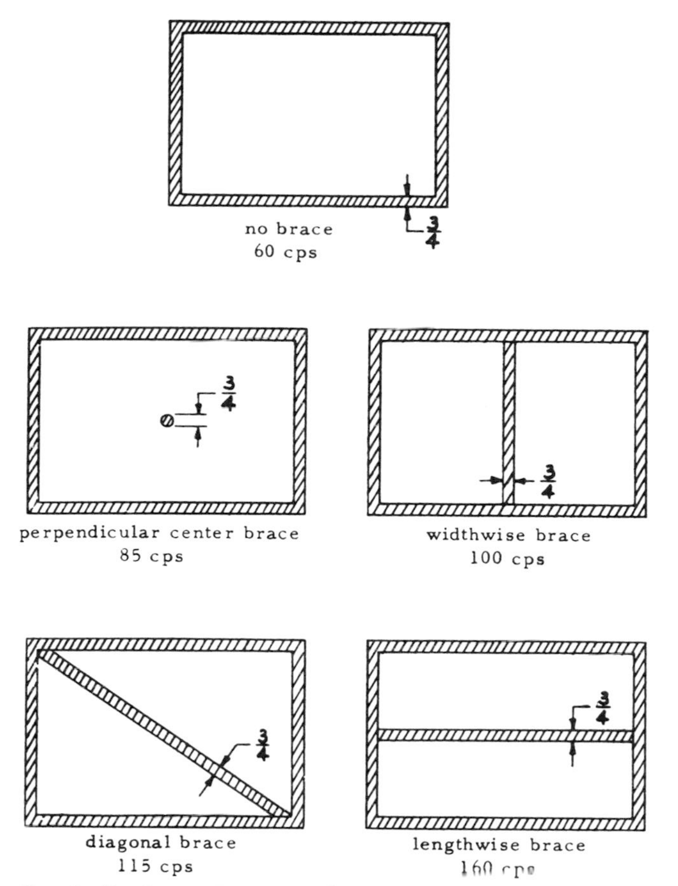

FIG. 6 Fundamental resonant frequency of a 12 in. × 18 in. × 0.020 in. steel panel, clamped at the edges, with various braces.

inversely proportional to the wall area.[6,7] Thus, a large wall generally must be thicker or better braced than a small one, for equivalent performance.

Wall Shape.—The resonant frequencies are not independent of wall shape. A long, narrow wall will have a much higher fundamental resonant frequency than a square wall of the same area,[8,9] and walls with unequal dimensions are therefore to be preferred. When one dimension is several times as large as the other, the fundamental resonance is relatively insensitive to small changes in the long dimension, but quite sensitive to changes in the short dimension. In fact, the frequency is theoretically almost proportional to the reciprocal of the square of the short dimension.

Wall Material.—Other factors being equal, a wall made of a material with a higher stiffness-to-weight ratio will have higher resonant frequencies. More precisely, the resonant frequencies are proportional to the square root of the ratio of Young's modulus to the material density.[10] One way of markedly increasing this ratio is to depart from the normal homogeneous wall construction and use a low-density, relatively low-stiffness core faced on both sides with a thin sheet of high-stiffness material. The resulting wall sandwich will not weigh much more than the core but will be much stiffer. The reason for this is that most of the bending stiffness of a panel results from the tensional stiffness of the material close to the surfaces. The core material may be porous or cellular in nature in order to reduce its density. Examples of possible core materials are soft wood, particle board, cellulose fiber, stiff foam plastics, and honeycomb cells or tubes of paper, metal, or plastic perpendicular to the panel faces. Examples of possible face materials are metal, plastic, hardboard, and paper.

At the present time, the most practical and immediately useful variety of sandwich panel appears to be honeycomb paper. This material is quite inexpensive and has a tremendous stiffness-to-weight ratio. Half-inch honeycomb paper is acoustically almost as good as half-inch plywood, yet it weighs about one-seventh as much.

Bracing.—The wall resonant frequencies may be raised by bracing the wall. Obviously, for a brace to be effective, its stiffness in the direction perpendicular to the wall surface must be adequate. The best kind of brace is one that is fastened along its length to the wall and completely bisects the inside surface of the wall into two areas. As a general rule, the brace should be positioned to minimize the diameter of circles that can be inscribed in each of these two resulting areas. Thus, with a rectangular wall, the best position for a single brace is parallel to the long dimension of the wall and roughly at the center of the short dimension. Such a brace breaks up the wall into two essentially independent panels, each of which has a fundamental resonant frequency more than twice as high as that of the unbraced wall, if the brace is stiff enough. The brace should be placed slightly off center to cause the resonant frequencies of the two resulting panels to be slightly different, so that at no frequency are they both transmitting appreciable sound. A good choice of position would be five per cent of the distance from the center to one edge of the short dimension. A brace parallel to the long dimension of the wall is considerably more effective than one parallel to the short dimension or one along a diagonal, especially if the wall is long and narrow. In situations where more than one brace is needed, the best arrangement is with all braces parallel to the long dimension and spaced so as to divide the wall into panels of slightly unequal widths.

In some instances it may be desirabe to use braces between and perpendicular to opposite walls of an enclosure. Such a brace is not nearly as effective as a side brace if it does not contact much wall area, but the brace itself need not be as rigid as a side brace because it is being stretched and squeezed rather than bent. Although a single brace of this kind between opposite wall surfaces is probably not worth while, it would be effective in stiffening side braces if terminated at the centers of the latter. Of course, effective results could be achieved by using a large number of perpendicular braces distributed over the wall surface.

Tests were made with 0.020 in. × 12 in. × 18 in. steel panels clamped at the edges and braced in various ways.

---

[6] *Ibid.*

[7] Timoshenko, *loc. cit.*

[8] Macduff and Felgar, *op. cit.*, Table 4.

[9] R. F. S. Hearmon, "The Frequency of Vibration of Rectangular Isotropic Plates," *J. Appl. Mech., Trans. Am. Soc. Mech. Engrs.* 74, 402 (1952).

[10] Timoshenko, *loc. cit.*

The bracing methods and corresponding fundamental resonant frequencies were as follows (see Fig. 6): without brace, 60 cps; wooden brace perpendicular to panel at its center, 85 cps; brace glued along entire short dimension of panel and at center of long dimension, 100 cps; brace glued along entire diagonal of panel, 115 cps; brace glued along entire long dimension and at center of short dimension, 160 cps.

Wall Curvature.—As mentioned previously, a long, narrow wall is preferable to a wall with equal dimensions, for a given thickness and area, because of the higher resonant frequencies of the former. Another important shape factor that may sometimes be varied is the degree of flatness of the wall surface. A wall that is curved in one or both dimensions is more rigid perpendicular to its surface than a flat wall, provided that it is adequately fastened along its edges. Consequently, it has a higher fundamental resonant frequency. The rigidity increases with increasing curvature. Basically, the increased stiffness results from the fact that the curvature increases the wall tension for a given flexure. The improvement of a wall with reasonable curvature over a flat one is so great that a curved panel of thin cardboard is frequently acoustically adequate.

The phenomenal improvement effected by a small amount of curvature is demonstrated by the following experiment with a 12 in. × 18 in. panel of 0.020 in. steel clamped at the edges. With a perpendicular brace at its center, the fundamental resonant frequency of the panel was 85 cps. When this brace was lengthened ⅜ in. to force the center of the panel outward, the resonant frequency rose to 175 cps.

If the use of curved walls is carried to its logical extreme, an enclosure results that is a surface of revolution such as a sphere, cylinder, or double cone. Enclosures of these shapes made of thin cardboard or sheet metal can give performance equivalent to that of rectangular enclosures of thick plywood. To test the concept of increased wall stiffness through cylindrical design, four loudspeaker systems were built and tested. All used 7 in. loudspeakers of the same kind with resonant frequencies of about 80 cps, mounted in the same manner in enclosures 18¼ in. long inside, one cubic foot in internal volume, and with ½ in. plywood end walls. Two enclosures were rectangular, one having ½ in. plywood side walls and the other ⅛ in. solid cardboard side walls. The other two were cylindrical, one having ⅛ in. solid cardboard side wall and the other a 0.020 in. steel side wall. Frequency-response curves were made in an anechoic chamber, and it was found that all units performed essentially identically except the rectangular cardboard model, which had a series of severe peaks and dips in the low-frequency region corresponding to wall resonances which could be detected by placing the fingers against the walls.

Loudspeaker Mounting.—When a hole is cut in a wall and a loudspeaker is mounted over it, the fundamental resonant frequency of the wall will usually be changed. The reason for this is that the loudspeaker is heavier and may be more or less stiff than the equivalent area of the usual wall material, and the effective stiffness and the mass of the wall are therefore changed, changing the resonance.

If the loudspeaker is small compared to the wall dimensions and is mounted near the center of the wall, the resonance will usually be lowered. This can be overcome by bracing the wall close to the loudspeaker or by moving the loudspeaker close to an edge or, preferably, corner of the wall. If, on the other hand, the loudspeaker diameter is almost as large as the smaller wall dimension, the desirable effect of raising the wall resonance may result.

WALL TESTS

An apparatus was constructed for testing the comparative sound transmission characteristics of 12 in. × 18 in. panels of various materials, thicknesses, shapes, and structures. A total of about ninety different panels was tested with this apparatus. It consists of a box with external dimensions of 18 in. × 13 in. × 14 in., made of ¾ in. plywood. A 12 in. loudspeaker is mounted in one of the 14 in. × 18 in. faces. In one of the 13 in. × 18 in. faces there is a 10½ in. × 16½ in. opening over which the test panels may be fastened.

Machine screws were partly embedded in the front edges of the opening, and screw holes were made in the test panels so that the latter could be clamped in place over the opening by wing nuts. Aluminum channel strips ¾ in. wide and 13/32 in. thick, with screw holes, were placed along the front panel edges under the wing nuts to hold the panel edges securely clamped along their length. Strips of foam polyurethane, ¾ in. wide and ⅛ in. thick, were cemented along the front edges of the opening to provide an airtight seal between them and the panel. The box was loosely filled with creped cellulose wadding to reduce standing waves.

A second box, with external dimensions of 18 in. × 14 in. × 12 in. was also made of ¾ in. plywood. This box contains no loudspeaker, but one 14 in. × 18 in. side is open. The edges of this side were covered with strips of polyurethane as above, and the box was loosely filled with creped cellulose wadding.

To test the relative sound transmission of a panel, the second box is placed open-side-up on a resilient pad and the first box is placed loudspeaker-side-down on top of the second. Thus, the front of the loudspeaker radiates into the second box while the back radiates into the first. When a test panel is clamped in place over the opening in the first box, sound radiated by the loudspeaker can emerge into the room only by passing through the panel or the walls of the boxes. With a test panel in place, a sinusoidal signal of varying frequency and constant voltage is fed to the loudspeaker. A microphone about two inches in front of the center of the test panel picks up sound radiated by the panel, and the output of the microphone is fed to a graphic recorder that makes a graph of output as a function of frequency. The resulting graph is then compared to that made with a ¾ in. plywood panel and to that made with no panel.

Another kind of test was applied to many of the panels. This was a test of the effects of the panel on the response of a loudspeaker system of which it is a part. Figures 2 through 5 were made with this apparatus. For this test, the first box is placed by itself panel-side-up on the resilient pad, with the loudspeaker facing forward. With the microphone a few inches in front of the loudspeaker, a graph of the system frequency response is made and compared to that made with a ¾ in. plywood panel and to that made with no panel. In addition, the directional characteristics of the system may be investigated by moving the microphone to different positions.

As a guide to the selection of wall materials for a particular application, some of the panels tested are grouped below according to the thickness of plywood that most closely approximates their performance. Of course, any panel may be improved by bracing.

Comparable to ¾ in. plywood: 1 in. honeycomb paper, convex 0.020 in. steel or aluminum coated with mastic, ¾ in. wood particle board, ½ in. wood particle board with 1/32 in. hardwood veneer glued to both sides.

Comparable to ½ in. plywood: ½ in. honeycomb paper, ½ in. plasterboard (U. S. Gypsum *Sheetrock*), ⅞ in. cellulose fiberboard, ½ in. wood particle board, ⅜ in. wood particle board with 1/32 in. hardwood veneer glued to both sides.

Comparable to 11/32 in. plywood: ⅜ in. plasterboard, ½ in. cellulose fiberboard, convex 0.020 in. steel or aluminum, flat 0.020 in. steel or aluminum plus ⅛ in. asphalt felt, convex 0.068 in. chipboard (cardboard), 11/32 in. wood particle board, 7/32 in. wood particle board with 1/32 in. hardwood veneer glued to one side.

Comparable to ¼ in. plywood: ¼ in. wood particle board, ⅛ in. tempered hardboard, 3/16 in. solid cardboard, 0.020 in. steel plus 7/32 in. corrugated cardboard, ¼ in. two-ply corrugated cardboard, cylindrically curved 0.068 in. chipboard.

SUMMARY

The basic function of enclosure walls is to prevent significant passage of sound through them. More specifically, wall vibration should not be sufficient to worsen the steady-state system response, and should cease soon after the loudspeaker stops moving in order to avoid hangover.

Normally, except in the vicinity of its first few resonant frequencies, even a quarter-inch plywood wall is adequately stiff and heavy to prevent deleterious transmission. Most walls cause trouble only near their first few resonant frequencies, the fundamental mode being the worst offender.

Adequate performance at the fundamental wall resonance depends on the use of sufficient absorbing material within the enclosure, sufficient damping of the wall material, and a sufficiently high resonant frequency. The damping of a thin wall of poorly damped material may be improved by bonding to the wall a layer of material with better inherent damping. The fundamental resonant frequency of a wall may be raised by using a material with a higher stiffness-to-weight ratio, by decreasing the wall area or at least the shorter surface dimension, by increasing the wall thickness, by bracing the wall, by curving the wall, or by replacing a homogeneous wall with one having a sandwich structure with stiff faces and a lightweight core. If possible, the wall resonances should be staggered so that no two walls have the same resonant frequency.

ACKNOWLEDGMENT

The author wishes to acknowledge the guidance, encouragement, and suggestions by E. S. White and J. E. Bridges.

THE AUTHOR

Peter W. Tappan received his B.S. degree in physics in 1952 and his M.S. degree in 1958 from Illinois Institute of Technology. He was employed by Motorola Inc. in 1951 and later that year joined the Physics Department of Armour Research Foundation, where he did research until 1956 on such projects as an X-ray intensification system, special tape recording heads, an electronic piano, and high-powered public address systems.

Mr. Tappan then went to the Warwick Manufacturing Corporation where he has been responsible for the acoustical research of that company and has worked on the design and development of speaker systems, phonograph pick-ups, and stereophonic and pseudostereophonic equipment.

Mr. Tappan is a member of the Audio Engineering Society, the Acoustical Society of America, the Chicago Acoustical and Audio Group, and the IRE Professional Group on Audio.

A Method of Testing Loudspeakers with Random Noise Input*

EDGAR VILLCHUR
Acoustic Research, Inc., Cambridge, Massachusetts

BEFORE discussing the subject indicated in the title, it is necessary to answer two questions. These are: a) what is the function of loudspeakers? and b) can loudspeakers be tested for the excellence with which they perform this function?

The answer to the second question is entirely dependent on the answer to the first. If we consider the purpose of loudspeakers to be the creation of pleasant, exciting, or dramatic sounds in their own right, then it should be clear that loudspeakers cannot be tested objectively. The best of wine tasters disagree. You cannot take a wine from a particular vineyard, put it into a test tube, and do a chemical analysis that will tell you with certainty whether particular people will prefer this wine to one from a different vineyard and/or vintage.

The supposed inability of objective testing to reveal the quality of a loudspeaker has become a first principle among the "hi-fi" writers and dealers who advise the public on the esoteric mysteries of sound reproduction. Explanations usually have to do with hearing differences in different individuals, differences of taste, and differences in room environment. All of these explanations make good sense once we accept the hypothesis that a loudspeaker is a new musical instrument, a creator rather than a reproducer of sound.

On the other hand, if the function of loudspeakers is merely to recreate with maximum accuracy sounds that have already had an objective existence, the explanations of why loudspeakers cannot be tested appear quite thin. Differences in individual hearing have no more to do with comparing a facsimile to its original than differences in vision affect the objective accuracy of a matching sample of color. The same hearing aberrations are brought into play with both the live and reproduced sound, and do not affect the process of matching. Taste may determine whether a listener prefers one or another symphony orchestra, or a small string group to a large brass band, but it cannot influence objective determination of the simple accuracy of reproduction. Room environment profoundly affects the final acoustic output of any sound-reproducing system, but this effect might just as well be used to establish the fact that amplifiers, pickups, needles, or turntables are not subject to objective evaluation. If there is to be compensation for room environment, it should not be sought in loudspeakers.

Taste can be a valid element in establishing preferences of one reproducing component over another in two instances:
1. Where the reproduced sound is accepted as an entity in itself, with little relation to the world of live concert music.
2. Where a choice must be made between different kinds of inaccuracy—for example, intermodulation distortion *vs* transient ringing.

In the late 1930's the Museum of Modern Art had a special exhibition in which American paintings were exhibited next to color reproductions of the same paintings in the same size. In many cases it was impossible to tell the difference, or the differences were very small. An observer could judge the accuracy of reproduction independently of his artistic taste, the kind of lighting employed, or whether

* Presented October 14, 1960 at the Twelfth Annual Convention of the Audio Engineering Society, New York.

he had astigmatic vision. The kind of evaluation that was called upon was entirely different from that involved in choosing between one painting and another, or between a Stradivari and a Guarneri violin.

The testing method to be described here bears a similarity to the Museum of Modern Art's exhibition efforts. In testing reproducing accuracy, this testing method makes direct reference to the original sound. Its genesis is in two types of experience—the staging of "live *vs* recorded" public concerts, and the use of white noise input for subjective loudspeaker testing.

In the live *vs* recorded concerts with which the author was associated, a string ensemble would record sections of a movement in a non-reverberant environment. Then, at the concert, live playing would be alternated with electronic reproduction at the same level. This was a direct A-B test between the live music and the reproduced music, with no time lag. Even the musical beat was not interrupted. Small differences in timbre, in transient attack and decay, or in other elements were painfully evident when something was wrong in the record-reproduce chain.

The use of white noise input, the second type of experience referred to, had been made standard procedure at the author's company (and undoubtedly others) as part of the testing program for speaker development. Some of the development personnel had worked up to the point where they thought they were experienced enough in listening to white noise to differentiate between "good" white noise and "bad" white noise. Nevertheless, during each test there was doubt and new soul searching in trying to decide which kind of noise best predicted reproducing accuracy. The test signal was, after all, produced by an electrical generator. It started out as a purely electrical signal without independent existence as sound, and there was no sure way of knowing which sound was right.

Each of these test techniques makes up part of a very powerful investigative tool. The white noise technique is able to reveal even subtle distortions in the texture of reproduced sound related to ringing, uneven presentation of acoustical energy in different parts of the frequency spectrum, dispersion, etc. The live *vs* recorded technique establishes a reference standard, providing validation of the test technique. The two together make up what has proven to be a very sensitive and reliable test for speaker evaluation.

The basic technique is to establish an acoustical reference sound (using a particular white noise generator and a particuiar speaker), and then to stage a live *vs* recorded display as was done with the string quartet.

A white noise generator and amplifier provide an input signal which is fed simultaneously to the "reference" speaker (placed in an anechoic chamber) and to one channel of a stereo tape recorder. The acoustical output of the reference speaker is picked up by the microphone and recorded on the second channel of the tape, as shown in Fig. 1. We then have a two-track tape in which one channel represents the electrical input signal that was fed to the speaker, and the other track represents a recording of the sound produced by that speaker.

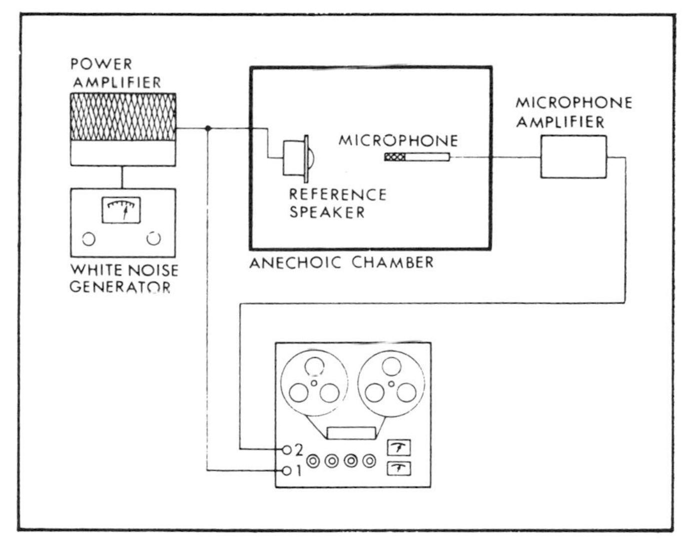

Fig. 1. Diagram of the test recording setup. The white noise generator, amplifier, and reference speaker make up a reference acoustical generator, whose sound is recorded in an anechoic chamber.

In the live *vs* recorded display the same reference speaker must be employed as standard, mounted on the same baffle. When the recording of the purely electrical input (Channel 1) is fed to the reference speaker, the sound produced is the same sound that had objective existence in the anechoic chamber, before it was picked up by the microphone. It is as though the live quartet performed again, during the live *vs* recorded display, the music that it had played when the original recording was being made. The system producing the random noise may be thought of as a reference acoustical generator.

The second channel represents a recording of the random noise that existed in the chamber. When the second channel is fed to a speaker under test, at the same volume level as is used for the reference sound, we have a true live *vs* recorded comparison: The speaker under test is expected to imitate the reference noise, working from a very accurate recording. If the speaker is perfect the sound will be the same as that from the reference speaker. The other elements in the system, assuming well matched channels in the tape record-reproduce system, will have little effect in creating differences in sound. A diagram of the test display setup is shown in Fig. 2.

If, on the other hand, the speaker under test has a particular type of coloration, this will be clearly evident. In the live *vs* recorded displays with a string quartet it was usually impossible to detect the switch-over from live to recorded sound. The verisimilitude of reproduced random noise, however, was never so close that the difference could not be detected. With the best speakers tested the differences were not too great; with lower quality speakers the differences were so gross that it seemed as though the speaker under test were being fed by a completely different type of noise, sometimes with a concentration of energy at some part of the frequency spectrum that was almost identifiable as a tone.

Once we had familiarized ourselves with the technique

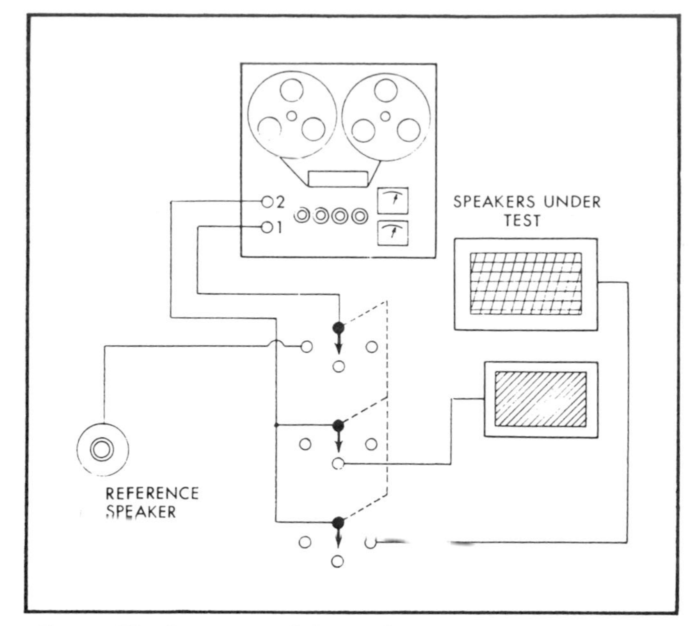

FIG. 2. The live *vs* recorded test display. The reference sound is recreated by playing Channel 1 of the tape through the reference speaker. This is the "live" display. The speaker under test is then asked to imitate the reference "live" sound from Tape Channel 2.

we then tried the same procedure with musical program material for the original electrical input. The results were similar although not quite as sensitive, and the kind of coloration predicted by the random noise comparisons was clearly present.

The above is the bare outline of the test technique, and a few comments on some of the details are in order. For one thing, the entire test relies on the ability to make a recording in a highly anechoic environment. If any reverberation is present in the recording made from the microphone, this will be introduced as a false note in the comparison display, an element not present on the channel that was recorded directly from the electrical generator. The reverberation imposed on the sound during the display must be the same for both the live and the recorded noise. As a matter of fact, the staging of this display in a normally reverberant environment is a distinct advantage in that integration of the sound radiated by the speaker at different angles from the axis is automatically taken into account.

The speaker under test may be of any type, and may consist of any number of separate radiators, but the reference speaker must be a single radiator. Theoretically it is not even necessary that we know what the reference speaker is, since we are only concerned with reproducing its sound, whatever that is. In practice the better the reference speaker the more sensitive the test. It is particularly important that the reference speaker have a good and uniform dispersion pattern. A multi-speaker system cannot be used as a reference speaker because the interference effects between the different drivers would hopelessly confuse the situation. These interference effects create severe aberrations of frequency response at the microphone in an anechoic environment, but they have little effect on the total sound in a reverberant room. We respond more to the integrated reflected room sound from a speaker than we do to the pressure that would represent the direct sound from that speaker at a particular radiating angle. In other words, in a reverberant environment we tend to hear the total acoustical power output of a speaker, rather than the pressure that would exist at our listening position in an anechoic environment.

One of the most critical elements in using this test technique successfully is the determination of the angle at which to place the microphone in relation to the reference speaker. It is necessary to choose a position for the microphone at such an angle to the speaker that radiation at this angle will fairly represent the total power response of the speaker. A perfect reproducer will then provide an accurate restaging of the original performance.

For example, suppose we have a speaker with flat high-frequency response to 20 kc on-axis, but whose response shows severe roll-off above 7 kc as soon as we get a little off-axis. Such a speaker radiates little significant energy above 7 kc, and when used in a normally reverberant room sounds that way from any listening position. If we made the recording on-axis and played this recording back through a perfect reproducer, the "recorded" sound would have much more high-frequency energy than the "live" sound. Conversely, a speaker may have relatively smooth response on-axis and severe peaks and dips off-axis. The greater the difference between on-axis and off-axis performance, the less suitable the speaker is to act as reference in this type of test. When we do find a speaker whose off-axis performance is not too different from its on-axis performance, we must then find the microphone position which will give a pressure recording most representative of the total integrated power output of the reference speaker.

In the case of the speaker used for the AES demonstration—a 2 in. mid-range dome-type direct radiator—we found 27½° off-axis (in any direction) to be the best. We arrived at this figure by experimental trial-and-error.

Both tape channels were recorded at the same recording level, and extreme care was taken to keep the playback levels of the reference speaker and of the speaker under test the same. This is not as easy as it sounds, because differences in coloration and frequency emphasis affect the listener's impression of loudness. Actually the level of the speaker under test was adjusted until the sound was most similar to the reference sound.

The two tape recorder channels were matched so that the total record-reproduce difference was no more than ½ db at any frequency. The matching of these channels is, of course, more important than the range of response, although it is desirable to have the complete frequency range.

The creation by a loudspeaker of an exact facsimile of sound on the spot, as it were, is not an exact test of its total function in home reproducing systems. A home loudspeaker system must recreate, within the home acoustical environment, both the original raw sound and the particular "mantle of reverberation" surrounding that sound in the recording hall, an element involving both time and space. The listener sitting in his living room will then hear something similar to what he would hear if he were at a concert. Success in anechoic facsimile reproduction does not necessarily solve the entire problem. Our tests indicate that it does, at the least, solve most of the problem, and that success or lack of success in facsimile reproduction, especially of random noise, is an excellent index of loudspeaker quality.

The test described is especially useful in comparing two or more speakers—to assign relative evaluations to each, or to test a particular design variation. The reliability of the test reading is very high in spite of its subjective nature because of the existence of the reference sound, and because of the absence of a time lag between comparisons. The very subjectivity serves to isolate those factors significant to aural perception.

The equipment used for recording and display at the AES convention demonstration consisted of the following: 1. H. H. Scott Random Noise Generator, Model 811A; 2. Dynakit Mark III Power Amplifier; 3. Acoustic Research 2″ AR-3 Mid-range Tweeter; 4. Acoustic Research's anechoic chamber; 5. Western Electric 640 AA Microphone (equalized to 20 kc); 6. Audio Instrument Company Microphone Preamplifier and Power Supply, Models 16W and 16P1; 7. Ampex Tape Recorder, Model 350-2, modified for channel matching; and 8. Sample speakers for testing—AR-3t, and unidentified "black box."

I wish to express my appreciation to Roy Allison, chief engineer and plant manager of Acoustic Research, for his invaluable assistance in setting up these tests, and to Mike Saslow, now of the University of California, for his suggestions with regard to the use of dual-track tape.

THE AUTHOR

Edgar Villchur received the M.S. degree in education from the City College of New York in 1940 and was a part-time instructor in electronics at New York University (Division of General Education) from 1951 to 1956.

He is president and director of research at Acoustic Research, Inc., a company that manufacturers loudspeaker systems and turntables of his designs and patents.

Mr. Villchur is the author of "Handbook of Sound Reproduction" and "Reproduction of Sound." He has contributed articles to several magazines and has lectured before various engineering groups. He is a Fellow of the Audio Engineering Society.

Constant Directional Characteristics from a Line Source Array*

David L. Klepper
Bolt Beranek and Newman Inc., Cambridge, Massachusetts

and

Douglas W. Steele
Massachusetts Institute of Technology, Cambridge, Massachusetts

A constant-length line-source loudspeaker system will have directional characteristics that vary with frequency. This paper discusses the use of acoustical loading to effectively decrease the length of the line-source with increasing frequency, maintaining nearly constant directional characteristics.

Line-source loudspeaker arrays, often called "column" loudspeakers, have recently become of great interest to sound-system contractors and equipment manufacturers in this country. These loudspeaker systems have been very popular in Europe because they could be easily assembled of relatively low-priced, cone-type loudspeakers to achieve considerable directivity in one plane. When used to replace conventional, single, cone-type loudspeakers in reverberant spaces (and properly aimed), they often have achieved dramatic improvements in speech intelligibility by apparently "cutting through" the room reverberation. Their greater directivity also gives the appearance of vastly greater efficiency when the listener is on or near on-axis.

Most of the recent commercial American line-source loudspeaker systems have been simple, straight-line arrays of identical type cone loudspeakers connected in some simple series-parallel arrangement. The following difficulties have been noted with nearly all such simple line sources, often reducing the quality of speech reinforcement systems:

1. Great roughness in response and lack of controlled directional characteristics at high frequencies, due to phase differences between individual loudspeakers, in turn caused by cone breakup and often emphasized by the series connections frequently used.

2. Narrowing of the major (on-axis) lobe at higher frequencies and broadening of the coverage at lower frequencies. Olson gives equations[1] for both continuous line sources and a series of point sources that demonstrate why any given line-source loudspeaker system, with all loudspeakers phased together, will have a major-lobe coverage angle that decreases with increasing frequency.

3. Strong minor off-axis lobes or side lobes at high frequencies; again Olson's equations indicate the inevitability of these side lobes, especially for a line actually made up of separated points.

4. Peaky and falling high-frequency response off-axis, even with uniform loudspeakers operating in phase. This is a natural corollary of factors 2 and 3.

Although these defects of most column loudspeakers have not prevented their application to many sound-system problems, the careful sound-system engineer may often desire the better results possible by overcoming these defects. We expect the practical results of such an improvement in line-source array design to include increased feedback rejection with properly placed microphone; more uniform coverage of the desired area; greater reduction of the energy in the reverberant field; and smoother frequency response in the area covered.

The problems caused by random differences in the phase response of the loudspeakers making up the line-source sys-

* Presented October 15, 1962 at the Fourteenth Annual Fall Convention of the Audio Engineering Society, New York.

[1] Harry F. Olson, *Acoustical Engineering,* (D. Van Nostrand Co., New York, 1957), pp. 35-36.

tem can, of course, be reduced by employing loudspeakers of known high quality and uniformity. We have designed a number of custom line-source loudspeaker systems over the past ten years and have generally been pleased with the uniformity of a number of commercially available speakers. We have also usually recommended simple parallel connections of loudspeakers with step-down transformers as required, and attempted to reduce side lobes and broadening main-lobe coverage at high frequencies by the use of padding in the lines feeding the loudspeakers at the outer edges. The improvement has been small, and predictable from Olson's equations for tapered line sources.[2] Curved-line sources have also been constructed and measured, and found to have generally rougher off-axis response at high frequencies.[3]

The only real solution to the problems inherent in a line source is the use of a line source of variable length, namely one that decreases in length with increasing frequency. From theory we know that a uniform line having a length equal to a constant times the wave length should have constant directional characteristics. Three previous attempts to approximate such a variable-length line source in practical loudspeaker systems were:

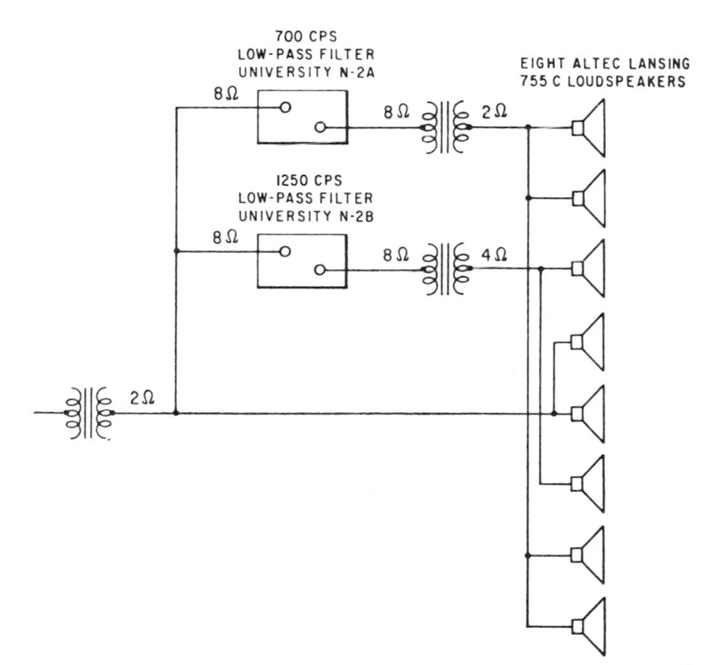

Fig. 1. Line-source loudspeaker with electrical filtering at Franklin Hall, Franklin Institute, Philadelphia, Pa.

1. The Electro-Voice LR-4S system, and similar custom-designed earlier systems employing filter networks to attenuate high-frequency signals at the outer loudspeakers. (For example, the system shown in Fig. 1.)

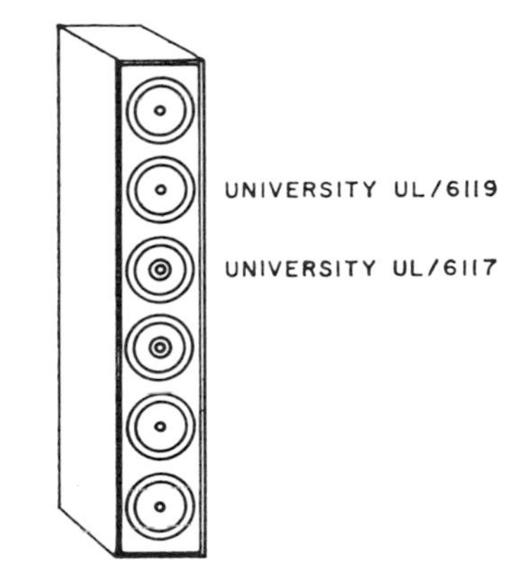

Fig. 2. Line-source loudspeaker with omission of high frequency "whizzer" in outer loudspeakers: University loudspeaker UCS-6.

2. A column using full-range loudspeakers only in the center, with outer loudspeakers that do not reproduce high frequencies. In one commercial example the cone-type of loudspeaker is employed throughout; each outer loudspeaker has its high frequency "whizzer" removed. (See Fig. 2.)

3. The "skewed" column or "barber pole" loudspeaker system, where the increasing directivity of the individual loudspeakers at higher frequencies is employed to reduce the line length.[4] (See Fig. 3.)

The remainder of this paper describes a fourth approach which effects a more precise reduction in the length of the line with increasing frequency. This approach uses acoustic loading in front of the line-source loudspeaker system.

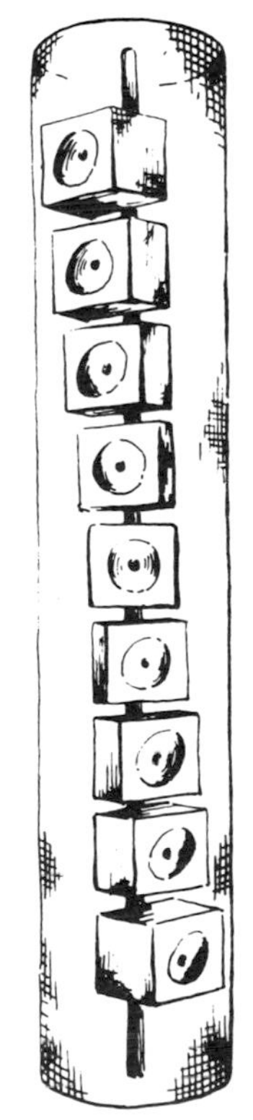

Fig. 3. "Barber pole" line source: Palais Chailot, Philips system.

[2] *Ibid.*, pp 37-39.
[3] M. F. Gardiner and D. L. Klepper, "Recent Studies of Line-Source Loudspeakers." Oral paper presented at the Spring 1960 Meeting of the Acoustical Society of America.
[4] D. Kleis, "Modern Acoustical Engineering," *Philips Technical Review*, **20**, 320 (1958-59).

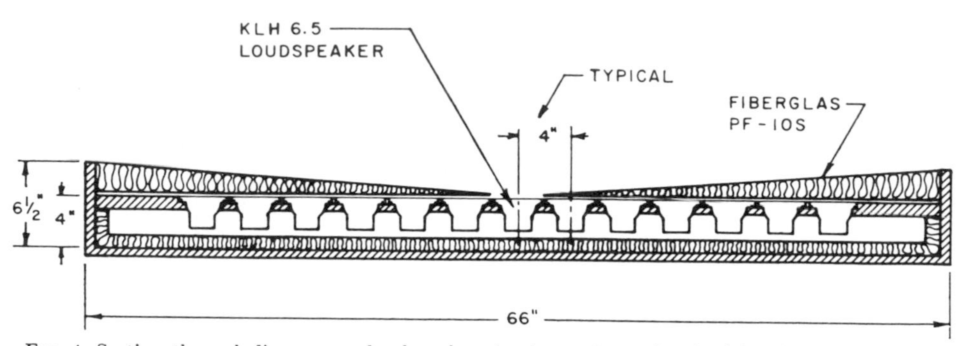

FIG. 4. Section through line-source loudspeaker (enclosure is made of ¾ in plywood).

Figure 4 shows the design of the line source used for the tests. It consists of 13 KLH Model 6.5 loudspeakers connected as parallel groups of three speakers each. The basic theory of operation is that at high frequencies the outer loudspeakers are attenuated so that they contribute essentially no sound energy. In this way the effective length of the line is reduced as frequency increases.

The glass fiber chosen for the wedges which are placed in front of the loudspeakers was O.C.F. PF-105. This particular type was picked because of its large attenuation, light weight, and rapid change of attenuation with frequency.[5] The shape of the wedge was calculated by making the attenuation due to the glass fiber equal to 3 db at the point where the length of the line is 1.75 wavelengths. This was chosen to make the beam width about 30°. Calculations showed that the phase shift due to the glass fiber is very small and would have its main effect in widening the beam (something that is desirable at high frequencies).

The KLH Model 6.5 loudspeaker was chosen for its extremely smooth frequency response and wide dispersion characteristics even at high frequencies. (See Fig. 5.) The wide dispersion is necessary if the line source is to have uniform *horizontal* coverage.

Measurements. Measurements were made with the following pieces of equipment: a Western Electric 640AA condenser microphone; an Altec M-11 microphone preamplifier; a McIntosh 50-w power amplifier; a custom-built polar plotter which automatically plots the polar response in db *vs* angle; a General Radio automatic level recorder; and a General Radio beat frequency oscillator.

The measurements of the line source were made in the M.I.T. anechoic chamber and were of two types. The first was the measurement of polar response at selected frequencies (400, 850, 1700, 2400, 3400, 4800, 6800 cps). The

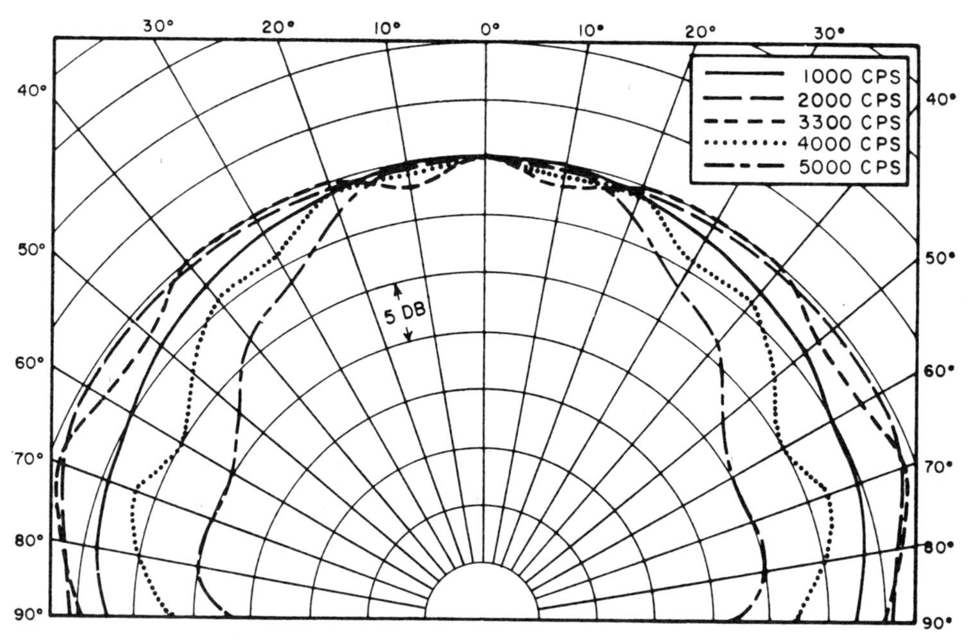

FIG. 5. Polar pattern: KLH 6.5 loudspeaker alone.

[5] The attenuation characteristics of PF-105 and other typical common porous materials are illustrated in: Leo L. Beranek, *Noise Reduction* (McGraw-Hill Book Co., New York, 1960), pp. 270-271, Fig. 12.22.

second was a measurement of frequency response for selected angles (every 10° from $-90°$ to $+90°$). In these tests the microphone was 17 ft from the center of the line source.

Figure 6 shows polar responses of the line source with no glass fiber wedge. As predicted, the beam width drops off with increasing frequency, and side lobes are very large. At 90° and 3400 cps the side lobe would be aimed directly toward the microphone in a typical reinforcement system.

Glass Fiber Loading. The enclosure for the line source was designed so that the glass fiber completely seals the air space in front of the covered speakers. This was done to take advantage of duct attenuation and thus reduce the side lobe at 90° and 3400 cps. Figure 7 shows the polar responses with the two glass fiber wedges in place. The beam widths are much more constant and the polar responses are reasonably smooth. The zero-degree frequency response curve made without the glass fiber wedge shows that between 1 and 3 kc the response of the line dropped about 15 db. (See Fig. 8.) The KLH Model 6.5 loudspeakers used in the lines have a frequency response which is down only 5 db at 19 kc. The reasons for the additional drop in the line source are the absorption of high-frequency energy from the outer loudspeakers and also cone-breakup, causing differences in the phase characteristics of the loudspeakers at high frequencies. Thus, the response is due to the addition of sound power rather than the addition of sound pressure as would be the case of the speakers all remained in phase.

To equalize the on-axis response of the line source, a network was designed to have a rising response above 2 kc to counteract the drop-off due to phase breakup. The response of the network and the resulting on-axis response of the line source are shown in Figs. 9 and 10.

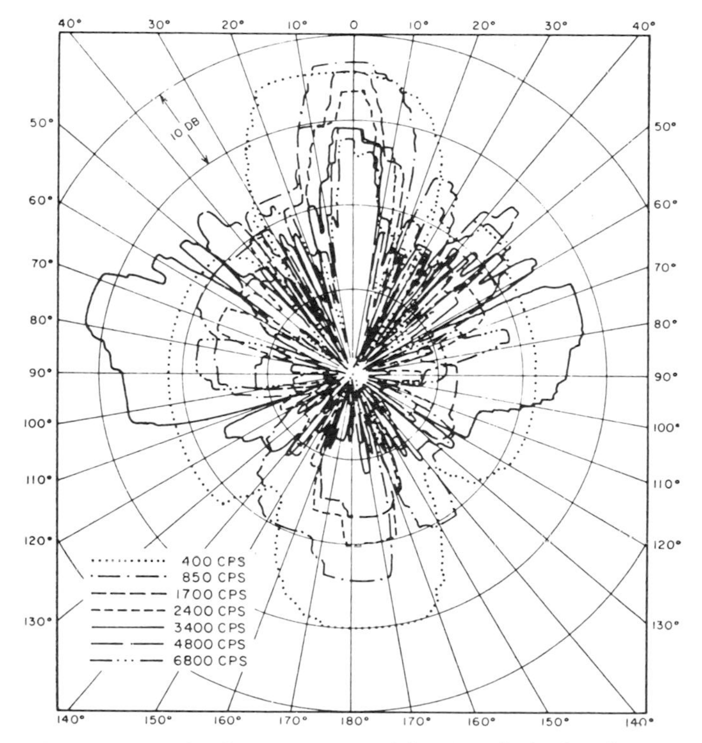

Fig. 6. Polar plot line source containing 13 4-in loudspeakers, no glass fiber.

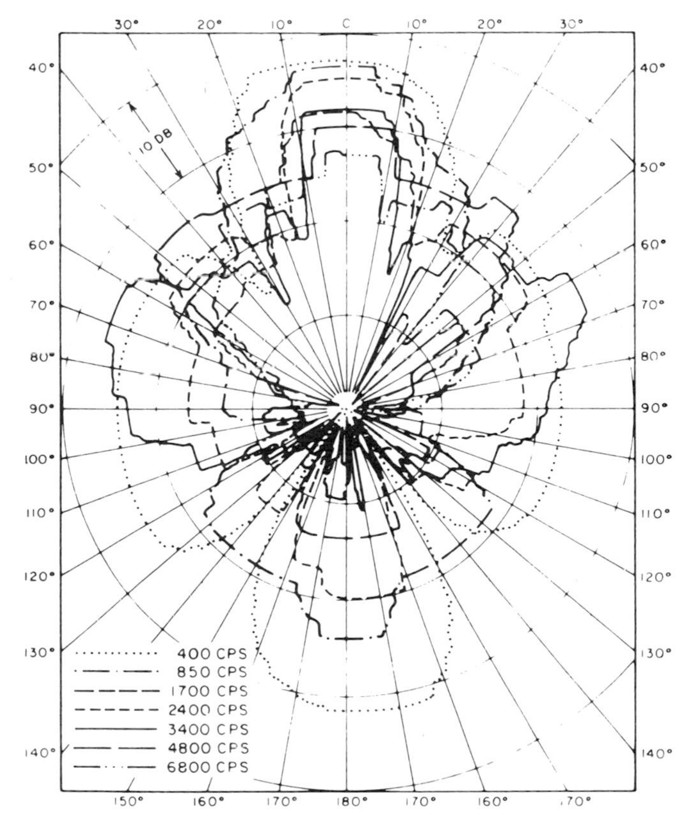

Fig. 7. Polar plot line source containing 13 4-in. loudspeakers with glass fiber wedges.

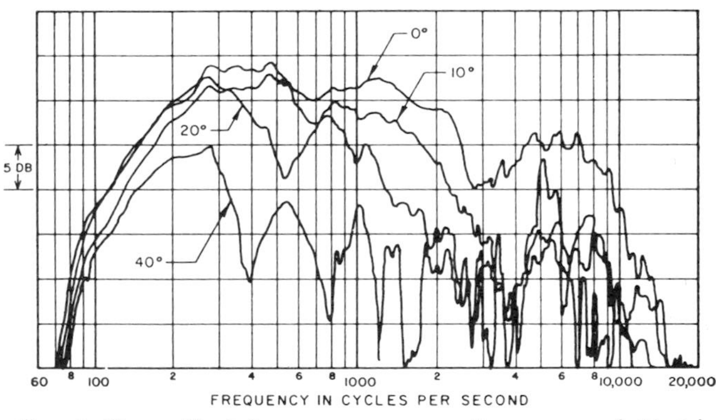

Fig. 8. Unequallized frequency response: line source of 13 4-in. loudspeakers without glass fiber wedges.

Use of the System. The system has been tested as part of a speech reinforcement system for the Tremont Temple Baptist Church in downtown Boston. In this application we assumed a vertical coverage angle of 25° and a horizontal coverage angle of 120°. The performing of the system was judged highly satisfactory with regard to providing coverage in the assigned area.

Further Improvements. In the line source, the spacing

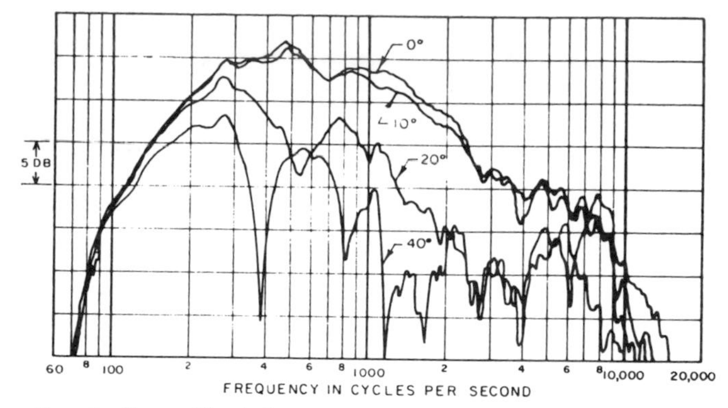

FIG. 9. Unequallized frequency response: line source of 13 4-in. loudspeakers with glass fiber wedges.

between all the speakers is 4 in. To reduce the size of the lobes at 3400 cps, it is recommended that the spacing between the speakers be made unequal to spread the energy of the side lobes over a wider frequency region. This will be tried in the near future.

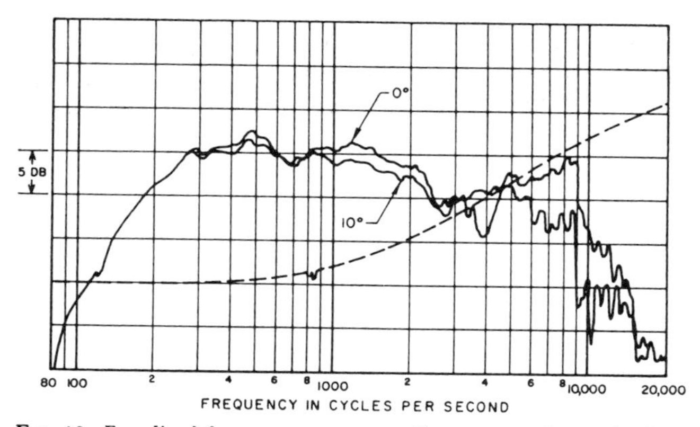

FIG. 10. *Equalized* frequency response: line source of 13 4-in. loudspeakers with glass fiber wedges.

Commercial Applications. This project was conceived as a study project, and we have no intention of marketing the loudspeaker system discussed. The features would appear to be applicable to numerous existing commercial line-source loudspeakers. A patent application is pending.

THE AUTHORS

David L. Klepper received the M.S. degree from the Massachusetts Institute of Technology in 1957; his B.S. degree was earned at the same school. While there, he designed a binaural microphone system that is now widely used for measurements in concert hall acoustics research. His experience also includes work with the U. S. Army Audio/Radio Section of the Psychological Warfare Board, 1955-1956, and with the Mystic Transformer Co., 1953-1954. In 1957 Mr. Klepper joined Bolt Beranek and Newman, Inc., where he currently supervises the integration of sound amplification system design with room acoustic design. His assignments in general architectural acoustics have included the design of numerous concert halls, auditoria, churches and exhibition halls.

Mr. Klepper has published several papers in his field. He is a member of Eta Kappa Nu, the Acoustical Society of America, the Audio Engineering Society, the Institute of Electrical and Electronic Engineers, and the Armed Forces Communications Electronics Association.

•

Douglas Steele was born in Boston, Mass., in 1940. He received the B.S. (1962) and M.S. (1963) degrees from the Massachusetts Institute of Technology, and is currently studying there towards a doctorate. He has worked with Mr. Klepper on line-source loudspeakers as a special course project in 1962, and has prepared a Master's Thesis on the effect of the normal modes of a room on sound reproduction.

Interrelation of Speaker and Amplifier Design*

Victor Brociner and Daniel R. von Recklinghausen
H. H. Scott, Inc., Maynard, Massachusetts

Anticipated improvement of performance has motivated amplifier designs using no audio transformers, particularly in speaker-amplifier combinations. However, direct coupling to the speaker involves several problems that may not all be obvious to the amplifier designer unfamiliar with speaker theory. This paper analyzes some of the pitfalls to be avoided.

INTRODUCTION

In THE continuing search for better sound reproduction it is necessary to analyze the *system* performing this function and not only the individual final links of the chain: the amplifier and the loudspeaker. In order to see what improvements are possible and what limitations there are, one must determine not only the capabilities of the amplifier and the loudspeaker separately but also the effect of one upon the other.

Efforts to improve amplifiers have recently been applied mainly to transistorized amplifiers. Lower power consumption has been obtained, which is of great importance in portable equipment. Class B operation of the output stage has been used to attain efficiency and has greatly reduced standby power. Reduced power consumption has also decreased amplifier weight—another important achievement for portable equipment.

MATCHING AND EQUALIZATION

In recent years, an idea of the 1920's has been revived whereby an amplifier and a loudspeaker comprise a complete integrated system.[1] The principal advantage claimed is that the amplifier and speaker are matched to each other. What *kind* of matching is involved? Impedance matching means that the nominal impedance of the loudspeaker is equal to the nominal load impedance required by the amplifier. This is easily accomplished with separate components. The major improvement that can be made in such a combination is that the amplifier can be designed to correct certain deficiencies that the loudspeaker might have. It must be remembered, though, that frequency response correction is possible only to a moderate degree. If a loudspeaker system has a marked lack of response in a given frequency range, boosting the amplifier response in that region will certainly improve the overall frequency response of the system; however, the power output capability of the amplifier restricts the degree of improvement, and the maximum audible volume of the loudspeaker system may actually be decreased. If the loudspeaker system has sharp resonance peaks, it is theoretically possible to compensate for those by a sharp dip in response of the amplifier. In practice, this is not very repeatable in production because the loudspeaker resonance and absorption resonance in the amplifier may vary in different units and also change with temperature, resulting in an overall response having a dip followed by a sharp peak, or vice versa. It is not only the frequency response of the amplifier that can be used for correction of the frequency response of the loudspeaker system, but also its internal impedance. The impedance curve versus frequency of a speaker is certainly not flat, and any finite impedance of the amplifier will affect the overall frequency response.

---

* Presented October 1963 at the Fifteenth Annual Fall Convention of the Audio Engineering Society, New York.

1. Daniel R. von Recklinghausen, "Mismatch Between Power Amplifiers and Loudspeaker Loads", *J. Audio Eng. Soc.* 6, 220 (1958).

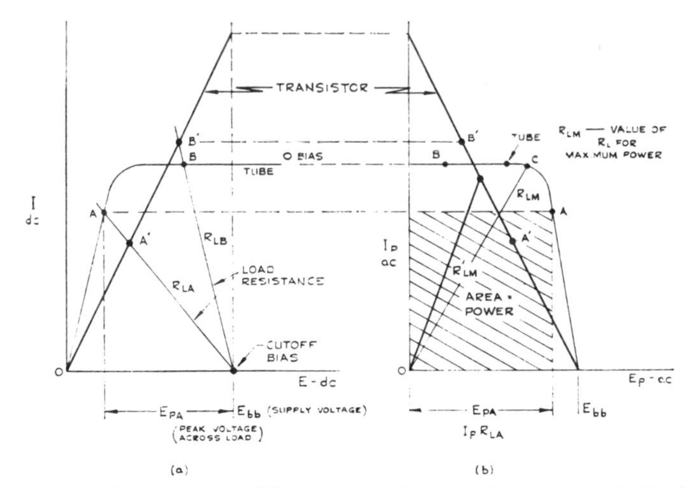

FIG. 1. Maximum possible current swing *vs* voltage across the load with R_L variable.

This raises the question of how a loudspeaker and an amplifier are really matched, and how matching should be accomplished. For this purpose, it is useful to consider the amplifier as a black box and analyze its output capabilities with various resistive and reactive loads. Previous work on this subject[2] has analyzed tube amplifiers, although transistor amplifiers are actually easier to analyze.

AMPLIFIER LOADING

As shown in Fig. 1, a tube amplifier is limited in its available output power primarily by two factors: maximum instantaneous output voltage and maximum instantaneous output current. The current-voltage diagram of such an amplifier is practically a rectangle. The maximum output voltage is definitely limited by the power supply voltage, and the maximum current is limited by the current the output stage can deliver at zero bias. (It is assumed that grid current is not permitted to flow.) In a transistor amplifier, such a current-limiting mechanism does not exist

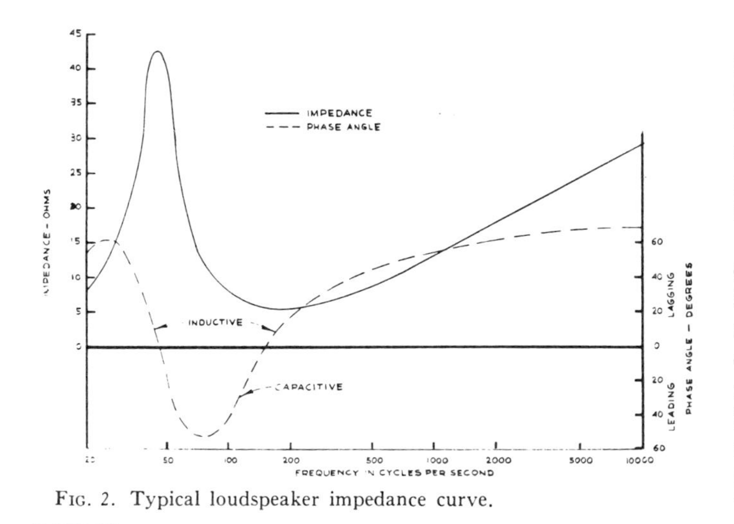

FIG. 2. Typical loudspeaker impedance curve.

2. Frederick V. Hunt, *Electroacoustics. Analysis of Transduction* (New York, John Wiley & Son, Inc.).

since a transistor is basically a current amplifier. Here, the maximum output voltage limitation still exists but the output current with any given load impedance is limited primarily by the saturation resistance of the transistors themselves and any fixed resistors that may be placed in series with the transistors to limit current to a safe value. Maximum output power of an amplifier occurs when the product of maximum available voltage and maximum available current is a maximum. Customarily, a tube amplifier is rated at such a point. (Point *C* in Fig. 1 b.) A transistor amplifier is usually rated and operated at a higher impedance point because operating such an amplifier at its maximum output capability causes overheating of the transistors. Since a speaker is not a purely resistive load and may at certain frequencies be an almost purely reactive load, it is also well to analyze the performance of amplifiers with purely reactive loads. Here, it is found that the performance of a tube amplifier is not drastically changed. A transistor amplifier, in this case, behaves rather like a

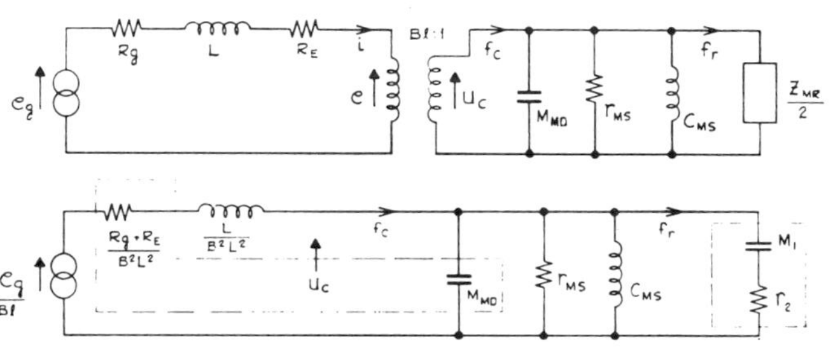

FIG. 3. *Top:* Mobility analog circuit of a direct-radiator speaker and amplifier. *Bottom:* Circuit with electrical quantities referred to the mechanical side and with approximate radiation mobility for low frequencies.

fixed resistor in series with a voltage generator, thereby permitting considerably higher reactive volt-ampere output than a tube amplifier under similar conditions.

SPEAKER CHARACTERISTICS

A speaker impedance is, as the name indicates, not a pure resistance; it varies with frequency, and has peaks and dips. Figure 2 shows a typical impedance curve, showing both magnitude and phase of the impedance. A slope rising with frequency is equivalent to an inductive component, and a falling impedance is equivalent to a capacitive component.

This frequency-varying loudspeaker impedance is, of course, the result of reactive loudspeaker elements. Figure 3 shows a "circuit diagram" of a single direct-radiator loudspeaker in a closed box. Actually, this circuit diagram is completely valid only for low and mid-frequency performance of a loudspeaker. It is drawn on the mobility basis, i.e., all elements moving at the same velocity are connected to a common point and an ideal transformer transforms this velocity into an electrical voltage, and vice versa. The resistor r_2 represents the radiation resistance of the loudspeaker—the element through which acoustic power is produced. From this diagram, it is possible to predict the integrated sound pressure *vs* frequency response of the loudspeaker. The response is the ratio of the equivalent voltage (integrated sound pressure) across the radiation resistance r_2 with the input voltage. The impedance of the loudspeaker can also be determined by dividing input voltage by input current, and the efficiency of the loudspeaker can be calculated. With most loudspeakers of the direct radiator type, efficiency is considerably less than 100%, and at mid-frequencies the input impedance of the loudspeaker is very nearly equal to the electrical voice coil resistance R_E. In an ideal loudspeaker without mechanical losses (r_{MS}) and infinite compliance (C_{MS}) the radiation resistance (r_2) and the equivalent capacitance representing the mass of the cone and voice coil (M_D) form an R-C low-pass filter with a low turnover frequency. The mass of the air (M_1) and the equivalent mechanical resistance of the voice coil and generator form a high-pass filter with a higher turnover frequency. Between those two turnover frequencies, the response of the loudspeaker will be approximately flat; if those two frequencies are separated by a factor of 10 to 1, then the voltage appearing across resistor r_2 is approximately one-tenth of the input voltage. Since one-tenth of the input voltage corresponds to one one-hundredth of the input power, such a loudspeaker would then have efficiency of 1%, which is certainly not an unusual value. This illustrates the type of compromise that has to be made between the efficiency and frequency response of a loudspeaker. It is readily seen that the farther apart the turnover frequencies are, the lower will be the point where the two curves intersect. The "gain-bandwidth product" remains constant while moving mass and speaker size are varied. The gain-bandwidth product itself is primarily determined by the power of the motor, i.e., by the product of active voice coil length and flux density in the airgap. The compliance of the box and of the suspension of the loudspeaker modify the low-frequency performance as shown in Fig. 4, where the individual high-pass and low-pass networks described above are also shown.

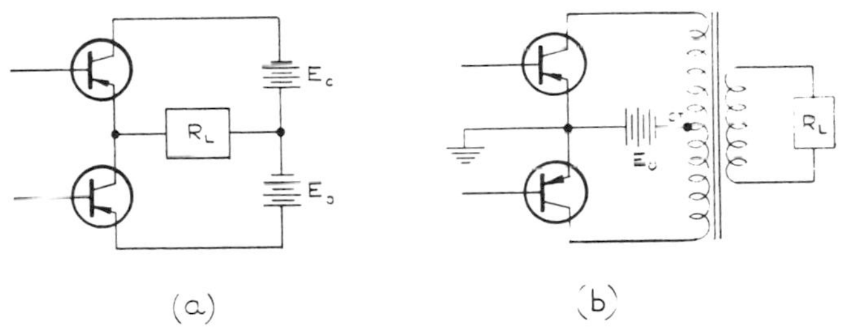

FIG. 5. Possible connections between speaker and amplifier. *a.* Series dc-connected stage; *b.* Parallel dc-connected stage.

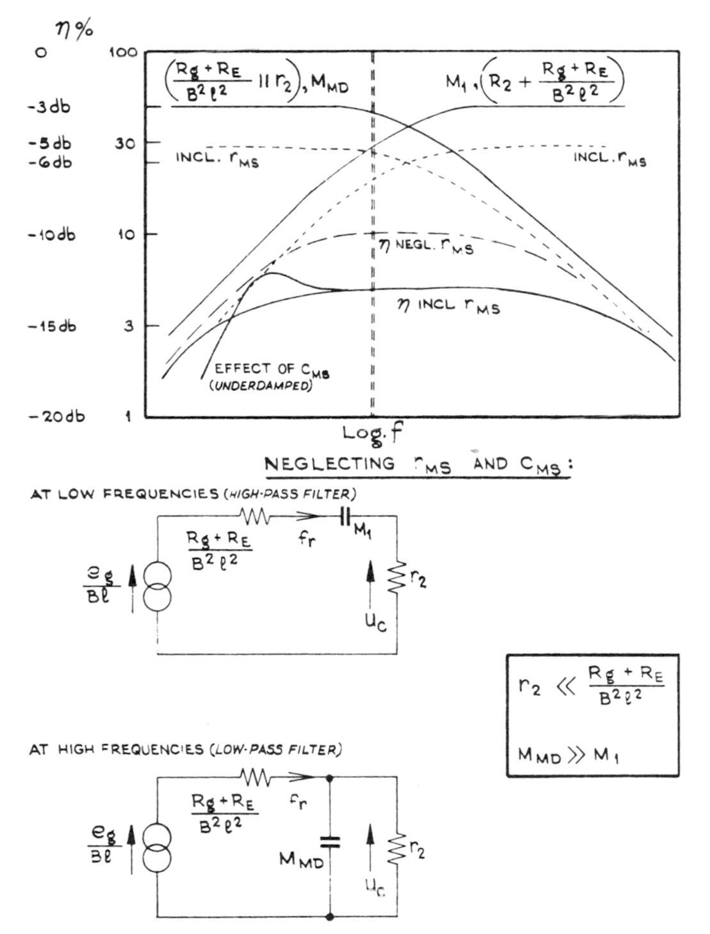

FIG. 4. Eg = amplifier open-circuit voltage; Rg = amplifier source resistance; L = voice coil inductance; R_E = voice coil resistance; fc = force = Bli; U_C = voice coil velocity; M_{MD} = mass of voice coil and diaphragm; r_{MS} = mechanical responsiveness of suspension = 1/(mechanical resistance); C_{MS} = mechanical compliance of suspension; Z_{MR} = mechanical radiation mobility for one side of diaphragm; = 1/(mechanical radiation impedance); M_1 = acoustic mass; and r_2 = acoustic responsiveness).

AMPLIFIER OUTPUT CAPABILITIES

As shown above, there is an optimum load impedance for the amplifier. Optimum performance of the overall system results when the speaker impedance is equal to the optimum load for the amplifier. The easiest and least painful way to match these impedances is by using a matching transformer. This is the usual procedure with tube amplifiers. With transistor amplifiers it is desired to eliminate the output transformer, and thus the loudspeaker itself must have the proper impedance.

The practical range of load impedances for which amplifiers can be designed is limited. Tube amplifiers without output transformers require loads in the range between 500 and 20,000 ohm. Transistor amplifier load impedances have optimum values from a few ohm to 50 ohm, as determined by the type of circuit, supply voltage, and output power capability. Impedances of dynamic direct-radiator loudspeakers seldom range lower than a couple of ohm or higher than 50 ohm. Before the advent of transistors, loudspeakers with voice coil impedances as high as 500 ohm were manufactured. However, production difficulties due to breakage of fine wire prevented these designs from being commercially practical. Ribbon and electrostatic loudspeakers basically have special impedance characteristics and usually include a built-in matching transformer for conversion of their basic impedance to a more usable value. The impedances of these loudspeakers with their matching transformers show more variation with respect to frequency than do those of direct radiator loudspeakers.

What designs are available for direct connection between speaker and amplifier? Output stages may be series or parallel push-pull connected with respect to the dc supply. The basic circuits are shown in Fig. 5.

The parallel-connected power stage requires an output transformer or center-tapped choke to permit connection to the speaker. However, for the purpose of analysis, transformers are ruled out, even those in disguise. A device for overcoming the difficulty is a loudspeaker with a center-tapped voice coil. Figure 6 shows how this makes possible

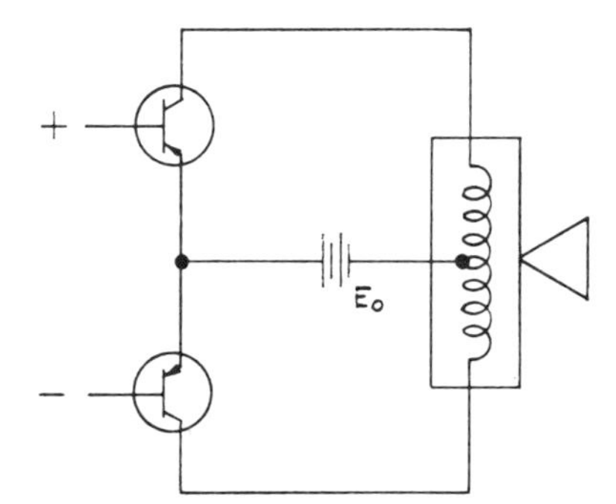

FIG. 6. Parallel dc-connected output stage using a speaker with center-tapped voice coil.

a transformerless amplifier with parallel dc-connected output transistors. At first sight, this seems an excellent circuit, with the supply voltage requirements of a transformer-coupled output stage and no net dc in the voice coil.

CONVENTIONAL PUSH-PULL AMPLIFIERS

In order to analyze the various amplifier-load combinations, it is necessary to remember the basic function of an amplifying device (be it a transistor or a tube) which is to act as a controlled time-varying impedance (R_D) between a supply voltage and a load impedance (R_L), as seen in Fig. 7*a*. If the resistance R_D is controlled so that a sinusoidal current flows in R_L, the basic circuit of a single-ended Class A amplifier is completed. The saturation resistance R_{sat} of the device is an inherent device characteristic and includes wiring and other external limiting resistors.

The maximum instantaneous current I_{max} in the transistor (or other device) is limited by device capabilities. In this circuit, it is $I_{max} = E_0/(R_1+R_{sat})$, where E_0 is the dc supply voltage. When the resistance R_D is controlled in such a way that a half-sinewave shaped current occurs, this stage acts as one-half of a push-pull circuit. To combine two such stages (appropriately controlled) in series (see Fig. 7*b*), the two load resistances R_L may be replaced by one single resistance R_L, since current flows in each R_D **only** half the time. This results in the standard series con-

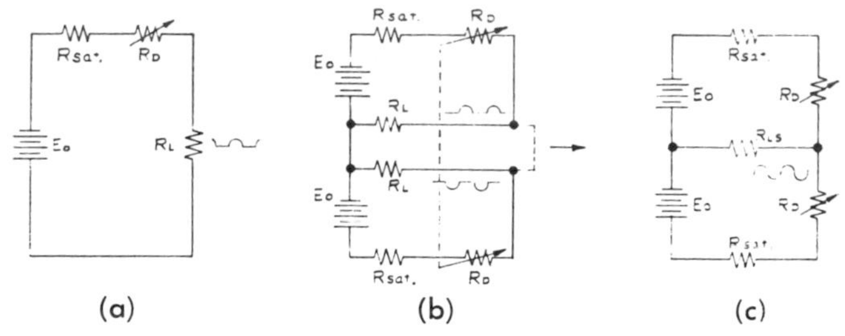

FIG. 7. Development of amplifier-load combination in series push-pull circuits.

nected circuit of Fig. 7*c* (shown with the R_D's replaced by transistors in Fig. 5*a*). If R_{sat} is assumed to be equal to zero, a total supply voltage of $2E_0$ is required and the maximum power output is given by $P_{max\,s} = (2E_0)^2/8R_L = E_0^2/2R_{L_S}$.

By an entirely analogous process the circuit of a standard parallel dc push-pull stage can be developed as shown in Fig. 8. Here, a transformer is required to invert the phase of one of the currents so that a sinusoidal current can flow in the ultimate load.

If transistors (or devices) identical in rating to those of the previous example are used, $I_{max} = E_0/(R_L+R_{sat})$ must be maintained as before, the total supply voltage required is E_0 (or one-half of the previous voltage), and the load resistance must be quadrupled. The total power consumption from the supply remains the same as before and so does the output power, which is given by

$$P_{max\,p} = E_0^2/2R_L = 2E_0^2/R_{L_P}.$$

CENTER-TAPPED SPEAKER CIRCUIT

Thus, if a parallel dc push-pull stage (without output transformer) is now connected to a center-tapped loudspeaker, the load resistance of each half voice-coil must be equal to R_L if the same supply voltage E_0 is used and I_{max} is maintained as before. Again, power input and power output remain as above: $P_{max\,cr} = E_0^2/2R_L$, remembering

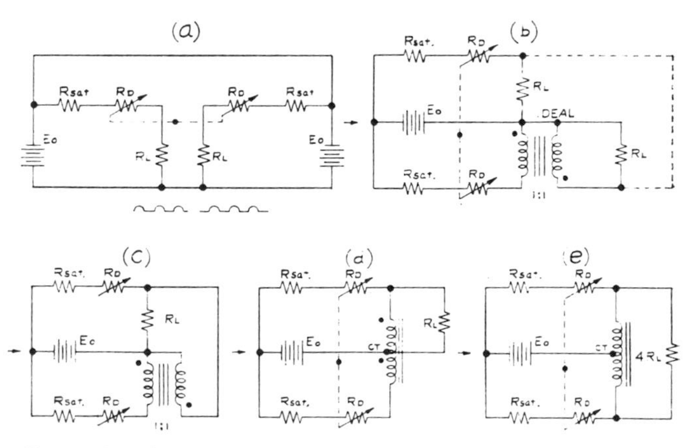

FIG. 8. Development of amplifier-load combination in parallel push-pull circuits.

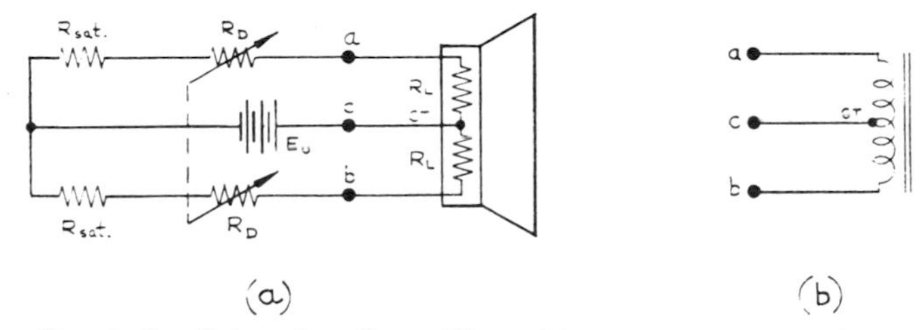

FIG. 9. Parallel push-pull amplifier with center-tapped speaker.

that R_L is the resistance of half the voice coil and each half-coil receives power half the time.

The addition of an autotransformer or center-tapped choke (of Fig. 9*b*) to the circuit of Fig. 9*a* then, in effect, connects both voice-coil halves in parallel, with each half receiving power at all times. This doubles peak current I_{max} input power and output power P_{max} because the effective load resistance is one-half of the previous load resistance. Thus, the addition of an autotransformer to the circuit of Fig. 9*a* converts this into a standard parallel dc push-pull circuit and raises ac and dc electrical power by 3 db. Therefore, transistors can be damaged by excessive peak current. For proper operation of the transistors, load resistance in each connection will have to be chosen so that I_{max} is not exceeded and the power increase cannot be realized.

What about the acoustic output of a loudspeaker with two separate voice coil halves? If it is presumed that this loudspeaker is essentially a "normal" loudspeaker with only an electrical center tap added to the voice coil, the rest of the loudspeaker structure being unchanged. Figure 10 shows the equivalent circuit of such a loudspeaker. Since a considerable effort is required to analyze such a circuit in detail, a simplified analysis will be presented.

When connected so that both electrical generators $e_g/2$ are identical and operate simultaneously, this loudspeaker operates identically to that of Fig. 3. If, as in a practical loudspeaker, the coupling between voice coil halves is relatively small, opening one of the generator connections (as is done alternately in the circuit of Fig. 9) will cause only one-half the velocity to be developed across the radiation resistance r_2. In this case the electrical power input is reduced to one-half its former value, since the current is unchanged, but flows in only half of the voice coil. In effect, one-half of the motor ($Bl/2$) is disconnected, thereby reducing the loudspeaker efficiency to one-half its former value. The reduction in efficiency is ***not*** accompanied by an increase in the bandwidth of the loudspeaker.

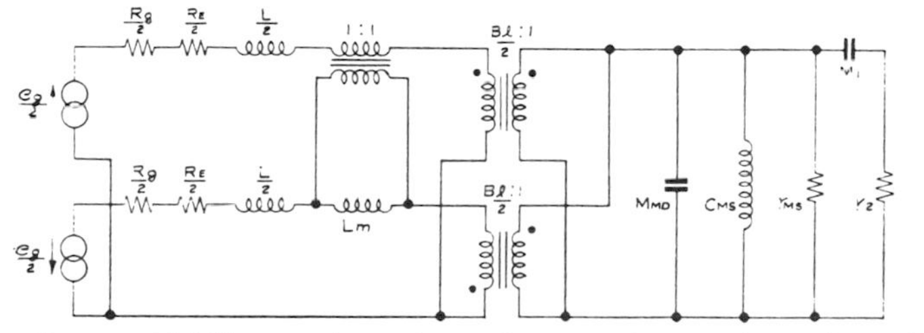

FIG. 10. Mobility analog of a direct radiator split voice-coil speaker and amplifier combination.

CONCLUSION

The reduction of loudspeaker efficiency is the most important disadvantage of using a loudspeaker with a center-tapped voice coil in a transformerless parallel dc push-pull amplifier circuit. This factor is not necessarily apparent to the amplifier designer. Alternately, if the loudspeaker designer desired to operate his loudspeaker at full effectiveness and did so by adding a center-tapped choke without changing loudspeaker impedance, he would create amplifier overload problems.

Of the parallel dc push-pull amplifier-loudspeaker combinations, only the transformer (or choke) coupled version will provide optimum results when properly matched. This is a major design consideration when the combination is to provide optimum performance while restricted by an available supply voltage of low value.

THE AUTHORS

V. BROCINER D. R. RECKLINGHAUSEN

Victor Brociner, a native New Yorker, received a B.S. in Mechanical Engineering from Columbia University in 1931. In 1937 he and two associates formed the Philharmonic Radio Company which pioneered in the high fidelity field, manufacturing a wide-band high-fidelity radio-phonograph. After World War II Mr. Brociner formed his own company, marketing high-fidelity amplifiers and loudspeakers. In 1958 he joined University Loudspeakers, Inc., as staff consultant, and in 1960 became director of engineering there. Since May, 1963, Mr. Brociner has been at H. H. Scott, Inc.

Mr. Brociner is a member of the Audio Engineering Society, the Institute of Electrical and Electronics Engineers, the Acoustical Society of America and the Radio Club of America.

•

Daniel R. von Recklinghausen was born in New York, N. Y., in 1925 and received a B.S. in electrical engineering from the Massachusetts Institute of Technology in 1951.

Previous to receiving his degree, he was employed at Rhode Schwarz, Munich, Germany and the Research Laboratory of Electronics, the High Voltage and Acoustics Laboratories of M.I.T., doing development work on uhf and shf meters and generators, reverberation devices and recording and studio facilities. He joined H. H. Scott, Inc., in 1951 as project engineer responsible for the development of sound analyzers, tuners, amplifiers and other acoustical instruments. In 1955 he became chief engineer.

Mr. von Recklinghausen is chairman of the Tuner Standards Committee of the Institute of High Fidelity Manufacturers and a member of the IHFM Amplifier Standards Committee. He has been a member of Panels 4 and 5 of the National Stereophonic Radio Committee and was chairman of subcommittees 4.1 and 5.4, N.S.R.C. He is a member of Tau Beta Pi Sigma X, and Etta Kappa Nu. He is a Fellow of the Audio Engineering Society, a Senior Member of the Institute of Electrical and Electronics Engineers and various IEEE professional groups.

Trends in Loudspeaker Magnet Structures*

R. J. PARKER

General Electric Company, Magnetic Materials Section, Edmore, Michigan

This paper describes the improvements in permanent magnet unit over the years. The influence this progress has had on magnetic circuit configurations and loudspeaker performance are reviewed. Future possibilities in terms of new permanent magnet unit properties and their significance to the loudspeaker industry are considered.

INTRODUCTION

As one reviews the history of permanent magnet materials it is of interest to note how the properties of available materials have influenced performance, cost, size, and reliability of electrical and electromechanical devices and equipments. The first uses of permanent magnets were in applications where permanent magnetism was an absolute necessity—the compass, the magneto, and the D'Arsonval meter. Weak fields produced by rather excessive volumes of early permanent magnet steels were tolerated in these early uses. With each significant increase in energy product and coercive force, the permanent magnet has challenged electromagnetism in some particular field of use. The permanent magnet challenged electromagnetism in loudspeakers in the early 1940's with inventions of Alnico 5, an Alnico magnet processed in a magnetic field with a resulting three-fold energy product improvement. Since then permanent magnets have had essentially no competition from wound excited structures. Improved volumetric efficiency, freedom of excitation watts, ease of installation and stability are well-recognized advantages of permanent magnetism. The permanent magnet is certainly a key component in the modern loudspeaker; as such it has great influence on speaker performance, cost, size, and stability.

BASIC RELATIONSHIP BETWEEN PERMANENT MAGNET PROPERTIES AND LOUDSPEAKER PERFORMANCE

In order to understand the role magnetism plays in determining the conversion efficiency and output of a loudspeaker one must examine the means by which electrical energy is delivered to a speaker voice coil.[1] The voice coil is generally coupled to the plate of a vacuum tube by means of an impedance matching transformer. It can be shown that the output P of a loudspeaker may be expressed as $P = i^2R_m$ where R_m is acoustical resistance and i is voice coil current. The output is also proportional to $(R_m/R + R_m)$ where R is the voice coil resistance. We may

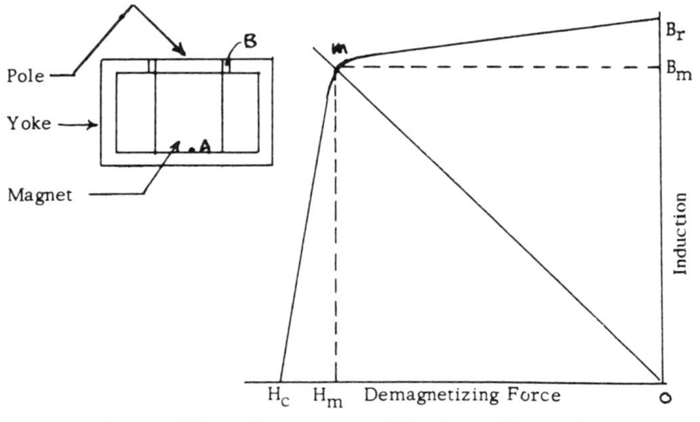

FIG. 1. Magnetic structure of the dynamic speaker.

also write $P = C/(Cl + l/x)$ where c is a constant and x is the ratio of (R_m/R). It is thus desirable to make R_m/R as large as possible, and x becomes a measure of speaker efficiency. R may be expressed in terms of the constants of the coil: $R = cl/a$, when e = specific resistance, l = winding length and a = wire cross-section. R_m is proportional to driving force squared, $N(B_g li)^2$ or $N(B_g l)^2$ per

* Presented October 15, 1963 at the Fifteenth Annual Fall Convention of the Audio Engineering Society, New York.

1. F. G. Spreadbury, *Permanent Magnets* (Isaac Pitman and Sons, London, 1949), p. 138.

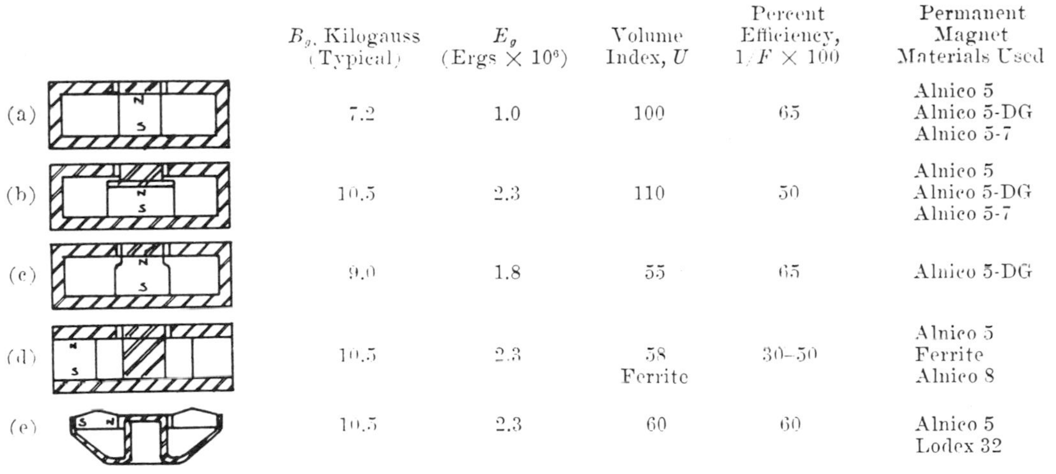

	B_g, Kilogauss (Typical)	E_g (Ergs × 10^6)	Volume Index, U	Percent Efficiency, $1/F \times 100$	Permanent Magnet Materials Used
(a)	7.2	1.0	100	65	Alnico 5 Alnico 5-DG Alnico 5-7
(b)	10.5	2.3	110	50	Alnico 5 Alnico 5-DG Alnico 5-7
(c)	9.0	1.8	55	65	Alnico 5-DG
(d)	10.5	2.3	58 Ferrite	30–50	Alnico 5 Ferrite Alnico 8
(e)	10.5	2.3	60	60	Alnico 5 Lodex 32

FIG. 2. Permanent magnetic circuits used in loudspeakers.

unit of current, where N is a constant determined by cone stiffness, suspension stiffness and frequency and B_g is air gap flux density. Therefore $X = R_m/R = NB_g^2l^2a/l = NB_g^2la/e = NB_g^2V_c/e$, where V_c is volume of conductor in gap. From this analysis we see that the speaker output depends on B_g^2, and consequently in loudspeaker work great efforts are exerted to maximize B_g. It is of course desirable to have high values of B_g because of the desirable influence on such important speaker characterstics as transient response and damping factor.

Figure 1 shows a typical speaker magnet circuit and the demagnetization unit property curve of a permanent magnet. In order to relate the permanent magnet properties to air gap density, B_g we must write the two fundamental design equations of the permanent magnet.[2] First, equating the rise of magnetomotive force in the permanent magnet to the drop across the gap, we have

$$L_m\, H_m = L_g\, H_g, \qquad (1)$$

where L_m = magnet length (cm), Lg = air gap length (cm) H_g = air gap unit potential per cm H_m = magnet potential per cm. Secondly, by equating the flux at points A and B in the circuit we may write

$$B_m\, A_m = B_g\, A_g\, F \qquad (2)$$

where B_m = magnet flux density per cm^2, A_m = magnet area per cm^2, B_g = air gap flux density lines per cm^2, A_g = air gap area (cm^2), F = leakage factor = total permeance/useful permeance. By multiplying Eq. (1) by Eq. (2) and substituting B_g for H_g (since in air they are numerically equal) we have

$$L_m\, A_m\, H_m\, B_m\, L = L_g\, A_g\, B_g^2\, F \qquad (3)$$
$$\text{or } V_m\, B_m\, H_m = V_g\, B_g^2\, F,$$

where V_m = magnet volume and V_g = air gap volume.

Solving Eq, (3) for B_g^2 we have

$$B_g^2 = V_m\, B_m\, H_m /\, F\, V_g.$$

B_g^2 is directly proportional to the volume of permanent magnet and also directly proportional to its available units of magnetic field energy, $B_m\, H_m$, and inversely proportional to volume of air gap and leakage factor F. In applying permanent magnets, it is thus desirable to operate the permanent magnet at a point on its demagnetization curve such that $B_m\, H_m$ is a maximum (point of maximum available energy) and in a circuit arrangement such that F will be a minimum.

The sound pressure output of a speaker is proportional to B_g *equals* $[V_m(B_mH_m)/FV_g]^{1/2}$, and in comparing sound pressure differences the decibel is commonly used. For a given configuration the change in sound pressure is related to gap density, B_g, magnet volume and magnet energy product as follows:

$$\text{decibels (db)} = 20 \log_{10} B_{g1}/B_{g2} = 10 \log_{10}(B_mH_m)_1/(B_mH_0)_2$$
$$= 10 \log_{10}V_1/V_2.$$

BASIC ARRANGEMENTS OF PERMANENT MAGNET CIRCUITS IN USE TODAY

Several commonly used permanent magnet circuits are shown in Fig. 2. In each case the magnetic circuit efficiency $1/F \times 100$ (% of total flux that is useful in gap flux) is given. The air gap energy $E_g = V_gB_g^2/8\pi$ ergs is indicated, and the nominal air gap density B_g. It is of interest to compare the total volume of each structure required to establish a given level of gap energy. A structure volume U has been calculated and indicated. U equals total structure space in cm^3/ Air gap energy, E_g, × 10^{-6}. Commonly used permanent magnet materials are also indicated with each structure. Fig. 3 shows the unit property curves for Alnico 5, Alnico 5-DG, Alnico 5-7, oriented Ferrite, and Lodex® 32 material. These are the materials generally used in loudspeakers. Alnico 5-DG and Alnico 5-7 are improvements over conventional Alnico 5 in terms of ori-

2. R. J. Parker and R. J. Studders, *Permanent Magnets and Their Application* (John Wiley and Sons, New York, 1962), p. 103.

® Registered trademark of General Electric Company.

ented crystal structure and improved energy product. Alnico 5-DG is a partial orientation obtained by chill casting, while Alnico 5-7 is a totally oriented crystal structure, achieved with crystal-growing and thermal control during solidification of the cast magnet. Alnico permanent magnets have usually been used in the center pole location because of their high indication levels. This location close to the gap allows rather high circuit efficiency. For gap density levels equal or above the operating induction level of the magnet, it is necessary to collect flux on a steped pole plug (EIA structure in Fig. 2b). The dual diameter system, Fig. 2c, allows pole tip operating densities approaching those of Fig. 2b but with improved efficiency. In this system the neck of the magnet is directional grain material and the sharp section change drives the neck to very high induction levels. Another advantage is the shallow height and a very minimum of return-path steel. For B_g levels above 11000, it is generally necessary to go to ring-type structures in

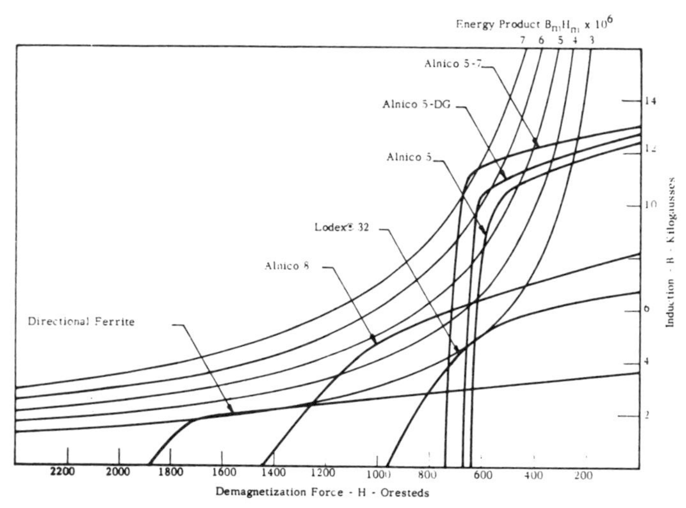

FIG. 3. Properties of permanent magnet units.

order to satisfy the permanent magnet design equations. Unfortunately as the magnet is moved away from its load (gap), low efficiency results due to the introduction of more unavoidable surface area which represents leakage radiation.

An interesting permanent magnet material gaining considerable status in loudspeaker industry is oriented Ferrite. From Fig. 3 we see that this material has low induction and high coercive force and is used in the form of short rings of very large cross section. The structure advantages are shallow depth, compactness, and freedom from the use of cobalt and nickel. However, the efficiency is low and high radiation is a problem in some equipments. Oriented Ferrite does illustrate the fact that an improved permanent magnet material is not necessarily one with an improved energy product.

Figure 2e shows a radial magnet system which has been used in limited quantities. Both Alnico 5 in large structures and the new Lodex® fine-particle magnet in small speakers have found application. A shallow structure and the possibility of achieving some economies by basket and return path are the principal advantages of this approach. More development effort is required in magnet fabrication techniques to make this approach feasible.

PERMANENT MAGNET IMPROVEMENT TRENDS AND THEIR SIGNIFICANCE TO THE LOUDSPEAKER INDUSTRY

We have seen from the foregoing relationships and magnet circuit descriptions that, ideally, for loudspeaker work we want high induction permanent magnets so that the magnet (source) can be located close to the load (gap) without the need for flux collecting techniques which are

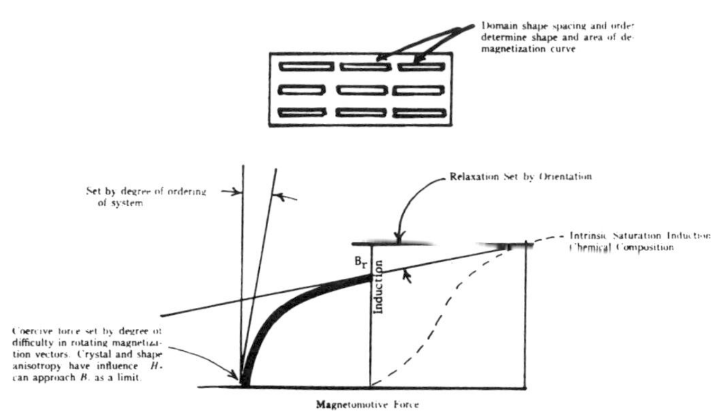

FIG. 4. Basic elements of a permanent magnet.

costly in terms of structure efficiency and produce undesirable field radiation that can create equipment problems.

Improvements in energy product, B_mH_m, are obviously desirable from the viewpoint of structure size and cost of related return path elements. As mentioned previously, a contribution can be made in the available energy per unit of cost without an improvement in energy product.

Let us examine the permanent magnet from the viewpoint of some basic physical considerations and determine the limitations and boundaries and speculate a bit on the trend in permanent magnet property improvement. The magnetization and demagnetization processes in terms of basic physics have only recently been understood. It is now apparent that all permanent magnet properties can be quite well explained in terms of fine-particle single-domain theory. The permanent magnet industry manufactures permanent magnets by metallurgical processes and now also by synthetically growing the ideally shaped particles by electrochemistry and assembling them into a finished magnet, yielding the Lodex® permanent magnet properties shown in Fig. 3. Whatever the process, it appears that fundamentally the properties of permanent magnets are governed by *1.* saturation induction (chemical composition); *2.* shape of the domains; *3.* spacing of the domains; and *4.* orientation or ordering of the domain system.

Figure 4 is an attempt to illustrate these features. For the future, it appears that there is some natural limit to improving saturation induction levels, which would be of great interest to the loudspeaker industry. This is because we know of no elements with higher saturation levels than Iron-Cobalt. We will undoubtedly make improvements in growing elongated domains which will be harder to rotate in a field and will thus produce higher coercive force values, H_c, in permanent magnets. Continued progress can be expected in orientation techniques. Directional grain magnets are well accepted. Techniques for orientation of the crystal edges in cast magnets by thermal and crystal-seeding means are already in limited commercial production. The synthetic particle magnets, although somewhat lower than cast magnets in energy product, offer excellent improvement possibilities, and work in this area has actually resulted in the basic knowledge to improve the cast magnets. Figure 5 shows the trend of energy product improvement with respect to time, which has an encouraging slope.[3] From the theory it appears that permanent magnets with energy products 4 to 5 times the best now available are possible within the known boundaries.

Permanent magnet studies and magnetism in general today represent a real frontier area of physics. Many research dollars are being spent and the possibilities of substantially improved energy products, coercive force, and available energy per dollar invested are excellent. As new unit properties and configurations become available the loudspeaker will most certainly reflect these changes.

3. F. E. Luborsky, *J. Appl. Phys.* 32, 171 (1961).

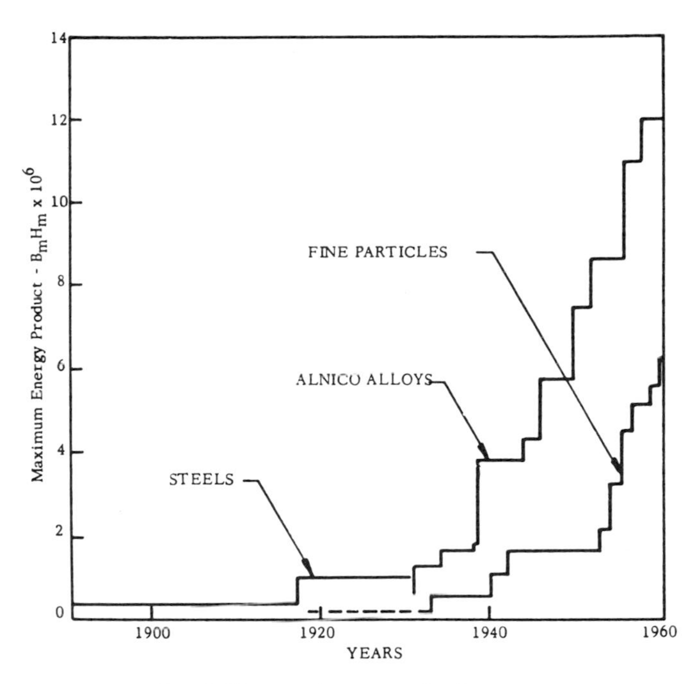

FIG. 5. Progress in magnet development.

THE AUTHOR

R. J. Parker received a degree in electrical engineering from the University of Vermont in 1945, and continued his studies in mathematics on the graduate level at Union College. During his employment with the General Electric Company he has worked primarily on magnetism and magnetic materials, and is currently manager of magnetic products engineering at General Electric's Magnetic Materials Section.

Mr. Parker is the coauthor of *Permanent Magnets and Their Application* (John Wiley and Sons, New York, 1962) and a member of the Institute of Electrical and Electronic Engineers.

Low-Frequency Response and Efficiency Relationships in Direct-Radiator Loudspeaker Systems*

ROY F. ALLISON
Acoustic Research, Inc., Cambridge, Massachusetts

Close control of Q_T at low-frequency resonance is required to maintain flat response in closed-box loudspeaker systems. Increasing the midband efficiency increases electrical damping. Over-damping and loss of low-frequency output may occur unless an optimal compromise is reached among midband efficiency and electrical, mechanical, and acoustic damping.

INTRODUCTION

THE performance of loudspeaker systems is most easily defined by different formulas for various frequency ranges, in which different elements become significant.

Above the first resonance frequency of a closed-box loudspeaker system, and below the frequency at which the diaphragm begins to become directional, there is a mass-controlled frequency region in which sound output is fairly uniform with frequency. This is so because the decrease in diaphragm movement with increasing frequency is balanced by a proportional increase in radiation resistance.

The region of uniform response may extend, in practical cases, from 100 cps or below to 400 cps or above. In terms of octaves covered this is a fairly wide range, and it serves as a convenient zero-decibel reference for evaluating the efficiency of the loudspeaker system. The radiated sound pressure in this range can be calculated as follows:[1]

$$|p|_c=\frac{e_gBl\rho_0}{(R_g+R_E)M_A4\pi rS_D}, \qquad (1)$$

where all units are in the mks system and $|p|_c =$ low-frequency reference sound pressure at distance r from the loudspeaker; $e_g =$ open-circuit voltage at the output terminals of the power amplifier; $B =$ air-gap flux density; $l =$ length of voice-coil wire in magnetic gap; $\rho_0 =$ density of air; $R_g =$ output impedance of power amplifier; $R_E =$ voice coil resistance; $S_D =$ effective area of the diaphragm; and $M_A =$ sum of the acoustic masses in the circuit, including those of the diaphragm and voice coil as well as the acoustic mass of the air loads on the front and the rear of the diaphragm.

This formula contains no surprises. It tells us that the sound pressure produced in this frequency range is directly proportional to the ac voltage applied to the voice coil, to the flux density of the field in which the voice coil is suspended, and to the length of voice coil wire in the gap. The sound pressure is inversely proportional to the sum of the amplifier output impedance and the voice coil resistance, to the distance from the loudspeaker, and to the product of acoustic mass and diaphragm area. It should be noted in passing that diaphragm size is included in the calculations for each of the acoustic masses because of the need for transforming them from mechanical masses to acoustic masses. Simply increasing the diaphragm size, without changing anything else, results in a smaller M_AS_D product. This in turn produces a higher resultant sound pressure. We shall follow Beranek in calling the output of the speaker system in this range the "reference sound pressure."

LOW-FREQUENCY RESPONSE

The output at the first resonance frequency of the system is related to the reference sound pressure by the Q of the resonance. Figure 1, also taken from Beranek,[2] shows system frequency response in the region of low-frequency

* Presented October 16, 1964 at the Sixteenth Annual Fall Convention of the Audio Engineering Society, New York.

1. L. L. Beranek, *Acoustics* (McGraw-Hill Book Company, New York, 1954), p. 225.

2. L. L. Beranek, *op. cit.*, p. 226.

resonance with Q_T as the parameter. Reference sound pressure is shown as zero decibels. With a Q_T of 1, sound pressure passes through the zero-decibel line exactly at the resonance frequency; there is a rise in response of less than 2 db just above the resonance frequency. This value of Q_T is, in my opinion, optimal. (Beranek believes that it should be slightly higher.) A value of 1 gives the flattest possible and most extended low-frequency response with no significant bass hangover. With higher values of Q_T the low-frequency response can be extended still more, but the peak which accompanies this extension can become audible as bass hangover. With lower values of Q_T, on the other hand, the low-frequency response is rolled off with no audible improvement in transient response. A Q_T of 0.5, representing what is known as critical damping, produces a frequency response which is 6 db down from reference level at the resonance frequency, and 2 db down a full octave above. "Critical damping," of course, is a technical term which does not imply optimal value.

Q_T is the same in concept as the Q of resonant electrical circuits: the familiar $\omega M/R$. In the case of a speaker system,

$$Q_T \equiv \omega_0 M_A / R_A; \quad (2)$$

the factor M is replaced by M_A, the acoustic mass, and R is replaced by R_A, the acoustic resistance. As the value of R_A increases, the resonance damping becomes greater and the value of Q_T decreases.

Let us take a more detailed look at the formula for Q_T.

$$Q_T \equiv \frac{\omega_0 (M_{AD} + M_{A1} + M_{AB})}{[B^2l^2/(R_g+R_E)S_D^2] + R_{AS} + R_{AB} + R_{AR}}. \quad (3)$$

Here M_A has been replaced by the individual masses which make it up: M_{AD}, the acoustic mass of the moving system of diaphragm and voice coil; M_{A1}, the radiation mass of the air acting on the front of the diaphragm; and M_{AB}, the acoustic mass of the air load presented by the box to the rear of the diaphragm. The acoustic resistance R_A is made up of four terms. There is the electrical damping resistance created by the back-emf, which is the fractional term $B^2l^2/(R_g+R_E)S_D^2$; R_{AS} is the acoustic term for the mechanical friction in the suspension elements and elsewhere, R_{AB} is the resistive component of the air load on the back of the diaphragm, and R_{AR} is the radiation resistance.

CONTROL OF Q_T

Obviously a great many factors affect Q_T, and thereby have a direct effect on very low-frequency response. Some are easily controlled and some are not.

The value of Q_T is directly proportional to ω_0, the resonance frequency expressed in radians per second. The resonance frequency can be increased by decreasing the diaphragm weight, or by increasing the suspension stiffness or using a smaller closed box. Decreasing the diaphragm weight also decreases the M_{AD} term (which accounts for most of the acoustic mass) and this tends to nullify the influence on Q_T of the increased value of ω_0. Increasing the stiffness of the suspension or enclosed air does not have this disadvantage. But a higher Q_T at a higher resonance frequency does not produce any higher output at the *original* resonance frequency; in other words, simply increasing the resonance frequency or decreasing it, without making other changes which affect Q_T, does not extend the low end significantly.

How about changing the diaphragm size? If this can be done with no change in mass, we have seen that increasing

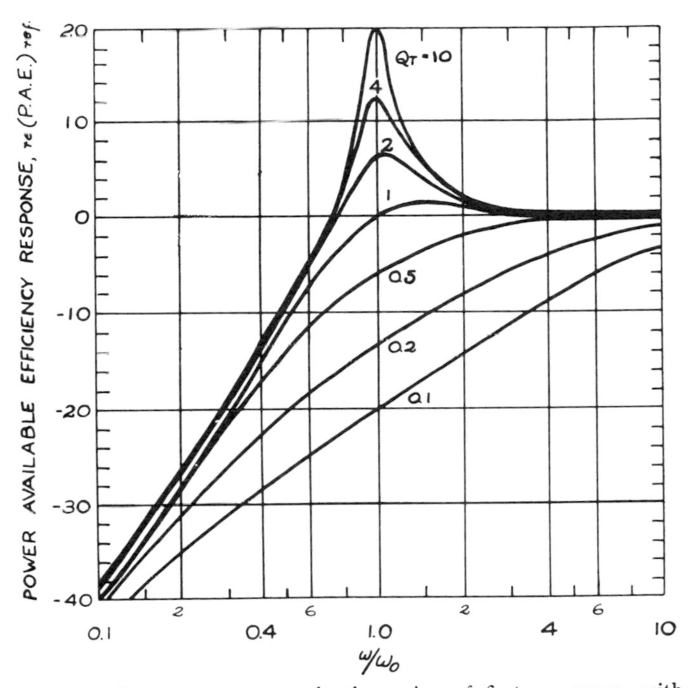

FIG. 1. Frequency response in the region of first resonance, with Q_T as parameter, for a direct-radiator closed-box loudspeaker system (after Beranek).

the diaphragm size increases the reference sound pressure. In the expanded formula for Q_T, diaphragm size is included in the calculations for so many of the terms (in order to convert them from mechanical to acoustic quantities) that it is not so easy to make a generalization. More often than not, however, increasing the diaphragm size with no other change would produce an increase in Q_T. Unfortunately, there is a practical limit to how big a diaphragm can be put into a small box.

Increasing the moving system mass (M_{AD}) will increase Q_T *provided* there is a simultaneous increase in suspension or box air stiffness, so that the resonance frequency remains the same. This gain in Q_T will be accompanied by a large decrease in reference sound pressure, of course, which the designer may not be willing to accept.

M_{A1}, the frontal radiation mass, and M_{AB}, the acoustic mass of the rear air load, are both determined primarily by diaphragm size, which was discussed previously. In practical cases, also, they are usually small compared with the total acoustic mass.

The radiation resistance R_{AR} is a function only of frequency in the extreme low-frequency range, where the diaphragm is very small compared to the wavelength, and as such is not susceptible of control.

The value of R_{AB}, the resistive air load on the back of the diaphragm, is a significant factor in the total acoustic resistance, particularly when the box is filled with Fiberglas. Filling the box with Fiberglas accomplishes two desirable objectives: first, it completely damps out internal reflections which would otherwise occur at frequencies for which the box dimensions are ½ wavelength or more. Second, the Fiberglas stuffing can change air compressions and rarefactions inside the box from adiabatic to isothermal, which in turn permits using a smaller box for the same air stiffness. These advantages are not insignificant ones, and should not be abandoned lightly in order to achieve a higher Q_T. Obtaining a high enough Q_T is often a problem with closed-box direct radiator systems; with other types of speaker systems the opposite problem is often found.

The suspension resistance term, R_{AS}, is determined by the sum of the internal friction of the suspension elements, edge damping compounds applied to the suspension, and hidden resistive elements. One example of a hidden resistance is air entrapped inside a magnet structure, which can escape only through small leaks in the structure as the voice coil assembly moves in and out.

Either back loading resistance or suspension friction can be significant in limiting Q_T, although friction need not be a limiting factor with proper design. In most cases, however, the major element in determining Q_T is the electrical damping term. The denominator of this term contains as a factor the diaphragm size, which has been discussed, and the sum of R_g and R_E. The value of R_g, the amplifier output impedance, is beyond the control of the designer of the speaker system. Amplifiers for general use invariably have a very low output impedance, and there is no prospect of any change. A high output impedance will increase Q_T; the designer of a complete amplifier and speaker system package obviously has an advantage in this respect that is denied one whose speaker systems are intended for universal use.

The value of R_E, the voice coil resistance, is generally determined by other requirements. Increasing the amount by which the voice coil extends outside the magnet gap will increase Q_T. Ordinarily, this should not be carried beyond an amount needed to provide for linear diaphragm excursion, because it entails the penalty of a severe reduction in reference sound pressure.

Note that the numerator of the electrical damping term is B^2l^2, while the numerator of the reference sound pressure formula contains Bl. This is the key to the most efficient way to adjust Q_T and the extreme low-frequency response. If all practical measures have been taken with the other terms, and Q_T is still too low, a small reduction in flux density will in most cases buy a big increase in Q_T. It should be noted that a decrease in flux density is generally accompanied by a decrease in cost also.

To cite a practical example: a small speaker system, the AR-4, was recently designed using an 8-in. woofer in a cabinet of a little less than one cubic foot. A reduction in flux density which dropped the reference sound pressure by 2 db provided a relative increase of 3 db at the resonance frequency. This was needed to make the low-frequency response flat. Yet the efficiency remains high enough to be perfectly satisfactory for home use.

CONCLUSION

In an effort to achieve completely unrealistic "efficiency" figures with a small speaker system, it is easy to overdamp the woofer. It can, as a matter of fact, hardly be avoided unless the resonance frequency is made high. In either case, low-frequency response suffers. To obtain flat response down to an acceptably low frequency it is necessary to keep close control of mechanical and acoustic resistive elements, and then to sacrifice whatever midband efficiency is required to optimize the electrical damping.

I should like to thank Edgar Villchur, President and Director of Research at Acoustic Research, Inc., for the many valuable suggestions and ideas he contributed towards this paper.

THE AUTHOR

Roy Allison has been a writer and editor of engineering trade journals in the radio communication and radio and television broadcast fields and was editor of *Audiocraft Magazine* and audio editor of *High Fidelity Magazine*. He joined Acoustic Research, Inc. in 1959 and became the company's chief engineer in 1960. He is now plant manager.

Mr. Allison is a member of the Audio Engineering Society and the Institute of Electrical and Electronics Engineers.

High-Power, Low-Frequency Loudspeakers*

JOHN K. HILLIARD

LTV Research Center, Ling-Temco-Vought, Inc., Anaheim, California

This paper discusses the generation, propagation, and detection of acoustic energy over a wide frequency and power level range. In particular, it describes an electro-pneumatic sonic generator which develops several kilowatts of acoustic energy. The photographs and charts illustrate several applications for this sonic generator; e.g., facilities to measure low frequency propagation and examples of metal fatigue and building structure damage criteria when exposed to high-level acoustic energy.

THE generation, propagation, and detection of acoustic energy is now being investigated over a wide frequency and power level range. Production of high intensity sound (over 120 db sound pressure level) extending up to 180 db is now achieved over a limited area. (A power level of 180 db corresponds to 100,000 watts per square foot.) Within the next year, several transducers having sinewave and white noise capabilities over a wide frequency range can be operated in parallel to develop well in excess of 100,000 acoustic watts.

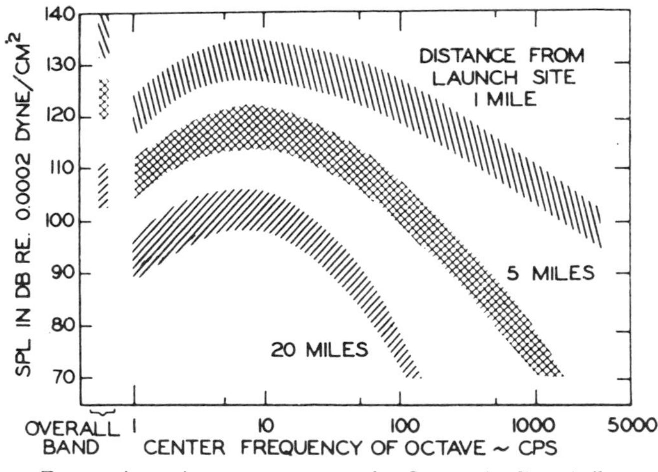

FIG. 1. Acoustic power spectrum for Saturn-Apollo missiles.

The demand for this large amount of acoustic energy comes from the need to make acoustic fatigue tests on full-scale missiles of the Apollo type and for propagation studies. The power spectrum for Saturn-Apollo is shown in Fig. 1. The peak power occurs at 5 to 20 cps. The total acoustic power produced with its thrust of 1.5 million pounds is approximately 50 million acoustic watts. The acoustic power generated is 0.6% of the total kinetic energy available and varies as the eighth power of the exit velocity. Although the exit velocity and the sound pressure level have not changed with the larger vehicles, the diameter has increased and therefore so has the total acoustic power.

At frequencies below 100 cps, the attenuation with distance is, under normal conditions, only that of the spreading loss or a reduction of 6 db for each doubling in distance. At these frequencies, tests on Saturn launch already provide data to indicate that at one mile the sound pressure level is 120 to 130 db.

The velocity of sound changes with temperature and wind conditions, and this variation tends to refract the sound rays. If the velocity increases with height, the sound rays are bent toward the ground and an increase or focus will occur in some areas—which may be at a factor of 10 db or more. Though the development of missiles requires almost daily firing of the engines, sites which are adjacent to residential areas—such as Huntsville, Cape Kennedy, Sacramento, Houston, and Vandenberg—must assure that firing is not made when an acoustic ray focusing condition exists.

At the Huntsville and Mississippi test sites, air modulated loudspeakers have been erected on 60-ft high towers. They radiate several kilowatts of acoustic power at low frequencies in the region of 30 to 60 cps. The sound level at a distance of 10 miles or more is above the ambient noise and so the propagation loss can be measured on a steady basis. By this method, the normal propagation is determined and firing is done only at these times.

The electro-pneumatic loudspeaker is a transducer in which the flow of compressed air through an orifice is modulated at audio and sub-audio frequencies by a voice coil driving a valve (Fig. 2). The valve consists of a set of

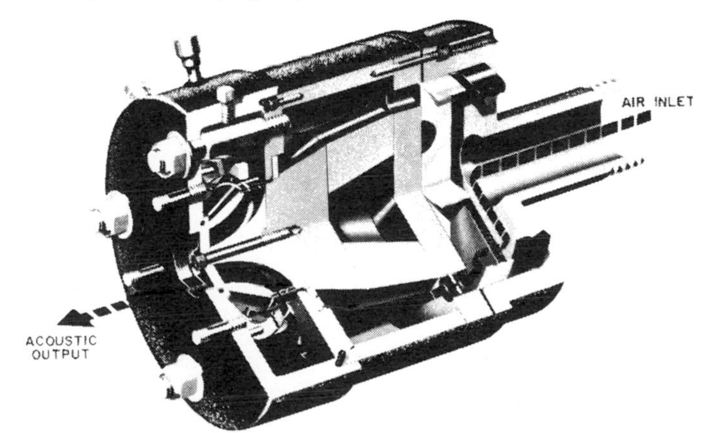

FIG. 2. Flow path of the electro-pneumatic transducer.

* Presented October 16, 1964 at the Sixteenth Annual Fall Convention of the Audio Engineering Society, New York.

outer and inner rings. The inner ring contains two rows of slots equally spaced around its circumference, each slot having a height of 0.060 in. The outer ring also contains slots of the same height, width, and spacing. The inner ring is fixed in a stationary position, and the outer ring is suspended in an RTV rubber annular support in a manner similar to that of conventional driver-type compression loudspeaker units. One edge of the rubber is bonded to the outer movable ring and the other edge is bonded to the inside of a fixed supporting ring. The rubber compliance is ¼ in. in width; the thickness is 0.03 in. The RTV rubber has excellent properties for long life in the presence of residual oil and heat associated with the air supply from conventional air compressors.

The voice coil is wound with a few turns of anodized aluminum ribbon and epoxy cement bonded to a fiberglass mounting ring. This assembly is then cemented to the outer moving ring. The impedance of the coil is approximately 4 ohm, and 100 w of audio power provides full modulation. The magnetic field is provided in the same manner as a compression or horn driver type loudspeaker. The compressed air flows up around the annular magnet and through holes in the top plate. At this point, it is directed at right angles into the movable slot. The outer and inner rings are spaced at a 50% opening with no signal, equivalent to Class A operation, with half of the total amount of air moving through the slots into the mouth of the units. With full modulation current in the coil, the outer slots completely open and close the port area which is 1.2 sq. in.

FIG. 3. Installation for the measurement of sound propagation.

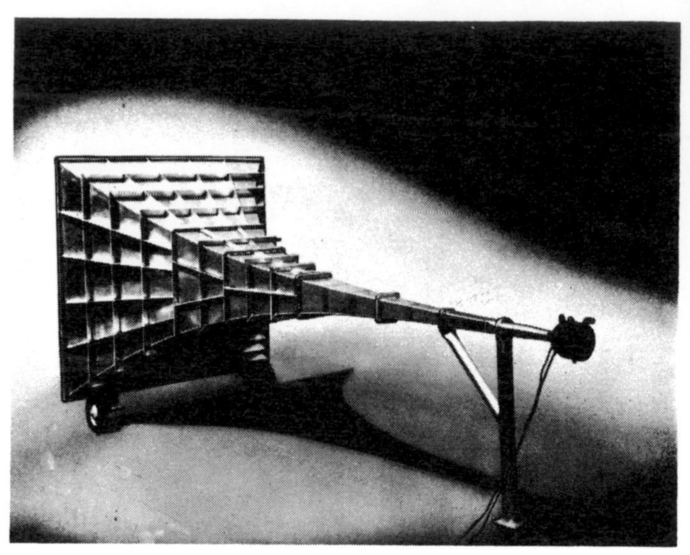

FIG. 1. Horn used in sound-propagation measurements.

Forty pounds per square inch at 500 cu. ft/min. is required from the air compression supply. An efficiency of 10 to 15% is obtained under operating conditions. The valve resonance is determined by the stiffness of the rubber compliance and the mass of the moving system. Where low frequencies only are generated, the resonance is made as low as possible. Where a wide band of frequencies are needed, the resonance is placed as high as possible, consistent with the maximum allowable current in the voice coil. Up to 10 amp of current can be used since a considerable cooling action is obtained by the flow of air around it.

The area of the mouth is twice that of the slots. The unit is attached to a horn by means of conventional throat adapters. The self-noise of the air through the valve without signal is 30 db below 100% modulation. As many as ten units are operated in parallel into a common throat, and the power increase is directly proportional to the number of units. A typical installation of the air modulators, horn, and tower for continuously measuring the propagation conditions is shown in Fig. 3. The horn is approximately 12 ft on a side and is capable of efficiently coupling the modulator to the air at frequencies down to 25 cps. Since the acoustic power is high, the horn must be sufficiently rugged in its construction to withstand continuous operation at full power (see Fig. 4).

The demand for higher acoustic testing power is forcing the design of larger and better sources. Models having a capacity of 25 to 100 kw are now being tested or in the process of being designed.

The testing of the larger missile engines will always be a problem, and acoustic isolation will become increasingly important. Until a new kind of fuel is developed, increased thrust can only come with increased diameter. The frequency of maximum output is inversely proportional to the diameter. It can therefore be determined that this frequency will be lowered with larger vehicles and that the next genera-

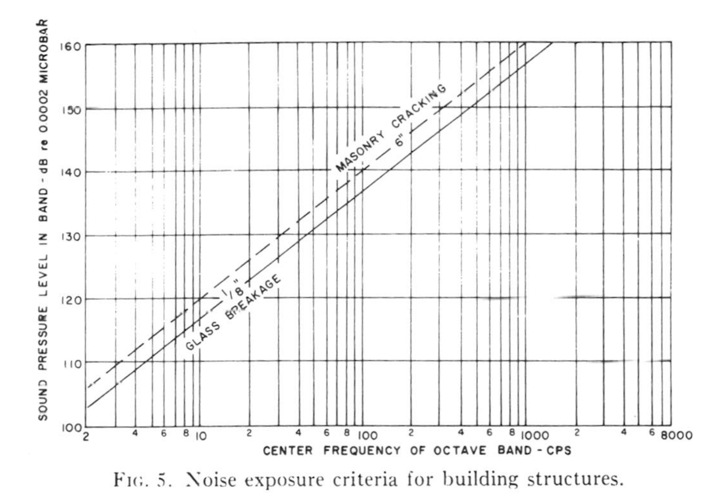

FIG. 5. Noise exposure criteria for building structures.

tion of vehicles could have an output 10 db higher than Saturn, or more than 120 db at four miles.

The walls and windows of buildings are most vulnerable to damage. Windows are resonant in the region of 45 cps and walls from 10 cps up to 20 or 30 cps, depending upon their thickness and unsupported area (Fig. 5). The lowest sound pressure where damage can be expected is at or near resonance, around 120 to 130 db SPL. Sonic booms will also start to show their damaging effects beginning at these levels. Simulation studies on these problems using powerful low-frequency loudspeakers is part of the overall research problem now in progress.

Air-modulated units have been limited to a frequency range below 1000 cps, but laboratory results to date indicate that good performance to 3000 cps is now practical. In metal-fatigue studies, panels composed of a typical structure of high-speed aircraft and missiles are placed in open-air or reverberant enclosures where they are exposed to sound. Both sinewave and random type spectra are used. Figure 6 illustrates the acoustic fatigue produced on a panel structure exposed to low-frequency jet engine noise generated by the air-modulated loudspeaker. In addition

FIG. 6. Panel structure showing acoustic fatigue induced by experimental low-frequency jet engine noise.

to their use for propagation and fatigue studies, voice warning and alerting of personnel is another application.

Another complementary development is that of microphones and calibration facilities having a capability below 1 cps. It is anticipated that this can be described in a subsequent paper.

BIBLIOGRAPHY

1. J. C. Burgess and V. Salmon, *Development of a Modulated Air Stream Loudspeaker* (Stanford Research Institute, December 30, 1955).

2. John V. Bouyoucos, *Self-Excited Hydrodynamic Oscillators,* Technical Memorandum No. 36, Office of Naval Research, July 31, 1955.

3. W. A. Meyer, *A Theoretical Analysis of the Performance of the LTV Air Modulated Speaker* (LTV Research Center, 1964).

4. R. D. Fay, "Plane Sound Waves of Finite Amplitude," *J. Acoust. Soc. Am.* (October, 1931).

5. Isadore Rudnick, "On the Attenuation of High Amplitude Waves of Stable Saw-Tooth Form Propagated in Horns," *J. Acoust. Soc. Am.* **30**, 339 (April, 1958).

6. J. K. Hilliard, "High Intensity Environmental Testing with Electro-Pneumatic Transducers," Fourth International Congress on Acoustics, Copenhagen (August 21-28, 1962).

7. J. K. Hilliard and W. T. Fiala, "Electro-Pneumatic Air Modulator for Fog Signals," *IRE Trans. Audio* **AU-10**, No. 4 (1962).

8. R. N. Tedrick *et al.*, "Studies in Far-Field Acoustic Propagation," *NASA Technical Note D-1277* (August, 1962).

THE AUTHOR

John K. Hilliard was born in Wyndmere, North Dakota, in 1901. His studies at Hamline University, St. Paul, Minnesota, resulted in a B.S. in physics in 1925 and were followed by graduate work in electrical engineering at the University of Minnesota. An honorary D.Sc. in engineering was conferred on him by Hollywood University (California) in 1951.

Dr. Hilliard spent fourteen years at the MGM studios working on the development of recording and reproducing film and tape equipment and designing microphones and loudspeakers for theaters. For many years he was engaged with high-intensity sound environmental equipment, designing a microphone for measurement of nuclear blast, high-speed boundary layer measurements, high-intensity environmental equipment to simulate jet and missile engine noise to evaluate fatigue of electronic equipment and air frame structures, microphones to pick up heart sound, communication equipment for telephone systems and anti-submarine warfare equipment.

From 1943 to 1960, Dr. Hilliard was with the Altec-Lansing Corporation as vice president in the Advanced Engineering Department where he worked with transducers and communication equipment. Presently he is Director of the LTV Research Center, Western Division, Anaheim, California.

In addition to membership in Eta Kappa Nu, the Armed Forces Committee on Hearing Bioacoustics, and the Institute of Environmental Engineers, Dr. Hilliard holds fellowships in the Acoustical Society of America, the Audio Engineering Society, Society of Motion Picture and Television Engineers, and the Institute of Electrical and Electronics Engineers. He is also an acoustic consultant at the Brain Institute, UCLA Medical School, Los Angeles.

Loudspeaker Phase Characteristics and Time Delay Distortion: Part 1

RICHARD C. HEYSER

Jet Propulsion Laboratory, California Institute of Technology, Pasadena, California

A technique is described for measurement of the complete frequency response of a loudspeaker, including amplitude and phase. A concept of time delay is introduced which provides a physical description of the effect of phase and amplitude variations as a frequency-dependent spatial smearing of the effective acoustic position of a loudspeaker.

INTRODUCTION In a previous paper a derivation was given for a new acoustic testing technique which allowed anechoic measurements to be taken in a normally reverberant environment [1]. The quantity measured was shown analytically to be the complex Fourier transform of the system impulse response of any signal with a fixed time delay. When applied to loudspeakers, this means that beside the conventionally measured pressure amplitude spectrum there is a pressure phase spectrum, which to the best information available to this author has not been as well investigated. In measuring both the amplitude and phase spectrum of some common loudspeaker types it was immediately evident that some peculiarities in the behavior of phase were not apparent from an inspection of amplitude alone. Since the measurement technique allows a subtraction of time delay incurred between the electrical stimulus applied to the loudspeaker terminals and the pressure wave incident upon the test microphone, it was apparent from the beginning that there was in many cases a frequency-dependent time delay in excess of that caused by the travelling of the pressure wave over the known distance from voice coil to microphone diaphragm. Attempts at understanding this delay in terms of an equivalent electronic transfer function were not satisfactory: the only concept of circuit time delay which might prove useful is that of group delay, also called envelope delay, and it was not evident exactly how one might go about application of this concept, particularly when open literature definitions are accompanied with disquieting phrases such as "... when the amplitude does not change rapidly with frequency ..." and "... if there is no absorption ...". In fact it is rather disturbing that a substitute more in alignment with nature is not used in those cases when this so-called time delay becomes negative, a condition found to be quite common in loudspeaker measurements. For this reason it became necessary to derive a time delay more in keeping with concepts of causality as well as to investigate the amplitude and phase relationships in loudspeakers. The resulting concept of a spatial "spreading out" of the effective acoustic position of a loudspeaker behind its physical position would appear to be a more unified approach to time delay in such a complicated network. This paper is a documentation of some characteristics which have been measured on typical loudspeakers, as well as the derivation of a concept of time delay useful for interpreting these characteristics. The ultimate purpose is to provide audio engineers working on loudspeaker design a criterion by which a loudspeaker may be equalized to provide a more perfect response than would be possible by the use of pressure response measurements alone.

THE LOUDSPEAKER AS A NETWORK ELEMENT

In considering the role of a loudspeaker in the reproduction of sound, it would appear logical to describe this device as a network element. Although a transducer of electrical to acoustic energy, a loudspeaker may dissipate power, store energy, modify frequency response, introduce distortion, and in general impart the same aberrations in its duty as any conventional electronic network. Unlike a conventional network, however, a loudspeaker interfaces with the spatial medium of a human interpreter and may possess characteristics in this medium, such as polar response and a time-delayed phenomenon, which are unlike a normal electronic network element. While recognition of these latter effects exists, measurement has proven cumbersome.

In the discussion to follow a loudspeaker will be considered as a general network element. This element will have some transfer function relating the output sound pressure wave to the applied electrical stimulus. The output of the loudspeaker will be considered to be its free-field response. Where severe interaction with its environment is desired, as for example in the case of a corner horn or wall-mounted dipole, then that portion of the environment will be included. No simplification to an equivalent circuit is sought; indeed, the system is assumed to be so complicated that the only knowledge one has is a direct acoustic response measurement.

DEFINITION OF FREQUENCY RESPONSE

The transfer function of a loudspeaker will be assumed independent of signal level. This considerably simplifies the analysis and is justified when one considers that deviations from linearity of amplitude are much less than deviations from uniform frequency response. This means that, as in linear circuit theory, one can now define the transfer function to be a function of frequency. Our concern then rests with determining the frequency response of a loudspeaker.

The frequency response of a loudspeaker will be defined as the complex Fourier transform of its response to an impulse of electrical energy. If one considers the magnitude of the frequency dependent pressure response, this definition coincides with the practice of using a slow sinewave sweep in an anechoic chamber and plotting the pressure response as a function of frequency [17]. This definition, however, also includes the phase angle as a frequency-dependent term. Thus if a loudspeaker has an amplitude response $A(\omega)$ and a phase response $\phi(\omega)$ the loudspeaker response $S(\omega)$ is

$$S(\omega) = A(\omega) e^{i\phi(\omega)}. \quad (1)$$

It quite frequently happens that the amplitude response is better characterized in decibels as a logarithmic function, $a(\omega)$, which leads to the simplified form

$$S(\omega) = e^{a(\omega)} e^{i\phi(\omega)}. \quad (2)$$

The frequency response of a loudspeaker will then consist of two plots. The plot of magnitude of sound pressure in decibels as a function of frequency, $a(\omega)$, will simply be called amplitude. The plot of phase angle of sound pressure as a function of frequency, $\phi(\omega)$, will be called phase. These taken together will completely characterize the linear loudspeaker frequency response by the relation

$$\ln S(\omega) = a(\omega) + i\phi(\omega). \quad (3)$$

Equation (3) allows us to state that the amplitude and phase are the real and imaginary components of a function of a complex variable. This complex function is thus a more complete definition of what is meant by the frequency response of a loudspeaker. From this we see that measuring amplitude alone may not be sufficient to specify total speaker behavior.

THE LOUDSPEAKER AS A MINIMUM PHASE NETWORK

The measurement of loudspeaker pressure response is not a new art, and substantial definitive data has existed for over 40 years [17]. With a few very rare exceptions these measurements have been of the amplitude response [23, 24, 25]. Indeed, it is common practice to call this the frequency response of a loudspeaker.

It is of more than casual concern to investigate the conditions under which the measurement of amplitude response is sufficient to characterize the complete behavior of a loudspeaker. Obviously, whenever this is the case, the measurement of phase is academic, and a conventional amplitude response measurement should continue as a mainstay of data. Referring to Eq. (3) one may inquire into the conditions under which a prescribed magnitude function results in a definite phase angle function and conversely.

For a complex function such as expressed in Eq. (3) there will exist a unique relationship between the real and imaginary parts, determined by a contour integral along the frequency axis and around the right half-plane, if the logarithm is analytic in this right half-plane [2]. A network which meets this requirement is called a minimum phase network. Thus, if a loudspeaker is a minimum phase network, the measurement of either phase or amplitude is sufficient to characterize the frequency response completely.

When one has a minimum phase network the amplitude and phase are Hilbert transforms of each other related by [2, 3, 5, 6]

$$a(\omega) = \frac{1}{\pi} P \int_{-\infty}^{\infty} \frac{\phi(x)}{\omega - x} dx \quad (4)$$

$$-\phi(\omega) = \frac{1}{\pi} P \int_{-\infty}^{\infty} \frac{a(x)}{\omega - x} dx, \quad (5)$$

where P indicates that the principal part of the integral is to be taken at the pole ω. These integrals are the counterpart of Cauchy's differential relations on the frequency axis and are a sufficient condition to ensure that the loudspeaker does not have an output prior to an input signal, that is, $f(t) = 0$ for $t < 0$. While it may appear absurd to even concern oneself with the obvious fact that a minimum phase network cannot predict the output, it is quite important to the concept of group delay for a minimum phase function. It can be shown that group delay is not coincident with signal delay for a minimum phase network [26].

Given that one seeks confirmation of minimum phase behavior in a loudspeaker, how can one determine when this condition is actually achieved? It is unfortunate that one cannot determine this from either amplitude or phase alone. This follows either from an analysis of Eqs. (4) and (5) or the Cauchy-Riemann equations (Eq. A2 in Appendix A) or from a consideration of the factors needed to say that there are no zeros in the right half-plane. Thus it would seem that it is necessary to measure both amplitude and phase in order to determine if a measurement of amplitude alone would have been sufficient. On its face value, this is a convincing argument for measuring phase.

Hard on the heels of such an analysis comes the query as to why one would be concerned whether a loudspeaker is minimum phase or not. The answer comes from a very important property of minimum phase networks which may be paraphrased [4] as: If a loudspeaker is a minimum phase network then it can be characterized as a ladder network composed of resistors, capacitors, and inductors, and there will always exist a complementing network which will correct the loudspeaker frequency distortion as closely as one chooses. Thus, if one assumes linearity, a minimum phase loudspeaker could be completely compensated to become a distortionless transducer.

Consider what this means if one does not have a minimum phase loudspeaker. Assume that a pressure response (amplitude) measurement is made on a loudspeaker in an anechoic chamber. The speaker will of course have peaks and dips in its response. One might naturally assume that by diligent work it would be possible to level out the peaks and fill in the dips by a combination of electrical and mechanical means to produce a loudspeaker with a considerably smoother measured response. However, if one does this with a non-minimum phase loudspeaker, even if it is non-minimum phase over only a portion of the spectrum, one will have a transducer with a smoother $\alpha(\omega)$ but quite probably a considerably distorted $\phi(\omega)$, having inadvertently created a complicated all-pass lattice network. As shown in Appendix B and elsewhere [26], this is equivalent to a dispersive medium. When program material is fed into this "equalized" loudspeaker the odds are that the sound heard by a listener will be considerably more unpleasant than that coming through the loudspeaker without benefit of such equalization.

The unhappy consequence of this type of experience will be an assumption that the anechoic chamber response bears little relationship to the quality of reproduction, and that perhaps the best loudspeakers were indeed made in a previous generation. If, on the other hand, one knew what portions of the frequency spectrum were minimum phase, equalization of that portion *would* improve the response, provided one did not attempt equalization on the remaining non-minimum phase portions. Thus if one is concerned with improving the quality of sound reproduction by means of passive or active equalization one is immediately interested in phase response of a loudspeaker and determination of minimum phase criteria.

TIME DELAY IN A LOUDSPEAKER

A network is said to be dispersive if the phase velocity is frequency-dependent, which means that the phase plot is not a linear function of frequency [11]. In pursuing the mathematical analysis of network transfer functions one eventually arrives at considerations of the effect of dispersion on time delay of a signal through a network. Perhaps the best that can be said of such considerations is that they are seldom lucid and almost never appear applicable to the problem at hand. One must nonetheless recognize that group delay (envelope delay) and phase delay are legitimate manifestations of the perturbations produced on a signal by a network. In this section we shall investigate some general considerations of time delay and apply them to the loudspeaker.

There is, of course, a very real time delay incurred by an acoustic pressure wave as it travels from loudspeaker to listener. The velocity of sound in air at a fixed temperature is constant, at least to the precision required for this discussion. Furthermore, this velocity is not a function of frequency. If a pressure wave travels a given distance at a given velocity it takes a period of time expressed as the quotient of distance to velocity.

When one considers the loudspeaker one can no longer assume a non-dispersive behavior. Appendix B contains a derivation of the effect of a dispersive medium (without absorption) on the transfer function of a network. It is shown that if the time lag is a function of frequency the effect will be an excess phase lag in the transducer transfer function. A very important result of this is that one should look first at the phase terms when considering time delay. Equations (4) and (5) indicate that, at least for a minimum phase network, either phase or amplitude give the same information. Bode [4] has shown that for a minimum phase network the phase lag, and hence to some measure time lag, of the low-frequency portions of the spectrum are governed by the amplitude function at high frequencies. Since it is known that the amplitude response of a loudspeaker must fall off at some sufficiently high frequency, there is some justification to believe that there will be an additional time delay in a loudspeaker due to the rolloff of high-frequency response. Stated another way, the acoustic position of a loudspeaker should, on the average, lie behind its physical position by an amount that is some inverse function of its high-frequency cutoff. The acoustic position of a woofer will be further behind the physical transducer than that of a tweeter. This important fact is quite frequently overlooked by engineers who consider that spatial alignment of voice coils is sufficient to provide equal-time path signals from multirange loudspeakers.

Having thus considered air path delay and time lag in the loudspeaker due to high frequency cutoff, one comes to the seemingly nebulous concept of dispersive lag in the transducer. Two types of so-called time delays have been defined for the purpose of expressing the distortion of a signal passing through a medium. These are phase delay and group delay, also called envelope delay [7-8]. Phase delay expressed in seconds is a measure of the amount by which a sinusoid disturbance of fixed frequency is shifted in phase after passing through a network. This conception is applicable only for a sinewave and only after total equilibrium is achieved, and is consequently of no use in considerations of the realistic problem of aperiodic disturbances. Therefore, we will not consider phase delay any further.

Group delay, also expressed in seconds, is an attempt at expression of the relative time shift of signal frequency components adjacent to a reference frequency. When used in this manner and applied to a medium with a substantial time delay (in the classic sense of distance traversed at a finite velocity) group delay is of benefit in distortion analysis. Group delay has caused a considerable confusion among engineers who have attempted to stretch the definition beyond the frequency range within which it is valid. Group delay is expressible very simply as the slope of the phase-frequency distribution; thus for a network with the transfer function of Eq. (2),

$$t_{Group} = -d\phi(\omega)/d\omega. \tag{6}$$

Group delay, although expressed in the dimension of time, is not a satisfactory substitute for the engineering concept of time delay which one intuitively feels must be present in a medium. There is a strong desire to ascribe a causal relation between an applied stimulus to a loudspeaker, for example, and the emergent pressure wave which as a premise, must have some time lag. There are, however, enough examples of total inapplicability—so called anomalous dispersion—to create suspicion regarding the primacy of group delay.

It can be shown that there is indeed a time delay phenomenon in a network more in alignment with engineering experience [26]. This delay is not necessarily single-valued, but may be multiple-valued or possibly a time distribution. An engineering interpretation which can be put on the time delay of a network may be secured by investigating the behavior of a given frequency component of an input signal as it finally emerges in the output. It is true that a sudden change in a parameter at the input will in effect create a broad spectrum around the particular frequency the delay of which we wish to characterize. However, this does not invalidate the premise that there will still exist a spectral component of this frequency, and one may legitimately ask what happens to that spectral component. It is shown that it may take some finite time for the component to appear at the output and that for a general network there may be many components of the same frequency arriving with different time delays.

This multiplicity of delayed outputs at a given frequency means that in the case of a loudspeaker one could also think in terms of a number of loudspeakers arrayed in space behind the physical transducer in such a way that the air-path delay of each produces the appropriate value of delay. Each frequency in the reproduced spectrum will then possess some unique spatial distribution of the equivalent loudspeakers. The emergent sound pressure wave will be a perfect replica of electrical signal only if these equivalent loudspeakers merge into one position for all frequencies since only then will there be no frequency-dependent amplitude or phase terms and all signal components will arrive at the same time [26].

Figure 1a is a highly schematic attempt at illustrating the phenomenon of loudspeaker time delay. A single loudspeaker is assumed, with a physical position in space indicated by the solid line. The effective position of the source of sound as a function of frequency is shown by speaker symbols which lie behind the physical location of the actual speaker by an amount determined by the delay time and velocity of sound in air. There may be many such equivalent perfect speakers distributed in space with more or less energy from each. The average position of the distribution of these equivalent speakers is

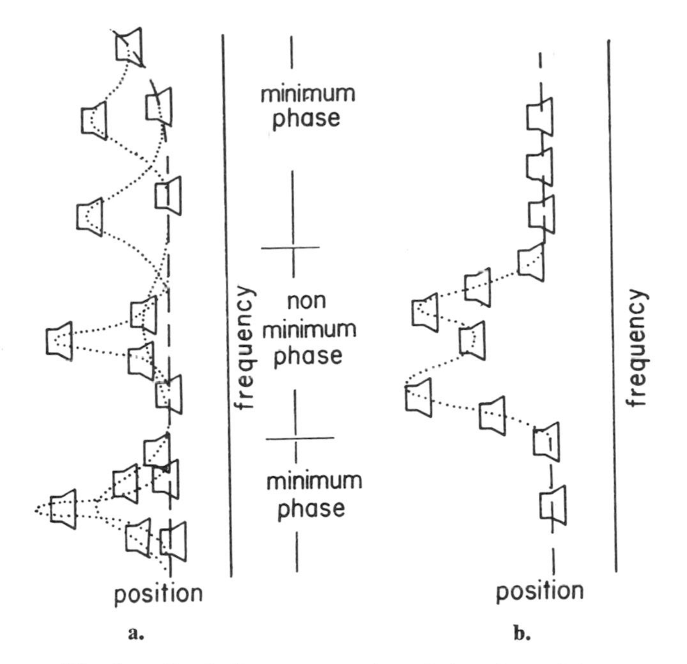

Fig. 1. **a.** Symbolic representation of the effect of frequency-dependent amplitude and phase variations of a single loudspeaker as equivalent to an assemblage of perfect loudspeakers distributed in space behind the physical position of the single loudspeaker. Each of the equivalent perfect loudspeakers has a flat amplitude and phase pressure response but assumes a frequency-dependent position indicated by the **dotted lines**, and in general differs in amount and polarity of energy radiated. The physical position of the actual radiator is indicated by the **solid line** while the average acoustic position determined by high-frequency cutoff lies behind this at the position of the **dashed line. b.** Symbolic representation of the acoustic effect of a response equalization based entirely on correcting the amplitude variations of the speaker of Fig. 1a. The frequencies at which the unequalized speaker is minimum phase may be corrected to perfect response indicated by a space-fixed perfect loudspeaker, but excess time delay results for non-minimum phase frequencies.

indicated by the dashed line, and corresponds to the delay attributed to high-frequency rolloff. Those frequencies at which the original loudspeaker is minimum phase are shown. Note that at no frequency will an equivalent speaker be found in front of the physical speaker. This is a result of the obvious fact that a loudspeaker can have no response prior to an input.

In Fig. 1b the result of amplitude equalization alone is symbolized. The equivalent speakers coalesce into one for the minimum-phase frequencies but spread out for all others.

TECHNIQUE OF MEASUREMENT

Analysis of the technique of time delay spectrometry has shown that the intermediate frequency amplifier contains the complex response of Eq. (2) with the frequency parameter ω replaced by a time parameter at [1]. This complex spectrum is convolved with a modifying term which is composed in turn of the convolution of the impulse response $i(t)$ of the intermediate frequency amplifier with the sweeping window function $w(t)$. The derivation of this relation is presented in a previous paper [1] and is sufficiently lengthy that it will not be reproduced here.

Equation (37) of that paper shows that if a loudspeaker is the subject of this test, the time function one finds in the intermediate frequency amplifier is $o(t)$, where

$$o(t) = (Gain\ Factor)[i(t) \otimes w(t)] \otimes S(at). \quad (7)$$

The effect of the convoluting, or folding integrals, indicated by the symbol $\otimes$ is a scanning and smoothing of the response $S(at)$. This means that if one observes appropriate precautions in sweep rate a, the intermediate frequency amplifier contains a signal which may be interpreted as

$$o(t) = Smoothed\ S(at). \quad (8)$$

Expressing this differently, one might say that the desired spectrum (Eq. 2) is contained in the equipment but all "sharp edges" have been smoothed off. The amount of smoothing is a function of the bandwidth of the equipment and the rapidity of the sweep. What is important is that there are no surprises or genuinely false patterns created by time delay spectrometry. If the loudspeaker contains a peak in response, then this peak will show in the analysis.

Having established the fact that time delay spectrometry will yield the complex transfer function of Eq. (2), it remains to see how both amplitude and phase may be extracted. It is assumed that the previous paper [1] will be used as reference for the basic technique. Figure 2 is a simplified block diagram of a time delay spectrometry configuration capable of measuring both amplitude and phase of a loudspeaker response.

In Fig. 2 a crystal oscillator is used as a source of stable fixed frequency. A countdown circuit derives a rate of one pulse per second which triggers an extremely linear sawtooth generator. This sawtooth provides a horizontal display to an oscilloscope as well as drive to a voltage-controlled sweep oscillator. The crystal oscillator is also used as a frequency source for two frequency synthesizers. A fixed frequency synthesizer converts the crystal frequency to the frequency of the intermediate frequency amplifier for the purpose of providing a reference to the phase detector. A tunable frequency synthesizer with digital frequency control is used to provide a precise offset frequency to down-convert the sweeping oscillator to the audio range; the filtered audio-range sweeping tone is then used to drive the speaker under test. A delay line is used between the sweeping oscillator and the microphone-channel balanced mixer for the purpose of precise cancellation of the time lag of the down-conversion lowpass filter. The intermediate-frequency amplifier containing the up-converted microphone spectrum feeds both a limiter-phase detector channel and a logarithmic amplifier-amplitude demodulator channel. The output of either the amplitude or phase detectors may be selected for display on the vertical axis of the oscilloscope which has the sawtooth horizontal drive.

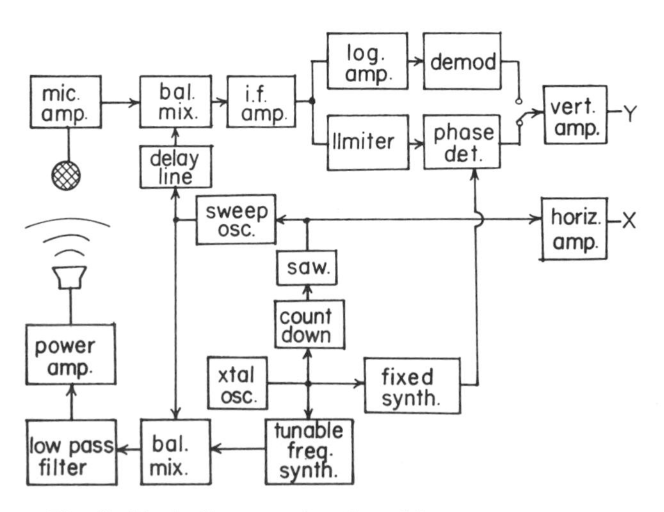

Fig. 2. Block diagram of a time delay spectrometry configuration capable of measuring both amplitude and phase frequency response of a loudspeaker.

It will be recognized that the demodulation of phase information has necessitated a considerable increase in circuit complexity over that required for amplitude alone. Particularly important is the fact that subtraction of the free air-path time lag and a stable display of phase not only requires a fixed offset frequency precisely divisible by the frequency of the sawtooth sweep but also necessitates a coherent phase-stable locked loop involving the time lag of the measurement air path.

As an illustration of the precision required, assume that one is measuring a response from dc to 20 kHz in a one second sweep and that an intermediate frequency of 100 kHz is being used. An offset of one part in 100,000 of the oscillator with respect to the phase standard will produce 360° of phase drift in one second. With a high-persistence phosphor, standard with spectrum analyzers, a distinct image blur will occur with a drift of 3.6° per sweep, yet this requires the oscillators to be offset by no more than one part in ten million. The use of a sampling attachment with an x-y plotter might require two orders of magnitude of stability over this value, i.e., oscillators which if multiplied up to 1,000 MHz would differ by no more than one Hz. This requires a self-consistent set of frequencies provided by obtaining all frequencies from a single oscillator.

Distance-measuring capability is similarly impressive. If one is measuring the phase response in the assumed 20 kHz band, one has a wavelength of approximately 650 mil at the highest frequency. A physical offset in distance of only 6 mil between loudspeaker and microphone will produce a 3.6° phase change at 20 kHz. This corresponds to a ½ μsec time difference in path length.

While the phase measurement provides an enormously sensitive measure of time delay, it should not be implied that it is at all difficult to obtain good data. It is unusual when there is sufficient motion of the air path or transducers to upset a phase measurement, and such an effect is visible within the time of two sweeps of the display.

In making measurements on a loudspeaker, the microphone is positioned at the desired speaker polar angle and at a distance consistent with the spectrum sweep rate and closest reflecting object. With the loudspeaker energized by the sweeping tone, the closest integer offset frequency is dialed which corresponds to the relation

$$F_0 = (X/c)(dF/dt) \quad (9)$$

where F_0 is the synthesizer offset in Hz, X is the distance from speaker to microphone in feet, c is the velocity of sound in feet per second, and the sweep rate is measured in Hz per second.

The amplitude response should be at or near its peak

value and require no further adjustment. The displayed phase response will quite generally be tilted with respect to the frequency axis at a slope which is proportional to the deviation of the offset oscillator from the proper value. An offset discrepancy of only two Hz will accumulate 720° of additional shift in a one second sweep. The proper offset frequency is easily found by observing the phase display and using that value which produces the most nearly horizontal phase plot. If the value is between two integer frequencies with a one second sweep, it may be helpful to slightly reposition the microphone toward or away from the speaker. Having found the required offset frequency it is more than likely that the display will pass through 360° at one or more frequencies, producing phase ambiguities. The phase of the offset synthesizer must then be slipped until the most nearly optimum display results. This is most readily done by dialing an offset which is 0.1 Hz above the integer Hz value, which will cause the phase display to move vertically by 36° per sweep. When the proper pattern is obtained the 0.1 Hz digit is removed, leaving a stationary pattern of phase *vs* frequency.

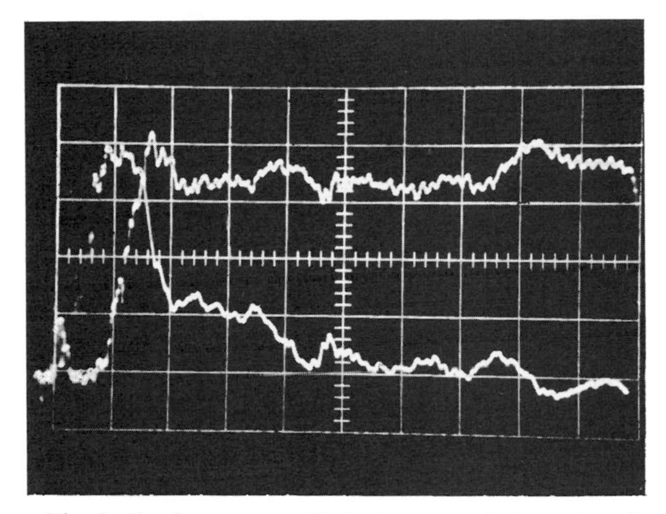

Fig. 3. Simultaneous amplitude (**upper**) and phase (**lower**) response of an inexpensive horn-loaded compression tweeter. Response is shown from dc to 10 kHz at 1 kHz per horizontal division. Amplitude is 10 dB per division and phase 60° per division.

MEASUREMENTS ON TYPICAL LOUDSPEAKERS

In the analysis of typical loudspeaker amplitude and phase characteristics it is desirable that a simultaneous display of both functions be made so that variations in either parameter at any given frequency may be compared. The oscillographs of this section are therefore dual-trace plots with the following characteristics: 1. The horizontal axis represents increasing frequency to the right with a linear scale; 2. Amplitude is the upper plot with logarithmic response and increasing signal as an upward deflection; 3. Phase is the lower plot with phase lead as an upward deflection. These characteristics, with the possible exception of a linear frequency scale, are among the standard conventions of network analysis.

Figure 3 is an example of an inexpensive horn-loaded compression tweeter. The plot extends from zero to 10 kHz with a frequency deflection factor of 1 kHz per cm (one cm is represented by a major division). The amplitude deflection factor is 10 dB per cm and the phase is 60° per cm. By referring to Fig. A-2 in the appendix it can be seen that this speaker is of the minimum phase type. The peaks at 1.6 kHz, 4 kHz, 7 kHz, and 8 kHz, and the dips at 4.6 kHz and 7.3 kHz have the appropriate phase fluctuation. Of particular interest is the peak at 1.6 kHz, identified by the phase change as a primary resonance in the driver occurring above horn cutoff.

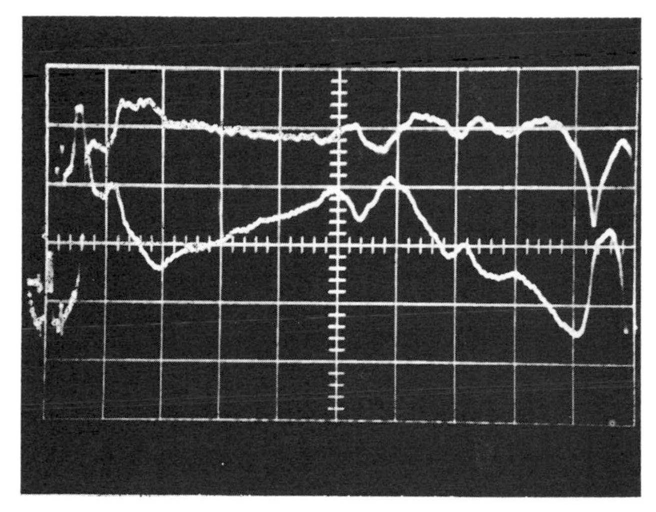

Fig. 4. Amplitude (**upper**) and phase (**lower**) response of midrange horn-loaded driver. Coordinates identical to those of Fig. 3.

Figure 4 is an example of a midrange horn-loaded speaker of the non-minimum phase type. Small variations are of minimum phase, including the dip at 9.4 kHz, but inspection of the phase identifies the fact that the speaker has a frequency-dependent spatial location. The acoustic position of the farthest forward equivalent speaker as determined by the offset frequency in the spectrometer is approximately 0.75 in. behind the position of the phase plug. This is in general agreement with the delay one would expect with a 10 kHz cutoff. From 2 kHz to 5.5 kHz the phase slope with independence of amplitude indicates a position which might be called Position 1. From 5.5 kHz to around 9.4 kHz the acoustic position

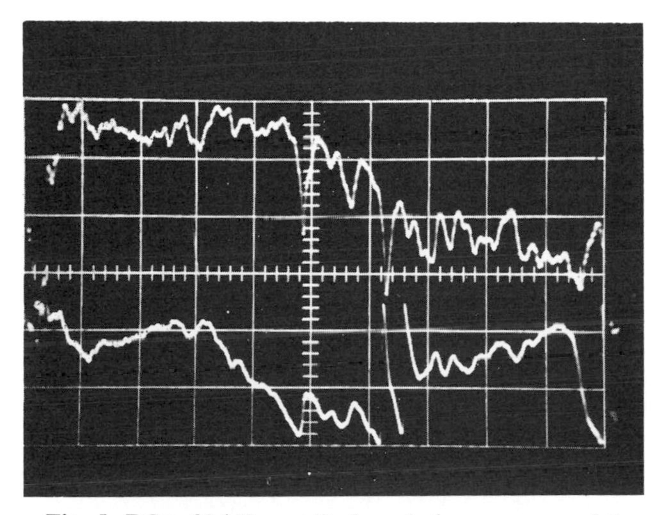

Fig. 5. DC to 20 kHz amplitude and phase response of the speaker of Fig. 4. Amplitude is 10 dB per division and phase 120° per division.

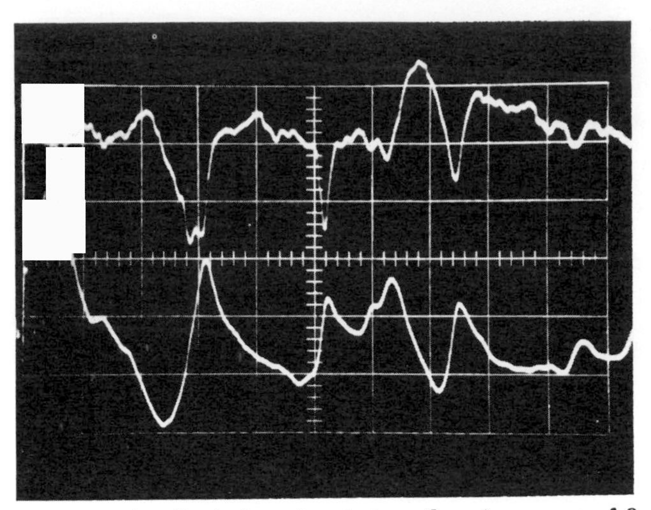

Fig. 6. Amplitude (upper) and phase (lower) response of 8 in. loudspeaker mounted in a reflex cabinet. Frequency scale is from dc to 2 kHz at 200 Hz per division. Amplitude is 5 dB per division and phase 30° per division.

can be seen to be behind Position 1 by almost 2 in. This is because the phase slope difference between the two regions differs by about 60° per kHz, which yields a time difference of 1/6 msec. The phase behavior between 1.1 kHz and 2 kHz in conjunction with the broad peak indicates a minimum phase resonance and not necessarily a change in location. This is further bolstered by observing that the phase slope from 800 Hz to 1.1 kHz is that of 2 kHz to 5.5 kHz. The high negative phase slope at the cutoff and the phase peak at 500 Hz is the minimum-phase behavior to be expected of the rapid drop in amplitude. The interpretation of the region around 1.5 kHz is that of a multi-pole resonance similar to a band-pass filter.

Figure 5 is the response from dc to 20 kHz for the speaker of Fig. 4. The behavior pattern shows definite non-minimum phase between 12 kHz and 14 kHz, with minimum phase elsewhere.

Figure 6 shows the on-axis behavior from dc to 2 kHz, at 200 Hz per cm, of an 8 in. speaker mounted in a reflex cabinet. The dip at 600 Hz coincides with the undamped back-wall reflection, and from the phase characteristic can be seen to be of the minimum phase type. This oscillograph was made with a five times expansion of a 10 kHz sweep in order that the space-equivalent bandwidth could be made small enough for measurement in a small room. For this reason the smoothing bandwidth is 70 Hz and the phase plot will appear slightly to the left of its proper frequency due to smoothing. By making the appropriate correction it can be seen that each of the peaks and dips is of the minimum phase type shown in Fig. A-2. The strong local fluctuations, such as the dips at 600 Hz, 1100 Hz, and 1500 Hz and the peaks at 400 Hz and 1350 Hz, produce phase fluctuations which are superimposed on the overall phase characteristic due to the low-frequency cutoff. This phase variation due to low-frequency cutoff is characteristically a high negative phase slope in the cutoff region and a smooth extension into the region of normal response.

The low-frequency behavior, which is strong due to the system response zero at dc is shown also in Fig. 7. This is a response measurement at 1 kHz per cm made from -5 kHz to $+5$ kHz passing through zero. It is a 15° off-axis response of an unenclosed paper whizzer-cone loudspeaker of the type normally used for replacement purposes in automobile radios. The required even and odd frequency characteristic of amplitude and phase is quite pronounced. For this loudspeaker the phase change is 180° at zero frequency, and does not commence its transition until within 200 Hz of zero. The apparent phase breakup below 100 Hz is due to strong low-frequency disturbances in the measuring room which captured the limiter when the loudspeaker signal dropped below their spectral distribution. This oscillograph demonstrates that the phase at zero frequency for which there is no loudspeaker output, may be obtained by centering the time delay spectrometry display at zero frequency and observing the point of symmetry as one approaches zero from both directions. This loudspeaker may be seen to have a minimum phase dip at 3.5 kHz and a possible minimum phase peak at 2.2 kHz, while the remainder of the spectrum is non-minimum phase. This is not unexpected since the response was obtained off-axis and the diffraction and reflection around the whizzer are substantial. Note in particular the absorption dips around 3.5 kHz which do not have substantial phase variations.

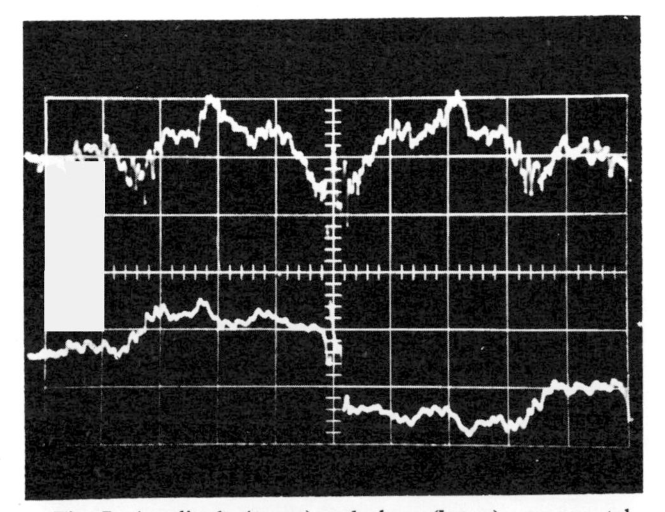

Fig. 7. Amplitude (upper) and phase (lower) response taken 15° off-axis on an unenclosed whizzer-cone speaker. Frequency scale is 1 kHz per division and extends from —5 kHz through dc to +5 kHz. The even frequency symmetry of amplitude and odd frequency symmetry of phase necessary for causality is readily discerned. Amplitude is 10 dB per division and phase is 120° per division.

Figure 8 shows the response of another horn-loaded compression tweeter. The scale factors for frequency, amplitude and phase are 1 kHz, 10 dB, and 30° per cm respectively. The spectrum encompasses dc to 10 kHz. With the possible exception of the region around 8.4 kHz the response is definitely minimum phase.

Figure 9 shows the response from dc to 20 kHz of a quality midrange electrostatic loudspeaker. This is also of minimum phase characteristic throughout the spectrum. The large apparent phase jump at 18 kHz is a phase detector transition through the equivalent 360° point.

An extremely difficult loudspeaker to measure, due to severe environmental dependence, is the full-range corner horn. The inclusion of the necessary walls and floor rather effectively nullifies a normally anechoic environ-

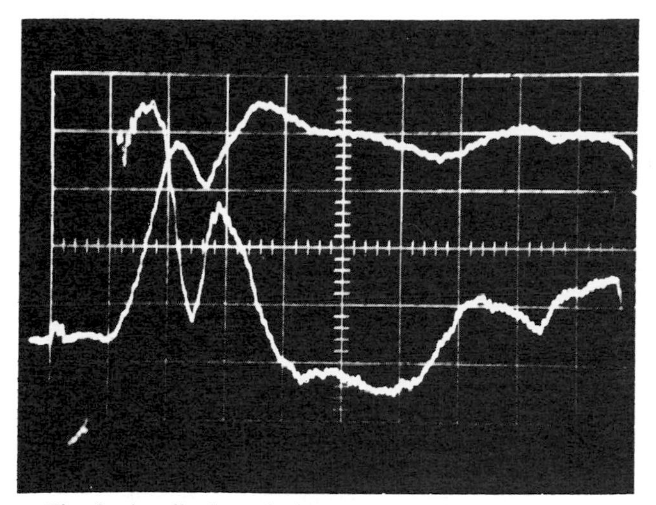

Fig. 8. Amplitude and phase response from dc to 10 kHz at 1 kHz per division of a moderately expensive horn-loaded compression tweeter. Amplitude is 10 dB per division and phase 30° per division.

ment. Figure 10a is for a measurement taken 3 ft on-axis in front of a medium-size corner horn enclosure. The frequency range covered is dc to 1 kHz at 100 Hz per cm. The amplitude scale is 10 dB per cm while the phase scale is 60° per cm. The response dip at 260 Hz was determined to be a genuine loudspeaker aberration and not a chance room reflection by the simple expedient of moving the microphone physically around and noting response. The basic response is seen to be reasonably uniform from about 70 Hz to well beyond 1 kHz with the exception of a strong minimum phase dip at 260 Hz. Figures 4, 8, and 10a compared near cutoff reveal a rather similar behavior pattern. According to the analysis of Appendix A the response dip at 260 Hz is minimum phase and removable. Figure 10b is the result of a simple inductance-capacitance peaking circuit placed between the power amplifier and loudspeaker terminals. The scale factors and magnitudes of Fig. 10b are identical to those of Fig. 10a to show a direct comparison before and after removing the minimum phase response dip. Because the network represents a loss, investigation of Fig. 10b reveals that the overall transfer gain was reduced by about

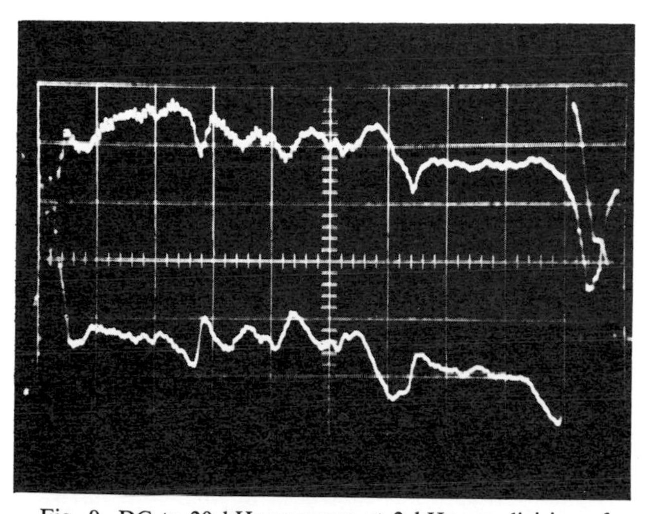

Fig. 9. DC to 20 kHz response at 2 kHz per division of a midrange electrostatic loudspeaker. Amplitude is 10 dB per division and phase is 60° per division.

20 dB with an additional 60° of incurred midrange phase lag. However, the response dip of Fig. 10a estimated at close to 20 dB has been effectively removed. The remaining response dip at 150 Hz may be seen to be an independent response aberration by comparing with Fig. 10a.

Investigation of the equalized response of Fig. 10b and other portions not illustrated revealed a smooth amplitude and phase response at frequencies which were harmonically related to 260 Hz. Thus, if room reflections did not constitute substantial energy at the microphone location, the squarewave response with a 260 Hz fundamental should have been improved. Figure 10c is the response to such a squarewave of the configuration of Figs. 10a and 10b. The upper trace is the response after equalization. The lower trace, made as a second exposure with the equalizer removed and system drive reduced accordingly, shows the unequalized response of Fig. 10a. There is no question that the transient behavior is improved. The squarewave frequency of Fig. 10c was chosen to show the improvement due to the response null removed, and was not deliberately modified for a more pleasing waveform after equalization. In fact, a substantial range of squarewave frequencies from about 70 Hz to 300 Hz show a distinct waveform improvement for the equalized speaker even with obvious room resonances.

CONCLUSION

This paper represents a preliminary report on loudspeaker frequency response measurement. An attempt has been made to provide a more rigorous approach to understanding the role that the neglected partner, phase, plays in the resultant performance of a loudspeaker. The measurement of phase as a spectral distribution and its correlation with response in the time domain has not received the attention which has been devoted to amplitude. There is, in fact, a substantial void in open literature discussion of phase distributions, which it is hoped will be partially filled by this paper. While there is rather complete agreement about the effect of peaks and dips on the response of a loudspeaker, one can usually expect animated discussion on the subject of phase variations. Part of the reason is the difficulty in instrumenting a phase measurement since phase is intimately related to time of occurrence. Thus measurements on magnetic recorders, disk recorders, loudspeakers and microphones are normally restricted to amplitude characteristics. Where lack of reverberation allows definite measurement of a source, measurements in the time domain by impulse testing or otherwise are used as a supplement to amplitude response measurements in the frequency domain [20]. By utilizing a different measurement technique it has been demonstrated here that loudspeaker phase response measurements may be made with the same facility and validity as amplitude response ones.

Having thus secured the capability of simultaneous measurement of amplitude and phase spectra, it is necessary to demonstrate a reasonable need for this capability. Looked at another way, any prior analysis which dictated a valid need for phase information would most certainly have precipitated a measurement technique. It

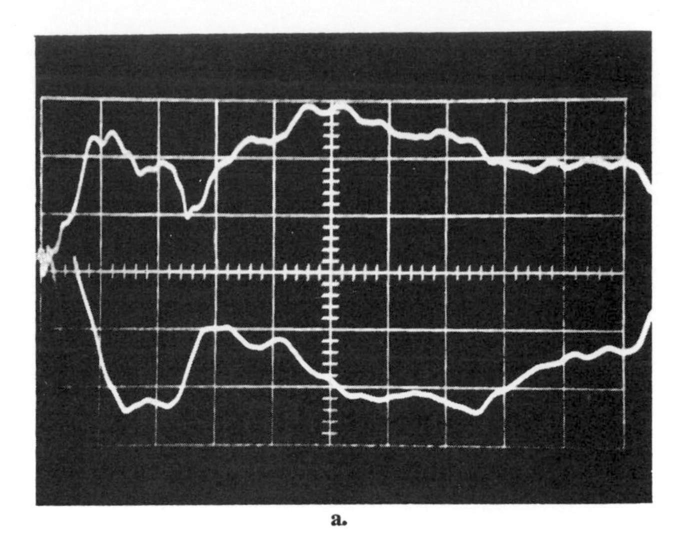

a.

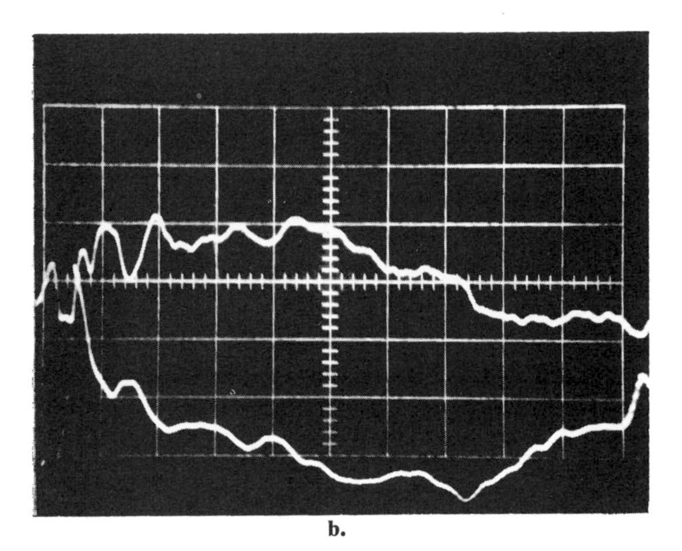

b.

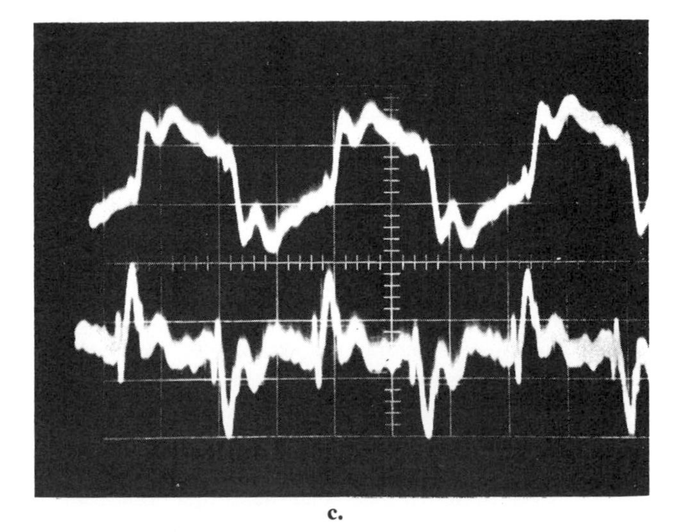

c.

Fig. 10. **a.** Three foot on-axis measurement of a corner horn loudspeaker system. Frequency scale is 100 Hz per division and covers dc to 1 kHz. Amplitude (**upper**) is 10 dB per division and phase (**lower**) is 60° per division. **b.** Result of equalization of the single major response dip of Fig. 10 a. **c. Upper** trace is the acoustic response to a square-wave of the equalized loudspeaker of Fig. 10b. **Lower** trace is the acoustic response of the unequalized loudspeaker of Fig. 10a. Vertical scale is uncalibrated pressure response and horizontal scale is 1 msec per division.

was required, then, to analyze the conditions under which it is necessary to have both amplitude and phase characteristics before one can say one knows everything about the frequency behavior. This led to electronic circuit analysis, where both spectra are normally considered, and a consideration of that class of networks known as minimum phase. The answer was not found completely in circuit analysis, since the very complex behavior of a loudspeaker quite frequently overtaxes the simplified concept of circuit time delay. The appendices to this paper help to bridge the gap in using circuit concepts for analysis of loudspeakers when one has both amplitude and phase spectra. Appendix A derives a simple graphical relationship between amplitude and phase which allows one to state whether a network under analysis is of the minimum phase type. This derivation was necessary since circuit analysis normally proceeds from a knowledge of the equations governing behavior, whereas loudspeaker characteristics are a product of a measurement on a system for which one has incomplete analysis.

Appendix B is a derivation of the inter-domain Fourier transformation relationship in the case of a dispersive medium without absorption. This is, of course, precisely what one finds with a loudspeaker if all minimum phase aberrations are removed. Surprisingly, this is also a common delay situation in many other branches of wave mechanics, yet the transform of a fixed delay of time or frequency (a special case of a non-dispersive medium) is the only form found in widely respected literature.

A head-on attack on the concept of time delay in a dispersive medium with absorption, which is a general characterization of loudspeakers, seems required. The concept of time delay in such a medium does not lack publication; however, such analysis is generally so specific that an engineer quite understandably hesitates in applying it to a general problem. An attack on this problem, discussed in a paper originally planned as a third Appendix to the present one [26], proceeds from the premise that a real-world system is causal; the output follows logically from the input and cannot predict the input. In pursuing this premise we were willing to accept a multiple-valued time behavior of spectral components. As a result, we found that there is indeed a concept of time delay of a system which is causal and makes engineering sense. Furthermore, there is a natural analogy between frequency and time which allows an engineer to draw from knowledge in one domain to add to comprehension in the other domain, and thus to relate modulation theory to time delay incurred by a complex frequency transfer function. Although a unique concept of time delay, the derivation involved is shown to be consistent with the work of Rayleigh [15], Brillouin, [16] and MacColl [9]. An important byproduct of this analysis is an explanation for the confusion created by attempts at using group delay in an absorptive medium. It is shown that the classic concept of group delay is not applicable to a minimum phase medium, and hence to any causal medium with absorption.

Thus, it is possible to identify the effect of amplitude and phase variations as equivalent to what would exist if the actual loudspeaker were replaced by a large number of perfect loudspeakers spread out in space in a frequency-dependent manner. With this approach to the interrelation of amplitude and phase, one can state from measured performance whether a given loudspeaker may be improved by electrical or mechanical means. Since it makes no difference whether the response characteristic is traceable to the loudspeaker, enclosure, or immediate environment, if the resultant behavior is minimum phase one knows that it can be improved.

Finally, some amplitude and phase spectra of typical loudspeakers have been included. The product of any mathematical analysis of phase and time delay would be questionable if it could not be applied to the practical physical problems of an audio engineer. It has been demonstrated by example that a loudspeaker may not be minimum phase. In the case where a loudspeaker is found to be minimum phase, a simple example was included to demonstrate that such minimum-phase response deficiencies can be removed by simple networks.

As more familiarity is gained with the phase response of loudspeakers it is likely that such measurement will become more commonplace. By relating the amplitude and phase characteristics to a seldom considered form of distortion, time delay, and by providing a visual means of determining whether this time delay distortion is removable by relatively simple means, it is hoped that a tool has been provided which will lead to improved quality of sound reproduction.

APPENDIX A

Relations Between Amplitude and Phase for Minimum Phase Network

Assume the transfer function of a network is

$$H(s) = A(s)e^{i\phi(s)} = e^{a(s)+i\phi(s)} \tag{A1}$$

where $a(s) = \ln A(s)$ and $s = \sigma + i\omega$. This will be defined as the transfer function of a minimum phase network if $a(s)$ and $\phi(s)$ are uniquely related each to the other. If either $a(s)$ or $\phi(s)$ are known, then everything is known about the network. This implies that there are no zeros or poles of the transfer function in the right-half s plane, since the derivatives must not only exist along the $i\omega$ axis for all values of the frequency ω but are related by the Cauchy-Riemann equations within and on the boundary of the right-half s plane [2,6]:

$$\frac{\partial a(s)}{\partial \sigma} = \frac{\partial \phi(s)}{\partial \omega}, \quad \frac{\partial a(s)}{\partial \omega} = -\frac{\partial \phi(s)}{\partial \sigma}. \tag{A2}$$

Taking further derivatives,

$$\frac{\partial}{\partial \sigma}\left(\frac{\partial a(s)}{\partial \sigma}\right) = \frac{\partial}{\partial \sigma}\left(\frac{\partial \phi(s)}{\partial \omega}\right), \tag{A3}$$

$$\frac{\partial}{\partial \omega}\left(\frac{\partial a(s)}{\partial \omega}\right) = -\frac{\partial}{\partial \omega}\left(\frac{\partial \phi(s)}{\partial \sigma}\right) \tag{A4}$$

$$= -\frac{\partial}{\partial \sigma}\left(\frac{\partial \phi(s)}{\partial \omega}\right),$$

from which it follows that

$$\frac{\partial^2 a(s)}{\partial \omega^2} = -\frac{\partial^2 a(s)}{\partial \sigma^2} \tag{A5}$$

and

$$\frac{\partial^2 \phi(s)}{\partial \omega^2} = -\frac{\partial^2 \phi(s)}{\partial \sigma^2}. \tag{A6}$$

If one assumes that the complex s plane is a topological map with $a(s)$ as the elevation, the situation is as plotted in Fig. A-1 for the simple one-pole one-zero

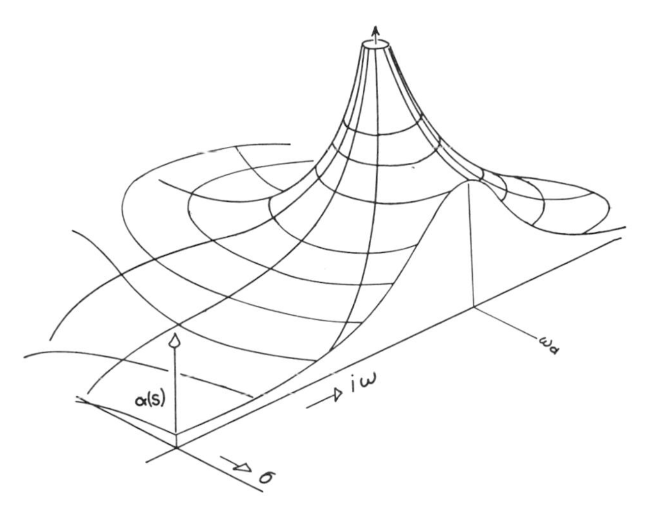

Fig. A-1. Representation of the topological plot of amplitude response in the complex s-plane. A section is taken along the $i\omega$ axis which corresponds to the curve normally considered as the amplitude response. The behavior near a pole in the left half s-plane is characterized and lines of steepest descent and of equipotential are shown.

function. For such a plot of $a(s)$ the lines of steepest descent for $a(s)$ are equipotential lines for $\phi(s)$. The lines of descent for $a(s)$ can originate only from those points at which $a(s)$ is positive or negative infinite, since no finite maxima or minima occur and there can only be saddle points where

$$dH(s)/ds = 0. \tag{A7}$$

Because there are no singularities in the right half-plane one can then state that for a point on the imaginary axis (where $\sigma = 0$ and the real-world concept of transfer function exists) when at or near a frequency of closest approach to a singularity such as ω_a in Fig. A-1,

$$\partial a(s)/\partial \sigma \text{ is a maximum negative value.} \tag{A8}$$

From Eq. A2, then, at this frequency

$$\partial \phi(s)/\partial \omega \text{ is a maximum negative value,} \tag{A9}$$

or, a point of inflection exists for $\phi(s)$,

$$\partial^2 \phi(s)/\partial \omega^2 = 0. \tag{A10}$$

At this point any penetration into the s plane along the direction of the σ axis must be along an equipotential line of phase and consequently a maximum rate of change of phase with respect to σ, since it follows from Eqs. A6 and A10 that

$$\partial^2 \phi(s)/\partial \sigma^2 = 0. \tag{A11}$$

This means that

$$-\frac{\partial}{\partial \sigma}\left(\frac{\partial \phi(s)}{\partial \omega}\right) = \frac{\partial^2 a(s)}{\partial \omega^2} \tag{A12}$$

$$= \text{maximum negative.}$$

This leads to the very simple rule for a minimum phase

network: At a local maximum or minimum in the transfer function, a frequency of maximum curvature of amplitude corresponds to a point of inflection of phase.

It may also be seen that the skew symmetry of Eqs. A2 allow a similar rule stating that a maximum curvature of phase corresponds to a point of inflection of amplitude.

Also, from inspecting the polarity of the functions it is evident that if one considers the direction of increasing frequency, when $\partial^2 a(\omega)/\partial\omega^2$ is a maximum positive then $\partial\phi(\omega)/\partial\omega$ is a maximum positive, while when $\partial^2\phi(\omega)/\partial\omega^2$ is a maximum positive then $\partial a(\omega)/\partial\omega$ is a maximum negative.

Note that these relationships should be held precisely only if the frequency under analysis is that which is closest to the singularity (pole or zero in transfer function) which produces the high rate of change of curvature. Perturbations on either side of the frequency of the singularity will adhere less to this pattern the further one proceeds from the singularity. Figure A-2 shows

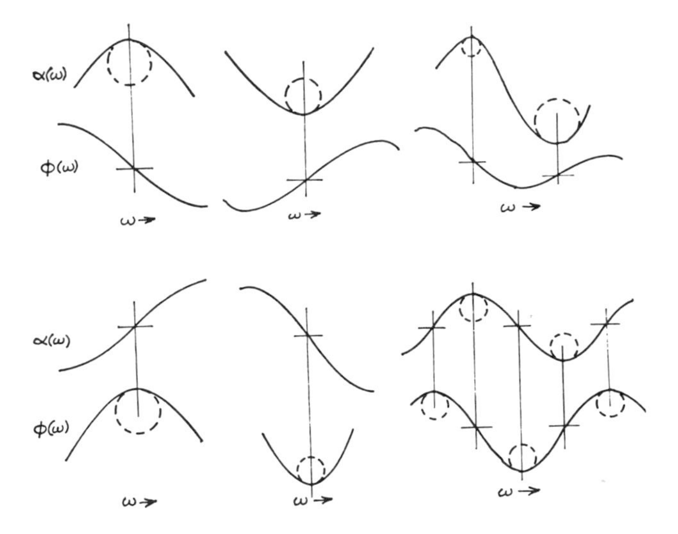

Fig. A-2. Characteristic amplitude and phase plots which may be used to identify minimum phase behavior. Points of maximum curvature are shown by **circles** around which the curve may be considered as bent, and associate points of inflection indicated by **horizontal lines.**

several simple cases of amplitude and phase functions which one can use to identify minimum-phase networks. Points of maximum curvature are shown by the dashed circle around which the curve might be thought of as bent. Points of inflection are shown by horizontal dashes. Note that the frequency scale is linear, amplitude is plotted logarithmically in dB with increasing gain as a positive quantity, and phase is plotted as an angle with the standard convention of phase lag as a negative angle.

APPENDIX B

Fourier Transform of Frequency-Dependent Delay

A medium in which a time-dependent disturbance propagates is said to be dispersive if the velocity in the medium, or time of traverse, varies with the frequency of the time dependence. If there are many frequency constituents in the initial form of the disturbance, then some time later these constituents are dispersed. The observed waveform at a fixed "down-stream" location will no longer be identical to the initial disturbance, and the resultant waveform will be a distortion of the original waveform even if no reduction in amplitude of these constituents has occurred.

Assume that the time delay for each frequency ω has been determined to be

$$T(\omega) = T_0 + \tau(\omega) \qquad \text{(B1)}$$

where T_0 is a fixed delay in seconds and $\tau(\omega)$ is a dispersive time delay. Since we are interested in frequency dependent factors, the frequency phase dependence becomes

$$\Theta(\omega) = \int_0^\omega T(\omega)\,d\omega = T_0\omega + \int_0^\omega \tau(\omega)\,d\omega. \qquad \text{(B2)}$$

This is the phase dependence of each frequency component comprising the dispersed output waveform. The expansion of all such components in a Fourier integral will yield the resultant time function at the output. Thus, for the case of an otherwise perfect transmission system, an input signal with a time dependence $g(t)$ and a frequency transform

$$G(\omega) = \int_{-\infty}^{\infty} g(t)e^{-i\omega t}dt \qquad \text{(B3)}$$

will produce an output from the dispersive medium of $f(t)$, where

$$f(t) = (1/2\pi)\int_{-\infty}^{\infty} G(\omega)e^{-i\Theta(\omega)}e^{i\omega t}d\omega. \qquad \text{(B4)}$$

The negative sign is used for time delay. This leads to the important finding that:

If $G(\omega)$ is the transform of $g(t)$, then

$$G(\omega)\cdot e^{\pm i\int_0^\omega T(\omega)d\omega}$$

is the transform of

$$g[t \pm T(\omega)].$$

By the same reasoning, if $g(t)$ is the transform of $G(\omega)$ then

$$g(t)\cdot e^{\pm i\int_0^t \Omega(t)dt}$$

is the transform of

$$G[\omega \mp \Omega(t)].$$

Note that the commonly encountered transform relations for a fixed delay constitute the special case of non-dispersive time delay.

REFERENCES

1. R. C. Heyser, "Acoustical Measurements by Time Delay Spectrometry," *J. Audio Eng. Soc.* **15**, 370 (1967).

2. C. H. Page, *Physical Mathematics* (D. Van Nostrand Co., Princeton, 1955), p. 220.

3. S. J. Mason and H. J. Zimmerman, *Electronic Circuits, Signals, and Systems* (Wiley, New York, 1960), p. 350.

4. H. W. Bode, *Network Analysis and Feedback Amplifier Design* (D. Van Nostrand Co., New York, 1955), p. 312.

5. Bateman Manuscript Project, *Tables of Integral Transforms* (McGraw Hill Book Co., New York, 1954), p. 239.

6. E. A. Guillemin, *The Mathematics of Circuit Analysis* (M.I.T. Press, Cambridge, 1965); p. 330.
7. W. R. Bennett and J. R. Davey, *Data Transmission* (McGraw Hill Book Co., New York, 1965), p. 84.
8. R. V. L. Hartley, "Steady State Delay as Related to Aperiodic Signals," *B.S.T.J.* **20**, 222 (1941).
9. S. Goldman, *Frequency Analysis Modulation and Noise* (McGraw Hill Book Co., New York, 1948), p. 102.
10. G. A. Campbell and R. M. Foster, *Fourier Integrals* (D. Van Nostrand Co., Princeton, 1961), p. 7.
11. M. J. Lighthill, "Group Velocity," *J. Inst. Math. Applics. I* (Academic Press, London, 1965), p. 1.
12. S. P. Mead, "Phase Distortion and Phase Distortion Correction," *B.S.T.J.* **7**, 195 (1928).
13. P. R. Geffee, *Simplified Modern Filter Design* (J. F. Rider, New York, 1963), p. 73.
14. S. Hellerstein, "Synthesis of All-Pass Delay Equalizers," *IRE Trans. on Circuit Theory* **PGCT-8**, No. 3, 215 (1961).
15. Rayleigh, *Theory of Sound* (Dover Press, London, 1945), Vol. 1, p. 301.
16. L. Brillouin, *Wave Propagation and Group Velocity* (Academic Press, London, 1960).
17. H. F. Olson, *Acoustical Engineering* (D. Van Nostrand Co., Princeton, 1960).
18. A. Papoulis, *The Fourier Integral and Its Applications* (McGraw-Hill Book Co., New York, 1962), p. 148.
19. D. Slepian and H. O. Pollak, "Prolate Spheroidal Wave Functions, Fourier Analysis and Uncertainty," *B.S.T.J.* **40**, 353 (1961).
20. E. D. Sunde, "Pulse Transmission by A. M., F. M., and P.M. In The Presence of Phase Distortion," *B.S.T.J* **40**, 353 (1961).
21. G. N. Watson, "The Limits of Applicability of the Principle of Stationary Phase," *Proc. Cambridge Phil. Soc.* **19**, 49 (1918).
22. C. Eckart, "The Approximate Solution of One-Dimensional Wave Equations," *Rev. Mod. Phys.* **20**, 399 (1948).
23. C. A. Ewaskio and O. K. Mawardi, "Electroacoustic Phase Shift in Loudspeakers," *J. Acoust. Soc. Am.* **22**, 444 (1950).
24. F. M. Weiner, "Phase Distortion in Electroacoustic Systems," *J. Acoust. Soc. Am.* **13**, 115 (1941).
25. F. M. Weiner, "Phase Characteristics of Condenser Microphones," *J. Acoust. Soc. Am.* **20**, L707 (1948).
26. R. C. Heyser, "Group Delay, Excess Delay, and Overall Time Delay," to be published.

THE AUTHOR

Richard C. Heyser received his B.S.E.E. degree from the University of Arizona in 1953. Awarded the AIEE Charles LeGeyt Fortescue Fellowship for advanced studies he received his M.S.E.E. from the California Institute of Technology in 1954. The following two years were spent in post-graduate work at Cal Tech leading toward a doctorate. During the summer months of 1954 and 1955, Mr. Heyser was a research engineer specializing in transistor circuits with the Motorola Research Laboratory, Phoenix, Arizona. From 1956 until the present time he has been associated with the California Institute of Technology Jet Propulsion Laboratory in Pasadena, California where he is a senior member of the JPL Technical Staff.

Mr. Heyser has presented several papers before the AES and is a member and fellow of the Audio Engineering Society, the Institute of Electrical and Electronic Engineers, as well as Tau Beta Pi, Pi Mu Epsilon, Phi Kappa Phi, Sigma Pi Sigma, and Sigma Xi. He is also a member of Theta Tau.

Loudspeaker Phase Characteristics and Time Delay Distortion: Part 2.

RICHARD C. HEYSER

Jet Propulsion Laboratory, California Institute of Technology, Pasadena, California

Fourier Integral concepts are explored for the relation existing between a function in the frequency domain and its time domain counterpart. A derivation is obtained for the effect of a loudspeaker's imperfect frequency response as a specific type of time delay distortion of the reproduced signal.

INTRODUCTION In an earlier paper [1] the definition of loudspeaker frequency response was expanded to include the phase of the pressure wave produced by an electrical stimulus as well as the conventionally measured amplitude. A technique of measurement was introduced which allowed a measurement to be made of this more complete response, and some examples were included of the response of common types of loudspeaker. Since the proper role of a loudspeaker is the acoustic reproduction of a time-dependent signal, the measurement of even the more complete frequency response is academic unless some inference can be obtained from this measurement as to whether the loudspeaker does its job well. Accordingly a presentation without proof was made of a means of visualizing the effect of imperfect loudspeaker frequency response as producing a time delay distortion equivalent to a frequency-dependent spatial distribution of otherwise perfect loudspeakers. It is the purpose of the present work to investigate the determination of temporal response from the more complete frequency response and develop this acoustic model.

In considering time response it must be remembered that engineers work in a causal world where cause distinctly precedes effect and time advances in its own inexorable fashion. No analysis performed on a network as complicated as a loudspeaker may be considered valid if it violates causality and allows the clock to run backward. Because of considerable mathematical complexity, the subject of time delay in a dispersive medium with absorption is generally avoided in most written material. The reader of such material is left instead with some simplified relations using the frequency phase spectrum, which for most systems yield time delay answers close to observed behavior. Those systems for which the answer violates a prior physical premise are considered anomalous. When all that is available on the frequency response of a loudspeaker is the pressure amplitude spectrum one cannot utilize the simplified temporal relations, and hence no questions arise. With the introduction of a means for measuring the complete frequency response one runs into immediate difficulty with application of the simplified concepts of time behavior because in many cases it is found that causality cannot be maintained.

In order to understand the distortion which a loudspeaker may impart to a time-dependent signal because of its imperfect frequency response, it becomes necessary to look more closely at the concept of frequency-dependent time delay and generate revisions required to present an understandable acoustic equivalent for an actual loudspeaker. This paper proceeds by first demonstrating why the common concept of group delay is not applicable to minimum-phase systems with absorption. Then a substitute for group delay is developed and is shown to provide the proper solution for some systems commonly considered to have anomalous behavior. Finally, a network concept is introduced which leads to an appropriate acoustic model for a loudspeaker.

GROUP DELAY, EXCESS DELAY, AND OVERALL TIME DELAY

Historically the concept of time delay in a dispersive medium was recognized as early as 1839 by Hamilton, but the distinction between phase delay and group delay seems to have been put on a firm foundation by Lord Rayleigh in publications in 1877 [2]. Rayleigh considered that group velocity represented the actual velocity of propagation of groups of energy in a medium. Group delay is defined to be the time delay in traversing a fixed distance at this group velocity [3]. To understand group delay one need only consider that the transformation from the analysis of a problem in the frequency domain to the solution in the time domain involves a Fourier Integral of the form

$$f(t)=(1/2\pi)\int_{-\infty}^{\infty} G(\omega)\, e^{a(\omega)}\, e^{i[\omega t+\phi(\omega)]}\, d\omega \qquad (1)$$

This may fall into a class of integral equations of the type

$$f(t)=\int F(s)e^{tg(s)}ds \qquad (2)$$

where $s=\sigma+i\omega$, $g(s)=x+iy$ is an analytic function, t is large, positive, and real, and $F(s)$ varies slowly compared with the exponential factor [4, 5].

Lord Kelvin's method of stationary phase evaluates integrals of this type by deforming the path of integration where possible through saddle points where x is constant and

$$\partial x/\partial\sigma=\partial x/\partial\omega=0 \text{ and } \partial y/\partial\sigma=\partial y/\partial\omega=0 \qquad (3)$$

For this path the modulus of $\exp[t\cdot g(s)]$ is constant while the phase varies. When all of these conditions are met, not only may an asymptotic solution be achieved but what is more important, Eq. (3) shows that the major contribution to the integral takes place where the phase is stationary and

$$dg(\omega)/d\omega=0. \qquad (4)$$

When these conditions are applicable the major contribution to the solution of Eq. (1) occurs at a time t such that

$$t=-d\phi(\omega)/d\omega. \qquad (5)$$

Since time commences in the analysis at initiation of input stimulus, this means that the time delay of the signal through the network is this value of t, called group delay.

Since the principle of stationary phase is a commonly used derivation of the network theory concept of group delay, it is of utmost importance to note the restrictions on the use of this derivation. The most important restriction is that the modulus remain a slowly varying function of frequency in that region of the frequency domain where the phase is changing the least. This means that when working with a network element this condition may be met by solutions which involve very long time delays, such as transmission lines, or when applied to networks that have no amplitude variation with frequency, such as all-pass lattices where $a(\omega)$ in Eq. (1) is always a constant.

In setting up relations for a network with absorption and short overall time delays, one gets an equation deceptively similar to Eq. (2) but with a substantial real as well as imaginary term in the exponent. The time function of Eq. (1) is an inversion integral evaluated along a path which is the entire imaginary axis from $-\infty$ through the origin to $+\infty$, closed to the left with a semicircle of infinite radius and the origin as center. This is done so as to encircle all singularities of the integrand for time greater than zero. The path of integration is restricted to the $i\omega$ axis when the expression of Eq. (1) is used and the real and imaginary parts of the exponent are related by the Cauchy-Riemann differential relations. Thus, even if $a(\omega)$ is generally a slowly varying function, just at that point on the $i\omega$ axis where the phase is stationary, $a(\omega)$ varies rapidly and one *cannot* use the principle of stationary phase. If the time delay of the network is small relative to several periods of the frequency under analysis, which is a condition commonly found in loudspeakers, then this inapplicability of stationary phase can lead to solutions for time delay which are absurd. Consider for example the circuit of Fig. 1. This network is certainly well behaved, yet the group delay is negative from zero frequency to the geometric mean of the transfer-function break points. Since obviously the output cannot predict the input, the only logical solution would be that the time delay of this network is not represented by group delay. There will of course exist a proper solution for time delay, but this requires a careful evaluation of the inversion integral through the saddle points of Eq. (3) where one may either use Kelvin's method of stationary phase with a path through the saddle points with x constant, or the method of steepest descent which chooses a path of integration so as to concentrate the large values of x in the shortest possible interval with y constant. The two methods are nearly equivalent, since the paths cross the same saddle points and can be deformed one into the other provided contributions from any singularities crossed are taken into account.

The minimum phase transfer function is the function with the minimum accumulation of phase lag (negative phase shift) as ω proceeds from dc to infinity. Because of this the accumulation of phase lag in a minimum phase

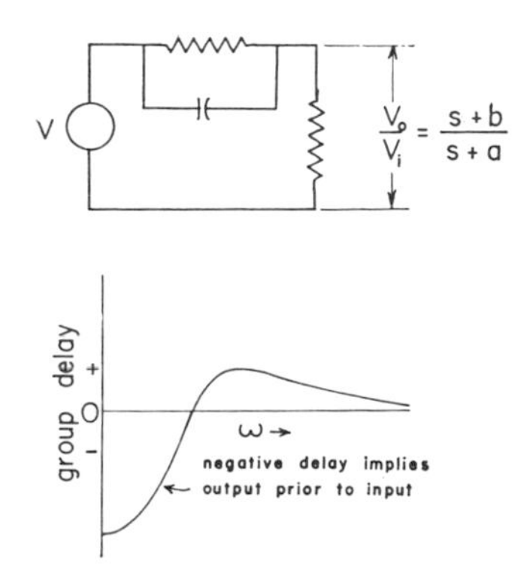

Fig. 1. A simple minimum phase circuit and its group delay, illustrating the inapplicability of group delay to such a causal circuit.

network may be negative as well as positive, as in the case of the circuit of Fig. 1. Since the Cauchy-Riemann equations actually define a minimum phase network and are necessary conditions that a circuit cannot predict the occurrence of a signal, the behavior of phase accumulation means that the group delay of Eq. (5) does *not* provide a measure of time lag in a minimum phase network.

While this might appear to destroy the concept of group delay for minimum phase networks, consider now the special non-minimum phase network called the allpass or flat network, with a constant amplitude of response [6, 7, 8]. For this network there is accumulated phase lag at a rate which is not negative at any frequency, yielding a group delay which is never negative. For this network, since $a(\omega)$ is constant, the principle of stationary phase is valid on the imaginary axis. The time delay thus calculated according to Eq. (5) is everywhere meaningful; this time delay of an allpass network with the transfer function

$$H(\omega)=e^{-i\theta(\omega)} \quad (6)$$

will be defined as excess delay

$$t_{\text{excess}}=d\theta(\omega)/d\omega. \quad (7)$$

One must be careful to observe that the excess delay is the time elapsed from the injection of a transient to the major contribution of the output waveshape. There may be minor ripples, or forerunners to use a phrase of Brillouin [9], which precede this major change as well as the latecomers which provide the effect commonly called ringing, but nonetheless the major change will occur at the time which was called excess delay.

If a network is minimum phase, there exists a unique relationship between amplitude and phase which allows a complete determination of phase from amplitude. If a network is non-minimum phase with a transfer function $H(\omega)$, there will exist a unique minimum phase network $G(\omega)$ with the same amplitude response, and an allpass network with a phase response $\theta(\omega)$ in cascade such that [10]

$$H(\omega)=G(\omega)e^{-i\theta(\omega)}=A(\omega)e^{-i\phi(\omega)}e^{-i\theta(\omega)}. \quad (8)$$

If the time delay characteristics of minimum phase networks and allpass lattices are considered, one can reconstruct the time behavior of any arbitrary physically realizable network. There will exist some total time delay of the network $H(\omega)$ which will be called t_{overall}. There will also exist some time delay for the minimum phase network $G(\omega)$ which will be called $t_{\text{min. phase}}$. The relation between these delays is

$$\begin{aligned} t_{\text{overall}} &= t_{\text{min. phase}}+t_{\text{excess}} \\ &= t_{\text{min. phase}}+[\partial\theta(\omega)/\partial\omega]. \end{aligned} \quad (9)$$

The commonly used group delay is the frequency slope of the total measured phase of $H(\omega)$, or from Eq. (5)

$$t_{\text{group}}=[\partial\phi(\omega)/\partial\omega]+[\partial\theta(\omega)/\partial\omega] \quad (10)$$

which may be expressed as

$$t_{\text{group}}=t_{\text{overall}}+\{[\partial\phi(\omega)/\partial\omega]-t_{\text{min. phase}}\}. \quad (11)$$

Consequently the group delay will be quite close to the overall time delay of the network if

$$t_{\text{overall}}>>\{[\partial\phi(\omega)/\partial\omega]-t_{\text{min. phase}}\}. \quad (12)$$

This is another verification that if a network has a sufficiently large overall time delay, then group delay may be considered a satisfactory substitute provided that the group delay of the equivalent minimum phase network is reasonably well behaved.

TIME DELAY AS A DISTRIBUTION

Turn now to a consideration of time delay in a general network. Attempts at a direct derivation of time delay do not seem particularly fruitful, since the classic definition requires that one make a sudden change in some parameter and see how long it takes before this change appears in the output; however, the moment a discontinuity is created in a time derivative of an electrical parameter, one no longer has that parameter but a large set of sideband frequencies which interfere with the measurement. Thus one is led to look for another solution which involves the relationship existing between frequency and time.

The relationship existing between a function in the time domain $f(t)$ and the same function in the frequency domain $F(\omega)$, is given by the Fourier integrals

$$f(t)=\frac{1}{2\pi}\int_{-\infty}^{\infty}F(\omega)e^{i\omega t}d\omega \quad (13)$$

and

$$F(\omega)=\int_{-\infty}^{\infty}f(t)e^{-i\omega t}dt. \quad (14)$$

There is an obvious symmetry which analytically lets a function in time commute with a function in frequency. Indeed, if a function were given in a dummy parameter and one did not know whether it was of time or frequency, there would be no way of ascertaining the proper domain. A remarkable fact would arise if one blindly inserted this function into the wrong equation: if the function were as well behaved as any related to a real world containing dissipation, the answer would be correct in form. This is because functions may be transferred in the Fourier integral if the sign of one of the parameters is reversed [11]. The implications of this are enormous, as many facts laboriously proven in one domain may automatically be transferred to the other domain. For example, as pointed out in a previous paper [12], if one terminates a time series there exists a frequency overshoot analogous to Gibbs' phenomenon.

The commutation of parameters, then, gives the remarkable simplification that the analysis of a distribution in time due to a complex transfer function is isomorphic with the frequency distribution due to complex modulation in time. This isomorphism considerably frees our imagination when trying to cope with the concept of the time delay of a frequency. If one imagines that the variation of amplitude with frequency of a frequency transfer function is analogous to the variation of amplitude with time of a time transfer function, one can imagine that there are "time sidebands" analogous to the frequency sidebands of modulation theory. In the case of frequency, all values from $-\infty$ through zero to $+\infty$ are allowed and we conveniently identify negative frequency as a phase reversal of a positive frequency. For the parameter time it is conventional to start analysis for a value of zero and assume no activity prior to this.

This merely requires that the time function have an even and odd component which cancel each other for all times less than zero. For such a time function which does not allow prediction, this means that the frequency function similarly has an even (amplitude) and odd (phase) component, although these will not necessarily cancel out at any frequency. This physical realizability criterion also means that the frequency transfer function must have complex conjugate poles and zeros in order to satisfy the even-odd requirement.

The concept of time delay of a frequency component is not complete, since the functions discussed so far are voltages in terms of either frequency or time. Consider, however, a frequency function which has a distribution that is forming as we observe in real time. This is called the running transform $F_t(\omega)$ [13, 14]

$$F_t(\omega) = \int_{-\infty}^{t} f(t)e^{-i\omega t}dt. \tag{15}$$

In this case there is a distinct relation between the distribution of sideband energy and time. There will exist a spectral distribution of frequencies corresponding to an instant in time which may be single-valued, multiple-valued, or a continuous distribution. By interchanging time for frequency one may infer that the time delay of a network for a given frequency may also be a distribution. This goes a long way toward clarifying the confusion created by investigators who attempt to come up with a single-valued number for the delay of a network. In those regions in which the actual delay distribution is small or single-valued, the simple group delay scores very well, but in regions of moderate to large dispersion group delay falls down completely and even yields absurdities.

By observing the conjugate behavior of time and frequency it should be apparent to anyone familiar with modulation theory that a network frequency transfer function

$$F(\omega) = A(\omega)e^{-i\phi(\omega)} = e^{a(\omega)}e^{-i\phi(\omega)} \tag{16}$$

represents a distribution of time delayed functions around the value

$$t_{\text{group}} = [d\phi(\omega)/d\omega]. \tag{17}$$

Furthermore, the group delay will represent the absolute delay of each component only if

$$a(\omega) = \text{constant}. \tag{18}$$

The distribution around the group delay in Eq. (17) is certainly consonant with the paired echo concept of Wheeler and MacColl [15] which treats the effect of minor deviations from the ideal transfer function by expanding the time function around these deviations.

DELAY IN MINIMUM PHASE NETWORK

Having recognized that the true network time delay of Eq. (19) may not necessarily be single-valued and may even be a finite distribution, we turn out attention to deriving the form of a minimum phase time $t_{\text{min. phase}}$ for several simple expressions.

As shown earlier, the group delay of a network with constant gain is the proper delay. Consider the single

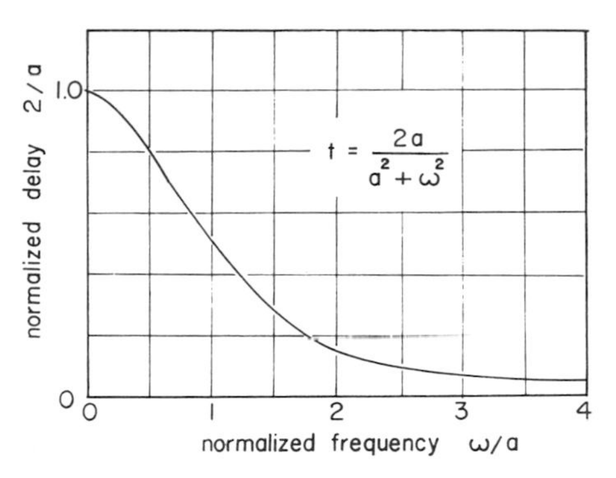

Fig. 2. Normalized plot of excess delay for a first-order allpass lattice.

pole allpass lattice function

$$L(\omega) = (s-a)/(s+a) = (i\omega - a)/(i\omega + a) \text{ for } \sigma = 0. \tag{19}$$

This is a constant gain function with a group delay

$$t_{\text{group}} = 2a/(a^2+\omega^2). \tag{20}$$

This is shown in Fig. 2. The time delay is maximum at zero frequency, and there is no delay at infinite frequency. There is also the very useful fact that single pole functions can be expressed as combinations of this lattice, for example,

$$\frac{1}{s+a} = \frac{1}{2a}\left(1 - \frac{s-a}{s+a}\right) \tag{21}$$

and

$$\frac{s+b}{s+a} = \frac{1}{2a}\left[(a+b) - (b-a)\frac{s-a}{s+a}\right]. \tag{22}$$

Equation (21) is that of a simple lowpass filter, and Eq. (22) describes the circuit of Fig. 1 if a is greater than b. The lefthand side of these equations is the commonly encountered system transfer function $H(s)$, consisting of a frequency-dependent amplitude and phase function. The system transfer function is the frequency transform of the time response to an impulse of voltage $h(t)$; thus,

$$H(s) = \int_{-\infty}^{\infty} h(t)e^{-st}dt. \tag{23}$$

Normally we think of the system transfer function as the quotient of output to input signal and use this concept to generate the common form expressed by the lefthand side by using a sinewave signal. This concept, however, is only valid if a sinewave is used, since there must in general be a time delay in a network; since Eq. (23) does not contain an explicit time dependence it is apparent that this time discrepancy is absorbed in the complex frequency spectrum and thus locked up so that we cannot readily predict time behavior without mathematical manipulation. The righthand sides of Eqs. (21) and (22) show alternate forms of the system transfer function, obtained purely from a special class of transfer functions which represents a known frequency-dependent time delay without a frequency-dependent amplitude. (Using this form allowed us to unlock the time behavior.)

Examining Eq. (21) it is apparent that the simple

lowpass filter can be considered to consist of two parallel constant-amplitude delay functions, one with no delay and the other the delay of Eq. (20). At very high frequencies these two delay signals cancel each other since they arrive at the same time and are of opposing polarity, while at low frequencies there is not a simultaneous output and hence no complete cancellation. A similar interpretation can be placed on Eq. (22).

Thus, the search for a meaningful concept of time delay in a circuit has revealed that there are simple allpass functions which possess a frequency-dependent time delay that fits out intuitive concept of delay; furthermore, a simple minimum-phase network for which the concept of group delay is invalid is now seen to be represented as a combination of allpass delay functions. Figure 3 shows the minimum phase time delay and group

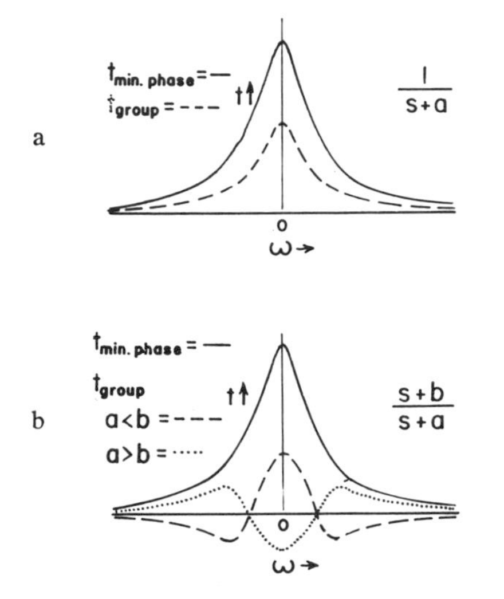

Fig. 3. Minimum phase delay and group delay. The actual minimum phase delay is double-valued and composed of a straight-line zero delay and a bell-shaped delay of the form of Fig. 2. The group delay is single-valued. **a.** Single-pole lowpass circuit. **b.** Single-zero single-pole transfer function.

delay for the single-pole functions of Eqs. (21) and (22). The minimum phase delay is seen to be double-valued for these single-pole functions. The strength of these delayed signals is obtained from the coefficients of Eqs. (21) and (22). It is immediately apparent that group delay is quite misleading for the function of Fig. 1, since this goes to negative time over a substantial portion of the frequency spectrum. The actual delay, as can be seen, never goes negative. Similarly, the group delay of Fig. 3a, although never negative, is nonetheless improper.

A NETWORK CONCEPT

The single-pole single-zero allpass lattice function of Eq. (19) is a primitive function which can be used as a building block for more complicated delays. Two lattices in cascade may, like relations (21) and (22), be composed of combinations of the constituent lattices; for example, if $a \neq b$,

$$\frac{s-a}{s+a}\cdot\frac{s-b}{s+b}=1+\frac{a+b}{a-b}\cdot\frac{s-a}{s+a}-\frac{a+b}{a-b}\cdot\frac{s-b}{s+b} \quad (24)$$

Similarly, one can expand other products of lattices as linear combinations of the individual lattices.

At first glance this would appear to invalidate the conclusion that the time delay of any allpass network is the frequency derivative of the phase function, as the latter is single-valued whereas Eq. (24) shows an expansion which is definitely multiple-valued. Reconciliation may be obtained by remembering that the principle of stationary phase yields the time at which the largest contribution will occur for the integral in Eq. (1). This time will be that of Eq. (7). We might expect that there will be prior contributions and these are discerned in the expansion on the right hand side of Eq. (24). If a sufficiently complicated network of such allpass functions were generated and an oscilloscope used to view the network output with a sudden input transient, the output waveform would be observed to have forerunners preceding the main signal transition. The only condition under which no forerunners would be observed is when the individual lattice sections are identical, in which case there can be no expansion such as Eq. (24). In other words, there is no linear combination for an iterated lattice,

$$[(s-a)/(s+a)]^N \quad (25)$$

and in this case the delay of Eq. (7) is the only delay. In this special case, if the frequency parameter a is very high, approaching infinity as rapidly as the number of identical sections n, then in the limit as n becomes large without limit this relation becomes the transfer function of ideal delay, [10]

$$e^{-T_0 s}=e^{-iT_0\omega} \text{ for } \sigma=0. \quad (26)$$

For all other iterated lattices the delay distribution will be a summation of the constituent delays and in the limit for such a dispersive network will be an integral expression (derived in an earlier paper [1]). The magnitude of terms on the righthand side of Eq. (24) and any such expansion is such that no single term contributes appreciably to the resultant output prior to the time indicated by Eq. (7). Instead each term is effectively nullified by a term representing a prior or later delay, and nullification is not substantially removed until the time of Eq. (7).

From the preceding discussion of forerunners it is quite easy to see how it is possible for a network with the transfer function and time delay of Fig. 3b to be cascaded with a complementing network to produce a constant-gain zero-delay output; thus,

$$(s+b)/(s+a)\cdot(s+a)/(s+b)=1. \quad (27)$$

While there is a finite delay component in Eq. (22), there is no necessity to envision a negative time delay to cancel the term of the form (24) which occurs in the cascaded combination, since each and every forerunner except a unity-gain zero-delay forerunner is cancelled completely. Some remarkable facts may now be deduced from the preceeding observations about network transfer functions which have all poles and zeros on the real σ axis.

1. Any network with simple poles and zeros restricted to the real σ axis may be considered as equivalent to a *parallel* combination of first-order allpass lattices. There will be one allpass lattice for each pole of the network transfer function. The pole, and hence time delay distribution, of each lattice will be determined by the asso-

ciate transfer function pole, while the strength and polarity of each lattice will be determined by the joint distribution of zeros and poles.

2. Higher order poles in the transfer function will yield series combinations of the associate lattices, with the number of lattice sections determined by the order of the pole.

3. Series combinations of networks may be considered as parallel combinations of the constituent lattices of each network.

Because of the associative property of the Fourier transform, the foregoing conclusions concerning the distribution of equivalent networks mean that since each lattice has a frequency-dependent time delay, the time delay of the network output is not single-valued but a multiple-valued combination of the primitive delays. Fig. 2 is a time-delay frequency distribution for the simple one-pole function. Any other minimum phase network which can be expressed as a rational function factorable to the form

$$\frac{(s+a)(s+b)\ldots}{(s+\alpha)(s+\beta)\ldots} \tag{28}$$

will have a time delay frequency function expressible as a sum of delays of the form of Eq. (20) and will have a graphical plot of delay *vs* frequency such as Fig. 4. To

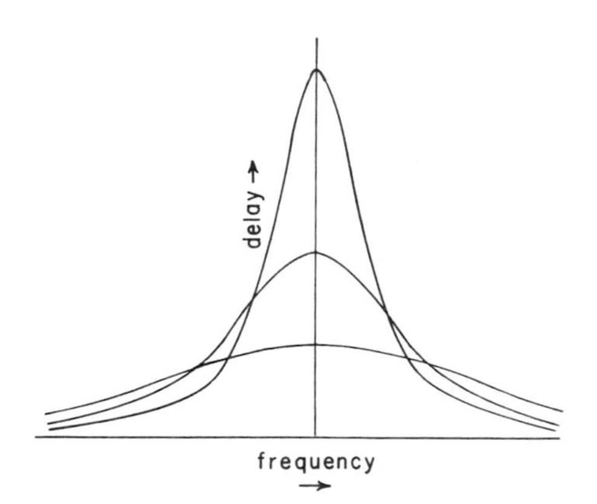

Fig. 4. The multivalued delays to be anticipated for a transfer function with a multiplicity of simple poles at the same frequency.

consider the time delay behavior of such a network, we may thus draw the equivalent network of Fig. 5, where each lattice is considered a frequency-dependent delay line with the delay of Eq. (20). A zero delay may be assumed due to a lattice with a pole at zero frequency. The gain and polarity of each delay line channel is assumed to be determined by a summing amplifier, for the sake of illustration only.

When dealing with a physical process which involves propagation with a frequency-independent velocity, such as sound in air, an equivalent interpretation of Fig. 5 would be that there is a distribution of otherwise perfect sources which assume a frequency-dependent position in space such that the delay due to the additional distance travelled at the velocity of propagation is identical to that of the equivalent delay line.

The allpass lattice of Eq. (19) has a single-pole and single-zero configuration on the real axis. This, as was seen, is quite satisfactory for discussing the time delay of

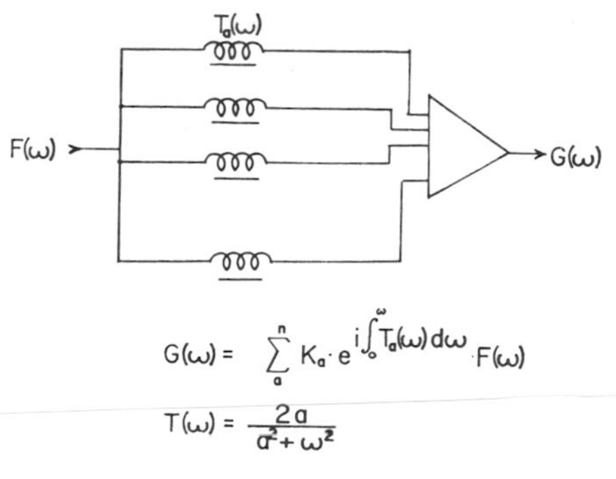

Fig. 5. Symbolic representation of a network with a transfer function expressible as a rational product of terms with poles and zeros. This network may be interpreted as a parallel combination of delay lines with constant amplitude transfer function but a frequency-dependent delay as shown. An input signal with spectral distribution $F(\omega)$ will produce the output $G(\omega)$.

any minimum-phase network with poles on the real axis, i.e., with the terms of Eq. (28) which do not have an imaginary component. A loudspeaker, however, generally has poles with an imaginary component, which leads to peaks and dips in the frequency response and damped ringing in the time response. For this case there exists one type of allpass lattice which, like Eq. (19) on the real axis, can be used to represent the time delay of any network with imaginary poles. This is the second-order lattice with conjugate complex poles and zeros and with the transfer function

$$\frac{(s-a+ib)}{(s+a+ib)} \cdot \frac{(s-a-ib)}{(s+a-ib)}. \tag{29}$$

There does not exist a simple one-parameter delay such as represented by Eq. (20); instead the delay relation now depends upon the position of a and b. The form of delay may be ascertained by allowing the expansion of Eq. (29) to be considered as two cascaded sections of the type of Eq. (19) with appropriate shift in complex frequency. Since the transfer function is now a sum of phase shifts, the time delay from Eq. (20), is [7]

$$t = \frac{2a}{a^2+(\omega-b)^2} + \frac{2a}{a^2+(\omega+b)^2}. \tag{30}$$

Obviously, if the term b approaches zero this becomes the transfer function of Eq. (25) with $n = 2$, so that the delay becomes twice that of Eq. (20). On the other hand, if for a given value of b the term a approaches zero, the phase shift in the vicinity of the frequency of b

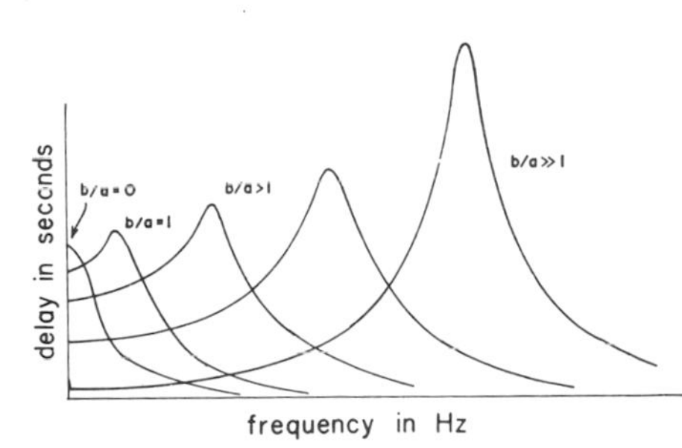

Fig. 6. Representation of the form of the excess delay of a second order allpass lattice.

becomes very large for a small change in frequency. In this case the time delay becomes large without limit. The nature of the delay time for various positions of the poles is shown in Fig. 6.

The form of the delay for the case where b is very much greater than a is the same as in Fig. 2, with the contribution of excess delay occurring at the frequency of b. This leads to the considerable simplification that as long as one is considering local variations in a loudspeaker response, one may consider all activity centered at the frequency of this variation and use the simple expression of Eq. (20). Because local loudspeaker fluctuations in phase and amplitude are usually significant, the equivalent delay and consequently the effective acoustic position relocation may be significant for the frequency of strong local fluctuation. A physical interpretation of this may be secured by observing what would happen if the loudspeaker were fed a transient signal which had in its spectrum this frequency of unusual delay. The pressure wave output would have all frequencies except this component, since for a short time this component will not have arrived. It is a calculable fact that removal of a component is tantamount to adding a cancelling-out of the phase-equivalent component to the original signal. Consequently, the output pressure transient will be perceived to have a "ringing" component at the frequency that is removed. Within some period of time the component frequency will arrive, gracefully one might add, since it is really a distribution of the form of Fig. 2, and the interpretation is that the ringing has now subsided. If the signal is removed from the loudspeaker terminals, the delayed component must persist for some time and the interpretation of this waveform would be that there is a ringing of the output with polarity reversed from the start-up transient.

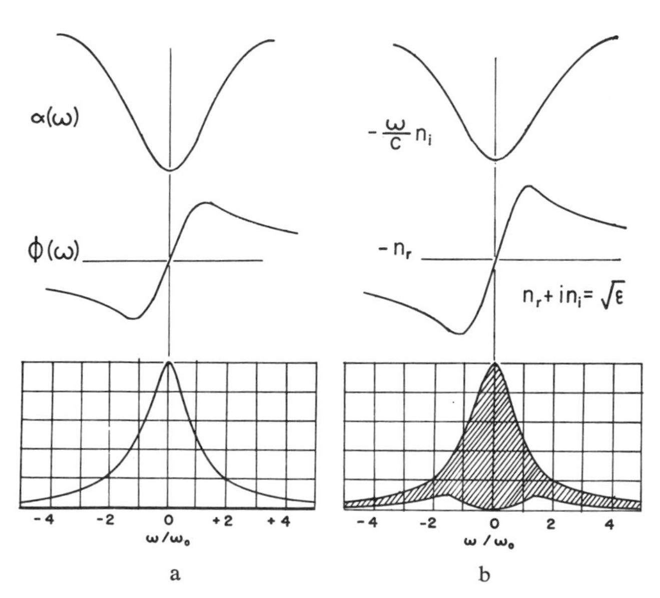

Fig. 7. **a.** Complete plot of amplitude, phase, and time delay (double valued) for the circuit of Fig. 1 with the frequency of maximum absorption at dc. **b.** Equivalent amplitude and phase characteristic of the transfer function of an electromagnetic wave passing through a single resonance dielectric medium exhibiting anomalous dispersion in which the group velocity by calculation can exceed the velocity of light in vacuum. The frequency dependent time delay (after Brillouin [9]) which has been normalized to the same center frequency of Fig. 7a is a continuum within the shaded region.

ANOMALOUS DISPERSION

A particularly significant distribution of amplitude and phase when discussing group delay is afforded by the transfer function for a real passive dielectric medium with a single simple resonance. The group velocity of a wave propagating in this medium could exceed the velocity of light and gave rise to the term "anomalous dispersion". The concept of group velocity established by Lord Rayleigh was so firmly entrenched that this solution posed a serious challenge to the theory of relativity. So great was this discrepancy that an exceedingly complicated solution was worked by Sommerfeld and Brillouin. Figure 7b is a plot of amplitude, phase, and time delay as worked out by Brillouin [9]. He observed that there was no unique delay, but depending upon sensitivity of apparatus there was a distribution of delays in the shaded region. For comparison with the solution above, Fig. 7a is a similar display for the function of Eq. (22) when a is greater than b. The agreement is quite satisfactory when one realizes that the index of refraction which plays the role of the network transfer function involves a square root of a function of the form of Eq. (22) and hence does not have a simple pole and zero but branch points. The branch points lead to the continuous distribution, whereas simple poles and zeros yield singular functions for time delay.

SUMMARY

A loudspeaker, when considered as a transducer of electrical signals to acoustic pressure, has a transfer function which has a frequency-dependent amplitude and phase response. The effect of these amplitude and phase variations may be considered to be the introduction of a time delay distortion in the reproduced pressure response. The response of an actual loudspeaker will be identical to the response one would have from an ensemble of perfect loudspeakers each one of which assumes a frequency-dependent position in space behind the actual loudspeaker. The number of equivalent loudspeakers, and hence the measure of time delay smearing, will increase with the complexity of the amplitude and phase spectrum. In those portions of the frequency spectrum where the actual loudspeaker is of minimum phase type, it is always possible to modify the response by mechanical or electrical means such that all equivalent loudspeakers merge into one position in space. When this is done there is no frequency-dependent time delay distortion, and the pressure response may be made essentially perfect. Attempts at minimum phase equalization of those portions of the frequency spectrum where the actual loudspeaker is non-minimum phase will not coalesce the equivalent loudspeakers but will leave a spatial distribution which is equivalent to a single perfect loudspeaker with a frequency-dependent position behind the actual loudspeaker.

REFERENCES

1. Richard C. Heyser, "Loudspeaker Phase Characteristics and Time Delay Distortion," *J. Audio Eng. Soc.* **17**, 30 (1969).

2. Rayleigh, *Theory of Sound* (Dover Press, London, 1945), Vol. 1, p. 301.

3. M. J. Lighthill, "Group Velocity," *J. Inst. Math. Applics. I* (Academic Press, London, 1965), p. 1.

4. G. N. Watson, "The Limits of Applicability of the

Principle of Stationary Phase," *Proc. Cambridge Phil. Soc.* **19**, 49 (1918).
5. C. Eckart, "The Approximate Solution of One-Dimensional Wave Equations," *Rev. Mod. Phys.* **20**, 399 (1948).
6. S. P. Mead, "Phase Distortion and Phase Distortion Correction," *B. S. T. J.* **7**, 195 (1928).
7. P. R. Geffee, *Simplified Modern Filter Design* (J. F. Rider, New York, 1963), p. 73.
8. S. Hellerstein, "Synthesis of All-Pass Delay Equalizers," *IRE Trans. on Circuit Theory* **PGCT-8**, No. 3, 215 (1961).
9. L. Brillouin, *Wave Propagation and Group Velocity* (Academic Press, London, 1960).
10. S. J. Mason and H. J. Zimmerman, *Electronic Circuits, Signals, and Systems* (Wiley, New York, 1960), p. 350.
11. G. A. Campbell and R. M. Foster, *Fourier Integrals* (D. Van Nostrand Co., Princeton, 1961), p. 7.
12. R. C. Heyser, "Acoustical Measurements by Time Delay Spectrometry," *J. Audio Eng. Soc.* **15**, 370 (1967).
13. A. Papoulis, *The Fourier Integral and Its Applications* (McGraw Hill Book Co., New York, 1962), p. 148.
14. D. Slepian and H. O. Pollak, "Prolate Spheroidal Wave Functions, Fourier Analysis and Uncertainty," *B. S. T. J.* **40**, 353 (1961).
15. S. Goldman, *Frequency Analysis Modulation and Noise* (McGraw Hill Book Co., New York, 1948), p. 102.

Mr. Heyser's biography appeared on page 41 of the January, 1969 issue of the Journal.

Modulation Distortion in Loudspeakers*

PAUL W. KLIPSCH

Klipsch and Associates, Inc., Hope, Arkansas

When comparing a loudspeaker with direct radiator bass system to one with horn loaded bass, the subjective judgment is that the one with the horn loaded bass is "cleaner". The difference in listening quality appears to be due to modulation distortion. The mathematical analysis of modulation distortion is reviewed and spectrum analyzer measurements are described which have been correlated with listening tests. The spectrum analyses corroborate the mathematical analysis and the listening tests offer a subjective evaluation. It is concluded that frequency modulation in loudspeakers accounts in large measure for the masking of "inner voices". Reduction of diaphragm excursions at low frequencies reduces FM distortion. Horn loading, properly applied, offers greatest reduction, while simultaneously improving bass power output capability.

INTRODUCTION The term *distortion* is defined herein as the generation of frequencies not originally present. Thus it is distinguished from frequency response errors. *Harmonic distortion* is the introduction of harmonics of the original frequencies and is not objectionable as such even at high amounts, because music consists largely of harmonics. Modulation distortion produces new frequencies which are inharmonically related to the original sounds and is therefore detectible and objectionable in much smaller amounts.

Amplitude modulation distortion derives from any nonlinearity which would produce harmonic distortion and appears as the inharmonic sum and difference frequencies or sidebands when two or more frequencies are mixed. The subject of amplitude modulation is covered in texts on radio engineering [1].

Great effort has been expended to reduce harmonic distortion in loudspeakers. Since harmonic distortion arises from the same causes as amplitude modulation (AM) distortion, it may tentatively be concluded that AM distortion in better loudspeakers is relatively small. This is not to dismiss AM distortion; the main effort in this paper is directed at total modulation distortion.

Frequency modulation distortion arises in a loudspeaker when diaphragm motion at some low frequency produces frequency shifts of some higher frequency due to the Doppler effect. The effect is similar to flutter in a defective tape player when the tape velocity is not constant within tolerable limits.

Experiments with an eccentric capstan on a tape machine indicate that flutter (frequency deviation) amounting to 0.35% is irritating if the modulating frequency is as high as 20 or 40 Hz [2].

Vast effort on the part of tape recorder manufacturers to attain wow and flutter levels below 0.1% deviation indicate that this problem is recognized. Yet much higher values are typically observed in loudspeakers.

The Doppler effect or the principle of alteration of pitch dates back to 1842 [3]. The familiar example is that of a moving vehicle, such as a locomotive, blowing a whistle. As the vehicle passes a listener the pitch of the whistle diminishes. The wavelengths observed are changed proportionally to the ratio of the velocity of the moving source to the velocity of sound.

A loudspeaker diaphragm vibrating at two frequencies, for example at 32 and 1000 Hz, would give rise to FM distortion. As the cone, vibrating at 1000 Hz, is moved toward and away from the observer, at the 32 Hz frequency there would arise a deviation from 1000 Hz dependent on the velocity of the diaphragm at the 32 Hz frequency.

If the velocity of the cone at the lower frequency were 0.5% of the velocity of sound, the frequency deviation of the higher frequency would be 0.5%.

Total modulation distortion is the combination of the amplitude and frequency modulation.

INITIAL OBSERVATIONS

Two loudspeakers, one with direct radiator bass and the other with horn-loaded bass, have been compared in listening tests. Nineteen out of 20 listeners judged that the one with the horn-loaded bass is "cleaner". Both loudspeakers were by the same manufacturer. Both had similar horn-loaded midrange and treble system with identical midrange and treble drive motors. The direct radiator unit offered a more extended bass range, with cutoff about 30 Hz compared to the horn-loaded bass cutoff of about 45 Hz. Thus, if the listener preference were predicated on frequency response the leaning should have been toward the direct radiator unit, but the opposite choice was indicated. The words "transparent", "better resolution", and "clarity of the inner voices" were applied to the speaker with the horn-loaded bass.

* Presented April 29, 1968 at the 34th Convention of the Audio Engineering Society, Los Angeles.

Single-frequency distortion tests indicated that both loudspeakers generate negligible harmonic distortion at the power levels used in the listening tests. Both showed accurate power linearity up to 120 dB SPL measured at 4 ft, as indicated by parallelism of frequency response curves run at 0.1, 1.0 and 10 W input. Hysteresis effects, if any, were below the resolving power of the measuring equipment used.

By elimination it appears that the cause of the difference in listening quality must be modulation distortion.

EARLY WORK ON FM DISTORTION

Frequency modulation distortion has long been recognized as a property of loudspeakers [4]. When two frequencies are radiated by the same diaphragm the higher frequency f_2 will be frequency-modulated by the lower frequency f_1 because of the Doppler shift due to the motion at the lower frequency. This frequency shift of the upper frequency will be proportional to the ratio of the diaphragm velocity at the lower frequency to the velocity of sound.

Let A_1 be the peak amplitude of motion due to f_1, then

$$x = A_1 \sin \omega_1 t \tag{1}$$

$$v = dx/dt = A_1 \omega_1 \cos \omega_1 t \tag{2}$$

or the peak velocity

$$V = A_1 \omega_1 .$$

The shift or deviation of a higher frequency will be proportional to V/c or $\Delta f_2 = (V/c) f_2$.

Writing $c = 13{,}500$ ips (velocity of sound),

$$\Delta f_2 = f_2 A_1 \omega_1 / 13{,}500. \tag{3}$$

For example, $A_1 = 1/8$ in., $f_1 = 28$ Hz, $\omega_1 = 176$, $V = 176/8 = 22$ ips, $V/c = 22/13{,}500 = 0.0016$.

If $f_2 = 600$ Hz, then $\Delta f_2 = 0.0016 \times 600 = 1$ Hz. In this example, therefore, the frequency deviation would be one Hz and the frequency f_2 would flutter between 599 and 601 Hz.

The amount of frequency shift, flutter, or deviation is easy to determine by simply measuring the diaphragm excursion at the lowest frequency, from which, knowing the frequency, the modulating velocity may be computed. The frequency modulation shift is simply this velocity divided by the velocity of sound multiplied by the modulated frequency.

Beers and Belar [4] derive a different measure for frequency modulation distortion, consisting of the effective amplitude of the sidebands.

Beers and Belar give

$$d = 0.033\, A_1 f_2 \tag{4}$$

where d = distortion factor (total rms value of sidebands as percent of amplitude of f_2), A_1 = amplitude of motion in inches at the lower frequency f_1, and f_2 = the higher or modulated frequency.

For the example given, where the cone excursion was 1/8 in. (amplitude $A_1 = 0.12$ in.) and the upper frequency $f_2 = 600$ Hz, $d = 0.033 \times 0.12 \times 600$ = approximately 2.4%. From the principles of frequency modulation, it may be seen that the sidebands consist of the sum and difference frequencies between the upper frequency f_2 and the modulating frequency f_1, as well as their higher orders; thus the sideband frequencies would be

$$f_2 \pm f_1$$
$$f_2 \pm 2f_1, \text{ etc.}$$

Note that the *amplitude* A_1 is a factor in determining the amplitude of the sidebands; the *velocity* V_1 determines the fraction of frequency shift of the modulated frequency.

FM ANALYSIS

The equation of frequency modulation is given by Terman [5]; in slightly rearranged form it is

$$e = E \sin[\omega_2 t + (\Delta\omega_2/\omega_1)\sin \omega_1 t], \tag{5}$$

where E is the amplitude of the "carrier" or higher frequency; $\omega_2 = 2\pi f_2$, with f_2 the higher or modulated frequency; $\omega_1 = 2\pi f_1$, with f_1 the lower or modulating frequency; and $\Delta\omega_2$ is the maximum deviation of the instantaneous frequency f_2.

Let

$$E = 1,\ m = \frac{\Delta\omega_2}{\omega_1} = \frac{(V/c)\,\omega_2}{\omega_1} = \frac{A_1\omega_1}{c}\cdot\frac{\omega_2}{\omega_1} = \frac{A_1}{c}\omega_2, \tag{6}$$

$$e = \sin(\omega_2 t + m \sin \omega_1 t) \tag{7}$$

$$\begin{aligned} &= J_0 m \sin \omega_2 t \\ &\quad + J_1 m[\sin(\omega_2+\omega_1)t - \sin(\omega_2-\omega_1)t] \\ &\quad + J_2 m[\sin(\omega_2+2\omega_1)t + \sin(\omega_2-2\omega_1)t] \\ &\quad + \text{etc.} \end{aligned} \tag{8}$$

Expressed as side band amplitudes [6], for $m << 1$,

$$\begin{aligned} e_0 &= J_0 m \cong 1 \\ e_1 &= J_1 m \cong m/2 \\ e_2 &= J_2 m \cong m^2/8, \text{ etc.} \end{aligned} \tag{9}$$

Using $c = 13{,}500$ ips,

$$\begin{aligned} e_0 &= 1 \\ e_1 &\cong 0.00023\, A_1 f_2 \\ e_2 &\cong 2.7 \times 10^{-8} (A_1 f_2)^2 \text{ etc.,} \end{aligned} \tag{10}$$

where e_1 is the magnitude of *each* of the 2 sidebands of first order; e_2 is magnitude of each second order sideband, etc.

Equations (10) and (4) can be compared. Consider the amplitude of one first-order sideband frequency

$$e_1 = 0.000233\, A_1 f_2 \tag{10}$$

where A_1 is the amplitude of motion due to f_1; if the second-order sidebands are small enough to be ignored, the effective value of both first-order sideband frequencies would be

$$\begin{aligned} E_1 &= 0.000233 \sqrt{2}\, A_1 f_2 \\ &= 0.00033\, A_1 f_2 \end{aligned}$$

which agrees with Beers and Belar's Eq. 4 where their coefficient of 0.033 was expressed in percent. Numerical example:

$A_1 = 1/8$ in.

$e_1 = 0.017$ (approx. −35 dB)

$e_2 = 0.00013$ (approx. −78 dB).

Two sidebands e_1 of 0.017 would represent an rms amplitude of

$$0.017 \times \sqrt{2} = 0.024,$$

which agrees with the 2.4% obtained using Beers-Belar's method.

Equations (8) through (11) state that the sidebands contain frequencies of $f_1 \pm f_2$, $f_1 \pm 2f_2$, etc. Equation (3) suggests the sidebands are limited to the deviation. Terman [5] offers the explanation that while the frequency is shifting the wave becomes lopsided, giving rise to other sinusoidal components.

Qualitatively it is hard to reconcile a one Hz deviation with a 28 Hz sideband component but these sideband frequencies become credible when viewed on the spectrum analyzer screen.

Beers and Belar draw several conclusions: 1. since the distortion factor d increases with f_2 the effect will be more severe in "high fidelity" applications, so that two loudspeakers should be used, one to radiate the low frequencies and the other for highs. (Recall that in 1943 a so-called two-way speaker was used mainly in theaters.) 2. It is difficult to evaluate FM distortion with listening tests because it cannot be readily isolated from other forms of distortion, and 3. FM distortion is probably masked by other forms of distortion.

When this was written in 1943, with AM radio and shellac disk records as the main media, it was probably true that FM distortion in loudspeakers was masked by other forms of distortion and noise. Now, with amplifiers exhibiting 0.05% distortion, FM radio eliminating some forms of distortion exhibited by AM and minimizing others, and with tape offering 55 dB or better S/N ratio, it is suspected that FM distortion in loudspeakers may be the major remaining defect in otherwise high-quality audio systems.

TOTAL MODULATION DISTORTION

Amplitude modulation gives rise to the same families of distortion sidebands ($f_2 \pm f_1$, etc.) as does frequency modulation. Using a spectrum analyzer, the indicated amplitude of each sideband component is the effective sum of the two kinds of distortion. Sometimes two sideband frequencies $f_1 + f_2$ and $f_1 - f_2$ are shown with different amplitudes. This is possibly due to a phase difference between the amplitude and frequency modulation components so that the effective sum of one side component differs from that of the other. The effective sum of both components will still represent the effective value of that particular order of modulation distortion. The effective sum of all sideband components will be the "total modulation distortion" for that particular combination of inputs.

No obvious way of separating amplitude and frequency modulation distortion has so far been described. But since the two kinds produce the same type of sidebands, the total modulation distortion is what causes listener distress. Fortunately the spectrum analyzer can be used to measure this total modulation distortion.

EXPERIMENTAL RESULTS

The experimental studies were performed with the following equipment:

Two oscillators, Hewlett-Packard HO2-207A GR 1310A;

Dual power amplifier, solid state "one of a kind", arranged to simplify two oscillators separately, feeding combined output to loudspeaker. Measurements indicate negligible distortion under conditions imposed;

Various control boxes;

B & K half-inch microphone;

Tektronix 564 storage scope with 3L5 spectrum analyzer and 2B67 time base.

Bass Loudspeakers

This must necessarily be merely a "progress report". It is doubtful if the work will ever be finished.

Table I compares the performance of four bass loudspeakers. Frequencies of 50 Hz and 300 Hz were used, and output at each frequency adjusted to give the stated SPL. (See Fig. 1).

The table confirms a rule which has long been known but not rigorously proved, namely that the higher the efficiency the lower the total modulation distortion. Another fact (not previously realized) is that the low-efficiency loudspeakers exhibit much higher total distortion than the computed FM distortion; highly efficient loudspeakers exhibit a total distortion only slightly greater than the computed FM distortion. The difference must be AM distortion. In the case of the high-efficiency horn loudspeaker, the individual sidebands were about 45 dB down from the 300 Hz signal. Combined distortion of oscillator, amplifier and analyzer could account for some of the total.

Let it be repeated that this work will never be finished. Results so far indicate a trend, and it is tentatively suggested that the last column in Table I be called "mud index".

Good loudspeakers are referred to as "clean" or "transparent", and poor speakers as "dirty" or "muddy". The magnitude of the modulation distortion is directly correlatable to the quality of "muddiness". Thus the term "mud index" may need no defense.

The main qualities of a loudspeaker have been considered to be: 1. Power output capacity, at 2. a corresponding distortion level, 3. polar response, and 4. frequency response.

If modulation distortion is quantitatively specified under 2. above, then it appears that loudspeakers can indeed be described as accurately as amplifiers.

Table I. Loudspeaker performance: bass loudspeakers.

	Output Sound Pressure Level (SPL) dB at 2 Feet	% Total Modulation Distortion (Effective Sideband Amplitude)
Large well-designed horn	100	0.7
15 in. driver in ported box 6.5 ft³	95	2.2
10 in. driver in sealed box 1.5 ft³	95	6.8
7 in. driver in sealed box 1.0 ft³	90	14.0

Midrange Loudspeakers

Again, this is only a progress report.

Tests were run on a high-quality midrange horn-type loudspeaker, a reflexed horn midrange and an 8 in. direct radiator (see Table II and Fig. 2).

Table II. Loudspeaker performance: midrange loudspeakers.

	Output SPL, dB at 2 ft	Modulation Distortion (Effective Sidebands)
Straight axis horn	100	less than 1%
Reflexed horn	100	approximately 5%
8 in. direct radiator	90	approximately 10%

As in bass loudspeakers, the distortion was approximately inversely proportional to efficiency. In the case of the reflexed horn the peak/trough ratio in the operating spectrum was about 24 dB; by choosing one frequency in the trough it was found that SPL values of only 90 dB could be obtained except under gross distortion. At 90 dB the total modulation distortion rose to 10%.

Experiments so far tend to indicate that plastic diaphragms in the compression drivers for horns exhibit slightly lower total modulation distortion and can handle larger power output than metallic diaphragms.

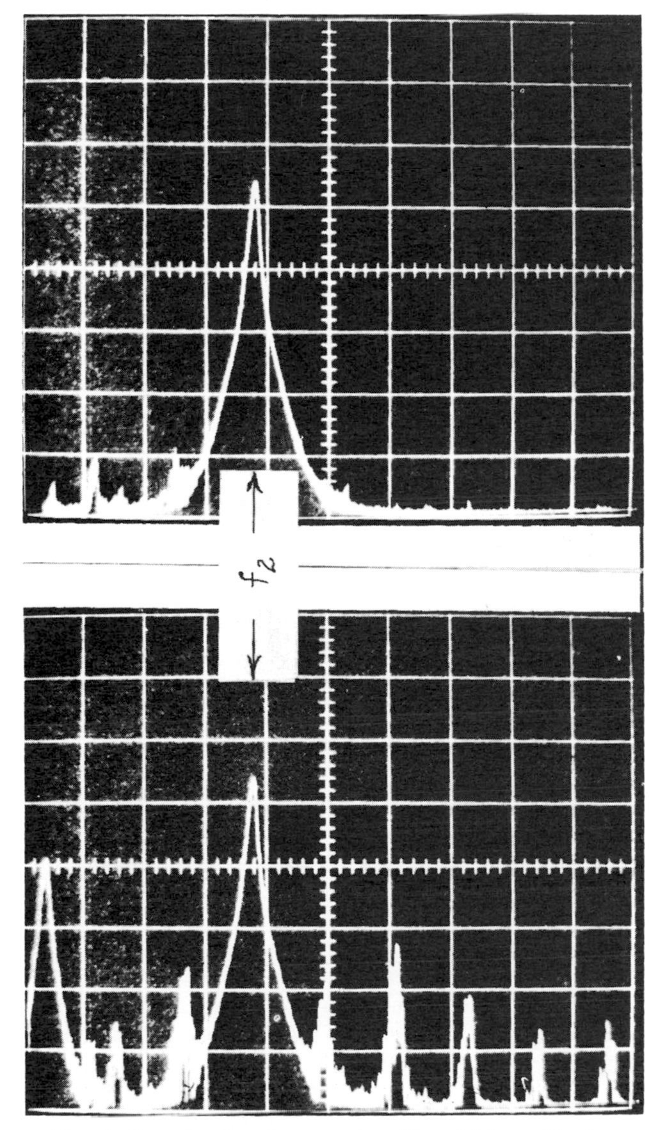

Fig. 1. Bass loudspeaker spectra. **Top**: high-quality horn-type unit at 100 dB SPL output at 2 ft. Total modulation distortion is obscured by ambient noise but may be on the order of 0.7%. **Bottom**: Ten-inch direct radiator in 1.5 ft^3 box (total enclosure) at 90 dB SPL output at 2 ft. (Vertical gain of analyzer changed to give same indicated level.) Total rms modulation distortion approximately 7%. f_1 = 50 Hz, f_2 = 300 Hz; vertical scale = 10 dB per div., horizontal scale = approximately 50 Hz per div. Note that f_1 does not show.

Upper Treble Loudspeakers

Horn type treble loudspeakers* display moderately high efficiency and the rule (which begins to look like a law) remains in force that the higher the efficiency the lower the distortion.

One "exotic" treble loudspeaker was tested. This was one of the ionized-air tweeters and it displayed over 30% rms amplitude of sum-and-difference sidebands when frequencies of 5000 Hz and 12500 Hz were mixed at 1 V input each. Listening tests showed an extreme distortion at all combinations of frequencies and at any amplitude high enough to read on a rectifier voltmeter. In fact, the "silky" highs of yesteryear's reports appear to be more "sizzly". This quality has fooled a lot of highly qualified listeners. It was surmised *a priori* that the distortion would be high. The "diaphragm" consists of the boundary between hot and cold air, and the ionized spot seems to be less than 0.1 in. in diameter. A natural conclusion would be that the modulation distortion would be of the order of 100 times as great as for a tweeter with a 1 in. diaphragm. The spectrum analyzer confirms this.

Well-designed horn tweeters with dynamic drive systems exhibit lower total modulation distortion than any other types tested here.

DEMONSTRATION TAPE

A tape was prepared of 50 Hz and 300 Hz tones mixed and played back on a small direct-radiator loudspeaker. The flutter was plainly audible.

Mozart's Concerto for Clarinet and Orchestra, third movement, contains sustained clarinet tones which tend to show even a small amount of flutter to an irritating degree. A small speaker which could execute ¼ in. of excursion at 28 Hz with almost no audible output was used to play a tape of the Concerto, while a 28 Hz oscillator tone was intermittently fed to the speaker. The resulting flutter was extremely irritating even though the modulating frequency was inaudible.

DISCUSSION

High Sound Pressures in the Throat of a Horn

Thuras, Jenkins and O'Neil [8] derive the ratio of second harmonic distortion to fundamental output of a horn

* Treble speakers are commonly referred to as "tweeters".

speaker at intense power output levels (10 W at 2000 Hz, for example) and particularly for intense pressure levels in the throat of the horn.

Whenever harmonic distortion occurs, modulation distortion likewise occurs.

This paper also mentions sum and difference frequencies. Using a horn of 200 Hz and inputs of 600 and 940 Hz, the authors detected sideband frequencies of 340 and 1540 Hz as well as the input fundamentals and harmonics. They stated that at higher power outputs the sound was very disagreeable and the fundamental tones could hardly be distinguished. Their analysis and measurements were concerned only with the harmonic distortion, and numerical data were not given for modulation distortion.

Goldstein and McLachlan [9] derive the harmonic distortion due to high pressures in the throat of a horn, but do not derive nor measure the modulation sidebands resulting from reproducing two frequencies simultaneously. They cite another paper [10] but call attention to an error of a factor of 4 in that paper.

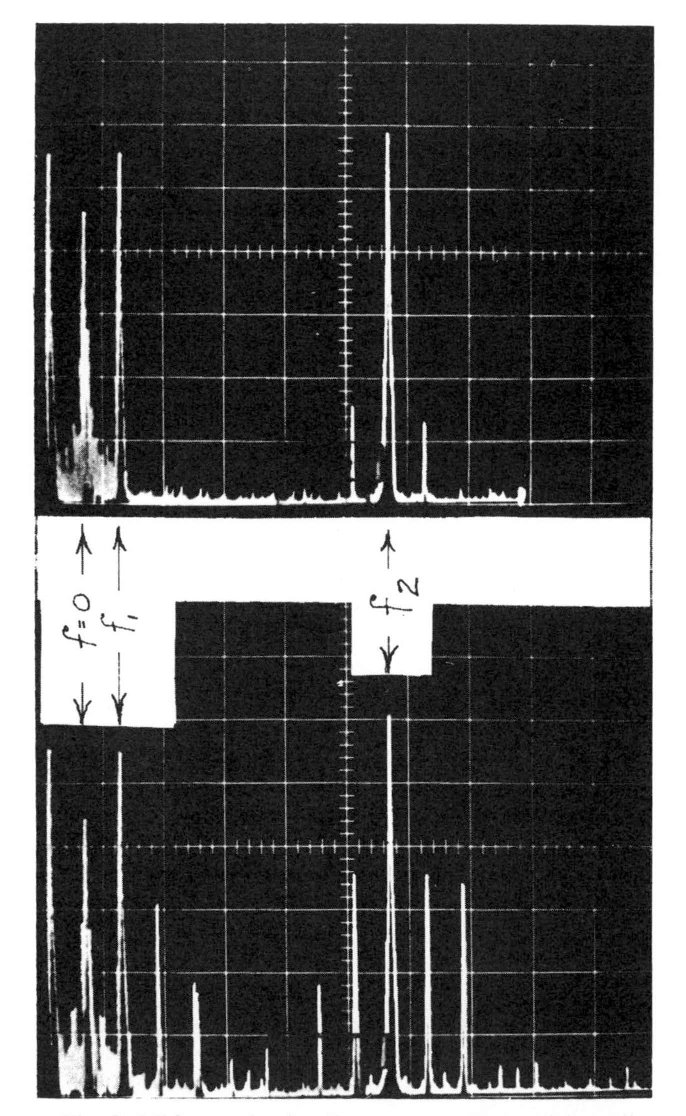

Fig. 2. Midrange loudspeaker spectra. **Top**: high-quality horn-type unit. Note absence of harmonics of the 510 Hz signal and sidebands of first-order only of 43 and 46 dB down (0.7% and 0.6%). Total rms modulation distortion, 0.9%. Output, 100 dB SPL at 2 ft. **Bottom**: typical 8 in. cone midrange loudspeaker of direct-radiator type. Note harmonics of f_1 at 23 and 35 dB down; modulation sidebands of first order at —25 dB (5.6%) and second-order sidebands of —26 dB (4.5% and —42 dB (.8%). Total rms modulation distortion, 9.1%. Output, 90 dB SPL at 2 ft. f_1 = 510 Hz, f_2 = 4.4 KHz; vertical scale = 10 dB per div., horizontal scale = approximately 500 Hz per div.

It appears obvious that second-order harmonic distortion and corresponding modulation distortion must occur in horn throats at "intense" sound pressure levels. The tests reported in the present paper involved output pressures in excess of what would be tolerable from direct radiators, but still with measured total modulation distortion on the order of ⅓ as great. Again, obviously, any device can be driven to a power level where severe distortion or failure must occur. The aim here was to deal with realistic power output levels when comparing the speaker types.

Impedance Variations with Horn Mouth Size

Wente and Thuras [11] used a bass loudspeaker with about 25 sq. ft of mouth and obtained about a 7:1 ratio of acoustic impedance. The bass horn used in present experiments had a mouth opening of 5.3 sq. ft, which with the mirror images formed by the walls in a corner produces an effective mouth area of 21 sq. ft. The motional impedance varies from 5 to 35 electrical ohm (7.5 to 38 voice coil ohm) measured over the 30 to 100 Hz range. Horns with very small mouths may exhibit acoustic impedance variations of 50:1 or more, and severe sound pressure response curve peaks and dips. Choosing a frequency at a deep response dip and forcing the input to achieve a given output could give rise to severe distortion. Even with such an inferior horn loudspeaker, the efficiency in a response dip is usually higher than for a direct radiator having the same effective area, and the distortion is lower.

There are exceptions: the reflexed midrange horn exhibited a 24 dB peak-trough difference in the response curve, and exhibited higher modulation distortion when one of the frequencies was in the bottom of the dip and the power was raised to give 100 dB SPL output. It was still, however, as good as the direct radiator. This is not a criticism of the horn, but of reflexing in such a way as to produce a violent anomaly in the response curve.

CONCLUSION

How much modulation distortion can barely be detected, how much is irritating, and how much is intolerable will vary with individual listeners, and will likely vary with any one individual as his habituation changes. What was "perfect sound reproduction" in 1905, 1925 and 1945 and what was 1955's major breakthrough is looked upon with more or less tolerance now. Our hearing has been educated to better things. In the demonstration tape, levels were chosen such that the results were unmistakable. Smaller amounts of distortion, even at and below the levels detectible by A-B comparison, may be objectionable by contributing to "listener fatigue". As people become more aware of loudspeaker faults it is reasonable to expect them to become more critical. James Moir [7] suggests that modulation distortion as low as 0.001% is detectable by ear. He does not indicate whether this numerical value is frequency deviation or sideband amplitude.

Modulation distortion cannot be eliminated in loud-

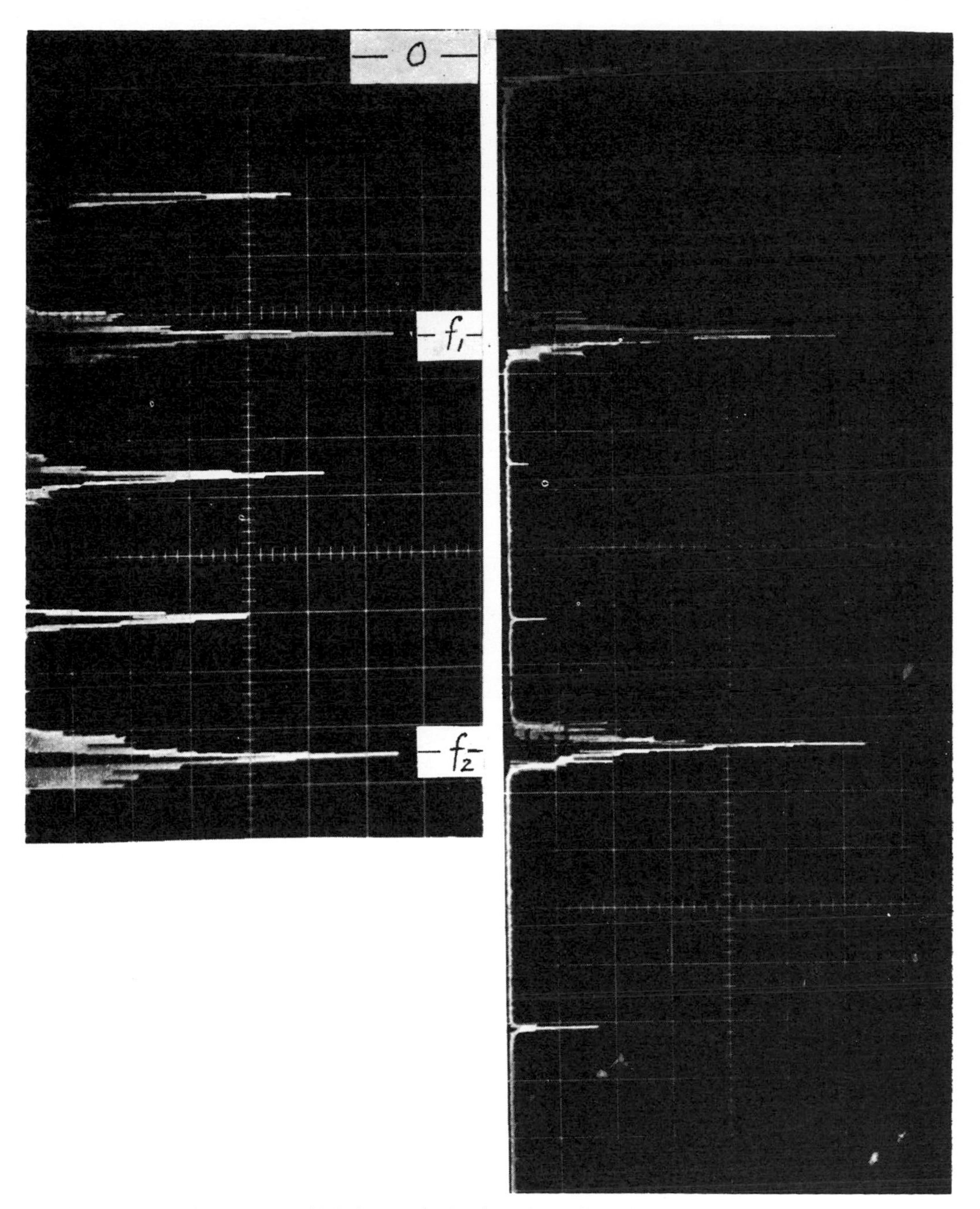

Fig. 3. Detailed spectra of high-frequency loudspeakers. **Top**: high-quality horn-type unit, paste-up of three overlapping ranges. **Bottom**: Ionized-air high-frequency loudspeaker, paste-up of two overlapping ranges. Note that the sidebands for the horn-type loudspeaker are 50 and 45 dB down from the amplitude of f_2, compared to 10 dB down (30%) distortion) for the ionized-air loudspeaker. f_1 = 5000 Hz, f_2 = 12.500 Hz at 0.5 V; vertical scale = 10 dB per div., horizontal scale = approximately 1 KHz per div.

speakers; the best that can be hoped for is minimization. If a diaphragm moves at all, it produces distortion. High-efficiency horn loudspeakers display much lower modulation distortion than the best direct radiators tested so far, and the rule seems to approach being a law that the higher the efficiency, the lower the distortion.

Among means to reduce distortion, one of the most obvious would appear to be to increase the diaphragm area. But the weight required to achieve rigidity, or the lack of rigidity, present other and more formidable problems. All large diaphragm speakers tested here exhibited audible "flexural" or "flapping" sounds.

Increasing the number of smaller direct-radiator loudspeakers has also been used. This also improves efficiency, although not to the extent realizable with well designed horns: however, the bulk and cost equal or exceed that of horns, and difficulties with polar response arise. Those observed here and elsewhere appear to have "muffled" sound, but whether this is due to the curtain of modulation distortion or to the curtain of a masking effect of enhanced bass has not been determined.

One further method of reducing the mud index in direct radiator loudspeakers is to taper the bass below about 70 Hz. Since little or no fundamental sound is radiated by a symphony orchestra below about 45 Hz, tapering would entail a loss of, say, 5 dB at the lowest

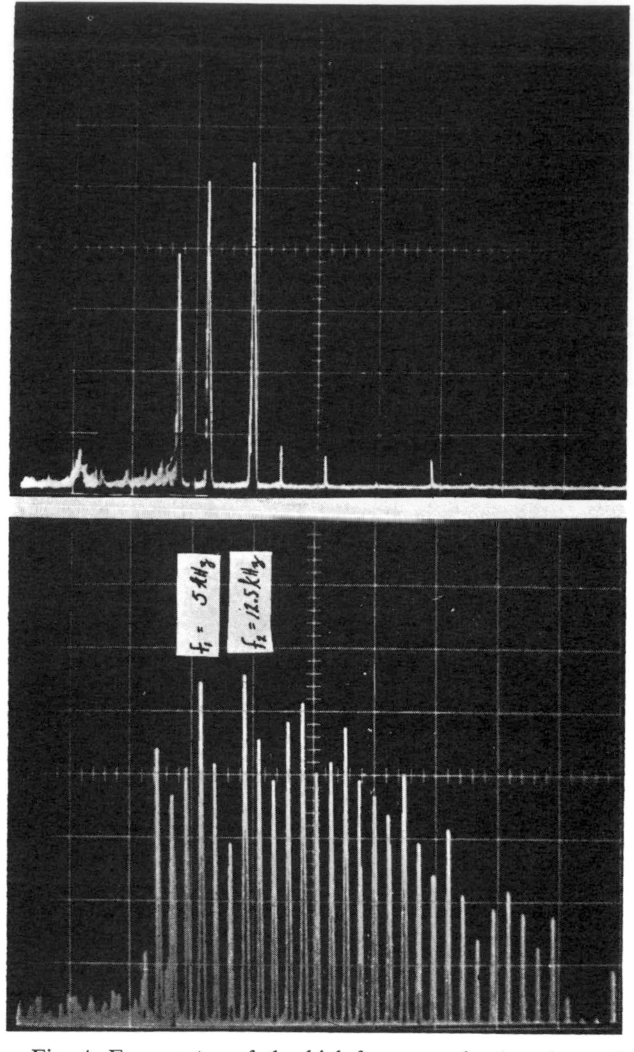

Fig. 4. Far spectra of the high-frequency loudspeakers of Fig. 3. **Top**: high-quality horn-type loudspeaker. **Bottom**: ionized-air loudspeaker. The B&K ½ in. microphone purports to be substantially flat to 40 KHz. Note that the ionized-air loudspeaker may be generating sidebands at much higher frequencies than shown; those in the audible range amount to 30% rms of the amplitude of f_2. $f_1 = 5000$ Hz, $f_2 = 12{,}500$ Hz at 0.5 V; vertical scale = 10 dB per div., horizontal scale = 10 KHz per div.

fundamentals radiated by a large orchestra, and modulation distortion would be reduced by more than 5 dB.

Apparently horn loading remains the best means to reduce diaphragm excursion and increase efficiency so as to minimize modulation distortion.

POSTLUDE

It was hoped early in these experiments that amplitude and frequency modulation could be distinguished, but so far this separation has been elusive. Pragmatically, the total modulation distortion is what affects quality, and when horn-type loudspeakers are shown to be capable of higher output at lower total modulation distortion, it seems fair to conclude that the sum of the amplitude and frequency modulation distortion is really the sought quantity.

However desirable it would be to measure each separately, this remains "beyond the scope of this paper".

REFERENCES

1. F. E. Terman, *Radio Engineers Handbook* (McGraw-Hill Book Co., New York, 1943), pp. 531-535.
2. Paul W. Klipsch, "Subjective Effects of Frequency Modulation Distortion" (Letter to the Editor), *J. Audio Eng. Soc.* **6**, 143 (1958).
3. Lord Rayleigh, *The Theory of Sound* (McMillan, 1878, reprint of 1940), Vol. II, pp. 155-156.
4. G. L. Beers and H. Belar "Frequency—Modulation Distortion in Loudspeakers", *Proc. IRE* **31**, 132 (Apr. 1943).
5. F. E. Terman, *Radio Engineering*, 3rd Ed., 1947. Equation (5) corresponds to Terman's Eq. 9-6.
6. B. O. Pierce, *A Short Table of Integrals*, Second Edition (Ginn and Co., Boston, 1910), Eq. 819, p. 96.
7. James Moir, "Doppler Distortion in Loudspeakers", *Hi Fi News* (England) Jan. 1967.
8. A. L. Thuras, R. T. Jenkins and H. T. O'Neil, "Extraneous Frequencies Generated in an Air Carrying Intense Sound Pressures", *J. Acoust. Soc. Am.* **6**, 173 (1935).
9. S. Goldstein and N. W. McLachlan, "Sound Waves of finite amplitude in an exponential Horn", *J. Acoust. Soc. Am.* **6**, 275 (1935).
10. Y. Rocard, *Comptes rendus* **196**, 161 (1933).
11. E. C. Wente and A. L. Thuras, "Symposium on Auditory Perspective: Loudspeakers and Microphones", *Trans. AIEE* **53**, 214 (1934).

ACKNOWLEDGEMENT

Appreciation is expressed for valued suggestions from G. L. Beers and Murlon S. Corrington.

THE AUTHOR

Paul W. Klipsch was born in 1904, in Elkhart, Indiana. He received the B.S. Degree in Electrical Engineering from New Mexico College for Agricultural and Mechanical Arts in 1926 (now New Mexico State University), and the E.E. from Stanford University in 1934.

He was employed in the testing department of General Electric Company from 1926 to 1928; at the Anglo-Chilean Consolidated Nitrate Corporation, Tocopilla, Chile from 1928 to 1931; the Independent Exploration Company, Houston, Texas from 1934 to 1936; the Subterrex Company, Houston, Texas from 1937 to 1941; and the U.S. Army Ordnance Department from 1941 to 1945 (Major, 1943, Lt. Col., 1953). At present, he is president of Klipsch and Associates, Inc., Hope, Arkansas, manufacturers of loudspeakers.

Mr. Klipsch has written many papers and holds patents in the fields of geophysics, acoustics, firearms, etc. He is a Fellow of the Audio Engineering Society, Fellow of IEEE, Member of the Acoustical Society of America, Tau Beta Pi, Sigma Xi, and is listed in Who's Who in Engineering.

Experimental Determination of Low-Frequency Loudspeaker Parameters*

J. ROBERT ASHLEY AND MARK D. SWAN

Colorado Springs Center, University of Colorado, Colorado Springs, Colorado

Methods for measuring the mechanical parameters of a loudspeaker have been previously described by Beranek [1] and Novak [2]. These methods are compared and combined with a simple program for a time-shared digital computer to give a method which requires a minimum amount of equipment and effort and yields excellent results.

INTRODUCTION Before one can do any design work on low-frequency baffles, one must know the mechanical parameters of the loudspeaker. The mass and compliance are needed to determine the resonant frequency and the optimum volume [3] for a vented cabinet. The flux density and voice coil wire length combine as a product, the *BL* product, along with the mechanical losses and electrical resistance to determine the total speaker Q factor which is needed in cabinet design.

This is not a new problem and Leo L. Beranek gives it an excellent treatment in Chap. 8 of his book *Acoustics* [1]. We have applied Beranek's theory to a wide variety of loudspeakers including the high-compliance low-resonance woofers, and have found such a variety of loudspeaker designs that we deem it essential to make measurements on a speaker before starting baffle design.

Processing the data from loudspeaker measurements involves a fair amount of arithmetic, which is both a source of occasional error and much boring labor. Since time-shared digital computer terminals are now becoming widely available, we have programmed this data-processing computation for the General Electric Time Sharing Service.

* Presented October 13, 1969 at the 37th Convention of the Audio Engineering Society, New York.

A REVIEW OF THE THEORY

The first parameter to be determined is the mechanical compliance of the suspension system, C_{MS}. (This is the reciprocal of mechanical stiffness.) We have found that the easiest way to make this measurement is to place the speaker with the cone pointed upward and the cone axis vertical. Known weights (in the range .1 to 1 kg) are placed on the cone and the displacement (change of position) is measured. Combining Beranek's Eqs. 8.41 and 8.42,

$$C_{MS} = \mathit{displacement/force} = \Delta x / 9.8 M' \quad \text{(M/N)} \qquad (1)$$

where the displacement is in meters and the added mass M' is in kilograms.

Once the loudspeaker is assembled, the moving system mass cannot be determined by weighing. Beranek suggests a perturbation technique which requires attaching a known mass to the diaphragm and measuring the shift in resonant frequency. One of the authors has used this method on over a dozen loudspeakers and destroyed only one cone assembly. The process is only moderately reliable because the position of the added mass (which should be as close to the voice coil as possible) can affect the measurement. Therefore, we prefer Beranek's alternate suggestion of first measuring the compliance and then measuring resonance to determine the moving system mass. If a vacuum tank is available, then the vacuum resonance and the compliance can be used to obtain the moving system mass by use of

$$M_{MD} = 1/C_{MS}(2\pi f_v)^2 \quad (2)$$

where f_v = vacuum resonance. However, a vacuum tank is not often available, and one must take the data in free air, i.e., with the speaker unbaffled and supported away from tables and walls. From Beranek's Eq. 8.37

$$M_{MD} = [1/C_{MS}(2\pi f_0)^2] - 3.15a^3 \quad (3)$$

where f_0 = free-air resonance. Note that one needs to know the effective piston radius a. Here we face the problem of determining just what is the actual cone outer diameter. This is a special problem for high-compliance suspensions with their multiple rolls and large width.

The cone radius also determines the cone area S_D which is the factor needed to convert acoustical loads on the diaphram to mechanical values. Novak [2] has suggested an alternate method of measuring the compliance of the suspension by checking the resonance in free air and then on a closed test box of known volume. Since the known volume of the test box actually gives the acoustic compliance of the box, this method then measures the acoustic compliance of the systems. Thus, we can rearrange Beranek's Eq. 8.15 as

$$C_{AS}/C_{AB} = 1.15(f_1/f_0)^2 - 1 \quad (4)$$

where C_{AS} = acoustic compliance of the speaker, f_0 = free-air resonance, f_1 = resonance on the test box, V_1 = volume of the test box, and

$$C_{AB} = V_1/1.4\times 10^5 \quad (5)$$

is the acoustic compliance of the test box (which is assumed to be small—say less than .5 m in maximum dimension).

The relationship between acoustic and mechanical compliance is simply

$$C_{MS} = C_{AS}/S_D^2 \quad (6)$$

which can be rearranged to give the effective cone area. The effective cone radius then, is

$$r = [(1/\pi)(C_{AS}/C_{MS})^{1/2}]^{1/2}. \quad (7)$$

We have found this to be an excellent way to check the validity of our measurements. First, the mechanical compliance is measured by placing known weights on the cone. Second, the acoustic compliance is measured by measuring the free-air resonance and the resonance on a closed box. If these two compliances used in Eq. 7 yield a value of the cone radius which is in reasonable agreement with a measured value, then the two independent measurements agree and the data can be used with confidence. In practice, we have found that the two methods of measuring cone radius agree to within a half centimeter in most cases.

With this degree of consistency in the compliance measurement, the computed value of moving system mass can also be regarded with a high level of confidence. We consider this added confidence sufficient justification for taking two independent determinations of compliance.

Although it is usually a negligible factor in determining the overall Q of a loudspeaker, the mechanical loss in the suspension can be determined by the half-bandwidth method described by Beranek. While measuring the free-air cone resonance electrically, we also record the frequencies where the voltage across the voice coil is 3 dB down from the value at resonance. From circuit theory, the Q is

$$Q = f_0/\Delta f = f_0/(f_2 - f_3) \quad (8)$$

and the mechanical resistance is found from Beranek's Eq. 8.40 as

$$R_{MS} = [\omega_0(M_{MD}+M_{MI})/Q] - 8.45\times 10^{-6}a^6 f^4 \quad (9)$$

where the mechanical air load resistance accounts for the last term and can usually be neglected.

The measured compliance and cone radius allow a simple computation of Novak's [3] optimum volume for a vented cabinet (bass reflex baffle). The optimum acoustic compliance of the box is related to the acoustic compliance of the loudspeaker by

$$C_{AB} = C_{AS}/1.44, \quad (10)$$

so that the optimum volume is

$$V_2 = 1.4\times 10^5 C_{AB} \approx 10^5 C_{AS}. \quad (11)$$

Novak [4] has pointed out what these equations clearly show, namely, that the optimum volume for a 12 in.-high compliance speaker is a relatively large number, say 10 ft^3. This reinforces Brociner's contention [5] that a small box should be driven by a small-diameter cone.

The most important factor in determining the damping of the loudspeaker in either a closed box or a vented box is the product of magnetic flux density and the length of the voice coil winding. Beranek's method of measuring the current required to restore the cone position to its resting point after a known mass is placed on the cone requires only the addition of an ammeter and adjustable dc power supply to the equipment used for the mechanical compliance measurement. Then, Beranek's Eq. 8.45 gives the BL product,

$$BL = 9.8M'/i \quad \text{(Wb/m)} \quad (12)$$

where M' is the added mass and i is the restoring current. We can also measure the voltage across the voice coil to determine the coil electrical resistance, although it is adequately accurate to simply use the ohmmeter of a reliable volt-ohm-milliammeter instrument.

The practical details of taking the data required for use in the equations will now be discussed.

TAKING THE DATA

Taking data for the mechanical compliance and the BL product can be combined into one setup, as shown in Fig. 1. The vernier caliper is used as a depth gage and first adjusted to measure the distance *D4* from the bar to a reference point on the cone. (The names for the distances and other data are the names used in the computer program of the next section.) Then a known mass *M4* is carefully placed in the cone. The mass to use

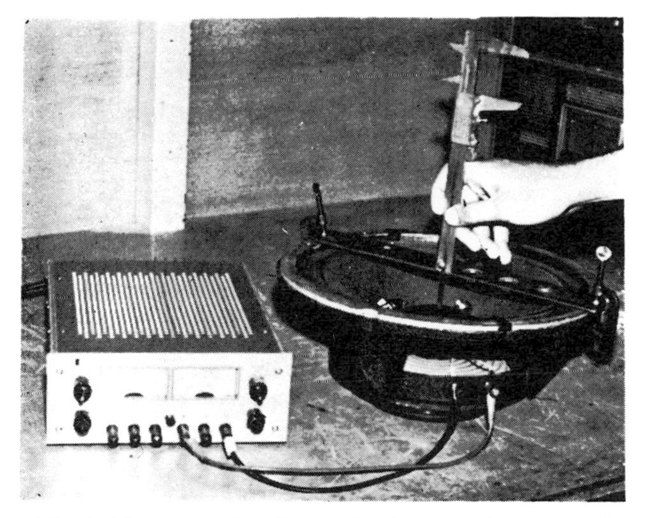

Fig. 1. Measurement of the mechanical compliance and the BL product. For the Jensen model W-12-NF woofer pictured here, the data were: M4 = .5139 kg; 12 = .62 A; D3 = 1.805 in.; D4 = 1.583 in.

in a given case is to some extent a function of the speaker compliance and allowable throw. We have found that .25 kg is a good value for a first try on small loudspeakers, and .5 kg is a good value for larger units. We have found that brass nuts for 1/4 to 3/8 in. thread make excellent weights. They can be distributed around the cone without applying sufficient force at any one point to damage the cone. An attempt to use steel weights proved quite unsuccessful: the leakage magnetic field from the speaker is sufficient to thoroughly confuse the data. For the mechanical compliance measurement, the objective is to flex the suspension to as large a displacement as possible without leaving the linear region. For high-compliance speakers, this displacement is about .5 cm; for low-compliance speakers, it is about .2 cm in large units and .1 cm in small units. (This implies that this method will not be accurate for low compliance speakers of less than 8 in. diameter.) If there is any doubt as to the length of the linear region, the displacement caused by several values of added mass should be measured and the data plotted.

Before disturbing the reading of the vernier caliper, the dc power supply is turned on and adjusted to bring the cone back to its reference position. The value of the current, *I2*, is recorded. Typically this will require current on the order of .5 to 1.0 A for 8 ohm speakers. For small speakers, this can represent an excessive dc power input and warp the voice coil if the current is applied for even a few tens of seconds. Therefore, one should try to use the smallest possible additional mass for 8 in. or smaller units. On larger units, the current should be applied only for the length of time required to obtain the data. (This is also a good opportunity to determine the phasing polarity of the speaker if it is to be used in a combination system or stereo system.)

After the current is measured, the power supply is turned off and the vernier caliper readjusted to measure the depth *D3* with the known mass *M4* in the cone. Since our caliper is graduated in inches, we record the data in inches and let the computer translate this to metric.

The second equipment setup is used to determine the free-air resonance *FO* and the Q, as shown in Fig. 2. The measurement of *FO* is done by tuning the frequency of the audio oscillator to obtain a peak reading on the VTVM. For best linearity and accuracy, the VTVM should be on a 100 mV scale for this measurement. To show the effect of nearby objects, the *FO* is first measured with the speaker resting cone-up on a table. Then, the speaker is held as shown at least 1 m from any plane surface. This latter value is the correct value of *FO*.

With the frequency set at *FO*, the oscillator output is adjusted to make the voltmeter read at the 0 point on the dB scale. Next, the frequency is increased to make the meter drop 3 dB, and the oscillator frequency *F2* is recorded. Similarly, the frequencey is decreased to find the 3 dB frequency below *FO* and the value of *F3* is recorded. These data are used with Eq. 8 to determine the mechanical Q of the moving system.

The final measurement uses the electrical equipment shown in Fig. 2 to measure the resonant frequency while the speaker is tightly held on a test box, as shown in Fig. 3. Here, the inside dimensions of the box are needed to compute the volume *V1* for use in Eq. 5. This box must be carefully constructed of 3/4 in. plywood with all six sides glued and screwed in place. All seams should be caulked and the box *is not* lined or filled with sound-absorbing material. A box of about .03 m^3 (about 2000 $in.^3$) can be used for 8 to 12 in. speakers. One word of caution: the hole in the test box *must be* larger than the effective cone area. This implies the use of an adapter for 8 in. speakers if the hole is made large enough for a 12 in. unit.

This completes the data-taking procedure. The numbers so determined are entered as DATA statements in the digital computer program of the next section.

COMPUTER PROCESSING OF THE DATA

Making the calculations for just two or three loudspeakers caused us to quickly tire of our desk calculators, slide rules, and human errors. Since rapid-response digital computing terminals are becoming more and more

Fig. 2. Measurement of the free-air resonance and the mechanical resistance. The 1 kohm resistor shown between the oscillator and voltmeter makes the oscillator appear as a constant-current generator to the speaker. For the Jenseon model W-12-NF woofer pictured here, the data were: F0 = 23.0 Hz; F2 = 25.6 Hz; F3 = 22.4 Hz.

Table I. Digital computer program used for the determination of loudspeaker parameters.

```
SPKR2      10:12    PX SYSF  4/23/69

100 LET P1 = 3.14159265
110 PRINT "        MECHANICAL PRØPERTIES ØF LØUDSPEAKERS"
120 PRINT
130 LET V1 = (11.2*8.65*22.5)
140 PRINT "THE VØLUME ØF ØUR TEST BØX IS ";V1;"CU.IN."
150 PRINT
160 LET V1 = V1*(.0254↑3)
170 PRINT USING 350
180 PRINT USING 360
190 READ T$, S$, M$, D1
200 READ F0, F1, F2, F3,
210 READ D3, D4, M4, I2
220 LET Q = F0/(F2 - F3)
240 LET C4 = .0254*(D3 - D4)/(9.8*M4)
250 LET B1 = (9.8*M4)/I2
270 LET C1 = V1*(1.15*((F1/F0)↑2) -1.0)/.14E6
280 LET D2 = 2*(SQR((SQR(C1/C4))/P1))/.0254
290 LET M3 = 1.0/(C4*((2*P1*F0)↑2))
300 LET M2 = M3 - 3.15*((D2/2)↑3)*(.0254↑3)
310 LET V2 = .14E6*C1/(1.44*(.0254↑3))
320 PRINT
330 PRINT USING 370, S$, D2, B1, M2, C4, V2, Q
340 GØ TØ 190
350: MØDEL      EFF. CØNE    BL PRØD.   MASS    CØMPLIANCE     ØPT. VØL.    Q
360:              DIA. IN.    WEB-MET     KG        M/N          CU. IN.
370:"          " ####.##      ###.##    #.####   #.######       ######.##   ####.#
375 DATA "JENSEN", "C-8282-2", "10 ØZ", 8
376 DATA 74, 88, 76.5, 70.2
377 DATA 1.199, 1.146, .2367, .66
380 DATA "UNIVERSITY", "C-8W", "10 ØZ.", 8
390 DATA 92, 106, 103, 81,
400 DATA .372, .268, .5139, .623
410 DATA "JENSEN", "C-10-PF", "14 ØZ.", 12
420 DATA 34.2, 66.0, 35.8, 33.0
430 DATA 1.599, 1.447, .5139, .63
432 DATA "JENSEN", "W-12-RF", "6.8 ØZ", 12
433 DATA 26, 75, 27.4, 24.8
434 DATA 1.788, 1.576, .5139, .94
440 DATA "JENSEN", "W-12-NF", "1-3/4 LB", 12
450 DATA 23.0, 72.5, 25.6, 22.4
460 DATA 1.805, 1.583, .5139, .62
470 DATA "B-A", "34B234", "10 ØZ", 12
480 DATA 75.0, 110, 77.2, 73.5
490 DATA 2.438, 2.402, .5139, .84
491 DATA "HERALD", "S-183A", "MED.", 12
492 DATA 68.5, 104.0, 73, 65,
494 DATA .520, .489, .2367, .49
500 END
```

available, we have programmed these computations for a typical system. The original program (Table I) was written in BASIC language and run on a terminal of the GE Mark I Time Sharing Service. Since some readers may not be familiar with this language or have access to a computer with this compiler, we include as Appendix A a translation to FORTRAN, which has been run on the GE system as well as on a CDC 6400 computer.

Statements 110 to 180 in the program set up titles for the tabulated output. Notice that Statement 130 computes the volume of the test box from the measured inside dimensions. This statement must be modified by each user to agree with the test box used. Statement 160 converts the test-box volume to cubic meters. Statements 190, 200 and 210 tell the computer to read the data which identifies and specifies each speaker. For reference, the names of the variables in these READ statements are tabulated and identified in Table II. (Some of these data are not used in this program but are included for use in other computations. It cannot be omitted from

Table II. Data elements for the program of Table I.

T$	Name of the manufacturer
S$	Model number identification
M$	Magnet weight (not used in the computation)
D1	Advertised speaker diameter
F0	Free-air resonance
F1	Resonance on the test box
F2	Upper 3 dB frequency
F3	Lower 3 dB frequency
D3	Depth measurement (in.) with mass in cone
D4	Depth measurement (in.) without mass in cone
M4	Mass used to displace the cone
I2	Current required to restore the cone position

Table III. Computation steps in the program of Table I.

220	Computes Q using Eq. 8
240	Computes C_{MS} using Eq. 1 and includes a convention from inches to meters
250	Computes the BL product using Eq. 12
270	Computes C_{AS} using Eq. 4
280	Computes the cone radius a using Eq. 7 and then converts the answer to diameter in inches
290	Computes the total mass $M_{MD} + M_{M1}$
300	Computes the moving system mass M_M by subtracting M_{M1}
310	Computes the Novak optimum volume using Eq. 11

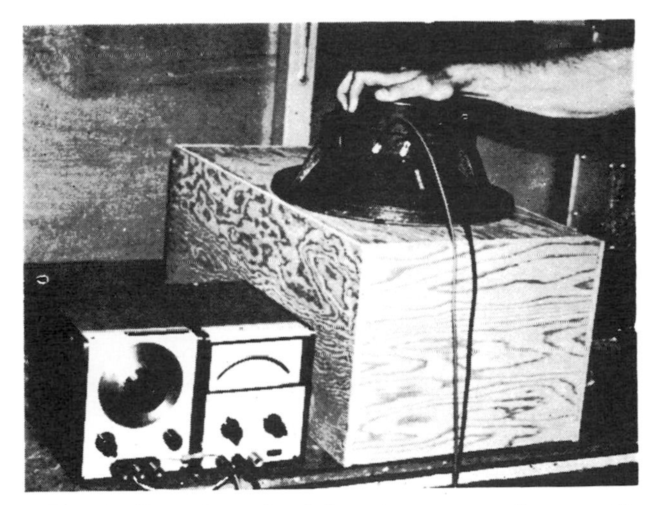

Fig. 3. Use of a closed box to measure the acoustic compliance of a loudspeaker suspension. This particular test box has an internal volume of 2180 in.[3] The resonance of the box and the Jensen W-12-NF woofer: F1 = 72.5 Hz.

the DATA Statements 375 ff without causing total confusion.)

The actual computation is done in Statements 220 through 310. The action of these statements is explained in Table III.

Statement 330 is the print statement which gives the output of the program. We have used the IMAGE format system available on the GE Mark I system to make the answer fit the width of the teletype page. Statement 340 tells the computer to repeat the computation for another speaker; the computer will do this until there is no data left. Finally, the data for the individual speakers is inserted after Statement 370.

The computer run for all the speakers we have measured is reproduced in Table IV. The effective cone diameter is within a quarter of an inch of the best

Table IV. Computer output resulting from the program of Table I.

```
SPKR2        10:09     PX SYSF  4/23/69

       MECHANICAL PRØPERTIES ØF LØUDSPEAKERS

THE VØLUME ØF ØUR TEST BØX IS  2179.8  CU.IN.

 MØDEL      EFF. CØNE    BL PRØD.   MASS     CØMPLIANCE     ØPT. VØL.     Q
             DIA. IN.    WEB-MET     KG          M/N         CU. IN.

C-8282-2       5.72         3.51    .0068      .000580        948.06    11.7

C-8W           5.62         8.08    .0046      .000525        797.19     4.2

C-10-PF        8.08         7.99    .0249      .000767       4969.42    12.2

W-12-RF        9.45         5.36    .0296      .001069      12971.56    10.0

W-12-NF        9.81         8.12    .0367      .001120      15783.31     7.2

34B234         9.48         6.00    .0193      .000182       2230.93    20.3

S-183A         8.34         4.73    .0122      .000339       2498.96     8.6

ØUT ØF DATA    IN 190



USED       6.33 UNITS.
```

APPENDIX A Translation of the Program of TABLE I to FORTRAN IV

```
                 PROGRAM LOUDSP(INPUT,OUTPUT)
000003         1 REAL M2,I2,M4,M3
000003         5 P1=3.14159265
000005        10 PRINT 15
000011        15 FORMAT (1H1,*   MECHANICAL PROPERTIES OF LOUDSPEAKERS*/)
000011        20 V1=(11.2*8.65*22.5)
000013        25 PRINT 30,V1
000021        30 FORMAT (1H *THE VOLUME OF OUR TEST BOX IS*,F10.3,*CU. IN.*/)
000021        35 V1=V1*(.0254**3.)
000026        40 PRINT 120
000032        45 PRINT 125
000036        50 READ 55,TS,SS,MS,D1,F0,F1,F2,F3,D3,D4,M4,I2
000072        55 FORMAT (3A10,I3,4F6.2,3F6.3,F4.2)
000072        60 Q=F0/(F2-F3)
000075        65 C4=.0254*(D3-D4)/(9.8*M4)
000102        70 B1=(9.8*M4)/I2
000105        75 C1=V1*(1.15*((F1/F0)**2.)-1.0)/.14E6
000116        80 D2=2.0*(SQRT((SQRT(C1/C4))/P1))/.0254
000130        85 M3=1.0/(C4*((2.0*P1*F0)**2.))
000137        90 M2=M3-3.15*((D2/2.0)**3.)*(.0254**3.)
000152       100 V2=.14E6*C1/(1.44*(.0254**3.))
000160       110 PRINT 130,SS,D2,B1,M2,C4,V2,Q
000202       115 IF (F0.GT. 0.0) GO TO 50
000205       120 FORMAT (1H * MODEL     EFF. CONE    BL PROD.    MASS    COMPLIANCE
                C    OPT. VOL.     Q*)
000205       125 FORMAT (1H *              DIA. IN.    WEB-MT.      KG        M/N
                C     CU. IN.*)
000205       130 FORMAT(1X,A8,1X,F7.2,5X,F6.2,2X,F6.4,3X,F8.6,10X,F9.2,6X,F6.1/)
000205           STOP
000206           END
```

APPENDIX B Computed Results from a CDC 6400 Digital Computer

MECHANICAL PROPERTIES OF LOUDSPEAKERS

THE VOLUME OF OUR TEST BOX IS 2179.800CU. IN.

MODEL	EFF. CONE DIA. IN.	BL PROD. WEB-MT.	MASS KG	COMPLIANCE M/N	OPT. VOL. CU. IN.	Q
C-8282-2	5.72	3.51	.0068	.000580	948.06	11.7
C-8W	5.62	8.08	.0046	.000525	797.19	4.2
C-10-PF	8.08	7.99	.0249	.000767	4969.42	12.2
W-12-RF	9.45	5.36	.0296	.001069	12971.56	10.0
W-12-NF	9.81	8.12	.0367	.001120	15783.31	7.2
34B234	9.48	6.00	.0193	.000182	2230.93	20.3
S-183A	8.34	4.73	.0122	.000339	2498.96	8.6

"guesstimate" made by laying a ruler across the speaker for all of these units. We estimate that all the parameters measured are accurate to within 5%.

The total cost of reading the data statements into the computer, doing the computation, and printing the answers was about $1.50 per loudspeaker in early 1969.

ACKNOWLEDGEMENTS

Mr. James F. Novak of the Jensen Manufacturing Division of the Muter Company gave us considerable assistance through phone conversations and correspondence. His confirmation of the measured values for several Jensen speakers was most valuable and encouraging. The data were taken and computer processed in the laboratories of the Colorado Springs Center of the University of Colorado.

The pictures used in the figures were taken at the Hewlett-Packard Colorado Springs Division.

REFERENCES

1. L. L. Beranek, *Acoustics* (McGraw Hill, New York, 1954).
2. J. F. Novak, "Performance of Enclosures for Low-Resonance High-Compliance Loudspeakers," *IRE Trans. Audio* **AV-7** (1959).
3. J. F. Novak, "Designing Hi-Fi Speaker Enclosures", *Electronics World*, (Jan. 1966).
4. J. F. Novak, oral communication, Jan. 1969.
5. V. Brociner, "Considerations of Speaker Size vs Cabinet in Low Frequency Reproduction," presented October 10, 1961 at the 13th Annual Convention of the Audio Engineering Society, New York.

THE AUTHORS

J. ROBERT ASHLEY MARK D. SWAN

J. Robert Ashley was born in Kansas City, Missouri in 1927. Becoming interested in home music systems while in high school, he took two years of electronics schooling while in the U.S. Navy. In 1952 he received the B.S. degree in electrical engineering from the University of Kansas. He then taught audio at that institution, and received the M.S. degree in electrical engineering there in 1956. For the following nine years, he worked as a research and development engineer with the Sperry Electronic Tube Division, doing microwave tube development and using analog computers in the study of electron beam focus. In 1967 he received the Ph.D. degree in electrical engineering from the University of Florida.

At present, Dr. Ashley is associate professor of electrical engineering at the Colorado Springs Center of the University of Colorado. Dr. Ashley is a senior member of the Institute of Electrical and Electronics Engineers, and a member of the Augio Engineering Society and the Simulation Council. He has been elected to Tau Beta Pi, Sigma Xi, Eta Kappa Nu, Sigma Pi Sigma, Kappa Eta Kappa, Sigma Tau, and Phi Kappa Phi.

•

Mark D. Swan was born in Ponca City, Oklahoma in 1946. He received the B.S. degree in electrical engineering from the University of Colorado in 1969.

While a senior, Mr. Swan's major areas of study were in control systems theory, communications theory, analog computation, and acoustics. He became interested in direct—radiator loudspeaker and enclosure design while taking a course in acoustics. The measurements discussed in this paper were made as part of a senior laboratory project. He began a tour of duty with the U.S. Navy in July, 1969.

Mr. Swan is a student member of the Institute of Electrical and Electronics Engineers and a member of Tau Beta Pi.

1970 through 1977

AUDIO

ES

Modulation Distortion in Loudspeakers: Part II

PAUL W. KLIPSCH

Klipsch and Associates, Inc., Hope, Arkansas

Modulation distortion in loudspeakers consists of amplitude modulation distortion (AMD) and frequency modulation distortion (FMD); the effective sum of these is the total modulation distortion (TMD). It appears that the first-order side frequencies are due mainly to frequency modulation and the second-order sideband frequencies are due to amplitude modulation. Small direct-radiator loudspeakers typically display large AMD and relatively less FMD, while horn loudspeakers display small FMD and negligible AMD.

INTRODUCTION Part I of this paper [1] defined the various kinds of distortion. The previous paper was concerned mainly with frequency modulation distortion (FMD), which appeared to be of greater importance than amplitude modulation distortion (AMD). Applying the spectrum analyzer to small direct radiators shows that AMD may exceed FMD by an order of magnitude.

ANALYSIS

A former colleague suggested that in a symmetrical system first-order sideband frequencies would not exist [2].
Let

$$y = k(x - mx^3) \qquad (1)$$

and assume this to be a reasonable approximation to the displacement y of a loudspeaker diaphragm for an applied force of x, to be considered valid over the range of

$$-2.0 < x < +2.0$$

Figure 1 illustrates this "stress–strain diagram", where, for example, $m = 0.1$, or

$$y = k(x - 0.1x^3). \qquad (2)$$

Now assume two equal sinewaves of unit amplitude,

$$x = \sin \omega_1 t + \sin \omega_2 t \qquad (3)$$

$$\begin{aligned} y = {} & \sin \omega_1 t + \sin \omega_2 t \\ & -0.1\,[\sin^3 \omega_1 t + 3 \sin^2 \omega_1 t \sin \omega_2 t \\ & \quad + 3 \sin \omega_1 t \sin^2 \omega_2 t \\ & \quad + \sin^3 \omega_2 t]. \end{aligned} \qquad (4)$$

Using $\sin^3 a = 3/4 \sin a - 1/4 \sin 3a$; $3 \sin^2 a \sin b = 3\,(1/2 - 1/2 \cos 2a) \sin b + 3\,(1/2 - 1/2 \cos 2b) \sin a = 3/2 \sin b - 3/2 \sin (a + 2b) - 3/2 \sin (a - 2b)$, etc., we obtain

$$\begin{aligned} y = {} & \sin \omega_1 t + \sin \omega_2 t \\ & -0.1\,[3/4 \sin \omega_1 t - 1/4 \sin 3\,\omega_1 t \\ & \quad + 3/4 \sin \omega_2 t - 1/4 \sin 3\,\omega_2 t \\ & \quad + 3/2 \sin \omega_1 t + 3/2 \sin \omega_2 t \\ & \quad - 3/2 \sin (\omega_1 t + 2\,\omega_2 t) \\ & \quad - 3/2 \sin (\omega_1 t - 2\,\omega_2 t) \\ & \quad - 3/2 \sin (\omega_2 t + 2\,\omega_1 t) \\ & \quad - 3/2 \sin (\omega_2 t - 2\,\omega_1 t)], \end{aligned} \qquad (5)$$

or

$$\begin{aligned} y = {} & 0.775 \sin \omega_1 t + 0.775 \sin \omega_2 t \\ & + 0.025 (\sin 3\,\omega_1 t + \sin 3\,\omega_2 t) \\ & - 0.15\,[\sin (\omega_1 t + 2\,\omega_2 t) \\ & \quad + \sin (\omega_1 t - 2\,\omega_2 t) \\ & \quad + \sin (\omega_2 t + 2\,\omega_1 t) \\ & \quad + \sin (\omega_2 t - 2\,\omega_1 t)]. \end{aligned} \qquad (6)$$

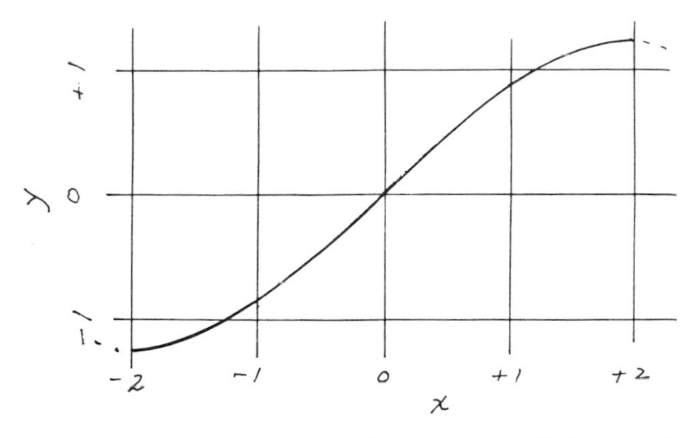

Fig. 1. Simplified stress–strain (force *vs* displacement) curve for suspended system of a loudspeaker, assuming symmetry of both magnetic and compliance systems.

The bracketed term in Eq. (6) shows modulation sideband frequencies of $f_1 \pm 2f_2$ and $f_2 \pm 2f_1$.

Note that these are second-order sidebands; there are no first-order sidebands of the form $f_2 \pm f_1$.

One may conclude that in a symmetrical system, such as illustrated in Fig. 1, only second-order amplitude-distortion sideband frequencies exist.

In Part I of this paper [1], an example was used wherein the amplitudes of the frequency modulation sideband frequencies were 0.017 (1.7%) for the first order and 0.00013 for the second order. These second-order amplitudes are 40 dB down lower than the first-order ones and not apt to show on an analyzer spectrogram.

Thus it appears that first-order sideband amplitudes can be attributed mainly to frequency modulation distortion and second-order sideband amplitude entirely to amplitude modulation distortion.

Of course, asymmetric nonlinearity would induce some first-order AMD, but it would seem that any second-order sideband frequencies must be almost entirely due to AMD.

INTERPRETATION

Examining Eq. (6) further, the fundamental signals, f_1 and f_2, which started out at unity are reduced to 0.775. There is a 2.5% third harmonic of each input signal. These effects are intuitively obvious, at least qualitatively. The amplitude of each sideband frequency which reads 0.15 amplitude becomes approximately 19% of the 0.775 fundamental output.

The bracketed terms show amplitudes of frequencies $f_2 \pm 2f_1$. This indicates that the symmetrical stress–strain systems depicted in Fig. 1 give rise to second-order sidebands, with complete absence of first-order sideband frequencies of $f_2 \pm f_1$.

The bracketed terms show amplitudes of frequencies of $f_1 \pm 2f_2$. Recognizing that $\sin(-a) = -\sin a$, it is logical to conclude that, with appropriate phase shifts, these sideband terms may be written as amplitudes of $2f_2 \pm f_1$.

This turns out to be a surprise. Early work with the sprectrum analyzer did not show these high-order terms for the simple reason they were not suspected and the "window" of the analyzer was not wide enough to include them. Therefore, in some of the new study the analyzer was adjusted to "see" out past $3f_2$.

TESTS OF MIDRANGE LOUDSPEAKERS

Two midrange loudspeakers were compared. One was a horn-loaded system designed for the 400 to 6000 Hz range, the other was an 8 in. direct-radiating cone designated by its manufacturer specifically for midrange application. Frequencies of $f_1 = 540$ Hz and $f_2 = 4400$ Hz were used, and inputs adjusted to give outputs of 100 dB SPL at 2 ft for f_1 and 92 dB for f_2. The vertical scale is 10 dB per major division.

Figure 2 shows the two spectrograms. The upper curve depicts the performance of the horn loudspeaker: the first peak is the amplitude of f_1, and no harmonics of f_1 are seen. The next large peak is the amplitude of f_2, flanked by two small first-order sideband amplitudes. The sideband amplitudes are nearly 40 dB below the amplitude of f_2, so that the total modulation distortion is slightly over 1%.

Since harmonic distortion of f_1 is not visible and

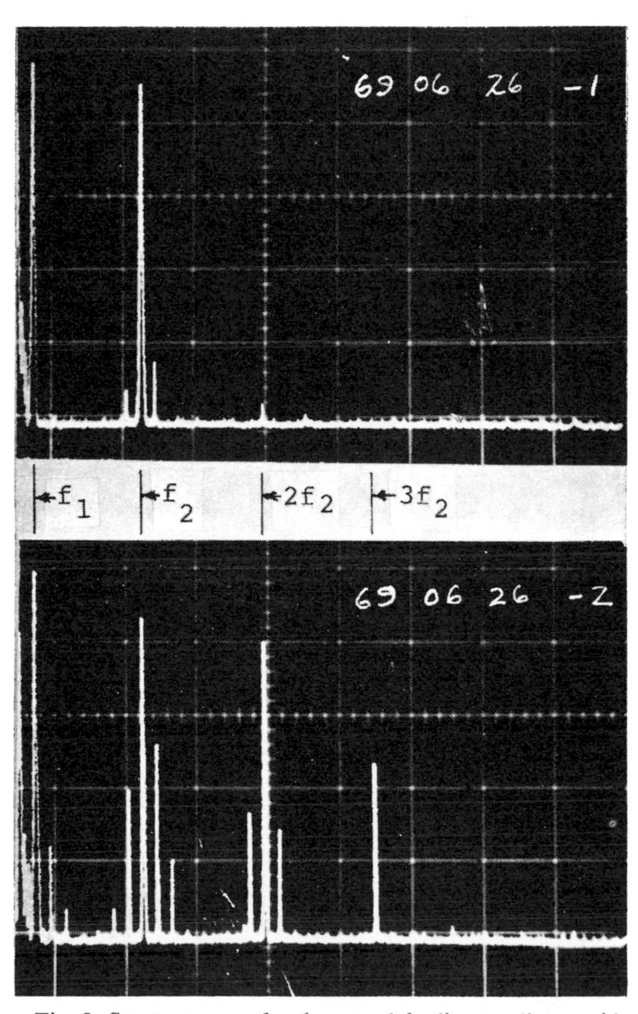

Fig. 2. Spectrograms of *a*. horn and *b*. direct-radiator midrange loudspeakers. Output 100 dB SPL at 2 ft for $f_1 = 540$ Hz, 92 dB for $f_2 = 4400$ Hz. Vertical scale 10 dB per major division. First two major peaks are f_1 and f_2. In top figure, the only significant distortion showing is the pair of sideband frequencies $f_2 \pm f_1$. In the bottom figure significant distortion components are $2f_1$, $f_2 \pm f_1$, $f_2 \pm 2f_1$, $2f_2$, $2f_2 \pm f_1$, and $3f_1$. Total distortion over 10%.

second-order sidebands of f_2 are below the resolution of the spectrum analyzer, it is to be assumed that amplitude modulation is negligible and that the sidebands are due to FMD.

The lower curve in Fig. 2 shows the spectrogram of the 8 in. direct radiator. As in the top figure, the first peak is the amplitude of f_1, but followed by small amounts of second and third harmonic distortion. Next is a large peak, amplitude of f_2, flanked by first- and second-order sideband amplitudes. Then comes the second harmonic $2f_2$ flanked by its sidebands of $2f_2 \pm f_1$, and finally $3f_2$. All the components predicted by Eq. (6) are represented. The magnitude of the $2f_2$ component is much larger than would be expected from Eq. (6) and remains unexplained, except that direct-radiator loudspeakers do unexplained things. Perhaps a nodal cone breakup was taking place and the microphone was in just the right place to maximize the fault. The fact that the second harmonic of f_1 predominates over the third harmonic suggests that the first-order sideband amplitudes of f_2 contain both AMD and FMD.

A significant observation is that the direct-radiator midrange loudspeaker had to be driven into a nonlinear range of cone travel to produce 100 dB SPL at 2 ft. This level corresponds to about 90 dB at a normal listening distance in a typical listening room. This is 1/100 the peak sound power one would demand for "realistic music reproduction", but one sees various orders of modulation distortion in amounts up to 15%. By contrast, the high-quality horn loudspeaker shows a mere 1% total modulation distortion at the same output power.

Another significant observation is that the high-quality horn displays only first-order modulation distortion, which is probably the irreducible frequency modulation type. Again, by contrast, the direct radiator shows a much higher level of first-order sideband components, suggesting suspension asymmetry plus higher FMD output.

TEST OF A FULL-RANGE LOUDSPEAKER

The speaker chosen for this test was a direct radiator consisting of several small cone loudspeakers of "long throw" capability and with a total area approximating that of a 12 in. cone loudspeaker. This system was intended for "full frequency range" and normally employed with an equalizer. The two frequencies were f_1 = 50 Hz and f_2 = 750 Hz, both adjusted to produce 95 dB SPL at 2 ft.

Figure 3 shows the spectrogram of this test. The first peak is the amplitude of the output of f_1. Following this, barely discernible, is the second harmonic ($2f_1$), followed by a strong $3f_1$ (about 20 dB down or 10% third harmonic). Fourth and fifth harmonics are significant.

The next major peak is f_2 (same amplitude as f_1, 95 dB) flanked by small (−30 dB) first-order sidebands ($f_2 \pm f_1$), in turn are flanked by larger second-order sidebands ($f_2 \pm 2f_1$). Still higher-order sidebands are visible.

From an analysis such as Eq. (6), and from the earlier paper, it would appear that there is about 3% FMD and 14% AMD. Apparently the FMD is not as serious as the AMD for this particular loudspeaker.

Sidebands of order higher than the second are not explained by Eq. (6); however, the derivation assumed symmetry, and some asymmetry existed as indicated by presence of a second harmonic of f_1.

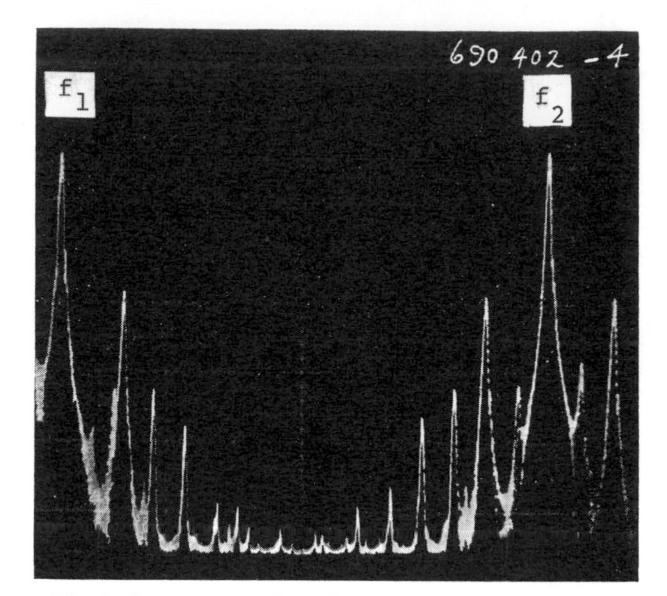

Fig. 3. Spectrogram of small full-range direct radiator employing several small cone loudspeaker elements and a preamplifier equalizer. First peak f_1 = 50 Hz, followed by a small $2f_1$ component, and $3f_1$, $4f_1$, etc. Second large peak, f_2 = 750 Hz, flanked by small first-order sidebands of $f_2 \pm f_1$ and larger sidebands of $f_2 \pm 2f_1$, and significant third- and fourth-order sideband frequencies. Total modulation distortion, approximately 14%. Input of both frequencies adjusted to produce 95 dB SPL at 2 ft.

It is easy to ignore sideband amplitudes of less than 3% when there are distortion amplitudes exceeding 10%. It would be interesting to find the causes of these unpredicted distortion products, but the cone loudspeaker with its infinite number of modes of vibration and breakup could take a lifetime of studying third order effects.

DISCUSSION

Beers and Belar [3] suggested using different speakers for bass and treble. An examination of Fig. 2 suggests that this expedient does not go far enough. Here is an example of a direct-radiator midrange loudspeaker such as is used in a three-way system, producing excessive distortion within its own normal band. The horn-loaded loudspeaker displays about 1/10 the distortion of the direct radiator.

In the case of the multiple loudspeaker whose performance is shown in Fig. 3, obviously the mere proliferation of the number of loudspeakers fails to reduce distortion to tolerable levels. In the companion paper a horn woofer was tested at 100 dB SPL and found to produce less than 1% total modulation distortion.

The frequency response curves of the three loudspeakers tested are shown in Figs. 4 and 5.

The solid curve in Fig. 4 shows the frequency response of the horn midrange, the distortion of which is shown in Fig. 2a. The partly dashed curve in Fig. 4 is for the direct radiator depicted in Fig. 2b.

Figure 5 shows the response (including equalizer) of the loudspeaker whose distortion is depicted in Fig. 3.

One should not expect a correlation between distortion

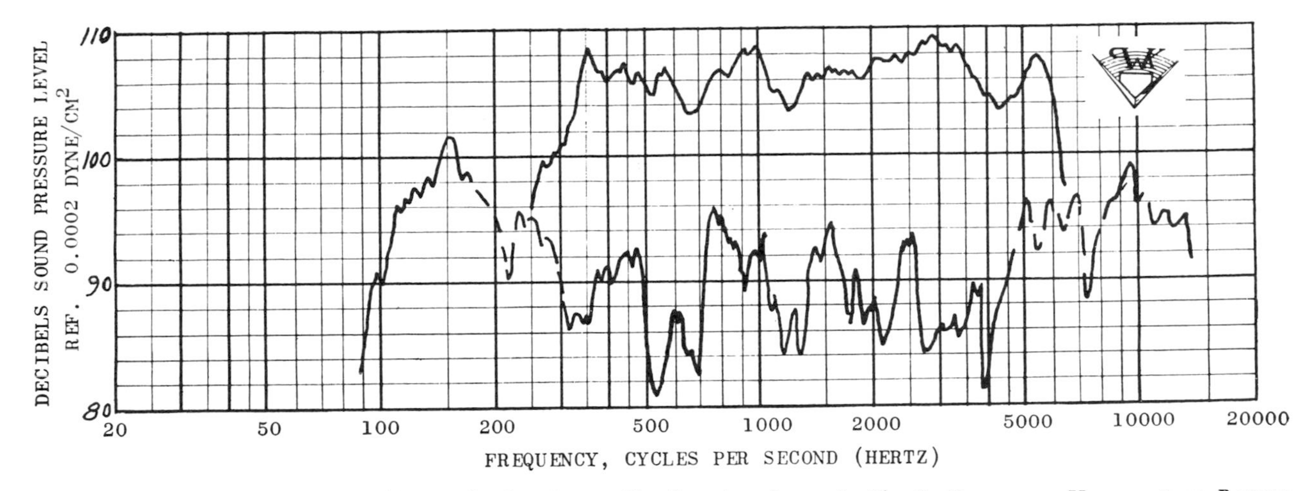

Fig. 4. Response curves of the midrange loudspeakers with distortion shown in Fig. 2. *Top curve*. Horn system; *Bottom curve*, 8 in. direct radiator, both at 1 W input.

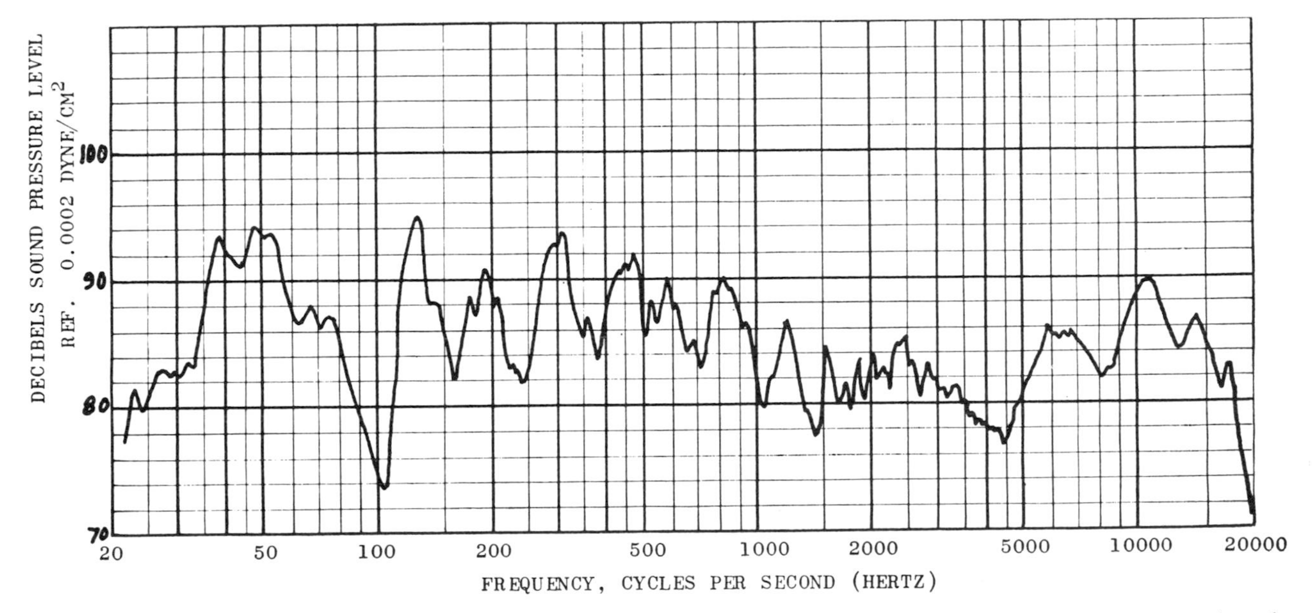

Fig. 5. Frequency response of the loudspeaker with distortion shown in Fig. 3. Input 0.5 W at 500 Hz, approximately 50 W at 40 Hz (difference due to equalizer); curve level coordinates corrected to 1 W input at 500 Hz.

of a loudspeaker and its frequency response, but in these cases it appears the response peak–trough ratio does correlate with the amount of total modulation distortion.

CONCLUSION

It is believed that Figs. 2 and 3 illustrate at least qualitatively what can be concluded from Eq. (6) and from Part I of this paper. The separation of FMD and AMD may not be absolute and precise, but it appears that first-order sideband components must be largely FMD and second-order components largely AMD. Further, it seems to follow that high-efficiency horns will display small FMD and negligible AMD compared to direct radiators, in which both forms of distortion are higher. Small direct radiators driven to output levels necessary for "realistic reproduction of music" may display a preponderance of AMD over FMD, and at objectionably high distortion levels.

A technical conclusion is that, to a reasonable approximation, the spectrum analyzer shows first-order sideband frequency components as FM distortion and second-order components as AM distortion.

A practical conclusion is that the inherently low distortion of properly designed horn-type loudspeakers is significant in the virtual elimination of amplitude modulation distortion and the reduction of frequency modulation distortion to nearly irreducible limits, and that this low distortion is the main contribution to the "cleanness" of sound reproduction from loudspeakers of this type.

REFERENCES

1. Paul W. Klipsch, Modulation Distortion in Loudspeakers, *J. Audio Eng. Soc.* **17**, 194 (1969).

2. John Eargle, personal communication.

3. G. L. Beers and H. Belar "Frequency—Modulation Distortion in Loudspeakers", *Proc. IRE* **31**, 132 (Apr. 1943).

THE AUTHOR

Paul W. Klipsch was born in 1904, in Elkhart, Indiana. He received the B.S. Degree in Electrical Engineering from New Mexico College for Agricultural and Mechanical Arts in 1926 (now New Mexico State University), and the E.E. from Stanford University in 1934.

He was employed in the testing department of General Electric Company from 1926 to 1928; at the Anglo-Chilean Consolidated Nitrate Corporation, Tocopilla, Chile from 1928 to 1931; the Independent Exploration Company, Houston, Texas from 1934 to 1936; the Subterrex Company, Houston, Texas from 1937 to 1941; and the U.S. Army Ordnance Department from 1941 to 1945 (Major, 1943, Lt. Col., 1953). At present, he is president of Klipsch and Associates, Inc., Hope, Arkansas, a firm which manufactures loudspeakers.

Mr. Klipsch has written many papers and holds patents in the fields of geophysics, acoustics, firearms, etc. He is a Fellow of the Audio Engineering Society, Fellow of IEEE, Member of the Acoustical Society of America, Tau Beta Pi, Sigma Xi, and is listed in Who's Who in Engineering.

The Development of a Sandwich-Construction Loudspeaker System*

D. A. BARLOW

Uxbridge, Middlesex, England

The development of a complete loudspeaker system is described, based on moving-coil loudspeakers with cones of sandwich construction of immense rigidity. Piston action is obtained over a wide range. Other features are described, such as the unique construction of the cabinet, which reduces 'boxy' coloration.

INTRODUCTION The diaphragm of the conventional moving-coil loudspeaker is made of molded paper. It is well known that under normal conditions of use, this is far from rigid, and only behaves as a rigid piston at low frequencies. Differences in amplitude between different parts of the cone can be detected at frequencies as low as 100 Hz, and diaphragm resonances occur from a few hundred Hz upwards; poor transient response and an irregular frequency response result. Molded paper is used for the diaphragm because it is convenient; by suitable choice of grade of paper, additives (e.g., cotton and wool fibers, bitumen, etc.) and cone profile, it is possible to damp many of these resonances and obtain a fairly smooth frequency response, although the transient response may still be unsatisfactory.

The efficiency of a loudspeaker is

$$\mu = \frac{B^2 r_{ma} m_1 \times 100\%}{\rho K_r (X_{ma} + X_{mc})^2 \times 10^3} \qquad (1)$$

where B = flux density, m_1 = voice coil mass in g, ρ = density of the conductor in g/cc, K_r = resistivity of the conductor in $\mu\Omega$/cc, r_{ma} = mechanical resistance of air load in mechanical Ω, X_{mc} = ω_{mc} = mechanical reactance of voice coil and cone in mechanical Ω, and X_{ma} = ω_{ma} = mechanical reactance of air load in mechanical Ω. (This ignores the mechanical reactance and resistance of the suspension.)

At mid-frequencies, above the fundamental resonant frequency, the output is level. At higher frequencies, the inertia of the moving parts causes the response to drop. Beranek [1] has shown that there is also the possibility of a second resonance, the electromechanical resonance of the electrical inductance of the voice coil with the mechanical mass of the cone and air load. This resonance usually occurs at high frequencies, outside the working range of the loudspeaker, and if (voice coil resistance + amplifier resistance) is more than (2π × frequency × voice coil inductance), the resonance does not occur at all.

In loudspeakers suitable for reproducing the low frequencies, having 8 to 12 in. diameter diaphragms of conventional weights, the response drops off above 1 to 2 kHz. It would be difficult to extend this by lightening the moving parts, and in any case, diaphragms of this size begin to become undesirably directional above this

* Based on a paper delivered Jan. 24, 1962 at the Brit. IRE (now IERE).

range. To obtain satisfactory performance, therefore, the diaphragm must behave as a rigid piston up to this range (and preferably well beyond), and smaller diaphragms must be used for reproducing the treble.

DIAPHRAGM AND CONE DESIGN

Diaphragm Stiffness

It is possible to obtain some improvement in stiffness of a paper cone by increasing the thickness, but there is a practical limit to this, as excessive weight will give low efficiency. An attempt is sometimes made to increase stiffness by means of corrugations, but this merely introduces compliances and the possibility of further resonances. An overall increase in stiffness might be obtained by using double-curvature indentations. For a thin paper cone, 4.8 in. diameter × .006 in. thick, McLachlan [2] found the first breakup resonance as low as 36.5 Hz. On a conventional paper cone, .02 in. thick × 10½ in. diameter, Yorke [3] found the first breakup resonances at 220–260 Hz, using a self-correcting optical scanning device to determine the actual movement of the whole of the cone [4]. This would not have been expected from the frequency response which was smooth in this region, probably because of cancellation effects between different parts of the diaphragm moving out of phase. Another method of determining the behavior of a diaphragm is by stroboscopic hologram interferometry [5].

As paper cones are thin, these resonances are bending modes. The stiffness of a material in bending, for any given geometry and edge condition, is proportional to Young's modulus and the cube of the thickness, ignoring variations in Poisson's ratio. The total weight of the diaphragm is fixed by the desired efficiency, so that thickness $\propto$ 1/density, i.e. stiffness $\propto$ modulus/density^3. On this basis, paper is much stiffer than metals (except beryllium) in spite of its much lower modulus, and lower-density materials such as expanded plastics are even stiffer, as may be seen in Table I. A method of obtaining still greater stiffness is sandwich construction [6, 7].

SANDWICH CONSTRUCTION

In bending, the maximum stress and strain occur at the outer fibers, the material at the neutral axis being unstressed. Better use of material can thus be made by concentrating it at the outer fibers. A familiar example is the tube. In the case of large areas, the same effect is obained by using a thin high-modulus material for the outer surfaces, and a light-weight material or form of construction for the core. To obtain maximum stiffness, the sandwich must be thick, the optimum proportions for a given total weight being given in convenient form by DeBrugne [8]:

$$\frac{\text{Optimum core thickness}}{\text{Optimum skin thickness}} = \frac{2}{\sqrt{g}-1}, \qquad (2)$$

$$g = \frac{1-E_a/E_s}{1-k/e}, \qquad (2)$$

where E_a = core modulus in psi, E_s = skin modulus in psi, k = weight of 1 cu.in. of core in lb, and e = weight of 1 cu.in. of skin in lb. This sandwich will of course be much stiffer than the same total weight of either material used separately.

The skin material should have the maximum ratio of modulus/density. Beryllium, the best material, is impractical due to difficulty of rolling and possible toxicity, so that aluminum is the obvious choice. The core should be as stiff as possible in the thickness direction and have minimum density. Honeycomb aluminum or impregnated paper are frequently used in aircraft construction and could be used for flat diaphragms. However, a cone is usual, being much stiffer than a flat sheet. Expanded polystyrene is the most practical material for the core of a cone, being of minimum density and easily molded to shape, and providing surfaces for glueing on other components.

Stiffness Tests

Comparative tests were made on cone paper, expanded polystyrene, and sandwich construction strips, each of the same length, width and weight (but different depths). These were loaded statically as simple cantilevers and the deflections measured. The stiffnesses were in the ratio 1:20:200 for the paper, expanded polystyrene, and sandwich strips respectively. Owing to the very small deflections of the expanded polystyrene and the sandwich strips and possible local crushing at the loading points, accurate measurement was difficult and the real stiffnesses were probably somewhat higher.

Diaphragm for Low Frequencies

The final design of cone was ⅜ in. thick × 10⅛ in. diameter, with .001 in aluminum skins glued on with epoxy resin. Other possible methods of coating such as expanding directly onto the foi!, electroplating, metal spraying and vacuum vapor deposition, were all found to be impractical. The total cone weight was 30 to 35 g, which enabled adequate sensitivity to be obtained without excessively high flux densities. The first breakup

Table I. Moduli and densities of various materials.

Material	Young's Modulus (gm/cm^2)	Density (gm/cc)	Modulus/ Density	Modulus/ (Density)^3
Steel	20×10^8	7.8	2.5×10^8	4.2×10^6
Titanium	11×10^8	4.5	2.4×10^8	12×10^6
Aluminium	7×10^8	2.7	2.6×10^8	36×10^6
Magnesium	4.2×10^8	1.85	2.3×10^8	66×10^6
Beryllium	25×10^8	1.9	13×10^8	360×10^6
Polystyrene	$.33 \times 10^8$	1.07	$.31 \times 10^8$	27×10^6
Cone paper	$.1 \times 10^8$	.42	$.24 \times 10^8$	135×10^6
Expanded Ebonite	$.00067 \times 10^8$	.064	$.01 \times 10^8$	260×10^6
Expanded Polystyrene	$.00033 \times 10^8$	.016	$.02 \times 10^8$	8000×10^6

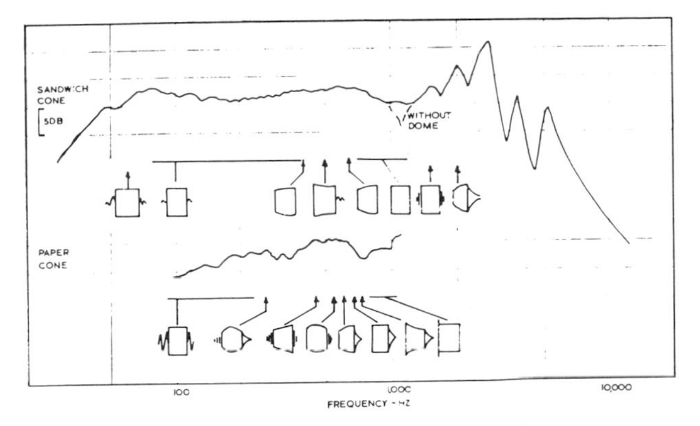

Fig. 1. Frequency and tone burst response of bass cones.

resonance was at 1500 to 1700 Hz. By comparison, unskinned cones of expanded polystyrene and flat skinned diaphragms with expanded polystyrene and honeycomb cores all gave first breakup resonances between 400 and 900 Hz.

The frequency response of the cone is given in Fig. 1. (The bass response depends on the mounting and will be discussed later). Measurements were made with a Bruel and Kjaer microphone 3 ft away, the loudspeaker being mounted on the parapet of a high building, thus approaching anechoic conditions. There were five main resonances, possibly corresponding to the five main tones of a bell. By examination with a crude probe microphone, it was found that the first peak corresponded to two diametral nodes. This is also the lowest mode for a flat plate, given by the formula

$$f = \frac{.193t}{R^2} \sqrt{\frac{Q}{\rho(1-\sigma^2)}} \qquad (3)$$

where Q = Young's modulus, σ = Poisson's ratio, ρ = density in g/cc, t = thickness in cm, and R = radius in cm.

The problem of the cone has so far proved intractable.

The addition of light stiffening radial ribs to the cone had no effect, as might be expected. The addition of a rigid rim also had no effect, possibly because the increase in weight offset any increase in stiffness. Tapering the cone to be thinner at the edge reduced the resonant frequency. For thin flat diaphragms, where the bending deflection is large compared to the shear deflection, the resonant frequency is proportional to 1/diameter^2 for a given thickness. In the present case, and also for flat diaphragms with aluminum core honeycomb, this was not true, as shown in Fig. 2.

Tone Burst Tests

Corrington [9] has shown that tone burst tests form a convenient means of testing the transient response. The tone burst consists of say, 16 cycles at the required frequency, followed by an interval, followed by a further 16 cycles, etc., the switching on and off being arranged to take place at zero level. The presence of "ringing", overshoot and "hangover" is readily seen in the resulting waveform from the loudspeaker. Where acoustic interference occurs between different units at crossover, results may mean very little.

Tone burst test results are indicated in Fig. 1. The major envelope shapes are shown, the transition between each usually being fairly gradual. The slight overshoot at 500 Hz is believed to be due to the surround and will be discussed later. The paper cone speaker referred to earlier is included for comparison; the breakup at 220–260 Hz is clearly shown.

Interference at Cone Apex

The plain cone was found to give a dip in the response at 1100 Hz, as described by Brittain [10]. This may be eliminated by means of a small bulbous obstacle mounted in front of, or attached to, the cone. A wide variety of shapes was tried, including pear shapes, discs, domes, truncated cones, wedges, etc. A spherically-curved dome glued to the cone was finally chosen as the most effective; it was also useful in preventing dust from entering the magnet gap. The diameter of the dome where it joins the cone should be between 35 and 42% of the cone diameter for a cone of 106° angle, and the radius of curvature of the dome should also equal this value.

It is interesting to note that when the dome was molded as part of the cone, with the skins covering the remainder of the cone surface, the first breakup resonance was lowered to 1200 Hz.

TREBLE UNIT

Originally it was not possible to mold the expanded polystyrene less than ¼ in. thick, and a variety of cones 2 to 5 in. in diameter × ⅛ to ¼ in. thick were made by machining from thicker material and glueing on the foil skins. In each case, the first breakup was between 2 and 4 kHz. Eventually, molded cones ⅛ in. thick × 2½ in. diameter were produced, using aluminum skins .00035" thick. No diaphragm resonance could be detected, either by means of lycopodium powder or impedance measurements. It is probable that the breakup resonances were above 5 kHz, above which frequency the response of a cone of this size and weight drops; further, voice coil resonances appear above this frequency and would obscure cone resonances.

To obtain satisfactory response in the range above 5 kHz, it is evident from the efficiency equation that extremely light diaphragms are necessary—say 50 mg total

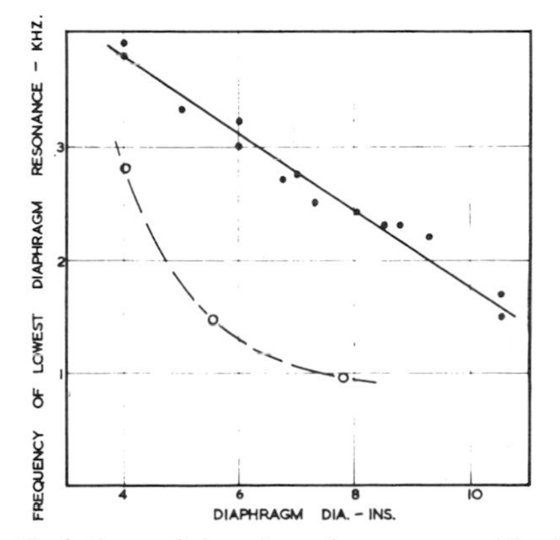

Fig. 2. Variation of breakup frequency with diaphragm diameter. ● = .001 in. aluminum skins on ⅜ in. expanded polystyrene cone; ○ = .001 in. aluminum skins on ⅜ in. aluminum honeycomb disc.

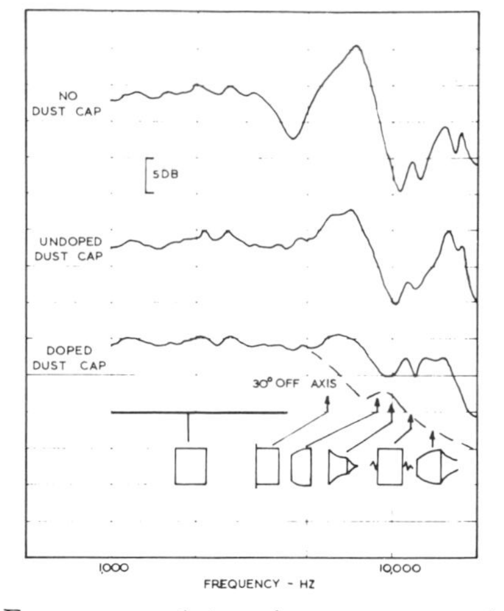

Fig. 3. Frequency and tone burst response of sandwich treble units.

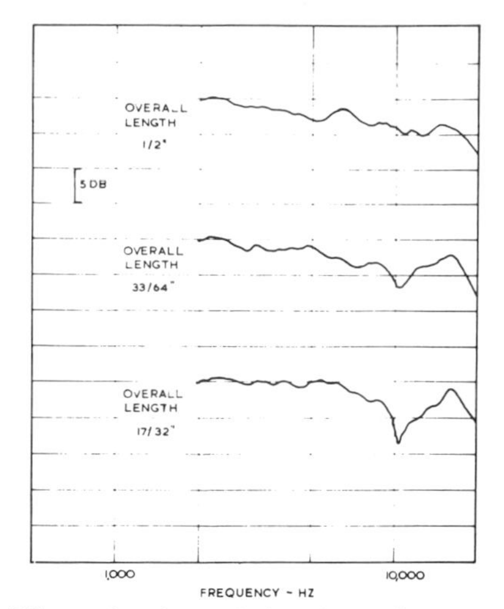

Fig. 4. Effect of voice coil length on frequency response of treble units.

mass for a 1 in. diameter diaphragm. To construct any type of diaphragm of this weight would not be easy, and to place the breakup resonances above, say, 20 kHz would be very difficult. It is just possible that this could be achieved by means of a sandwich ribbon diaphragm, in which most of the moving mass is the conductor.

Voice Coil Resonances

A 1 in. diameter voice coil was used with the 2½ in. diameter sandwich cone. The winding was in aluminum, as this gave about 2 dB more output than a copper coil due to the reduction in the total moving mass. Resonances occurred at 8, 12, and 16 kHz, and by judicious choice of materials it was possible to damp these and obtain a level response within ± 3 dB up to 15 kHz. A dome-shaped dust cap in soft molded fabric was used, analogous to the dome on the bass unit, to avoid an interference dip at 4.5 kHz. It was found that by applying a viscous damping material to the dust cap (originally for rendering it airtight) the first coil resonance at 8 kHz was suppressed, instead of giving a peak of up to 7 dB; further, the response above 12 kHz was raised to the general level (Fig. 3). For the doping of the dust cap to be effective, the coupling between cone and coil and between cone and dustcap must be good. The dustcap does not necessarily have to touch the voice coil, but perfect joints are essential—if only 95% of the contact area is glued, the 8 kHz peak will appear. To obtain a smooth response, the voice coil must resonate at suitable frequencies; the dip at 10 kHz was later eliminated by reducing the length of the voice coil former, as shown in Fig. 4. Tone burst tests showed good results up to 5 kHz, after which the voice coil resonances gave some ringing (Fig. 3).

Since ordinary aluminum wire easily kinked and broke, annealed wire was used. The ends are tinned ultrasonically in tin-zinc solder (to reduce the risk of corrosion). The tinned ends are wrapped several times around the tinned copper lead-out wires to ensure good contact, and are soldered and then covered with lacquer to reduce the risk of corrosion. In this way, few coils have become open-circuited and no corrosion has been found.

It is well known that loose turns on the voice coil can cause buzzing. It was found that even a very small area of wire or paper not properly stuck, detectable only by destroying the coil, gave an intolerable whine over a range of frequencies, in spite of the waveform appearing satisfactory. (This suggests that the ear is more sensitive than the eye in examining sinewaves). Other minor causes of buzzing at certain frequencies or "uncleanness" over a range of frequencies which were dealt with were vibration of leads and tagstrips, and chassis not firmly in contact with cabinet or magnet top plate.

Saturation of Magnet Poles

It is sometimes argued that if the magnet pole pieces are saturated, there will be less rise in impedance at high frequencies, so that reponse will not fall off due to less power transfer. An attempt was made to achieve this by machining the poles of a magnet assembly to concentrate the flux over a smaller area (see Fig. 5), but little advantage was gained.

Paper Cone Treble Unit

Before thin moldings in expanded polystyrene became available, a paper cone unit was used. It is known that a slight flare to the cone will often give a smoother response than either a straight-sided or a severely flared one, and this was found to be the case for this unit, shown in Fig. 6. Tone burst tests showed up cone resonances, in addition to voice coil resonances. And

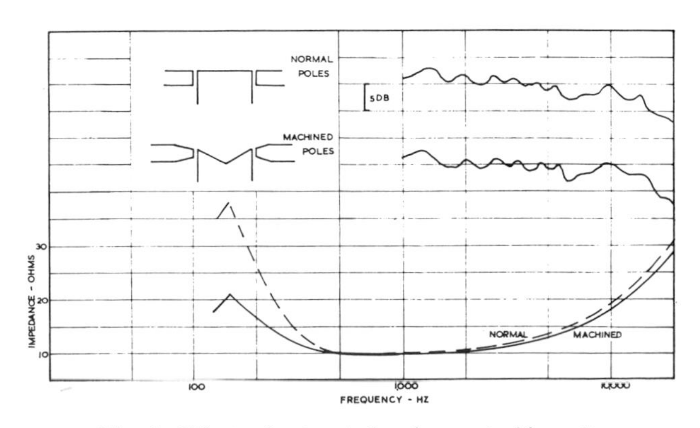

Fig. 5. Effect of saturated poles on treble unit.

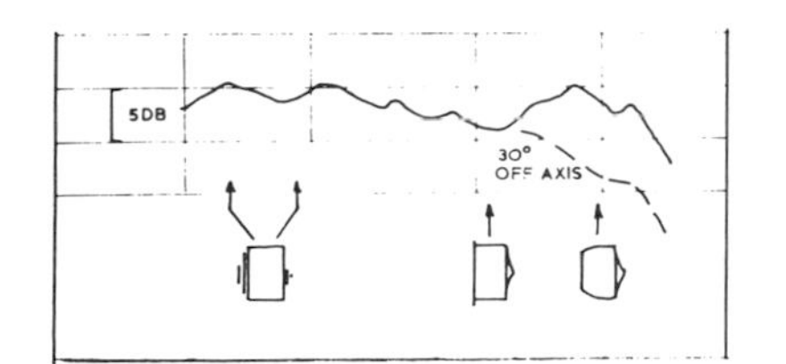

Fig. 6. Frequency and tone burst response of paper-cone treble unit.

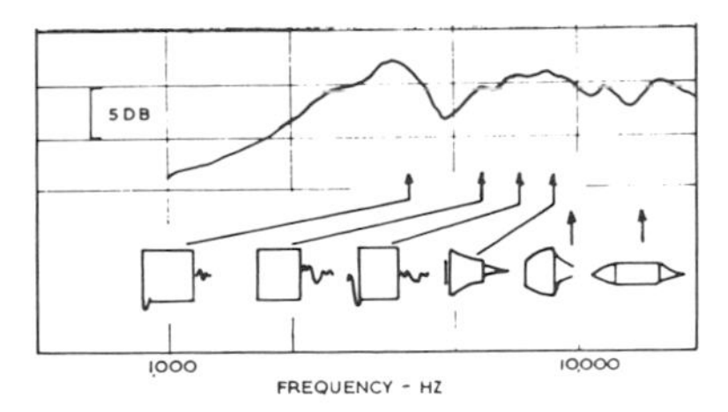

Fig. 7. Frequency and tone burst response of ribbon unit.

damping compounds applied to the cone had no effect.

Other Methods of Reproducing the Treble

As satisfactory sandwich construction for the treble was difficult at first, other methods of reproducing the treble were considered.

1. Twin-Cone Twin-Coil Loudspeakers.—These offer no advantage. They take various forms but are all open to the same objection, viz., that the fundamental resonance of the small cone or coil falls within the audio range.

2. Ribbon Speakers.—Conventional ribbon speakers suffer from longitudinal, transverse, and torsional resonances. It is well known that in ribbon microphones the profile of the corrugations in the ribbon is critical, and absorbent materials are used to damp the resonances [11]. Tone burst tests on a very good ribbon loudspeaker are given in Fig. 7. The ribbon is extremely fragile and it may be difficult to obtain sufficient sensitivity to match moving-coil loudspeakers.

3. Blatthaller-Type Loudspeakers.—A recent version of the Blatthaller loudspeaker consists of a flat expanded polystyrene diaphragm, about 4 in. $\times$ 4 in. with a zig-zag ribbon conductor fixed to the rear and moving between magnet poles. This is doubtless an attempt to drive the diaphragm all over, but will not prevent the diaphragm from resonating. A brief consideration of the diaphragm and conductor weights and magnet size shows that efficiency must be very low, and this was found to be the case—about 15 dB below that of a conventional moving coil speaker. However, above 2 kHz, the output rose and was level from 3 to 14 kHz, although rather directional, as shown in Fig. 8.

The rise in response is believed to be due to the resonance of the inertia of the diaphragm with the acoustical capacity formed by the air trapped between the magnet poles and the rear of the diaphragm. This effect is well-known in horn loudspeakers, where it is often used to boost the treble response, after which a more rapid cutoff is obtained. The diaphragm must obviously have resonances in the audio range, and there was some evidence of these on tone burst tests, although they tend to be swamped by the main resonance.

4. Pressure-Type Units.—Similar results with less directionality may be obtained by means of a suitably designed pressure-type unit, used with or without a horn. The response of a unit of this type for use without a horn is shown in Fig. 9, together with the effect of removing the perforated front plate. As before, the efficiency for the diaphragm size and weight would be very low, and the acoustic capacitance is formed by the air trapped behind the phase plate. Tone burst tests showed some ringing in spite of the very smooth frequency response. The design of such a unit is critical and largely a matter of chance; as shown in Fig. 9, two other units of similar general design gave very poor results.

5. Electrostatic Loudspeakers.—Hunt [12] has shown that the basic distortion in a push-pull electrostatic loudspeaker with constant charge is extremely low, and Walker [13] has described some of the design problems. The diaphragm resonances have been described by Malmé [14] and used to reinforce the lack of bass due to limited baffle size. With good design, the resonances at high frequencies may be less in evidence than the voice-coil resonances in a moving-coil loudspeaker, judging by tone burst tests and listening to white noise above 5 kHz. Test results on some commercial units are given in Figs. 10 and 11. The efficiency is 5 to 10 dB below that of most moving-coil loudspeakers, and they tend to be directional. Design of a full-range electrostatic loudspeaker is a difficult compromise between size, amplitude, bass distortion, power-handling capacity, efficiency, etc.

6. High-Voltage Discharge Loudspeakers.—Klein [15] has described a transducer consisting of a high-voltage

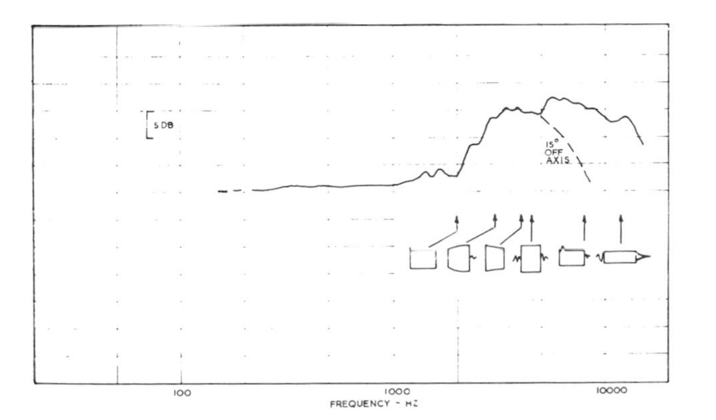

Fig. 8. Frequency and tone burst response of Blatthaller-type unit.

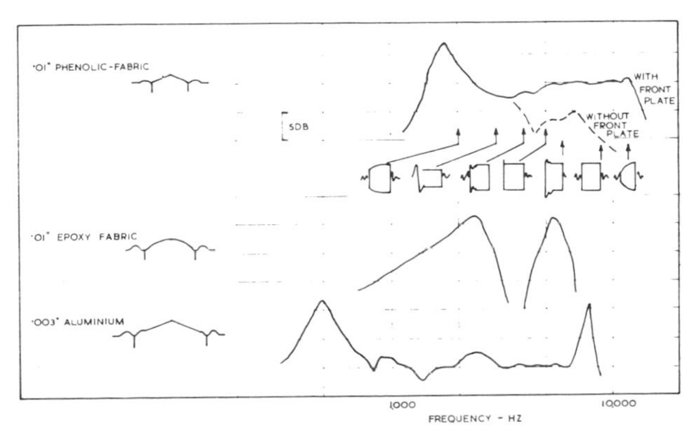

Fig. 9. Frequency and tone burst response of pressure units without horns.

discharge modulated by the audio signal, which is reminiscent of Dudell's singing arc. Radio-frequency bias is used, and the discharge tube outlet is loaded by a horn. Since the mass of the moving parts is virtually nil, the device should be free from resonances. Unfortunately, the audible output without distortion is very low, and there are practical difficulties in providing a high power RF supply with low distortion and without interference with other equipment. Falkus [16] has demonstrated an American modification, but since the effective diaphragm diameter is only 3/16 in., the power handling capacity is very low, and a multiplicity of units would be required if distortion is to be avoided. It is not certain whether the efficiency is equal to that of moving-coil systems.

Shirley [17] has demonstrated a somewhat similar device, using a corona discharge. The discharge plates radiate directly without a horn and constitute a push-pull triode output stage, fed from driver tubes. Considerable further development would be required. Another possibility is electrical modulation of gas flames [18].

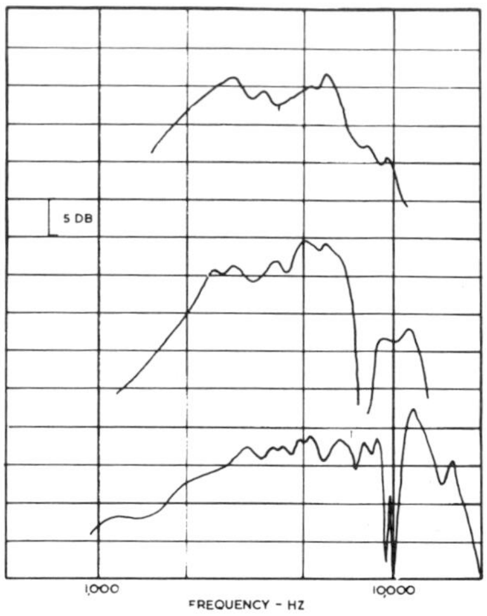

FINAL LOUDSPEAKER SYSTEM

Bass Unit

A 2 in. diameter voice coil is used with a winding length of ¾ in. The magnet top plate is 5/16 in. thick and the center pole is undercut to give symmetrical leakage fields on each side of the gap. Distortion measurements at 12 W input at 57 Hz showed that the undercut reduced the total harmonic distortion from 6.3 to 5.3%. The magnet cavity is filled with sulphur to avoid possible resonance[1]. A clearance of .018 in. all around the voice coil in the magnet gap was ample to allow for large excursions and easy centering of the coil.

The rear suspension is a flexible deep corrugated-fabric molding, and the rim suspension a half roll in doped fabric, lightly molded to shape. It is well-known that a corrugated-paper surround is quite unsuitable for appreciable amplitudes. A molded-fabric surround is better, but resonates even if heavily doped. The half-round surround rolls on itself and shows the least tendency to resonate. It must be very lightly impregnated, just enough to hold its shape; too much impregnation gives crackling at high amplitudes. Thin rubber has been used for this type of surround but it is not so dead as doped

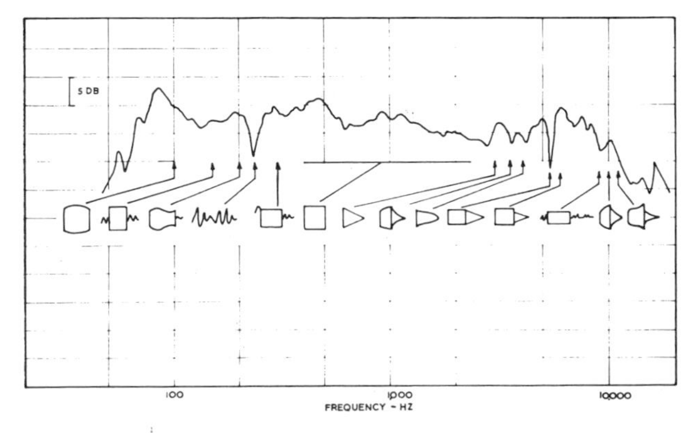

Fig. 10. Frequency and tone burst response of full-range electrostatic unit.

1. Suggested by Mr. H. J. Leak.

Fig. 11. Frequency response of three electrostatic treble units.

fabric and slight resonances in the 400 to 800 Hz region can be detected with lycopodium powder, and by careful listening. Polyvinyl chloride (PVC) with an external plasticizer is dead and is easily hot-vacuum-formed to shape, but the stiffness varies with temperature and there is likely to be some hardening with time. The dope for the molded-fabric surround must render it airtight and as dead as possible. Viscous liquids, even with thickening agents, slowly drain away, leaving the pores of the fabric open. The various types of rubber film are not sufficiently dead. The final choice of dope is an emulsion of PVC-acrylic copolymer without external plasticizer; the material is permanently tacky, having been polymerized to this stage instead of being fully polymerized to the rigid condition. It is stable and easily applied. It varies little with temperature, unlike certain mixtures which depend for their viscosity on being in the melting range at room temperature.

Figure 12 shows load-deflection and dc volts-deflection curves for the bass unit. Good linearity is obtained over a throw of ⅜ in. The maximum amplitude under extreme conditions in practice was found to be 3/16 in. The half-roll surround, not being axially symmetrical, could give even harmonic distortion. This could be avoided by using two of them back-to-back or in the form of a tube, as suggested by Olson [19].

Treble Unit

The treble unit cone has a flat doped-cloth surround and corrugated rear suspension. A half-roll surround, even though heavily doped, resulted in response irregularities in the 5 kHz region. The flat cloth surround allows sufficient movement to give low distortion at 4 W input (representing a very high sound output) down to 300 Hz, the fundamental resonance being at 150 to 200 Hz. The voice coil is 1/16 in. longer than the magnet gap. The clearance all around the voice coil is .015 in.; .010 in. could only be used with difficulty, in spite of the amplitude being very small.

Crossover Filter

A half-section 900 Hz crossover of constant resistance type is used, modified to give a somewhat steeper cutoff

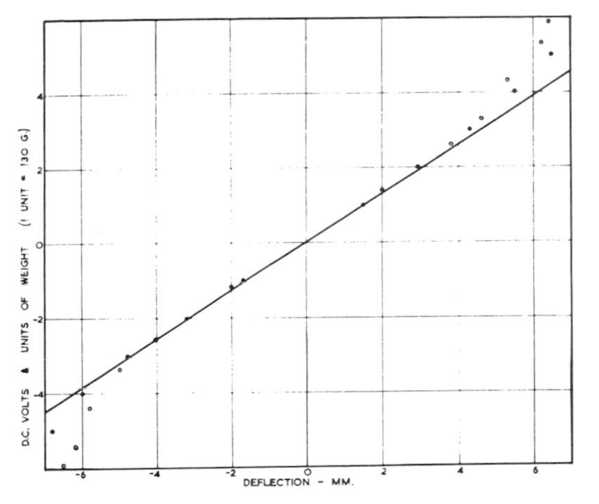

Fig. 12. Deflection characteristics of bass unit suspension. ● = weight deflection; ○ = voltage deflection.

to the bass unit, so that the input at the breakup resonances is always less than —25 dB. The impedance curve of the system is given in Fig. 13. Reversible electrolytic condensers were used and it was found that the contact resistance of the wire ends could vary over each cycle, giving distortion; strip ends avoided this. All-welded construction would obviously be desirable.

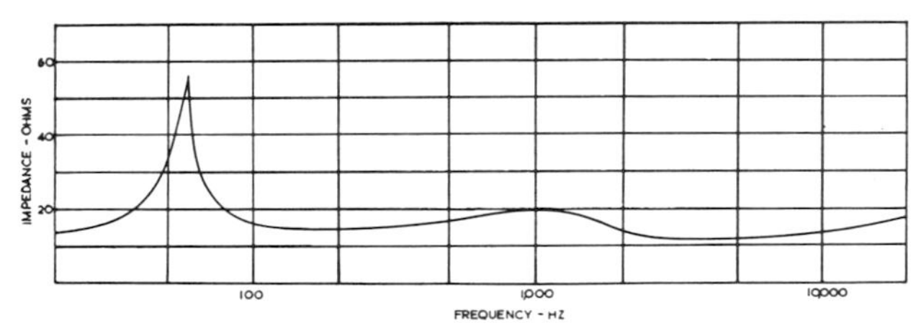

Fig. 13. Impedance of sandwich loudspeaker system.

Mounting of Bass Unit

Flat baffles and open-backed cabinets were rejected because of the inherent loss of bass with this type of mounting in any practical size.

Horns were rejected because of the large size needed and the irregular response, even when the mouth size is fairly large and care is taken with the design of the folds. Thus a commercial horn system was found to have an irregular response, quite apart from interference dips due to folds, and doubtless due to resonance of the various cavities formed by folding; further, it cut off sharply below 80 Hz, in spite of being designed with a cutoff frequency of 40 Hz. The drive unit was removed from the horn and mounted in a totally enclosed cabinet of much smaller volume, where it gave a much smoother curve with a more extended bass response (the output was, of course, lower) as shown in Fig. 14. Horns are only nonresonant if they are straight, infinitely long, and with infinitely large mouth.

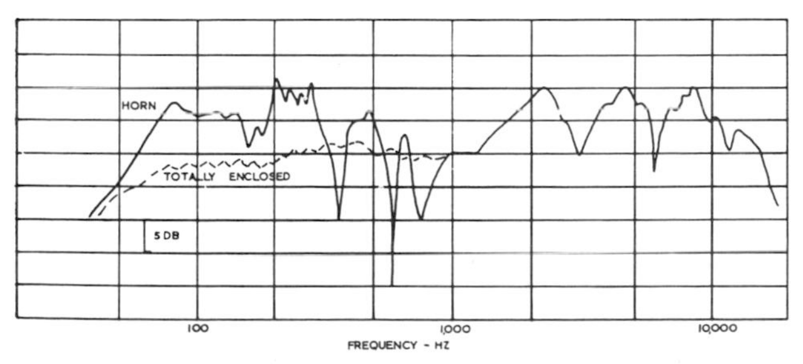

Fig. 14. Frequency response of folded-horn loudspeaker.

There are various sorts of pipe enclosures, for example Voigt's quarter-wave pipe, the labyrinth, and variations on this [1, 20]. The quarter-wave pipe is essentially a resonant device. The labyrinth was found to give an irregular response with many impedance peaks, doubtless due to resonances of the lengths of folds and interference at the bends, as shown in Fig. 15. Completely filling the labyrinth with absorbent cotton wadding damped many of these, but the basic objection to any folded device remains. Further, the large quantity of absorbent needed overdamps the bass in any practical design (unless perhaps high internal impedance amplifiers are used). The bass response falls off from approximately 200 Hz, despite the large cabinet volume.

The remaining types of enclosure are the totally enclosed, the reflex, and variations on these. It is sometimes said that the reflex is more efficient than the totally enclosed cabinet. In the mid-frequency range, this is not true, as the action of each is the same; at low frequencies, the response depends on numerous factors. In each type of enclosure, the free air resonance of the loudspeaker is raised by an amount depending on the volume—the loudspeaker mass resonates with its own compliance and that of the enclosed air; in the reflex enclosure, the port or pipe has a small additional effect, further raising the resonant frequency by a small amount. This effect is often observed with a totally enclosed cabinet, when a slight air leak raises the resonance by 1 or 2 Hz. There are numerous formulas, for the design of reflex cabinets, but the final design must be checked with actual response curves. For a 1.7 ft^3 cabinet with the present drive unit, a 5 in long, 2 in diameter pipe gave the most level and extended bass response (identical to that obtained with the same cabinet totally enclosed).

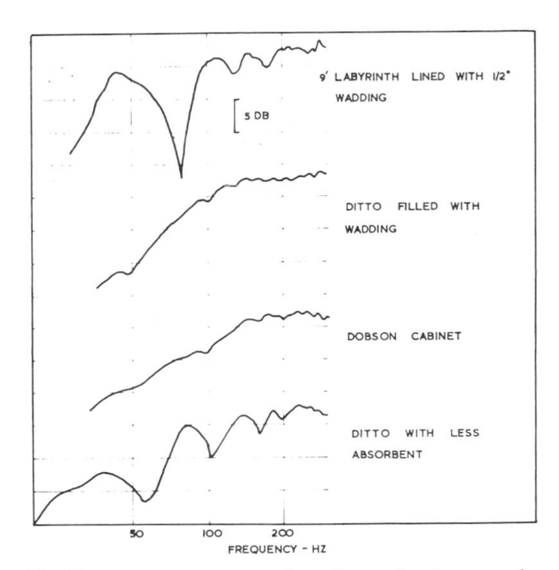

Fig. 15. Frequency response of various pipe-type enclosures.

The theory of the reflex cabinet has been examined at length by Thiele [21]. There is a condition in which for a given cabinet volume and loudspeaker unit, the reflex cabinet will give a more extended bass response than the total enclosure. This has also been pointed out by Reith [22], quoting Keibs [23]. The cabinet should be of such a volume that when closed it raises the resonance of the unit by a factor of 1.56. The pipe is designed so that its acoustic inductance resonates with the acoustic capacitance of the air in the cabinet at the free-air resonance of the speaker. The Q for the unit alone should be .83 at its resonance. The —3 dB point of the system will then be at the free-air resonance of the loudspeaker, which is about 70% of the —3 dB point for the same system enclosed. The rate of cutoff of the reflex cabinet will approach 18 dB/octave, compared with 12 for the closed box. It is possible that ringing may be noticed with the steeper cutoff of the reflex cabinet.

For a 1.7^3 ft box and a 10 in. diameter cone, a loudspeaker was taken with a free-air resonance of 45 Hz, rising to 74 Hz (1.64 times) in the box. A 2½ in. diameter hole in the cabinet gave a minimum impedance at 41 Hz, thus approximately fulfilling the above conditions. An extension of the response was obtained (see Fig. 16), although the steeper rate of cutoff was not found. It is possible that better matching would have given better results, but variations of this order would be expected in production. However, with this size of loudspeaker it is quite easy to obtain a free-air resonance much lower than 45 Hz, in fact lower than 25 Hz. Under these conditions, the bass response in a 1.7 ft^3 cabinet is extended much further (see Fig. 16). This optimum condition for a reflex cabinet would be useful for much larger cabinets and perhaps also for small cabinets and loudspeakers, where the free-air resonance is rather high.

At very low frequencies, in this case below 20 Hz, the enclosed air of the closed box prevents excessive movement of the cone when accidentally subjected to low-frequency components of switch clicks, scraping of the pickup stylus, etc.; in contrast, the pipe of the reflex cabinet allows the air to move freely in and out, and excessive cone amplitude and damage may result. (This does not mean that the reflex cabinet gives more output at these frequencies than the closed box.) It was also noticed that at low frequencies air could be heard swishing in and out of the pipe. This effect could not be reduced by using larger-diameter pipes, as the increased length necessary gave resonances in the audio range.

With the closed box, critical damping is obtained with a Q of ½, when the response is -6 dB at resonance, whereas for a level response the Q must be 1 (see Fig. 17). Novak [24] has shown that in a reflex cabinet designed to give level response, the Q is about .35 and damping is thus overcritical. A–B listening tests on a reflex cabinet with a removable bung did not show any audible difference.

The Q depends on several factors: *1.* Cabinet size—small cabinets give high Q. *2.* Amplifier output

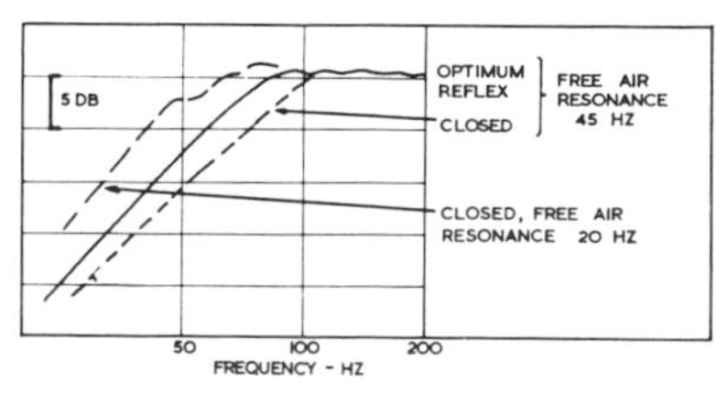

Fig. 16. Frequency response of optimum reflex *vs* totally enclosed cabinets.

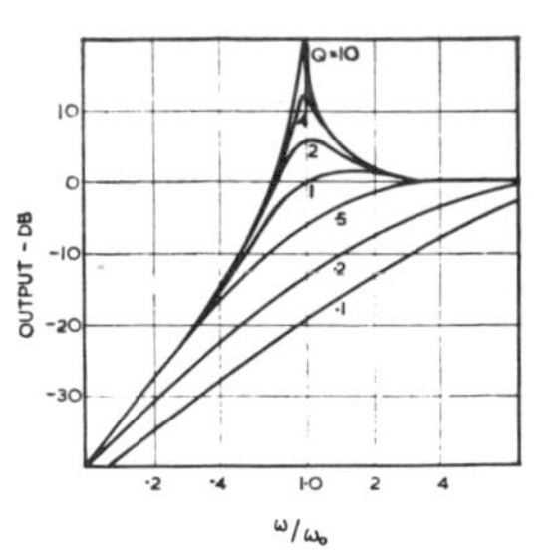

Fig. 17. Effect of Q on bass response of loudspeaker in a totally enclosed box. (After Beranek [1].)

impedance—low impedance, as for all modern amplifiers, gives low Q. *3.* Mechanical losses in the speaker suspension—these reduce Q. *4.* Magnetic gap field strength—higher flux reduces Q. This is perhaps the most important factor. *5.* Acoustical resistance of absorbent material in the cabinet—this reduces Q.

If a fair quantity of absorbent is used, it tends to produce isothermal rather than adiabatic conditions in the enclosed air. Under isothermal conditions, the velocity of sound is reduced, so that the wavelength is reduced and the cabinet appears larger. The bass resonance is thus reduced in frequency—in the present case by about 10%, the cabinet being about half full. The maximum reduction is about 18%; if enough absorbent is used to obtain this, the absorption is excessive and there is no extension of the extreme bass. Various absorbents were tried, including cotton wool, glass fiber (three types), wood wool, copper wool, soft felt, asbetsos fiber. rubberized hair, cellulose wadding, kapok, and bonded acetate fiber; the latter was cheap and pleasant to handle.

With a low-resonance speaker, say 20 Hz, good bass response can be obtained with a cabinet volume of 1½ to 2 ft^3, giving a resonance of about 60 Hz. The response is level to this frequency and then drops off at 12 dB/octave. With the present system, clean organ notes down to 30 Hz can be clearly heard. One of the few records containing such notes is CBS SBRG 72132, Saint-Saëns Symphony No. 3. A lower resonant frequency in the cabinet could be obtained by using a heavier cone, a further 40 g lowering the resonance to 47 Hz. In some designs, weights have been added for this reason, but sensitivity is lost and higher-power amplifiers are necessary. (This may be responsible for the idea that closed-box loudspeakers have low efficiency). A more compliant suspension gives little further reduction in resonant frequency in the cabinet, as most of the stiffness is already provided by the enclosed air.

One modification of the reflex is the "drone cone" [25]. This consists of an undriven diaphragm mounted in the port, so that all the air moves in phase, unlike the normal port where there may be a loss of energy due to phase shift and air friction. This device might be useful where a high enough Q cannot otherwise be obtained. A similar device has been used commercially to extend the bass response. In the present case, a variety of cones were tried, but no improvement was obtained.

Another modification of the reflex cabinet involves the use of an acoustic resistance, consisting of drilled holes in the cabinet wall or porous material covering part of the port [26, 27]. An impedance curve of a reflex cabinet, taken with a high impedance source, has two peaks, namely the main resonance already described (at about

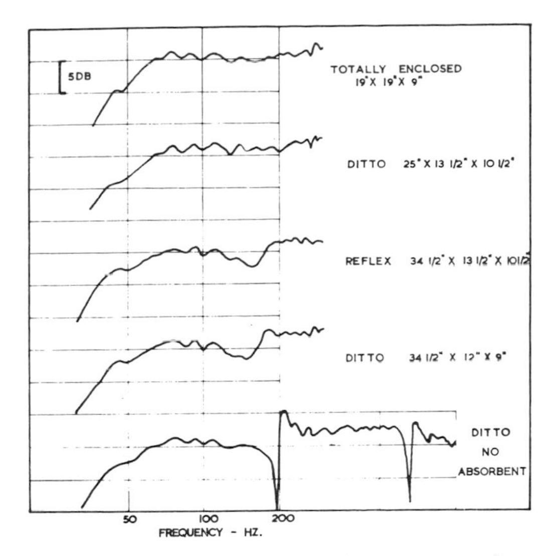

Fig. 18. Effect of cabinet shape on bass response: frequency curves for cabinets of various shapes.

65 Hz in the present case) and a second peak at a very low frequency perhaps 8 Hz. The existence of this lower peak does not mean that there is any useful output this region. The acoustic resistance apparently damps the upper peak so that it is no longer detectable in impedance measurements. There is of course no such peak on the response curve, and to apply more damping at this point must mean considerable loss of bass.

Cabinet Shape

The influence of cabinet shape is shown in Fig. 18. This suggests that the height/width ratio should not exceed 2 if the 150 Hz dip is to be avoided. It had previously been thought that a cabinet with unequal principal internal dimensions, in say the ratio 5:3:2, as is often used for listening rooms, would be best, as room eigentones are then spread over a range with none being individually prominent. However, in loudspeaker cabinets, it seems that air column resonances in the largest dimension predominate. A spherical cabinet is perhaps the ideal.

It is interesting to note (Fig. 18) that with no absorbent, the third harmonic is apparent, as also are adjacent small peaks. The addition of a very small quantity of absorbent suppresses the peaks and the harmonic and reduces the fundamental, but no amount of absorbent will completely eliminate the dip. The use of an acoustic resistance halfway along the cabinet halves the effective volume and length, so that the dip no longer appears, but there is then no advantage over a cabinet of half the length.

Cabinet Construction

The bass response of one stout experimental cabinet was less than was expected. It was constructed with removable front and rear panels, each fixed with 12 screws. The bass response was improved by glueing in the front panel and using 20 screws on the back panel, as shown in Fig. 19. In view of this it was decided to use all-glued construction, with back and front glued in and the bass unit screwed on from the outside, access to the cabinet being obtained via the bass unit mounting hole.

It is well known that the cabinet produces its own coloration or boxy tone, although the response curve only indicates this in extreme cases. In an effort to overcome this, very heavy construction such as brick or concrete has been used. At very low frequencies, cabinet radiation will be stiffness-controlled and can be reduced by increasing the rigidity of the walls. At high frequencies, radiation will be mass-controlled and can be reduced by increasing the weight of the walls. However, at the panel resonant frequencies radiation will be very high, perhaps exceeding that of the loudspeaker. These resonances are responsible for the coloration and can be reduced by damping.

There is also the coincidence effect, described by Beranek [28]. Above the critical frequency, sound impinging on a panel at a certain angle will have the same projected wavelength (in the plane of the panel) as that of the flexural wave in the panel. Although there may be no mechanical resonance at this frequency, the panel will radiate strongly. Like mechanical resonances, this radiation may be reduced by damping. For the ⅜ in. thick plywood used for the present cabinet, the critical frequency is about 2 kHz, where there is little power being fed to the bass speaker. In passing, it may be noted that the coincidence effect could apply also to loudspeaker diaphragms, although in any practical case the critical frequency would be supersonic.

Methods of damping panels have been discussed by Lloyd [29] and Beranek [28]. There are two chief methods. One consists of applying a damping compound in sufficient quantities to one or both panel surfaces. This is usually more effective when a given quantity is applied to one side only, as the damping layer is then subjected to higher strains and dissipates more energy. The other method consists of using two thinner panels, bonded with a damping material. This method was used in cabinets demonstrated at the London Audio Fair in April 1960. Briggs [30] has used a sand filling between two plywood skins. This would damp the skins in compression, but might not be so effective when the sand is in tension.

Q Measurements

Structural resonances of loudspeaker cabinets have been discussed by Moir [31] and Tappan [32]. Moir uses a simple method of measuring the effectiveness of damping treatments. This consists of testing a cantilever by driving from a small vibration generator near the clamped end, and measuring the amplitude of vibration from a pickup coil and light magnet fixed to the free end of the cantilever. The Q of the main resonance can thus be readily obtained, and this gives a direct measure of the value of each method of construction. (The methods

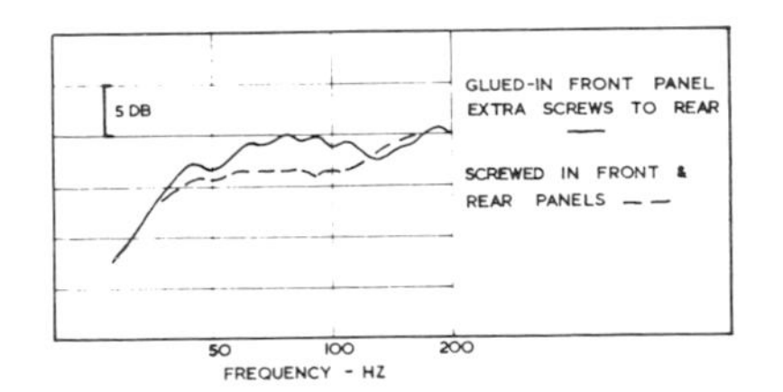

Fig. 19. Effect of type of construction on bass response.

used by manufacturers and others are often complex and there may be poor agreement between the different methods).

On materials used in normal cabinet construction, such as plywood, chipboard, blockboard and softwood, the Q was 30 to 45. The double panel bonded with bitumen had a Q of 15; thus, although this was an improvement, further reduction of Q was desirable. Moir has suggested that as the Q of air column resonances in rooms is about 15, the Q of cabinet walls should be less than this. It was difficult to reduce the Q of the bonded panels below 15 unless the bonding layer was very thick, which would make cabinet construction rather difficult. The lowest Q was obtained with very thick layers of high-efficiency commercial damping compounds on one surface. The Q of the compounds under these conditions of measurement was 5, representing the lowest attainable value.

A variety of materials were tested for both forms of construction, and some for possible use for cabinet walls. Tested alone, asbestos-cement, concrete, clay tiles, fiber-filled rigid plastics, paper and fabric-filled phenolic sheet, etc., all gave Qs between 20 and 25. Vulcanized fiber, cone paper, cardboard, corkboard, papiêr maché, wood-wool-cement and lead all gave Qs between 10 and 20. Lower values could only be obtained by using damping compounds.

Using the double-panel method, various rubbers and gasket materials had no effect, doubtless because they were elastic at the amplitudes involved. The harder and thicker grades of felt gave Qs down to 10, but were very expensive.

Many commercial damping compounds take several days to dry when applied in the thick layers required here. Sheet damping materials must therefore be used, glued to the cabinet walls. The most effective material for a given weight was a micaceous PVC, the most economical one being a bituminous felt. This latter material usually has an indented surface, so that it is not glued all over, but gives additional damping due to friction when used on metal panels. With cabinets, this did not happen, perhaps because the amplitudes were too low—indeed, if the felt were not well glued all over, it did not damp the panel; unglued areas were free to vibrate and could be detected by rapping the panel.

Shorter [33] has used a layer of fiberboard firmly bonded to the inside surface of the cabinet and he claims considerable reduction in cabinet radiation by this treatment, which adds only 11% to the weight. In the present tests, ½ in. fiberboard had a Q of 10 to 15 and had no effect whatever on ½ in. plywood; further, a sandwich-construction panel consisting of two skins of ⅛ in. hardboard bonded to a core of ¾ in. thick fiberboard gave a Q of over 40, fully equal to that of the hardboard alone. It was generally observed that if a damping compound were to be effective, a considerable weight must be used.

Recently, Cooke and Fincham [39] have likewise measured the output of cabinets, by suspending a small loudspeaker system inside closed cabinets and measuring the output of the cabinet walls while being driven by the air pressure generated by the small system. Bituminous felt reduced the transmission by up to 20 dB, compared to undamped panels, especially at the higher modes of vibration. They have also shown that transmission of rear radiation back through the cone (the "regurgitation effect") is reduced by 10 dB with a sandwich cone, as compared to a paper one.

Details of the Final Cabinet

The total weight of the complete system is limited by practical considerations to about 50 lb. Since it is obviously better to use heavily damped panels of medium thickness rather than thick undamped panels of the same total weight, ⅜ in. plywood was used with 9/16 in. thick bituminous felt glued inside, giving a Q of 6.

The wooden block on which the crossover components are mounted acts as a packing piece between the back of the bass unit and the inside surface of the back of the cabinet, and a brass bolt clamps all three together. This stiffens the rear panel and couples some of the weight of the bass unit to it, thus reducing the Q and supporting the weight of the magnet.

As the bass unit is mounted from the front of the cabinet, a decorative grille board is used to cover the front. The cut-out in the grille board was at first made equal to the diameter of the cone + surround, but this was found to give a 3 dB hump in the 1500 Hz region; absorbent packing around the opening between the grille board and the front of the cabinet did not reduce the effect, nor did bevelling the edge of the cut-out. It was therefore increased in area to a rectangular shape. Cross arms were used across this opening to support the grille cloth and reduce any tendency to flap at large cone excursions. Parallel arms give a sharp interference dip at 3200 Hz; although this would not matter as it affected the bass unit only, tapered arms were nevertheless used to reduce the effect.

Nichols [34] and Olson [35] have shown that diffraction may occur at the edge of a cabinet, giving peaks and dips in the response curve. The positions and magnitudes of the peaks and dips depend on the microphone distance and cabinet shape, and are due to interference between the direct sound and sound reflected at the cabinet edge. The effect occurs up to quite high frequencies and is less pronounced if the source does not approximate a point. The effect can be reduced by mounting the loudspeaker eccentrically and bevelling the cabinet edges. In the case of the bass unit no such effects were observed and bevelling of the cabinet edges had no effect, doubtless because the loudspeaker is almost as wide as the cabinet. With the treble unit, this effect was noticed as irregularities in the 1 to 4 kHz region, and a smoother response was obtained by mounting the unit off-center. This also avoids a sharp dip due to cancellation at the board edge of the back and front radiation.

It is well known that in mounting a loudspeaker on a board behind the cut-out, the hole acts as a short pipe and reflection and diffraction take place at the hole edge, and that this can be reduced by bevelling. Thus a ¾ in. thick board gave a 12 dB dip at 5500 Hz, which was reduced to 5 dB by bevelling. It is often said that the loudspeaker should be mounted from the front of the board. This was found to avoid the 5500 Hz dip, but it introduced peaks and dips in the 1 to 3 kHz region. The best arrangement was a thin board with the loudspeaker mounted halfway through the thickness, with both edges and loudspeaker frame bevelled. The treble unit is thus mounted on the grille board and isolated from the bass unit by means of a cavity at the rear. This cavity is lined

Fig. 20. Complete system, showing method of mounting and construction.

with absorbent, to reduce a resonance at 320 Hz. In other words, the treble unit is, in effect, mounted on a small baffle.

The grille cloth is specially woven to give good obscuration with minimum high-frequency absorption. If the air spaces between the threads are not less than about .02 in. wide, and provided the cloth is not too thick, absorption is very small—in this case about ½ dB up to 14 kHz, except for 1½ to 2 dB loss at 8 kHz. This latter loss is a function of distance from the loudspeaker, occurs with a variety of cloths, and is probably a reflection effect. For comparison, light furnishing fabrics give up to 5 dB loss, increasing with frequency. The grille cloth did not completely hide the aluminum skin of the bass cone, so a layer of thin black cotton cloth was added over the bass cut-out. The black cloth must be carefully chosen: two layers of open mesh are not as effective as one layer of closer weave in obtaining the desired obscuration.

The complete system is shown in Fig. 20. The method of mounting the bass and treble units can be seen, as well as the use of bituminous felt to damp panel resonances. A sectioned bass cone is shown in Fig. 21. The skins have been peeled back to show the construction.

Balance Between Bass and Treble

Shorter [33] has described how small differences in mean level between bass and treble units, even though the actual curves be very far from flat, give great differences in the character of the sound. Frequently manufacturers fit a treble unit having much greater sensitivity than the bass unit with a variable resistance and leave the user to match the two. This cannot be done without proper measuring equipment. The present units are therefore designed with similar sensitivities.

If the treble unit level is more than 2 dB above the bass unit level, a very "forward" tone is produced; on single-channel signals, the sound appears to come from just behind the grille cloth. This is most realistic on solos, but large orchestras equally appear to be just behind the grille cloth. This impression of listening to a hole in a box is accentuated if the loudspeaker is very directional. If the treble level is more than 2 dB below the bass, the sound appears to come from deep inside the box and the point source effect is absent. When the correct balance is obtained, and especially if the treble is well distributed, there is a pleasant absence of the "hole in a box" feeling, the exact position of the treble unit being difficult to locate, and the tone is neither forward nor recessive.

DOPPLER DISTORTION

Doppler distortion has been studied by Beers and Belar [36] and summarized by Rettinger [37]. Moir [38] has demonstrated that for single loudspeakers covering the whole frequency range the distortion can be very unpleasant, but that where the range is divided between two or more loudspeakers the distortion is very small.

MEASURED VALUES

With two or more units, acoustic interference occurs which destroys the value of the results obtained in the crossover region and an octave on each side, results depending on microphone position. Units must therefore be measured separately and the curves combined. Tone burst tests and squarewave tests are likewise valueless, and intermodulation distortion values varying by a factor of 10 times may be obtained merely by moving the microphone 1 in. Intermodulation tests with a small constant difference between the two frequencies might be possible.

The maximum amplitude reached by the bass unit with 12 W input was about 3/16 in. at 60 Hz, when second harmonic was 2.8% and third harmonic 2.2%. This compares with values obtained by a European broadcasting authority (Fig. 22). The same cabinet as a reflex gave a maximum amplitude of ⅛ in. with 2.5% second and 1.4% third harmonic distortion. Mounting the loudspeaker in a wall gave values of 1.7% and 1.7% for an amplitude of 3/16 in. This suggests that this is the residual suspension mechanical and magnetic distortion, and that the air distortion of the cabinet forms roughly ⅓ of the total, below which it would be impossible to go without using a larger cabinet. It will be noted that except for the very low frequencies, the distortion is less than 1%.

The system will accept well over 15 W peak speech and music without distress. Inputs of 15 W rms sinewave

Fig. 21. Sectioned bass cone, showing construction.

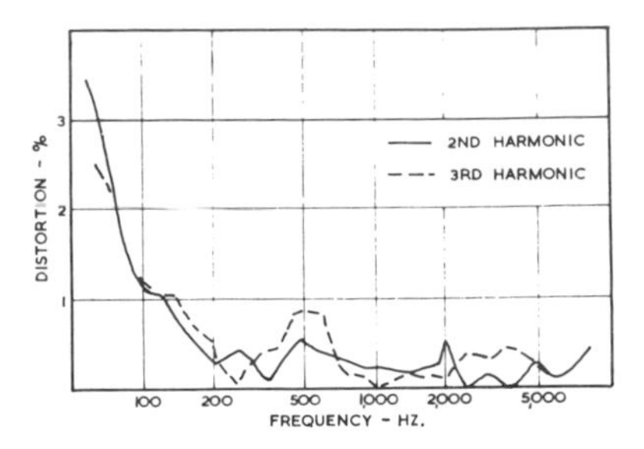

Fig. 22. Distortion curves for sandwich loudspeaker at 10 W rms input.

above 1 kHz will cause overheating of the treble unit voice coil. It is interesting to note that if the magnet is removed, the treble voice coil rapidly overheats at a 4 W input, indicating that the magnet conducts much of the heat away. The amplitudes are too small for appreciable cooling by movement of the air.

PRODUCTION TESTING

The loudspeakers are tested with sinewaves, white noise, and music, and the bass resonance and first breakup resonance are checked. The sensitivity and response of the treble units are measured, using an 18 in. felt-lined cube with the speaker and microphone mounted on opposite faces. The cube is an open framework with internal felt baffles, and gives a consistent, if not anechoic, result. The response is held within ± 3 dB. The cube accentuates any resonances present, which suggests that the same may be true of listening rooms, rather than loudspeaker resonances being swamped by room resonances.

ALTERNATIVE DESIGNS

Smaller Systems

The size of the cabinet, 26 in. × 15 in. × 12 in., may be a difficulty where space is limited. A smaller version, 18½ in. × 11 in. × 8 in., was therefore developed. Since a smaller cone with less throw would suffice, a 10 in. × 6 in. cone was used. The maximum amplitude, at resonance, was ⅛ in. with 12 W input at 90 Hz, after which the response drops off at 12 dB/octave. This gives adequate bass on some types of music, and bass boost can be used without producing audible frequency doubling, but on heavy organ and orchestral music some "body" is missing.

The treble unit is the same as for the standard system, but mounted differently, so that some irregularities due to diffraction could not be avoided. The elliptical bass cone gave a larger number of less pronounced breakup resonances than the circular cone, starting at the same frequency, 1500 Hz, corresponding to the 10 in. dimension. It was found that if a thin pressed-steel chassis were used for the bass unit, there was an additional impedance peak at about 80 Hz when the loudspeaker was mounted in the cabinet. This varied in magnitude according to whether the axis of the loudspeaker was vertical or horizontal, and was evidently the resonance of the flexing of the frame with the mass of the magnet.

Very Small Systems

Some manufacturers have developed very small systems, as low as 300 in.^{3} internal volume. The bass is very good considering the size, but audible frequency doubling takes place on heavy orchestral and organ music. A large change in cabinet volume gives a relatively small change in frequency response, so that only about an octave is lost, compared with a 1½–2 ft^3 cabinet.

These very small cabinets show what could be done by radio manufacturers to provide better quality at little extra expense. Table radios and record players could be made with excellent bass response, if a single unit with more throw than is usual were fitted.

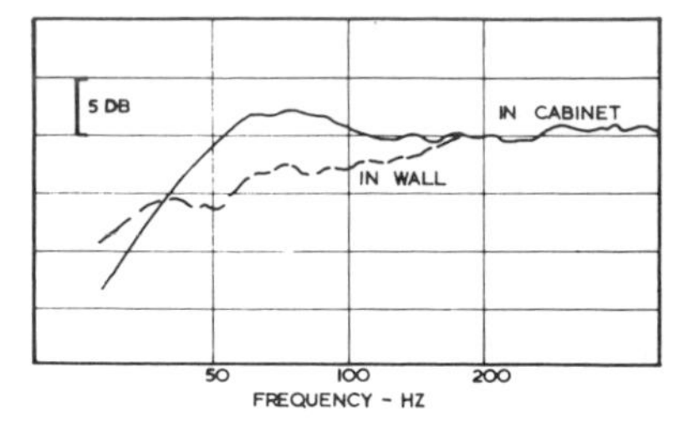

Fig. 23. Bass response of loudspeaker mounted in wall.

Very Large Cabinets

Large cabinets, say several cubic feet, have low Q, and loss of bass results. A loudspeaker mounted in a wall, representing the extreme case, is shown in Fig. 23. In an attempt to extend the bass response, a 5.6 ft^3 cabinet was constructed in ¾ in. veneered chipboard, and lined with 1⅛ in. thick bituminous felt. A standard bass unit was used; with the cabinet closed, a small extension of the bass was obtained, using the minimum amount of absorbent material inside the cabinet. An improvement was obtained by converting this to a reflex cabinet with a 12 in. long 4 in. diameter pipe. Swishing noises in the pipe were prevented by means of a 1 in. thick disc of rubberized hair glued in the pipe. This material is very open and is self-supporting, unlike cloth which flaps. Too great a resistance to air flow naturally rendered the cabinet equivalent to being closed. The free-air resonance of the loudspeaker was 21 Hz, which matched the cabinet for the optimum condition described previously. It will be seen from Fig. 24 that the response falls far short of the theoretical. In A–B listening tests with some records, the standard cabinet appeared superior to the large one, due to the greater output in the 60–150 Hz range, although the superiority of the large cabinet was evident on records with extreme bass.

The reason for the discrepancy between theoretical and practical results is unknown. The Q of the system is rather low and series resistance was used to increase this,

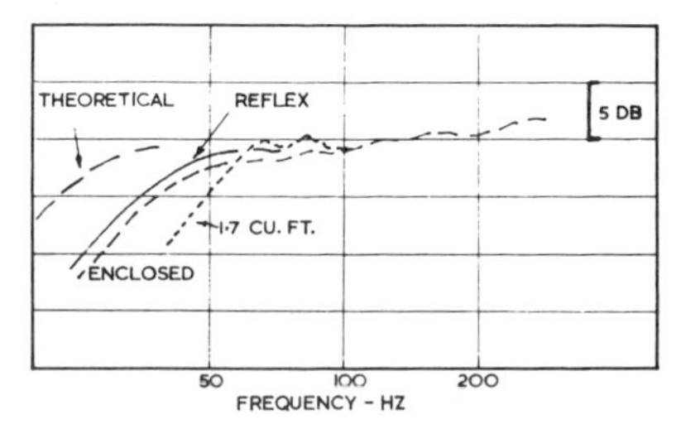

Fig. 24. Response of loudspeaker mounted in 5.6 ft^3 cabinet.

and although there was some increase in output in the 50 Hz region, there was no improvement in the extreme bass. It is possible that the cabinet is not rigid enough in the 30 Hz region, and a concrete cabinet could be used to test this.

REFERENCES

1. L. L. Beranek, *Acoustics* (McGraw-Hill, New York, 1954).
2. N. W. McLachlan, *Loudspeakers* (Dover Publications, New York, 1960).
3. R. Yorke, Private communication (Jan. 1965).
4. R. Yorke, Lecture to Brit. IRE, London, Nov. 29, 1961.
5. Anon., *Wireless World* **73**, 471 (1967).
6. D. A. Barlow, "Rigidity of Loudspeaker Diaphragms," *Wireless World* **64**, 564 (1958).
7. D. A. Barlow, U.S. Pat. 3,111,187.
8. N. A. DeBruyne, *Brit. Plastics* **14**, 162 (1942).
9. M. S. Corrington, "Correlation of Transient Measurements on Loudspeakers with Listening Tests," *J. Audio Eng. Soc.* **3**, 35 (1955).
10. F. H. Brittain, "Metal Cone Loudspeaker," *Wireless World* **58**, 440 (1952).
11. "Ribbon Microphone," B.B.C. Monograph (1953).
12. F. V. Hunt, *Electro-Acoustics* (Harvard Univ. Press, Cambridge, 1954).
13. P. J. Walker, "Wide-Range Electrostatic Loudspeakers," *Wireless World* **61**, 208, 265, 381 (1955).
14. C. I. Malmé, "A Wide-Range Electrostatic Loudspeaker," *J. Audio Eng. Soc.* **7**, 47 (1959).
15. F. L. D., "Loudspeaker Without Diaphragm," *Wireless World* **58**, 2 (1952).
16. A. E. Falkus, "The Ionic Loudspeaker for the Reproduction of High Frequencies," *British Kinematography Sound & Television Soc. J.* **48**, 132 (1966).
17. G. Shirley, "The Corona Wind Loudspeaker," *J. Audio Eng. Soc.* **5**, 23 (1957).
18. W. R. Babcock, K. L. Baker, and A. G. Cattaneo, "Electrical Modulation of Gas Flames," *Nature* **216**, 676 (1968).
19. H. F. Olson and J. Preston, U.S. Pat. 2,814,353.
20. A. R. Bailey, "A Non-Resonant Loudspeaker Enclosure Design," *Wireless World* **71**, 483 (1965).
21. A. N. Thiele, "Loudspeakers in Vented Boxes," *Proc. IRE Australia* **22**, 487 (1961).
22. B. C. Reith, "Bass Reflex Enclosures (Ltr.)," *Wireless World* **73**, 38 (1967).
23. L. Keibs, "Physical Conditions for Optimum Bass Reflex Cabinets," *J. Audio Eng. Soc.* **8**, 258 (1960).
24. J. F. Novak, "Performance of Enclosures for Low Resonance High Compliance Loudspeakers," *J. Audio Eng. Soc.* **7**, 29 (1959).
25. H. F. Olson, J. Preston, and E. C. May, *J. Audio Eng. Soc.* **2**, 219 (1954).
26. C. G. McProud, *Audio* **40**, Nos. 6, 7 (1956).
27. E. J. Jordan, "Loudspeaker Enclosure Design," *Wireless World* **62**, 75 (1956).
28. L. L. Beranek, "The Transmission and Radiation of Acoustic Waves by Structures," *Proc. Inst. Mech. Engs.* **173**, 12 (1959).
29. D. H. Lloyd, *Metal Industry* **75**, 371 (1949).
30. G. A. Briggs, *Loudspeakers* (Wharfedale Wireless Works, 1958).
31. J. Moir, "Structural Resonances in Loudspeaker Cabinets," *J. Brit. Sound Recording Assoc.* **6**, 183 (1961).
32. P. W. Tappan, "Loudspeaker Enclosure Walls," *J. Audio Eng. Soc.* **10**, 224 (1962).
33. D. E. L. Shorter, "A Survey of Performance Criteria and Design Considerations for High Quality Monitoring Loudspeakers," *Proc. IEEE* **105**, Pt. B (Nov. 1958).
34. R. H. Nichols, *J. Acoust. Soc. Am.* **18**, No. 1, 151 (1946).
35. H. F. Olson, "Direct Radiator Loudspeaker Enclosures," *Audio Engineering* **35**, 34 (1951). [Reprinted in *J. Audio Eng. Soc.* **17**, 22 (1969).]
36. G. L. Beers and H. Belar, "Frequency Modulation Distortion in Loudspeakers," *Proc. IRE* **31**, 132 (Apr. 1943).
37. V. Rettinger, *Audio* **43**, 7 (1959).
38. J. Moir, Lecture to Brit. Sound Recording Assoc., London, Apr. 17, 1964.
39. R. Cooke and L. Fincham, Lecture to British Kinematography Sound & Television Soc., London, Mar. 16, 1969.

THE AUTHOR

Donald A. Barlow was born in 1924 in Birmingham, England. He graduated in metallurgy at Birmingham University in 1943 and gained an external M.Sc. in 1955. He worked in the Research Department of Aluminium Laboratories Ltd. on mechanical properties and plastic deformation until 1959, when he joined H. J. Leak & Co. Ltd. to develop his invention of the sandwich cone. Mr. Barlow is now with Rank-Wharfedale Ltd. as Senior Acoustics Research Engineer. He is the author of a number of papers, including one on record groove deformation which received a Letter of Recognition from the Audio Engineering Society. Donald Barlow's work on groove deformation is a spare time activity.

Constant-Voltage Crossover Network Design*

RICHARD H. SMALL

School of Electrical Engineering, University of Sydney, Sydney, N.S.W., Australia

Consideration of the electroacoustic behavior of common loudspeaker drivers leads to the general crossover network design requirement of constant total voltage transfer. Conventional passive networks satisfy this requirement only if the cutoff slopes are limited to 6 dB per octave. Active crossover networks with steeper cutoff slopes can also be designed to meet this requirement, but these networks do not provide a rapid transition between drivers. Regardless of the network chosen, the drivers used must have useful frequency ranges which overlap by about four octaves.

INTRODUCTION Most high-quality loudspeaker systems used today are of the multiple-driver type. These systems contain two or more drivers, each designed for optimum performance over a limited portion of the system frequency range. One advantage of this approach is that the useful system frequency range may exceed that of the best single wide-range driver. Secondly, by dividing the signal spectrum among several drivers, total modulation distortion [1] of the system may be reduced.

An essential part of every multiple-driver loudspeaker system is the crossover network, also often called the dividing network. This network is responsible for dividing the signal to be reproduced into two or more separate signals on the basis of frequency; each driver receives the particular range which it is designed to reproduce.

Two important varieties of crossover network are in common use. One is the passive network which is constructed entirely of passive components and connected between a single power amplifier and a set of drivers [2], [3]. The other is the active network, or electronic crossover [4] which is connected ahead of a set of power amplifiers, one for each driver.

* Presented at the 12th National Radio and Electronics Engineering Convention, Institution of Radio and Electronics Engineers Australia, Sydney, May 1969. Published in *Proc. IREE Australia* **31** (1970), and republished here with the permission of the Institution.

Traditional performance standards for crossover networks rely on simple electrical principles, without regard to the electroacoustic performance of drivers. The most common and familiar criterion is that of constant total power transfer, which is the basis of constant-resistance passive network designs [5].

A generally valid criterion for the division of the electrical signal in a multiple-driver system must take into account the driver transfer characteristics and the mechanism of recombination of the separate acoustic outputs. While the specific transfer characteristics of drivers depend on the driver design, one important feature common to all types of driver is a linear steady-state amplitude relationship between driving voltage and radiated sound pressure [6], [7]. The combined output of two drivers radiating together is found by superposition, i.e., the total sound pressure at any point is the linear sum of the two individually radiated sound pressures, phase difference being taken into account [8].

To simplify the derivation of a generally valid network performance criterion, two assumptions are made. The first is that the drivers are mounted so closely together that the path lengths to any point in the environment differ by much less than a wavelength at the crossover frequency. The second is that the amplitude and phase versus frequency characteristics of the drivers are identical (though not necessarily smooth) in the cross-

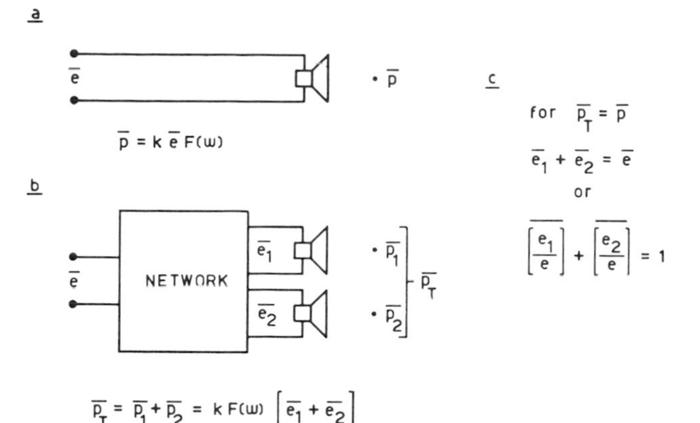

Fig. 1. Comparison of the performance of a single driver at **a** with two such drivers operated from a crossover network at **b** yields the network design requirement **c**.

over region. The practical significance of these assumptions will be discussed shortly.

CONSTANT VOLTAGE TRANSFER

The problem of crossover network design is illustrated in its simplest form in Fig. 1. In Fig. 1**a**, a single driver is connected to a voltage source; in Fig. 1**b**, two drivers identical to the first operate from the same voltage source via a crossover network. In the transfer expressions, superior bars indicate vector quantities and p is the (sinusoidal) sound pressure at a fixed distance from the driver(s), e is the (sinusoidal) driving voltage, k is a sensitivity constant, and $F(\omega)$ is the amplitude and phase characteristic of the specified drivers. Fig. 1**c** shows that the system of Fig. 1**b** will radiate the same sound pressure as the single driver of Fig. 1**a** if the crossover network satisfies the condition that the vector sum of the individual voltage transfer functions is unity.

For the general case of a crossover network having low-pass and high-pass voltage transfer functions defined by $G_L(s)$ and $G_H(s)$, respectively, the requirement is that

$$G_L(s) + G_H(s) = 1. \qquad (1)$$

It is emphasized that Eq. (1) is a vector relationship. The sum of the network voltage transfer functions must be both unity in amplitude and zero in phase for all values of frequency. This condition of unity total voltage transfer has also been derived from transient considerations in an earlier paper by Ashley [9]. In practice, the total voltage transfer may have any constant amplitude. While unity will be used for convenience in analysis, the derived performance criterion will henceforth be referred to as constant voltage transfer and the networks which meet this criterion as constant-voltage crossover networks.

The derivation of Eq. (1) assumes two conditions: that the drivers are mounted closely together and that they are identical. The first condition was not imposed solely to simplify the derivation; it is the only way to ensure uniform addition of the driver outputs for both direct and reflected sound throughout the listening area. If large driver spacings are employed, there is no ideal solution to the crossover design problem; hence any attempt to improve crossover network design must be accompanied by efforts to achieve the close driver spacing assumed.

In practice, some driver spacing is unavoidable, and the resulting path length difference introduces unwanted phase shift into the acoustic addition of the driver outputs. The most severe effects occur for driving signals of equal amplitude and nearly 180° phase difference, because the addition in this case is very sensitive to small additional phase shifts. Any choice in the design of crossover networks should therefore favor a solution which gives the least phase difference between outputs when the amplitudes are comparable.

The second condition appears at first to limit the usefulness of the derived performance criterion, because the drivers used in multiple-driver systems are seldom identical and often of completely different types. However, this condition is satisfactorily met by many practical driver combinations, for example, two direct radiators, each operating in its piston range.

If differences in the transfer characteristics of two drivers can be established and represented by a simple model, equalizing networks can be designed for use with one or both of the drivers to produce the required similarity of response. The network plus equalizers then constitute a correct "crossover network" for this specific set of drivers. By treating the problem of equalization separately, it is possible to design crossover networks having universal applicability. If a selected set of drivers cannot be equalized for use with a constant-voltage network, then these drivers will not produce ideal results with any network design.

CONVENTIONAL NETWORK RESPONSES

The ability of conventional crossover networks to provide constant voltage transfer is determined by examining the voltage transfer characteristics of these networks. Because the customary amplitude versus frequency response plots lack important phase information, these are supplemented here with the voltage transfer functions in polynomial form and polar plots of these functions. Low-pass functions are designated by G_L and high-pass functions by G_H. The form of these functions is simplified by adopting a normalized frequency variable $s_n = s/\omega_0$, ω_0 being the nominal crossover frequency.

Figure 2 presents the polynomial functions and plots for first-order (6 dB per octave) constant-resistance crossover networks. The same information is provided in Fig. 3 for second-order (12 dB per octave) networks and in

a $\quad G_L = \frac{1}{1 + s_n}; \quad G_H = \frac{s_n}{1 + s_n}; \quad s_n = \frac{s}{\omega_0}$

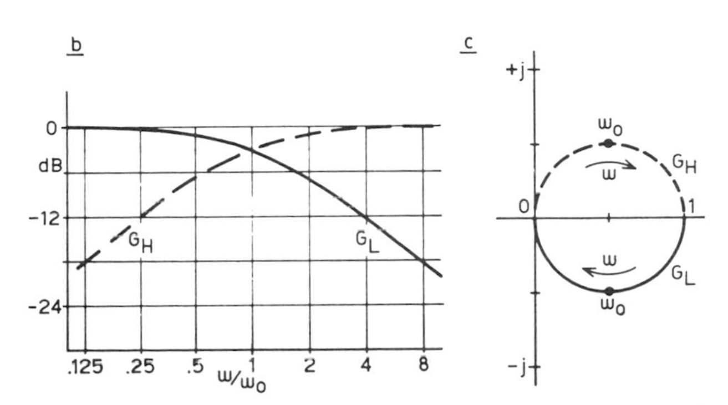

Fig. 2. First-order constant-resistance crossover network performance: **a** voltage transfer functions; **b** amplitude versus frequency response; **c** polar plots.

a $G_L = \frac{1}{1+\sqrt{2}s_n + s_n^2}$; $G_H = \frac{s_n^2}{1+\sqrt{2}s_n + s_n^2}$; $s_n = \frac{s}{\omega_0}$

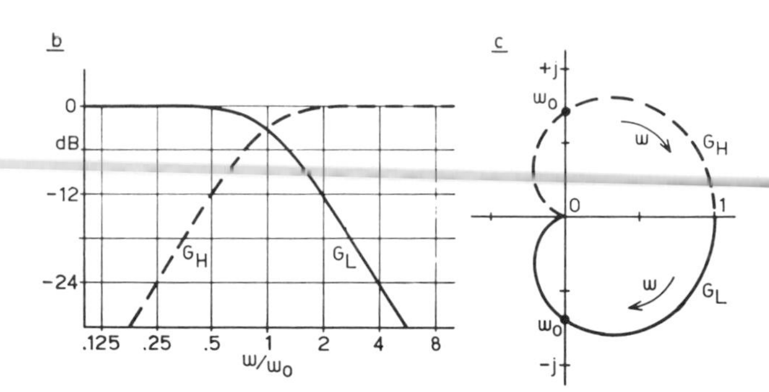

Fig. 3. Second-order constant-resistance crossover network performance: **a** voltage transfer functions; **b** amplitude versus frequency response; **c** polar plots.

a $G_L = \frac{1}{1+2s_n+2s_n^2+s_n^3}$; $G_H = \frac{s_n^3}{1+2s_n+2s_n^2+s_n^3}$; $s_n = \frac{s}{\omega_0}$

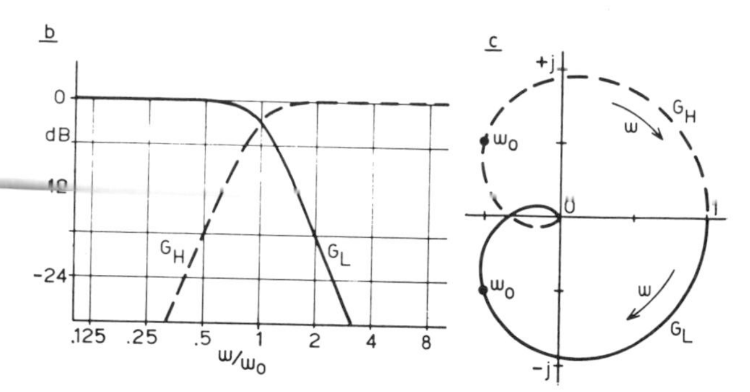

Fig. 4. Third-order constant-resistance crossover network performance: **a** voltage transfer functions; **b** amplitude versus frequency response; **c** polar plots.

Fig. 4 for third-order (18 dB per octave) networks. The constant-resistance designs result in Butterworth (maximally flat) responses for all cases.

An important feature of the pairs of polynomial functions presented is that in all cases,

$$G_L(s_n) = G_H(1/s_n). \quad (2)$$

It is this property which results in symmetry about the crossover frequency for the pairs of transfer plots and symmetry about the real axis for the pairs of polar plots.

Another important feature of the polynomial expressions is that the numerators consist of only one term. This feature is consistent in conventional active crossover network designs also. The single-term numerator is the result of choosing the simplest and most economical circuit which yields a given cutoff slope. It is also the reason for the failure of high-order conventional networks to provide constant voltage transfer, as can be shown by adding the low-pass and high-pass voltage transfer functions for each network to obtain the total response. Only the first-order conventional design results in constant voltage transfer. In the higher order designs, the shortage of numerator terms results in a nonunity total response. The second-order network has a null at crossover; the third-order network, while possessing a constant total amplitude, exhibits a complete phase reversal at crossover.

Higher order responses, which have steeper cutoff slopes, are traditionally desired because the more rapid attenuation outside the pass band eases the bandwidth requirements of the drivers. It is therefore of interest to investigate whether steep cutoff slopes can be obtained with constant voltage transfer, and to examine the extent to which the driver performance requirements may thereby be eased.

NETWORKS WITH CONSTANT VOLTAGE TRANSFER

The condition for constant voltage transfer is that the polynomial voltage transfer functions of a network sum to unity, Eq. (1). The simplest way of achieving this is to select a denominator polynomial common to both transfer functions and then to divide the terms of the denominator polynomial between the two numerators. The order of the denominator polynomial and the assignment of the terms to the numerators will determine the cutoff slopes of the two transfer functions.

If symmetrical responses having equal cutoff slopes are desired, then Eq. (2) must also be satisfied. This is achieved by selecting a denominator polynomial having symmetrical coefficients ($c_0 = c_n$, $c_1 = c_{n-1}$, etc.) and dividing the terms equally between the two numerators.

The effect of these requirements on the polar plots of the transfer functions is quite interesting. It is easily shown that if Eq. (1) is satisfied, the polar plots of G_L and G_H will be identical in shape and size (the geometrical condition of congruency) and will lie in positions such that if one is rotated 180° about the point +½, 0 in the plane of the plot, it will coincide with the other. Note that this condition is satisfied in Fig. 2, where the two plots are identical semicircles, but not in Fig. 3 or Fig. 4.

As seen in the previous section, the condition imposed by Eq. (2) results in the polar plots of the transfer functions being symmetrical to each other about the real axis. Thus the polar plots of symmetrical constant-voltage functions must exhibit both congruent shapes and symmetry to each other about the real axis. These simultaneous conditions produce symmetry about the line Re = +½ for each function plot as well.

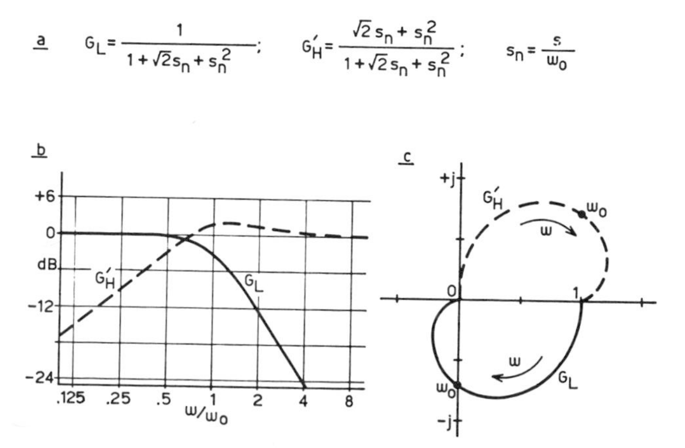

Fig. 5. Asymmetrical constant-voltage transfer functions based on conventional second-order low-pass network: **a** voltage transfer functions; **b** amplitude versus frequency responses; **c** polar plots.

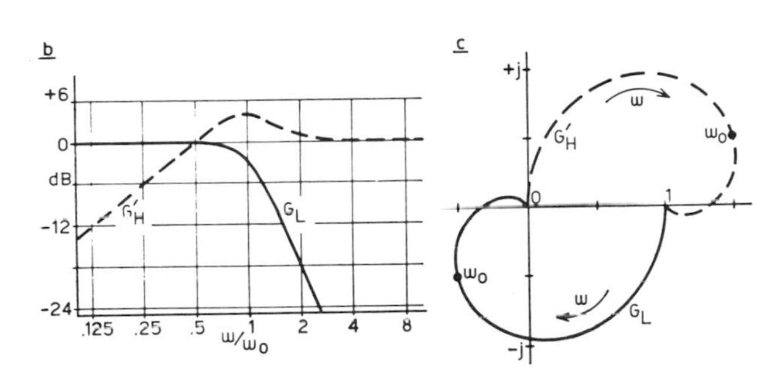

Fig. 6. Asymmetrical constant-voltage transfer functions based on conventional third-order low-pass network: **a** voltage transfer functions; **b** amplitude versus frequency responses; **c** polar plots.

Asymmetrical Networks

Taking the conventional low-pass responses of Figs. 3 and 4, the matching high-pass responses which give constant voltage transfer are easily derived, both from the polynomial functions and from the polar plots. The new function pairs are presented in Figs. 5 and 6. Note the identical shapes of the polar plots for each pair of functions. In both cases, the ultimate slope of the high-pass function is only 6 dB per octave. This is inherent in the initial choice of G_L which leaves the point $+1,0$ at an angle of $-90°$ and thus compels G'_H to leave the origin at an angle of $+90°$

Symmetrical Networks

Second Order: The simplest polynomial functions which satisfy Eq. (1) and (2) and result in second-order (12 dB per octave) responses are

$$G_L(s_n) = (1+as_n)/(1+as_n+as_n^2+s_n^3)$$
$$G_H(s_n) = (as_n^2+s_n^3)/(1+as_n+as_n^2+s_n^3).$$

For stability the coefficient a must be greater than unity. The actual choice of a determines the amount of peaking in the response and the phase difference at crossover. Choosing $a = 2+\sqrt{3}$ gives $|G(\omega_0)| = 1.0$, with 120° of phase difference between the two outputs, and approximately 2 dB of peaking in the pass band of each response. See Fig. 7 for plots of these functions.

Third Order: The simplest satisfactory polynomials are

$$G_L(s_n) = (1+as_n+bs_n^2)/(1+as_n+bs_n^2+bs_n^3+as_n^4+s_n^5)$$
$$G_H(s_n) = (bs_n^3+as_n^4+s_n^5)/(1+as_n+bs_n^2+bs_n^3+as_n^4+s_n^5).$$

For stability, a must be greater than unity, and b must be greater than $a+1$. If $|G(\omega_0)|$ is again chosen to be unity, the relationship between a and b is fixed at $a = (2-\sqrt{3})(b-1)$. A value of b can then be found which is high enough to keep the response peak below, say, 3 dB. The function $G_L(s_n)$ above has been investigated with the aid of a computer for various combinations of a and b. Response plots for $b = 21$ and $a = 5.36$ appear in Fig. 8.

General Considerations: The restriction of $|G(\omega_0)|$ to a value of unity was not arbitrary. This choice is consistent with the desire to avoid phase differences at crossover of nearly 180°, as explained earlier. At ω_0, $\text{Re}(G) = +\frac{1}{2}$ for all symmetrical constant-voltage functions. Therefore, choosing $|G(\omega_0)| = 1$ gives $\angle G = \pm 60°$, or a phase difference of 120° at crossover. $|G(\omega_0)|$ cannot be decreased much below unity without producing large peaks in the pass band.

Restriction of the pass band peak is also based on rational criteria. (The shape of the polar plots shows that a peak must be present in all constant-voltage network responses except first order.) If one driver has a large excess input, constant voltage transfer requires that a large out-of-phase component be applied to the second driver. Large peaks thus produce undesirably large phase differences at the frequency of peaking. Equally important considerations are the power capability of the amplifiers and the power rating of the drivers, both of which must be increased in proportion to the amount of peaking.

Features of Constant-Voltage Networks

Inspection of the voltage transfer characteristics of the various constant-voltage networks discussed reveals an interesting fact: in every case, asymmetrical or symmetrical, there is a broad overlap region on the frequency

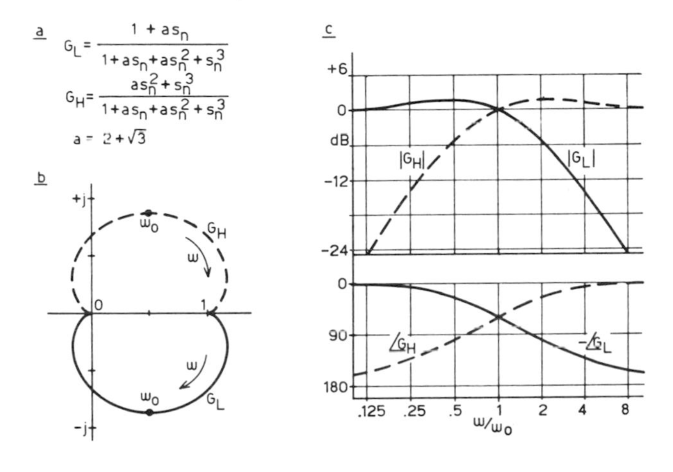

Fig. 7. Second-order symmetrical constant-voltage transfer functions **a**, their polar plots **b**, and their amplitude and phase versus frequency responses **c**.

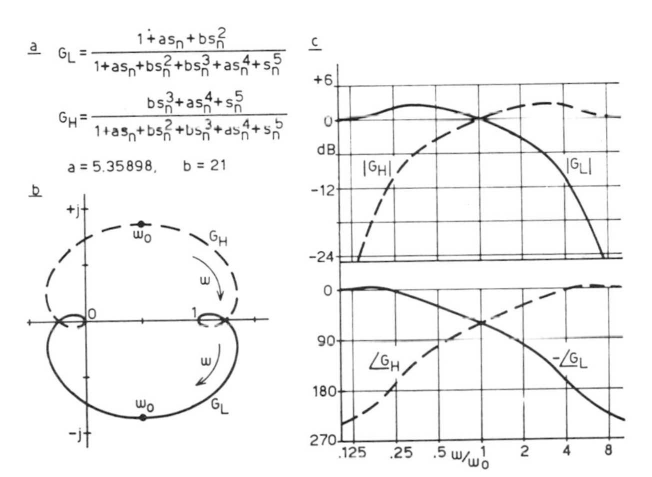

Fig. 8. Third-order symmetrical constant-voltage transfer functions **a**, their polar plots **b**, and their amplitude and phase versus frequency responses **c**.

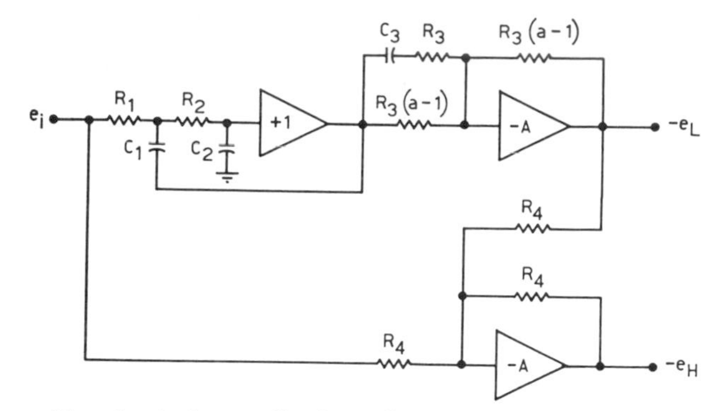

Fig. 9. Active realization of second-order symmetrical constant-voltage crossover network.

scale which is about four octaves wide between the -12 dB points of the related function pairs. This general rule holds for all the responses investigated; it can be overcome only by permitting undesirably large peaks or phase differences. Thus a steep ultimate cutoff slope does not help materially to reduce the overlap region where both drivers must operate satisfactorily and have closely similar characteristics.

For the general case of symmetrical networks, each driver must be designed to operate for two octaves beyond the nominal crossover frequency—at both ends of its range for a midrange driver. Over the four-octave overlap range, the driver characteristics must be closely similar or must be made so by the use of equalizers.

If it is necessary to cut off one driver rapidly due to an uncontrollable response irregularity, this can be done using an asymmetrical network. But the other driver must then have a well-behaved response for three octaves or more beyond the nominal crossover frequency.

REALIZATION OF CONSTANT-VOLTAGE NETWORKS

Active Networks

Given polynomial expressions for a desired response, such as those of the previous section, network circuits may be developed using the techniques of circuit synthesis [10], [11]. For example, the second-order symmetrical response of Fig. 7 requires a low-pass function $G_L(s_n) = (1+as_n)/(1+as_n+as_n^2+s_n^3)$. This function may be factored to

$$G_L(s_n) = (1+as_n)/(1+s_n)\,[1+(a-1)s_n+s_n^2].$$

Thus one way of synthesizing the network function is to cascade a shelf network with another network giving a damped pole-pair, as shown in the upper part of Fig. 9.

The complementary high-pass function may similarly be generated by a cascaded shelf network and second-order high-pass filter. However, if the low-pass response can be produced with unity gain at low frequencies, the high-pass response can then be obtained simply by means of a difference amplifier connected between the input and output of the low-pass circuit [12]. This is possible because of the constant-voltage property, Eq. (1). If the low-pass response is realized with a net phase inversion as in Fig. 9, a summing amplifier may be used to recover the high-pass response as shown in the lower part of the figure [9, p. 243].

The synthesis techniques described are applicable to all functions discussed earlier. All polynomials can be broken down into first-order and second-order polynomial factors, and the response functions can then be synthesized in cascade using the methods of [10] and [11].

First-order active networks are trivial. The simplest synthesis uses two complementary passive *RC* networks, with buffer amplifiers if necessary to eliminate loading errors.

Terminated Passive Networks

It was shown earlier that only the first-order variety of conventional passive networks exhibits constant voltage transfer. Higher order constant-voltage responses cannot be obtained with driver-terminated passive networks due to the nature of the required transfer function zeros.

Suitable first-order passive networks are presented in Fig. 10. Effective operation of such networks depends upon correct resistive termination, which is often assumed to be provided by loudspeaker drivers. This assumption is in fact usually false, and may lead to highly undesirable system responses (see next section).

Where resistive termination can be ensured, the series network of Fig. 10**b** is inherently advantageous because tolerances in component values, both in the crossover network and in the termination, will have no effect on the total network voltage response. Because the drivers are connected in series across the amplifier output, the sum of the voice-coil voltages must always be equal to the driving voltage.

NETWORK TERMINATION AND DRIVER EQUALIZATION

Figure 11**a** is a plot of the magnitude of the voice-coil impedance versus frequency for a typical moving-coil driver. The peak at 55 Hz is produced by the mechanical resonance of the moving system, the rising characteristic above 2 kHz by the self-inductance of the voice coil. This driver resembles a constant resistance only over the limited frequency range of 150–1000 Hz.

Termination of a constant-resistance crossover network with nonresistive drivers has two effects on system operation: first, the impedance presented to the amplifier is not resistive and may upset the stability or response of the amplifier; second, the voltage response of the network may be altered.

Regarding the impedance presented to the amplifier, the most common problem is reduced loading of the crossover network by the driver (due to the fundamental reso-

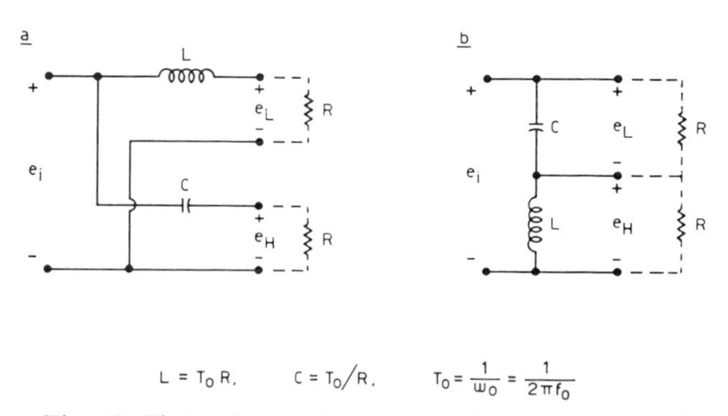

Fig. 10. First-order passive terminated crossover networks: **a** parallel network; **b** series network.

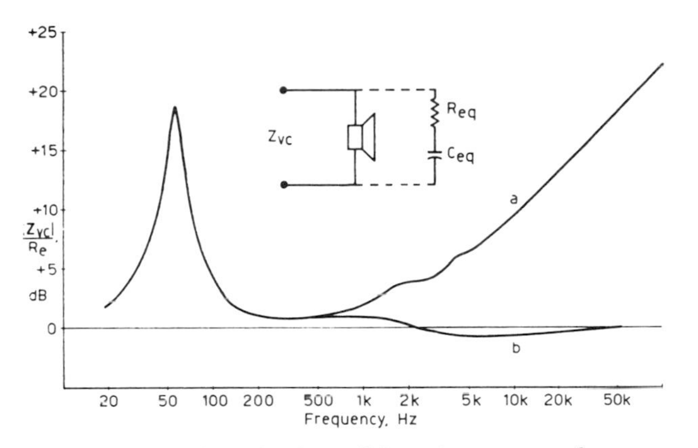

Fig. 11. Modulus of voice-coil impedance versus frequency for: **a** a typical moving-coil driver; **b** the same driver with voice-coil inductance equalizer.

nance of a tweeter or the large voice-coil inductance of a woofer) at a frequency where series resonance occurs in the crossover network. Series resonance can occur in the series first-order network and all higher order passive networks. The result is an unusually low network input impedance at resonance, which may cause overload and distortion in the amplifier or a troublesome ringing in the system transient response [13], [14].

The network voltage response is altered whenever the load impedance departs from the design value near crossover or in the stop band of each driver. (In the pass band, the voltage transfer is always close to unity and is not sensitive to load variations.)

Both difficulties may often be overcome by the use of simple impedance equalizers placed across the driver voice-coil terminals and adjusted to present the crossover network with a nearly constant resistive load.

Equalization of the voice-coil inductance, for example, is obtained with a series *RC* network. If the voice-coil inductance and dc resistance are L_e and R_e, respectively, then the required equalizer components are $R_{eq} = R_e$ and $C_{eq} = L_e/R_e^2$. The network load impedance is then equal to R_e. Figure 11**b** shows the equalization achieved on the driver of Fig. 11**a** using such a network. Losses in L_e make the equalization slightly inexact, but the impedance variations are less than 1 dB.

Electrodynamic drivers designed for low-frequency use usually have larger values of voice-coil inductance than drivers designed for high-frequency use. Unless the crossover frequency can be kept below the frequency at which the woofer voice-coil impedance begins to rise, equalization of the driver impedances to maintain correct network voltage response may not result in correct system acoustic response at crossover. This is because driver cone motion is the result of force developed from current flow in the voice coil; different values of voice-coil inductance thus produce amplitude and phase differences in the voltage-to-cone-motion characteristics of the drivers.

One satisfactory solution to this problem is to redesign the passive network to include the woofer voice-coil inductance, as suggested [5, p. 108]. A parallel network must be used, and the design value of crossover inductance is reduced by the amount of the voice-coil inductance. This solution, which requires no impedance equalizer, is limited to cases where the voice-coil inductance is less than the required crossover inductance; also, it cannot be used with drivers which have special cone treatment to offset the response effects of the voice-coil inductance.

In an active crossover system, the above condition is treated as a general response equalization problem. The lag caused by the larger voice-coil inductance is equalized by a complementary lead network in the amplifier. Ordinary driver response irregularities, if not too severe, may also be corrected by equalizers installed in the amplifiers [15].

A special equalization problem occurs when a direct-radiator driver is combined with a horn-loaded or electrostatic driver. The problem is that the direct-radiator diaphragm motion is mass controlled, while that of the other types is resistance controlled. The result is a constant phase difference of 90° between the two driver transfer characteristics [16]. This constant phase difference cannot be exactly equalized, although approximate networks may be designed to reduce the system amplitude errors in the overlap region.

MULTIPLE CROSSOVERS

Multiple crossover networks exhibiting overall constant voltage transfer may be developed from the single-crossover principles developed earlier. The design criterion for an n-way crossover network having voltage transfer functions $G_1, G_2, \cdots, G_n$ is that the vector sum of *all* transfer functions is unity, i.e.,

$$G_1+G_2+\cdots+G_n = 1. \tag{3}$$

Equation (3) can be satisfied by simple cascading of networks (active or passive) which satisfy Eq. (1).

For passive first-order constant-resistance networks the method is to replace the resistive load at one or each output of a first network with another network having its own resistive loads. Figure 12 shows a three-way passive network using two cascaded single-crossover networks of the series type. The configuration shown gives minimum losses (one inductor only) in series with the woofer. Both networks affect the output of the second, giving a band-pass response to the midrange driver and an extra reduction of low-frequency drive to the tweeter. This "extra reduction" is a natural result of the constant voltage transfer property of the network. Four-way passive crossover networks are easily developed by extension of the above technique.

Figure 13 illustrates one of the many possible ways of developing a four-way active crossover network by cas-

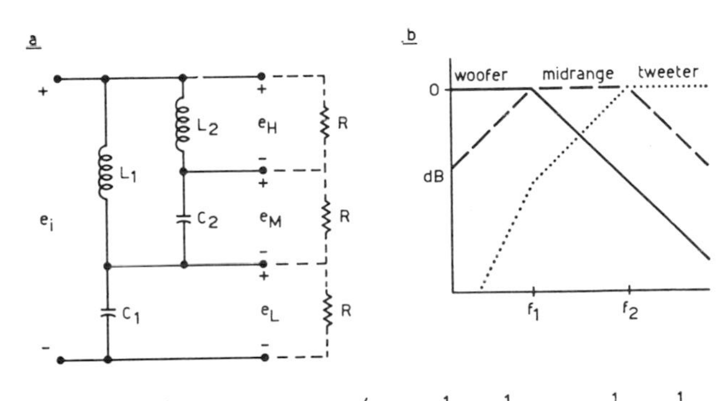

Fig. 12. Three-way series passive network with constant voltage transfer: **a** network circuit; **b** asymptotes of network voltage responses.

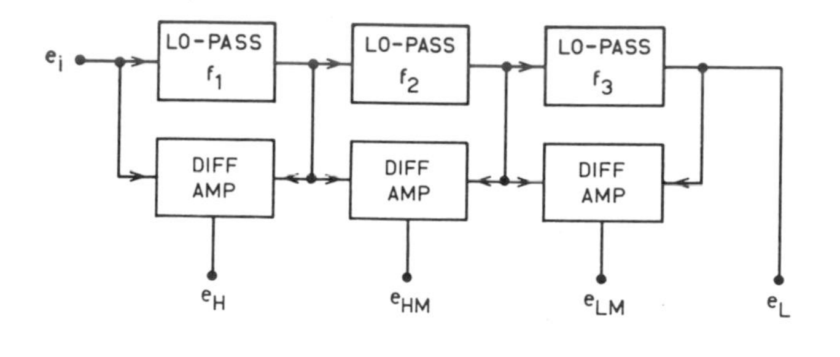

Fig. 13. Block diagram of four-way active crossover network with constant voltage transfer.

cading. This particular approach uses only three low-pass filters. Constant voltage transfer is assured by the difference amplifier recovery technique; hence the filters may be of any selected design so long as the derived high-pass responses are suitable for the drivers used.

TESTING CROSSOVER NETWORKS

Any completed crossover network design may be tested for constant voltage transfer by fairly simple means. Such tests may serve either to evaluate the performance of an existing network or to aid in the adjustment of one newly designed.

Active networks and passive parallel networks normally possess a terminal common to all outputs. It is then a simple matter to connect the various outputs to a summing network or summing amplifier. A sensitive test is to apply a square-wave input and to observe the total network output with an oscilloscope. The frequency of the square wave is adjusted to the vicinity of each crossover in turn. This test quickly reveals any departure from constant voltage transfer.

Constant voltage transfer can also be checked with sine waves. An oscilloscope having horizontal input and similar vertical and horizontal amplifiers can be used to display output versus input and thus provide simultaneous amplitude and phase indication.

The load presented to the amplifier by passive networks can also be checked simply. The method is to drive the network, with its driver loads, from a high-resistance source and to observe the voltage at the network input terminals [13, p. 26]. The high-resistance source may be either a generator with high output impedance or a normal loudspeaker amplifier having a resistor added in series with its output. Sine-wave drive can be used to obtain an impedance versus frequency plot, while square-wave drive with oscilloscope output indication will very sensitively reveal any impedance irregularities.

PHYSICAL INSTALLATION OF DRIVERS

As stated earlier, it is highly desirable that the drivers be mounted closely together so that the path lengths from each driver to listeners or to reflecting surfaces are equal over the greatest possible area. The ideal condition is approached only in a few coaxial designs which provide nearly coplanar location of the voice coils. This solution is not available to three- and four-way systems using separate drivers; for these systems, some compromise mounting method must be used.

In direct-radiator systems, it is almost invariably necessary to mount all drivers on the same baffle, which results in the radiating surfaces being more or less coplanar. The driver spacings then determine the path length differences in various directions. Because tolerable path length differences are related to the signal wavelength, the driver spacing is more important for the higher crossover frequencies.

If the drivers are mounted in a vertical line with the higher frequency units in the upper positions, the sound addition will be reasonably uniform in the horizontal plane at the level of the upper drivers. This is the area that is normally occupied by listeners.

CONCLUSION

The design of crossover networks is inextricably linked with the driver mounting problem.

For ideal mounting conditions, constant-voltage crossover networks provide an exact solution. The most interesting feature of these networks is the consistently wide overlap region. Response in the overlap region must be carefully considered when selecting and mounting drivers for a multiple-driver loudspeaker system.

For systems having unavoidably large driver spacings, there is no perfect crossover design. Intuition suggests, however, particularly when room reverberation is considered, that in this case constant power transfer (constant-resistance) networks would provide the best results on average.

The most desirable crossover network for general use would seem to be the simple first-order network. This network provides both constant voltage transfer and constant power transfer, the least phase difference of any network design, as well as economy and simplicity of construction.

REFERENCES

1. P. W. Klipsch, "Modulation Distortion in Loudspeakers," *J. Audio Eng. Soc.* **17**, 194 (1969).
2. J. K. Hilliard, "Loudspeaker Dividing Networks," *Electronics* **14**, 26 (January 1941).
3. E. J. Jordan, *Loudspeakers* (Focal Press, London, 1963), ch. 8.
4. N. H. Crowhurst, "Electronic Crossover Design," *Audio* **44**, 19 (September 1960).
5. N. H. Crowhurst, "The Basic Design of Constant Resistance Crossovers," *Audio Eng.* **37**, 21 (October 1953).
6. L. L. Beranek, *Acoustics* (McGraw-Hill, New York, 1954), p. 188.
7. J. E. Benson, "Theory and Design of Loudspeaker Enclosures," *Proc. IREE Australia* **30**, 269 (September 1969).
8. A. H. Davis, *Modern Acoustics* (G. Bell and Sons, London, 1934), p. 6.
9. J. R. Ashley, "On the Transient Response of Ideal Crossover Networks," *J. Audio Eng. Soc.* **10**, 241 (1962).
10. R. P. Sallen and E. L. Key, "A Practical Method of Designing RC Active Filters," *IRE Trans. Circuit Theory* **CT-2**, 74 (1955).
11. N. Balabanian and B. Patel, "Active Realization of Complex Zeros," *IEEE Trans. Circuit Theory* **CT-10**, 299 (1963).
12. R. M. Mitchell, "Transient Performance of Loudspeaker Dividing Networks," *Audio* **48**, 24 (January 1964).
13. V. Brociner, "Problems of Matching Speakers to Solid-State Amplifiers," *Electron. World* **77**, 23 (January 1967).

14. D. R. von Recklinghausen, "Mismatch Between Power Amplifiers and Loudspeaker Loads," *J. Audio Eng. Soc.* **6**, 220 (1958).
15. M. A. K. Hamid and L. B. Shulakewych, "Loudspeaker Compensation Using Integrated Circuits," *IEEE Trans. Broadcast & TV Receivers* **BTR-15**, 41 (1969).
16. W. R. Stroh, "Phase Shift in Loudspeakers," *IRE Trans. Audio* **AU-7**, 120 (1959).

THE AUTHOR

Richard H. Small was born in San Diego, California in 1935. He received a BS from California Institute of Technology in 1956, and an MSEE from Massachusetts Institute of Technology in 1958. Following this, for six years (1958 to 1964) he was engaged in electronic circuit design for high-resolution mass spectrometers and other analytical instruments at the Research Center of Consolidated Electrodynamics Corporation, a subsidiary of Bell & Howell Company.

During 1962, Mr. Small visited Norway as an OEEC Growing Points Fellow, and worked on the design of control circuits for semiautomatic machine tools at Norwegian Technical University. In 1964 he was employed in electronic and mechanical design for the Industrial Division of World Design Center, Tokyo.

Since moving to Australia in 1965, Mr. Small has worked as a Teaching Fellow in the School of Electrical Engineering, University of Sydney, and as a private consultant. He is presently a Commonwealth Postgraduate Research Student in the School of Electrical Engineering, University of Sydney, researching the field of direct-radiator electrodynamic loudspeaker systems.

Mr. Small is a member of the Audio Engineering Society, the Institute of Electrical and Electronics Engineers, and the Institution of Radio and Electronics Engineers, Australia.

PHASE AND DELAY DISTORTION IN MULTIPLE-DRIVER LOUDSPEAKER SYSTEMS

RICHARD H. SMALL

School of Electrical Engineering, The University of Sydney, Sydney, Australia

The results reported by Ashley [1] for a third-order Butterworth crossover network having an all-pass amplitude characteristic and a 360-degree phase rotation are most interesting. I avoided looking at networks of this class in my recent paper [2] through both cowardice and ignorance of the subjective effects.

It would be interesting to know how much (and how rapid) phase rotation can be tolerated in loudspeaker systems. Some preliminary experiments carried out by Dr. R. H. Frater of this University suggest that phase rotation which is undetectable in a monaural loudspeaker system can seriously degrade image formation when two such systems are used for stereo reproduction.

Existing standards for stereo reproduction [3] concentrate on channel differences and give no guide to the perceptability of identical phase or delay anomalies in both channels. It seems that questions about phase and delay distortion have always been more numerous than the answers available [4–9]. Perhaps Prof. Ashley's intrepid students will have the time and opportunity to reduce the disparity.

REFERENCES

1. J. R. Ashley, "Operational Amplifier Implementation of Ideal Electronic Crossover Networks," *J. Audio Eng. Soc.* **19**, 7 (1971).
2. R. H. Small, "Constant-Voltage Crossover Network Design," *J. Audio Eng. Soc.* **19**, 12 (1971).
3. "Sound Broadcasting and Television," CCIR Doc. of XI Plenary Assembly, Oslo, 1966, Vol. 5, Rep. 293-1.
4. J. R. Ashley, "Phase Shift in Audio Systems," *IEEE Trans. Audio and Electroacoustics* (Corresp.) **AU-14**, 50 (1966).
5. J. K. Hilliard, "Notes on How Phase and Delay Distortions Affect the Quality of Speech, Music and Sound Effects," *IEEE Trans. Audio* **AU-12**, 23 (1964).
6. J. H. Craig and L. A. Jeffress, "Effect of Phase on the Quality of a Two-Component Tone," *J. Acoust. Soc. Am.* **34**, 1752 (1962).
7. W. R. Stroh, "Phase Shift in Loudspeakers," *IRE Trans. Audio* **AU-7**, 120 (1959).
8. C. A. Ewaskio and O. K. Mawardi, "Electroacoustic Phase Shift in Loudspeakers," *J. Acoust. Soc. Am.* **22**, 444 (1950).
9. P. W. Tappan, "Phase Distortion," *IEEE Trans. Audio.* (Editor's Corner) **AU-12**, 21 (1964).

Loudspeakers in Vented Boxes: Part I*

A. N. THIELE

Australian Broadcasting Commission, Sydney, N.S.W. 2001, Australia

An investigation of the equivalent circuits of loudspeakers in vented boxes shows that it is possible to make the low-frequency acoustic response equivalent to an ideal high-pass filter or as close an approximation as is desired. The simplifying assumptions appear justified in practice and the techniques involved are simple.

The low-frequency performance of a loudspeaker can be adequately defined by three parameters, the resonant frequency f_s, a volume of air V_{as}, equivalent to its acoustic compliance, and the ratio of electrical resistance to motional reactance at the resonant frequency Q_e. From these three parameters, the electroacoustic efficiency η can be found also. A plea is made to loudspeaker manufacturers to publish these parameters as basic information on their product. The influence of other speaker constants on these parameters is investigated.

When f_s and V_{as} are known, a loudspeaker box can be designed to give a variety of predictable responses which are different kinds of high-pass 24-dB per octave filters. For each response, a certain value of Q is required which depends not only on the Q_e of the loudspeaker but also the damping factor of the amplifier, for which a negative value is often required.

The usual tuning arrangement leads to a response which can be that of a fourth-order Butterworth filter. This, however, is only a special case, and a whole family of responses may be obtained by varying the volume and tuning of the box. Also an empirical "law" is observed that for a given loudspeaker the cutoff frequency depends closely on the inverse square root of the box volume. The limitations of this "law" may be overcome by the use of filtering in the associated amplifier. For example, for a given frequency response, the box volume can be reduced at the price of increased low-frequency output from the amplifier and vice versa, with little change in the motion required of the loudspeaker.

Acoustic damping of the vent is shown to be unnecessary. Examples are given of typical parameters and enclosure designs.

Editor's Note: The theory of vented-box or bass-reflex loudspeaker baffles has always seemed to have an air of mystery, probably because the total electroacoustic system has four degrees of freedom and seems four times as complicated as the closed-box baffle with its two degrees of freedom. Beranek gives a good foundation for theoretical analysis and Novak has performed numerous valuable calculations. Those working in the design of loudspeakers have used these analysis techniques and probably asked essentially the same seven questions that A. N. Thiele recognized at the turn of the previous decade.

The seven questions and their answers were published in the August 1961 issue of the *Proceedings of the IRE Australia*, and the elegance of the answers adequately justifies republication of Thiele's work in the *Journal of the Audio Engineering Society*. In his classic discourse Thiele observes that the topology of the equivalent circuit (Fig. 1) is simply that of a high-pass filter. If suffi-

* Presented at the 1961 I.R.E. Radio and Electronic Engineering Convention, Sydney, N.S.W., March 1961. Reprinted from *Proceedings of the IRE Australia*, vol. 22, pp. 487-508 (Aug. 1961). The author was formerly with E.M.I. (Aust.) Ltd., Sydney, N.S.W.

cient simplification can be justified, Thiele reasons that the methods of modern network synthesis should be applicable to loudspeakers. This is a profound observation because it means that once the system transfer function is chosen, a logical sequence can be followed to specify driver and baffle parameters. This is much more efficient than the cut and try methods based on either analysis or measurements.

Although the idea is profound because of its simplicity, much work is required to develop, utilize, and demonstrate its use. In the interest of compatibility with format in this Journal, we have received permission from A. N. Thiele to republish his work in two parts. This first part develops the synthesis approach and summarizes all of vented-box design in a table of 28 alignments. The second part will apply the method and draw some very pertinent conclusions about efficiency, driver Q, box volume, and amplifier output impedance.

The high point of this work is Table I which gives 28 alignments for vented-box loudspeakers. I have been so impressed with this table that I have written a Fortran program to quickly apply Thiele's synthesis methods to any loudspeaker with adequately known parameters. This program and a run or two for typical woofers will be published after Part II.

In considering this manuscript for republication, Thiele has suggested that after 10 years his only change of attitude would be to change the emphasis in Section XIV (Part II). In contrast to the original preference for use of a closed box (which is still quite valid), Thiele would now emphasize the use of a vented box for measurements. This is indeed a trifling matter and in concurring with Thiele's opinion, I can only add emphasis to how well this paper has passed the test of time—it is just as pertinent now as it was ten years ago.

J. R. Ashley

I. INTRODUCTION:

The technique of using a vented box to obtain adequate low-frequency response from a loudspeaker has been known for many years. The principle seems simple, yet the results obtained are variable. Since comparatively cheap and reliable methods of acoustic measurement, especially at low frequencies, virtually do not exist, the only check of results is the "listening test." The listening test is after all the final criterion of the performance of an electroacoustic system, but as a method of adjusting for optimum it is very poor indeed. Quite apart from one's prejudices and memories of previous "acceptable" equipments, the adjustment of a vented box in ignorance of the loudspeaker parameters involves two simultaneous adjustments, box tuning and amplifier damping. And again there is a strong temptation to adjust the low-frequency response to something other than flat to "balance" response errors at high frequencies, when in fact the two problems should be tackled separately.

For a long time it has seemed to the writer that the methods of design of vented boxes were unsatisfactory, leaving a number of questions unanswered.

1) What size of box should be chosen? Usually it seems the larger the better, but how much better is a large box and what penalty does one pay for a small box? And for a given speaker, what *is* a "large" box or a "small" box?

2) What amplifier damping should be used? In general the answer is, the heavier the damping the better, though with high-efficiency speakers this could cause a loss of low frequencies. But then again, negative damping is sometimes used, especially in the United States. And when vented enclosures often give excellent results, why should they be known by some as "boom boxes"?

3) Is it advisable or necessary to use acoustic damping to flatten the response? Some claim good results [1] while others [2] warn against it. The general principle of flattening response with parasitic resistance, and thus dissipating hard-won power, seems wrong, especially in an output stage and when a maximum bandwidth is sought. The principle seems to apply equally to an amplifier–loudspeaker–box combination and a video output stage.

4) To what frequency should the vent be tuned? The conventional answer is to tune it to the loudspeaker resonant frequency, but Beranek [3, p. 254] mentions that "for a very large enclosure, it is permissible to tune the port to a frequency below the loudspeaker resonance," while small boxes are sometimes tuned above loudspeaker resonance.

5) What should be the area of the vent? The conventional answer is to make it equal to the piston area of the loudspeaker, but Novak [2] states that "it is permissible to use any value of vent area," and again "the vent area should not be allowed to be less than 4 in^2." Again, should we use only a hole for the vent or should we use a duct or tunnel?

6) If we equalize the amplifier to correct deficiencies in the speaker and enclosure, what penalties result for example in distortion? Can we trade amplifier size for box size?

7) Assuming that we know how to design a box (and associated amplifier) given the loudspeaker parameters, how may the parameters be measured?

There are other questions that could be asked but the seven above seem the most important; at any rate, they are the ones that the present paper hopes to answer.

II. DERIVATION OF BASIC THEORY

The theory of operation of loudspeakers in vented boxes has been covered so many times in the literature [3, pp. 208-258], [4] that it should be unnecessary to repeat it here; therefore only sufficient of the theory will be quoted to make the present approach intelligible.

This approach derives from Novak [2] to whom the reader is referred, not only for his method, but for his introductory paragraph . . . "Trade journals tell of 'all new enclosures, revolutionary concepts, and totally new principles of acoustics' when in reality there is a close identity with enclosure systems described long ago in well-known classics on acoustics." This should be framed and hung on the audio engineer's wall alongside Lord Kelvin's dictum. The present paper is the result of a different emphasis on, and interpretation of, Novak's treatment. It should be emphasized that, unless stated specifically otherwise, the results apply only to the "piston range" of the speaker. This is the region where the circumference of the speaker is less than the wavelength of radiated sound, i.e., below 400 Hz for a 12-inch speaker, and below 1 kHz for a 5-inch speaker. The performance of loudspeakers above the piston range is another subject altogether.

We will be dealing later with a simplified equivalent

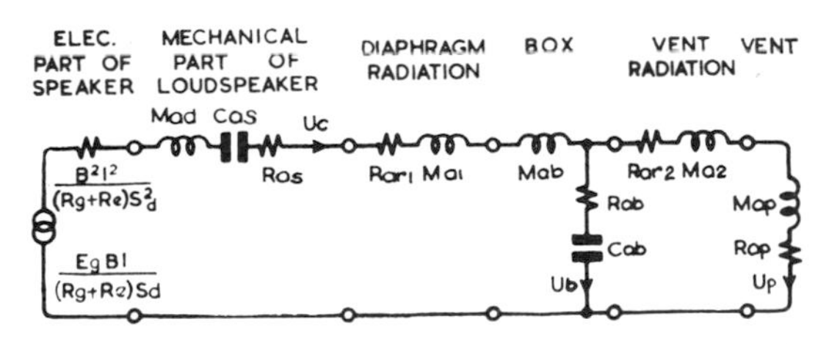

Fig. 1. Complete (electromechanical) acoustical circuit of loudspeaker in vented box (after Beranek [3]).

circuit, but first consider Fig. 1 in which the complete equivalent circuit of the loudspeaker and enclosure is given in acoustical terms.

We note that there are three possible equivalent circuits, electrical, mechanical, and acoustical. To convert from electrical to mechanical units,

$$Z_m = B^2l^2/Z_e \quad (1)$$

where

- Z_e electrical impedance
- Z_m equivalent mechanical impedance
- B magnetic flux density in air gap
- l length of wire in air gap.

Again to convert from mechanical to acoustic units,

$$Z_a = Z_m/S_d^2 \quad (2)$$

where

- Z_a acoustical impedance
- S_d equivalent piston area of diaphragm (usually taken as area inside first corrugation).

Taking then in Fig. 1 the first impedance after the generator which is the acoustical equivalent of the electrical resistance of the amplifier output impedance R_g in series with the voice coil resistance R_e, we can see that the various equivalents for this impedance are

$$Z_e = R_g+R_e \quad (3)$$
$$Z_m = B^2l^2/(R_g+R_e) \quad (4)$$
$$Z_a = B^2l^2/S_d^2(R_g+R_e). \quad (5)$$

In Fig. 1,

- E_g open-circuit voltage of audio amplifier
- M_{ad} ($= M_{md}/S_d^2$) acoustic mass of diaphragm and voice coil
- M_{md} mechanical mass as usually measured
- C_{as} acoustic compliance of suspension
- R_{as} acoustic resistance of suspension
- R_{ar1} acoustic radiation resistance for front side of loudspeaker diaphragm
- M_{a1} acoustic radiation mass (air load) for front side of loudspeaker diaphragm
- M_{ab} acoustic mass of air load on rear side of loudspeaker
- R_{ab} acoustic resistance of box
- C_{ab} acoustic compliance of box
- R_{ar2} acoustic radiation resistance of vent
- M_{a2} acoustic radiation mass (air load) of vent
- M_{ap} acoustic mass of air in vent
- R_{ap} acoustic resistance of air in vent
- U_c volume velocity of cone
- U_b volume velocity of box
- U_p volume velocity of port, or vent.

The advantage of using this large complete equivalent circuit in the first place is that the equivalent circuit of the loudspeaker in a totally enclosed box may be shown by removing the mesh representing the vent. To represent the speaker operated in an infinite baffle, C_{ab} and R_{ab} are short-circuited. If the speaker is operated in open air (unbaffled), the circuit is as in an infinite baffle, but the values of R_{ar1} and M_{a1} are modified [see 4, Fig. 5.2]. The details of these circuits are very well covered in [3] from which Fig. 1 and the accompanying symbols are taken.

To make the circuit more manageable, we simplify it to Fig. 2.

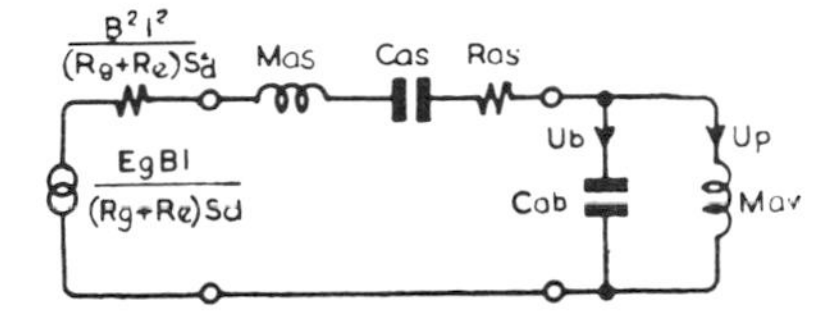

Fig. 2. Simplified acoustical circuit of loudspeaker in vented box.

1) The three acoustic masses M_{ad}, M_{a1}, and M_{ab} are lumped together to make a single mass M_{as}. However, we must be careful to remember that this is an artifice. M_{as} is not fixed, and some error results by assuming it to be so. For example, the reduction of M_{ab} and hence of M_{as} when the speaker is tested in open air causes a rise in resonant frequency, which must be accounted for in measurements, as in Section XIV.

2) R_{ar1} and R_{ar2} are neglected in the equivalent circuit, even though they are responsible for the acoustic output of the loudspeaker. The whole essence of Novak's theoretical model which makes a simple solution possible is that a loudspeaker is a most inefficient device. In measurements of fifty loudspeakers using the method of Section XIV covering a wide range of sizes and qualities, efficiencies ranged between 0.4% and 4%. For this reason, the radiation resistances may be safely neglected. Since radiation resistance varies with frequency squared, this simplifies analysis considerably. For, as pointed out in [3, p. 216], the radiation resistance of a loudspeaker in a "medium-sized box (less than 8 ft^3)" is approximately the radiation impedance for a piston in the end of a long tube. And the radiation resistance of the vent (or port) is the same. Thus

$$R_{ar1} = R_{ar2} = \pi f^2 \rho_o/c \quad (6)$$

where ρ_o is the density of air and c is the velocity of sound in air.

Note that the radiation resistance is independent of the dimensions of the piston or vent. Note also that Eq. (6) is an approximation which is accurate only in the piston range of the loudspeaker (compare [3, Fig. 5.7] or [4, Fig. 5.2]).

3) M_{a2} and M_{ap} are lumped together as M_{av}, the total air mass of the vent.

4) R_{ab} and R_{ap} are neglected since for most practical purposes their Q is very high compared with that of the loudspeaker, especially when its damping is properly controlled by the amplifier.

For example, it will be shown later that the Q of speak-

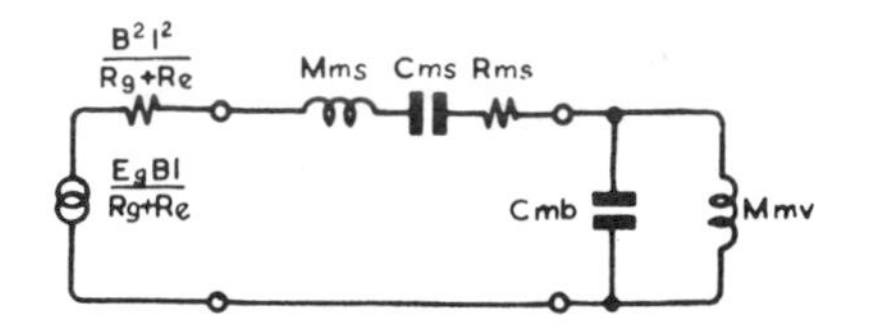

Fig. 3. Simplified mechanical circuit of loudspeaker in vented box.

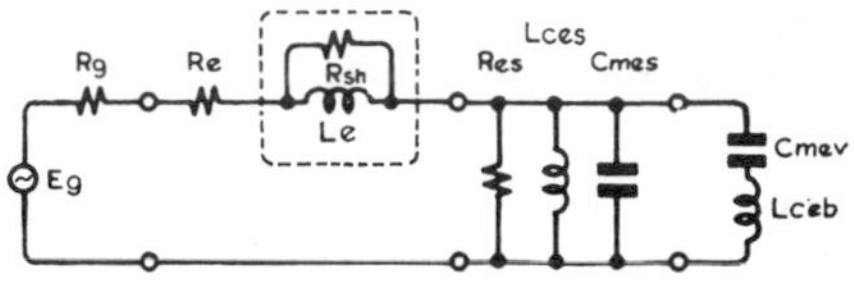

Fig. 4. Simplified electrical circuit of loudspeaker in vented box.

er plus amplifier for a vented box will usually lie between 0.3 and 0.5. The Q of the vent, on the other hand, can be found by combining [3, Eqs. (5.54) and (5.55)] to give

$$Q_v = \omega M_{ap}/R_{ap} = (S_v f/\mu)^{1/2}(l'+1.70a)/(l'+2a) \quad (7)$$

where

- Q_v effective Q of vent
- S_v area of vent (assumed to have constant cross section)
- l' actual length of vent
- a effective radius of vent
- μ kinematic coefficient of viscosity; for air at NTP, $\mu = 1.56 \times 10^{-5}$ m²/s.

Thus if $S_v = 4$ in², the bottom limit specified by Novak, and $f = 25$ Hz, then $Q_v = 64$.

Since these are the smallest values of S_v and f likely to be found in practice, it is clear that little error will result from this source, and this is confirmed in Section XI. In the preceding discussion, the effect of M_{a2} and R_{ar2} has been neglected, but in no case investigated has the total Q_v fallen below 30.

5) As a result of measurements of fifty loudspeakers, it appears that the Q_a of the speaker due to R_{as} lies usually between 3 and 10, so that this does not affect matters greatly, but since R_{as} can be lumped with the equivalent electrical resistance (see Eq. (8)) and because it has some importance in the loudspeaker measurements of Section XIV, it is included in Fig. 2

The mechanical equivalent circuit (Fig. 3) is derived from Fig. 2 by multiplying all the acoustical impedances by the conversion factor S_d^2 as in Eq. (2). Thus these impedances represent the mechanical impedances at the loudspeaker diaphragm due to the whole acoustical–mechanical circuit. Since the conversion is obtained by multiplying by a constant, the form of the circuit remains the same. However, when the conversion is made from Fig. 3 to Fig. 4, the electrical equivalent circuit, it can be seen from Eq. (1) that an impedance inversion takes place. Thus all series elements become parallel elements, inductances become capacitances, and vice versa. Thus L_{ces} is the electrical inductance due to the compliance of the loudspeaker suspension, C_{mes} is the electrical capacitance due to the mass of the loudspeaker cone, C_{mev} is the electrical capacitance due to the mass of the vent, and L_{ceb} is the electrical inductance due to the compliance of the box. In Fig. 4 an additional pair of circuit elements which were neglected in the earlier circuits have been added within the dashed lines. These are the inductance and shunt resistance (largely due to eddy current loss in the pole piece and front plate) of the voice coil.

It is hoped that this will not cause confusion. These elements contribute very small effects at the low frequencies we are considering, but show the reason for the shape of the resulting electrical impedance curve of Fig. 5 above f_n. However, this will be of greater importance when we come to testing procedures in Section XIV.

III. DERIVATION OF RESPONSE CURVE

The expression for the frequency response of the system is obtained by analysing the circuit of Fig. 2. To simplify the expression, we lump all the series resistance into a total acoustic resistance,

$$R_{at} = R_{as} + [B^2l^2/(R_g+R_e)S_d^2]. \quad (8)$$

Now we have seen already that the radiation resistances of speaker and vent must always be the same. And since the radiated sound depends on the sum of the volume velocities U_c and U_p (or rather their difference, since U_p derives from the back pressure of the speaker), then the acoustic power output is

$$W_{ao} = |U_c - U_p|^2 R_{ar1} \quad (9)$$

while the nominal electrical input power is

$$W_{ei} = E_g^2 R_e/(R_g+R_e)^2. \quad (10)$$

Thus the efficiency is

$$\eta = W_{ao}/W_{ei} = [|U_c-U_p|^2 R_{ar1}(R_g+R_e)^2]/(E_g^2 R_e). \quad (11)$$

Analyzing the circuit, we find that

$$(U_c-U_p)/[E_gBl/S_d(R_g+R_e)] = 1/pM_{as} \times \left[\frac{p^4M_{as}M_{av}C_{as}C_{ab}}{\left\{\begin{array}{l}p^4M_{as}M_{av}C_{as}C_{ab}+p^3M_{av}C_{as}C_{ab}R_{at}\\ +p^2(M_{as}C_{as}+M_{av}C_{as}+M_{av}C_{ab})+pC_{as}R_{at}+1\end{array}\right\}}\right]. \quad (12)$$

To make the expression easier to manage we write $E(p)$ for the expression inside the square bracket on the right-hand side which is a fourth-order high-pass filtering function. Also if $j\omega$ is written for p, the steady-state response $E(j\omega)$ *is* found. We also convert pM_{as} from the operational form to the steady-state form $j\omega M_{as}$, and then substitute

$$M_{ms} = M_{as}S_d^2. \quad (13)$$

This puts the expression for mass into a more intelligi-

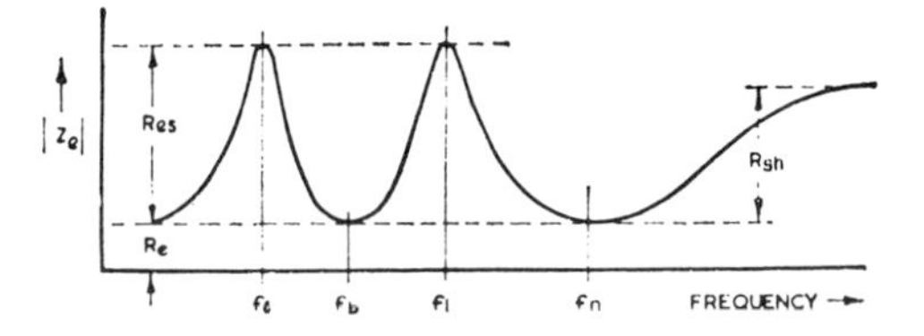

Fig. 5. Typical impedance curve of loudspeaker in vented box.

ble form, but it is emphasized that the total loudspeaker mechanical mass M_{ms} includes not only the mass of the cone plus voice coil, but also the mechanical equivalent of the acoustic air load. The latter is only a small part of the total, but varies with the speaker's environment, e.g., box volume [3]. Thus if we substitute Eqs. (6), (12), and (13) in Eq. (11),

$$\eta = \rho_o B^2 l^2 S_d^2 |E(j\omega)|^2 / 4\pi c R_e M_{ms}^2 \quad (14)$$

or

$$\eta = (\rho_o/4\pi c)(B^2 l^2 S_d^2 / R_e M_{ms}^2)|E(j\omega)|^2. \quad (15)$$

Thus the expression for efficiency contains three parts:
1) a constant part containing physical constants,
2) a constant part containing speaker parameters,
3) a part $|E(j\omega)|^2$ which varies with frequency.

IV. CONTROLLING THE FREQUENCY RESPONSE

The problem of greatest interest is the control of frequency response; so we consider first (3), $|E(j\omega)|^2$, or preferably its operational form $E(p)$. To make this easier to manage we substitute in $E(p)$ of Eq. (12)

$$T_s^2 = (1/\omega_s)^2 = M_{as}C_{as} \quad (16)$$
$$T_b^2 = (1/\omega_b)^2 = M_{av}C_{ab} \quad (17)$$
$$Q_t = (M_{as}/C_{as})^{1/2}/R_{at} \quad (18)$$

where ω_s is the resonant frequency. ω_b is the box resonant frequency, or more exactly, the frequency at which the acoustic mass of the vent resonates with the acoustic capacitance of the box. It should not be confused, as is often done, with f_h or f_l of Fig. 5, which are by-products of f_s and f_b (see Eqs. (105) and (106)).

Q_t is the total Q of the loudspeaker when connected to its amplifier. The acoustic resistance in the loudspeaker R_{as} has a small effect, but usually the resistances reflected from the loudspeaker resistance R_e *and the amplifier* R_g contribute the greater part of Q_t. Then $E(p)$ of Eq. (12) becomes

$$E(p) = \frac{p^4 T_b^2 T_s^2}{\left\{ \begin{array}{l} p^4 T_b^2 T_s^2 + p^3 (T_b^2 T_s/Q_t) \\ + p^2 [T_b^2 + T_s^2 + T_b^2 C_{as}/C_{ab}] + p(T_s/Q_t) + 1 \end{array} \right\}} \quad (19)$$

For many purposes this is more conveniently written as

$$E(p) = 1/\{1 + 1/pQ_t T_s + (1/p^2)[1/T_b^2 + 1/T_s^2 + C_{as}/C_{ab}T_s^2] + 1/p^3 T_b^2 T_s Q_t + 1/p^4 T_b^2 T_s^2\}. \quad (20)$$

This expression corresponds to Novak's expression for the modulus in his Eq. (15) which is simplified into his Eq. (16). (Note that in the captions for his Figs. 7, 9, 11, 12, and 13, a positive sign is wrongly substituted for a negative sign).

As stated before, this is a fourth-order high-pass function, that is, it has an asymptotic slope in the attenuation band of 24 dB per octave, and can be written in the general form

$$E(p) = 1/\{1 + x_1/pT_0 + x_2/p^2T_0^2 + x_3/p^3T_0^3 + 1/p^4T_0^4\} \quad (21)$$

which is defined by a time constant T_0 ($= 1/\omega_0$, the nominal cutoff frequency) and three coefficients x_1, x_2, x_3 which determine the shape of the response curve. In fact, the general expression is often written with a constant x_0 and x_4 instead of the two unity coefficients in the denominator of Eq. (21); but the expression can always be reduced to the form of Eq. (21) by division of the whole expression by a constant, and suitable adjustment of T_0 and the x coefficients. Considering Eq. (20) now from the viewpoint of what can be done with a given speaker, the parameters C_{as} and T_s are fixed. Thus there are three variables Q_t, T_b, and C_{ab}, and it is possible to achieve any desired shape of curve (i.e., any desired combination of the three x coefficients); but in doing so T_0 is determined (see Eq. (27)).

For identity between the two Eqs. (20) and (21), the coefficients of the various powers of p must be identical, that is,

$$x_1/T_0 = 1/Q_t T_s \quad (22)$$
$$x_2/T_0^2 = 1/T_b^2 + 1/T_s^2 + C_{as}/C_{ab}T_s^2 \quad (23)$$
$$x_3/T_0^3 = 1/Q_t T_b^2 T_s \quad (24)$$
$$1/T_0^4 = 1/T_b^2 T_s^2. \quad (25)$$

From these, the relationships can be established

$$T_b/T_s = x_1/x_3 \quad (26)$$
$$T_0/T_s = (x_1/x_3)^{1/2} \quad (27)$$
$$Q_t = 1/(x_1 x_3)^{1/2} \quad (28)$$
$$C_{as}/C_{ab} = (x_1 x_2 x_3 - x_3^2 - x_1^2)/x_1^2. \quad (29)$$

The Hurwitz criteria [5] for stability of a network defined by Eq. (21) are
1) all the x coefficients are positive,
2) $x_1 x_2 x_3 - x_3^2 - x_1^2$ is positive.

If (1) and (2) are true, then all the parameters determined by the four Eqs. (26)–(29) are positive and therefore realizable. Thus we have in the four equations a set of simple relationships which enable us to achieve, for any speaker, any shape of low-frequency cutoff (fourth-order) characteristic. The only requirement is that we have sufficient freedom to choose a suitable box resonant frequency $1/T_b$, box volume C_{ab}, and total Q of speaker plus amplifier Q_t, and can accept the resulting value of T_0.

The first parameter T_b presents no practical difficulty; the second, C_{ab}, can cause trouble if space is limited, but in this case, as shown in Section VII, we can work backward and choose a suitable response characteristic to suit the box size; the third, Q_t, is controlled by the source impedance of the amplifier. If the required Q_t is greater than the speaker's natural Q, a positive output impedance will be required of the amplifier and this can be controlled by the usual negative feedback techniques. If less, a negative output impedance will be required, and this can be achieved by applying feedback from a separate winding on the voice coil, or by a combination of positive current and negative voltage feedback. There is a practical limit here if the degree of negative impedance required is too large, but this will be discussed in Section XII.

V. SOME PRACTICAL RESPONSE CURVE SHAPES

Fourth-Order Butterworth Response

Armed with Eqs. (26)–(29) we can calculate the parameters required for different response characteristics. The most obvious one to try first is the fourth-order maximally flat (Butterworth)[1] characteristic for which

$$|E(j\omega)| = 1/[1+(\omega_o/\omega)^8]^{1/2} \quad (30)$$

or

$$|E(j\omega)|^2 = 1/[1+(\omega_o/\omega)^8] \quad (31)$$

and, in the operational form,

$$E(p) = 1/(1+2.613/pT_o+3.414/p^2T_o^2 +2.613/p^3T_o^3+1/p^4T_o^4). \quad (32)$$

Note that in Eq. (31) and others which will follow, the ratio of any two frequencies, say ω_a/ω_b, is identical to f_a/f_b. Note also that all Butterworth responses are 3 dB down when $\omega = \omega_o$, i.e., $\omega T_o = 1$.

A characteristic of Butterworth responses, though not peculiar to them, which simplifies calculations even further is that in all cases

$$x_1 = x_3. \quad (33)$$

Thus in this class or response,

$$T_b = T_s \quad (34)$$
$$T_o = T_s \quad (35)$$
$$Q_t = 1/x_1 \quad (36)$$
$$C_{as}/C_{ab} = x_2-2. \quad (37)$$

Thus in the fourth-order case where

$$x_1 = x_3 = 2.613 \quad (38)$$
$$x_2 = 3.414 \quad (39)$$

we have

$$Q_t = 0.383 \quad (40)$$
$$C_{as}/C_{ab} = 1.414. \quad (41)$$

This is alignment no. 5 of Table I. The term "alignment" seems appropriate since the problem is similar to the choice of alignments for other filters, e.g., RF and IF amplifiers. This is obviously the conventional type of box alignment, for the box frequency f_b is identical with the speaker resonant frequency f_s, and also the frequency f_3 with which the response is -3 dB. Note that because of the rapid change of attenuation the response is only -0.9 dB at $1.2f_s$.

However, it also shows that a true maximally flat characteristic is obtained only if the correct values of box size C_{as} and especially Q_t are chosen also. It is easy to show from Eq. (20) that in any alignment, at the upper resonant frequency (f_h of Fig. 5), the response is

$$E(j\omega) = j(Q_t\omega_h/\omega_s)/[1-(\omega_b^2/\omega_h^2)] \quad (42)$$

that is, the response varies directly with Q_t. Also at the box resonant frequency, f_b

$$E(j\omega) = (C_{ab}/C_{as})(\omega_b^2/\omega_s^2) \quad (43)$$

that is, the response is independent of Q_t. (The response at f_l is similar to Eq. (42) when ω_h is replaced by ω_l, but as this is in the attenuation band, it is less important.) Thus if Q_t is twice the optimum value, there will be a response peak 6 dB high. Now as a general rule a speaker with a Q of about 0.4, as required in this case, is usually of high quality.

A Q of 0.8 is typical of a medium quality speaker and a Q of 1.6 is typical of a low ("popular" or "skimped-magnet") quality speaker. Thus these speakers would have response peaks (at $1.76\omega_s$ in this case) of 6 dB and 12 dB, respectively, if fed from a zero output impedance amplifier, 12 dB and 18 dB if fed from an amplifier with impedance equal to loudspeaker resistance R_e (e.g., pentode with 6-dB negative voltage feedback), and even more with higher amplifier impedances. Hence the expression "boom box."

An amplifier with negative output impedance half that of the loudspeaker resistance R_e, a quite feasible figure, would correct the medium quality speaker, and reduce the peak on the cheaper one to 6 dB. An amplifier with a negative output impedance three quarters of R_e, to correct the cheaper speaker, is possible but would need care in respect of stability (see Section XII).

[1] Hence the expression Butterworth box. However, in spite of the phonetic similarity, butter boxes are not in general suitable as loudspeaker enclosures.

Fifth-Order Butterworth Response

This has the characteristic

$$|E(j\omega)|^2 = 1/[1+(\omega_o/\omega)^{10}]. \quad (44)$$

The operational form can be factorized to

$$E(p) = 1/[(1+1/pT_o)(1+\sqrt{5}/pT_o +3/p^2T_o^2+\sqrt{5}/p^3T_o^3+1/p^4T_o^4)] \quad (45)$$

which is the characteristic of two filters in cascade: 1) a first-order filter which can be provided by a CR network with a time constant T_o, and 2) a fourth-order filter provided by a loudspeaker and box for which

$$T_o = T_s = T_b \quad (46)$$
$$Q_t = 0.447 \quad (47)$$
$$C_{as}/C_{ab} = 1. \quad (48)$$

The alignment, no. 10 of Table I, has the advantage if the extra box size can be tolerated (a smaller value of C_{as}/C_{ab} means a larger box) that a maximally flat response can be obtained down to the loudspeaker resonant frequency, while at the same time, a very simple "rumble" filter tapers off the input to the amplifier in the attenuband. This helps the amplifier, but more importantly it greatly reduces the maximum flux density in the output transformer and also the maximum excursion of the loudspeaker (see Section X and Fig. 10).

Sixth-Order Butterworth Response

This has the characteristic

$$|E(j\omega)|^2 = 1/[1+(\omega_o/\omega)^{12}] \quad (49)$$

while the operational form may be factorized to

$$E(p) = 1/[(1+1.932/pT_o+1/p^2T_o^2)(1+1.414/pT_o+1/p^2T_o^2)(1+0.518/pT_o+1/p^2T_o^2)]. \quad (50)$$

As in the previous case, the overall alignment is achieved by providing one factor with an external filter, in this case second order, and making the fourth-order response of the loudspeaker plus box the product of the two remaining factors. Thus we can obtain the identical response in three different ways. These are listed in Table I as alignments no. 15, 20, and 26, the three separate classes depending on whether the auxiliary electrical circuit has the lowest, middle, or highest x value of the three factors in the alignment. Not only do the three alignments produce the same response, but as shown later (Section X and Fig. 10) the cone excursions are identical.

	Alignment Details				Box Design				Auxiliary Circuits				Approximately Constant Quantities	
	No.	Type	k	Ripple (db)	f_3/f_s	f_3/f_b	C_{as}/C_{ab}	Q_t	f_{aux}/f_3	y_{aux}	Peak Lift (db)	f_{pk}/f_3	$\frac{C_{as}f_s^2}{C_{ab}f_3^2}$	$\frac{Q_t f_b}{f_s}$
Quasi-Third Order	1	QB_3	—	—	2.68	1.34	10.48	.180	—	—	—	—	1.47	.360
	2	QB_3	—	—	2.28	1.32	7.48	.209	—	—	—	—	1.44	.362
	3	QB_3	—	—	1.77	1.25	4.46	.259	—	—	—	—	1.43	.367
	4	QB_3	—	—	1.45	1.18	2.95	.303	—	—	—	—	1.41	.371
Fourth Order	5	B_4	1.0	—	1.000	1.000	1.414	.383	—	—	—	—	1.41	.383
	6	C_4	.8	—	.867	.935	1.055	.415	—	—	—	—	1.41	.384
	7	C_4	.6	0.2	.729	.879	.729	.466	—	—	—	—	1.37	.386
	8	C_4	—	0.9	.641	.847	.559	.518	—	—	—	—	1.36	.392
	9	C_4	—	1.8	.600	.838	.485	.557	—	—	—	—	1.35	.398
Fifth Order	10	B_5	1.0	—	1.000	1.000	1.000	.447	1.00	—	—	—	—	—
	11	C_5	.7	—	.852	.934	.583	.545	1.43	—	—	—	—	—
	12	C_5	.4	0.25	.724	.889	.273	.810	2.50	—	—	—	—	—
	13	C_5	.355	0.5	.704	.882	.227	.924	2.93	—	—	—	—	—
	14	C_5	.278	1.0	.685	.877	.191	1.102	3.60	—	—	—	—	—
Sixth Order Class I	15	B_6	1.0	—	1.000	1.000	2.73	.299	1.00	−1.732	+6.0	1.07	—	—
	16	C_6	.8	—	.850	.868	2.33	.317	1.01	−1.824	+7.7	1.06	—	—
	17	C_6	.6	—	.698	.750	1.81	.348	1.02	−1.899	+10.1	1.05	—	—
	18	C_6	.5	—	.620	.698	1.51	.371	1.03	−1.930	+11.6	1.05	—	—
	19	C_6	.414	0.1	.554	.659	1.25	.399	1.04	−1.951	+13.2	1.04	—	—
Sixth Order Class II	20	B_6	1.0	—	1.000	1.000	1.000	.408	1.00	0	—	—	—	—
	21	C_6	.8	—	.844	.954	.722	.431	1.10	− .438	+0.2	2.36	—	—
	22	C_6	.6	—	.677	.917	.500	.461	1.21	− .941	+1.1	1.77	—	—
	23	C_6	.5	—	.592	.902	.414	.484	1.27	−1.200	+1.9	1.63	—	—
	24	C_6	.414	0.1	.520	.890	.353	.513	1.31	−1.414	+3.0	1.55	—	—
	25	C_6	.268	0.6	.404	.876	.276	.616	1.37	−1.732	+6.0	1.47	—	—
Sixth Order Class III	26	B_6	1.0	—	1.000	1.000	.732	.518	1.00	+1.732	—	—	—	—
	27	C_6	.268	0.6	.778	.911	.110	1.503	2.73	0	—	—	—	—
	28	QB_3	—	—	.952	.980	1.89	.328	1.08 mean	—	6.0	0	—	—

Table I. Summary of loudspeaker alignments.

This illustrates a general principle that box size can be exchanged for amplifier power. The only additional penalties are as follows:

1) additional heating of the voice coil by signals in the region of the cutoff frequency, and
2) the requirement of a smaller value of Q_t as the box volume is decreased.

The performance required of the auxiliary filtering is given in the last four columns of Table I, whose terms are illustrated in Fig. 6. Instead of the parameter x in the expression

$$E(p) = 1/(1+x/pT_o+1/p^2T_o^2) \tag{51}$$

the response shapes are defined in Table I by the parameter y in the expression

$$|E(j\omega)|^2 = 1/[1+y(\omega_o/\omega)^2+(\omega_o/\omega)^4] \tag{52}$$

where

$$y = x^2-2 \tag{53}$$

as given in a previous paper [6]. When y is zero or positive there is no peak in the response as shown in Fig. 6, but when y is negative there is a peak whose frequency and amplitude are given in Table I. The amplitude of response at the nominal cutoff frequency f_{aux} of this auxiliary filter is given by

$$|E(j\omega)| = 1/(2+y)^{1/2}. \tag{54}$$

Chebyshev Responses

If the real values of the poles of a Butterworth function are all multiplied by the same factor k, which is less than one, a Chebyshev or "equal ripple" function results [7]. Chebyshev filters are characterized by a flat response in the passband except for ripples which are equal in amplitude, (see curve 8 of Fig. 8). Beyond cutoff, the response falls at a rate whose maximum is greater than the asymptotic slope. Typical values are tabulated in Table I with the type names C_4, C_5, and C_6 representing Chebyshev responses of fourth, fifth, and sixth order. It will be seen from the table that a considerable change in alignment occurs before the ripples become serious in magnitude. For our purpose here, the Chebyshev responses provide a means of carrying the useful response of the speaker plus box combination well below the speaker resonant frequency f_s (which is also cutoff frequency f_o in the Butterworth cases). This is done by tuning the box to below f_s, but not as low as the cutoff frequency (defined here as f_3, the frequency where the response is 3 dB down). The box size C_{ab} is increased, and to some extent, so is Q_t.

The increase in useful low-frequency response is considerable. In alignment no. 9, a response down to $0.6f_s$ is obtainable without amplifier assistance, if a ripple of 1.8 dB can be tolerated. In alignment no. 25, where a maximum lift of 6 dB is required from the amplifier before its response falls off, a flat response can be obtained down to nearly $0.4f_s$.

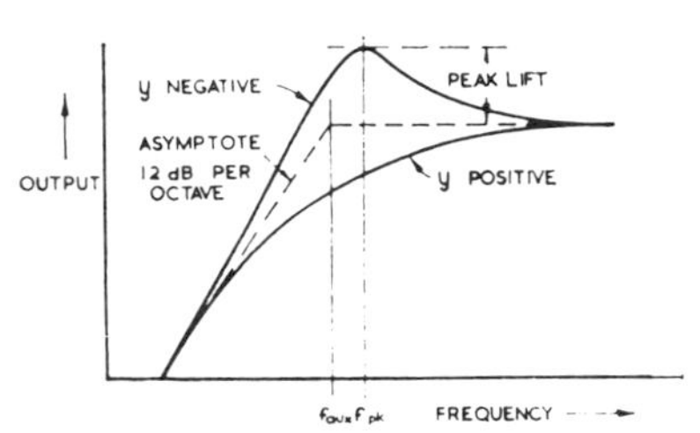

Fig. 6. Typical curves for second-order auxiliary filter, illustrating terms used in Table I.

Quasi-Butterworth Third-Order Responses

This long name disguises a class of responses characterized by

$$|E(j\omega)|^2 = 1/[1+y_3(\omega_o/\omega)^6+y_4(\omega_o/\omega)^8] \quad (55)$$

that is, in the expression for the modulus of the fourth-order filter, there are zero coefficients for the second and fourth powers of frequency, with nonzero coefficients for both the eighth *and* sixth powers. This type of response yields a series of alignments, nos. 1–4 of Table I, in which the cutoff frequency (again defined here as the frequency f_3 where the response is 3 dB down) is above the speaker resonant frequency. So also is the box resonant frequency, but again, not to the same extent. As the cutoff frequency is made higher, these alignments require smaller box volumes, and lower values of Q_t.

VI. GENERAL DISCUSSION OF TABLE I

It will be seen that alignments no. 1–9 provide a means of varying the cutoff frequency of a loudspeaker–box combination over a wide range. The last two columns for these alignments illustrate two interesting properties which remain substantially constant ($\pm 5\%$) over this wide range.

1) The expression $C_{as}f_s^2/C_{ab}f_3^2$ is substantially constant around 1.41. This means that if a given speaker for which C_{as} and f_s are constant is placed in different boxes to provide different cutoff frequencies, the box volume will vary with inverse frequency squared. This illustrates a fact long known to designers of vented boxes, but rather blurred by the exponents of "revolutionary new concepts," that the bigger the box, the better the low-frequency response. It is also interesting to note that

$$C_{as}f_s^2 = 1/4\pi^2 M_{as} = S_d^2/4\pi^2 M_{ms} \cong 1.41 C_{ab}f_3^2 \quad (56)$$

that is, for a given cutoff frequency of the combination, the box size varies with the square of diaphragm area S_d^2 and inversely with M_{ms}. In other words, if the mass of the loudspeaker M_{ms} is fixed and the compliance C_{as} is varied to give a different resonant frequency f_s, then the box volume C_{ab} for a given cutoff frequency f_3 remains substantially constant. To this extent, and also in the expression for efficiency (Eq. (66)) the compliance of the loudspeaker is *unimportant*.

2) $Q_t f_b/f_s$ lies around 0.38. If Eq. (18) is rewritten as

$$Q_t = \omega_s M_{as}/R_{at} \quad (57)$$

then the expression above becomes $\omega_b M_{as}/R_{at}$ which can be thought of as the total Q of the speaker at the box resonant frequency. This remains nearly constant throughout alignments no. 1–9.

Certain alignments, no. 13, 14, and 27 with no. 12 as a borderline case, which require auxiliary filtering with large attenuation at the cutoff frequency of the whole system, must be considered suspect, since they postulate high acoustic efficiencies in the region of cutoff. Remember that the basis of the theory is that the overall efficiency is low. In the borderline case, no. 12 for example, the peak efficiency will be just above cutoff frequency and will be approximately 2.5^2 times the loudspeaker efficiency. If the loudspeaker is 4% efficient, this means a maximum overall efficiency of 25%. Around this point, the basic assumptions will become inaccurate, especially if resistive losses in the box are large.

Similarly, for reasons of cone excursion (considered in Section X), alignments with smaller values of f_3/f_b such as nos. 17–19 should be avoided if possible. These particular alignments which do give good low-frequency responses in small box volumes would probably be unpopular anyway since they make such great demands on amplifier output in the region of cutoff.

Alignment no. 28 is interesting in that it represents the result of "pure" bass lift. In the other alignments which use "amplifier aiding," the response often rises near cutoff, but always falls off ultimately at lower frequencies at a rate of 6 or 12 dB per octave. In this way, although increased amplifier output may be required over a comparatively narrow range of frequencies, a greatly decreased output, and with it, a greatly decreased cone excursion, is required at the lower frequencies. But in alignment no. 28, a simple low-frequency lift of 6 dB, such as results from a network with two resistors and a capacitor, is required. The mean frequency of lift (at which the lift is 3 dB) is $1.08f_3$. However, since the maximum lift continues to the lowest frequencies, the amplifier would be more likely to cause intermodulation distortion with "rumble" components. However it does give some decrease of box volume compared with alignment no. 5.

It should be emphasized that these alignments are by no means the only ones possible. They have been chosen as the ones most likely to be useful and as showing the

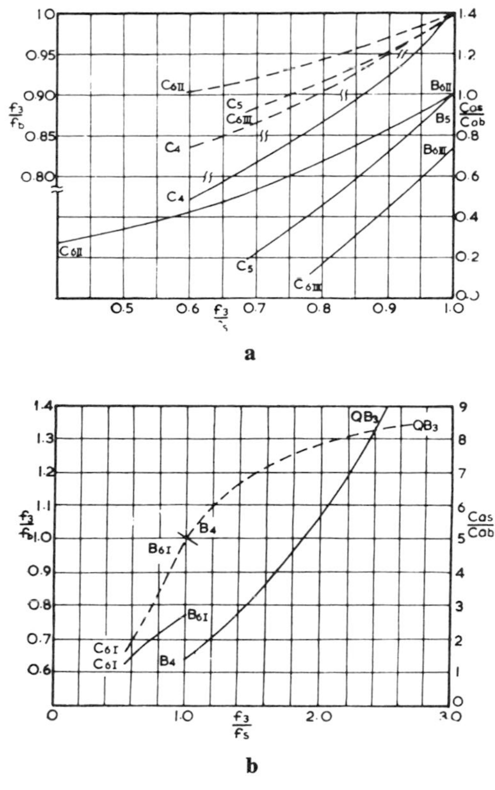

Fig. 7. f_3/f_b (dashed curves) and C_{as}/C_{ab} (solid curves) versus f_3/f_s. **a.** For design of medium and large boxes; alignment types B_4–C_4, B_5–C_5, and B_6–C_6 class II and III. **b.** For design of small boxes; alignment types QB_3–B_4 and B_6–C_6 class I.

trend of results. If more sophisticated filtering in the amplifier is possible, the choice widens greatly, e.g., there are six alignments for the eighth-order Butterworth response, each with its fourth-order amplifier filter and the ratios C_{as}/C_{ab} of 0.518, 0.681, 1.000, 1.316, 1.932, and 2.543.

Another possibility would be the use, instead of the "quasi-Butterworth" responses, of "sub-Chebyshev" responses, i.e., response functions derived by multiplying the real coordinates of the Butterworth poles by a constant k which is *greater* than 1.

In answer to the question proposed in 1) of Section I—What is a large box?—it would appear that a medium sized box would be one for which V_b is about the same value as V_{as}, say C_{as}/C_{ab} lies between 1 and 1.414. For large boxes, C_{as}/C_{ab} is less than 1, for small boxes C_{as}/C_{ab} is greater than 1.414. Table I shows that smaller boxes demand a smaller value of Q_t. Thus if Q_t is not properly controlled, the smaller boxes will tend to cause a greater peak at f_h, while larger boxes will cause the peak to diminish. Fig. 7 is plotted from the points of Table I. Typical response curves for alignments no. 3, 5, and 8 are given in Fig. 8.

VII. TO DESIGN A BOX FOR A GIVEN LOUDSPEAKER

First, the following three loudspeaker parameters must be known: 1) the resonant frequency f_s, 2) the Q values Q_a and Q_e, the latter being usually the controlling factor. This is discussed in more detail in Section IX, Eqs. (71) and (72), and 3) the acoustic compliance C_{as}. This is expressed most conveniently as V_{as}, the volume of air whose acoustic compliance is equal to that of the speaker.

Since in general the acoustic compliance, from [3, Eq. (5.38)] is given by

$$C = V/\rho_0 c^2 \tag{58}$$

then

$$C_{as}/C_{ab} = V_{as}/V_b \tag{59}$$

where V_b is the volume of the box.

The design is commenced in one of two ways:

1) If the box size is limited, V_b is taken as the assigned value. Remember this is the net volume, and that the bracing and the volume displaced by the loudspeaker and the vent (say 10%) must be subtracted from the gross volume. From this value and the known value of V_{as}, the ratio C_{as}/C_{ab} is found, and thence either from Fig. 7 or interpolation from Table I, the values of f_3/f_s, f_3/f_b, and Q_t. Hence f_3 and f_b are found.

2) If a certain frequency response is required, then f_3 is the starting point. The ratio f_3/f_s is found, then from Fig. 7, or by interpolation from Table I, f_3/f_b, C_{as}/C_{ab}, and Q_t. Hence f_b and V_b are found.

The choice of alignment will depend largely on what can be done with the amplifier circuits. For a straightforward amplifier with no filtering, alignments no. 1–9 would be chosen. If a slightly larger box is possible, alignments no. 10 and 11, with their simple CR input filtering make it possible to ease the power handling requirements of both speaker and amplifier. If a more sophisticated design of input filtering is possible as described in Sections V and XII, alignments 15–17 can be used to obtain good acoustic output from small boxes at the expense of higher electrical power output from the amplifier, while alignments no. 20–25 are the most suitable if a fair sized box is available and only moderate lift is required from the amplifier, although in all the fifth- and sixth-order cases, the power required from the amplifier and the excursion demanded of the speaker decrease rapidly below cutoff.

Having found f_b and V_b, the vent dimensions may be found using the methods of the standard texts [8]. However, the following adaptation of the method has proven useful for calculation. The standard form is

$$V_b = 1.84 \times 10^8 S_v/\omega_b^2 L_v \tag{60}$$

where S_v is the cross-sectional area of the vent, in square inches, and L_v is the effective length of the vent, in inches, which includes its actual length together with an end correction.

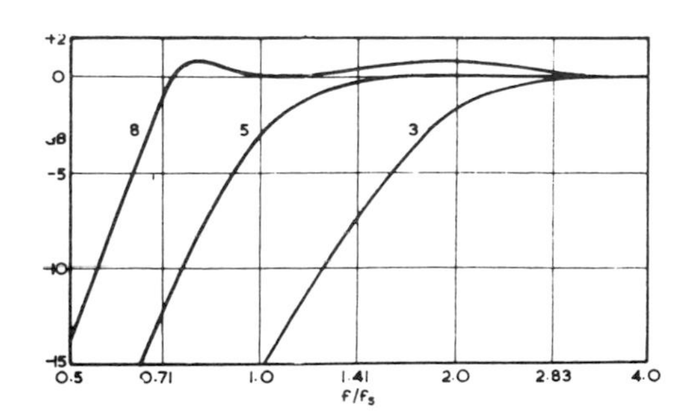

Fig. 8. Typical response curves for identical loudspeakers, but different box sizes. C_{as}/C_{ab} = 0.56, 1.41, and 4.46, corresponding to alignments no. 8, 5, and 3 (types C_4, B_4, and QB_3) of Table I.

This is written more conveniently as

$$L_v/S_v = 1.84 \times 10^8/\omega_b{}^2 V_b. \quad (61)$$

The quantity L_v/S_v, which has the dimension of inches^{-1}, is equivalent to an inductance (acoustic mass) which resonates at ω_b with a capacitance (acoustic compliance) equivalent to V_b. When L_v/S_v is found, a value is chosen for the vent area S_v. It has been shown already in connection with Eq. (6) that the radiation resistance, and therefore the operation of the vented box, is independent of the value of S_v. Now it is usually stated that S_v should normally be the same as the effective radiating area of the cone [8], i.e., S_d. However, this will often involve an excessive length of vent, especially in small boxes and at low cutoff frequencies, because, since L_v/S_v is fixed, the volume L_vS_v displaced by the vent varies as $S_v{}^2$. At the same time, a small amount of distortion is generated in the vent (see [1, Eq. 6.33]) which is a maximum near the box resonant frequency ω_b and is proportional to L_v. On the other hand, Novak [2] quotes 4 in^2 as the lower unit.[2] As shown before, a small area vent has still a high value of Q. However, it will also have higher alternating velocities of air, and this will limit the amount of acoustic power that can be handled linearly. The only advice that can be given is to design the vent area as large as possible in the particular circumstances, up to a limit equal to the piston area.

The maximum length of L_v is usually quoted as $\lambda/12$ where λ is the wavelength of sound at the loudspeaker resonant frequency f_s. The actual requirement is that the vent, which is essentially a transmission line, should look like a lumped constant mass at all the frequencies for which the box is effective. That is, it must still be rather shorter than $\lambda/4$ at frequencies somewhat above f_h of Fig. 5. The value of f_h with respect to f_s will depend on the box tuning. But it also varies with C_{as}/C_{ab}; with a smaller box, f_h is higher.

With the chosen area of vent, first calculate the part of L_v/S_v due to the end correction. This length L'' is usually quoted as

$$L'' = 1.70R \quad (62)$$

where R is the effective radius of the vent, i.e.,

$$(L_v/S_v)_{end} = 0.958/\sqrt{S_v}. \quad (63)$$

This applies to pipes with both ends flanged. When a free-standing pipe is used, the end correction is

$$L'' = 1.46R \quad (64)$$

and

$$(L_v/S_v)_{end} = 0.823/\sqrt{S_v}. \quad (65)$$

In a pipe the end correction is not usually a large part of L_v/S_v. It forms the larger part when the vent is a simple hole in the front panel and then Eq. (63) is correct.

A method favored by the writer, if styling permits, is to build a shelf into the bottom of the box as in Fig. 9, with a spacing l from the back panel equal to the height

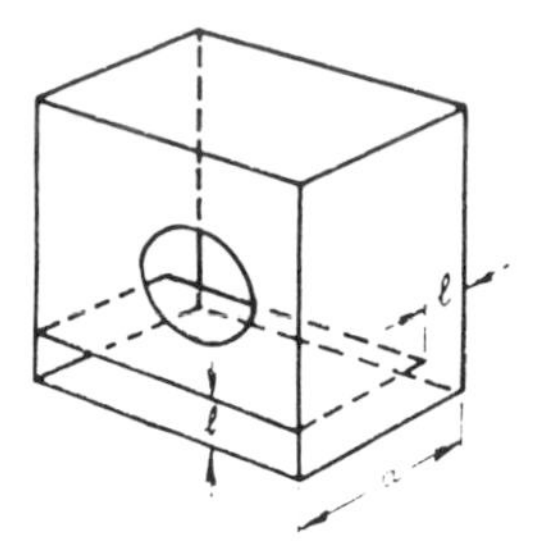

Fig. 9. Simple method of making a tunnel or duct.

of the opening in the front panel. In this case, the effective length of the tunnel is the box depth d plus the end correction as given by Eq. (62) and allowances for thickness of lumber. This vent is tuned by varying l.

When $(L_v/S_v)_{end}$ is found, it is subtracted from the required value of L_v/S_v, and from this, the actual length L_v' is calculated. If this value is unsuitable, another value of S_v is tried and so on (see Appendix).

With regard to box dimensions, it is desirable to take all precautions to prevent strong standing waves. If a corner box is made, the problem is usually fairly easy to solve since the box sides are splayed at least in two dimensions. If a rectangular box is made, and if styling allows, the inside dimensions should be in the preferred ratio for small rooms, that is, 0.8:1.0:1.25 or 0.6:1.0:1.6. In any case, the speaker should be mounted away from the center of the front panel.

The need for sound sealing, with good glued joints, adequate bracing, and adequate damping of the internal surfaces has been stressed often before, so no more need be said of it here. The same is true for the improvement in performance that is obtained by placing the box in the corner of the room, and also by building the sides of the box right down to the floor. However, this last does not seem to be realized sufficiently and the current fad for mounting all furniture on legs causes much unnecessary loss of performance in loudspeaker boxes.

Finally the value of Q_t required by the alignment is compared with the values Q_a and Q_e available, and suitable adjustments are made to the amplifier to achieve a correct overall Q_t. This is dealt with in Section XII, and a worked example is given in the Appendix.

REFERENCES

1. E. J. Jordan, "Loudspeaker Enclosure Design," *Wireless World*, vol. 62, pp. 8-14 (Jan. 1956); pp. 75-79 (Feb. 1956).
2. J. F. Novak, "Performance of Enclosures for Low-Resonance High-Compliance Loudspeakers," *IRE Trans Audio*, vol. AU-7, pp. 5-13 (Jan.-Feb. 1959).
3. L. L. Beranek, *Acoustics* (McGraw-Hill, London, 1959).
4. H. F. Olson, *Elements of Acoustical Engineering*, 2nd ed. (Van Nostrand, Princeton, N.J., 1947), pp. 154-156.
5. O. W. Eshbach, Ed., *Handbook of Engineering Fundamentals* (John Wiley, New York, 1936), pp. 8-60.
6. A. N. Thiele, "Television IF Amplifiers with Linear Phase Response," *Proc. IRE (Aust.)*, vol. 19, p. 655 (Nov. 1958).
7. J. L. Stewart, *Circuit Theory and Design* (John Wiley, New York, 1956), pp. 159-163.
8. F. Langford-Smith, *Radiotron Designer's Handbook*, 4th ed. (A. W. V. Co., Sydney, 1952), p. 847.

[2] This is presumably for the particular case he considers where f_b is 25 Hz, and the acoustic output power is high. For a higher box resonant frequency and/or lower power, an even smaller vent area seems permissible.

THE AUTHOR

Neville Thiele was educated at the University of Queensland and the University of Sydney, graduating as Bachelor of Engineering in 1952. He joined the staff of E.M.I. Australia Ltd. in 1952 as a development engineer in the Special Products Division. During 1955 he spent six months in England, Europe and the United States and on return was responsible for the development of E.M.I. Australia's television receiver. He was appointed advance development engineer in 1957.

Mr. Thiele joined the Australian Broadcasting Commission in 1962, and is now senior engineer, design and development, responsible for the Federal Engineering Laboratory, and with design investigation of equipment and systems for sound and vision broadcasting.

Loudspeakers in Vented Boxes: Part II*

A. N. THIELE

Australian Broadcasting Commission, Sydney, N.S.W. 2001, Australia

Editor's Note: Part I of *Loudspeakers in Vented Boxes* was published in the May, 1971 issue of the Journal.

VIII. LOUDSPEAKER EFFICIENCY

In Eq. (12) an expression was derived for the efficiency of a loudspeaker in a box, which consists of three parts. We have considered, in the meantime, the third part which varies with frequency. We now consider the first two parts. Thus the basic efficiency

$$\eta_{ob} = (\rho_o/4\pi c)(B^2l^2S_d^2/R_eM^2_{ms}). \qquad (66)$$

If this experience is compared with Beranek's Eq. (7.19) it will be seen to give one quarter of his value, after the differences in notation are allowed for.

1) Multiplication by 100 to give percentage.

2) The definition of "nominal input power" in Eq. (10) of this paper as the power delivered by the amplifier into the nominal speaker impedance R_e[3]. Beranek's treatment is based on the idea of maximum power transfer when the load impedance is equal to the generator impedance, as in his Eq. (7.14). If this condition, $R_g = R_e$, is substituted in his Eq. (7.19), one of the conditions for agreement with Eq. (66) is satisfied. However, in dealing with the output power from an amplifier, the writer prefers to consider the power delivered into the load without regard to the output impedance R_g, for the relationship of R_g to the optimum load impedance depends in the first place on the nature of the output device, transistor, pentode, or triode. Furthermore, R_g can be manipulated by feedback techniques (see Section XII) to almost any desired value without affecting the condition for optimum output power. Hence the treatment in this paper.

3) The lumping in this paper of all mechanical mass into M_{ms}.

The additional multiplication factor of one quarter arises from the following.

4) Beranek's figure being for the radiation from *both* sides of the diaphragm, giving twice the output from one side.

5) The assumption in this paper that the radiation resistance in a box is that of a piston at the end of a long tube [3, p. 216]. This radiation resistance is one half of that of a piston in an infinite baffle.

Thus the results are consistent. We will continue here to use η_{ob}, unless stated otherwise. But it is important to define efficiency in terms of actual use and to remember that the value of η_{ob}, being the basic efficiency in a box, is one half the efficiency on an infinite baffle and one quarter of the efficiency, if radiation from both the front and back of a speaker in an infinite baffle is considered.

To simplify the understanding of Eq. (66), we make a further substitution. It can be shown that

$$l^2/R_e = V_{cu}/2\sigma \qquad (67)$$

where σ is the resistivity of the conductor and V_{cu} is the volume of the conductor assumed to be completely within the air gap. In so far as the conductor overlaps the air gap a correction factor would be applied. Then

[3] The nominal impedance of a loudspeaker is usually taken as the minimum impedance at mid-frequencies, at f_n in Fig. 5. This is a little greater than R_e; but for simplicity, and it is hoped without too much confusion, the nominal impedance is taken here as R_e.

* Reprinted from *Proceedings of the IRE Australia,* vol. 22, pp. 487–508 (Aug. 1961). For Part I see *J. Audio Eng. Soc.,* vol. 19, pp. 382-392 (May 1971).

Eq. (66) becomes

$$\eta_{ob} = (\rho_o/8\pi c\sigma)(B^2 S_d^2 V_{cu}/M^2_{ms}) \quad (68)$$

that is, once the voice coil conductor material, and therefore σ, is chosen, the loudspeaker efficiency depends on the four parameters in the second bracket. Without digressing too far into the problem of loudspeaker design, it is noted that this shows the two basic questions in loudspeaker design for good efficiency at low frequencies.

1) How to make the product B^2V_{cu} a maximum for a given magnet, since the larger V_{cu} is made, the wider and/or deeper is the air gap, and hence the lower is B.

2) How to make S_d^2/M_{ms}^2 a maximum, since the larger the area the greater the mass for a given cone thickness. If thickness is reduced, break-up problems increase due to nonlinearity of the piston drive. In conventional designs the mass of the voice coil is small (less than 20%) compared with the mass of the cone, so there is little interaction between V_{cu} and M_{ms}.

The writer prefers to express efficiency as an electroacoustic conversion loss

$$dB_{ca} = 10 \log_{10} \eta. \quad (69)$$

For example, 1% efficiency is equivalent to 20-dB electroacoustic conversion loss. This facilitates comparisons between different designs and estimations of the acoustic level (in phons) which a speaker will provide with a given amplifier and listening room (see Appendix).

IX. RELATIONSHIP OF EFFICIENCY η, Q, AND BOX VOLUME

First we take Eq. (57) and break Q_t into two component parts, one due to the acoustic resistances and the other due to electrical damping, so that

$$1/Q_t = 1/Q_a + (1/Q_e)[R_e/(R_g+R_e)]. \quad (70)$$

Then from Eqs. (8) and (57), the acoustic Q of the loudspeaker

$$Q_a = \omega_s M_{as}/R_{as} \quad (71)$$

and the electrical Q of the loudspeaker

$$Q_e = \omega_s M_{as} R_e S_d^2/B^2l^2 \quad (72)$$

i.e.,

$$Q_e = 2\sigma\omega_s M_{ms}/B^2V_{cu}. \quad (73)$$

Again if we consider the approximate relationship established in Table I that

$$C_{as}f_s^2/C_{ab}f_3^2 \cong \sqrt{2} \quad (74)$$

thus, converting the acoustic compliance of the box into the equivalent volume of air, the box volume

$$V_b \cong (\rho_o c^2/\omega_3^2\sqrt{2})(S_d^2/M_{ms}) \quad (75)$$

remembering that this approximate relationship holds only in the absence of amplifier assistance.

Now considering together Eqs. (68), (73), and (75), the following points emerge.

1) The same considerations that ensure high efficiency also ensure a low Q_e, except that Q_e is independent of the projected piston area S_d and depends only on the *first* power of the cone mass M_{ms} instead of the second power.

2) The box volume depends, apart from the choice of cutoff frequency f_3, only on S_d^2 and M_{ms}. Reduction of box volume by reduction of S_d involves an increased cone excursion, which is inversely proportional to S_d and ω_b^2, for a given acoustic power. If the box volume is reduced by increasing M_{ms}, η is decreased even more (see Eq. (68)), necessitating increased amplifier power. It would seem that the well-known R–J enclosure works this way. The opening in front of the cone is restricted, and this increases the air mass loading M_{a1} of Fig. 1 in the same manner as a vent. Thus M_{ms} is increased and the box volume V_b, i.e., C_{ab}, for a given low-frequency cutoff is reduced, but at the price of reduced efficiency throughout the piston range.

3) The best way of increasing η and lowering Q_e is to increase the flux density B. But if one starts with a reasonably high value of B in the first place, the cost of obtaining an extra decibel of efficiency increases rapidly. So again to obtain a given amount of acoustic power at a given price, a compromise must be struck between the sizes of magnet, box, and amplifier. However, this discussion does show the reason for the large magnet, long throw, heavy cone designs used overseas in small "bookshelf boxes."

Note that Q_a in Eq. (71) depends only on acoustic reactance and resistance, that is, Q_a is independent of B.

Substituting Eqs. (58) and (73) in (68), we obtain the interesting relationship

$$\eta_{ob} = \omega_s^3 V_{as}/4\pi c^3 Q_e \quad (76)$$

where V_{as} is the volume of air equivalent to the acoustic compliance of the loudspeaker, or

$$\eta_{ob} = 8.0 \times 10^{-12} f_s^3 V_{as}/Q_e \quad (77)$$

where V_{as} is in cubic inches. *Thus the basic efficiency of the speaker can be calculated from the three parameters which are used for the design of the box.* A physical explanation of the variation of η and Q_e is given at the end of Section XII.

X. EXCURSION OF LOUDSPEAKER CONE

In the derivation of Eq. (12) it was found that

$$U_c/(U_c - U_p) = 1 - 1/\omega^2 M_{ac} C_{ab}$$
$$= 1 - (\omega_b/\omega)^2. \quad (78)$$

Thus the acoustic output power radiated by the cone alone is

$$W_{aoc} = W_{e}\eta_{ob}[1-(\omega_b/\omega)^2]^2 |E(j\omega)|^2. \quad (79)$$

Now starting from the relationship

$$W_{aoc} = (R_{ma}\dot{x}^2)10^{-7} \quad (80)$$

which is [4, Eq. 6.13], where R_{ma} is the mechanical radiation resistance and $\dot{x}$ is the rms velocity of the piston in cm/s, it is possible to derive an expression for peak cone movement,

$$x_{pk} = 1.31 \times 10^5 \sqrt{W_{aoc}}/f^2 S_d \quad (81)$$

or

$$x_{pk} = 5.17 \times 10^6 \sqrt{W_{aoc}}/\omega^2 S_d \quad (82)$$

where x_{pk} is in inches (note that this x which stands for excursion is unrelated to the shape parameter x of Eq.

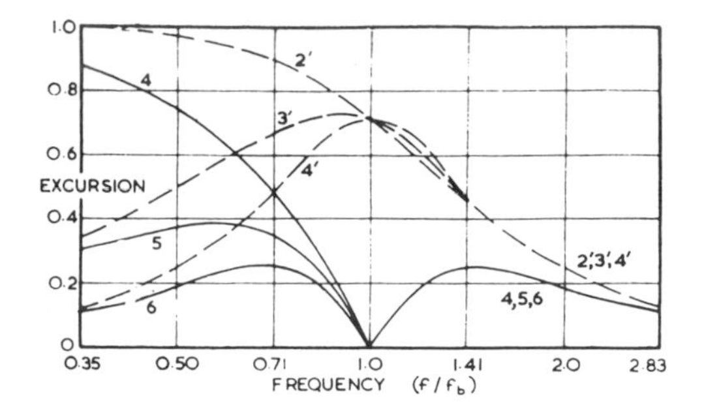

Fig. 10. Normalized cone excursion versus normalized frequency for various orders of Butterworth response with loudspeaker in vented box (solid curves) and in infinite Baffle (dashed curves). Curves are numbered for order of response. Normalized excursion is $|(f_b/f)^2 - (f_b/f)^4| \cdot |E(j\omega)|$, part of Eq. (84).

(21) et seq.), S_d is in square inches, and W_{aoe} is in watts. Again allowance is made for the fact that the loudspeaker is mounted in a box so that the radiation resistance is half the value for an infinite baffle. Thus Eqs. (81) and (82) will give values for displacements which are $\sqrt{2}$ times those given in [4, Fig. 6.9]. Thus

$$x_{pk} = 5.17 \times 10^6 (\eta_{ob} W_{ei})^{1/2} [1 - (\omega_b/\omega)^2] |E(j\omega)| / \omega^2 S_d. \tag{83}$$

If we write this expression as

$$x_{pk} = [1.31 \times 10^5 (\eta_{ob} W_{ei})^{1/2} / f_b{}^2 S_d] [(\omega_b/\omega)^2 - (\omega_b/\omega)^4] |E(j\omega)| \tag{84}$$

it is apparent that there are two parts, one fixed for a given speaker and box (note frequency f_b in this expression) and one that varies with frequency. This latter expression is plotted in Fig. 10 for various Butterworth responses, in which box, speaker, and cutoff frequencies are identical. The solid curve 4 gives the excursion of the classical fourth-order Butterworth alignment no. 5 of Table I. Solid curve 5 refers to the fifth-order Butterworth alignment no. 10, which includes a simple auxiliary filter. Solid curve 6 refers to the sixth-order Butterworth alignment which is identical for nos. 15, 20, and 26, since both frequency response and box resonant frequency are the same in each. For comparison, the dotted curves give the excursions for the same speaker in an infinite baffle (totally enclosed box) with the same power. Dotted curve 2 applies to a speaker with a second-order Butterworth response ($Q_t = 0.707$). Dotted curve 3 applies to a third-order Butterworth response ($Q_t = 1$, with a simple auxiliary filter). Dotted curve 4 applies to a fourth-order Butterworth response ($Q_t = 1.307$, with a second-order auxiliary filter). The frequency response is the same as solid curve 4, but it is obtained by different means. The curves show the following.

1) The excursion below resonance is reduced greatly in both vented box and infinite baffle when an auxiliary highpass filter is used. The first-order auxiliary filter gives a good improvement especially in view of its simplicity. The second-order auxiliary filter not only allows a greater reduction of cone excursion, it also allows the use of three separate box alignments for the same response and allows box volume to be traded for amplifier power in the case of the vented box. The Butterworth curves with second-order auxiliary filters are symmetrical about the center frequency. There seems little need therefore to use more elaborate filtering.

2) Even more important, the excursion of the cone is reduced greatly when the loudspeaker is placed in a vented box. The curve predicts zero excursion at the box frequency. This arises from the assumption that the Q of the box circuit is infinite. While this cannot be achieved completely in practice, the excursion at the box frequency will be low so long as the ratio of Q of the box to Q of the speaker is high, as demonstrated in Section II.

Of course, if resistance is deliberately introduced into the box circuit, as by making the vent from a number of small holes or by stretching fabric across the vent, the Q will be greatly reduced and some of the advantage of the vented box will be lost, as shown in the next section. Fig. 10 refers only to Butterworth responses. In Fig. 11, a plot is made of the function $|(\omega_b/\omega)^2 - (\omega_b/\omega)^4|$ against frequency. If, for example, in a Chebyshev response the frequency response is known, the excursion at different frequencies can be found by reading off the function at a given frequency on Fig. 11 and multiplying it with the frequency response. The rapid rise of the function between normalized frequencies of 1 and 0.71 shows why responses should be preferred in which f_b is not too much greater than f_3. Thus with respect to cone excursion, an alignment in the group 20–25 would be preferred to its counterpart in the group 15–19 which has a lower value of f_3/f_b.

It would seem that in published ratings of loudspeakers, the maximum excursion x_{max} would be more useful than the conventional rating of maximum input power. The latter might save the loudspeaker from a melted voice coil, but when mechanical damage or undistorted acoustic output are of interest, x_{max}, along with the kind of baffle and the alignment, determine the performance.

XI. BOXES WITH RESISTIVE LOADING OF VENT

Good results have been reported with resistively loaded vents [1]. These were therefore investigated using both series and parallel loading of the vent as shown in Fig. 12. In both cases, the resistance was assumed to be constant with respect to frequency and the response function was found to be of third order.

This, by the way, explains a discrepancy between the statements in [3, p. 244] and in [2, p. 11] that the drop in response below cutoff is 18 dB per octave, even though [2, Eq. 15)], which is equivalent to Eq. (20) of this

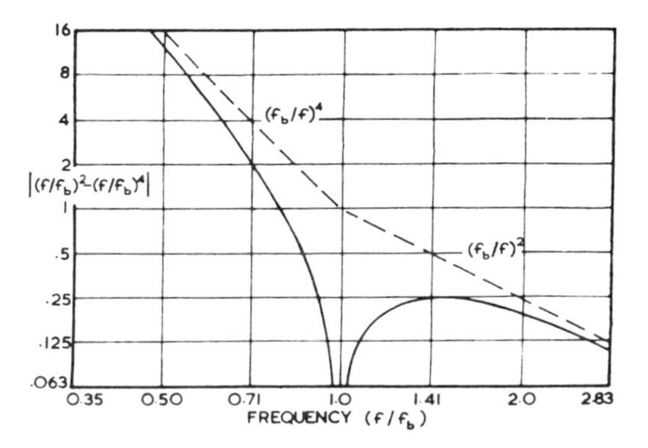

Fig. 11. Function $|(f_b/f)^2 - (f_b/f)^4|$ versus normalized frequency f/f_b. The function, part of Eq. (84), is used to compute excursion when frequency response $|E(j\omega)|$ is known.

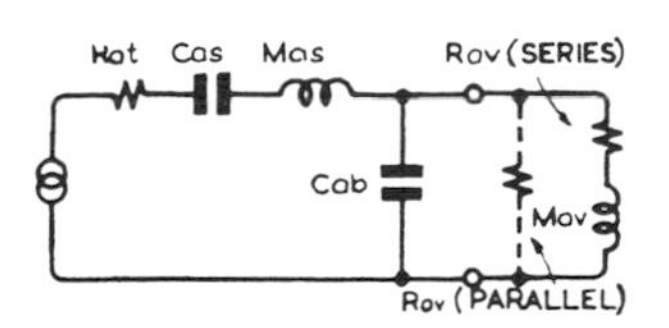

Fig. 12. Equivalent acoustic circuit of loudspeaker and box showing added acoustic damping in series or parallel with vent.

paper, obviously has an asymptotic slope of 24 dB per octave. In the practical case, where resistance loading of the vent however small will be encountered, the asymptotic slope will eventually be 18 dB per octave; but so long as the original simplifying assumptions hold, the response in the region that concerns us will be effectively 24 dB per octave.

The expressions are, for the case of series resistance loading,

$$E(p) = 1/\{1+(1/p)(1/Q_bT_b+Q_bT_b/T^2_s)+(1/p^2)(1/T_s^2+1/T_b^2+C_{as}/C_{ab}T_s^2)+Q_b/p^3T_s^2T_b\} \quad (85)$$

when

$$1/Q_t = T_s/Q_bT_b+Q_bT_b/T_s \quad (86)$$

and Q_b is defined as the ratio of acoustic mass resistance to series acoustic resistance of the vent at the *box* resonant frequency.

For the case of parallel resistance loading,

$$E(p) = 1/\{1+(1/p)(Q_bT_b/T_s^2+1/Q_bT_b+C_{as}T_b/C_{ab}T_s^2Q_b)+(1/p^2)(1/T_s^2+1/T_b^2+C_{as}/C_{ab}T_s^2)+Q_b/p^3T_s^2T_b\} \quad (87)$$

when

$$1/Q_t = Q_bT_b/T_s+T_s/Q_bT_b+C_{as}T_b/C_{ab}T_sQ_b \quad (88)$$

and Q_b in this case is the ratio of parallel acoustic resistance across the vent (series resistance being assumed negligible) to acoustic mass reactance. Note the inversion of the expression for parallel Q_b compared with that for series Q_b. Since these equations are of third order and there is one extra variable Q_b, there are two extra degrees of freedom in the design. However, one is removed if an all-pole function is desired, hence Eqs. (86) and (88). Before an alignment is commenced, one other parameter must be fixed arbitrarily. The ratio C_{as}/C_{ab} seems the easiest to handle for this purpose. Thus in a third-order Butterworth alignment, if C_{as}/C_{ab} is made 1.414, for comparison with the fourth-order Butterworth alignment no. 5 of Table I, the results are as given in Table II.

Table II. Parameters for third-order Butterworth alignment with resistive vented loading.

Method of Loading	f_3/f_s	f_3/f_b	C_{as}/C_{ab}	Q_t	Q_b
Series Resistance	1.317	1.285	1.414	0.379	2.22
Parallel Resistance	1.420	1.120	1.414	0.352	2.25
No Resistance (Alignment No. 5, for comparison)	1.000	1.000	1.414	0.383	∞

It will be seen that although the box had the same volume, the cutoff frequencies for the resistively loaded alignments are 1.32 and 1.42 times higher than no. 5 of Table I. Compared with previous alignments (no. 1–9 of Table I) those of Table II are most inefficient in utilization of box volume, there is no compensating freedom to use a larger value of Q_t, in fact it needs to be a little smaller, finally and more important, the excursion of the speaker near cutoff frequency is greatly increased. For these reasons, the use of acoustic damping seems to be unjustified. It is realized that the cases treated here use resistances which are constant with frequency. Some acoustic resistances, as described for example in [3, Eqs. (5.54) and (5.56)], vary with frequency and might have a somewhat different effect. However, the use of added damping with the attendant dissipation of input power seems to be wrong in principle, unless a suitable alternative cannot be found. It is believed that the method outlined already provides the suitable alternative.

Effect of Losses in Box and Vent

Having established that intentional loading of the vent is undesirable, it is of interest to know the effect on the ideal response, obtained by assuming zero loss, of small unavoidable losses in the box and vent. We will only consider performance at the box resonant frequency, since at this frequency 1) the box circuit contributes most, in the ideal case all, of the acoustic output, and 2) the losses in the box circuit are greatest.

In the ideal case, the transfer impedance connecting the input force $E_gBl/S_d(R_g+R_e)$ with the vent volume velocity U_p in Fig. 2, at the box resonant frequency ω_b, is $j\omega_bM_{av}$. If now we express all the losses in the vent *and* the box as Q_b, the "Q of the box and vent circuit," the transfer impedance, and thus the frequency response at ω_b is reduced by a factor which we will call the maximum box loss $(A_b)_{max}$. Then, to a close approximation,

$$(A_b)_{max} = 1/[1+(1/Q_tQ_b)(C_{ab}/C_{as})(\omega_b/\omega_s)]. \quad (89)$$

If we apply the approximations of parts 1) and 2) of Section VI for the "unassisted" alignments no. 1–9 of Table I, Eq. (89) is simplified to

$$(A_b)_{max} = 1/[1+(1.85/Q_b)(f_b^2/f_3^2)] \quad (90)$$

that is, for a given value of Q_b, the box loss increases with higher values of f_b/f_3 and thus, larger box sizes.

To illustrate the effect of box loss, Eq. (89) is applied to various alignments. Taking first the classical alignment, no. 5 of Table I, the maximum box loss is 0.5 dB when Q_b is 30 and 1.5 dB when Q_b is 10. Taking other, extreme, alignments when Q_b is 30, the losses for alignments no. 1, 9, 19, and 25 are 0.3 dB, 0.7 dB, 0.5 dB, and 0.7 dB, respectively. Thus it can be seen that a Q_b of 30 will have little effect on any alignment. With a Q_b of 10, the losses are 0.9 dB, 1.9 dB, 1.5 dB, and 2.2 dB, respectively, i.e., when the box Q is reduced three times, the maximum box loss is increased approximately three times in each case. A method of measuring Q_b is given at the end of Section XIV and illustrated in the Appendix.

Table III. Change of output impedance R_g with type of feedback.

	Negative	Positive
Voltage Feedback	R_g Decreases	R_g Increases
Current Feedback	R_g Increases	R_g Decreases

XII. AMPLIFIER CIRCUITS

Negative Output Impedance

It is essential to the method that the overall Q_t of the loudspeaker plus amplifier be properly controlled within $\pm 10\%$ for ± 1 dB accuracy of response. As explained in Section V, if Q_t is twice the optimum value, a 6-dB peak results. Similarly if Q_t is too small, there will be a dip in the response. Thus it is important that the speaker Q_e be known, either from information supplied by the manufacturer or by measurement, and that the amplifier output impedance be then adjusted to give the required overall value of Q_t. It is assumed in the following that the available speaker Q_e is larger than the required Q_t. This is the more usual case, especially with lower priced loudspeakers. But if it is smaller, a suitable adjustment can easily be made, for example, by changing the positive current feedback to negative current feedback.

The subject of amplifier output impedance control properly requires another paper, which it is hoped will be presented later. For the present only some general results will be given.

If feedback is applied to an amplifier, not only does its gain change, but its effective output impedance R_g changes also; not its optimum load impedance which remains unchanged by feedback but the impedance which is seen when looking back into the amplifier output terminals. The effect of applying different kinds of feedback is shown in Table III.

The terms voltage feedback and current feedback refer of course to feedback of a voltage which is proportional to output voltage and output current, respectively. In the latter case, this is usually achieved by placing a small resistor in series with the load, and taking the voltage drop across it for feedback. It will be seen that not only does negative voltage feedback reduce the output impedance R_g, positive current feedback reduces R_g also, and to the greater extent that R_g can be made zero or negative.

Negative output impedance is characteristic of oscillators; one therefore tends to be wary of it as tending to instability. But this can only happen when the positive output impedance presented by the load is less than the negative impedance presented by the amplifier. Now the impedance of a loudspeaker in a box, typified by Fig. 5, can never be less than its dc resistance R_e of Fig. 4. The only exception is at very high frequencies, where the shunt capacitance of the connecting leads takes effect. But unless the leads are very long and the nominal impedance of the speaker is high, this will not usually take effect within the bandwidth of the amplifier. And in any case, we will want to eliminate the negative impedance characteristic at the higher audio frequencies for reasons that will be discussed later. Thus a negative impedance amplifier can be made completely stable apart from gross misadjustment, such as connecting a loudspeaker of much lower impedance than the design figure or short-circuiting the output leads.

The method of applying mixed feedback is shown in Fig. 13. It will be seen that if the sense of the voltage developed across the potential divider R_3 and R_4 is negative, then the voltage developed across the current feedback resistor R_2, usually made less than 1/10 the nominal impedance of the speaker to minimize power loss, will be positive. The circuit shows why this method is sometimes described as bridge feedback. Usually the circuit is arranged to be unbalanced at all frequencies so that the net feedback is always negative, but it need not necessarily be so. For example, if no net negative feedback is desired, so that there is no overall gain reduction with nominal load, the bridge will be balanced at nominal load.

Physically, the circuit can be thought of as having a certain amount of feedback with nominal load, in which the negative voltage feedback is partially neutralized by the voltage from the positive current feedback resistor. If the impedance Z_1 is open-circuited, the current feedback from R_2 disappears leaving a greater amount of negative feedback. Thus the output voltage may be less on open circuit than on nominal load. This is the effect we describe as negative output impedance. Its extent, or whether it is seen at all, will depend on the original gain and output impedance of the amplifier and the value of the feedback resistor R_2. Thus if we have, as in Fig. 4, a loudspeaker resistance R_e, and make the effective output impedance of the amplifier R_g equal to, say, $-0.6R_e$, the total effective impedance of R_g+R_e becomes $+0.4R_e$. And if the Q_e of the loudspeaker is 1.0, this will make the overall Q_t a value of 0.4 by applying a maximum of 1.0/0.4 times, i.e., 8.0 dB, extra gain reduction by negative feedback when the impedance of the speaker becomes high, as at f_h and f_l of Fig. 5. (Need it be emphasized that this form of damping does not dissipate amplifier output power, except in the small current feedback resistor. It reduces power by feedback at the source.)

This fact necessitates a degree of additional care in the design of negative impedance amplifier. For when the load is open-circuited, the negative feedback rises to the maximum; in this case a gain reduction of 8 dB above the nominal value, and the stability margin will be reduced. The size of the negative impedance will in practice be limited either by this consideration or by the need for a feedback resistor so large that it dissipates an appreciable part of the output power.

An alternative method of control damping uses a feedback winding closely coupled to the voice coil. In this way, feedback can be taken effectively from the junction of R_e and L_e in Fig. 4. Simple negative feedback

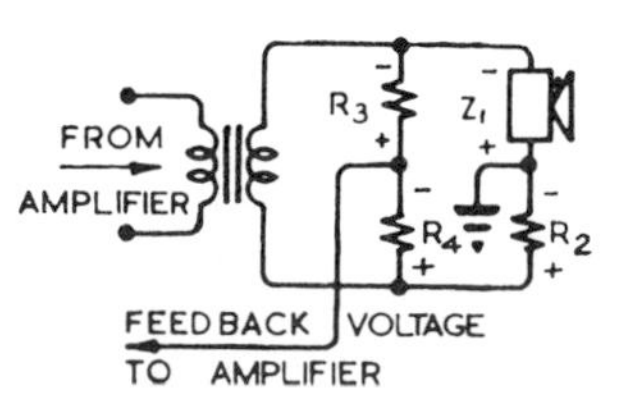

Fig. 13. Method of applying mixed feedback (positive current and negative voltage).

then reduces an effective output impedance which is the sum of $R_g + R_e$. Thus Q_t is reduced in the same way as before. Since the impedance of the feedback circuit is usually high compared with the voice coil impedance, the feedback winding can be made of very fine wire. In fact, if it is wound bifilar with the main winding with wire 16 B&S gauges smaller, it will fit into the air spaces between the larger wires. It thus takes up no more space in the air gap and adds less than 3% to the mass of the copper in the voice coil. Unfortunately, such a winding is difficult to achieve in production and is thus rarely, if ever, used.

If negative impedance is applied, it reduces the output voltage whenever the load impedance is high, i.e., not only in the region of f_l and f_h in Fig. 5, but also at frequencies above f_n where the impedance rise is due to the inductance L_e of Fig. 4. At high frequencies, this contributes nothing to the acoustic damping of the speaker, but simply reduces the high-frequency response, in the case quoted above, a maximum of 8 dB. This is usually undesirable, so the negative impedance should be eliminated at the higher audio frequencies. One method among several possible is shown in Fig. 14**a**. Here an inductance L_2 is added to the feedback resistor R_2 with a time constant L_2/R_2 matching that of the speaker, usually in the range of 30–60 μs. This can be easily done by winding a solenoid of copper wire which combines resistance R_2 and inductance L_2. However, since this achieves its result by feeding back an increasing positive voltage to neutralize an increasing negative voltage, quite small unbalance between the two can cause instability at high frequencies.

On the other hand, consider the circuit of Fig. 14**b** where the lower resistor of the negative feedback potential divider R_4 becomes two resistors R_5 and R_6 in series. Suppose that a suitable set of resistors R_2, R_3, and R_4 has been found to give the correct gain and output impedance for low frequencies with the dotted connection open-circuited. It is then possible to find a tapping point on R_4 (i.e., the junction of R_5 and R_6) such that the same gain is obtained on nominal load whether the dotted connection is open circuit or short circuit. This is done by connecting the nominal load and making R_5 and R_6 a potentiometer whose wiper is grounded through a switch. The wiper is adjusted until the gain is the same with the switch open or closed. In the open-circuit condition, the output impedance will be the value originally chosen, but on short circuit, most of the positive current feedback will be eliminated. If then a capacitor is substituted for the switch as shown in Fig. 14**b**, the output impedance will change from a negative value at low frequencies to a small value, either positive or negative depending on the

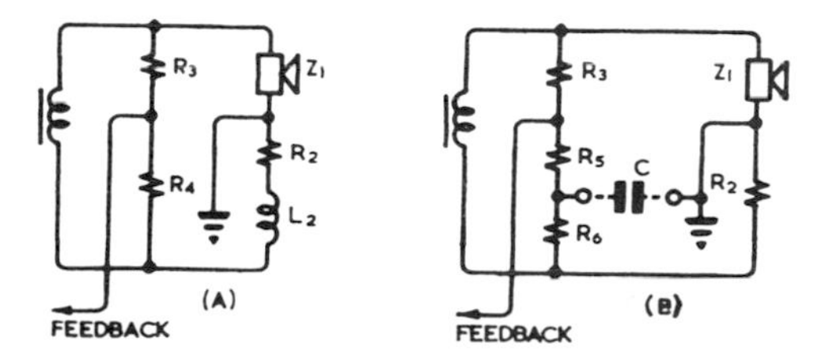

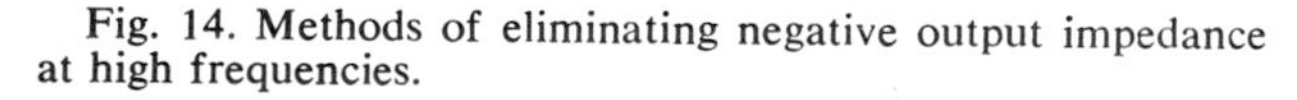
Fig. 14. Methods of eliminating negative output impedance at high frequencies.

particular circuit. The frequency of changeover, which should be, say, two octaves above f_h, depends on the capacitance C and the resistances R_5 and R_6. At the same time, the gain of the amplifier on nominal load stays constant over the whole audio range.

Auxiliary Filters

The auxiliary filtering needed for sixth-order alignments is best provided by circuits using RC networks in a feedback loop ahead of the main amplifier. In general it is unwise to use the main amplifier feedback loop to provide both negative impedance and high-pass filtering. It is hoped to deal with this in a later paper, but for the moment the reader's attention is directed to the extensive literature, of which [9] and [10] are examples, concerning low-frequency filters without inductors, which use resistors, capacitors, and tubes in comparatively inexpensive combinations.

Maximum Power at Maximum Impedance

The electrical impedance seen at the terminals of a loudspeaker varies greatly with frequency, but output stages deliver maximum power into a comparatively narrow range of impedances. To consider the maximum acoustic power that can be delivered by an amplifier through a loudspeaker, we return to the equivalent electrical circuit of Fig. 4, together with the impedance curve of Fig. 5. For this purpose, we ignore for the moment the inductance L_e with its electrical shunt loss R_{sh} and assume that the curve of Fig. 5 reaches a final value of R_e above f_n.

The acoustic output depends on the voltage across R_{es}, which includes the electrical equivalent of the radiation resistance R_{ar1}. Since R_{ar1} varies with frequency squared, the voltage across R_{es} needs to vary inversely with frequency to maintain constant acoustic power. At the higher frequencies the motional impedance is much lower than R_e and is controlled by the reactance of C_{mes}, which is equal to B^2l^2/M_{ms}. Thus the condition for flat response is achieved, often described as mass control.[4]

If B is varied while R_e remains constant, the motional impedance at any given high frequency within the piston range will increase with B^2. The electrical equivalent of radiation resistance, though small, will increase and with it the ratio, again small, of acoustic power radiated to electrical power input. Thus efficiency varies with B^2. At the same time the increase of motional impedance while the resistance R_e remains constant causes Q_e, the electrical Q, to decrease inversely with increasing B^2.

But as the frequency decreases, the motional impedance rises, reaching at f_h and again at f_l a maximum value of R_{es} which is usually several times the resistance R_e. Thus at these peaks the motional impedance, which at high frequencies was negligible compared with R_e, is now the major part of the total impedance. Suppose for simplicity that it comprises all of the speaker impedance. This time when B is varied and the motional impedance

[4] This should not be confused with the technique of mass control practiced by politicians and advertising people. In that context, the reactance is usually assumed to result from the equivalent of a compliance, and hence to decrease with signal frequency.

varies as B^2, then for a given acoustic power output the voltage across R_{es}, which is virtually the input voltage, will need to increase with increasing B. Summarizing, for a fixed acoustic power output, an increase of B will decrease the input voltage required at high frequencies, and increase the input voltage required at the impedance peaks. Also Q_e will decrease.

With a load impedance much larger than nominal, the criterion of performance of the amplifier becomes, not output power, but the undistorted output voltage on open circuit. This will always be larger than the undistorted output voltage at nominal load; how much larger will depend on the design of the amplifier.

Now if the Q_t required for a flat frequency response is identical with the Q_e of the loudspeaker, then if we ignore Q_a, the generator impedance R_g must be zero. Thus for a constant acoustic power output the same voltage will be required at the loudspeaker terminals at all frequencies, and all impedances, so that at the frequency f_h somewhat more maximum acoustic power is available than at higher frequencies.

If the Q_t required is less than Q_e, R_g will need to be negative, and for constant acoustic power and amplifier output voltage, at the junction of R_g and R_e in Fig. 4, will fall at f_h. But if the Q_t required is greater than Q_e, R_g will need to be positive, and the amplifier output voltage for constant acoustic power will rise at f_h. If the ratio of increase of voltage required is greater than the ratio of amplifier undistorted output voltages on open circuit to on-load, it is possible for less maximum acoustic power to be available in the region of f_h than at other frequencies in the useful band. But since low values of Q_e are normally associated with high efficiency, this is only likely to occur with high-efficiency, usually high-quality speakers. It should not cause trouble until Q_e is less than half Q_t, and even then the maximum acoustic power in most program material is less at frequencies below 100 Hz than around 400 Hz.

Thus there is a paradox that a highly efficient speaker may deliver less power around f_h than at higher frequencies, while a less efficient speaker delivers more. This will depend on the ratio of Q_e to Q_t and of amplifier undistorted output voltage off-load to on-load.

Related to this topic is the flattening of the impedance characteristic which is usually considered to be a good feature of vented boxes. Reference to Fig. 5, and comparison with Fig. 16, shows that, with the simplifying assumption that the resistive losses in the box and vent are negligible, the height of the impedance peak $R_e + R_{es}$ peaks at f_h and f_l and raise the minimum impedance at f_b. But this is incidental, and the relative heights are of little importance. Thus the idea of tuning the box so that the impedance peaks at f_h and f_l are equal, misses the real point. In the impedance curve of a loudspeaker in a box, the most useful information is not the values of the impedances, so long as box and vent damping is not too severe, but the values of the frequencies f_h, f_b, and f_l. Knowledge of these three frequencies alone enables a box alignment to be checked by Eqs. (105) and (106).

It should be clear that flatness of the impedance characteristic is no indication of flatness of acoustic response. Take as an analogy a coupled pair of tuned circuits. When the output voltage, or more exactly the transfer impedance, is maximally flat, the input impedance has two peaks. If one parameter is known, say the ratio of primary to secondary Q, the transfer impedance can be deduced from the input impedance, just as we do for loudspeakers in Eqs. (105) and (106). But a flat input impedance characteristic does not indicate a flat transfer impedance. In a loudspeaker, the impedance characteristic has greater peaks, whose height depends purely on the acoustic damping, though this contributes little to the overall system damping, and thus the overall frequency response.

XIII. EFFECTIVE REVERBERATION TIME

An objection sometimes made to the use of vented boxes is that the slope of attenuation beyond cutoff, 24 dB per octave, is much steeper than the 12 dB per octave of a speaker on an infinite baffle, and therefore the transient response is worse. In a low-pass filter, the ringing associated with steep attenuation slope is virtually removed by the use of Thompson or critically damped responses. But in high-pass filters such as are considered here, there is always some overshoot with filters of order two or more. To estimate its effect on a listener we use the concept of "effective reverberation time."

Imagine that we have a source of sound in a room which has built up a steady field. The source is then stopped. The sound in the room does not stop immediately, but dies away gradually. The time taken for the sound to decay is called the reverberation time, defined as the time taken for the sound pressure in the room to fall 60 dB from its original value. In small rooms the reverberation time will probably lie between 400 ms for a highly damped room to 1 s or more for a live one.

When the sound passes through two reverberant rooms in cascade, the law of the resulting overall reverberation time is not well establishd, but calculations on cascaded high-pass filters suggest that rms addition gives at least a guide. In any case it would appear that an added reverberation time of 200–300 ms should not appreciably color the reproduction.

When a transient is applied to a filter and it rings, the effect is perceived by the ear, or brain, as an extension of the transient event in time. Hence the expression "hang-over." To express the effect of the ringing then, an idea is borrowed from architectural acoustics, and the effective reverberation time of a filter is defined as the time taken, after a step function is applied, for the amplitude of the envelope of ringing to fall 60 dB below the amplitude of the original step function.

For the higher order filter functions, with two or more second-order factors, only the most lightly damped factor need be considered. For, by the time the ringing due to the most lightly damped factors is 60 dB down, the ringing due to the more heavily damped factors is negligible. This eases computation greatly.

Actually, at low frequencies the reverberation time defined above will be rather longer than the time the sound is perceived by the listener. To see why, we consult the much abused Fletcher–Munson curves [4, Fig. 12.11].

Suppose, for example, that the original sound is at 100-phon level. This is probably the maximum a system could reproduce, or a listener tolerate. Now at 50 Hz the threshold of hearing is 51 dB above reference level, that is, 49 dB below our arbitrary listening level. At 25 Hz the threshold of hearing is 67 dB above reference

Table IV. Reverberation times for various alignments.

Type of response	B_2	C_2	C_2	B_4	C_4	B_6	C_6	C_6	C_6
Q_t (for second order alignments)	0.707	1.000	1.414	—	—	—	—	—	—
k (for sixth order alighments)	—	—	—	—	—	1.000	0.600	0.414	0.268
Alignment numbers	—	—	—	5	8	15, 20, 26	17, 22	19, 24	25, 27
Time (in periods of cutoff frequency)	1.63	2.24	3.17	2.87	7.09	4.77	6.79	9.67	14.86
Time for 50 c/s cutoff (mS)	33	45	63	57	142	95	136	193	297

level, that is, only 33 dB below our arbitrary listening level. At 25 Hz, therefore, the effective reverberation time for the listener cannot be greater than the time in which the sound level falls 33 dB, i.e., about half the reverberation time as defined conventionally. Thus at low frequencies in general, the conventional definition based on a 60-dB fall in level yields a reverberation time rather longer than a listener will hear. (This is probably the reason for the observed increase in optimum reverberation time at low frequencies, see [4, Fig. 11.11].)

In a filter which cuts off sharply, the major ringing frequency will be close to the cutoff frequency. Also for a given shape of response curve the reverberation time can be expressed as a certain number of cycles of the cutoff frequency (see Table IV), i.e., the reverberation time increases with decreasing cutoff frequency. On the other hand, below, say, 50 Hz, its effect on the listener will decrease at approximately the same rate. Thus for all filters of a given response curve shape, the figure for 50 Hz should give a rough idea of the maximum reverberation time, as perceived by the listener.

Calculated reverberation times are given in Table IV. The first three alignments are of second order, corresponding to a loudspeaker on an infinite baffle. For these, the values of Q_t are shown. Note that the reverberation time, though low, doubles as Q_t increases from 0.707 to 1.414, that is, when the frequency response goes from maximally flat to a 4-dB peak. The times for 50-Hz cutoff are all below 200 ms, except for the last ($k = 0.268$), which is the very steepest.

It thus appears that a properly adjusted vented box, even with amplifier assistance (auxiliary filtering), need cause no perceptible coloration due to ringing. But it is important to emphasize that the adjustment must be correct. Table IV shows that the addition of a 4-dB peak to the response of a speaker on an infinite baffle can double the reverberation time. Being low in the first place it remains tolerable. But in the case of a vented box, particularly with an auxiliary filter, a doubled reverberation time would be more serious. Again, this emphasizes the importance of adequate damping (for correct value of Q_t) by the amplifier.

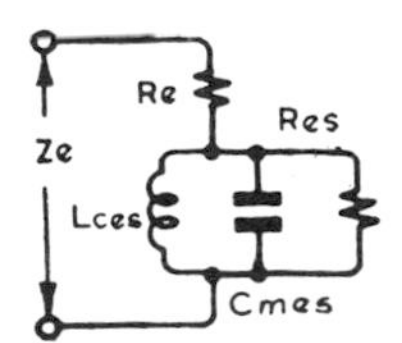

Fig. 15. Simplified equivalent electrical circuit of loudspeaker.

XIV. MEASUREMENT OF LOUDSPEAKER PARAMETERS

In earlier sections it was shown how the required response can be obtained from a loudspeaker and box if several parameters are known. The question remains, how are these parameters found?

Properly, this information should be available from the loudspeaker manufacturer. This is particularly important for equipment produced in quantity, where it is important to know not only the mean values but also the tolerances. However, in the absence of published figures, or to check them, the following procedure will provide the information.

Procedures for measuring Q are given in [2, p. 13], but the method used seems too laborious and inaccurate. The method outlined hereafter can be understood by considering Figs. 15 and 16. Figure 15 is derived from Fig. 4; only this time we omit the vented box and we ignore L_e and R_{sh} which take effect at much higher frequencies. Now

$$Q_a = \omega_s C_{mes} R_{es} \tag{91}$$

$$Q_e = \omega_s C_{mes} R_e. \tag{92}$$

These quantities, defined earlier in Eqs. (71) and (72) in terms of the acoustic equivalent circuit, are defined here in terms of the electrical equivalent circuit. We define r_0 as the ratio of the impedance at resonance, $R_{es} + R_e$, to the dc resistance of the voice coil R_e. Now we take another arbitrary impedance which is presented at two other frequencies f_1 and f_2 on the flanks of the curve, and we call its ratio to the dc resistance r_1. Then

$$f_1 f_2 = f_s^2. \tag{93}$$

Physically, this means that the curve is symmetrical on a logarithmic frequency scale. In experimental work it provides a handy check. Now we can find

$$Q_a = [f_s/(f_2 - f_1)][r_0^2 - r_1^2)/(r_1^2 - 1)]^{1/2} \tag{94}$$

and

$$Q_e = Q_a/(r_0 - 1). \tag{95}$$

If additionally we choose r_1 such that

$$r_1 = \sqrt{r_0} \tag{96}$$

then Eq. (94) is simplified to

$$Q_a = \sqrt{r_0}\, f_s/(f_2 - f_1). \tag{97}$$

The interesting feature of these expressions is that they involve no approximations, and thus hold for all values of Q. Furthermore around the value $\sqrt{r_0}$ the curve has its greatest slope. Thus the frequencies f_1 and f_2 can be

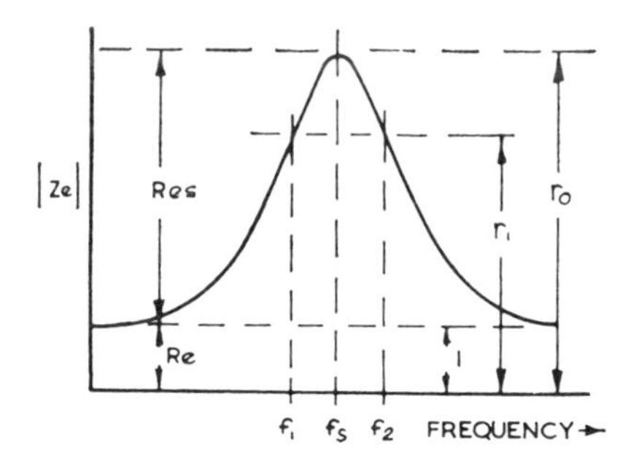

Fig. 16. Typical impedance curve of loudspeaker, modulus of Z_e in Fig. 15.

found most accurately. This is especially important since the calculation involves a comparatively small difference between large numbers f_2-f_1.

Usually Q_a takes account of the acoustic resistances in the loudspeaker. But if the voice coil has a short-circuited turn by accident or design, e.g., an aluminum former, this will appear in Q_a, even though its physical nature is similar to Q_e. (But eddy current losses in the pole piece or front plate appear in R_{sh}.)

Fig. 17 shows the test circuit. V is a voltmeter of impedance much higher than the loudspeaker. Throughout the readings, the generator is adjusted so that the reading of V is constant. The value is not of great importance, but a standard test figure is one volt. The accuracy of this voltmeter is not important so long as it is independent of frequency. A is an ac ammeter which reads the current into the speaker with the fixed voltage across its terminals. Again, since we are interested only in the shape of the impedance curve, the absolute accuracy of this instrument is not important so long as the meter reading is linear. However, to set the relative current due to R_e, first we measure R_e with dc on a Wheatstone bridge, and then a calibrating resistor R_c of similar value. Connecting R_c to the test terminals and applying the standard test voltage at say, f_s, a current value I_c is found on the ammeter A. Then the current I_e which corresponds to R_e is found by

$$I_e = I_c R_c / R_e. \qquad (98)$$

Now the loudspeaker is suspended in air as far from reflecting surfaces as is practical and connected to the test terminals instead of R_c. The generator is adjusted to the speaker resonant frequency f_s, indicated by minimum current I_o. Thus r_o is found:

$$r_o = I_e / I_o. \qquad (99)$$

Now the current $\sqrt{(I_e I_o)}$ is found corresponding to the ratio $\sqrt{r_o}$ and the frequencies either side of resonance, where this current value is read. These are f_1 and f_2 and they should be read to as close an accuracy as the test gear will allow. Eq. (93) provides a check on the

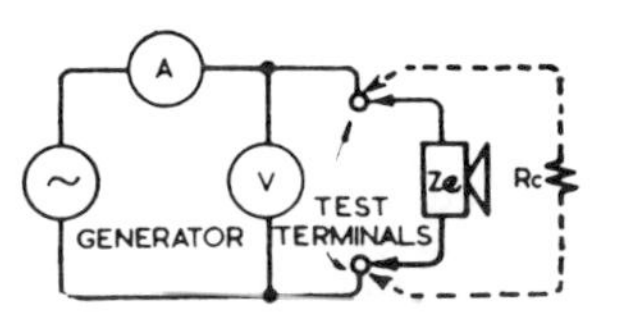

Fig. 17. Test circuit schematic for measurement of loudspeaker parameters.

method, and Eqs. (97) and (95) give Q_a and Q_e.

The next problem is to find the value of V_{as}, the volume of air equivalent to the loudspeaker compliance. For this, the loudspeaker is placed in a totally enclosed unlined box whose internal volume V_b is known, remembering that allowance must be made for bracing and the volume displaced by the speaker. It is important that this box be free of air leaks. If these occur we will read part of the curve of Fig. 5, around f_h. Thus care should be taken, not only in the construction of the box and in the mounting of the speaker, but also in the way the speaker leads are taken through the walls of the box. Solid terminals are preferred.

Another precaution may be necessary. In Figs. 15 and 16, from which we derived Eqs. (93), (94), (95), and (97), we assumed that the effect of the inductance L_e is negligible. In fact, L_e interacts with the parallel combination of L_{ceo} and C_{mes} to produce a series resonance at f_n in Fig. 5, where the nominal impedance is measured. If this frequency, usually 400–600 Hz, is well above the speaker resonance f_s, so that there is little disturbance of the curve at f_2 of Fig. 16, the accuracy of the measurements will be unaffected. But if f_s is above 150 Hz, which can occur with small speakers and becomes even more likely when the speaker is placed in the box for the last test, the likelihood of inaccurate results increases.

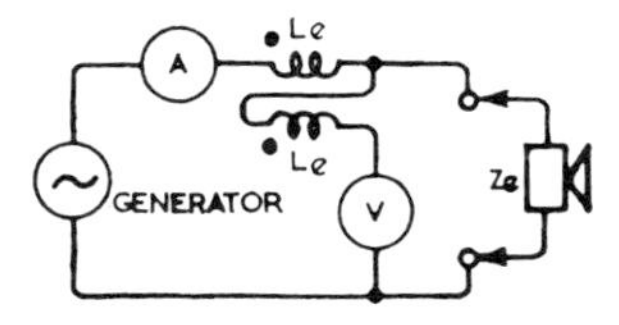

Fig. 18. Modification of Fig. 17 to cancel effect of loudspeaker inductance L_e.

This could be avoided by connecting in the circuit of Fig. 18 a bifilar inductance whose value L_e in each half is equal to the inductance of the voice coil. It is preferable, and not difficult, to wind this with an air core. In measuring L_e of the loudspeaker, it is important to measure it at a frequency well away from f_n, say, 10 kHz. Also it is important to measure it as an inductance in parallel with a resistance (D or tan δ scale, *not* the Q scale of a bridge), for the Q of the inductance at 10 kHz is usually of the order of one which can lead to serious error if the measurement is made as an inductance in series with a resistance. With a high-impedance voltmeter V, error due to series resistance of the inductor should be negligible.

If the new resonant frequency in the closed box f_{sc} is found, the ratio of volume is usually given as

$$V_{as}/V_b = (f_{sc}/f_{sa})^2 - 1 \qquad (100)$$

where f_{sa} is the resonant frequency of the speaker in air which we previously called f_s. However, this expression ignores the change in the acoustic mass M_{as} of 1.05 to 1.25 times which results from placing the speaker in the box. A more accurate method is to repeat the previous procedures for finding Q_e. Then if we call Q_{ea} and Q_{ec} the values of Q_e measured in air and in the closed box, respectively, then

$$V_{as}/V_b = [(f_{sc}Q_{ec})/(f_{sa}Q_{ea})] - 1. \qquad (101)$$

Also the ratio of the acoustic masses in air and in the closed box

$$M_{asa}/M_{asb} = f_{sc}Q_{ea}/f_{sa}Q_{ec} \quad (102)$$

should lie between 0.8 and 0.95.

With V_b known, V_{as} can be calculated. The size of V_b is not critical, but should not be too large, otherwise the ratio f_{sc}/f_{sa} becomes close to unity, and the accuracy of the V_{as}/V_b calculation falls. This can be seen from Eq. (100). Finally the values of f_{sa} and Q_{ea} are adjusted to take account of the change in M_{as} when the speaker is placed in the box. Thus

$$f_{sb} = f_{sa}(M_{asa}/M_{asb})^{1/2} \quad (103)$$

$$Q_{eb} = Q_{sa}/(M_{asa}/M_{asb})^{1/2}. \quad (104)$$

Thus the efficiency η_{ob} can be calculated from Eq. (77). This gives the result, rather surprising at first sight, that the electroacoustic conversion efficiency of a loudspeaker in the piston range can be calculated from electrical measurements alone.

The following alternative method is useful, particularly when the loudspeaker has to be placed in a box whose size is already determined or as a final check on a previously calculated box, or again if it becomes too difficult to seal the loudspeaker in the test box.[5]

First the vent, if adjustable, is made to resonate with the box somewhere near the speaker resonant frequency, but this is not very important. Then the three frequencies f_l, f_b, and f_h of Fig. 5 are found as accurately as possible. Special care is needed in reading f_b as the curve has a flat bottom.

From these readings we find f_{sb}, the resonant frequency of the speaker when mounted in the box,

$$f_{sb} = f_h f_l / f_b \quad (105)$$

and the compliance ratio C_{as}/C_{ab}, i.e.,

$$V_{as}/V_b = (f_h^2 - f_b^2)(f_b^2 - f_l^2)/f_h^2 f_l^2. \quad (106)$$

With the speaker resonant frequency in air f_{sa} already known and f_{sb} known from Eq. (105), we find the mass ratio M_{asa}/M_{asb} from Eq. (103), and then Q_{eb} from Eq. (104). Q_a is adjusted to Q_{ab} in a similar manner. By reference to Table I and Fig. 7, a suitable alignment can be found, thus setting the final values of f_b and Q_t. Note that Q_t is due to the parallel combination of 1) Q_{ab} and 2) Q_{eb} modified by the amplifier.

To estimate the value of Q_b, the "Q of the box and vent circuit," we measure I_b, the current through the speaker at f_b, with the input voltage held constant as before. Then

$$Q_b = (\omega_b/\omega_s)(C_{ab}/C_{as})[(1/Q_e) + (1/Q_a)][(I_b - I_o)/(I_e - I_b)]. \quad (107)$$

[5] Experience gained since the writing of this paper shows that accurate results are more easily obtained with this second method. Using a vented box is especially preferred if the speaker being measured has a low resonant frequency and if the testing box is fairly small. In such cases, small leaks in the "totally enclosed" box or around the loudspeaker pad ring can produce a virtual vent which produces the familiar twin peaks of loudspeaker impedance. But if the lower peak is below the limit of measurement, say, below 10 or 15 Hz, it could easily happen that the remaining upper peak would be taken as the single peak of a closed-box system with dire results.

Note that, because the difference between I_e and I_b will be small, the readings must be taken carefully.

Comparing Eq. (107) with Eq. (89), it can be seen that

$$(A_b)_{max} = 1/\{1 + [Q_a Q_e/Q_t(Q_a + Q_e)][(I_e - I_b)/(I_b - I_o)]\}. \quad (108)$$

This greatly simplifies the estimation of $(A_b)_{max}$.

A worked example of this method is given in the Appendix.[6]

XV. EXPERIMENTAL WORK

When the work was started from which this paper derived, it was necessary first to find the parameters for a number of loudspeakers. To date about fifty have been measured. In the case of one speaker, the effect of a number of modifications was observed; in the rest, usually one and occasionally two or three samples have been checked. The results obtained give confidence in the method. For example, from the readings and knowing other parameters, it is possible to calculate the flux density, and the values obtained give good correlation with readings on a flux meter. Changes of parameters during production can also be detected.

Some generalizations from the results have been mentioned earlier. For example, it was found that Q_a varies between about 3 and 10, which is high compared with the Q_t values of 0.2 to 0.6 required in Table I. Thus it was apparent that acoustic resistance usually has little effect on the damping of a speaker in a well-designed system. Values of Q_e varied from 0.2 to 0.5 in the case of high-quality speakers, through 0.5 to 1.0 in the better commercial grades of speakers, to 2 and even 3 in the case of some low-priced speakers.

Similarly efficiencies, for radiation from one side of an infinite baffle, ranged from −24 dB (0.4%) for low-priced speakers through −20 dB (1%) for medium-grade to −14 dB (4%) for high-quality speakers.

However, one must resist the tempting generalization that it is possible to rate the overall quality of a speaker by its Q_e or even its efficiency. For example, if efficiency is made higher and Q_e lower by reducing the cone mass M_{ms}, trouble with "break up" may result at middle frequencies. In fact while the best 8-in speaker tested had a Q_e of 0.33, there was one sample with good clean response at high frequencies with a high Q_e of 1.7 and another with Q_e below 1 which was less acceptable. It must be remembered that these readings, and the paper in general, are concerned only with low-frequency performance.

As a result of the design theory, a number of boxes have been made. In the absence of reliable measurements of sound pressure, all that can be said is that they gave a good improvement in clean low-frequency response, and that the cutoff frequencies are near the predicted values. Some particularly gratifying results have been obtained

[6] Experimental work, using the above method indicates that in practical boxes Q_b is often of the order of 10. This difference from the calculated values of 30 or more may be due to frictional losses in the timber. It is shown in Section XI that when Q_b is 10, the frequency response error is still only 1 to 2 dB. However, if there are sufficient air leaks, or if the cavity damping is excessive, as when the box is completely stuffed with underfelt, Q_b can fall below 5.

with 5-in speakers in modest boxes with response down to 80 Hz.

XVI. CONCLUSION

The work described herein was begun as an advanced development project in an attempt to obtain good low-frequency response from loudspeakers in small boxes. Unfortunately, no "revolutionary concept" was uncovered that offers something for nothing. On the other hand, it has provided a reasonably precise method of design that was previously lacking.

In general, a system with good flat response down to a predictable cutoff frequency can be designed, if the necessary parameters Q_e (and Q_a), V_{as}, and f_s are known for the loudspeaker. The box volume is closely proportional to the inverse square of cutoff frequency, which can be varied over a wide range. The output impedance R_g of the amplifier has a large effect in controlling the response, especially at f_h, the higher frequency of maximum impedance. Whether R_g needs to be positive, zero, or negative depends on the type of alignment and the Q parameters of the speaker. On the evidence available, acoustic resistance damping of the vent has no advantage, and is wasteful of box volume or bandwidth.

The advantages accruing from a predictable design include the possibility of optimum design of "rumble" filters. At frequencies below cutoff where negligible acoustic output is produced, these relieve the amplifier and loudspeaker of high signal amplitudes and thus minimize an annoying source of intermodulation distortion. Carried a step further, the use of auxiliary electrical filters makes it possible to trade box volume for low-frequency power capability of the amplifier.

Another way of reducing box volume is to increase the mass of the loudspeaker cone. But since this also reduces efficiency, it may be considered as a further example of trading amplifier size for box size, only this time the amplifier must deliver increased power over the whole audio spectrum. Again, the box volume may be reduced if a smaller diameter loudspeaker is used. The danger here is that the speaker excursion increases, but it is a good solution if the speaker is capable of a long linear excursion, or if the power output and/or low-frequency response is restricted.

The size of the magnet, or more precisely the flux density B, has a great influence on performance. Both efficiency, hence acoustic output, and Q_e vary with B^2; so it is clear that the saving of pennies on a smaller magnet can be poor economy.

The parameters needed for vented-box design can be measured with normal electrical measuring equipment together with a test box of known net internal volume. Nevertheless it is suggested to loudspeaker manufacturers that it is in their interest, as well as the user's, to publish typical values of Q_e, Q_a, V_{as}, and x_{max}, as well as f_s. These parameters are more useful to the system designer than, for example, flux density or total flux. Their publication would help ensure that the manufacturer's product is used to the best possible advantage.

The totally enclosed box has been mentioned only in passing, since it is well covered in [2]. But it should be noted that if a totally enclosed box is chosen with the same volume as that of alignment no. 5, the cutoff frequency is 1.55 times higher. With smaller boxes, the advantage decreases, though with practical sizes it is still appreciable. With larger totally enclosed boxes, the cutoff frequency can never fall below f_s, while the Chebyshev vented box alignments can extend the response considerably below f_s.

The greatest advantage of a vented box over an infinite baffle is the reduction of loudspeaker excursion, permitting higher power output or lower distortion. To this advantage, the present paper adds, it is hoped, a greater flexibility in design. The only apparent disadvantage of a vented box is in the transient response, but in fact the ringing is only perceptible with a misadjusted alignment. With proper adjustment, the effective reverberation time, though longer than that of a properly adjusted infinite baffle, is not long enough to appreciably color the sound in the listening room.

Finally, it is emphasized again that the acoustic response is due to the combination of speaker plus box plus amplifier as an integrated whole.

APPENDIX: WORKED EXAMPLE

This refers to a purely imaginary speaker, the readings being chosen to simplify the calculations. However, the readings would be typical of a medium-quality 8-in speaker.

Measurement of Speaker Parameters Q_a, Q_e, V_{as}, and f_s

With a Wheatstone bridge we find

dc resistance of speaker $R_e = 4.00$ ohms
dc resistance of calibrating resistor $R_c = 5.00$ ohms.

Now we place R_c in the test circuit of Fig. 17 and find that when V reads 1 volt,

$$I_c = 180 \text{ mA}.$$

Now

$$I_cR_c = 0.180\times 5.00 = 0.900.$$

Since this is 10% below the observed reading of 1 volt, one or both of the meters is inaccurate, but this is unimportant so long as their readings are constant with frequency and the reading of ammeter A is linear.

Then from Eq. (98),

$$I_e = I_cR_c/R_e = (0.180\times 5.00)/4.00 = 225 \text{ mA}.$$

We now suspend the loudspeaker in air as far from reflecting surfaces as possible and read the minimum current I_0 which is 25 mA at 55.0 Hz (f_{sa}, the speaker resonant frequency in air).

Then from Eq. (99),

$$r_0 = I_e/I_0 = 225/25 = 9$$

$$\sqrt{r_0} = \sqrt{9} = 3$$

$$\sqrt{(I_0I_e)} = \sqrt{(225\times 25)} = 75 \text{ mA}.$$

With the voltmeter V reading a constant 1 volt, the ammeter A reads 75 mA at 44.0 and 68.75 Hz.

First we use this reading to check $f_{sa} = \sqrt{(44.0\times 68.75)}$ from Eq. (93) $= 55.0$ Hz as before. Then from Eq. (97),

$$Q_a = f_a\sqrt{r_0}/(f_2-f_1) = (55\times 3)/(68.75-44) = 6.67$$

and from Eq. (95),

$$Q_e = Q_a/(r_o-1) = 6.67/(9-1) = 0.833.$$

The speaker is now placed in a vented box whose net volume is 1000 in^3 and we read the frequencies defined in Fig. 5,

$$f_h = 100\text{ Hz};\quad f_b = 60\text{ Hz};\quad f_l = 30\text{ Hz}.$$

Then from Eq. (105),

$$f_{sb} = f_h f_l / f_b = (100\times 30)/60 = 50\text{ Hz}$$

and from Eq. (106),

$$V_{as}/V_b = (f_h^2-f_b^2)(f_b^2-f_l^2)/f_h^2 f_l^2.$$

Computation is easier if we rewrite Eq. (106) as

$$V_{as}/V_b = (f_h+f_b)(f_h-f_b)(f_b+f_l)(f_b-f_l)/f_h^2 f_l^2$$

i.e.,

$$\begin{aligned} V_{as}/V_b &= (100+60)(100-60)(60+30)(60-30)/100^2\times 30^2 \\ &= (160\times 40\times 90\times 30)/(100\times 30\times 100\times 30) \\ &= 1.92 \end{aligned}$$

i.e.,

$$V_{as} = 1.92\times 1000 = 1920\text{ in}^3.$$

In the vented box, the speaker resonant frequency has dropped $f_{sb}/f_{sa} = 50/55 = 0.909$ times. Thus from Eq. (103),

$$M_{asa}/M_{asb} = (0.909)^2 = 0.826$$

and from Eq. (104),

$$Q_{ab} = 6.67/0.909 = 7.33$$

while

$$Q_{eb} = 0.833/0.909 = 0.917.$$

At f_b the current I_b was read as 220 mA. Then from Eq. (107), the Q of the box plus vent

$$\begin{aligned} Q_b &= (f_b/f_s)(C_{ab}/C_{as})[(Q_a+Q_e)/Q_a Q_e][(I_b-I_o)/(I_e-I_b)] \\ &= [60\times(7.333+0.917)\times(220-25)]/[50\times 1.92\times 7.33\times 0.917\times(225-220)] \\ &= (60\times 8.25\times 195)/(50\times 1.92\times 7.33\times 0.917\times 5) \\ &= 29.9. \end{aligned}$$

From Eq. (108) the maximum box loss in the quasi-Butterworth alignment described below, where $Q_t = 0.347$, is

$$\begin{aligned} (A_b)_{max} &= 1/\{1+[Q_a Q_e/Q_t(Q_a+Q_e)][(I_e-I_b)/(I_b-I_o)]\} \\ &= 1/\{1+(7.33\times 0.917\times 5)/(0.347\times 8.25\times 195)\} \\ &= 1/1.060 \end{aligned}$$

which is equivalent to 0.5 dB.

Efficiency η from Eq. (77)

$$\begin{aligned} \eta_{ob} &= 8.0\times 10^{-12} f_s^3 V_{as}/Q_e \\ &= (8.0\times 50^3\times 1920)/(10^{12}\times 0.917) \\ &= 2.09\times 10^{-3} \end{aligned}$$

which is equivalent to -26.6 dB in a box, or -23.6 dB on an infinite baffle (i.e., a true infinite baffle, not a totally enclosed medium-sized box which gives the same efficiency as a vented box), or -20.6 dB on a true infinite baffle, taking into account radiation from both front and back.

Thus if the speaker is mounted in a box and fed with a 5-watt amplifier, the acoustic power output will be

$$W_{ao} = \eta_{ob} W_{ei} = 5\times 2.09\times 10^{-3} = 0.0104\text{ Watt}.$$

If we assume a listening room of 16 × 12½ × 10 = 2000 ft^3, then from [4, p. 418, Fig. 11.12] an acoustic power of 0.003 watt provides +80-dB intensity level. Our output is 10.4/3 times, i.e., 5.4 dB greater than this; therefore the system is capable of a peak +85-dB intensity level.

Peak Excursion x_{pk}

We assume an alignment where the box is tuned to the same frequency as the loudspeaker, i.e., 50 Hz. This is typical of Butterworth alignments. Then the fixed part of the expression for x_{pk} in Eq. (84) is

$$(1.31\times 10^5\times \sqrt{W_{ao}})/f_b^2 S_d.$$

Now if the effective piston diameter is 7 in, i.e.,

$$S_d = \pi\times 3.5^2 = 38.5\text{ in}^2$$

then the expression becomes

$$1.31\times 10^5\times\sqrt{0.104}/(50^2\times 38.5) = 0.139\text{ in}.$$

Now the maximum value of the frequency-sensitive expression for a vented box in the useful band (above f_b) in Fig. 10 is approximately one quarter. Thus

$$x_{pk} = 0.139/4 = \pm 0.035\text{ in}$$

compared with ±0.098 in in a totally enclosed box (infinite baffle).

Box Design

First suppose we wish to obtain the best results with the original 1000-in^3 box. Allowing 10% for the bracing and volume displaced by the speaker, the optimum inside dimensions would be $\sqrt[3]{1100}\times(0.8,\ 1.0,\ 1.25)$ in, i.e., 8.28 × 10.33 × 12.9 in, say 8¼ × 10¼ × 13 in. This would need to be checked in case the original assumption of 10% was incorrect. Assuming that the dimensions are

Table V. Computation of three Butterworth alignments for imaginary speaker.

Type of alignment		QB_3	B_4	B_5	B_6(i)
C_{as}/C_{ab}		1.92	1.414	1.000	2.732
V_b (cubic inches)		1000	1358	1920	704
Box	Height (in.)	13	14	16	11½
	Width (in.)	10¼	11½	13	9
	Depth "d" (in.)	8¼	9	10	7½
Cutoff frequency f_3 (c/s)		58.5	50	50	50
Box frequency f_b (c/s)		54.7	50	50	50
L_v/S_v (in.$^{-1}$)		1.56	1.37	0.97	2.65
S_v (in.^{2})		7.69	10.07	16.25	4.50
Vent height "l" (in.)		¾	⅞	1¼	½
Q_t		.347	.383	.447	.299
$(Q_e)_{total}$		.364	.404	.476	.312
R_g/R_e		−.600	−.560	−.481	−.660

correct, then in a box similar to Fig. 9, the width of the vent will be 10¼ in. The length of the tunnel will be $d = 8\frac{1}{4}$ in, together with two thicknesses of timber (say ½ in each) plus a ½-in square stiffener on the top rear edge of the shelf, giving a total tunnel length of 9¾ in.

The simplest alignment for $C_{as}/C_{ab} = 1.92$ is a third-order quasi-Butterworth between alignments no. 4 and 5. From Fig. 7 (b),

$$f_3/f_s = 1.17, \text{ thus } f_3 = 50\times 1.17 = 58.5 \text{ Hz}$$

$$f_3/f_b = 1.07, \text{ thus } f_b = 58.5/1.07 = 54.7 \text{ Hz}.$$

Thus

$$\omega_b{}^2 = 1.18\times 10^5$$

and for the tunnel, from Eq. (61),

$$\begin{aligned}(L_v/S_v)_{required} &= 1.84\times 10^8/\omega_b{}^2 V_b \\ &= 1.84\times 10^8/1.18\times 10^5\times 10^3 \\ &= 1.56 \text{ in}^{-1}.\end{aligned}$$

Now if the tunnel height l = ¾ in, then area

$$S_v = 10\tfrac{1}{4}\times \tfrac{3}{4} = 7.69 \text{ in}^2$$

and

$$\begin{aligned}(L_v/S_v)_{end} &= 0.958/\sqrt{S_v} \\ &= 0.958/\sqrt{7.69} \\ &= 0.34 \text{ in}^{-1}\end{aligned}$$

$$\begin{aligned}(L_v/S_v)_{tunnel} &= 9.75/7.69 \\ &= 1.27 \text{ in}^{-1}.\end{aligned}$$

Thus

$$(L_v/S_v)_{available} = 1.61 \text{ in}^{-1}$$

which is about as close as can be obtained with the tolerances on the small dimension (¾ in) of l.

Amplifier Output Impedance R_g

Now by interpolation,

$$Q_t = 0.347$$

and since $Q_{ab} = 7.33$, $Q_{eb} = 0.917$, and from Eq. (70),

$$1/Q_t = 1/Q_a + 1/Q_e(1+R_g/R_e).$$

Thus

$$1/0.347 = 1/7.33 + 1/0.917(1+R_g/R_e).$$

Hence

$$R_g/R_e = -0.60.$$

Notes

1) $(L_v/S_v)_{end}$ is small compared with $(L_v/S_v)_{tunnel}$, and since the vent area is already small compared with the piston area, a simple hole in the front panel would be quite impractical as a vent. Its area would need to be about 1 in².

2) The dimension l (¾ in) is fairly critical.

3) Q_a has little effect on Q_t. The negative impedance required is fairly high but quite practical.

For comparison three Butterworth alignments have also been computed for this imaginary speaker so that the effect of amplifier filtering can be assessed (Table V). All three have cutoff frequencies of 50 Hz. But while B_4 has no filtering, B_5 has a simple CR filter which is −3 dB at 50 Hz (CR = 3180 μs), and B_6 has a peak 6 dB high at 53.5 Hz before it falls off at the rate of 12 dB per octave ($y = -1.732$, f_{aux} = 50 Hz).

ACKNOWLEDGMENT

The writer must acknowledge his heavy indebtedness to Novak's original paper [2], as well as to a number of his colleagues, including W. Buckland, D. A. Drake, J. G. Elder, M. C. Plumley, and N. K. Snow, who in many discussions have helped to hammer out the ideas presented. Special thanks are due to J. A. Lane who carried out most of the early experimental work and to K. W. Titmuss who continued it.

REFERENCES

1. E. J. Jordan, "Loudspeaker Enclosure Design," *Wireless World*, vol. 62, pp. 8-14 (Jan. 1956); pp. 75-79 (Feb. 1956).
2. J. F. Novak, "Performance of Enclosures for Low-Resonance High-Compliance Loudspeakers," *IRE Trans. Audio*, vol. AU-7, pp. 5-13 (Jan.-Feb. 1959).
3. L. L. Beranek, *Acoustics* (McGraw-Hill, London, 1959).
4. H. F. Olson, *Elements of Acoustical Engineering*, 2nd ed. (Van Nostrand, Princeton, N.J., 1947), pp. 154-156.
5. O. W. Eshbach, Ed., *Handbook of Engineering Fundamentals* (John Wiley, New York, 1936), p. 8-60.
6. A. N. Thiele, "Television IF Amplifiers with Linear Phase Response," *Proc. IRE (Aust.)*, vol. 19, p. 655 (Nov. 1958).
7. J. L. Stewart, *Circuit Theory and Design* (John Wiley, New York, 1956), pp. 159-163.
8. F. Langford-Smith, *Radiotron Designer's Handbook*, 4th ed. (A.W.V. Co., Sydney, 1952), p. 847.
9. R. P. Sallen and B. L. Key, "A Practical Method of Designing RC Active Filters," *IRE Trans. Circuit Theory*, vol. CT-2, No. 1, pp. 74-85 (Mar. 1955).
10. A. N. Thiele, "The Design of Filters Using only RC Sections and Gain Stages," *Electron. Eng.*, pp. 31-36 (Jan. 1956); pp. 80-82 (Feb. 1956).

Active and Passive Filters as Loudspeaker Crossover Networks*

J. ROBERT ASHLEY AND ALLAN L. KAMINSKY†

University of Colorado, Colorado Springs, Colo. 80907

This tutorial paper defines the function of a crossover network and then explores methods of meeting this function. For moderately priced two-way loudspeakers, a passive network at about 800–1600 Hz will continue to dominate the designs of the future. However, the use of active filters (electronic crossover networks) and buffer amplifiers offers the most significant means of loudspeaker improvement in the next decade. As one typical factor, crossover frequencies need to be lowered and crossover slopes increased, and the active filter is the only economical method of doing this.

INTRODUCTION: The crossover or frequency dividing network plays a most important role in the performance of high-quality loudspeaker systems. To date, individual drivers have not been capable of reproducing all frequencies present in music that are detectable by the human ear. The crossover network is a particular type of filter that allows various drivers, each suited to a particular range of frequencies in the audio spectrum, to be combined into a system capable of wide frequency coverage. The function of the crossover network then is simply to divide the frequency spectrum so that signals of the appropriate frequency range are directed to the appropriate driver of a multidriver loudspeaker system.

We have noted in the past a strong tendency to separate the filter problem from the overall loudspeaker system problem; consequently, some rather poor systems have been designed. As a symptom of the general ignorance of the system aspects of the crossover problem, consider the fact that most networks marketed separately do not specify the slope of the system transfer characteristic in the stop band. As a result, the novice tends to visualize a stone wall at a certain magic point in the frequency spectrum with tones to the left and to the right of this stone wall obediently marching off to their respective drivers. It seems a shame to destroy this illusion by noting that a filter with a stop band defined by a square corner and infinite slope is a classic example of a physically nonrealizable filter.

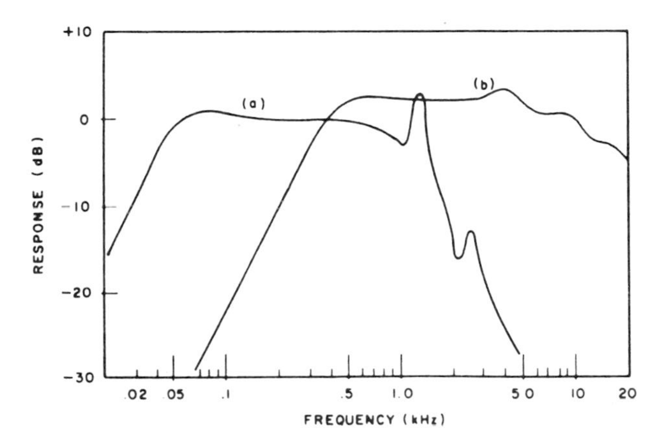

Fig. 1. Typical transfer characteristics. (a) 10-inch woofer; (b) 3-inch tweeter.

* Presented October 12, 1970, at the 39th Convention of the Audio Engineering Society, New York.

† Formerly with Rectilinear Research Corp., Bronx, N.Y.

The purpose of this paper is to study active and passive filter networks for use as loudspeaker crossover networks. We discuss the problem from a total system standpoint and point out the need for overlap in the responses of the drivers, the effect of driver impedance variations, the need to consider phase shift in the drivers and filter networks, etc. To keep the results from becoming too abstract, we use, as a typical example, the two-way direct radiator loudspeaker system which is a mainstay of the present audio equipment market. Such a loudspeaker, with a 10-inch woofer and a 3-inch tweeter in a 1.5-ft^3 closed box seems to have the blend of price, size, and performance which best satisfies the present market. By simple shifts of the frequency axes, the results we present can be applied to systems using different driver sizes.

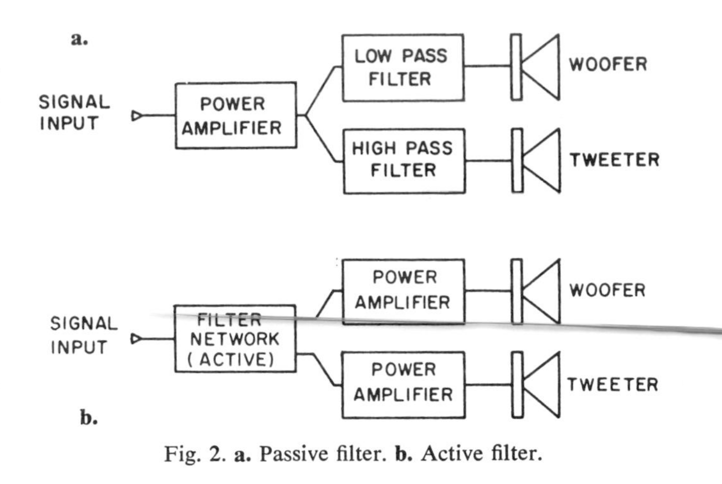

Fig. 2. **a.** Passive filter. **b.** Active filter.

DIRECT RADIATOR LOUDSPEAKER RESPONSE

Before we can consider the filter design aspect of the crossover problem, we must have a good idea of what the capabilities of the direct radiator loudspeaker are. Beranek gives an excellent general discussion of this problem [1, ch. 7]. Applying this theory to a 10-inch woofer with a correctly designed magnet [2] yields a driver with a transfer characteristic similar to that shown in Fig. 1, curve (a). The low frequency fall-off is caused by the failure of the system to maintain a constant acceleration characteristic below the resonant frequency. The 12-dB per octave fall-off above 1 kHz is caused by the radiation resistance reaching a constant value for this size cone [2]. The "spike" in the response is quite typical of the woofers we have measured and is caused by a standing wave along the cone as shown in [1, Fig. 7.9]. (Most woofers for closed-box systems have heavier (thicker) cones than the one referenced by Beranek and this accounts for a slight increase in the frequency of the spike.) In addition to these factors, the direct radiator loudspeaker becomes markedly more directive above 1 kHz, and the angle of the cone adds to this problem. Thus, the crossover network must inhibit woofer excitation above 1 kHz and direct this portion of the spectrum to the tweeter.

The tweeter obeys the same laws of nature as the woofer, but the lower mass, diameter, and compliance yield the curve shown in Fig. 1, curve (b). If the tweeter magnet is chosen properly, the efficiency will be equal to or slightly greater than the efficiency of the woofer because the mass and diameter decrease in such a way as to cause their individual effects to be canceled. This is desirable in a passive network system since the balance adjustment can then be made on the tweeter channel. The only parameter that does not scale directly is the frequency at which standing waves appear in the cone. Consequently, tweeters show considerable "roughness" in their high-frequency response and the only reasonable solution is to use a three-way system with a 1-inch driver for the upper end of the spectrum.

In addition to proper frequency division, the crossover network must protect the tweeter from the low-frequency end of the spectrum for two reasons. First, most of the power in the music spectrum [3] is concentrated below 1 kHz and the output of a 100-watt amplifier delivering the full music spectrum would be quite sufficient to destroy (by heat) the physically small and light-weight voice coil of the tweeter. Second, since the direct radiator tweeter is also operating in an acceleration mode, its displacement (for constant acoustic power output) must increase rapidly (12 db per octave) as frequency decreases. The tweeter cone does not have room to move more than a couple of millimeters; consequently, the crossover network must protect the tweeter from low tones to prevent the generation of gross harmonic distortion.

The driver considerations detailed above define the function of the crossover network and indicate that the role it plays is critical to proper overall loudspeaker system performance. From the standpoint of the drivers alone, the crossover network should have the highest possible slope in the stop band regions. We will see that this is more easily said than done when the total problem is considered.

PASSIVE AND ACTIVE FILTERS

Networks that achieve the frequency division desirable for crossover action in a multidriver loudspeaker system fall into two general categories. The type of network most commonly employed in commercially available systems is illustrated in Fig. 2**a**. In this arrangement, the composite signal to be reproduced is brought up to the level necessary to drive the transducers before any filtering is performed. The subsequent filtering, which is done at high level, is achieved by networks synthesized solely with passive (i.e., *R, L, C*) elements. Such filters are popular since a system employing passive filters requires only one power amplifier, and since the crossover network dissipates very little power and may be completely contained within the box that houses the various drivers of the loudspeaker system. This is usually considered to be a desirable state of affairs since most loudspeaker systems are presently marketed independently of power amplifiers.

The second general technique for solving the crossover problem is illustrated in Fig. 2**b**. Here the filtering necessary for frequency division is performed at low level. The various low-level signals are then routed through the separate power amplifiers that service the individual drivers of the loudspeaker system. The low-level filter used in the arrangement can be synthesized with either passive or active (with amplifiers) networks. Since the active network can be synthesized with only resistors, capacitors, and operational amplifiers [3], the current trend is to make electronic crossover networks with active filters. Although the cost of operational amplifiers at

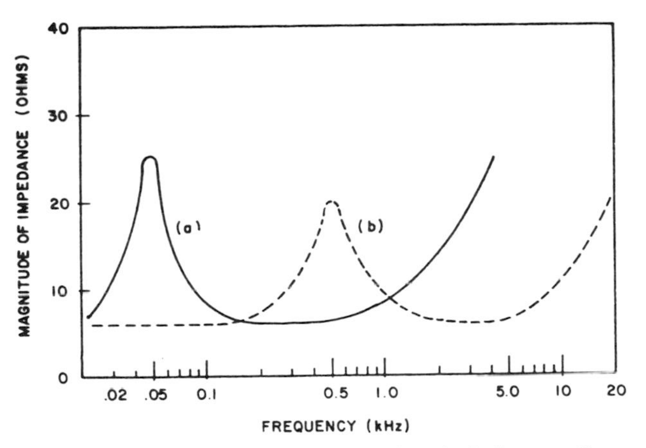

Fig. 3. Impedance characteristics of typical direct radiator driver loudspeakers. (a) 10-inch woofer; (b) 3-inch tweeter.

one time made synthesis of active crossover networks a strictly academic problem, recent advances in solid-state technology have increased the viability of active filters.

FILTER TERMINATIONS

It is most enlightening to study some of the problems inherent in the design of a passive crossover network. Most networks of this type are synthesized on the assumption that the network is terminated by a pure and constant resistance. The validity of this assumption, however, is questionable. Beranek [1] and Small [4] note that the impedance of the direct radiator loudspeaker is anything but a pure and constant resistance. As shown in curve (a) of Fig. 3, the impedance versus frequency characteristic of our typical 10-inch woofer has two significant deviations from constant resistance behavior. The low-frequency peak is caused by the mechanical resonance employed to achieve satisfactory low-frequency response in a direct radiator loudspeaker. The rise at the high-frequency end of the range is caused by the voice coil inductance. If the woofer is not designed for "long throw," this rise will occur above the frequency where other considerations have significantly decreased the woofer response. However, most small-box woofers are "long throw" to allow the motion required in the low bass region. The long-throw voice coil is usually double wound and some three centimeters long. This much wire near the soft iron of the pole piece will have a very significant inductance. Typically, the voice coil inductance of a long-throw woofer will give an automatic 6-dB per octave crossover at 600–800 Hz. In passive networks this inductance can be included as part of the inductor connected in series with the woofer if and only if the crossover frequency is lower than 600 Hz.

It is also interesting to note that the driver impedance of some 10 ohms causes passive filter elements (especially the capacitors) to be rather large. Intuitively we expect this since capactive reactances of tens of ohms can only be attained with tens or hundreds of microfarads at crossover frequencies less than 1 kHz.

The use of an active filter with separate buffer amplifiers to energize the various drivers alleviates most of these problems. With respect to the termination impedance of the filter, it is obvious that the buffer power amplifier isolates the driving point impedance of the loudspeaker from the output of the filter. The input impedance of the buffer amplifier can be made any desired value of pure and constant resistance and this eliminates the termination impedance problem for either active or passive realizations of the low-level crossover filters. Also, the very low Thevenin impedance of low-distortion power amplifiers is more suitable for exciting variable impedance driver units. *Thus, the buffer amplifier is better for both the filter termination and the loudspeaker driving source.*

The other problem caused by the loudspeaker as a termination impedance is the size of capacitors. The low-level filter can be synthesized for characteristic impedances of the order of kilohms, and this reduces capacitor size to the order of tenths of a microfarad. Passive filters which require inductors would be unwieldy as tens of henries would be required; however, the whole idea of active filter synthesis is to avoid the use of inductors, so this is not a significant problem. Thus, the inclusion of buffer power amplifiers allows the use of active filters synthesized with only resistors, capacitors, and operational amplifiers. The cost is much less than the cost of a good passive filter network at the 10-ohm level; furthermore, the availability of inexpensive 5-watt integrated-circuit power amplifiers alters the economic consideration regarding buffer amplifiers. If a high-slope crossover network is desired, it is actually less expensive to use operational amplifiers in active filters and integrated-circuit power amplifiers rather than a single power amplifier and a passive filter. Regarding marketing and compatibility problems, we will retreat to our ivory tower and offer no comments.

In the following sections we discuss several types of passive filters suitable for insertion between a single power amplifier and the driver loudspeakers. We will use the assumption of constant terminating impedance with the advice that a fair proficiency with computers is required to do otherwise. Then we summarize the use of active filter techniques with buffer power amplifiers for each of the driver loudspeakers.

BUTTERWORTH PASSIVE FILTERS

Various classes of filters may be employed in crossover design. A review of the approximation problem of modern network synthesis [5] gives a worthwhile comparison of modern filters. Bessel filters may be used since they have excellent phase and transient response characteristics. However, the frequency response change in the crossover region is too gradual for most loudspeakers. The Chebyshev equal-ripple filters achieve excellent frequency division with attendant wide fluctuations in input impedance. The best compromise between frequency response and input impedance seems to be the Butterworth characteristic. As pointed out by Ashley [7], the well-known 6- and 12-dB per octave constant resistance crossover networks are actually first- and second-order Butterworth filter networks.

The Butterworth low-pass characteristic

$$T[j(\omega/\omega_0)]T^*[j(\omega/\omega_0)] = \frac{1}{1+(\omega/\omega_0)^{2n}} \quad (1)$$

where

$$\omega_0 = 2\pi f_c \quad (2)$$

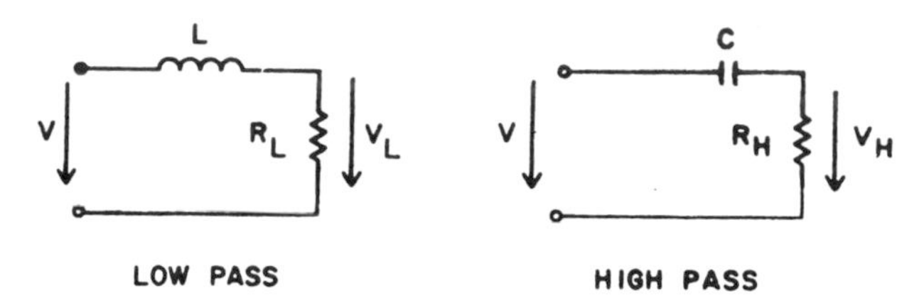

Fig. 4. First-order filter.

and f_c is the crossover frequency, is realized by implementing the low-pass transfer operator

$$T(p/\omega_0) = \frac{1}{B_n(p/\omega_0)} \tag{3}$$

where

$$p = d/dt = j\omega \tag{4}$$

$$s = p/\omega_0 \tag{5}$$

and $B_n(p/\omega_0)$ is a Butterworth polynomial of order n. These are given in Table I for reference.

Table I. Butterworth polynomials.

n	$B_n(s)$
1	$s+1$
2	$s^2+\sqrt{2}s+1$
3	s^3+2s^2+2s+1
4	$s^4+2.6131259s^3+3.4142136s^2+2.6131259s+1$
5	$s^5+3.2360680s^4+5.2360680s^3+5.2360680s^2+3.2360680s+1$

Consider now the first-order filter of Fig. 4. Clearly,

$$\frac{V_L}{V} = \frac{R_L/L}{s+R_L/L} \tag{6}$$

$$\frac{V_H}{V} = \frac{s}{s+1/R_HC}. \tag{7}$$

It is apparent that if

$$\omega_0 = \frac{R_L}{L} = \frac{1}{R_HC} \tag{8}$$

then

$$V_L+V_H = V \tag{9}$$

that is, if this first-order network is used, the sum of the outputs is a perfect replica of the input. This would seem to be a desirable property for a crossover network to have. Note that this first-order constant resistance filter is a Butterworth filter, with a stop-band slope of 6 dB per octave on both channels. Now the usual slope of a tone control circuit with the control in a maximum position is 6 dB per octave; thus, it is easy to observe how little the signals are actually attenuated in the stop-band region of this type of filter. The obvious consequence of this is that the two drivers must overlap in frequency response for about a 4-octave range; that is, the woofer must have nearly flat response through two octaves above crossover frequency and the tweeter must have nearly flat response for two octaves below crossover frequency. The curves we have presented for our typical 10-inch woofer and 3-inch tweeter do not meet this requirement, and we have found very few commercially available units where this requirement is met. The result is "roughness" in the crossover region which can be both measured and heard.

The obvious solution to this overlap problem is to increase the attenuation of the crossover filters in their stop-band region. That is to say, use a higher order Butterworth filter such as the second-order or 12-dB per octave constant resistance crossover network.

The schematic diagram of a second-order filter appears in Fig. 5. Here,

$$V_L/V = (\omega_{0L})^2/\{s^2+2\zeta_L\omega_{0L}s+(\omega_{0L})^2\} \tag{10}$$

where

$$(\omega_{0L})^2 = 1/L_LC_L$$

and

$$\zeta_L = (1/2R_L)\sqrt{L_L/C_L}. \tag{11}$$

Also,

$$V_H/V = s^2/\{s^2+2\zeta_H\omega_{0H}s+(\omega_{0H})^2\} \tag{12}$$

where

$$(\omega_{0H})^2 = 1/L_HC_H$$

$$\zeta_H = (1/2R_H)\sqrt{L_H/C_H}. \tag{13}$$

Now, if

$$\omega_{0L} = \omega_{0H} = \omega_0$$

$$\zeta_L = \zeta_H = \zeta = 1/\sqrt{2} \tag{14}$$

then this second-order crossover network is a second-order Butterworth filter. Note, in this case, that

$$(V_L+V_H)/V = (s^2+\omega_0^2)/(s^2+\sqrt{2}\omega_0s+\omega_0^2) \tag{15}$$

and observe that at the crossover frequency,

$$s = j\omega_0 \tag{16}$$

so that

$$(V_L+V_H)/V|_{s=j\omega_0} = 0. \tag{17}$$

This indicates a severe problem in the form of a "hole" in the frequency response at the crossover frequency. Ashley [6] demonstrated to the 13th Convention of the Audio Engineering Society that this "hole" can be heard.

One common solution to this problem that is currently employed by a number of loudspeaker manufacturers is to invert the polarity of, say, the woofer in the loudspeaker system. The information then received by the listener is actually

$$(V_H-V_L)/V = (s^2-\omega_0^2)/(s^2+\sqrt{2}\omega_0s+\omega_0^2). \tag{18}$$

This eliminates the hole at the crossover point as far as magnitude is concerned; however, a somewhat extraordinary phase characteristic is then produced.

For either the inverted or noninverted driver connec-

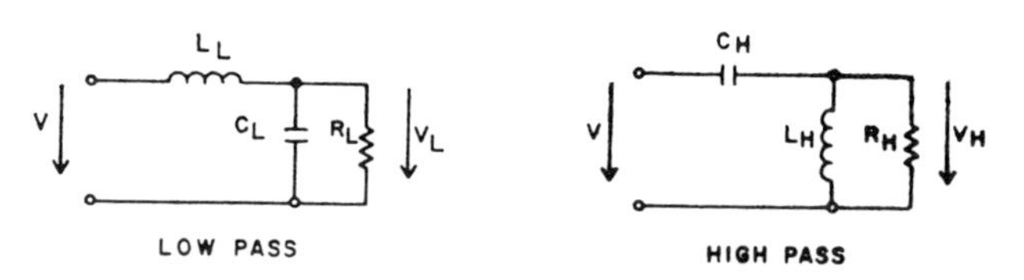

Fig. 5. Second-order filter.

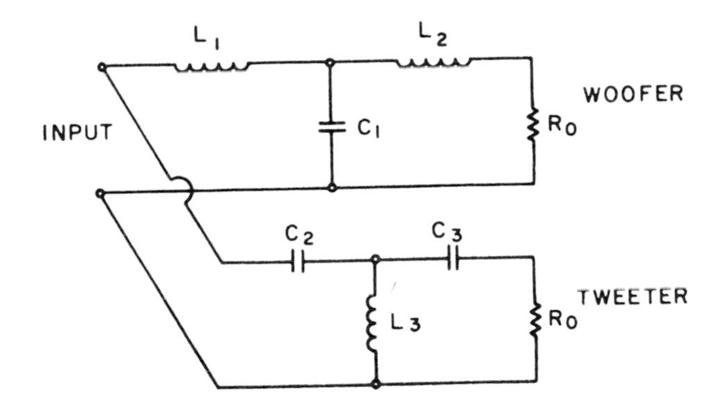

DESIGN EQUATIONS

LOW PASS SECTION

$$L_1 = \frac{3 R_0}{4 \pi f_c}$$

$$L_2 = \frac{R_0}{4 \pi f_c}$$

$$C_1 = \frac{2}{3 \pi f_c R_0}$$

HIGH PASS SECTION

$$C_2 = \frac{1}{3 \pi f_c R_0}$$

$$C_3 = \frac{1}{\pi f_c R_0}$$

$$L_3 = \frac{3 R_0}{8 \pi f_c}$$

Fig. 6. Third-order Butterworth filters as an 18-dB per octave constant-resistance frequency dividing network.

tion, the total power (without regard to cancellation because of phase) delivered by the loudspeakers is constant with frequency. Furthermore, the response of each filter output is down 3 dB at the crossover frequency and the slope is 12 dB per octave in the stop band. The requirement for more components is the usual reason for rejecting this kind of filter, but we feel that the actual decrease in sound quality (caused by the hole or extraordinary phase characteristic) is the more significant reason for not using this type of network.

Seeing the trouble that occurs in going from a first- to a second-order Butterworth filter might tend to make us ignore the third-order Butterworth in spite of its 18-dB per octave slope in the stop band. One author [7] was convinced that the hole at crossover frequency would be such a problem that the Butterworth filters above first-order would not be very useful for crossover networks. Then, Henne demonstrated with an analog computer [3]

Table II. Element values for third order Butterworth filters with 8 ohm drivers.

F_C (HZ)	L_1 (MH)	L_2 (MH)	C_1 (UF)	C_2 (UF)	C_3 (UF)	L_3 (MH)
100.00	19.10	6.37	265.26	132.63	397.89	9.55
125.89	15.17	5.06	210.70	105.35	316.05	7.59
158.49	12.05	4.02	167.37	83.68	251.05	6.03
199.53	9.57	3.19	132.94	66.47	199.42	4.79
251.19	7.60	2.53	105.60	52.80	158.40	3.80
316.23	6.04	2.01	83.88	41.94	125.82	3.02
398.11	4.80	1.60	66.63	33.31	99.94	2.40
501.19	3.81	1.27	52.93	26.46	79.39	1.91
630.96	3.03	1.01	42.04	21.02	63.06	1.51
794.33	2.40	.80	33.39	16.70	50.09	1.20
1000.00	1.91	.64	26.53	13.26	39.79	.95
1258.93	1.52	.51	21.07	10.54	31.61	.76
1584.89	1.21	.40	16.74	8.37	25.10	.60
1995.26	.96	.32	13.29	6.65	19.94	.48
2511.89	.76	.25	10.56	5.28	15.84	.38
3162.28	.60	.20	8.39	4.19	12.58	.30
3981.07	.48	.16	6.66	3.33	9.99	.24
5011.87	.38	.13	5.29	2.65	7.94	.19
6309.57	.30	.10	4.20	2.10	6.31	.15
7943.28	.24	.08	3.34	1.67	5.01	.12
10000.00	.19	.06	2.65	1.33	3.98	.10

that the third-order Butterworth filter crossover network has flat voltage and power frequency response with a gradual change in phase across the band. As demonstrated at the 38th Convention of the Audio Engineering Society, this change in phase across the band cannot be heard. This means that the third-order Butterworth filter must receive serious consideration as a high-level crossover network.

Straightforward application of the methods of modern network synthesis [5] yields the third-order Butterworth crossover network of Fig. 6. This filter will have 3-dB attenuation at the crossover frequency (as do all Butterworth filters) and a slope of 18 dB per octave in the stop band. Listening to the individual channels when this filter is used, it becomes evident that a much higher attenuation exists in the stop band than when a first-order filter is used; indeed, this filter is not a bad approximation to the "stone wall" effect previously described.

We note in passing that a fourth-order Butterworth crossover network will have the same problem as a second-order filter and is not to be recommended. However, the fifth-order filter does have the same properties as the third-order filter, except for a total phase shift change of 720° instead of 360°. Weinberg [5] gives all the information needed to synthesize all of the Butterworth filters, and his tables will quickly yield the fifth-order filter. Since the third-order filter seems to be of considerable importance, we have used a computer to generate Table II giving the element values for 8-ohm drivers.

QUASI-SECOND-ORDER PASSIVE CROSSOVER NETWORKS

In the previous section, we described the frequency response problem with second-order constant-resistance filters that led Ashley [6] to suggest a buffered crossover network which forced the phasor voltages applied to the drivers to add up to the applied voltage. The use of buffer amplifiers makes possible a true 12 dB/octave slope in the high-pass filter. (See the second order curves of Fig. 14). This basic idea has been generalized for passive filters by Small's development of what he has termed a "constant voltage crossover network." [4] Working independently on a commercially available loudspeaker system, Kaminsky generalized the series connected first-order Butterworth filter by relaxing the constant input impedance constraint and obtained the quasi-second-order filter shown in Fig. 7. Here

$$\frac{V_L}{V} = \frac{s+(R_L+R_H)\omega_0/2R_L\zeta}{R_H C(s^2+2\zeta\omega_0 s+\omega_0{}^2)} \tag{19}$$

$$\frac{V_H}{V} = \frac{s(s+2\zeta R_H\omega_0/[R_L+R_H])}{s^2+2\zeta\omega_0 s+\omega_0{}^2} \tag{20}$$

where

$$\omega_0{}^2 = 1/LC$$

$$\zeta = (R_L+R_H)/(2R_LR_H)\sqrt{L/C}. \tag{21}$$

Observe that

$$V_L+V_H = V \tag{22}$$

as, indeed, it must if Kirchhoff is to be satisfied. If, as is usually the case,

$$R_L = R_H = R \tag{23}$$

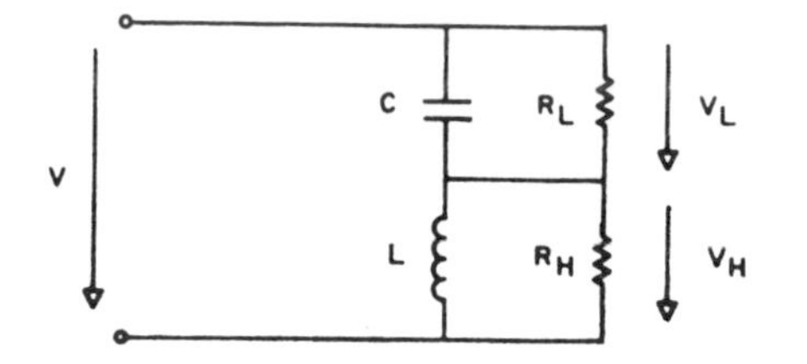

Fig. 7. A simple quasi-second order passive crossover network.

(19) and (20) reduce to

$$\frac{V_L}{V} = \frac{s+\omega_0/\zeta}{RC(s^2+2\zeta\omega_0 s+\omega_0{}^2)}. \tag{24}$$

$$\frac{V_H}{V} = \frac{s(s+\zeta\omega_0)}{s^2+2\zeta\omega_0 s+\omega_0{}^2}. \tag{25}$$

If $\zeta = 1$, then this configuration specifies a first-order filter. However, suppose that $\zeta = 0.5$. Then a straight-line Bode plot reveals the approximate behavior of the filter to be as follows. The low-frequency channel cuts off at 12 dB per octave at ω_0 and 6 dB per octave above $2\omega_0$; the high-frequency channel cuts off at 12 dB per octave at ω_0 and 6 dB per octave below $0.5\omega_0$. Hence, the appellation of quasi-second-order seems appropriate for this filter. This is illustrated in Fig. 8.

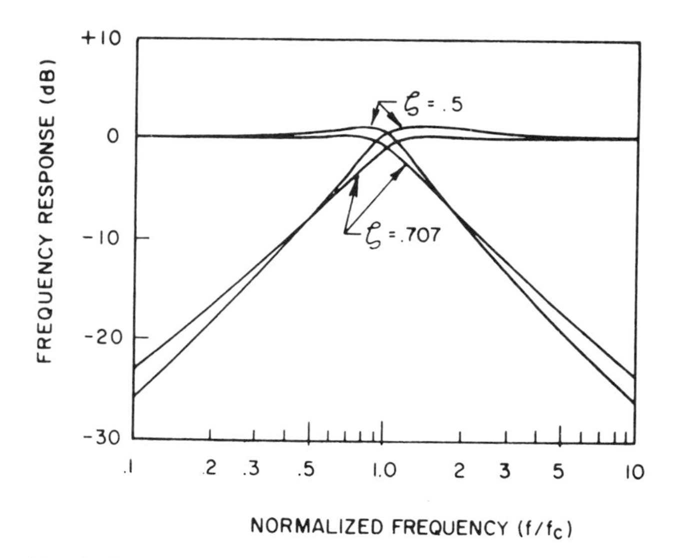

Fig. 8. Frequency response of the quasi-second order filters.

The class of filters exemplified in this section (such filters are possible for any order) have desirable characteristics that do not stop at the lack of phase error. One of these is that the quasi-second-order filter has half the components of a conventional second-order filter. The other is that component tolerances are not as important as in conventional crossover networks, since a slight error in the crossover point affects both channels in a complementary manner.

Computer-generated element values for this crossover network with 8-ohm terminations are listed in Table III.

ACTIVE FILTERS FOR CROSSOVER NETWORKS

In the preceding sections we have demonstrated that an active filter network followed by buffer amplifiers is a better solution to the crossover problem, from the standpoint of flexibility and economics, than is a system with passive high-level filters. In this section we survey some of the better techniques for synthesizing active filters with high-gain operational amplifiers.

First-order filters can be realized by simple *R-C* networks, but the slope of 6 dB per octave in the stop bands is not high enough to justify the system complexity. A straightforward realization of second-order high- and low-pass filters will have exactly the same hole at the crossover frequency that plagued the second-order Butterworth passive network. The third-order conventional Butterworth high- and low-pass filter networks do have flat frequency response and can be synthesized with only two operational amplifiers. This attractive filter is shown in Fig. 9. Application of the tables of values for Butterworth filters, as given in Foster [8], yields the typical component values shown in Table IV. (This filter, with a crossover frequency of 318 Hz, was demonstrated at the 38th Convention of the Audio Engineering Society.) The values for the high-pass filter are based on a characteristic impedance of 20 kΩ.

The real advantage of the active-filter approach is that the constant-voltage crossovers are simple to synthesize. Following Small [4], we consider both symmetrical and asymmetrical crossover characteristics. We restrict our

Table III. Element values for quasi-second-order filters with 8 ohm drivers.

	ZETA = 1/SQRT(2)		ZETA = 1/2	
F_C (HZ)	L (MH)	C (UF)	L (MH)	C (UF)
100.00	9.00	281.35	6.37	397.89
125.89	7.15	223.48	5.06	316.05
158.49	5.68	177.52	4.02	251.05
199.53	4.51	141.01	3.19	199.42
251.19	3.58	112.01	2.53	158.40
316.23	2.85	88.97	2.01	125.82
398.11	2.26	70.67	1.60	99.94
501.19	1.80	56.14	1.27	79.39
630.96	1.43	44.59	1.01	63.06
794.33	1.13	35.42	.80	50.09
1000.00	.90	28.13	.64	39.79
1258.93	.72	22.35	.51	31.61
1584.89	.57	17.75	.40	25.10
1995.26	.45	14.10	.32	19.94
2511.89	.36	11.20	.25	15.84
3162.28	.28	8.90	.20	12.58
3981.07	.23	7.07	.16	9.99
5011.87	.18	5.61	.13	7.94
6309.57	.14	4.46	.10	6.31
7943.28	.11	3.54	.08	5.01
10000.00	.09	2.81	.06	3.98

Table IV Element values for operational amplifier filters.

F HZ	C0 (UF)	C1 (UF)	C2 (UF)	C3 (UF)	C5 (UF
100.00	.07958	.37797	.41237	.05173	.15915
125.89	.06321	.30023	.32756	.04109	.12642
158.49	.05021	.23848	.26019	.03264	.10042
199.53	.03988	.18943	.20667	.02593	.07977
251.19	.03168	.15047	.16417	.02059	.06336
316.23	.02516	.11952	.13040	.01636	.05033
398.11	.01999	.09494	.10358	.01299	.03998
501.19	.01588	.07541	.08228	.01032	.03176
630.96	.01261	.05990	.06536	.00820	.02522
794.33	.01002	.04758	.05191	.00651	.02004
1000.00	.00796	.03780	.04124	.00517	.01592
1258.93	.00632	.03002	.03276	.00411	.01264
1584.89	.00502	.02385	.02602	.00326	.01004
1995.26	.00399	.01894	.02067	.00259	.00798
2511.89	.00317	.01505	.01642	.00206	.00634
3162.28	.00252	.01195	.01304	.00164	.00503
3981.07	.00200	.00949	.01036	.00130	.00400
5011.87	.00159	.00754	.00823	.00103	.00318
6309.57	.00126	.00599	.00654	.00082	.00252
7943.28	.00100	.00476	.00519	.00065	.00200
10000.00	.00080	.00378	.00412	.00052	.00159

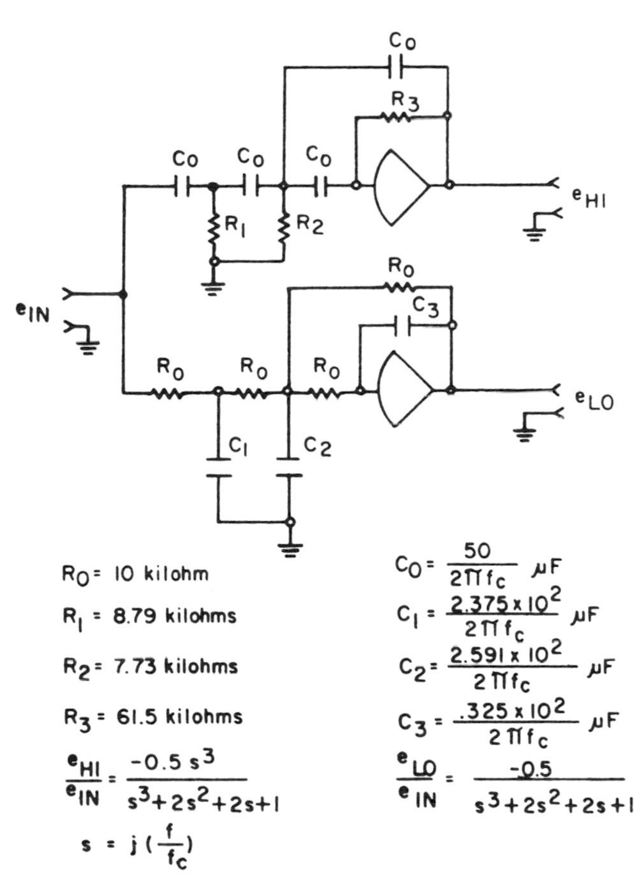

Fig. 9. Realization of the third-order Butterworth electronic crossover network with Rauch filters.

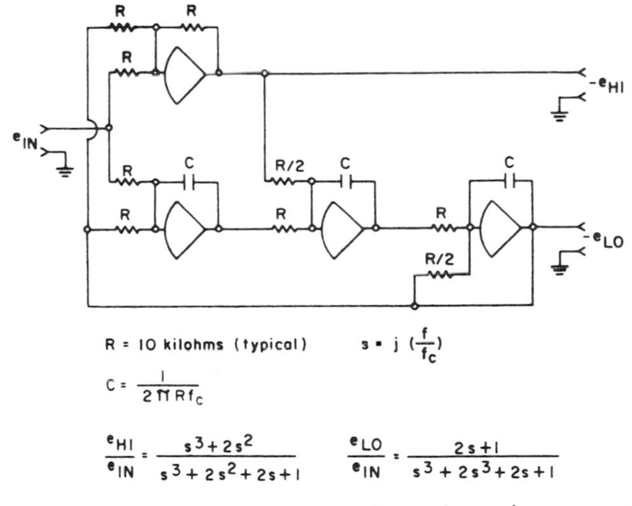

Fig. 11. Symmetrical constant-voltage electronic crossover network with third-order Butterworth characteristic function.

methods to those employing high-gain operational amplifiers because of the availability of inexpensive, high-performance, integrated-circuit devices.

The simplest approach to either symmetrical or asymmetrical electronic crossover synthesis is to use the method suggested by Ashley [6], [7] which requires only one filter network. The second-order symmetrical filter is shown in Fig. 10. In this case, we have chosen to synthesize a low-pass filter and then derive (by subtraction) the high-frequency output. This requires one less operational amplifier than synthesizing the high-pass filter and deriving the low-frequency output. Observe that the damping coefficient ζ can be modified by changing only two resistors, and that the crossover frequency f_c is controlled by two capacitors. (The capacitor size for 10-kΩ resistors is given in column C5 of Table IV.) This network is the electronic analog of the quasi-second-order passive crossover network and will have the frequency response of Fig. 8.

Applying this same approach to a filter with a third-order characteristic function yields the symmetrical network of Fig. 11. Here we have combined the function of the summing operational amplifier in such a way that this network requires only four operational amplifiers. Since this is the same number required for the second-order network, there is considerable motivation to use this network and obtain the 12-dB per octave slope in both pass

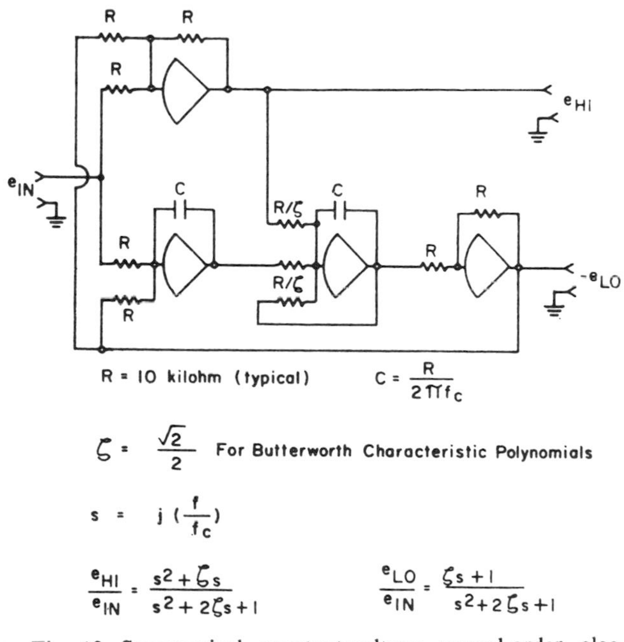

Fig. 10. Symmetrical constant-voltage second-order electronic crossover network.

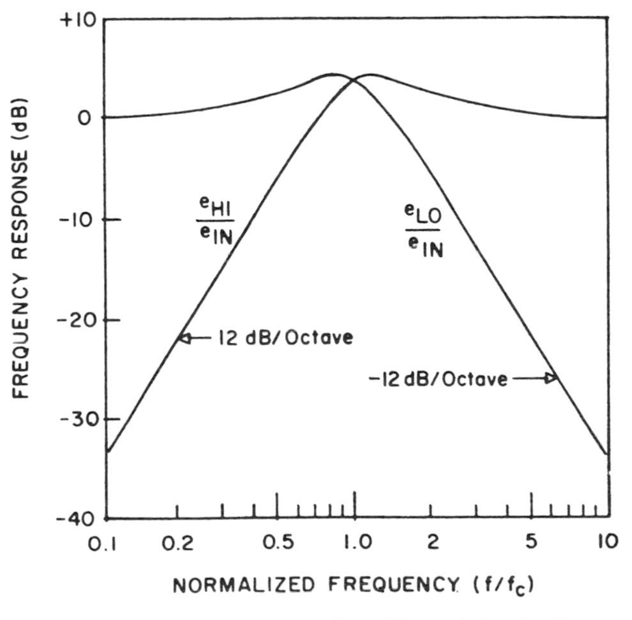

Fig. 12. Frequency response of modified third-order Butterworth electronic crossover network.

bands as shown in Fig. 12. Again, capacitor sizes are given in the C5 column of Table IV.

It is possible to synthesize higher order filters of this type with the cost measured in additional operational amplifiers. Since the third-order filters offer a significant improvement in performance as compared to presently available passive filter networks, we will leave the rather obvious details to those who can demonstrate a justifying need for such systems.

The synthesis of asymmetrical constant-voltage networks can be accomplished, for up to third-order characteristics functions, as shown in Fig. 13. Here the basic filter section is a high-pass active network and the low-frequency channel is derived by subtraction. The resultant high-pass characteristic is desirable because the frequency response shown in Fig. 14 is better matched to the capabilities of both buffer amplifiers and driver units. The third order Butterworth high-pass filter in Fig. 13 can be constructed using the capacitor values of Table IV. This simple network is a good solution to the crossover problem if the woofer driver has extended response in the high-frequency range.

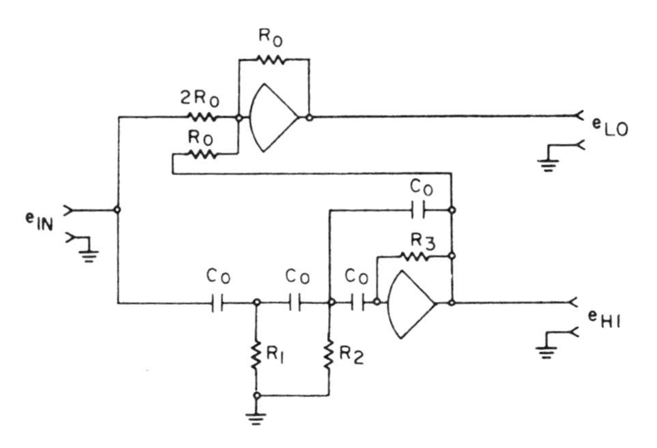

$$\frac{e_{HI}}{e_{IN}} = \frac{-0.5\,s^3}{s^3+2s^2+2s+1} \qquad \frac{e_{LO}}{e_{IN}} = \frac{-0.5\,(2s^2+2s+1)}{s^3+2s^2+2s+1}$$

$$s = j\left(\frac{f}{f_c}\right)$$

Fig. 13. Asymmetrical constant-voltage active filter crossover network with third-order Butterworth characteristic function.

CONCLUDING REMARKS

The consideration of all aspects of the crossover problem for direct radiator loudspeaker systems points to several optimum designs for various size and power capabilities. The two-way loudspeaker constrained to a 2-ft³ box should have a 10-inch woofer and a 3-inch tweeter with a $\zeta = 0.5$ quasi-second-order passive crossover network designed for a crossover frequency of about 800 Hz. Decreasing the box size would call for a smaller woofer and an increase in the crossover frequency. Substitution of a passive third-order Butterworth filter for the quasi-second-order filter would result in a slight improvement in performance near the crossover frequency, but it is doubtful if this improvement is worth the added cost for this kind of loudspeaker system.

The next significant level of system performance im-

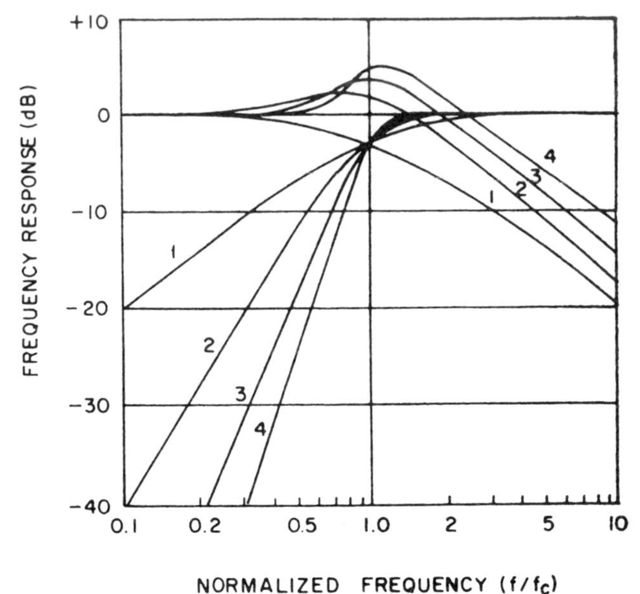

Fig. 14. Frequency response of asymmetrical crossover networks with Butterworth characteristic functions.

provement requires a larger cabinet and a three-way system. Using a 5-ft³ box, a 12-inch woofer, 5-inch mid-range, and 1-inch tweeter leads to a most interesting crossover network design. Small [4] gives the network needed for three-way constant-voltage crossover and the crossover frequencies should be set at 500 and 2500 Hz. (Kaminsky has designed a similar network for a commercially available three-way system.)

Further increase in system performance will require a still larger cabinet and more woofer cone area. A 10-ft³ box with two 12-inch woofers is an elaborate enough starting point to justify the active filter approach. Proper selection of a low-mass large-magnet 8-inch mid-range driver will allow a 5-watt buffer amplifier to match a 30-watt buffer amplifier driving the woofers. The low-frequency electronic crossover at 316 Hz should be the symmetrical third-order network of Fig. 10. The crossover to a 2-inch tweeter at 1585 Hz can be done with a $\zeta = 0.5$ quasi-second-order network. Such a loudspeaker system would be nearly the ultimate which could be achieved with direct radiator drivers.

REFERENCES

1. L. L. Beranek, *Acoustics* (McGraw-Hill, New York, 1954).
2. J. R. Ashley and T. A. Saponas, "Wisdom and Witchcraft of Old Wives' Tales About Woofer Baffles," *J. Audio Eng. Soc.* **18**, 524 (1970).
3. J. R. Ashley and L. M. Henne, "Operational Amplifier Implementation of Ideal Electronic Crossover Networks," *J. Audio Eng. Soc.* **19**, 7 (1971).
4. R. R. Small, "Constant-Voltage Crossover Network Design," *Proc. IREE Australia*, 66 (1970) and *J. Audio Eng. Soc.* **19**, 12 (1971).
5. L. Weinberg, *Network Analysis and Synthesis* (McGraw-Hill, New York, 1960).
6. J. R. Ashley, "On the Transient Response of Ideal Crossover Networks," *J. Audio Eng. Soc.* **10**, 241 (1962).
7. J. R. Ashley, "Butterworth Filters as Loudspeaker Frequency Dividing Networks," *Proc. IEEE* (Letters) **58**, 959 (1970).
8. E. J. Foster, "Active Low-Pass Filter Design," *IEEE Trans. Audio* **AU-13**, 104 (1965).

THE AUTHOR

Allan L. Kaminsky was born in Brooklyn, New York in 1941. He received the B.S. degree in electrical engineering from Newark College of Engineering in 1966, and M.S. and Ph.D. degrees from Columbia University in 1967 and 1970 respectively.

After receiving his doctorate, Kaminsky was associated with Rectilinear Research Corporation. He is currently Assistant Professor of Electrical Engineering and Computer Science at the University of Colorado.

Dr. Kaminsky is a member of Eta Kappa Nu, Tau Beta Pi, Sigma Xi, the Association for Computing Machinery, the Institute of Electrical and Electronics Engineers, the American Association for the Advancement of Science, and the Audio Engineering Society.

•

Note: Dr. Ashley's biography appeared in the October, 1970 Journal.

PROJECT NOTES / ENGINEERING BRIEFS

ELECTRICAL VERSUS ACOUSTICAL PARAMETERS IN THE DESIGN OF LOUDSPEAKER CROSSOVER NETWORKS

G. L. AUGSPURGER

Perception Inc., Box 39536, Los Angeles, Calif. 90039

The current interest in distortionless crossover network design prompts the following observations. First, while Ashley and Henne [1] mention that listening tests do not necessarily agree with theoretical criteria, neither their paper nor Small's [2] suggests the practical step of measuring the combined acoustical output from the system rather than the electrical input to the loudspeakers as a guide to what is "ideal" and what is not. In this way, Small's requirement that the two loudspeakers be equalized to have identical amplitude and phase characteristics through the crossover region is not an absolute necessity, since the needed equalization becomes an integral part of the network design.

Second, a factor that helps explain the discrepancy between the theory and audible results is the relation of direct on-axis sound to total radiated acoustic power through the crossover region. This deserves more detailed discussion than is supplied in Small's otherwise excellent analysis.

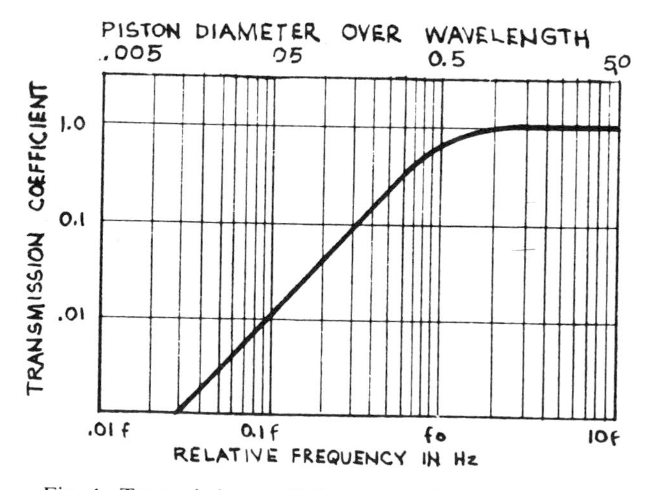

Fig. 1. Transmission coefficient versus frequency for circular piston in very large flat baffle.

Fig. 1 is derived from the familiar graph of the radiation resistance seen by a circular piston operating in a very large flat baffle. Following the example of Locanthi [3], the effect is shown as transmission coefficient, drawn as a simple 6-dB per octave rolloff below f_0. f_0 is the frequency of ultimate loading, which is assumed to be that frequency at which the diameter of the piston is $\lambda/2$. (These are simplifications, but sufficiently accurate for our purpose.)

A mass-controlled piston operating below f_0 exhibits uniform on-axis response and uniform power response. Above f_0, on-axis response remains uniform, but power response rolls off because the device becomes more and more directional. A "resistance-controlled" (constant velocity) piston exhibits uniform power response above f_0, but on-axis response rises because of increasing directionality unless a dispersive device, such as an acoustic lens, is used. Practical loudspeakers generally fall somewhere between the two categories [3].

Fig. 2a represents a loudspeaker mounted in a very large flat baffle and radiating into a semireverberant listening room. An auditor is located on the axis of the loudspeaker at some arbitrary point at least several diameters away. For a voltage $\bar{e}$ across the voice coil terminals, a sound pressure $\bar{p}$ is produced at the auditor's location. This sound pressure is made up of a direct component plus a reverberant component. In a typical home listening situation, the reverberant component predominates.

In Fig. 2b a second identical loudspeaker has been added. The two are connected in parallel (the simplest network of all) and mounted as close together as possible, following Small's dictum that ". . . it is the only way to ensure uniform addition of the driver outputs for both direct and reflected sound throughout the listening area." The sound pressure at the auditor's location is the vector sum of the pressures produced by the two loudspeakers.

Fig. 2c shows the same two loudspeakers separated by a distance equal to several wavelengths. The axes of the two loudspeakers intersect at the auditor's location, and

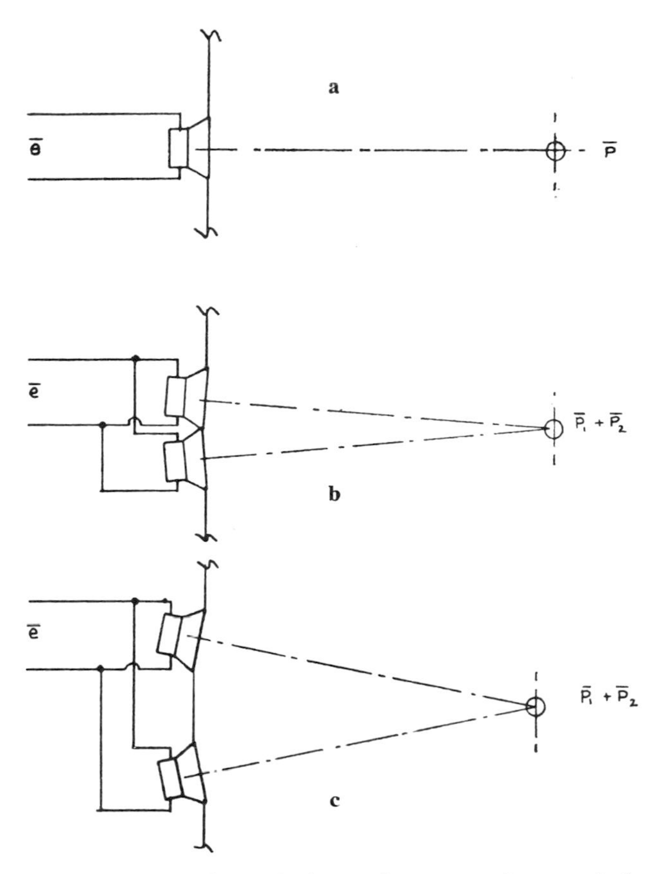

Fig. 2. Comparison of the performance of **a**, a single loudspeaker with **b** two such loudspeakers mounted very close together and **c** mounted several wavelengths apart.

the distance from the auditor to either speaker is the same as in the preceding examples.

Suppose that, in all three situations, the loudspeakers are operated at frequencies well below f_0. In Fig. 2b their outputs combine in phase through a full 180° solid angle. By connecting two speakers in parallel we have doubled the electrical power input, yet the acoustical power output has gone up 6 dB, or a factor of four. This is explained by the fact that the combined radiating area of the two pistons moves f_0 down a half-octave and correspondingly raises the transmission coefficient 3 dB. In this instance, therefore, both direct and reverberant sound pressures are raised 6 dB compared with a single speaker.

However, if the speakers are widely separated as in Fig. 2c, the transmission coefficient remains unchanged. Therefore, although $\bar{p}_1 + \bar{p}_2 = 2\ \bar{p}$ for direct sound at the auditor's location, sound pressures throughout the listening room add in random phase, and total acoustic power is doubled, compared with a single speaker . . . the change in reverberant sound pressure is 3 dB less than the change in direct sound pressure.

What happens if the loudspeakers are operated at frequencies above f_0? Keeping our attention at Fig. 2c, there are no changes in the relationships. Compared with a single speaker, direct sound pressure increases 6 dB, but reverberant sound pressure increases only 3 dB.

In the situation of Fig. 2b, even though the speakers are mounted as close together as possible, there can be no increase in the transmission coefficient beyond unity. Again, therefore, direct sound pressure increases 6 dB while reverberant sound pressure increases only 3 dB. It seems that close spacing, by itself, is not enough.

The implications for practical crossover network design are discouraging. For most "constant-voltage" networks to produce the intended results, not only must the two loudspeakers have identical characteristics through the crossover region and be mounted very close together, they also must be small compared with any wavelength through the crossover region. Consider a 12-inch woofer and 3-inch midrange radiator; if we allow only one octave on either side of crossover rather than the two octaves recommended by Small, the highest permissible crossover frequency is still only about 250 Hz.

While a 250-Hz crossover is not common, it is certainly possible. But, maintaining the same philosophy in the high-frequency range requires closely coupled direct radiators having diameters less than 1 inch. Even if one assumes this to be within the realm of possibility for a home loudspeaker system, there remains the problem of high-quality high-power loudspeaker systems for theatres and auditoriums, where requirements dictate that transducers (whether direct radiators or horns) be operated above f_0.

A possible answer to the dilemma is to drive high- and low-frequency loudspeakers in quadrature. Under this condition, referring again to Fig. 2, for frequencies

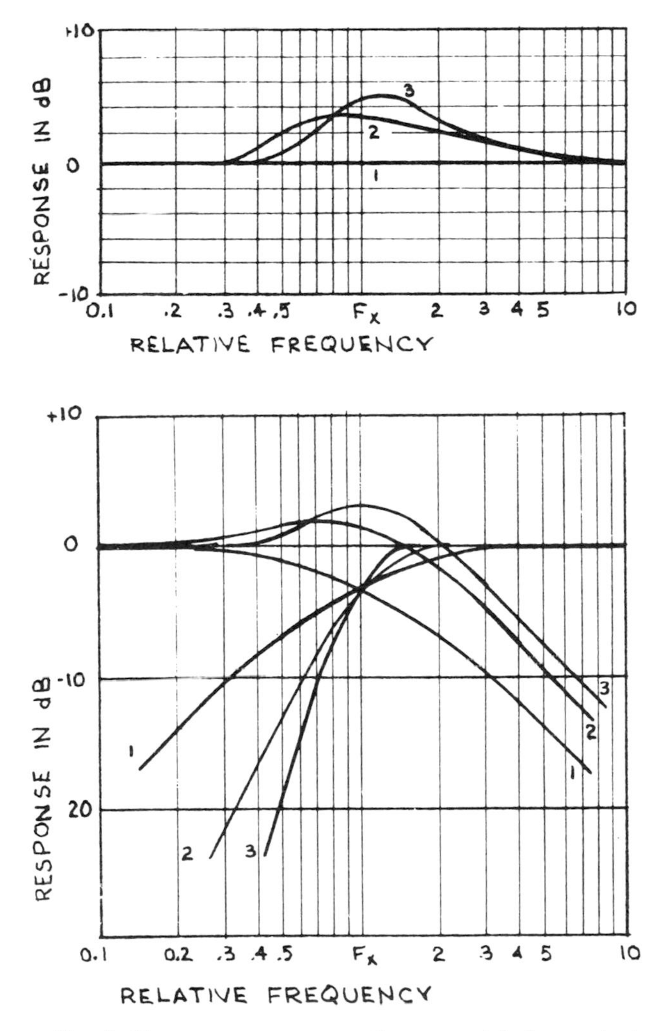

Fig. 3. Frequency response of asymmetrical constant-voltage crossover networks. **a.** In terms of power response as arithmetic sum of both channels. **b.** In terms of two channels independently [1].

above *or* below f_0, both direct and reverberant sound pressures are 3 dB greater than for a single speaker. It would seem, then, that for uniform response with practical loudspeakers, an ideal network not only should meet criteria for constant-voltage transfer and phase linearity, but also should provide a constant 90° phase difference between the two outputs and unity power transfer when the outputs are summed arithmetically. Which somehow brings us back to the good old first order 6-dB per octave constant-resistance configuration.

For example, Fig. 3 compares the response of the first-order constant-resistance network (curve 1 in both graphs) with that of second- and third-order asymmetrical constant-voltage networks. When the higher order networks are used with loudspeakers operating above f_0, one can expect a hump in perceived response through the crossover region because reverberant response sums as the total power from the two channels.

One might consider making use of the 90° phase relationship (mentioned by Small) between a resistance-controlled horn-type tweeter and a mass-controlled cone-type woofer. By connecting these to a second-order constant-resistance network, the 90° difference between transducer outputs should combine with the 180° difference between network outputs to achieve the desired quadrature shift. (Whether by accident or design, several commercial loudspeaker systems are made up of these three types of components.) Unfortunately, the added 90° phase difference increases, rather than compensates for, the inherent delay distortion of the network.

If one must make a choice, experience suggests that the ear is far more sensitive to a small change in level than to a small departure from phase linearity (delay distortion). This is confirmed by the experiments of Ashley and Henne. An interesting listening comparison between phase-linear and non-phase-linear network response can be set up quite simply by making use of another unique property of the first-order constant-resistance network. By reversing the phase of one set of outputs, delay distortion is introduced without affecting any of the other properties of the network.

Of course, one can reverse the phase of any crossover network, and often with substantially different results. For example, Small states that the second-order constant-resistance network has a null at crossover. Analytically yes, but this circuit is normally used with the phase of one channel reversed, giving (vectorially) a 3-dB bump rather than a null. Small and Ashley both indicate that the phase shift of the third-order constant-resistance network varies from 0° to 360°. But if one channel is reversed, the maximum phase shift is only 180° and delay distortion is similarly halved.

These effects are illustrated in Fig. 4. Frequency has been plotted linearly so that delay at any frequency is proportional to the slope of the curve at that frequency. For clarity the curves have been separated vertically and do not repreesnt absolute phase relationships. It is interesting that, when connected in reverse phase, all three networks have a maximum phase shift of 180°, or ± 90° from the crossover frequency. When outputs are summed vectorially, first- and third-order networks provide uniform voltage transfer, in contrast to the 3-dB peak of the second-order circuit. By definition, all three circuits provide constant (arithmetic) power transfer.

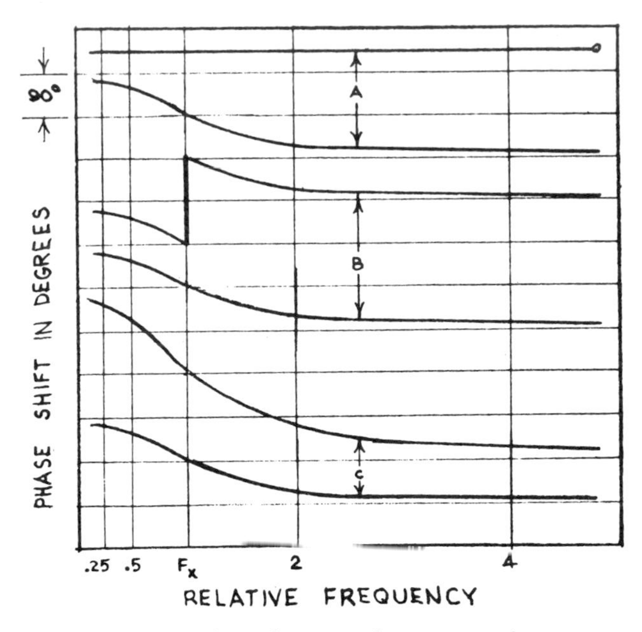

Fig. 4. Phase shift of summed outputs of constant-resistance networks. Lower curves show effect of phase reversal in one channel. **a.** First-order network. **b.** Second-order network. **c.** Third-order network.

In conclusion, because of the importance of the reverberant field in most listening situations, it is highly desirable that the crossover network provide uniform sound pressure level through the crossover region, for both direct and reverberant sound at the normal listening location. Therefore, when transducers have similar characteristics, first- and third-order constant-resistance networks give the greatest promise of achieving an imperceptible crossover; in the case where the transducers add a 90° phase shift, the second-order circuit probably is a better choice. Using operational amplifiers, higher order networks are quite practical and may prove to be even more desirable.

REFERENCES

[1] J. R. Ashley and L. M. Henne, "Operational Amplifier Implementation of Ideal Electronic Crossover Networks," *J. Audio Eng. Soc.*, vol. 19, pp. 7-11 (19671).

[2] R. H. Small, "Constant-Voltage Crossover Network Design," *J. Audio Eng. Soc.*, vol. 19, pp. 12-19 (1971).

[3] B. N. Locanthi, "Application of Electric Circuit Analogies to Loudspeaker Design Problems," *Re Trans. Audio*, vol. PGA-1, (Mar. 1952).

[4] R. M. Mitchell, "Transient Performance of Loudspeaker Dividing Networks," *Audio*, vol. 48, p. 24 (Jan. 1964).

About the Author: George L. Augspurger received his B.A. degree from Arizona State University at Tempe, M.A. from UCLA, and has done additional postgraduate work at Northwestern University. After working in sound contracting and television broadcasting, he joined James B. Lansing Sound, Inc. in 1958 where he served as Technical Service Manager and, later, as Manager of the company's newly-formed Professional Products Department. In 1968 he was appointed JBL's Technical Director.

In October, 1970 he left JBL to devote full time to Perception Inc., a consulting group specializing in architectural acoustics and audio system design. Mr. Augspurger is a member of the Audio Engineering Society, Acoustical Society of America, and United States Institute of Theatre Technology.

Application of Electric Circuit Analogies to Loudspeaker Design Problems*

BART N. LOCANTHI

California Institute of Technology, Pasadena, Calif.

Electric circuit analogies are derived for three types of loudspeaker systems: direct radiator in an infinite baffle, direct radiator in a reflex enclosure, and horn loudspeaker. The data are in good agreement with data taken from experimental ascoustica units.

Editor's Note: It is with pleasure that we publish this 1952 tutorial paper from the *IRE Transactions on Audio*. Mr. Locanthi has simply substituted the new I.S. units for the old c.g.s. system.

INTRODUCTION: Electrical engineers and physicists are frequently concerned with the task of obtaining solutions to electromechanical problems. These people are generally well versed in electric circuit theory. By transforming all of the mechanical "constants" of an electromechanical system to their equivalent electrical quantities, an electric circuit analogy is developed from which the qualitative performance may be quickly judged. Furthermore, quantitative data may be obtained by making appropriate measurements in the electric circuit.

It will be demonstrated in the paper that electric circuit analogy data are in good agreement with data taken from the following experimental acoustical units: 1) direct radiator in an infinite baffle, 2) direct radiator in a reflex enclosure, and 3) horn loudspeaker.

Especially in view of the good agreement between the electric circuit analog data and those obtained from an experimental horn loudspeaker, which was treated partly as a lumped parameter system and partly as a distributed parameter system, there can be little doubt as to the power of this type of analysis.

Electric circuit analogies are derived in this paper for the three types of loudspeaker systems described. The analog computer at the California Institute of Technology was used to obtain data from the electric circuit analogies.

Electric circuit analogies for electromechanical systems have been known for at least 50 years [1]. It is the purpose of this paper to demonstrate the application of electric circuit analogies to certain loudspeaker design problems. In particular, the direct radiator in an infinite baffle, the direct radiator in a "reflex" type enclosure, and the horn loudspeaker will be discussed. Throughout the discussion, the mobility analogy will be used (i.e., voltage represents velocity and current represents force). The only major assumptions that will be made to facilitate the analysis are 1) the cone or diaphragm has no resonant modes and moves as a uniform piston, and 2) the resistance losses in the suspension of the moving system are negligible compared to the radiation losses.

CASE I: DIRECT RADIATOR IN AN INFINITE BAFFLE

A diagram of a direct radiator in an infinite baffle is shown in Fig. 1. Let

* Presented at the 1952 IRE National Convention, March 3-6, New York. Reprinted from *IRE Transactions on Audio*, vol. PGA-6, March 1952.

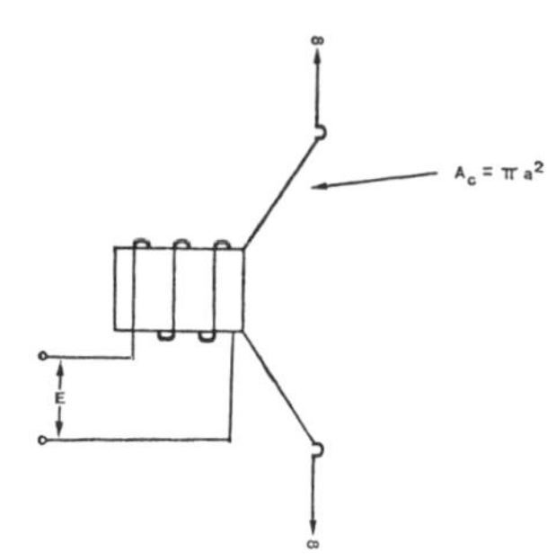

Fig. 1. Direct radiator loudspeaker in infinite baffle.

M = total effective mass of moving system (i.e., cone, voice coil, and effective air mass), kg
R_a = radiation resistance in mechanical ohms, N · s/m
C_m = effective compliance of suspension and back enclosure, if any, m/N
i = applied current to driving coil, amperes
l = wire length of driving coil, meters
T = flux density in region of driving coil tesla
R = dc resistance of driving coil, ohms
W_a = acoustic power radiated, watts
x = displacement of moving system, meters
L = inductance of driving coil, henrys
E = applied voltage to driving coil, volts

In all the following analogies a voltage generator of zero source impedance will be assumed. However, it should be clear that an amplifier of finite source impedance may be represented by an amplifier of zero source impedance in series with the appropriate impedance. Insofar as the overall system performance is concerned, the amplifier source impedance may be considered as an additional element of the series electrical impedance $(R_i + j\omega L_1)$.

The following two equations then describe the system [1], [2]:

$$L\frac{di}{dt} + R_i = (E - E_1) \tag{1}$$

$$\frac{M}{(Tl)^2}\frac{dE_1}{dt} + \frac{R_a E_1}{(Tl)^2} + \frac{1}{C_m (Tl)^2}\int E_1\, dt - i = 0. \tag{2}$$

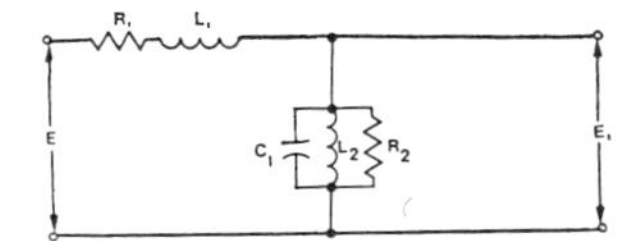

Fig. 2. Direct radiator loudspeaker in infinite baffle.

The electric circuit which satisfies (1) and (2) is shown in Fig. 2, where

$$R_1 = R \qquad L_1 = L \qquad C_1 = \frac{M}{(Tl)^2}$$

$$R_2 = \frac{(Tl)^2}{R_a} \qquad L_2 = C_m (Tl)^2 \qquad E_1 = (Tl)\frac{dx}{dt}$$

$$W_R = \frac{E_1^2}{R_2} = \dot{x}^2 R_a \quad \text{watts.}$$

The parallel combination of C_1, L_2, and R_2 may be said to represent the inverse mechanical impedance of this moving system multiplied by $(Tl)^2$ As the factor (Tl) is increased, the impedance of the parallel combination of C_1, L_2, R_2 increases as $(Tl)^2$ relative to the series electrical impedance of R_1 and L_1. Clearly, then, if (Tl) is increased far enough, E_1 will equal E for a relatively wide range of frequencies. The bandwidth for which $E_1 = E$ increases as $(Tl)^2$. If one refers to Fig. 3, which shows the radiation resistance per square meter of a piston, set in an infinite baffle, as a function of the ratio of piston diameter to wavelength of radiated sound, he will see that $E_1 = E$ is not a desirable condition for all frequencies. $E_1 = E$ implies a constant velocity condition and clearly, in this case, for D/λ less than 0.5, the acoustic output will drop at the rate of 6 dB/octave. It might be interesting to note that $D/\lambda = 0.5$ for a 15-inch radiator at approximately 440 Hz.

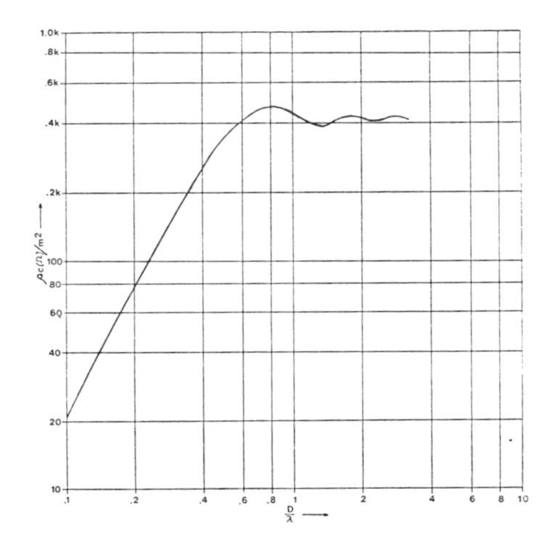

Fig. 3. Piston vibrating in infinite baffle.

Below $D/\lambda = 0.5$, the velocity of the radiator must increase inversely as the frequency if the acoustic power radiated is to be independent of frequency. The usual method for providing this frequency–velocity characteristic is to make use of the mechanical "resonance" of the loudspeaker. The insertion loss of this electromechanical equalizer is determined by the smallest D/λ down to which the response is to be uniform and the maximum variation in the low-frequency response which can be tolerated. If one sets the maximum variation in

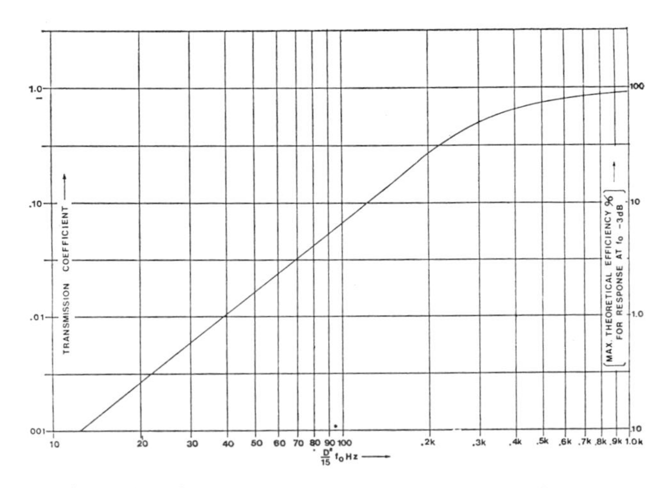

Fig. 4. Maximum transmisssion coefficient and theoretical efficiency, direct radiator loudspeaker.

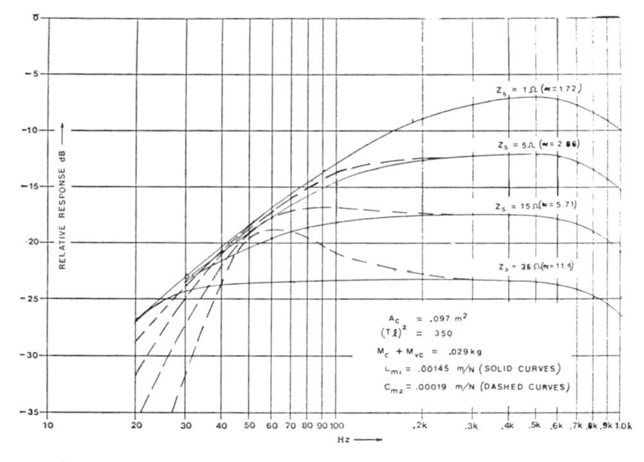

Fig. 5. Relative response 15" diameter, direct radiator loudspeakers.

low-frequency response at ± 1.5 dB, he may use the data in Fig. 3 and the concept of insertion loss to produce the curve shown in Fig. 4. The midrange (i.e., $D/\lambda = 0.5$) insertion loss is plotted as a function of $D/15f_0$, where D is the diameter of the piston radiator in inches and f_0 is the low frequency at which the response is to be down 3 dB for infinite suspension compliance.

Fig. 5 shows the relative acoustic output as a function of frequency for several values of α

$$\alpha = \frac{R_1 \times 10^2}{(Tl)^2}$$

and for two different suspension compliances. The larger compliance was chosen to provide a system resonance in the infinite baffle of 20 Hz, while the smaller compliance was chosen to provide a system resonance of 55 Hz in the infinite baffle. The ordinate zero dB represents a midrange efficiency of 100 percent. It should be observed that only a slight improvement in response for the $\alpha = 5.71$ curve was produced by using a mechanism having the smaller suspension compliance. For the $\alpha = 10.44$ curve, the rise of 5 dB as system resonance would be held to be objectionable by many listeners.

Note the excellent correlation between the data shown in Figs. 4 and 5, even though two widely different system resonances were used. Fig. 4 is for some systems slightly pessimistic from an efficiency point of view.

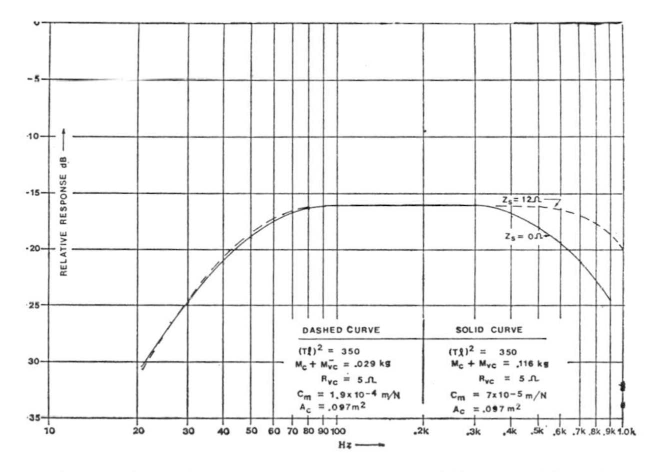

Fig. 6. Relative response of two different 15" direct radiator loudspeakers.

However, the extent to which this is so is small.

Fig. 6 shows the relative response curves obtained for two different 15-inch loudspeaker mechanisms possessing the same electromechanical coupling coefficients and the same system resonances (when mounted in an infinite baffle). The mechanisms differed in only one respect: the cone plus voice coil mass of one unit was four times heavier than that of the other. The heavy unit was driven by an amplifier which presented a zero source impedance while the lighter unit was driven by an amplifier which presented a 12-ohm source impedance.

CASE II: DIRECT RADIATOR IN A REFLEX ENCLOSURE

A diagram of a direct radiator in a reflex enclosure is shown in Fig. 7. The port in a reflex enclosure may be treated as a zero length tube; the usual end conditions for both ends of a tube apply at the port. In most cases, the inner surface of the enclosure is covered with sound-absorbing material. At such low frequencies as are likely to be encountered near the Helmholtz resonance of the port, the absorption coefficient of the lining may be neglected. The major loss for the port is then radiation into the space away from the enclosure.

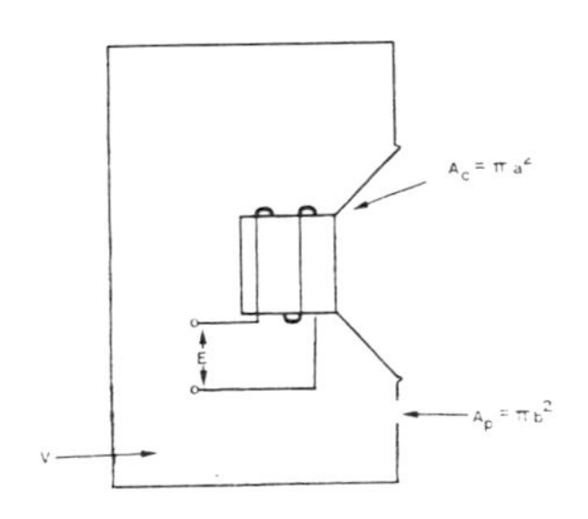

Fig. 7. Reflex enclosure loudspeaker.

The effective air mass acting at the port is approximately twice that due to the reactive component of the radiation impedance of one end of the tube, while the resistance offered by the port is the real part of the radiation impedance of the open end of the tube [3]. For constant pressure in the enclosure, the particle velocity at the port is proportional to the cone velocity and to the ratio of the cone area to the port area. The dimensions of the reflex enclosure are assumed to be small compared to the wavelength of sound for frequencies in the neighborhood of the Helmholtz resonance. The absorption coefficient of the material which lines the enclosure should be of sufficient magnitude at the resonant modes of the enclosure above the port resonance to damp them out.[1]

The port is coupled to the back of the cone by the compliant air of the enclosure. Let

ρ_0 = density of air, kg/m³
$\pi a^2 = A_c$ = cone area, m²
$\pi b^2 = A_p$ = port area, m²
V = volume of enclosure, m³
c = velocity of sound, m/s.

[1] For a discussion which treats the variation of C_v from the uniform pressure case see [4].

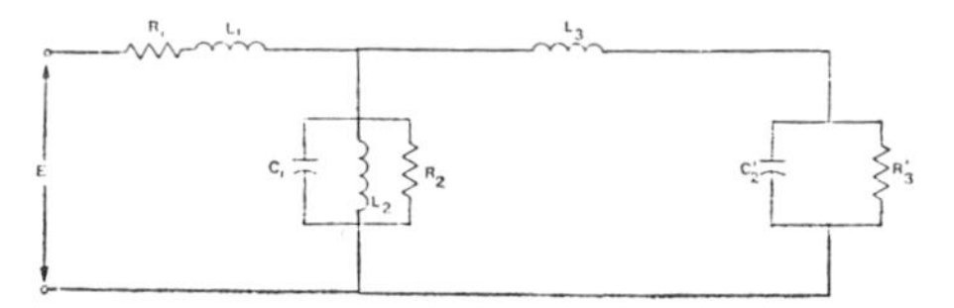

Fig. 8. Reflex enclosure loudspeaker without mutual impedance.

Then the compliance of the cone against the enclosure with the port closed satisfies the following equation:

$$C_v = \frac{V}{\rho_0 c^2 A_c^2}.$$

Let M_{ap} represent the total air mass effective at the port, and R_{ap} the radiation resistance of the port. If one assumes that there is no coupling between the port and the cone outside the enclosure, he obtains the electric circuit analogy shown in Fig. 8 [5], where

$$R_1 = R \qquad L_1 = L \qquad R_3 = \frac{(Tl)^2}{R_{ap}}$$

$$R_2 = \frac{(Tl)^2}{R_a} \qquad L_2 = C_m (Tl)^2 \qquad C_2 = \frac{M_{ap}}{(Tl)^2}$$

$$R_3' = \left(\frac{A_p}{A_c}\right)^2 R_3 \qquad L_3 = C_r (Tl)^2 \qquad \frac{N_s}{N_p} = \frac{A_c}{A_p}.$$

$$C_1 = \frac{M}{(Tl)^2} \qquad C_2' = \left(\frac{A_c}{A_p}\right)^2 C_2$$

It has been the author's experience that the impedance versus frequency curves for the analogy in Fig. 8 do not agree well with those of experimental units. The major differences appear to have been the frequencies at which the two low-frequency impedance maxima occur. The principal source of the discrepancy seems to be the omission of external coupling between the cone and port.

An approximate determination of the mutual impedance between the piston and the port may be determined in the following manner.

The pressure at a point p, distant R from the center of the vibrating piston and in the same plane (see Fig. 9), may be obtained by solving the following equation:

$$p(y) = \frac{i\rho_0 \omega u_0 e^{i\omega t}}{2\pi} \iint_s \frac{ds}{h} e^{-ikh}$$

The solution may be approximated by expanding e^{-ikh}/h in an infinite series and integrating the first four terms [6].

$$\frac{Zm'}{A_p} = \rho_0 f \pi a^2 \left[k - 1/6\, k^3 \left(R_0^2 + \frac{a^2}{2} \right) \right]$$
$$+ i\rho_0 f \left[4\frac{a^2}{R_0} B\left(\frac{a^2}{R_0^2}\right) - \frac{2k^2 a^2 R_0}{9} \left\{ \left(5 + 3\frac{a^2}{R_0^2}\right) K\left(\frac{a^2}{R_0^2}\right) - \left(1 + 7\frac{a^2}{R_0^2}\right) D\left(\frac{a^2}{R_0^2}\right) \right\} \right]$$

where B, K, and D are the complete elliptic integrals defined and tabulated in [7].

The inclusion of the mutual impedance terms modifies the electric circuit analogy shown in Fig. 8 to the extent shown in Fig. 10, where

$$R_1 = R \qquad L_1 = L$$

$$L_2 = C_m (Tl)^2 \qquad C_1 = \frac{M}{(Tl)^2} - C_3$$

$$L_3 = C_r (Tl)^2 \qquad C_2' = \frac{M_{ap}}{(Tl)^2} \left(\frac{A_c}{A_p}\right)^2 - C_3$$

$$\frac{1}{R_2} + \frac{1}{R_4} = \frac{R_a}{(Tl)^2} \qquad C_3 \cong \frac{2\rho_0 A c^2}{\pi^2 R_0 (Tl)^2} B\left(\frac{a^2}{R_0^2}\right)$$

$$R_3' + \frac{1}{R_4} = \frac{R_{ap}}{(Tl)^2} \frac{A_c^2}{A_p} \qquad R_4 \cong \frac{(Tl)^2}{A_c^2 \rho_0 f k}.$$

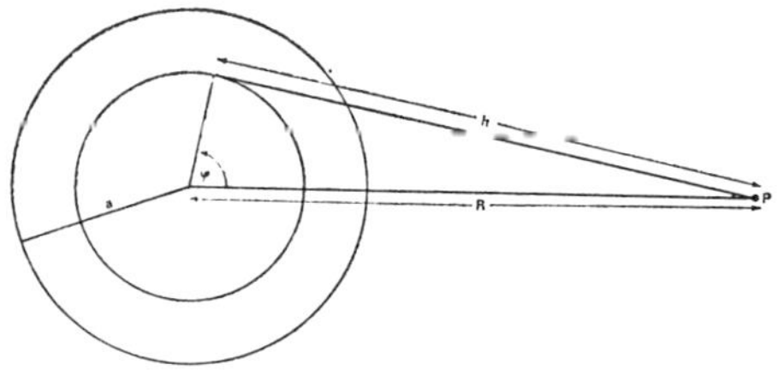

Fig. 9. Geometrical configuration.

It was found that this approximation modified the analogy shown in Fig. 8 so as to bring the impedance measurements of the electric circuit analogy into good agreement with those of experimental units. The inclusion of the mutual impedance into the electric circuit analogy for the reflex enclosure has been observed to produce the following differences from the electric circuit analogy which does not include the effect of the mutual impedance.

1) A reduction of the resonance frequency, which occurs above the port resonance, by 4 to 7 Hz out of an average of 65 Hz for several designs considered;

2) an increase of the resonance frequency, which occurs below the port resonance, by 2 to 4 Hz out of an average of 25 Hz for the several designs considered;

3) a sharper cutoff in response below the port resonance frequency.

No difference in the frequency at which the port resonance occurs has been observed between the electric circuit analogy which includes the effect of the mutual impedance and the electric circuit analogy which does not include the mutual impedance.

Figs. 11–14 show computed response curves for two different loudspeaker mechanisms mounted in two different reflex enclosures. Fig. 15 shows the computed relative acoustic output as a function of frequency for the same loudspeaker mechanism when mounted in two different types of enclosures. The amplifier source impedance was adjusted in each case to provide the same de-

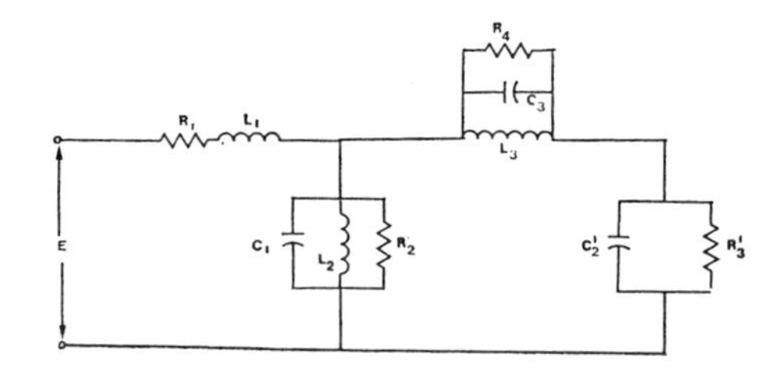

Fig. 10. Reflex enclosure loudspeaker with mutual impedance.

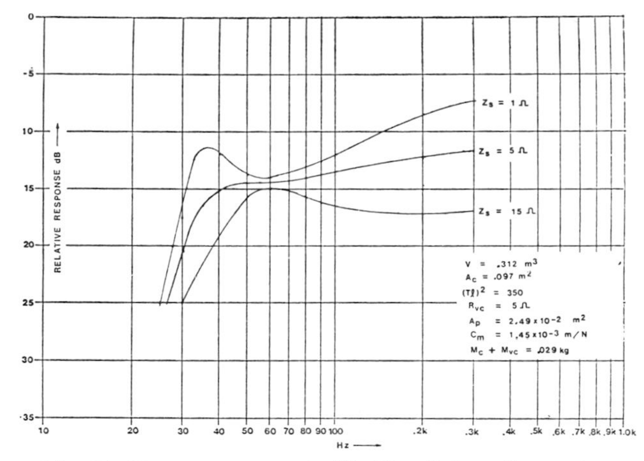

Fig. 11. Response curves (solid, Fig. 5) in reflex enclosure 0.312 m³ and port area 0.0249 m².

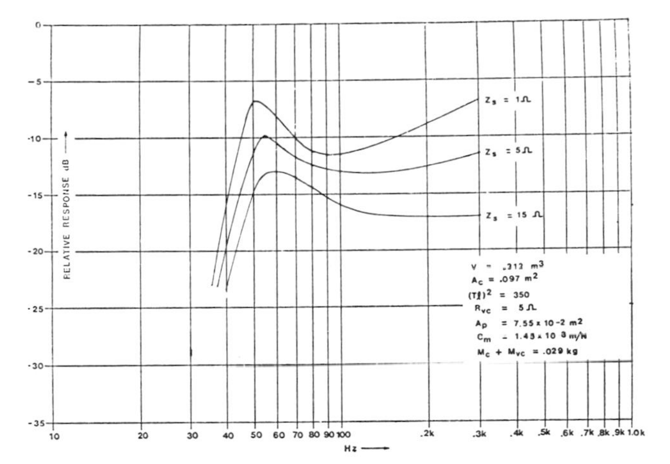

Fig. 12. Response curves (solid, Fig. 5) in reflex enclosure of 0.312 m³ and port area 0.0755 m².

gree of relative flatness in response. In the lower part of Fig. 15 are plotted the relative cone displacements as a function of frequency required to produce the response curves shown above. Note that a 6-dB improvement in overall efficiency is easy to attain with the reflex enclosure over the infinite baffle design and with no greater peak-to-peak displacement down to 40 Hz.

Many designs which provide a relatively high frequency port resonance (i.e., 70 to 100 Hz) produce considerable low-frequency distortion when driven at frequencies from 30 to 65 Hz. Below the port resonance, the acoustic loading of the cone or diaphragm is very low, large cone excursions ensue, producing very little radiation at the fundamental driving frequency and considerable harmonic distortion.

The electric circuit analogy is, of course, applicable to modified Helmholtz resonators in which a tube of finite length is used. The total mass effective at the port is then that due to both end corrections plus that due to air contained within the tube. The Helmholtz resonance frequency satisfies the following equation:

$$f_h \cong \frac{1}{2\pi}\sqrt{\frac{1}{M_{ap}C_r}} = \frac{bc}{2}\sqrt{\frac{3}{V(3\pi l+16b)}}$$

where all parameters are as before and l is the axial port length.

In the case of enclosures of small volume, the area of the port required for a given low resonance frequency may be so small that friction losses in the port may exceed radiation losses. Heavy, large diameter dummy cones with soft suspensions may be substituted for the air mass in the port to obtain low-frequency Helmholtz resonances in small enclosures.

CASE III: HORN LOUDSPEAKER

Generally the cross-sectional area of a horn (Fig. 16) is proportional to the throat area S_0 and to some analytic function of x, the distance of the section from the horn throat, i.e.,

$$S = S_0 f(x)$$
$$S_m = S_0 f(l).$$

One is invariably confronted with an unavoidable air volume V_f between the driving diaphragm or cone and the horn throat whenever it is desired to make the particle velocity at the horn throat greater than the cone velocity. Occasionally, a judicious choice of back air volume V_b can be made to place the gravest mode of the system where it will extend the low-frequency response.

The diaphragm is coupled to the throat through the compliant air volume V_f where

$$C_{V_f} = \frac{V_f}{\pi^2 \rho_0 c^2 a^4} \quad \text{(m/N)}$$

and a is the radius of the diaphragm in meters.

The force acting on a massless piston in a horn throat

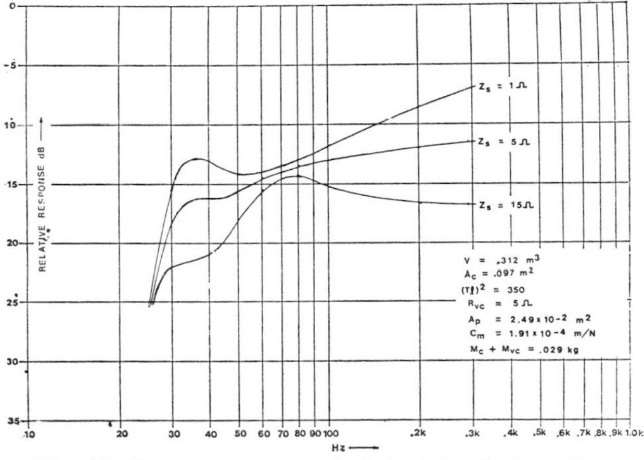

Fig. 13. Response curves (dashed, Fig. 5) in reflex enclosure of 0.312 m³ and port area 0.0249 m².

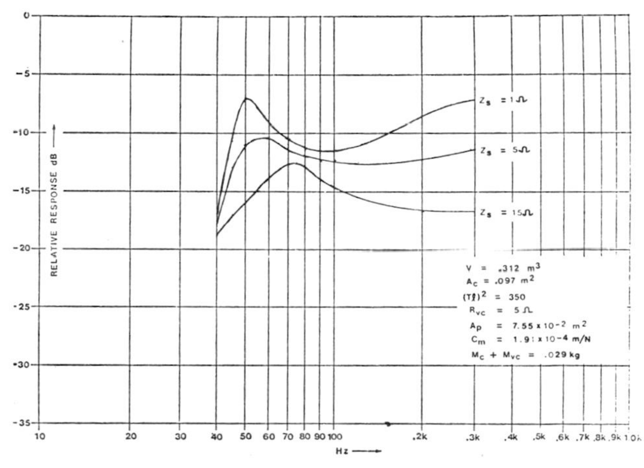

Fig. 14. Response curves (dashed, Fig. 5) in reflex enclosure of 0.312 m³ and port area 0.0755 m².

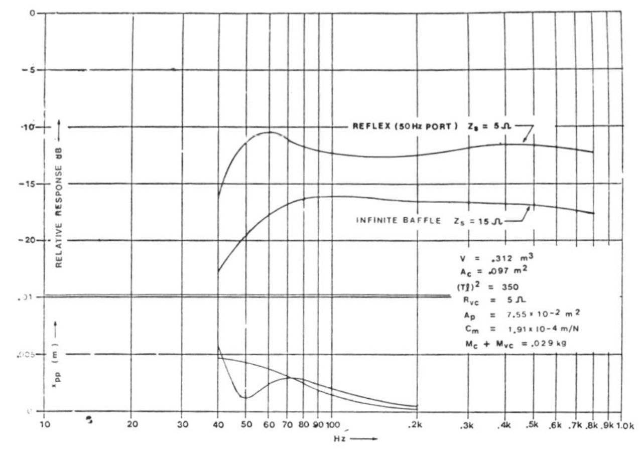

Fig. 15. Relative response and displacement vs. frequency of reflex enclosure and infinite baffle loudspeakers.

is pS_0. If the piston has a velocity u, the inverse mechanical impedance of this piston is

$$Z^{-1} = u/pS_0. \tag{3}$$

What is desired is an electric circuit analogy for the horn such that the electrical impedance looking into the analogous circuit is

$$Z^{-1} = u/pS_0.$$

Consider the approximate differential equation which describes the propagation of plane pressure waves down a cylindrical tube of varying cross section.

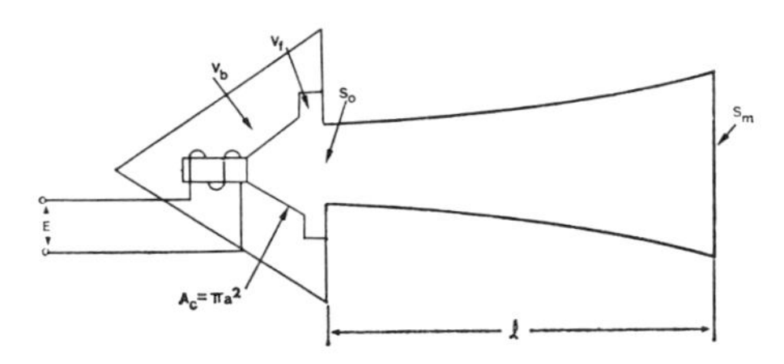

Fig. 16. Horn loudspeaker.

Let S_0 be the throat area. Then $S = S_0 f(x)$ and

$$\frac{\partial}{\partial x}\left[\frac{1}{\rho} S_0 f(x) \frac{\partial p}{\partial x}\right] dx = \frac{1}{\rho c^2} S_0 f(x) \frac{\partial^2 p}{\partial t^2} dx. \tag{4}$$

Integrating with respect to t yields

$$\frac{\partial}{\partial x}\left[\frac{1}{\rho} S_0 f(x) \int \frac{\partial p}{\partial x} dt\right] dx = \frac{1}{\rho c^2} S_0 f(x) \frac{\partial p}{\partial t} dx. \tag{5}$$

In finite differences form (5) becomes

$$\frac{1}{\Delta x}\left[\frac{S_0 f(x_n + \tfrac{1}{2})}{\rho} \int (p_{n+1} - p_n)\, dt + \frac{S_0 f(x_n + \tfrac{1}{2})}{\rho} \int (p_{n-1} - p_n)\, dt\right] = \frac{1}{\rho c^2} S_0 f(x_n) \left(\frac{\partial p}{\partial t}\right)_n \Delta x. \tag{6}$$

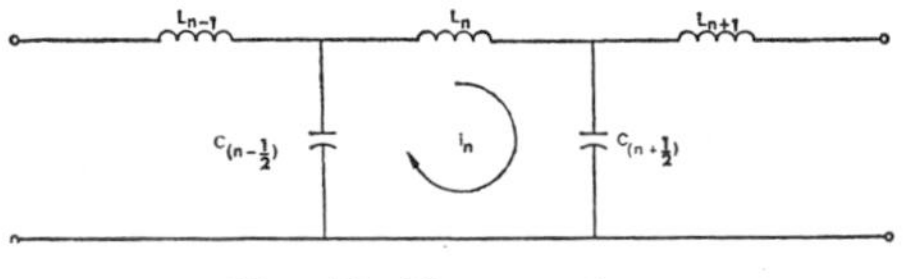

Fig. 17. Horn only.

Consider the electric circuit shown in Fig. 17

$$\frac{1}{C_n + \tfrac{1}{2}} \int (i_{n+1} - i_n)\, dt + \frac{1}{C_n - \tfrac{1}{2}} \int (i_{n-1} - i_n)\, dt = L_n \frac{d_{i_n}}{dt}. \tag{7}$$

If $i_n \approx p$, then

$$L_n = \frac{S_0 f(x) \Delta x}{\rho c^2}$$

$$C_{n+\frac{1}{2}} = \frac{\rho \Delta x}{S_0 f(x_n + \tfrac{1}{2})}$$

$$E_{n+\frac{1}{2}} \approx -\frac{S_0 f(x_n + \tfrac{1}{2})}{\rho \Delta x} \int (P_{n+1} - P_n)\, dt = -\frac{S_0 f(x_n + \tfrac{1}{2})}{\rho} \int \frac{dp}{dx} dt,$$

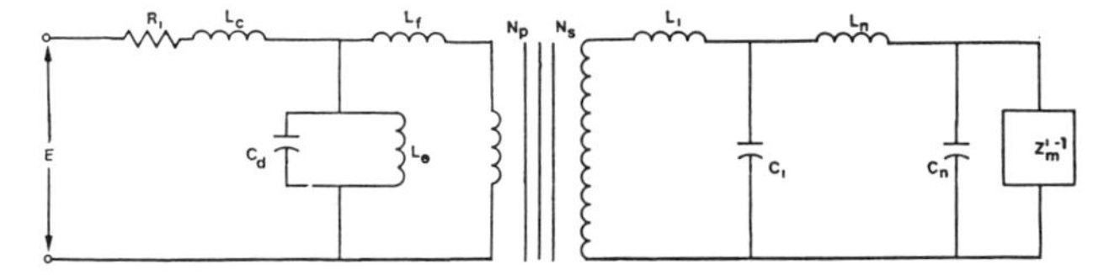

Fig. 18. Horn loudspeaker.

But $dp/dx = -\rho du/dt$ from continuity considerations, so that

$$E_{n+\frac{1}{2}} \frac{S_0 f(x)}{\rho} (\rho u) = S_0 f(x) u$$

$$\frac{E}{i} = \frac{S_0 f(x) u}{P}. \tag{8}$$

At the throat $f(x) = 1$, and the impedance indicated by (8) is high by S_0^2.

The impedance of the horn network must then be changed by S_0^2 to match the proper boundary condition at the throat:

$$L'_n = \frac{1}{S_0^2} L_n = \frac{f(x_n) \Delta x}{\rho c^2 S_0} \tag{9}$$

$$C'_{n+\frac{1}{2}} = S_0^2 C_n = \frac{\rho S_0 \Delta x}{f(x_{n+\frac{1}{2}})}. \tag{10}$$

At any point along the horn, now, the characteristic impedance is

$$Z_0^{-1} = \sqrt{\frac{L'_n}{C'_{n+\frac{1}{2}}}} = \sqrt{\frac{f(x_n)}{\rho c^2 S_0} \cdot \frac{f(x_{n+\frac{1}{2}})}{\rho S_0}} = \frac{f(x)}{\rho c S_0} \tag{11}$$

at $x = l$, i.e., the end of the horn.

The mouth area $S_m = S_0 f(l)$. The inverse mechanical impedance at the horn mouth, at high frequencies, is

$$Z_m^{-1} = \frac{1}{\rho c S_m}. \tag{12}$$

Clearly, then, the calculated terminating impedance must be multiplied by S_m^2/S_0^2 in order to provide the proper termination at the horn mouth.

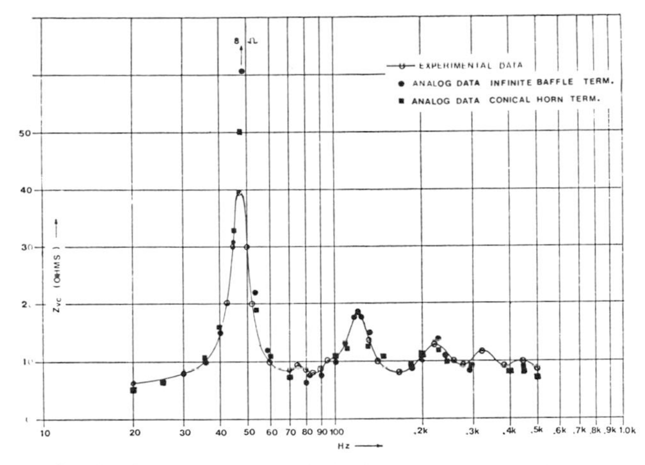

Fig. 19. Measured electrical impedance vs. frequency data compared to calculated electrical impedance vs. frequency data for experimental horn loudspeaker.

The total analogy for the horn and its proper termination including the driving piston and front and back air volumes is shown in Fig. 18, where

R_1 = dc resistance of driving coil, ohms
L_c = inductance of driving coil, henrys
$C_d = M_d/(Tl)^2$, where M_d is the total effective mass of diaphragm
$L_e = (Tl)^2 C_e$, where C_e is the total effective compliance of diaphragm suspension and back enclosure, if any
$L_f = (Tl)^2 C_f$, where C_f is the compliance of diaphragm against front cavity with horn throat closed

$$\frac{n_p}{n_s} = \frac{S_0}{S_d},$$ where S_0 is the throat area; S_d the diaphragm area

$$L_n = (Tl)^2 \frac{f(x_n)\Delta x}{\rho c^2 S_0}, \quad \text{henrys}$$

$$C_n = \frac{1}{(Tl)^2} \cdot \frac{\rho S_0 \Delta x}{f(x_n)}, \quad \text{farads}$$

$$Z_{m'}^{-1} = \left(\frac{S_m}{S_0}\right)^2 Z_m^{-1} (Tl)^2$$

where Z^{-1} is the inverse mechanical terminating impedance for horn mouth.

Having developed the complete electric circuit horn analogy, it was felt desirable to check the analog computer results against measurement on some existing experimental horn unit. Through the kindness of Mr. George Bretell of the 20th Century Fox Film Corporation, I am able to show in Fig. 19 a comparison between the measured voice coil impedance of the drivers of Mr. Bretell's horn and the impedance looking into the electric circuit analogy which was calculated to represent his experimental unit. It might be of some interest to mention here that the direct current resistance of the drivers was 4 ohms. The horn was designed to fit into a room corner, however, the mouth was approximately one foot from each wall. At very low frequencies the room corner (conical horn) termination at the horn mouth produced the better agreement between the analog data and those taken from the experimental unit. At higher frequencies the infinite baffle flange termination for the horn mouth produced the better agreement between the analog data and those taken from the experimental unit.

Fig. 20 is a comparison of the transmission coefficients for conical, hyperbolic, and exponential horns as determined from the results of electric circuit analogies along with transmission coefficients calculated for the semi-infinite cases. The "short" horns analyzed were all of the same length (2.4 m), mouth area 1.21 m^2, and throat area of 10^{-2} m^2.

It should be realized that a horn of 2.4-m length is hardly a short horn. Nevertheless, disagreement exists between the transmission coefficients obtained from the electric circuit analogies and those calculated for the semi-infinite cases. Needless to say, a shorter horn shows even greater deviations. Furthermore, below the cutoff frequencies of the exponential and hyperbolic horns, the three horns show essentially identical transmission characteristics. Certainly if the exponent m of an exponential horn is small and if the horn is short, the differences between the exponetial, hyberbolic, and conical horns of the same mouth and throat areas and of the same lengths are quite small, and the differences in acoustical performance are negligible.

CONCLUSION

It has been demonstrated that electric circuit analogies may accurately represent the three major types of loudspeaker systems used today. While resistance losses in the suspension of the moving system have not been considered, these losses, if known, may easily be introduced into the analogies. All the computations for curves presented in this paper were handled by one man who spent less than forty hours preparing data for the electric circuit analog computer, obtaining data from the computer, and plotting the results.

If one were to consider only those loudspeaker mechanisms which are currently available, the following comments are in order.

1) Loudspeaker mechanisms may be designed to operate in "infinite" baffles, providing uniform acoustic output down to about the resonant frequency of mechanism, mounted in the baffle. The overall efficiency of a mechanism of given cone dimension is reduced as the low-frequency range of the reproducer is extended. The infinite baffle design is the most inefficient of all those considered in this paper (i.e., 0.5 to 4 percent).

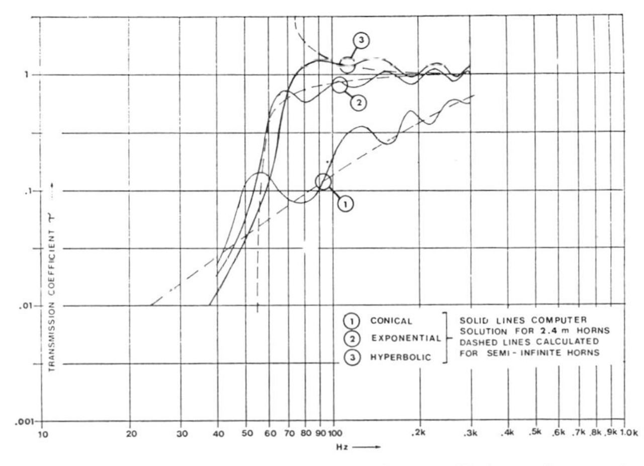

Fig. 20. Comparison of transmission coefficients for conical, hyperbolic and exponential horns.

2) The loudspeaker mechanisms designed for either horn or reflex enclosure application should possess higher electromechanical coupling coefficients than mechanisms designed specifically for use in infinite baffles.

While the horn efficiency may be of the order of 50 percent compared to the 15 percent efficiency of the reflex enclosure design, the reflex enclosure design appears to be more compact than the horn for comparable low-frequency performance.

APPENDIX

In the paper the following terms occur frequently:

ρ = density of air (1.2 kg/m^3)
c = velocity of sound in air (3.44×10^2 m/s)
$\rho c^2 = 1.42 \times 10^5$
$$k = \frac{2\pi f}{c}.$$

For a discussion in which the radiation impedance of a vibrating piston set into an infinite plane is derived, see [8, pp. 143-147].

Let

R_a = mechanical resistance of a piston radiating into one half of the infinite space (mechanical ohms)

M' = effective air mass acting on one side of a piston set into an infinite baffle, kg

a = radius of piston, meters

$$R_a = \pi a^2 \rho c \left[1 - \frac{J_1(2ka)}{ka} \right], \quad \text{mechanical ohms} \quad (13)$$

$$M' = \frac{\pi \rho}{2k^3} K_1(2ka), \quad \text{kg.} \quad (14)$$

Clearly both R_a and M' are functions of frequency. For small values of k,

$$R_a \cong \frac{\pi a^4 k^2 \rho c}{2}$$

$$M' \cong \frac{8 \rho a^3}{3}.$$

For large values of k,

$$R_a \cong \pi a^2 \rho c$$
$$M' \cong 0.$$

If the back side of the radiating piston is enclosed so that no radiation takes place in the backward direction, it is still necessary to add an air mass correction for the air on the back side of the radiator. Depending somewhat on the shape of the enclosure, the effective air mass may vary however, added values of 0.7 M' to M' produce results in good agreement with experimental data.

For a discussion which treats the parallel representation of the radiation impedance, the reader should examine [9].

In many designs $(Tl)^2$ will be of the order of 10^2. Even so, however, one may find that the capacitors required for an electric circuit analogy may be several hundred microfarads, and that the inductors will be fractions of a millihenry. Furthermore, it may be considered too expensive to solve problems on a one-to-one frequency basis. For example, a design which is to be investigated in the region of 30 Hz will require inductors of reasonably high Q, say 50 or 60. Such inductors are large and expensive. In order to solve problems practically on an electric circuit type of analog computer, it is frequently desirable to make both frequency and impedance base changes. These changes are usually not made until all the circuit constants are calculated for the problem on its original frequency and impedance base.

If we let α represent the impedance base change factor and β the frequency base change factor, then $Z_{\alpha\beta}$, $R_{\alpha\beta}$, $C_{\alpha\beta}$, and $L_{\alpha\beta}$ represent the elements in the new system, while Z, R, C, and L represent the elements in the original system.

$$Z_{\alpha\beta} = \alpha Z \quad (15)$$
$$f_{\alpha\beta} = \beta f \quad (16)$$

then

$$R_{\alpha\beta} = \alpha R \quad (17)$$
$$L_{\alpha\beta} = \alpha L / B \quad (18)$$
$$C_{\alpha\beta} = (1/\alpha\beta) C. \quad (19)$$

REFERENCES

[1] R. L. Wegel, *AIEEE Trans.*, vol. 40 (Oct. 1921).

[2] W. P. Mason, *Electro-mechanical Transducers and Wave Filters* (D. Van Nostrand, Princeton, N.J., 1942), p. 90. Also, M. S. Gardner and J. L. Barnes, *Transients in Linear Systems* (John Wiley, New York, 1942), pp. 60-62.

[3] A. H. Davis, *Modern Acoustics* (Macmillan, New York, 1934), pp. 120-121.

[4] W. F. Meeker, F. H. Slaymaker, and L. L. Merrill, "Acoustical Impedance of Closed Rectangular Loudspeaker Housings," *J. Acous. Soc. Am.*, vol. 22, no. 2 (Mar. 1950) p. 206.

[5] C. O. Caulton, E. T. Dickey, and S. V. Perry, "The Magic Voice," *Radio Eng.*, vol. 16, no. 10 (1936) p. 8.

[6] S. J. Klapman, "Interaction Impedance of a System of Circular Pistons," *J. Acoust. Soc. Am.*, vol. 11, (1940), p. 289.

H. Stenzel, *Berechnung von Schallvörgangen* (Springer, Berlin, 1939), pp. 76 ff.

[7] E. Jahnke and F. Emde, "Tables of Higher Functions," pp. 77-85.

[8] I. B. Crandall, *Theory of Vibrating Systems and Sound* (D. Van Nostrand, Princeton, N.J.)

[9] B. B. Bauer, "Notes on Radiation Impedance," *J. Acoust. Soc. Am.*, vol. 15 (1944), p. 283.

[10] P. M. Morse, *Vibration and Sound* (McGraw-Hill, New York).

[11] H. F. Olson, *Elements of Acoustical Engineering* (D. Van Nostrand, Princeton, N.J.)

[12] G. W. Stewart and R. B. Lindsay, *Acoustics* (D. Van Nostrand, Princeton, N.J.)

THE AUTHOR

Bart N. Locanthi received a B.S. in physics from Cal Tech in 1947. He was vice president in charge of engineering at J. B. Lansing Sound, leaving in 1970 to become an independent consultant. Mr. Locanthi is a member of the AES, IEEE, SMPTE, ASA where he is a Fellow, Chairman of the writing group on Loudspeaker Measurement Standards, and member of the Technical-Administrative Committee on Engineering Acoustics.

Determination of Loudspeaker Signal Arrival Times* Part I

RICHARD C. HEYSER

Jet Propulsion Laboratory, California Institute of Technology, Pasadena, Calif.

Prediction has been made that the effect of imperfect loudspeaker frequency response is equivalent to an ensemble of otherwise perfect loudspeakers spread out behind the real position of the speaker creating a spatial smearing of the original sound source. Analysis and experimental evidence are presented of a coherent communication investigation made for verification of the phenomenon.

INTRODUCTION: It is certainly no exaggeration to say that a meaningful characterization of the sound field due to a real loudspeaker in an actual room ranks among the more difficult problems of electroacoustics. Somehow the arsenal of analytical tools and instrumentation never seems sufficient to win the battle of real-world performance evaluation; at least not to the degree of representing a universally accepted decisive victory. In an attempt to provide another tool for such measurement this author presented in a previous paper a method of analysis which departed from traditional steady state [1]. It was shown that an in-place measurement could be made of the frequency response of that sound which possessed a fixed time delay between loudspeaker excitation and acoustic perception. By this means one could isolate, within known physical limitations, the direct sound, early arrivals, and late arrivals and characterize the associated spectral behavior. In a subsequent paper [2] it was demonstrated how one could obtain not only the universally recognized amplitude spectrum of such sound but also the phase spectrum. It was shown that if one made a measurement on an actual loudspeaker he could legitimately ask "how well does this speaker's direct response recreate the original sound field recorded by the microphone?" By going to first principles a proof was given [3] that a loudspeaker and indeed any transfer medium characterized as absorptive and dispersive possessed what this author called time-delay distortion. The acoustic pressure wave did not effectively emerge from the transducer immediately upon excitation. Instead it emerged with a definite time delay that was not only a function of frequency but was a multiple-valued function of frequency. As far as the sonic effect perceived by a listener is concerned, this distortion is identical in form to what one would have, had the actual loudspeaker been replaced by an ensemble of otherwise perfect loudspeakers which occupied the space behind the position of the actual loudspeaker. Furthermore, each of the speakers in the ensemble had a position that varied in space in a frequency-dependent manner. The sonic image, if one could speak of such, is smeared in space behind the physical loudspeaker.

This present paper is a continuation of analysis and experimentation on this phenomenon of time-delay distortion. The particular emphasis will be on determining how many milliseconds it takes before a sound pressure wave in effect emerges from that position in space occupied by the loudspeaker.

* Presented April 30, 1971, at the 40th Convention of the Audio Engineering Society, Los Angeles.

APPROACH TO THE PROBLEM

The subject matter of this paper deals with a class of measurement and performance evaluation which constitutes a radical departure from the methods normally utilized in electroacoustics. Several of the concepts presented are original. It would be conventional to begin this paper by expressing the proper integral equations, and thus promptly discouraging many audio engineers from reading further. Much of the criticism raised against papers that are "too technical" is entirely just in the sense that common language statements are compressed into compact equations not familiar to most of us. The major audience sought for the results of this paper are those engineers who design and work with loudspeakers. However, because the principles to be discussed are equally valuable for advanced concepts of signal handling, it is necessary to give at least a minimal mathematical treatment. For this reason this paper is divided into three parts. The first part begins with a heuristic discussion of the concepts of time, frequency, and energy as they will be utilized in this paper without the usual ponderous mathematics. Then these concepts are developed into defining equations for loudspeaker measurement, and hardware is designed around these relations. The second part is a presentation of experimental data obtained on actual loudspeakers tested with the hardware. The third part is an Appendix and is an analytical development of system energy principles which form the basis for this paper and its measurement of a loudspeaker by means of a remote air path measurement. The hope is that some of the mystery may be stripped from the purely mathematical approach for the benefit of those less inclined toward equations, and possibly provide a few conceptual surprises for those accustomed only to rigorous mathematics.

TIME AND FREQUENCY

The sound which we are interested in characterizing is the result of a restoration to equilibrium conditions of the air about us following a disturbance of that equilibrium by an event. An event may be a discharge of a cannon, bowing of a violin, or an entire movement of a symphony. A fundamental contribution to analysis initiated by Fourier [4] was that one could describe an event in either of two ways. The coordinates of the two descriptions, called the domains of description, are dimensionally reciprocal in order that each may stand alone in the ability to describe an event. For the events of interest in this paper one description involves the time-dependent pressure and velocity characteristics of an air medium expressed in the coordinates of time, seconds. The other description of the same event is expressed in the coordinates of reciprocal time, hertz. Because these two functional descriptions relate to the same event, it is possible to transform one such description into the other. This is done mathematically by an integral transformation called a Fourier transform. It is unfortunate that the very elegance of the mathematics tends to obscure the fundamental assertion that any valid mathematical description of an event automatically implies a second equally valid description.

It has become conventional to choose the way in which we describe an event such that the mathematics is most readily manipulated. A regrettable consequence of this is that the ponderous mathematical structure buttressing a particular choice of description may convince some that there is no other valid mathematical choice available. In fact there may be many types of representation the validity of which is not diminished by an apparent lack of pedigree. A conventional mathematical structure is represented by the assumption that a time-domain characterization is a scalar quantity while the equivalent reciprocal time-domain representation is a vector. Furthermore, because all values of a coordinate in a given domain must be considered in order to transform descriptions to the other domain, it is mathematically convenient to talk of a particular description which concentrates completely at a given coordinate and is null elsewhere. This particular mathematical entity, which by nature is not a function, is given the name impulse. It is so defined that the Fourier transform equivalent has equal magnitude at all values of that transform coordinate. A very special property of the impulse and its transform equivalent is that, under conditions in which superposition of solutions applies, any arbitrary functional description may be mathematically analyzed as an ordered progression of impulses which assume the value of the function at the coordinate chosen. In dealing with systems which transfer energy from one form to another, such as loudspeakers or electrical networks, it is therefore mathematically straightforward to speak of the response of that system to a single applied impulse. We know that in so doing we have a description which may be mathematically manipulated to give us the behavior of that system to any arbitrary signal, whether square wave or a Caruso recording.

In speaking of events in the time domain, most of us have no reservations about the character of an impulse. One can visualize a situation wherein nothing happens until a certain moment when there is a sudden release of energy which is immediately followed by a return to null. The corresponding reciprocal time representation does not have such ready human identification, so a tacit acceptance is made that its characterization is uniform for all values of its parameter. An impulse in the reciprocal time domain, however, is quite recognizable in the time domain as a sine wave which has existed for all time and will continue to exist for all time to come. Because of the uniform periodicity of the time-domain representation for an impulse at a coordinate location in the reciprocal time domain, we have dubbed the coordinate of reciprocal time as frequency. What we mean by frequency, in other words, is that value of coordinate in the reciprocal time domain where an impulse has a sine wave equivalent in the time domain with a given periodicity in reciprocal seconds. So far all of this is a mathematical manipulation of the two major ways in which we may describe an event. Too often we tend to assume the universe must somehow solve the same equations we set up as explanation for the way we perceive the universe at work. Much ado, therefore, is made of the fact that many of the signals used by engineers do not have Fourier transforms, such as the sine wave, square wave, etc. The fact is that the piece of equipment had a date of manufacture and we can be certain that it will some day fail; but while it is available it can suffice perfectly well as a source of signal. The fact that a mathematically perfect sine wave does not exist in no way prevents us from speaking of the impulse response of a loudspeaker in the time domain, or what is the same thing, the frequency response in the reciprocal time domain. Both descriptions are spectra in that the event is functionally dependent upon a single-valued coordinate and is arrayed in terms of that coordinate. If we define, for any reason, a zero coordinate in one domain, we have defined the corresponding epoch in the other domain. Since each domain representation is a spectrum description we could state that this exists in two "sides." One side is that for which the coordinate is less in magnitude than the defined zero. The form of spectral description in the general case is not dependent on the coordinate chosen for the description. Thus we could, by analogy with communication practice which normally deals with frequency spectra in terms of sidebands, say that there are time-domain sidebands. The sideband phenomenon is the description of energy distribution around an epoch in one domain due to operations (e.g., modulation) performed in the other domain. This phenomenon was used by this author to solve for the form of time-delay distortion due to propagation through a dispersive absorptive medium [3].

Fourier transform relations are valid only for infinite limits of integration and work as well for predictive systems as they do for causal. There is no inherent indignation in these transforms for a world with backward running clocks. The clock direction must be found from some other condition such as energy transformation. As pointed out previously [3], this lack of time sense led some investigators to the erroneous conclusion that group delay, a single-valued property, was uniquely related to real-world clock delay for all possible systems and has led others to the equally erroneous conclusion that a uniform group delay always guarantees a distortionless system. When we consider working with causal systems, where our clocks always run forward at constant rate, we must impose a condition on the time-domain representation that is strongly analogous to what the communication engineer calls single sideband when he describes a frequency attribute. We must, in other words, say that the epoch of zero time occurs upon stimulation of the system and that no energy due to that stimulation may occur for negative (prior) time. The conditions imposed on the other domain representation, frequency domain, by this causal requirement are described as Hermitian [21]. That is, both lower and upper sidebands exist about zero frequency and the amplitude spectrum will be even symmetric about zero frequency while the phase spectrum is odd symmetric.

The mathematical simplicity of impulse (and its sinusoidal equivalent transform) calculations has led to a tremendously useful series of analytical tools. Among these are the eigenvalue solutions to the wave equation in the eleven coordinates which yield closed form [10]. However, these are mathematical expansions which, if relating to one domain wholly, may be related to the other domain only if all possible values of coordinate are assumed. Tremendous mathematical frustration has been experienced by those trying to independently manipulate expressions in the two domains without apparently realizing that each was a description of the same event. Having assumed one description, our ground rules of analysis prevent an arbitrary choice of the description in the other domain. Because the time- and frequency-domain representations are two ways of describing the same event, we should not expect that we could maintain indefinite accuracy in a time-domain representation if we obtain this from a restricted frequency-domain measurement, no matter how clever we were. If we restrict the amount of information available to us from one domain, we can reconstruct the other domain only to the extent allowed by the available information. This is another way of expressing the interdomain dependence, known as the uncertainty principle. Later we shall consider the process of weighting a given spectrum description so as to minimize some undesirable sideband clutter when reconstructing the same information in the complementing spectral description.

When dealing with very simple systems, no difficulty is encountered in using a frequency-only or time-only representation and interpreting joint domain effects. But the very nature of the completeness of a given domain representation leads to extreme difficulty when one asks such seemingly simple questions as, "what is the time delay of a given frequency component passing through a system with nonuniform response?" A prior paper demonstrated that there is a valid third description of an event [3]. This involves a joint time–frequency characterization which can be brought into closed form if one utilizes a special primitive descriptor involving first-order and second-order all-pass transmission systems. In some ways this third description, lying as it does between the two principal descriptions, may be more readily identified with human experience. Everyone familiar with the score of a musical piece would be acutely aware of a piccolo solo which came two measures late. A frequency-only or time-only description of this musical fiasco might be difficult to interpret, even though both contain the information. Other joint domain methods have been undertaken by other investigators [5].

Applying this third description to a loudspeaker provided the model yielding time-delay distortion. It was shown that the answer to the time of emergence of a given frequency component had the surprise that at any given frequency there were multiple arrivals as a function of time. The nature of the third description was such that one could envision each frequency arrival as due to its own special perfect loudspeaker which had a frequency-dependent time delay which was single valued with frequency. If the system processing the information (in this case a loudspeaker) has a simple ordered pole and zero expansion in the frequency domain, then the arrival times for any frequency are discrete. If the expansion has branch points, then the arrival times may be a bounded distribution. The general problem for which this provides a solution is the propagation of information through a dispersive absorptive medium. Even though this characterization of information-bearing medium best fits a loudspeaker in a room, as well as most real-world propagation problems, attempts at solutions have been sparse [6], [7].

The equipment available to us to make measurements on a loudspeaker, such as oscilloscopes and spectrum analyzers, work in either of the primary domains and so do not present the third-domain results directly. This does not mean that other information processing means, perhaps even human perception of sound, work wholly in the primary domains. Within the restrictions of the uncertainty principle, which is after all a mathematical limitation imposed by our own definitions, we shall take a given frequency range and find the time delay of all loudspeaker frequency components within that range. The nature of this type of distortion is illustrated schematically in Fig. 1. If a momentary burst of energy $E(t)$ were fed a perfect loudspeaker, a similar burst of energy $E'(t)$ would be observed by O some time later due to the finite velocity of propagation c. More generally an actual loudspeaker will be observed by O to have a time smeared energy distribution $\epsilon(t)$. As far as the observer is concerned, the actual loudspeaker will have a spatial smear $\epsilon(x)$.

ENERGY, IMPULSE AND DOUBLET

Anyone familiar with analysis equipment realizes that the display of Fig. 1 will take more than some simple assembly of components. In fact, it will take a closer scrutiny of the fundamental concepts of energy, frequency, and time. The frequency-domain representation of an event is a complex quantity embodying an amplitude and a phase description. The time-domain representation of the same event may *also* be expressed as a complex quantity. The scalar representation of time-domain performance of a transmission system based on impulse excitation, which is common coinage in communication engineering [9], is the real part of a more general vector. The imaginary part of that vector is the Hilbert transform [2], [4] of the real part and is associated with a special excitation signal called a doublet by this author. For a nonturbulent (vortex free) medium wherein a vector representation is sufficient, the impulse and doublet responses completely characterize performance under conditions of superposition. For a turbulent medium one must use an additional tensor excitation which in most cases is a quadrupole. For all loudspeaker tests we will perform, we need only concern ourselves with the impulse and doublet response.

Any causal interception of information from a remote source implies an energy density associated with the actions of that source. The energy density represents the amount of useful work which could be obtained by the receiver if he were sufficiently clever. For the cases of interest in this paper, the total energy density at the point of reception is composed of a kinetic and a potential energy density component. These energy density terms relate to the instantaneous state of departure from equilibrium of the medium due to the actions of the remote source.

If we wish to evaluate the amount of total work which could be performed on an observer, whether microphone diaphragm or eardrum, at any moment, such as given in Fig. 1, then we must evaluate the instantaneous total energy density. In order to specify how much energy density is available to us from a loudspeaker, and what time it arrives at our location if it is due to a predetermined portion of the frequency spectrum, we must choose our test signal very carefully and keep track of the ground rules of the equivalence of time and frequency descriptions. We may not, for example, simply insert a narrow pulse of electrical energy into a loudspeaker, hoping that it simulates an impulse, and view the intercepted microphone signal on an oscilloscope. What must be done is to determine first what frequency range is to be of interest; then generate a signal which contains only those frequencies. By the process of generation of the excitation signal for a finite frequency band, we have defined the time epoch for this signal. Interception of the loudspeaker acoustic signal should then be made at the point of desired measurement. This interception should include both kinetic and potential energy densities. The total energy density, obtained as a sum of kinetic and potential energy densities, should then be displayed as a function of the time of interception.

The foregoing simplistic description is exactly what we shall do for actual loudspeakers. Those whose experiments are conducted in terms of the time domain only will immediately recognize that such an experiment is commonly characterized as physically unrealizable in the sense that having once started a time only process, one cannot arbitrarily stop the clock or run it backward. In order to circumvent this apparent difficulty we shall make use of the proper relation between frequency and time descriptions. Rather than use true physical time for a measured parameter, the time metric will be obtained as a Fourier transform from a frequency-domain measurement. Because we are thus allowed to redefine the time metric to suit our measurement, it is possible to alter the time base in any manner felt suitable. The price paid is a longer physical time for a given measurement.

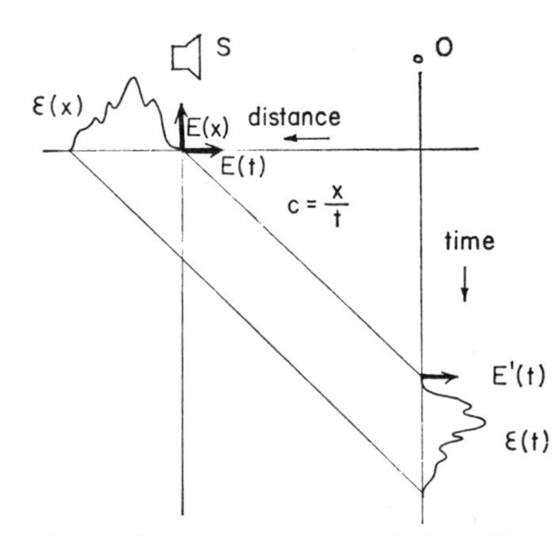

Fig. 1. Symbolic representation of time–distance world line for observer O perceiving energy from loudspeaker S.

A loudspeaker energy plot representing one millisecond may take many seconds of real clock time to process, depending upon the time resolution desired. The process utilized will coincide in large measure with some used in coherent communication practice, and the amount by which the derived time metric exceeds the real clock time will correspond to what is called filter processing gain. The basic signal process for our measurement will start with that of a time delay spectometer (TDS) [1], [16]. This is due not only to the basic simplicity of instrumentation, but the "domain swapping" properties of a TDS which presents a complex frequency measurement as a complex time signal and vice versa.

ANALYSIS, IMPULSE AND DOUBLET

If we consider that a time-dependent disturbance $f(t)$ is observed, we could say that either this was the result of a particular excitation of a general parameter $f(x)$ such that

$$f(t) = \lim_{\lambda \to \infty} \int_{-\infty}^{\infty} f(x) \frac{\sin \lambda (t-x)}{\pi (t-x)} dx \quad (1)$$

or it was the result of operation on another parameter $F(\omega)$ such that

$$f(t) = \int_{-\infty}^{\infty} F(\omega) e^{i\omega t} d\omega. \quad (2)$$

Eq. (1) is known as Fourier's single-integral formula [4, p. 3] and is frequently expressed as

$$f(t) = \int_{-\infty}^{\infty} f(x) \delta(t-x) dx \quad (3)$$

where $\delta(t-x)$ is understood to mean the limiting form shown in Eq. (1) and is designated as an impulse because of its singularity behavior [10].

The functions $f(x)$ and $F(\omega)$ of Eqs. (2) and (3), Fourier's two descriptions of the same event, are thus considered to be paired coefficients in the sense that each of them multiplied by its characteristic "driving function" and integrated over all possible ranges of that driving function yields the same functional dependence $f(t)$. This paired coefficient interpretation is that expressed by Campbell and Foster in their very significant work [8].

Eq. (3) may be looked upon as implying that there was a system, perhaps a loudspeaker, which had a particular characterization $f(x)$. When acted upon by the driving signal $\delta(t-x)$, the response $f(t)$ was the resultant output. Conversely, Eq. (2) implies that there was another equally valid characterization $F(\omega)$ which when acted upon by the driving signal $e^{i\omega t}$ produced the same response $f(t)$.

The functions $f(x)$ and $F(\omega)$ are of course Fourier transforms of each other. The reason for not beginning our discussion by simply writing down the transform relations as is conventional practice is that to do so tends to overlook the real foundations of the principle. To illustrate that these functions are not the only such relations one could use, consider the same system with a driving signal which elicits the response

$$g(t) = \lim_{\lambda \to \infty} \int_{-\infty}^{\infty} f(x) \left\{ \frac{\cos \lambda (t-x) - 1}{\pi (t-x)} \right\} dx \quad (4)$$

which as before we shall assume to exist as the limiting form

$$g(t) = \int_{-\infty}^{\infty} f(x) d(t-x) dx. \quad (5)$$

Also,

$$g(t) = \int_{-\infty} F(\omega) \{-i \operatorname{sgn}(\omega)\} e^{i\omega t} d\omega. \quad (6)$$

Obviously this is an expression of the Hilbert transform of Eqs. (2) and (3) [2], [4]. It is none the less a legitimate paired coefficient expansion of two ways of describing the same phenomenon $g(t)$. By observing the way in which $\delta(t-x)$ and $d(t-x)$ behave as the limit is approached in Eqs. (1) and (4), it is apparent that both tend to zero everywhere except in a narrow region around the value where $t=x$. Thus there is not one, but at least two driving functions which tend toward a singularity behavior in the limit. As we shall see, these two constitute the most important set of such singularity operators when discussing physical properties of systems such as loudspeakers. Because of the nature of singularity approached by each, we shall define them as impulse and doublet, respectively. The following definitions will be assumed.

The impulse operator is approached as the defined limit

$$\delta(t) = \lim_{a \to \infty} \frac{\sin at}{\pi t}. \quad (7)$$

The impulse operator is not a function but is defined from Eq. (3) as an operation on the function $f(x)$ to produce the value $f(t)$. $\delta(t)$ is even symmetric. The application of an electrical replica of the impulse operator to any network will produce an output defined as the impulse response of that network. The Fourier transform $F(\omega)$ of this impulse response $f(t)$ is defined as the frequency response of the network and is identical at any frequency to the complex quotient of output to input for that network when excited by a unit amplitude sine-wave signal of the given frequency.

The doublet operator is approached as the defined limit

$$d(t) = \lim_{a \to \infty} \frac{\cos at - 1}{\pi t}. \quad (8)$$

The doublet operator is not a function but is defined from Eq. (5) as an operation on the function $f(x)$ to produce the value $g(t)$. $d(t)$ is odd symmetric. The application of an electrical replica of the doublet operator to any network will produce an output defined as the doublet response of that network. The doublet response is the Hilbert transform of the impulse response. The Fourier transform of the doublet response is identical to that of the impulse response, with the exception that the doublet phase spectrum is advanced ninety degrees for negative frequencies and retarded ninety degrees for positive frequencies.

In addition to the above definitions, the Fourier transform of the impulse response will be defined as being of minimum phase type in that the accumulation of phase lag for increasing frequency is a minimum for the resultant amplitude spectrum. The Fourier transform of the doublet response will be defined as being of nonminimum phase.

It must be observed that the doublet operator defined here is not identical to that sometimes seen derived from the impulse as a simple derivative and therefore possessing a transform of nonuniform amplitude spectral density [9, p. 542]. The corresponding relation between the doublet operator $d(t)$ and the impulse operator $\delta(t)$ prior to the limiting process is

$$d(t) = -\frac{1}{\pi} \frac{d}{dt} \int_{-\infty}^{\infty} \delta(x) \ln \left| 1 - \frac{t}{x} \right| dx. \quad (9)$$

The distinction is that the doublet operator defined here has the same power spectral density as the impulse operator. Furthermore as can be seen from Eq. (9), the doublet operator may be envisioned as the limit of a physical doublet, as defined in classical electrodynamics [10].

ANALYTIC SIGNAL

We have thus defined two system driving operators, the impulse and the doublet, which when applied to a system produce a scalar time response. Although the relation between the time-domain responses is that of Hilbert transformation, if one were to view them as an oscilloscope display, he may find it hard to believe they were attributable to the same system. However, the resultant frequency-domain representations are, except for the phase reference, identical in form. We will now develop a generalized response to show that it is not possible to derive a unique time behavior from incomplete knowledge of a restricted portion of the frequency response.

Symbolizing the operation of the Fourier integral transform by the double arrow $\leftrightarrow$, we can rewrite Eqs. (2) and (6) as the paired coefficients

$$f(t) \leftrightarrow F(\omega) \qquad (10)$$

$$g(t) \leftrightarrow -i(\operatorname{sgn} \omega)F(\omega). \qquad (11)$$

Multiplying Eq. (10) by a factor $\cos \lambda$ and Eq. (11) by $\sin \lambda$ and combining,

$$\cos \lambda \cdot f(t) + \sin \lambda \cdot g(t) \leftrightarrow F(\omega)[\cos \lambda - i(\operatorname{sgn} \omega) \sin \lambda]. \qquad (12)$$

The frequency-domain representation is thus

$$\begin{array}{ll} F(\omega)e^{-i\lambda}, & 0 < \omega \\ F(\omega)e^{i\lambda}, & 0 > \omega. \end{array} \qquad (13)$$

In this form it is apparent that if we were to have an accurate measurement of the amplitude spectrum of the frequency response of a system, such as a loudspeaker, and did not have any information concerning its phase spectrum, we could not uniquely determine either the impulse response or doublet response of that loudspeaker. Such an amplitude-only spectrum would arise from a standard anechoic chamber measurement or from any of the power spectral density measurements using noncoherent random noise. This lack of uniqueness was pointed out in an earlier paper [2]. The best that one could do is to state that the resultant time-domain response is some linear combination of impulse and doublet response.

Because the time domain representation is a scalar, it is seen that Eq. 12 could be interpreted as a scalar operation on a generalized time-domain vector such that

$$\operatorname{Re}[e^{-i\lambda}h(t)] \leftrightarrow F(\omega) \cdot e^{-i\lambda\{\operatorname{sgn} \omega\}} \qquad (14)$$

where $\operatorname{Re}(x)$ means real part of and where the vector $h(t)$ is defined as

$$h(t) = f(t) + ig(t). \qquad (15)$$

This vector is commonly called the analytic signal in communication theory, where it is normally associated with narrow-band processes [11], [12]. As can be seen from (14) and the Appendix, it is not restricted to narrow-band situations but can arise quite legitimately from considerations of the whole spectrum. This analytic signal is the general time-domain vector which contains the information relating to the magnitude and partitioning of kinetic and potential energy densities.

The impulse and doublet response of a physical system, which in our case is the loudspeaker in a room, is related to the stored and dissipated energy as perceived. This means that if one wishes to evaluate the time history of energy in a loudspeaker, it is better sought from the analytic signal of Eq. (15). It is not sufficient to simply use the conventional impulse response to attempt determination of energy arrivals for speakers. The magnitude of the analytic signal is an indication of the total energy in the signal, while the phase of the analytic signal is an indication of the exchange ratio of kinetic to potential energy. The exchange ratio of kinetic to potential energy determines the upper bound for the local speed of propagation of physical influences capable of producing causal results. We call this local speed the velocity of propagation through the medium. From the basic Lagrange relations for nonconservative systems [13] it may be seen that the dissipation rate of energy is related to the time rate of change of the magnitude of the analytic signal. If the system under analysis is such as to have a source of energy at a given time and is dissipative thereafter with no further sources, the magnitude of the analytic signal will be a maximum at that time corresponding to the moment of energy input and constantly diminishing thereafter. The result of this is that if we wish to know the time history of effective signal sources which contribute to a given portion of the frequency spectrum, it may be obtained by first isolating the frequency spectrum of interest, then evaluating the analytic signal obtained from a Fourier transform of this spectrum, finally noting those portions of the magnitude of the analytic signal which are stationary with time (Hamilton's principle) [10].

It becomes apparent that by this means we will be able to take a physical system such as a loudspeaker in a room and determine not only when the direct and reflected sound arrives at a given point, but the time spread of any given arrival. Because we will be measuring the arrival time pattern for a restricted frequency range, it is important to know what tradeoffs exist because of the spectrum limitations, and how the effects can be minimized.

SPECTRUM WEIGHTING

We will be characterizing the frequency-dependent time delay of a loudspeaker. The nature of the testing signal which we use should be such that minimum energy exists outside the frequency band of interest, while at the same time allowing for a maximum resolution in the time domain. This joint domain occupancy problem has been around for quite some time and analytical solutions exist [14]. For loudspeaker testing where we wish to know the time-domain response for a restricted frequency band, we can use any signal which has a frequency spectrum bounded to the testing band with minimum energy outside this band [19], [20]. An intuitive choice of a signal with a rectangular shaped frequency spectrum which had maximum occupancy of the testing band would not be a good one, because the time-domain characterization while sharply peaked would not fall off very rapidly on either side of the peak. The consequence of this is that a genuine later arrival may be lost in the coherent sideband clutter of a strong signal. A much better choice of band-limited spectrum would be one which places more energy in the midband frequency while reducing the energy at band edge. Such a spectrum is said to be weighted. The weighting function is the frequency-dependent multiplier of the spectral components. An entire uniform spectrum is spoken of as unweighted, and a uniform bounded spectrum is said to be weighted by a rectangular function.

The proper definition of spectrum weighting must take into account both phase and amplitude. If a rectangular amplitude, minimum phase weighting is utilized, the resultant time function will be given by Eq. (1) without the limit taken. The parameter λ will be inversely proportional to the bandwidth. If rectangular amplitude but nonminimum phase weighting is utilized, then the time function will be given by Eq. (4).

It should be obvious that one can weight either the time or frequency domain. Weighting in the time domain is frequently referred to as shaping of the pulse response. The purpose in either case is to bound the resultant distribution of energy. Two types of weighting will be utilized in this paper. The first is a Hamming weighting [14, p. 98] and takes the form shown in Fig. 2**a**. As used for spectral limitation, this is an amplitude-only weighting with no resultant phase shift. Although this type of weighting cannot be generated by linear circuits, it can be obtained in an on-line processor by nonlinear means. The second weighting is a product of two functions. One function is the minimum phase amplitude and phase spectrum of a tuned circuit. The other function is shown in Fig. 2**b**. This second weighting is that utilized in a TDS which will be used as a basic instrument for this paper.

Reference to the earlier paper and its analysis discloses that within the TDS intermediate frequency amplifier (which of course could be centered at zero frequency), the information relating to a specific signal arrival is contained in the form

$$o(t) = [i(t) \otimes w(t)] \otimes S(at) \tag{16}$$

where $\otimes$ signifies convolution, $S(at)$ is the complex

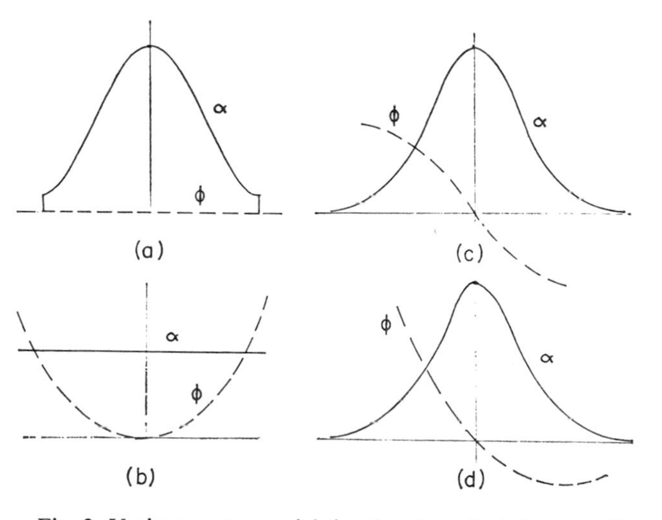

Fig. 2. Various system weighting functions including amplitude (solid line) and phase (dashed line) utilized to bound the resultant energy when taking a Fourier transform. **a.** Hamming weighting. **b.** Quadratic phase all-pass weighting. **c.** Passive simple resonance weighting. **d.** Simple TDS weighting formed as a product of **b** and **c.**

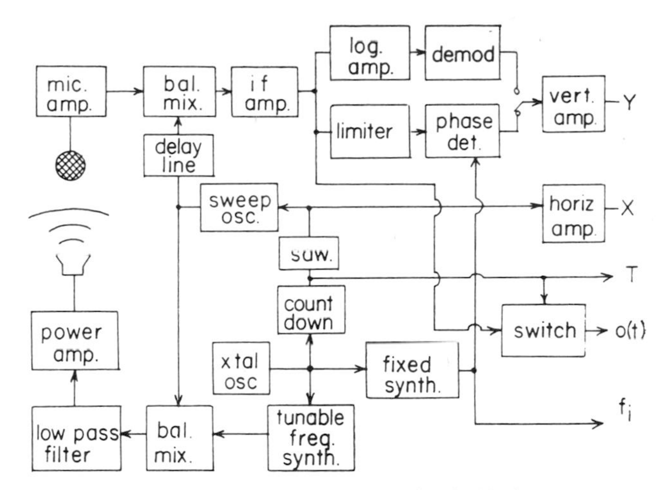

Fig. 3. Block diagram of simple TDS

Fourier transform of the impulse response of the system under test, $i(t)$ is the impulse response of the intermediate frequency amplifier, and $w(t)$ is the window function defined as the impulse response of a quadratic phase circuit. It can be seen that the TDS provides a weighting of the time domain arrivals of that signal selected in order to give an optimum presentation of the frequency spectrum.

TRANSFORMATION TO TIME

We will now consider how to convert a measured frequency response to the analytic signal. We must start of course by having the loudspeaker frequency response available. Assume then that the system under test is evaluated by the TDS. The block diagram of this is reproduced in Fig. 3 from an earlier paper. As before, a tunable frequency synthesizer is used. Assume that the output of the intermediate frequency amplifier is taken as shown. This output signal will be of the form of Eq. (16), but of course translated to lie at the center of the intermediate frequency. Because the frequency deviation of the sweep oscillator is restricted to that portion of the frequency spectrum of interest (dc to 10 kHz, for example), the signal $o(t)$ is representative of this restricted range. The duration of sweep will be a fixed value of T seconds, so that $o(t)$ is a signal repetetive in the period T. Assume that we close the switch for $o(t)$ shown in Fig. 3 for a period of T seconds and open it prior to and following that time. The signal characterization out of this switch is

$$e^{i\omega_i t} \,|\, i(t) \otimes w(t) \otimes S(at) \,|\, \mathrm{Rect}\,(t-T) \tag{17}$$

where the rectangular weighting function is defined as,

$$\mathrm{Rect}\,(t-T) = \begin{matrix} 1, & 0<t<T \\ 0, & \text{elsewhere.} \end{matrix} \tag{18}$$

Assume we now multiply the signal by the complex quantity

$$e^{-i\omega_i t}\, e^{i\Omega t} \tag{19}$$

and the product is in turn multiplied by a weighting function $A(t)$. If we take the integral of the product of these functions, we have

$$\int_{-\infty}^{\infty} [\mathrm{Rect}(t-T)] \cdot A(t) \cdot \{i(t) \otimes w(t) \otimes S(at)\} e^{i\Omega t} dt. \quad (20)$$

The infinite limits are possible because of the rectangular function which vanishes outside the finite time limits. The integral of Eq. (20) may now be recognized as a Fourier transform from the t domain to the Ω domain. This may be expressed in the Ω domain as

$$a(\Omega) \otimes [I(\Omega) \cdot e^{-i\Omega^2/2a} \cdot h(\Omega)] \quad (21)$$

where $a(\Omega)$ is the transform of the weighting in the t domain, $I(\Omega)$ is the frequency response of the intermediate frequency amplifier expressed in the Ω domain, the exponential form is the quadratic phase window function, and $h(\Omega)$ is the Ω domain form of the analytic function shown in Eq. (15). The reason that this is $h(\Omega)$ and not the impulse response $f(\Omega)$ is that we have assumed a TDS frequency sweep from one frequency to another, where both are on the same side of zero frequency.

What we have done by all this is instrument a technique to perform an inverse Fourier transform of a frequency response. The answer appears as a voltage which is a function of an offset frequency Ω. Even though we energized the loudspeaker with a sweeping frequency, we obtain a voltage which corresponds to what we would have had if we fed an infinitely narrow pulse through a perfect frequency-weighted filter to a loudspeaker. We now say that by changing an offset frequency Ω, the answer we see is what would have been observed had we used a pulse and evaluated the response at a particular moment in time. By adjusting the offset frequency we can observe the value that would be seen for successive moments in time.

SINGLE- AND DOUBLE-SIDED SPECTRA

We will be making measurements in the frequency domain and from this calculate the time-domain energy arrivals. If our measurement includes zero frequency, we have shown earlier how one could invoke the odd symmetry requirement to define "absolute" phase [2]. By so doing we have eliminated the parameter λ from Eq. (13). It is thus possible to calculate either the impulse or doublet time response in a unique manner. However, since the lower and upper sidebands are redundant in the frequency domain, care must be taken in using Eq. (20) that only one sideband, for example, positive frequencies, be used and the other sideband rejected. Failure to do this will result in an improper calculation not only of impulse and doublet response, but of the analytic signal as well. If one is aware of this single-sided versus double-sided spectrum pitfall, he may use it to advantage. For example, if a perfectly symmetric double-sided spectrum is used, the analytic signal calculation will yield the impulse response directly, as can be seen from Eq. (12).

Most loudspeaker measurements are made in a single-sided manner. For example, one may wish to know what time distribution arises from the midrange driver which works from 500 Hz to 10 kHz. In this case, because zero frequency is not available it may not be possible to define the parameter λ of Eq. (13), even if both amplitude and phase spectra are measured. Because of this an unequivocal determination of the impulse response (potential energy relation) or of the doublet response (kinetic energy relation) may be impossible. One may always determine the analytic signal magnitude (potential plus kinetic energy relation). The time position of effective energy sources can be determined by noting the moments when the effective signal energy is a maximum.

INSTRUMENTATION

The loudspeaker energy arrivals are obtained from the analytic signal. The signals of interest are first isolated from the remainder of the room reflections by means of a TDS. This measurement is the frequency domain description of the loudspeaker anechoic response, even though the loudspeaker is situated in a room. This loudspeaker description, although mathematically identical to a frequency-domain description, has been made available within the TDS in the time domain. In order to take a Fourier transform of this frequency-domain description to obtain the time-domain analytic signal, we must multiply by a complex sinusoid representing the time epoch, multiply this in turn by a complex weighting function, and then integrate over all possible frequencies (Eq. 20). This process would normally require substantial digital computational facilities for a frequency-domain measurement; however, the "domain swapping" properties of a TDS allow for straightforward continuous signal processing. Fig. 4 is a block diagram of the functions added to the TDS of Fig. 3 to effect this process. The signal from the intermediate frequency amplifier of the TDS is buffered and fed to two balanced mixers. By using an in-phase and quadrature multiplier of the same frequency as the intermediate frequency, the two outputs are obtained which are Hilbert transforms of each other and centered at zero frequency. Each of these is then isolated by low-pass filters and processed by identical switching multipliers controlled by a cosine function of the sweep time to effect a Hamming weighting. The net output of each weighting network is then passed through sampling integrators. At the start of a TDS sweep, the integrators are set to zero by

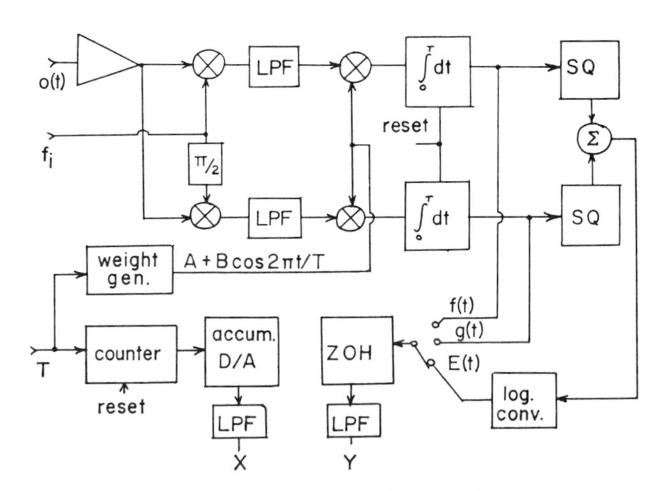

Fig. 4. Block diagram of Fourier transformation equipment attaching to a TDS capable of displaying time-domain plots. **a.** Impulse response $f(t)$. **b.** Doublet response $g(t)$. **c.** Total energy density $E(t)$.

the same clock pulse that phase locks the TDS offset frequency synthesizer so as to preserve phase continuity. Each integrator then functions unimpeded for the duration of the sweep. If the proper phase has been set into the offsetting synthesizer, the output of one integrator at the end of the sweep will correspond to the single value of the impulse response for the moment of epoch chosen, while the other will correspond to doublet response. If the proper phase has not been selected, then one integrator will correspond to a linear combination such as expressed in Eq. (12), while the other integrator will correspond to the quadrature term.

If one desires to plot the impulse or doublet response, the appropriate integrator output may be sent to a zero-order hold circuit which clocks in the calculated value and retains it during the subsequent sweep calculation. This boxcar voltage may then be recorded as the ordinate on a plotter with the abscissa proportional to the epoch. One trick of the trade which is used when horizontal and vertical signals to a plotter are stepped simultaneously, is to low-pass filter both channels with the same cutoff frequency. The plotter will now draw straight lines between interconnecting points.

If one is interested in the magnitude of the analytic signal (14), which from the Appendix, to be published December 1971, is related to energy history, then the most straightforward instrumentation is to square the output from each integrator and linearly add to get the sum of squares. A logarithmic amplifier following the sum of squares will enable a signal strength reading in dB without the need for a square root circuit. By doing this, a burden is placed on this logarithmic amplifier since a 40-dB signal strength variation produces an 80-dB input change to the logarithmic element. Fortunately, such an enormous range may be accommodated readily by conventional logarithmic elements. For graphic recordings of energy arrival, the output of the logarithmic amplifier may be fed through the same zero-order hold circuit as utilized for impulse and doublet response.

The configuration of Fig. 4 including quadrature multipliers, sampled integrators, and sum of squares circuitry is quite often encountered in coherent communication practice [17], [18]. This circuit is known to be an optimum detector in the mean error sense for coherent signals in a uniformly random noise environment. Its use in this paper is that of implementing an inverse Fourier transform for total energy for a single-sided spectrum. An interesting byproduct of its use is thus an assurance that no analytically superior instrumentation as yet exists for extracting the coherent loudspeaker signal from a random room noise environment.

CHOICE OF MICROPHONE

The information which our coherent analysis equipment utilizes is related to the energy density intercepted by the microphone. The total energy density in joules per cubic meter is composed of kinetic energy density E_T and potential energy density E_V, where [22, p. 356]

$$E_T = \frac{1}{2}\rho_0 v^2$$

$$E_V = \frac{1}{2}\rho_0 c^2 s^2. \qquad (22)$$

The equilibrium density is ρ_0, v is the particle velocity, s is condensation or density deviation from equilibrium, and c is velocity of energy propagation.

At first glance it might be assumed that total energy may not be obtained from either a pressure responsive microphone which relates to E_V or a velocity microphone relating to E_T. The answer to this dilemma may be found in the Appendix. One can always determine one energy component, given the other. Hence a determination of acoustic pressure or velocity or an appropriate mixture of pressure and velocity is sufficient to characterize the energy density of the original signal.

This means that any microphone, whether pressure, velocity, or hybrid, may be used for this testing technique, provided that a calibration exists over the frequency range for a given parameter. This also means that any perceptor which is activated by total work done on it by the acoustic signal will not be particular, whether the energy bearing the information is kinetic or potential. There is some reason to believe that human sound preception falls into this category.

REFERENCES

[1] R. C. Heyser, "Acoustical Measurements by Time Delay Spectrometry," *J. Audio Eng. Soc.*, vol. 15, p. 370 (1967).

[2] R. C. Heyser, "Loudspeaker Phase Characteristics and Time Delay Distortion: Part 1," *J. Audio Eng. Soc.*, vol. 17, p. 30 (1969).

[3] R. C. Heyser, "Loudspeaker Phase Characteristics and Time Delay Distortion: Part 2," *J. Audio Eng. Soc.*, vol. 17, p. 130 (1969).

[4] E. C. Titchmarsh, *Introduction to the Theory of Fourier Integrals* (Oxford Press, London, 2nd ed., 1948).

[5] C. H. Page, "Instantaneous Power Spectra," *J. Appl. Phys.*, vol. 23, p. 103 (1952).

[6] L. Brillouin, *Wave Propagation and Group Velocity* (Academic Press, New York, 1960).

[7] H. G. Baerwald, "Über die Fortpflanzung von Signalen in dispergierenden Systemen," *Ann. Phys.*, vol. 5, p. 295 (1930).

[8] G. A. Campbell and R. M. Foster, *Fourier Integrals* (D. Van Nostrand, Princeton, N.J., 1961).

[9] E. A. Guillemin, *The Mathematics of Circuit Analysis* (M.I.T. Press, Cambridge, Mass., 1965).

[10] E. U. Condon and H. Odishaw, *Handbook of Physics* (McGraw-Hill, New York, 1967).

[11] R. S. Berkowitz, *Modern Radar* (John Wiley, New York, 1967).

[12] L. E. Franks, *Signal Theory* (Prentice-Hall, Englewood Cliffs, N.J., 1969).

[13] T. v. Karman and M. A. Biot, *Mathematical Methods in Engineering* (McGraw-Hill, New York, 1940).

[14] R. B. Blackman and J. W. Tukey, *Measurement of Power Spectra* (Dover, New York, 1959).

[15] A. W. Rihaczek, *Principles of High-Resolution Radar* (McGraw-Hill, New York, 1969).

[16] R. C. Heyser, "Time Delay Spectrometer," U.S. Patent 3,466,652, Sept. 9, 1969.

[17] A. J. Viterbi, *Principles of Coherent Communication* (McGraw-Hill, New York, 1966).

[18] H. L. VanTrees, *Detection, Estimation, and Modulation Theory* (John Wiley, New York, 1968).

[19] T. A. Saponas, R. C. Matson, and J. R. Ashley, "Plain and Fancy Test Signals for Music Reproduction Systems," *J. Audio Eng. Soc.*, vol. 19, pp. 294-305 (Apr. 1971).

[20] A. Schaumberger, "Impulse Measurement Techniques for Quality Determination in Hi-Fi Equipment, with Special Emphasis on Loudspeakers," *J. Audio Eng. Soc.*, vol. 19, pp. 101-107 (Feb. 1971).

[21] R. Bracewell, *The Fourier Transform and Its Applications* (McGraw-Hill, New York, 1965).
[22] D. H. Menzel, *Fundamental Formulas of Physics* (Prentice-Hall, Englewood Cliffs, N.J., 1965).
[23] E. A. Guillemin, *Theory of Linear Physical Systems* (John Wiley, New York, 1963).
[24] I. S. Gradshteyn and I. M. Ryzhik, *Table of Integrals, Series and Products* (Academic Press, New York, 1965), Eq. 3.782.2.
[25] B. B. Baker and E. T. Copson, *The Mathematical Theory of Huygens' Principle* (Oxford Press, London, 1953).

THE AUTHOR

Richard C. Heyser received his B.S.E.E. degree from the University of Arizona in 1953. Awarded the AIEE Charles LeGeyt Fortescue Fellowship for advanced studies he received his M.S.E.E. from the California Institute of Technology in 1954. The following two years were spent in post-graduate work at Cal Tech leading toward a doctorate. During the summer months of 1954 and 1955, Mr. Heyser was a research engineer specializing in transistor circuits with the Motorola Research Laboratory, Phoenix, Arizona. From 1956 until the present time he has been associated with the California Institute of Technology Jet Propulsion Laboratory in Pasadena, California where he is a senior member of the JPL Technical Staff.

Mr. Heyser has presented several papers before the AES and is a member and Fellow of the Audio Engineering Society, the Institute of Electrical and Electronic Engineers, as well as Tau Beta Pi, Pi Mu Epsilon, Phi Kappa Phi, Sigma Pi Sigma, and Sigma Xi. He is also a member of Theta Tau.

Determination of Loudspeaker Signal Arrival Times* Part II

RICHARD C. HEYSER

Jet Propulsion Laboratory, California Institute of Technology, Pasadena, Calif.

EXPERIMENT

The information to be determined is the time delay of total acoustic energy that would be received from a loudspeaker if fed from an impulse of electrical energy. Because we are interested in that energy due to a preselected portion of the frequency band, we may assume that the impulse is band limited by a special shaping filter prior to being sent to the loudspeaker. This filter would not be physically realizable if we actually used an impulse for our test; but since we are using a method of coherent communication technology, we will be able to circumvent that obstacle. Fig. 5 shows three responses for a midrange horn loaded loudspeaker. The frequency band is dc to 10 kHz, and each response is measured on the same time scale with zero milliseconds corresponding to the moment of speaker excitation. The driver unit was three feet from the microphone. Curve (a) is the measured impulse response and is what one would see for microphone pressure response, had the loudspeaker been driven by a voltage impulse. Curve (b) is the measured doublet response and is the Hilbert transform of (a). In both (a) and (b) the measured ordinate is linear voltage. Curve (c) is the total received energy on a logarithmic scale. Here the interplay of impulse, doublet, and total energy is evident.

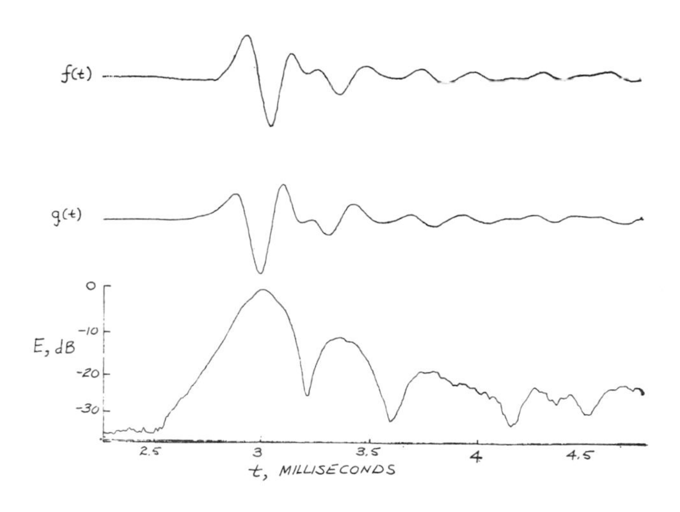

Fig. 5. Measured plots of impulse response $f(t)$, doublet response $g(t)$, and total energy density E for a midrange horn loudspeaker for spectral components from dc to 10 kHz.

* Presented April 30, 1971, at the 40th Convention of the Audio Engineering Society, Los Angeles. For Part I, please see pp. 734-743 of the October 1971 issue of this *Journal*.

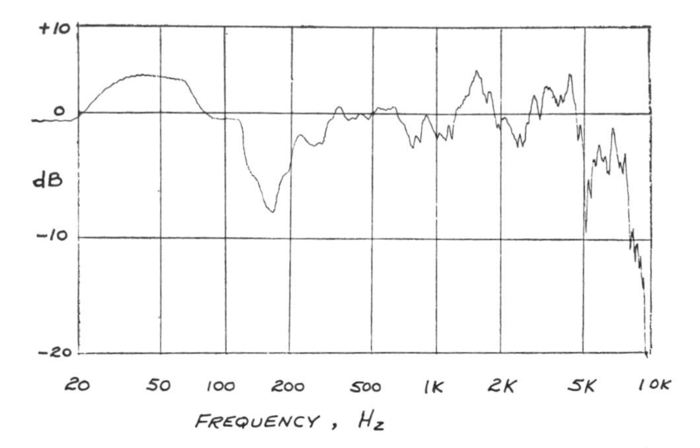

Fig. 6. TDS plot of frequency response (amplitude only) of an eight-inch open-back cabinet mounted loudspeaker with microphone to cone air path spacing of three feet.

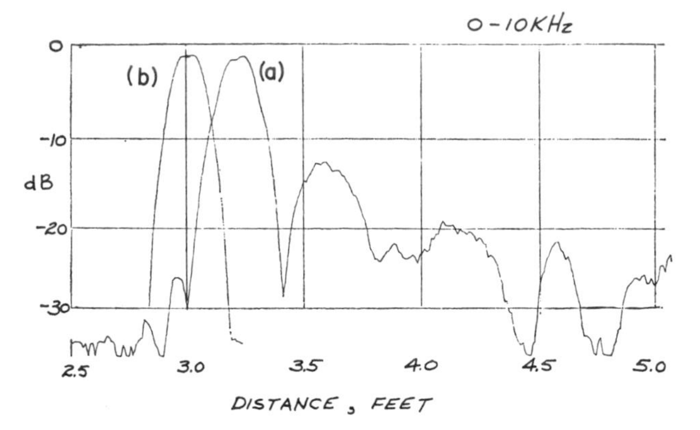

Fig. 7. Curve (a)—Energy-time arrival for loudspeaker of Fig. 6, taking all frequency components from dc to 10 kHz. Curve (b)—Superimposed measured curve to be expected if loudspeaker did not have time-delay distortion.

Fig. 6 is the TDS measured amplitude frequency response of a good quality eight-inch loudspeaker mounted in a small open-back cabinet. For simplicity the phase spectrum is not included. Fig. 7 is the time delay of energy for the speaker of Fig. 6. Superimposed on this record is a plot of what the time response would have been, had the actual loudspeaker position and acoustic position coincided and if there were no time-delay distortion. It is clear from this record that time-delay distortion truly exists. If one considers all response within 20 dB of peak, it is evident that this loudspeaker is smeared out by about one foot behind its apparent physical location. It should be observed that the response dropoff above 5 kHz coincides with a gross time delay of about three inches, as predicted by earlier analysis (Part I, [2]).

Fig. 8 is a plot of energy versus equivalent distance in feet for a high-efficiency midrange horn loaded driver. The band covered is 500 Hz to 1500 Hz and includes the region from low-frequency cutoff to midrange. The physical location of the driver phase plug is shown, and it may be seen that the acoustic and physical positions differ by nearly one foot. Fig. 9 is the same driver, but the band is 1000 Hz to 2000 Hz. The acoustic position is now closer to the phase plug and a hint of a double hump in delay is evident. Because the bandwidth is 1000 Hz, the spatial resolution available does not allow for more complete definition of acoustic position for this type of display.

Fig. 10 is a data run on an eight-inch wide range loudspeaker without baffle. A scaled pseudo cross section of the loudspeaker is shown for reference. The frequency range covered is dc to 20 kHz. Although the time-delay value may vary from one part of the spectrum to another, it is apparent that a wide frequency range percussive signal may suffer a spatial smear of the order of six inches.

Fig. 11 is a medium-quality six-inch loudspeaker mounted in an open-back cabinet. The position of main energy is, as predicted, quite close to that which would be assumed for a cutoff at about 5 kHz. The secondary hump of energy from 3 to 3.5 milliseconds is not due to acoustic energy spilling around the side of the enclosure, but is a time delay inherent in the loudspeaker itself.

Fig. 12 is the energy received from an unterminated midrange driver excited from dc to 10 kHz. The effect of untermination is seen as a superposition of an exponential time delay, due to a relatively high Q resonance, and internal reverberation with a 0.3-millisecond period.

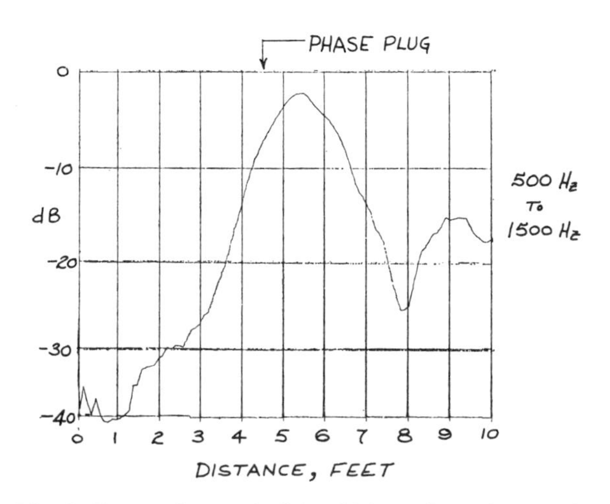

Fig. 8. Energy-time arrival for high-quality midrange horn loudspeaker for all components from 500 Hz to 1500 Hz. Measured position of phase plug is shown.

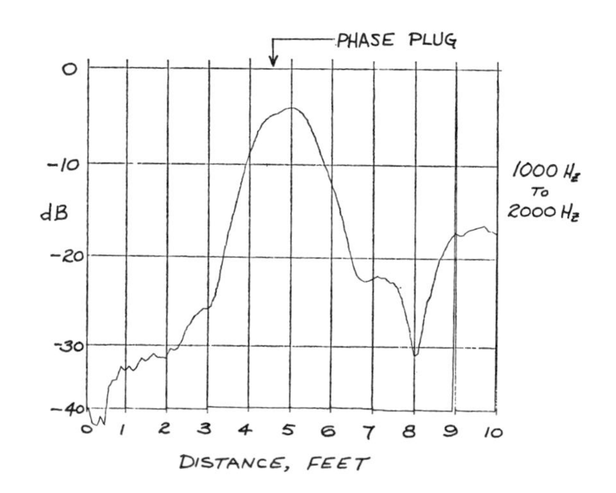

Fig. 9. Same loudspeaker as Fig. 8, but excitation is from 1000 Hz to 2000 Hz.

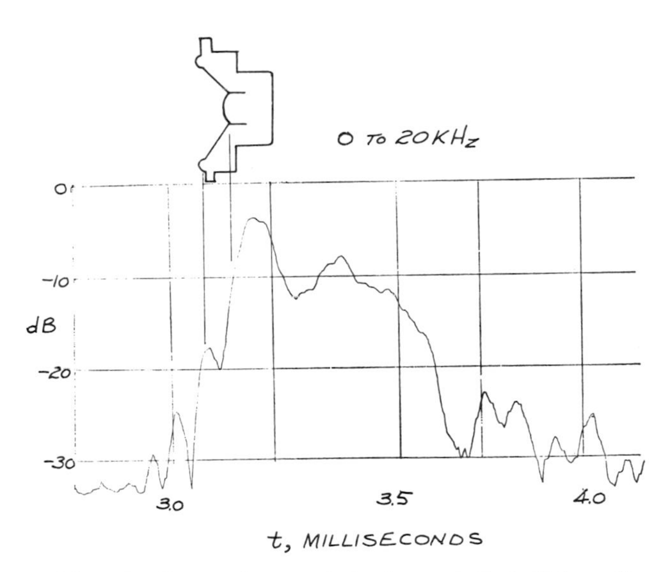

Fig. 10. Energy-time arrivals for unbaffled high-quality eight-inch loudspeaker. Frequency band is dc to 20 kHz and phantom sketch of loudspeaker physical location is included for identification of amount of time-delay distortion relative to speaker dimensions.

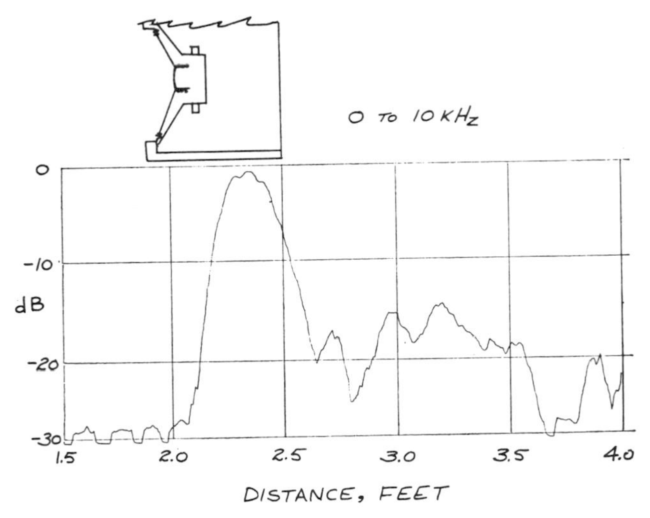

Fig. 11. Energy-time arrivals for open-back cabinet mounted medium-quality eight-inch loudspeaker. Frequency band is dc to 10 kHz and loudspeaker position shown to approximate scale.

Fig. 13 shows the effect of improper termination by a horn with too high a flare rate. The resonance is more efficiently damped, but the internal reverberation due to acoustic mismatch still exists. This is a low-quality driver unit.

Fig. 14 is the time delay distortion of the midrange driver discussed at some length elsewhere (Part I [2, Fig. 4]. The internal delayed voices are plainly in evidence.

Fig. 15 is a high-quality paper cone tweeter showing the time-delay distortion for the dc to 10-kHz frequency range. The multiplicity of reverberent energy peaks with about a 0.13-millisecond period is due to internal scattering within the tweeter. It is not at all clear from the frequency response taken alone that such an effect exists; however, by observing the time-delay characteristic it is possible to know what indicators to look for upon reexamination of the complete frequency response.

Fig. 16 is the time display of a multiple-panel high-quality electrostatic loudspeaker. This is a 1–5-kHz response taken along the geometric axis of symmetry, coinciding with the on-axis response. The physical position of the closest portion of radiating element occurs at a distance equivalent to 2 milliseconds air path delay. Fig. 17 is the same speaker 15 degrees off axis. Not only is the total energy down, but the contribution of adjacent panels is now evident.

Figs. 18 and 19 are dc to 25-kHz on-axis and 15-degree off-axis runs on a high-quality horn loaded compression tweeter. The positions of mouth, throat, and voice coil are shown in the on-axis record and several interesting effects are observable which do not show up in normal analysis. There appears to be a small acoustic contribution due to the horn mouth. This effect has been repeatedly seen by this author in such units. One possible explanation is that a compressional or shear body wave is actually introduced in the material of the horn (or cone in direct radiators) which travels at least as fast as the air compressional wave and causes an acoustic radiation from the bell of the horn itself. Also an

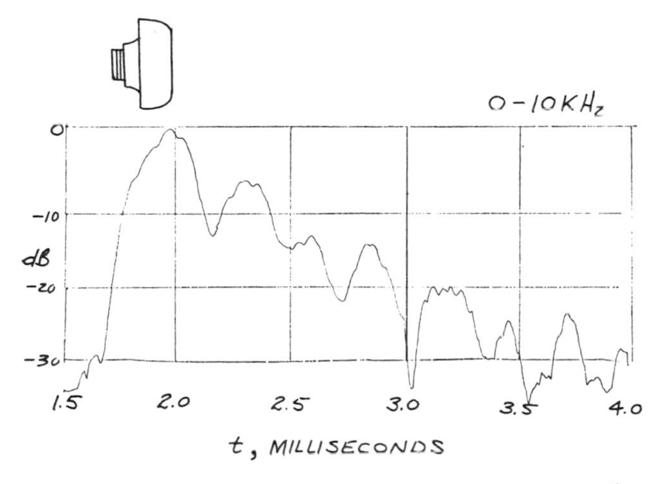

Fig. 12. Energy-time arrivals of unterminated low-quality midrange driver unit. Frequency range is dc to 10 kHz and physical position of driver shown.

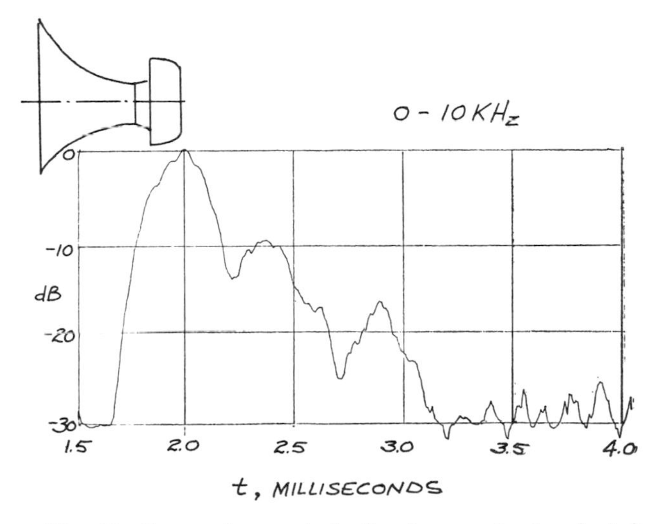

Fig. 13. Energy-time arrivals for improperly terminated driver unit of Fig. 12.

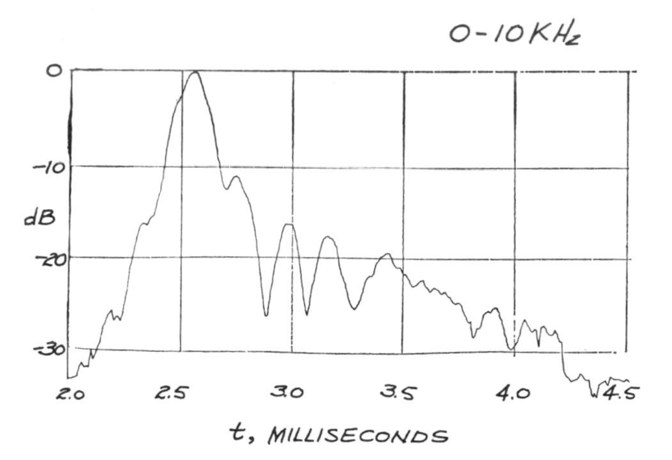

Fig. 14. Dc to 10 kHz energy-time arrivals for midrange horn loaded loudspeaker exhibiting distinct nonminimum phase frequency response.

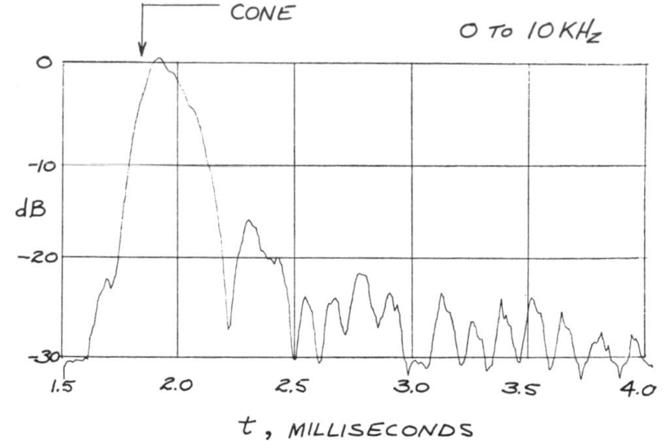

Fig. 15 Dc to 10 kHz energy-time arrivals of paper cone tweeter exhibiting distinct reverberation characteristic.

internal reverberation is observable following emergence of the main loudspeaker energy. This reverberation appears to be due to acoustic scattering off the sides of the internal structure of the horn itself. This may be inferred from the 0.12-millisecond period seen in Fig. 18, which coincides with the on-axis geometry, together with the replacement by a different behavior 15 degrees off axis as seen in Fig. 19. This suggests that closer attention might be paid to the details of mechanical layout of such horns whose acoustic properties may have been compromised for improved cosmetic appeal.

It has been noted by several authors that a network which introduces frequency-dependent phase shift, only without amplitude variation, quite often cannot be detected in an audio circuit, even when the phase shift is quite substantial. Because such networks create severe waveform distortion for transient signals while not apparently effecting the listening quality of such signals, it is assumed by inference that phase distortion must be inaudible for most systems. Fig. 20 is a measurement made through a nominal 2-millisecond electrical delay line with and without a series all-pass lattice. The network used is a passive four-terminal second-order lattice with a 1-kHz frequency of maximum phase rate. The frequency range is dc to 5 kHz, and an electronic delay is used to show the overall time delay on a scale comparable to that used for loudspeaker measurements. Although the lattice does indeed severely disturb the impulse response waveform, it is interesting to note that the total energy is not greatly effected when one considers a reasonable band of frequencies. Since this time-delay distortion, which agrees with calculated values, is due to an analytically perfect signal, it is not at all unlikely that a multimiked program heard over any loudspeaker possessing the degree of time-delay distortion measured in this paper would not appear to show this particular phase-only distortion. In view of the amount of time-delay distortion evident in most loudspeakers, it might be presumptuous to assume that this effect is totally inaudible in all systems.

SUMMARY AND CONCLUSION

A ground rule has been utilized in assessing the linear performance of a loudspeaker in a room. This rule is that the quality of performance may be associated with the accuracy with which the direct sound wave at the position of an observer duplicates the electrical signals presented to the loudspeaker terminals. Although it is realized that there are many criteria of performance,

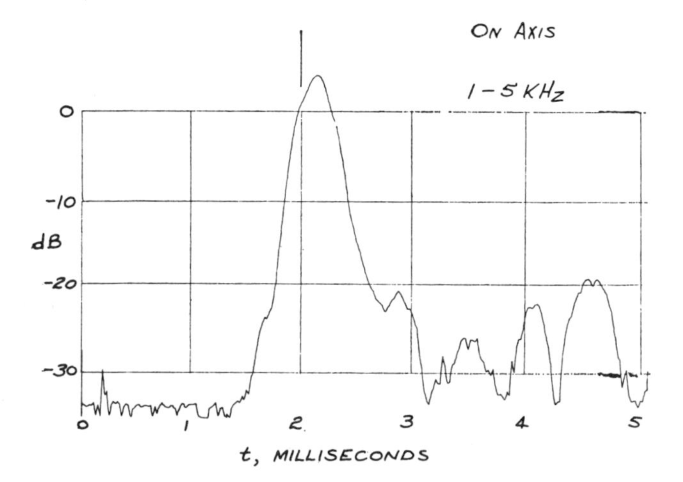

Fig. 16. On-axis energy-time response of high-quality electrostatic multi-panel midrange speaker with position of closest panel equivalent to air path delay of 2 milliseconds and 1-5-kHz excitation.

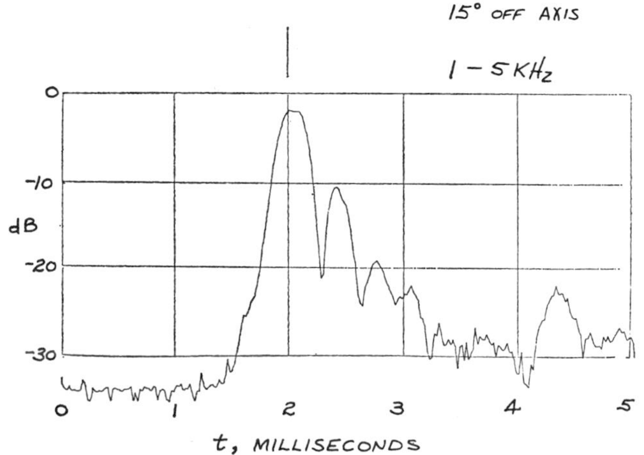

Fig. 17. 15-degree off-axis energy-time response of electrostatic loudspeaker of Fig. 16.

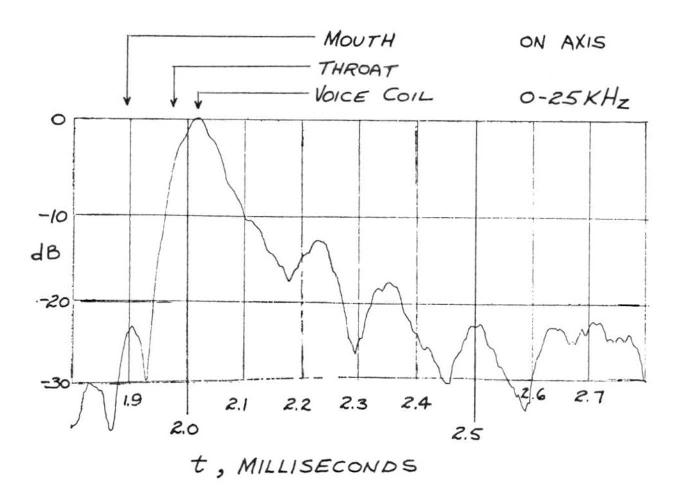

Fig. 18. On-axis energy-time response of a high-quality horn loaded compression tweeter. Frequency excitation is dc to 25 kHz and positions of mouth, throat, and voice coil shown.

this assumption of equivalence of acoustic effect resulting from an electrical cause has the advantage that it yields to objective analysis and test. The difference between the total sound due to a loudspeaker in a room and the same loudspeaker in an anechoic environment, for example, may be simplified to the following model. In an anechoic environment we have one loudspeaker at a fixed range, azimuth, and elevation with respect to an observer. In a room we have the original anechoic

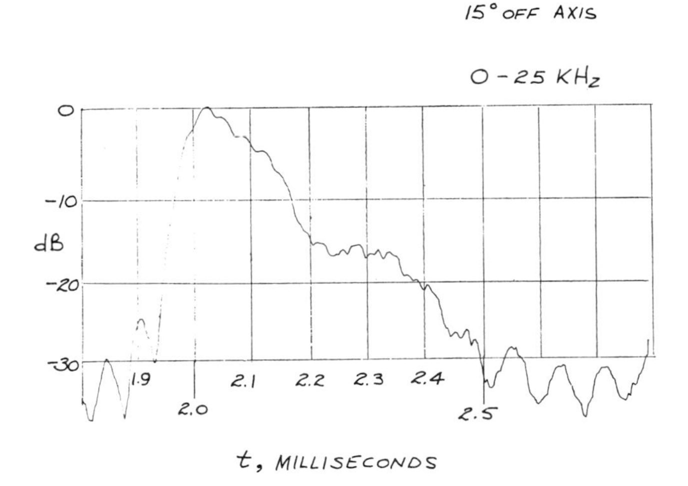

Fig. 19. 15-degree off-axis energy-time response of speaker of Fig. 18.

loudspeaker, but in addition we have a multiplicity of equivalent loudspeakers assuming various positions of range, azimuth, and elevation. The additional loudspeakers, in this room model, all have the same program material as the anechoic loudspeaker, but of course suffer time delays in excess of the direct path delay of the anechoic loudspeaker. Also each room model loudspeaker has a frequency response unique to itself. The groundrule of loudspeaker quality may be applied to each equivalent source in turn and the composite effect analyzed for total quality of response in the room.

A purely mathematical analysis of any single loudspeaker in this room model disclosed that there is a direct tie between frequency response and time smear of signal received by an observer. The analysis showed that if we were to isolate any speaker to an anechoic environment, we could duplicate the acoustic response as closely as we desired for any given observer by replacing the original speaker and its frequency response aberrations with a number of perfect response loudspeakers. Each of these perfect response loudspeakers in this mathematical model occupies its own special frequency-dependent position in space behind the apparent physical position of the original imperfect loudspeaker. The result of this is that the acoustic image of a sound source is smeared in space behind the originating speaker. Perhaps another way of looking at this is that even in an otherwise anechoic environment an actual loudspeaker could be considered to be a perfect transducer imbedded in its own special "room" which creates an ensemble of equivalent sources. The type of distortion caused by this multiplicity of delayed equivalent sources has been called time-delay distortion.

A measurement of the amount of time-delay distortion in an actual loudspeaker in a room has now been made. The anechoic frequency response, both amplitude and phase, was first isolated by time-delay spectrometry for the specific portion of frequency spectrum of interest. The complex frequency response was then processed by real-time continuous circuitry to yield the complex time response.

Plots of the complex time vector components as a function of equivalent time of arrival for a variety of loudspeakers have been presented. The existence of time-delay distortion has been verified by this direct experimental evidence. It has been shown that the equivalent spatial smear for even the better class of loudspeaker may amount to many inches and that the equivalent acoustic source is always behind the apparent physical source location. It has not been possible to plot the individual joint time–frequency components predicted mathematically. This is because these components overlap in the time and frequency domains and a single-domain time presentation, even though band limited, cannot separate simultaneous arrival components. Sufficient experimental evidence has been presented to show that these components do exist to an extent necessary to create

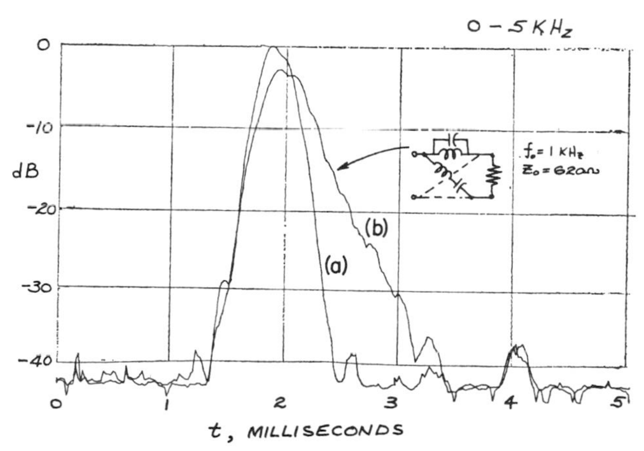

Fig. 20. Energy-time response. Curve (a)—Electrical delay line with 2-millisecond delay and excitation from dc to 5 kHz. Curve (b)—Delay line of (a) in series with second-order all-pass lattice which exhibits severe impulse response distortion due to rapid phase shift at 1 kHz.

the acoustic image smear detected by an observer.

Several energy principles have been originated and proved. While originally developed to determine techniques for investigating time-delay distortion, these principles reach far beyond simple loudspeaker testing. It has been shown that the unit impulse is but one component of a more generalized tensor. For nonturbulent systems the tensor becomes a simple two-component vector. This is the case for most acoustic and electronic situations of energy propagation. The conjugate term to the unit impulse is the unit doublet. In an acoustic field generated by a loudspeaker, one can associate the potential energy density with the impulse response of the loudspeaker. When one does this he may then associate the kinetic energy density with the loudspeaker doublet response. The total energy density may be associated with the vector sum of impulse and doublet response. Inasmuch as it is the total energy density which is available to perform work on an eardrum or microphone diaphragm, the majority of experimental data presented in this paper has been the time of arrival of this parameter.

It has also been shown that potential and kinetic energy densities are not mathematically independent if one is careful with his energy bookkeeping. What this means for acoustic radiation from a loudspeaker is that either the impulse or doublet response is sufficient to determine total performance if one has the proper tools at his disposal. But one should be cautious of gross simplification in the event that impulse or doublet response is utilized independently. As with any incomplete analysis, certain truths may not be self-evident.

An interesting area of speculation is opened up when one realizes that any reasonably well-behaved acoustic transducer placed in a sound field is capable of yielding information concerning the total energy density if associated with a suitable means of data processing. One cannot help but incautiously suggest that a closer look at the human hearing mechanism might be justified to determine whether total sound energy detection rather than potential energy (pressure) could shed a light on some as yet unexplained capabilities we seem to possess in the perception of sound.

Note: Mr. Heyser's biography appeared in the October 1971 issue.

Determination of Loudspeaker Signal Arrival Times* Part III

RICHARD C. HEYSER

Jet Propulsion Laboratory, California Institute of Technology, Pasadena, Calif.

APPENDIX

Energy Relations as Hilbert Transforms

A fundamental approach to a complicated system may be made through that system's energy relations. Accordingly we present the following principles.

1) In a bounded system the internal energy density E is related to its potential and kinetic energy density components V and T by the vector relation

$$\sqrt{E} = \sqrt{V} + i\sqrt{T}$$

where the vector components are Hilbert transforms of each other.

2) In a bounded system a complete description of either the kinetic or potential energy density is sufficient to determine the total internal energy density.

3) By appropriate choice of coordinates within a bounded system, the available energy at a point of perception due to a signal source at a point of transmission may be partitioned as follows.

a) The potential energy density is proportional to the square of the convolution integral of the signal with the system impulse response.

b) The kinetic energy density is proportional to the square of the convolution integral of the signal with the system doublet response.

* Presented April 30, 1971, at the 40th Convention of the Audio Engineering Society, Los Angeles. For Parts I and II, please see pp. 734-743 and pp. 829-834 of the October and November issues of this *Journal*.

The first law of thermodynamics defines an exact differential function known as the internal energy (Part I, [10])

$$dE = dQ - dW, \qquad \text{joules} \qquad (23)$$

which equals the heat absorbed by the system less the work done by the system. By integration the energy may be obtained as a function of the state variables, and in particular for the class of electroacoustic situations of concern for this paper, it may be composed of kinetic energy and potential energy T and V,

$$E = T + V, \qquad \text{joules.} \qquad (24)$$

By taking the time rate of change of the components of (23) and expressing this in engineering terms, we have (Part I, [23, p. 124])

$$\frac{d(T + V)}{dt} = P - 2F, \qquad \text{watts} \qquad (25)$$

which asserts that the time rate of change of energy equals the power drawn from the system less the energy dissipated as heat within the system.

Properly speaking, the internal energy of a system is that property which is changed as a causal result of work done on or by that system. Energy, per se, is not generally measured. We may, however, describe and measure the energy density. Energy density is a measure of the instantaneous work which is available to be done by a system at a particular point in space and time if the total energy partitioned among the state variables could be annihilated. Energy density for state variables s is expressed as $E(s)$ and has the dimensions of joules per unit of s. The energy densities of joules per second and joules per cubic meter will be utilized in this paper. Energy density may be partitioned, for nonturbulent systems, into kinetic and potential densities. The methods by which we measure energy density, even for acoustic systems, may take the form of mechanical, electrical, or chemical means. The dynamical considerations which gave rise to Eqs. (23) and (24) naturally led to the terms kinetic and potential. When dealing with electrical or chemical characterizations, such terms are difficult to identify with the processes involved. This author has found it convenient to identify potential energy as the energy of coordinate configuration and kinetic energy as the energy of coordinate transformation.

Assume that the ratio of total kinetic to potential energy density at any moment is related to a parameter θ such that

$$\sqrt{T} / \sqrt{V} = \tan \theta. \tag{26}$$

From (24) and (26) it is possible to define the vector

$$\sqrt{E} = \sqrt{V} + i\sqrt{T}. \tag{27}$$

This is shown in Fig. A-1. We know from physical considerations that the internal energy of any bounded system is not only finite but traceable to a reasonable distribution of energy sources and sinks. If, for example, we measure the acoustic field radiated from a loudspeaker, we know that the value of that field at any point does not depend upon the way in which we defined our coordinate system. We can state, therefore, that $\sqrt{E}$ is analytic in the parameter t and is of class $L^2(-\infty, \infty)$ such that

$$\varepsilon = \int_{-\infty}^{\infty} |\sqrt{E}|^2 \, dt < \infty. \tag{28}$$

When conditions (27) and (28) are met it is known that the vector components of (27) are related by Hilbert transformation (Part I, [4, p. 122]). Furthermore,

$$\int_{-\infty}^{\infty} (\sqrt{T})^2 \, dt = \int_{-\infty}^{\infty} (\sqrt{V})^2 \, dt = \varepsilon/2 \tag{29}$$

which means that not only is it possible to express the kinetic and potential energy determining time components as Hilbert transforms, but when all time is considered, there is an equipartition of energy.

The relationship between kinetic and potential energy density is true for a bounded system, that is, one in which a boundary may be envisioned of such an extent as to totally enclose at any moment the total energy due to a particular signal of interest. A proper summation of the energy terms within that boundary for the signal of interest would then disclose a partitioning in accordance with principle 1). A measurement of the energy density at a microphone location due to a remote source will only yield a part of the total energy density of that source. The relation (27) will therefore not necessarily be observed by the microphone at any given moment. Thus, for example, the pressure and velocity components at a point in an expanding sound wave from a source will be related by what is called the acoustic impedance of the medium and are not necessarily at that point related by Hilbert transformation. However, we know that the source of sound was, at the moment of energization, a bounded system and was therefore governed by the physics of (27). If the medium of propagation is such that a given energy component imparted by the source is preserved in form between source and microphone, we may take that microphone measurement and reconstruct the total energy-time profile of the source by analytical means. This observation is the basis for the measurements of this paper.

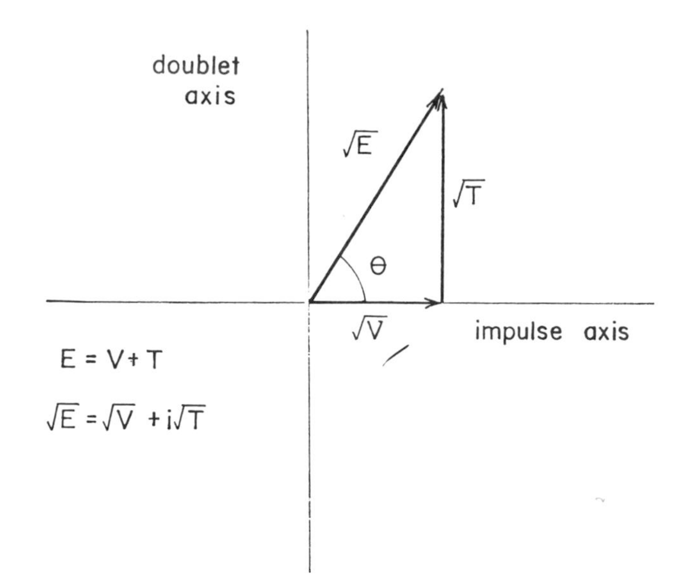

Fig. A-1. Root energy density plane defined such that one axis is system impulse response while quadrature (Hilbert) axis is doublet response.

Any vector obtained from (Eq. 27) by a process of rotation of coordinates must possess the same properties. This surprisingly enough is fortunate, for although from dynamical arguments the components shown in (Eq. 27) are the most significant, it quite frequently happens that an experiment may be unable to isolate a purely kinetic component. This does not inhibit a system analysis based on total energy since we can obtain the total vector by adding our measured quantity to a quadrature Hilbert transform and be assured of a proper answer.

For verification of principle 3) we must consider that class of kinetic and potential energy related signals which could serve as stimulus to a system for resultant analysis. In particular we seek a signal form which when used as a system stimulus will suffice to define within a proportionality constant the system vector (27) by an integral process. This is done so as to parallel the analytical techniques which use a Green's function solution to an impulse (Part 1, [10]) and of course the powerful Dirac delta. Because we are dealing with quadrature terms we have not one but two possible energy stimuli. Consider the special representation of (27),

$$\sqrt{V(x)} = \frac{1}{\sqrt{2\pi a}} \frac{\sin ax}{x} \tag{30}$$

$$\sqrt{T(x)} = \frac{1}{\sqrt{2\pi a}} \frac{\cos ax - 1}{x}.$$

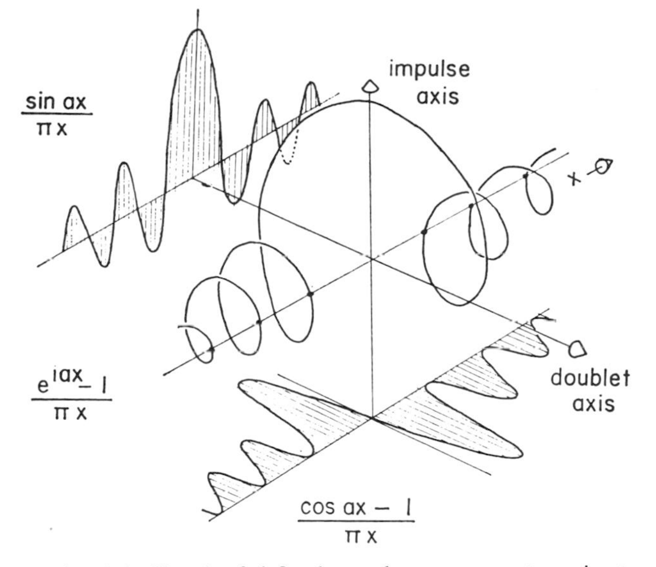

Fig. A-2. Sketch of defined complex energy vector prior to allowing the parameter a to become large without limit. Impulse (7) and doublet (8) are shown as orthogonal projections from this vector.

The energy density represented by this is obtained from (24) as

$$E(x) = \frac{\sin^2 ax + 1 - 2\cos ax + \cos^2 ax}{2\pi ax^2}$$

$$= \frac{1 - \cos ax}{\pi ax^2}. \tag{31}$$

The total energy represented by (31) as a becomes large without limit is (Part I, [24])

$$\varepsilon = \lim_{a \to \infty} \int_{-\infty}^{\infty} \frac{1 - \cos ax}{\pi ax^2} dx = 1. \tag{32}$$

Thus in the limit the quadrature terms of (30) produce a representation of unit total energy which exists only for $x = 0$ and is null elsewhere. To see this more clearly rewrite (27) with (30) components as

$$e(y) = \frac{1}{\sqrt{2\pi}} \frac{\sin \sqrt{a}y}{y} + i \frac{1}{\sqrt{2\pi}} \frac{\cos \sqrt{a}y - 1}{y} \tag{33}$$

where $y = \sqrt{a}\,x$. The vector (33) is as shown in Fig. A-2 with its quadrature components as projections. If we took the limiting form of (33) as $\sqrt{a}$ became large without limit, this would approach the impulsive vector

$$\epsilon(y) = \delta(y) + id(y) \tag{34}$$

where by definition

$$\delta(y) = \text{unit impulse} = \lim_{\lambda \to \infty} \frac{\sin \lambda y}{\pi y}$$

$$d(y) = \text{unit doublet} = \lim_{\lambda \to \infty} \frac{\cos \lambda y - 1}{\pi y} \tag{35}$$

This impulsive vector is symbolized in Fig. A-3 as its quadrature projections. It may be readily seen that $\delta(y)$ is identical to the impulse commonly referred to as the Dirac delta (Part I, [10, p. I-168]). To this author's knowledge this particular unit doublet has not received previous recognition.

In order to justify the designation of the energy-related vector $\epsilon(y)$ as impulsive, consider the magnitude squared form shown in (31). It is known that (Part I, [4, p. 35])

$$\lim_{\lambda \to \infty} \int_{-\infty}^{\infty} f(y) \frac{1 - \cos \lambda(x - y)}{\pi\lambda(x - y)^2} dy = f(x). \tag{36}$$

In the limit, utilizing (33),

$$f(x) = \int_{-\infty}^{\infty} f(y)\{\epsilon(x - y) \cdot \epsilon^*(x - y)\} dy \tag{37}$$

where the asterisk denotes complex conjugation. Thus the magnitude squared of the vector (34) is an impulse in the Dirac delta sense, although the generating vector is composed of an impulse and a doublet.

We know from classical analysis that the response at a receiving point due to injection of a Dirac delta at a transmitting point is a general system describing function. If the system is such as to allow superposition of solutions, then we can state that the total energy density at the receiving point due to an arbitrary forcing function $x(t)$ at the transmitting point is obtained from

$$\sqrt{E(t)} = \int_{-\infty}^{\infty} x(\tau)\, h(t - \tau) d\tau \tag{38}$$

where the describing function $h(t)$ is the normalized system response to the Dirac delta of total energy (34). Likewise the potential energy component $V(t)$, also obtainable from a Dirac delta, has a similar form with its own describing function. It must therefore follow that there is a kinetic energy describing function obtained as the response to the unit doublet as assumed from the generating form of (30). By this argument $\epsilon(y)$ could be regarded as a unit energy impulsive vector composed of equal portions of potential energy producing impulse and kinetic energy producing doublet. The assumption that the impulse is related to potential energy is drawn by analogy of form from classical mechanics in the assumption that the difference in state following an off-setting impulse of position is positional displacement, while the difference of state following the doublet is velocity. Relating to circuit theory, suppose a single resonance circuit is excited by a unit impulse of voltage.

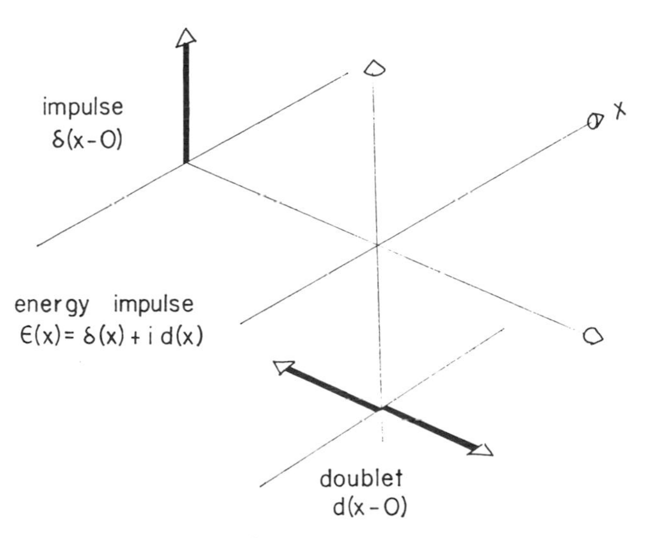

Fig. A-3. Sketch of limiting form assumed by components of Fig. A-2 when a is allowed to go to the limit. Note that the defining envelope of both impulse and doublet even as the limit is approached is proportional to the reciprocal of coordinate x.

At the instant following application of the impulse the capacitor has a stored charge (potential energy $\frac{1}{2}CV^2$) while the inductor has no current (kinetic energy $\frac{1}{2}LI^2$). Thereafter, the circuit exchanges energy under the relations (24) and (26). Should a unit doublet of voltage be applied, one would have as initial conditions a current in the inductor with no net charge in the capacitor. If one did not choose to identify the impulse with potential energy solely, he could multiply (34) by the unit vector of Eq. (14) to obtain

$$e^{i\lambda}\{\delta(t) + id(t)\} \tag{39}$$

so as to redistribute the initially applied energy in the proper manner. Regardless of how one does this, it should be evident that a general description of system energy density must involve both the impulse and doublet response, not just the impulse response.

It might logically be asked why the need for a doublet response has not been previously felt with sufficient force to generate prior analysis. The answer is found in principle 2). An analysis based on either the impulse or doublet can be used to derive a complete system analysis by appropriate manipulation. The physical reason why one cannot use solely the impulse response or doublet response is that a measurement made on one system parameter, such as voltage, velocity, or pressure, can only express the momentary state of energy measured by that parameter. One scalar parameter of the type available from linear system operation does not represent the total system energy. A complete mathematics of analysis could be generated based completely on the doublet driving function and obtain the same results as a mathematics based on the impulse. This is because in order to get a complete answer, the complementing response must be calculated for either approach. Among the examples which spring to mind for the need of impulse and doublet analysis jointly is Kirchoff's formulation of Huygens' principle for acoustics (Part I, [25, p. 43]) and the impulse and doublet source solutions for electric and magnetic waves (Part I, [10]).

The response of a system $h(t)$ to the unit energy operation (34) is, from Eqs. (3), (5), and (15),

$$h(t) = f(t) + ig(t) = \int_{-\infty}^{\infty} f(x)\,\epsilon(t-x)\,dx. \tag{40}$$

The system response $h(t)$ is the analytic signal composed of the impulse response $f(t)$ and the doublet response $g(t)$. From (25) the time position of energy sinks and sources is found from the local minima and maxima of

$$\frac{d}{dt}|h(t)|. \tag{41}$$

While it is readily proved that the analytic signal $h(t)$ has a single-sided spectrum, this fact is of little value to our present consideration of energy. We assume that the parameter under analysis is a scalar or may be derived from a scalar potential. We assert that the sources of energy, which relate to the effective sources of sound, may be determined by considering both the kinetic and

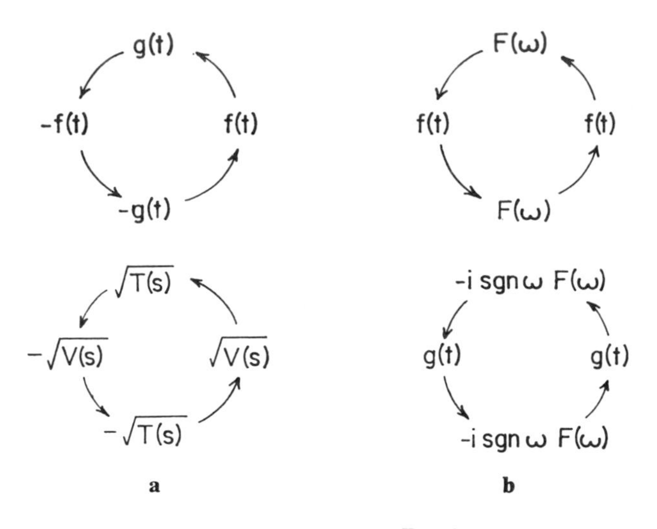

Fig. A-4. Symbolic representation of functional changes brought about by successive applications of **a.** Hilbert transformation to conjugate functions of same dimensional parameter; **b.** Fourier transformation to functions of reciprocal dimensional parameter.

potential energies. These may be obtained separately as scalar components of the vector analytic signal. A local maximum in the magnitude of the analytic signal is due to a local source of energy and not an energy exchange.

The total energy of (24) is a scalar obtained by squaring the defined vector components of (27). The Hilbert transform relations exist between the vector components of (27) and subsequently of (40). Although two successive applications of Hilbert transformation produce the negative value of the original function (skew reciprocity), the energy being obtained as a square is uneffected. The Fourier transform relating two descriptions of the same event is reciprocal in order that no preference be displayed in converting from one domain to the other (Fig. A-4). The Hilbert transform, being skew reciprocal, does show a preference. This is also separately derived from the Cauchy–Riemann relations for the analytic function (27). It should be observed that the geometric relation between analytic functions derived in [2, Appendix A] of Part I must hold between the impulse and doublet response. Hence it is possible to generate a reasonably accurate sketch of the form of a doublet response from an accurate impulse response measurement. From these one could infer the form of total energy of a given system.

There is a strong generic tie between the imaginary unit $i = \sqrt{-1}$ and the generalized Hilbert transform in that two iterations of the operation produce a change of sign while four iterations completely restore the original function. One must surely be struck by the analogy of the energy related vectors (27) and (40) to the quadrature operation of the imaginary unit which is known to be related to the system-describing operations of differentiation and integration.

Note: Mr. Heyser's biography appeared in the October 1971 issue.

Horn-Loaded Electrostatic Loudspeaker*

JOSEF MERHAUT

Technical University, Prague, Czechoslovakia

An electrostatically driven foil diaphragm is loaded acoustically by a horn having the throat area 10 times smaller than that of the diaphragm. The resulting acoustical transformation enables one to increase considerably the frequency range. Cross section of a patented arrangement, design data, dimensions, and results are presented.

LIST OF SYMBOLS

- f frequency
- S_i input cross-sectional area of horn
- S_d area of diaphragm of driver
- S cross-sectional area
- f_0 critical (cutoff) frequency of horn
- k transformation ratio
- g exponent of flaring of horn
- c_0 propagation velocity of sound in air
- x coordinate
- ρ_0 static density of air
- r_i specific (acoustical or mechanical) impedance (per unit area) at input of horn
- r_d specific impedance at diaphragm
- p sound pressure
- v particle velocity in air
- v_i particle velocity at input of horn
- v_d velocity of diaphragm
- d thickness of air gap
- ν_m mechanical tension on edge of diaphragm per unit length
- ν_e mechanical tension in diaphragm caused by electrostatic forces
- u rms value of signal voltage upon each system
- U_0 dc polarizing voltage
- K electroacoustic transducer ratio
- C_0 static capacity of each system in driver
- ϵ_0 permittivity of vacuum
- m_a equivalent acoustic mass of diaphragm
- c_{a0} equivalent acoustic compliance of diaphragm
- ρ_m mass of diaphragm per unit area
- b width of diaphragm
- l length of diaphragm
- r_{ar} acoustic resistance due to radiation
- c_{an} negative compliance of system
- E_0 intensity of electric field in air gap
- μ viscosity of air
- r_{av} acoustic resistance due to viscous losses in air gap
- c_{ax} acoustic compliance of air volume between diaphragm and each solid electrode
- κ Poisson's constant for adiabatic compression
- p_0 static air pressure
- ω angular frequency, $\omega = 2\pi f$.
- $\omega_{1,2}$ low (high) limiting angular frequency for 3-dB decay
- $f_{1,2}$ low (high) limiting frequency for 3-dB decay
- Q quality factor of system
- Δ decay in dB due to finite length
- β wavenumber, $\beta = \omega/c_0$
- P_r radiated acoustic power
- I sound intensity due to P_v
- a ratio of voltages, $a = u/U_0$
- P_e apparent electrical power to loudspeaker
- η^* efficiency of loudspeaker
- η excursion of diaphragm
- η_0 excursion η for $x = 0$
- $F_{1,2}$ forces upon diaphragm
- ξ coordinate
- W volume velocity
- η' relative decay.

* Presented October 24, 1968, at the 35th Convention of the Audio Engineering Society, New York.

INTRODUCTION: A disadvantage of most loudspeakers is that their vibrating parts are large with respect to the wavelength in the vibrating mechanism. The diaphragm of a loudspeaker usually does not vibrate in phase, e.g., as a piston, but has parasitic oscillations in the higher modes. As these parasitic oscillations usually have a relatively high quality or Q factor, the frequency response of such a loudspeaker shows sharp peaks and dips which cannot be equalized electronically.

The said disadvantage does not occur in loudspeakers with small thin diaphragms, based on the electrostatic principle. But these loudspeakers normally have relatively small acoustic radiation impedance and this causes trouble at low and middle frequencies.

HORN-LOADED ELECTROSTATIC LOUDSPEAKER

This disadvantage is eliminated in a new design of the electrostatic loudspeaker described in this paper. The diaphragm of this unit is heavily loaded by a high acoustic resistance using a velocity transformation, which will be described later.

The author has shown elsewhere [1], [2] that the acoustic impedance of a membrane which is loaded with a high specific acoustic resistance has a smooth frequency response, without any peaks and dips. The velocity transformation is achieved [3]–[5] by attaching an exponential or hyperbolic horn, having an input area S_i which is smaller than that of the diaphragm S_d.

Such horns have a critical frequency f_0, given by

$$f_0 = \frac{gc_0}{4\pi} \tag{1}$$

where g is the exponent determining the flaring of the horn. For the exponential horn the cross-sectional area is

$$S = S_i \, e^{gx} \tag{2}$$

where x denotes the distance from the throat.

It is known that when the horn is long enough and the frequency f is large compared to f_0, its specific input impedance, i.e., the impedance per unit area, approaches the value of $c_0\rho_0$, c_0 being the propagation velocity of sound and ρ_0 the static density of the medium.

In practice, the horn is always used above the critical frequency f_0, and therefore we usually assume that the specific input impedance has the value $c_0\rho_0$. If the acoustic pressure at the diaphragm as well as at the throat of the attached horn is p, and if the particle velocity at the input of the horn is v_i, the specific input impedance z_i is

$$z_i = \frac{p}{v_i} = c_0\rho_0 \tag{3}$$

Let us introduce the transformation ratio $k = S_d/S_i$. Now the particle velocity at the diaphragm v_d is, for the reason of continuity, k times smaller than v_i. Therefore the specific impedance loading the diaphragm z_d is

$$z_d = \frac{p}{v_d} = k\frac{p}{v_i} = kz_i = k\rho_0 c_0 \tag{4}$$

when $f >> f_0$. This means that z_d is real and k times larger than in the case without the transformation. This effect is well known in the electrodynamic horn loudspeakers, but is not common in the electrostatic units.

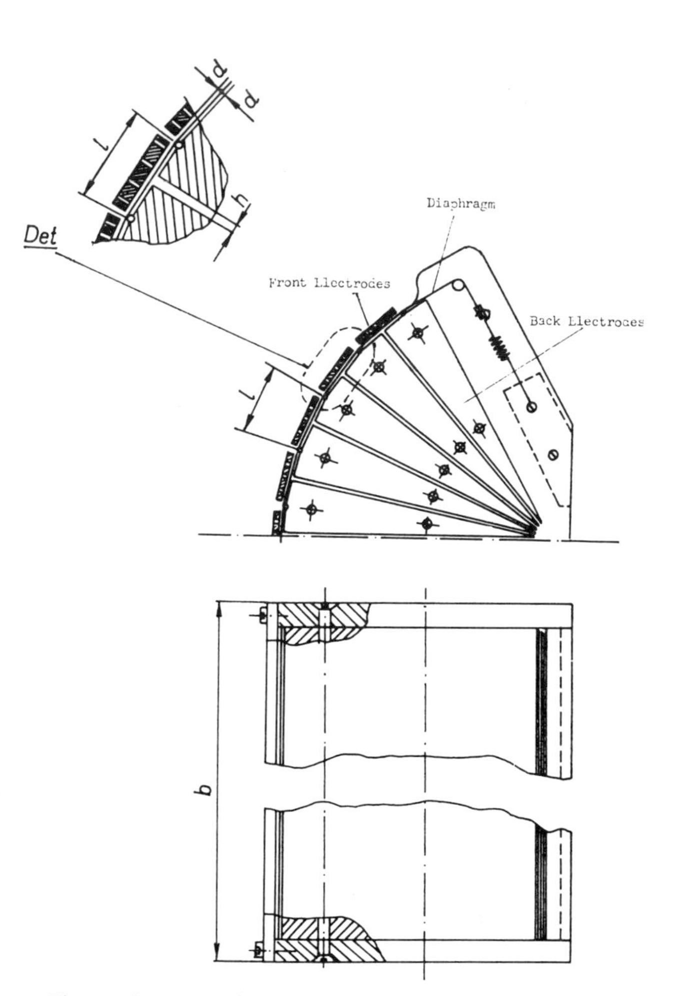

Fig. 1. Cross section of new electrostatic horn-loaded driver.

The author has succeeded in designing a suitable configuration permitting an easy use of the velocity transformation (Fig. 1). The loudspeaker diaphragm is made of a thin metalized polyester foil and located between two solid electrodes. The inner electrode is composed of segments having the shape of wedges, fastened between two plates, made of an insulating material. The outer electrode is conventional, e.g., it consists of perforated plates. The air gap d between the diaphragm and each of the solid electrodes is 0.30 mm. Between the adjacent wedges there are slits of constant cross section connecting the diaphragm to the input of the horn. These slits may be considered as prismatic guides with no flaring. It is known that such waveguides loaded at the output by a real specific impedance $c_0 \, \rho_0$ have the same specific impedance $c_0 \, \rho_0$ at their input. This is the case for frequencies f larger than the critical frequency f_0 of the attached horn. All the slits have the same length, causing equal phase shift.

The diaphragm is of rectangular shape and uniformly stretched with a tension ν_m per unit length. The distance d from the inner electrodes is maintained by spacers placed on each wedge. The system is polarized by dc voltage U_0 between 600 and 800 V.

ANALOG DIAGRAM AND FREQUENCY RESPONSE

The analog diagram containing the acoustical elements

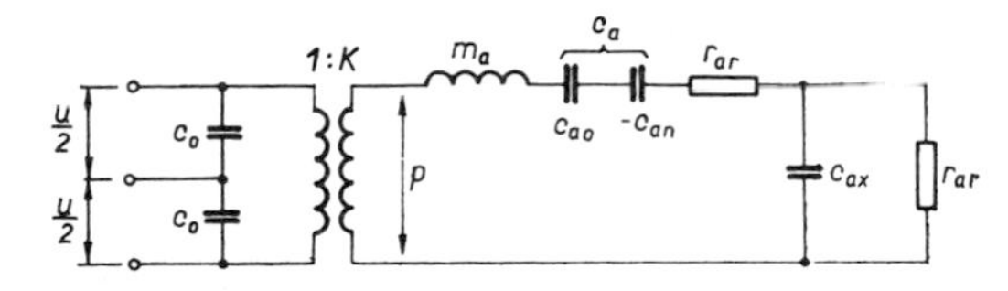

Fig. 2. Analog diagram of electrostatic horn-loaded loudspeaker.

for one part of the diaphragm between two spacers is shown in Fig. 2. The electroacoustic transducer ratio K is [1]

$$K = \frac{U_0 C_0}{Sd}$$

where

$$C_0 = \frac{\varepsilon_0 S_d}{d}$$

$$\varepsilon_0 = 8.85 \times 10^{-12}.$$

K may be also written

$$K = \frac{\varepsilon_0 U_0}{d^2}.$$

From [2], if the diaphragm is loaded with a specific impedance $k\ c_0\ \rho_0$, no higher modes need be considered. So we may substitute for the said part diaphragm a single acoustic mass m_a, and one acoustic compliance c_{a0}. If the specific mass of the foil used for the diaphragm is ρ_m per unit area for m_a, we have

$$m_a = \frac{\rho_m}{bl} \tag{5}$$

and the compliance c_{a0}, according to [1], is

$$c_{a0} = \frac{bl^3}{12\ \nu_m}. \tag{6}$$

The acoustic resistance r_{ar} representing the real load of the diaphragm by the horn for $f >> f_0$ is

$$r_{ar} = k\frac{c_0\rho_0}{bl}. \tag{7}$$

There is a negative acoustic compliance c_{an} in the system caused by the electrostatic forces, which is given by

$$c_{an} = \frac{bl^3}{12\ \nu_e} \tag{8}$$

where

$$\nu_e = \frac{\varepsilon_0 E_0{}^2 l^2}{8d} \tag{9}$$

as derived in Appendix I.

The resulting acoustic compliance c_a is given by

$$\frac{1}{c_a} = \frac{1}{c_{a0}} - \frac{1}{c_{an}} = \frac{12(\nu_m - \nu_e)}{bl^3}. \tag{10}$$

The acoustic resistance r_{av} in Fig. 2 represents the losses caused by the viscous friction in the inner air gap. It is given by

$$r_{av} = \frac{\mu l(1 - 1/k)^3}{2bd^3} \tag{11}$$

as derived in Appendix II.

The acoustic compliance c_{ax} in Fig. 2 is that of the air cushion between the diaphragm and the inner electrode. Its value is

$$c_{ax} = \frac{bld}{\kappa p_0}. \tag{12}$$

Eq. (12) may also be written

$$c_{ax} = \frac{bld}{c_0{}^2\rho_0}. \tag{13}$$

The acoustic pressure generated by the diaphragm responding to electrostatic forces is (for a push–pull system)

$$p = \frac{1}{2}\frac{\varepsilon_0}{d^2}\left(\left(U_0 + \frac{u}{2}\right)^2 - \left(U_0 - \frac{u}{2}\right)^2\right) \tag{14}$$

which can be simplified as

$$p = \frac{\varepsilon_0 U_0}{d^2}u = \frac{\varepsilon_0 E_0}{d}u. \tag{15}$$

From Eq. (15) it may be seen that for a blocked diaphragm (and also for very small excursions of it, as it is here) the pressure p does not contain higher harmonics, even when the instantaneous values of u are larger than the dc polarizing voltage U_0. (This would not be the case for a single system, where u has to be much smaller than U_0 and u must in no case exceed U_0.) The value of U_0 has, however, influence on the sensitivity of the system. (For practical reasons it is recommended to keep the peak value of u on a system smaller than or equal to U_0.) The ideal frequency response, resulting from the diagram in Fig. 2, is given in Fig. 3. In the lower part of the frequency response, the dashed curve represents the ideal case for $f_0 = 0$ (e.g., with an ideal horn). The solid line represents the response with a horn of infinite length, but with a finite critical frequency f_0.

The lower limiting frequency is given by

$$2\pi f_1 = \omega_1 = \frac{1}{c_a r_{ar}}. \tag{16}$$

If we introduce Eqs. (10) and (7) into Eq. (16), we have

$$\omega_1 = \frac{12(\nu_m - \nu_e)}{kc_0\rho_0 l^2}. \tag{17}$$

At the upper part of the frequency response the shape of the curve is affected by the resonance of m_a and c_{ax} occurring at the frequency f_2 given by

$$2\pi f_2 = \omega_2 = \frac{1}{\sqrt{m_a c_{ax}}}. \tag{18}$$

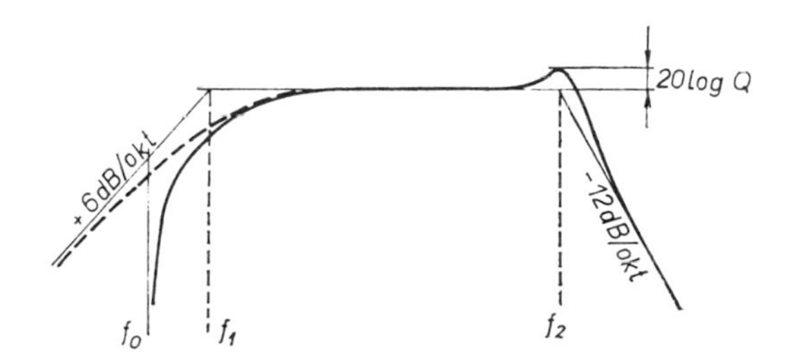

Fig. 3. Theoretical frequency response.

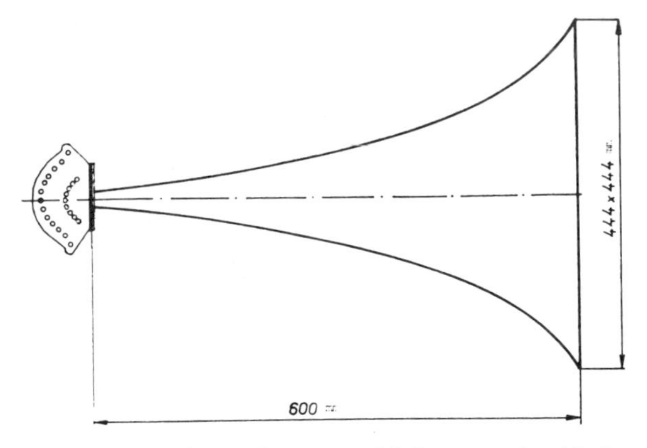

Fig. 4. Dimensions of exponential horn used with loudspeaker.

If we substitute Eqs. (5) and (13) for m_a and c_{ax} into Eq. (18), we obtain

$$\omega_2 = c_0\sqrt{\frac{\rho_0}{\rho_m d}}. \qquad (19)$$

Between the frequencies f_1 and f_2 the resistance r_{ar} is larger than the reactances $\omega\ m_a$ and $1/\omega\ c_a$. For $f > f_2$ the curve is asymptotic to a straight line with a slope of —12 dB per octave caused by m_a and c_{ax}. The eventual peak at f_2 is controlled by the Q of the circuit.

$$Q = \frac{r_{ar}}{\omega_2 m_a}. \qquad (20)$$

When we insert into Eq. (20) Eqs. (7), (18), and (5), we obtain

$$Q = k\sqrt{\frac{\rho_0 d}{\rho_m}}. \qquad (21)$$

In order to obtain a favorable response in the vicinity of frequency f_2, there is an advantage in choosing Q near unity. From Eqs. (21) and (13) and the condition Q = 1 we get, for the upper limiting frequency,

$$\omega_2 = \frac{k c_0 \rho_0}{\rho_m}. \qquad (22)$$

From Eqs. (22) and (17) it may be seen that both limiting frequencies f_1 and f_2 are shifted k times, so that the flat part of the frequency response is about two decades wider if k is, for instance, 10. Furthermore, in the region between f_1 and f_2 the system is resistance controlled. This is an asset for the transient response of the loudspeaker. In the experimental model where Q = 1,

$$f_1 = 235 \text{ Hz}$$
$$f_2 = 17.9 \text{ kHz}.$$

The critical frequency of the horn used with the model was f_0 = 220 Hz. The horn was an exponential one, having the outer dimensions as shown in Fig. 4. The modulus of its input acoustic impedance as a function of frequency is shown in Fig. 5. The values have been measured by the method described in [6].

In the preceding considerations concerning the frequency response, one phenomenon affecting the higher frequencies was not discussed. It is the delay caused by the traveling of the sound waves along the diaphragm to the input of the waveguide, causing a phase shift. The decay Δ resulting from this effect is apparent in the very high frequency range and is

$$\Delta = 20 \log \eta = 20 \log \frac{2}{kl}\sqrt{2\left(1 - \cos\frac{\beta l}{2}\right)} \qquad (23)$$

where $\beta = \omega/c_0$ and Δ = 2.3 dB, as derived in Appendix III.

ACOUSTIC POWER AND EFFICIENCY

The acoustic pressure p in the system is given by Eq. (15). For a polarizing voltage U_0 = 800 V and an ac voltage u = 2 × 200 V rms, the pressure p = 31.6 N/m² or 123.2 dB above 2 × 10⁻⁵ N/m².

The acoustic power P_v delivered by the loudspeaker is given by

$$P_v = S_d \frac{p^2}{k \rho_0 c_0}. \qquad (24)$$

For U_0 = 600 V and u = 2 × 400 V rms, P_v = 10 mW. If we assume that the loudspeaker radiates uniformly into a half-space, then at a 1-m distance the acoustic power would be

$$I_v = \frac{P_v}{2\pi} = \frac{10 \times 10^{-3}}{2\pi} = 1{,}59 \times 10^{-3} \text{ W/m}^2.$$

When we insert expression (15) into Eq. (24), we have

$$P_v = \frac{S_d \epsilon_0^2 E_0^2 u^2}{k d^2 c_0 \rho_0}. \qquad (25)$$

The voltage u must be in a certain relation with U_0. Let us introduce the ratio $a = u/U_0$. The $u = a\ E_0\ d$, which gives, together with Eq. (25),

$$P_v = \frac{S_d \varepsilon_0^2 E_0^4 a^2}{k c_0 \rho_0}. \qquad (26)$$

When we define the efficiency of the system η^* as the ratio

$$\eta^* = \frac{P_v}{P_e} 100\%$$

where

$$P_e = u^2 \frac{\omega C_0}{2},$$

and using Eq. (25), we have

$$\eta^* = \frac{2\varepsilon_0 E_0^2}{k d c_0 \rho_0 \omega}. \qquad (27)$$

For U_0 = 800 V and f = 1 kHz, we obtain η^* = 1.6%.

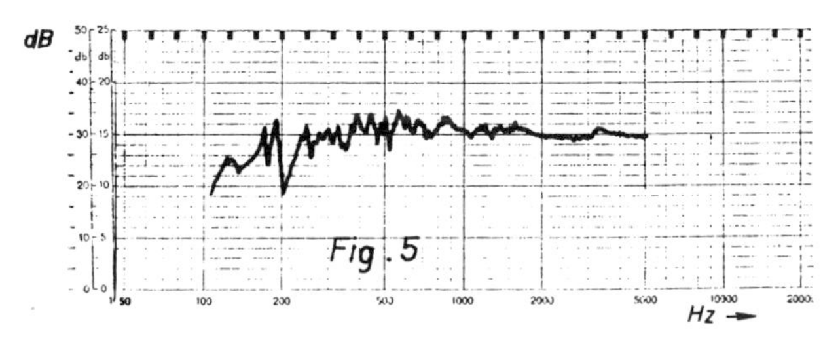

Fig. 5. Modulus of input acoustic impedance of horn of Fig. 4 as a function of frequency.

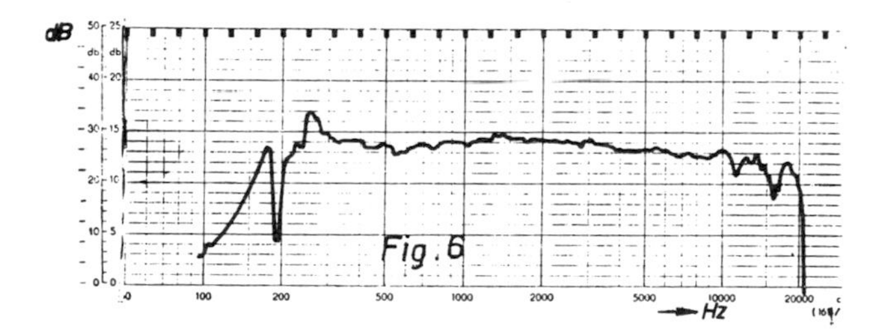

Fig. 6. Sound pressure level measured at input of horn as a function of frequency.

DIAPHRAGM EXCURSION

The normal velocity of the diaphragm v corresponding to the acoustic pressure p is approximately (for $f >> f_0$)

$$v = \frac{p}{kc_0\rho_0} \tag{28}$$

and from it the rms value of the displacement of the diaphragm η is

$$\eta = \frac{v}{\omega} = \frac{p}{\omega k c_0 \rho_0}. \tag{29}$$

EXPERIMENTAL RESULTS

Frequency Response at Throat of Horn

A half-inch measuring condenser microphone was inserted through the wall of the horn near the throat. The axis of the microphone was perpendicular to the wall of the horn, and the surface of the diaphragm was identical with the inner surface of the wall of the horn. The sound pressure level thus measured is shown in Fig. 6 as a function of frequency. The sharp dip above 200 Hz is caused by the critical frequency f_0 of the horn. The fluctuations above f_0 are caused by the variations in the input impedance of the horn. The irregularities above 10 kHz are caused by diffraction effects and may be regarded as measuring errors.

Table I

f (Hz)	Harmonic (%)			
	Second	Third	Fourth	Fifth
1000*	2.3	0.5	0.15	0.07
1000**	1.05	0.03	0.01	
500	1.4	0.6	0.1	0.07
1000	1.7	0.38	0.1	0.07
2000	1.3	0.6	0.2	0.02
4000	2.1	0.35	0.1	
8000	0.6			

* $u = 800$ V.
** $U_0 = 800$ V.

Frequency Response in Axis of Loudspeaker at 1 m

The frequency response of the model loudspeaker as measured at 1 m from the mouth of the horn on axis is shown in Fig. 7. The slope of the curve up to 1200 Hz corresponds to the transition from a spherical wave to a plane wave.

Harmonic Distortion

The harmonic distortion was measured as the frequency response at the throat of the horn by means of the measuring microphone and a wave analyzer for $U_0 = 600$ V dc and $u = 600$ V rms, unless otherwise stated. For each fundamental frequency f the amount or harmonics in percent is shown in Table I.

The new driver is shown in Fig. 8.

CONCLUSION

It is believed that the new concept in electrostatic loudspeaker design described in this paper constitutes a valuable contribution to the state of the art.[1] Experimental models built in accordance with the outlined theory have yielded very satisfactory results. Measurements have shown unusual agreement with theoretical considerations.

APPENDIX I

The negative acoustic compliance is caused by the mechanical tension ν_e which has its origin in the pulling electrostatic forces. For no ac signal to the loudspeaker, e.g., (Fig. 9) if $u = 0$, and for the excursion of the diaphragm $\eta(x)$—the forces acting upon the element dS of the area of the diaphragm from both electrodes are

$$dF_{1,2} = \frac{1}{2}\frac{\varepsilon_0 U_0^2 dS}{(d \pm \eta)^2} = \frac{\varepsilon_0 E_0^2}{2}\frac{b\,dx}{(1 \pm \eta/d)^2}. \tag{30}$$

The resulting force dF acting upon dS is given by

$$dF = dF_2 - dF_1. \tag{31}$$

For $\eta << d$, Eqs. (30) and (31) give

$$dF = 2\varepsilon_0 E_0^2 \eta \frac{b}{d} dx. \tag{32}$$

From the equilibrium of the moments of forces in the

[1] The design is covered by Czechoslovak patent 130731. Patent applications for the United States as well as other countries have been filed.

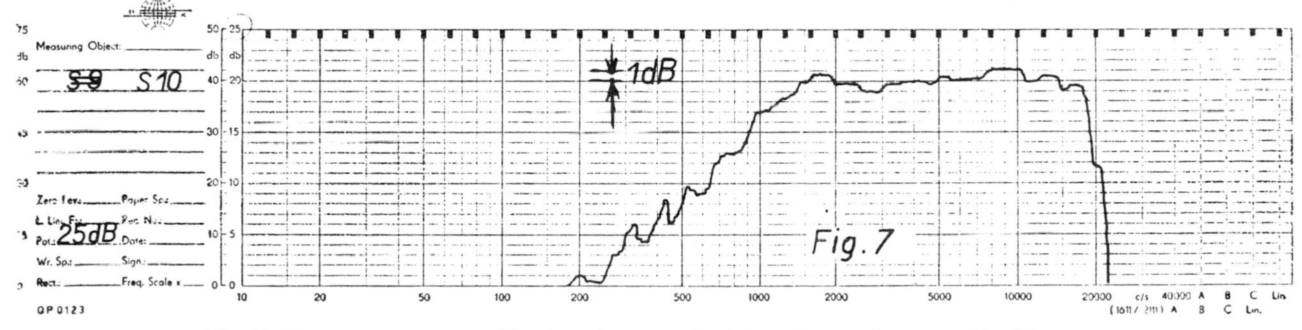

Fig. 7. Frequency response of loudspeaker on axis at 1-m distance from mouth of horn.

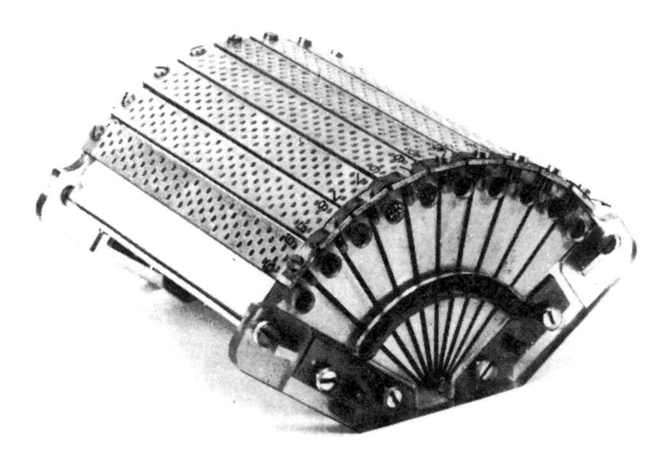

Fig. 8. New electroacoustic driver.

cross section $x = 0$, we may write for one half of the diaphragm the condition

$$\int_0^{l/2} x dF = \nu_b b \eta_0 \quad (33)$$

and hence,

$$\nu_e = \frac{2\varepsilon_0 E_0^2}{d} \int_0^{l/2} \frac{\eta}{\eta_0} x dx. \quad (34)$$

If we consider as in [1] the parabolic deflection

$$\frac{\eta}{\eta_0} = 1 - \left(\frac{2x}{l}\right)^2,$$

Eq. (34) gives after integration

$$\nu_e = \frac{\varepsilon_0 E_0^2 l^2}{8d}. \quad (35)$$

APPENDIX II

Acoustic Resistance Due to Viscous Friction

Let us introduce the coordinates x and ξ according to Fig. 10, where a cross section of one half of the part of the diaphragm between two separators is known. Let us consider that the diaphragm is moving in phase with a constant velocity v. The volume velocity $W(\xi)$ flowing through the air gap along the diaphragm at the cross section with coordinate ξ to the waveguide is

$$W(\xi) = \int_\xi^{l/2} v b d\xi = vb\left(\frac{l}{2} - \xi\right). \quad (36)$$

An element of the gap having length $d\xi$ has the acoustic resistance [3]

$$\frac{12\mu d\xi}{bd^3}.$$

The pressure decay over this elementary resistance is

$$dp = W(\xi) \frac{12\mu d\xi}{bd^3}. \quad (37)$$

The pressure $p(x)$ at x is given by the integral

$$p(x) = \int_x^{l/2} dp = \frac{12\mu v}{d^3} \int_x^{l/2} \left(\frac{l}{2} - \xi\right) d\xi. \quad (38)$$

Eq. (38) after integration leads to

$$p(x) = \frac{6\mu v}{d^3}\left(x^2 - lx + \frac{l^2}{4}\right). \quad (39)$$

The value of the pressure $p(x)$ averaged over the surface of the diaphragm is

$$p_m = \frac{1}{bl/2} \int_{h/2}^{l/2} p(x) b dx = \frac{2}{l} \int_{h/2}^{l/2} p(x) dx. \quad (40)$$

After substituting the expression (39) for $p(x)$ into Eq. (40), we obtain

$$p_m = \frac{\mu v (l - h)^3}{2ld^3}. \quad (41)$$

From it the specific resistance per unit area of the diaphragm is

$$r_{sv} = \frac{p}{v} = \frac{\mu (l - h)^3}{2ld^3} \quad (42)$$

Because the ratio h/l is determined by the transformation ratio k and $h = l/k$, Eq. (42) may be written

$$r_{sv} = \frac{\mu l^2 (1 - 1/k)^3}{2d^3}. \quad (43)$$

According to Eq. (43) the acoustic resistance r_{av} for the whole diaphragm is

$$r_{av} = \frac{r_{sv}}{bl} = \frac{\mu l (1 - 1/k)^3}{2bd^3}. \quad (44)$$

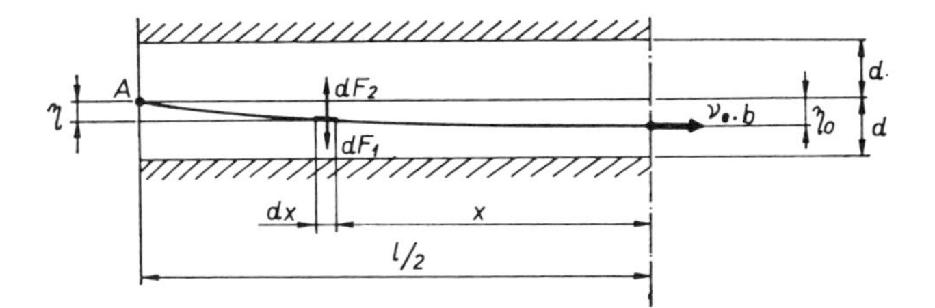

Fig. 9. Cross section of air gap; forces acting upon the diaphragm due to excursion.

APPENDIX III

Loss of Acoustic Pressure Caused by Phase Shift

When the acoustic wave passes along the diaphragm toward the input of the slits between the wedges of the inner electrode, a phase shift proportional to βx occurs, where $\beta = \omega / c_0$. The resulting acoustic pressure p_v at

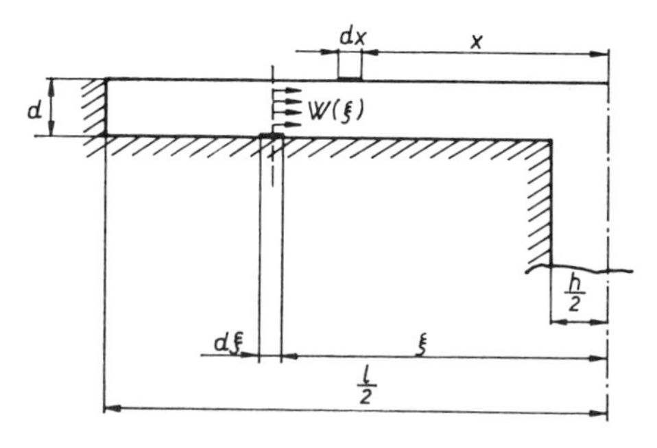

Fig. 10. Cross section of air gap; viscous losses due to particle velocity.

the entrance of the slits may be written

$$p_v = \frac{1}{S}\iint_s pdS\, e^{-j\beta x}. \tag{45}$$

For the element of area dS we may substitute bdx into Eq. (45), and we thus obtain

$$p_v = \frac{1}{bl/2}\int_0^{l/2} pbdxe^{-j\beta x}. \tag{46}$$

Let us introduce the relative decay

$$\eta' = \left|\frac{p_v}{p}\right|. \tag{47}$$

Substituting Eq. (46) into Eq. (47), we have

$$\eta' = \left|\frac{2}{l}\int_0^{l/2} e^{-j\beta x}dx\right|. \tag{48}$$

Eq. (48) leads after solution to

$$\eta' = \left|\frac{2}{j\beta l}\left(1 - \cos\frac{\beta l}{2} + j\sin\frac{\beta l}{2}\right)\right| \tag{49}$$

and this again yields

$$\eta' = \frac{2}{\beta l}\sqrt{2\left(1 - \cos\frac{\beta l}{2}\right)}. \tag{50}$$

REFERENCES

[1] J. Merhaut, "A Contribution to the Theory of Electroacoustic Transducers," *Acoustica*, vol. 19, (1967/68) p. 283.

[2] J. Merhaut, "Some Aspects of Electrostatic Transducers," *Radio Electron. Eng.*, vol. 36, (1968) p. 175.

[3] H. F. Olson, *Elements of Acoustical Engineering* (Van Nostrand, Princeton, N. J., 1947).

[4] L. L. Beranek, *Acoustics* (McGraw-Hill, New York, 1954).

[5] N. W. McLachlan, *Loud Speakers* (Clarendon Press, Oxford, 1934).

[6] J. Merhaut, "Method of Measuring the Acoustical Impedance," presented at the 76th Meeting of the Acoustical Society of America, Cleveland, Ohio (Nov. 1968).

THE AUTHOR

Josef Merhaut was born in Prague, Czechoslovakia, on November 5, 1917. He began his university studies in 1936 at the Technical University of Prague. During the war, when the universities in Czechoslovakia were closed, he was with Telegrafia AG. He finished his studies in 1946 and received his first doctorate degree in 1948. In 1961 he received the (Dr.Sc.) degree. His dissertation was on loudspeaker intermodulation distortion.

From 1946 to 1964 Dr. Merhaut was with Tesla National Corporation, where he became Director of the Researche Institute of Electroacoustics. He was nominated Professor in 1964 and since 1965 he has been with the Technical University of Prague.

Since 1966, Professor Merhaut has been a corresponding member of the Czechoslovac Academy of Sciences. He is a member of the Acoustical Commission of the Czechoslovac Academy of Sciences, the Acoustical Society of America and the Audio Engineering Society.

Simplified Loudspeaker Measurements at Low Frequencies*

RICHARD H. SMALL

School of Electrical Engineering, University of Sydney, Sydney, N.S.W., Australia

The effective free-field frequency response and harmonic distortion of a direct-radiator loudspeaker system can be measured at low frequencies without establishing free-field radiation conditions. The technique is based on measurement of the acoustical pressure within the system enclosure and is simple and inexpensive. It provides useful response measurements up to about 200 Hz, and harmonic distortion measurements up to about 100 Hz.

Editor's Note: An acoustic anechoic chamber for testing loudspeaker systems down to 20 Hz is a frighteningly expensive structure. Neither my University nor Mr. Small's University has such a facility and right now I am not convinced that the data from an anechoic chamber relates well enough to the home or auditorium environment to convince universities to invest scarce dollars in such facilities. Even more pertinent to most of the members of the AES is the fact that only a fortunate few have access to these chambers while the number wanting to measure loudspeaker systems must exceed several thousand.

The outdoor measurement technique so well described by Shearman [1] is adequate but I can testify from personal experience that wind, rain, (snow in Colorado) and motorized vehicle noise are sufficiently annoying that an alternate method is badly needed. This Mr. Small has provided and the elegant simplicity of his method commends it to your understanding and use.

I had the pleasure of presenting this paper to the 41st. AES Convention and the familiarity gained with this work leads to anticipation of your question "is the method accurate and valid?" In his modest way, Small understates (Sec. 5) the accuracy of the method. In some previous work, one of my students (Mark Swan) measured pressure in a vented box and on-axis frequency response outdoors to verify some computer solutions. We were not clever enough to appreciate the significance of the excellent agreement of box pressure with theory but we had proved that the basic assumptions made by Small are quite valid. Some of my students are presently doing the experimental work needed to give complete verification of Small's method. A Project Note should appear in a few months to present this verification. In the meantime, if you want to make a very simple and accurate measurement of your loudspeaker system's low frequency response or distortion, I advise you to measure first and ask questions later.

J. R. Ashley

I. INTRODUCTION: The measurement of loudspeaker system characteristics is customarily carried out under free-field radiation conditions so that it will reflect only the properties of the loudspeaker system and not those of the environment. However, it is often difficult to establish true free-field radiation conditions at low frequencies. Outdoor test facilities are notoriously difficult to establish and maintain [1], while large indoor anechoic chambers do not provide a true free field at very low frequencies and must be carefully calibrated.

The measurement method described in this paper is based on the fact that the low-frequency output of a small direct-radiator loudspeaker system is directly related to

* Presented May, 1971, at the 13th National Radio and Electronics Engineering Convention, Institution of Radio and Electronics Engineers Australia, Melbourne, and October 5, 1971, at the 41st Convention of the Audio Engineering Society, New York. Published in *Proc. IREE Australia,* vol. 32, pp. 299–304 (Aug. 1971), and republished here with the permission of the Institution.

the acoustic pressure within the system enclosure. This pressure is essentially unaffected by the system acoustic load, and is the same in a reverberant environment as in an anechoic environment.

II. BASIC THEORY

A direct-radiator loudspeaker system radiating into a hemispherical (2π steradian) free field is illustrated in Fig. 1. The steady-state rms pressure inside the enclosure is p_B, the total output volume velocity crossing the enclosure boundaries is U_0, and the rms sound pressure at a distance r from the system is designated p_r.

If the enclosure has negligible absorption losses, it can be represented at very low frequencies by an acoustic compliance C_{AB} which is related to the internal volume of air V_B by [2, p.129]

$$C_{AB} = V_B/\rho_0 c^2 \qquad (1)$$

where ρ_0 is the density of air (1.18 kg/m^3) and c is the velocity of sound in air (345 m/s). Fig. 2 presents the acoustical analogous circuit of such an enclosure (impedance analogy). From analysis of this circuit, the relationship between output volume velocity and internal pressure is

$$U_0 = p_B \omega C_{AB} \qquad (2)$$

where ω is the steady-state radian frequency.

The relationship between p_r and U_0 for the radiation conditions of Fig. 1, regardless of the type of system or the number of enclosure apertures contributing to the total U_0 [3, p. 270], is

$$p_r = (\rho_0/2\pi r)\ \omega U_0 \qquad (3)$$

and the radiated power is [2, p. 189]

$$P_A = (\rho_0/2\pi c)(\omega U_0)^2. \qquad (4)$$

If the loudspeaker system is removed from the anechoic environment, the pressure p_B and the volume velocity U_0 do not change significantly. These quantities are not noticeably affected by the acoustical load [4. p. 489], provided the environment is not a high-Q acoustical resonator and is spacious compared to the enclosure volume. It should thus be possible to determine the basic low-frequency free-field response and power output of a direct-radiator loudspeaker system by measuring the enclosure pressure while the system is located in any reasonable environment and then using the relationships in Eqs. (1)–(4).

A signal representing output volume velocity is obtained by multiplying the enclosure-pressure signal by a factor proportional to frequency as required by Eq. (2). This process must then be repeated to obtain a signal representing free-field sound pressure, as required by Eq. (3). An electronic differentiation circuit has exactly the desired property, i.e., a gain proportional to frequency, so two such circuits will perform the required operations. For calculation of radiated power, the pressure-measuring transducer must be calibrated, and the enclosure compliance and differentiation time constants must be known accurately. However, if only the relative frequency response is desired, calibration is not necessary.

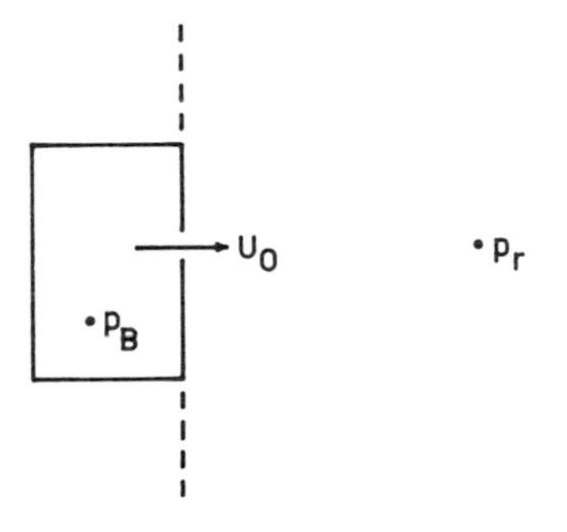

Fig. 1. Loudspeaker system radiating into hemispherical free field.

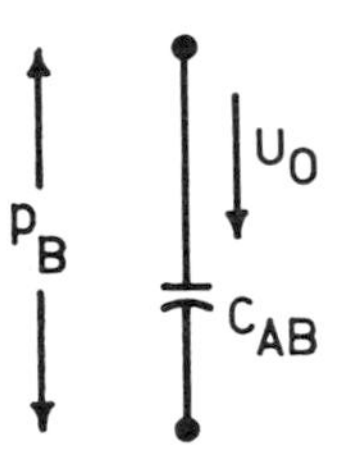

Fig. 2. Acoustical analogous circuit of lossless enclosure.

III. EQUALIZATION

The preceding theory offers a simple means of obtaining the free-field response of a loudspeaker system having negligible enclosure losses, but only for very low frequencies. In particular, Eq. (1) is valid, i.e., C_{AB} is a constant, only for frequencies low enough that the wavelength of sound is greater than eight times the smallest dimension of the enclosure [2, p. 217]. This is a frequency limit of about 50 Hz for a moderate size enclosure.

Unfortunately, this is not a sufficient bandwidth for the study of loudspeaker systems. The response of many systems has not yet leveled off at this frequency, and to adequately observe the complete cutoff behavior of the system it is necessary to obtain a bandwidth of about 200 Hz. This can be done with quite reasonable accuracy by equalizing the factors that tend to contribute errors at higher frequencies.

Compliance Shift

At very low frequencies, all air in the enclosure is compressed equally and Eq. (1) is valid. At higher frequencies, the compression is no longer uniform and the effective compliance is reduced. The major factor in this compliance reduction is the air-load mass on the rear of the driver diaphragm which moves with the diaphragm at high frequencies without compression. The magnitude of this effect depends on the effective volume of the air-load mass compared to the enclosure volume; it is negligible for a small driver in a large enclosure but can amount to several dB error for a large driver in a small enclosure. The volume occupied by the air-load mass is typically $2.2a^3$, where a is the effective radius of the diaphragm [2, p. 217].

The compliance shift can be equalized by passing the enclosure-pressure signal through a shelf attenuator having an attenuation at high frequencies corresponding to the reduction of compliance. The attenuation must be fully effective at the frequency at which the rear air-load mass resonates with the enclosure compliance. This frequency depends somewhat on the shape of the enclosure but is generally about $100(a/V_B)^{1/2}$ Hz, where a is in meters and V_B is in cubic meters. Good experimental results were obtained by centering the shelf equalizer at one third this frequency, but no rigorous theoretical justification for this location has been established.

Enclosure Losses

The presence of enclosure absorption losses means that the enclosure cannot be represented by a pure compliance but must be represented instead by a series compliance and resistance as shown in Fig. 3. R_{AB} is the series acoustic resistance due to the enclosure losses.

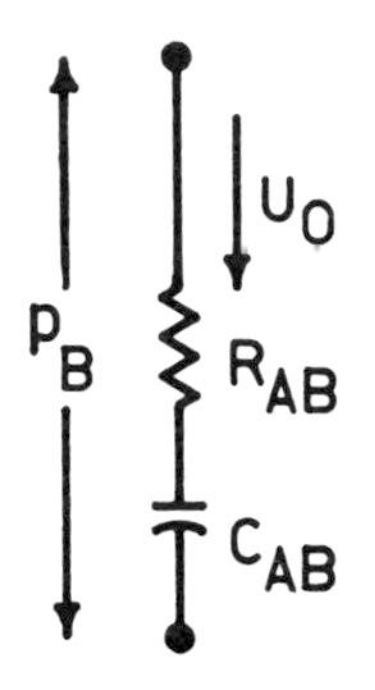

Fig. 3. Acoustical analogous circuit of enclosure with absorption losses.

If the value of R_{AB} is assumed to be independent of frequency, the relationship between enclosure pressure and volume velocity becomes

$$U_0 = p_B \left| \frac{j\omega C_{AB}}{1 + j\omega C_{AB} R_{AB}} \right| . \quad (5)$$

The presence of R_{AB} may then be equalized by placing a resistor of suitable value in series with the input capacitor of the differentiation circuit used to implement Eq. (2). The correct value of resistance can be determined from measurement of the system voice-coil impedance and subsequent calculation of the enlosure losses. The measurement method is given in the Appendix.

Even where the enclosure losses are very low, it is advisable to keep a minimum-value resistor in series with *both* differentiating capacitors to limit the differentiating bandwidth to about 1 kHz. This prevents excessive buildup of noise at high frequencies from interfering with the desired sound-pressure signal.

Pressure Uniformity and Standing Waves

At frequencies above about 50 Hz but still low enough for the wavelength to be longer than the enclosure dimensions, the pressure in the enclosure becomes noticeably nonuniform. The region nearest the driver is below average pressure, while the region farthest from the driver is above average pressure [2, pp. 32–33]. This condition increases in severity as the wavelength approaches the dimensions of the enclosure, but its effects can be tempered by careful placement of the pressure-sensing transducer. The best transducer location must be found by trial and error; it is often near the geometrical center of the enclosure volume. Above about 200–250 Hz, the magnitude and gradient of pressure changes and the development of standing waves within the enclosure render the method useless.

TABLE I. Loudspeaker System Data.

	Closed-box System	Vented-box System
Physical Data		
Enclosure volume, l	28	38
Driver diameter, m	0.25	0.35
Diaphragm radius, m	0.10	0.14
Small-Signal Parameters		
Driver resonance, Hz	25	25
Closed-box resonance, Hz	61	60
Vented-box resonance, Hz	—	45
Compliance ratio	5.3	5.1
System Q	1.65 at 61 Hz	0.22 at 25 Hz
Enclosure Q	15 at 61 Hz	12 at 45 Hz

IV. APPLICATIONS

Where a calibrated pressure transducer is available, it should be possible to test and calibrate sound sources and testing chambers below about 50 Hz. With careful equalization, the frequency response of small direct-radiator loudspeaker systems can be measured up to about 200 Hz.

The harmonic distortion of a loudspeaker system may also be measured if all major Fourier components of the signal representing sound pressure fall within the frequency range for which the response measurement is valid. This would usually include fundamental frequencies up to 50 Hz, with useful results often available up to 100 Hz.

An ideal transducer for measuring enclosure pressure is a condenser microphone with FET preamplifier. This type of transducer has a pressure response which is flat down to about 2 Hz, and high-quality models are usually supplied with calibration curves.

A tweeter loudspeaker driver having a closed back and high resonant frequency (above 1 kHz) may also be used as a sensing transducer. At low frequencies the output voltage of this transducer is proportional to the rate of change of pressure within the enclosure, i.e., this transducer already includes one of the required differentiation operations and thus operates with simpler circuitry. Unfortunately, the high-Q mechanical resonance usually present in this type of transducer makes distortion measurement difficult due to the unavoidable resonant-frequency component in the output which is accentuated by differentiation.

A typical test setup for the measurement of response and harmonic distortion, including equalization networks, is shown schematically in Fig. 4. If a tweeter is used as the transducer, the second differentiation stage is omitted.

The simplicity of the measurement technique suggests its usefulness for design as well as evaluation. It is particularly well suited to the final adjustment of a loudspeaker system designed in accordance with approximate analytical methods because the measured response includes the effects of all system losses and any frequency dependence of the system component values with the exception of enclosure resistance. This application is analogous to the use of familiar sweep alignment techniques in making final adjustments to the response of theoretically designed electrical filters or tuned amplifiers.

V. EXPERIMENTAL MEASUREMENTS

Two loudspeaker systems, one closed-box type and one vented-box type, were selected to illustrate the measurement technique. The low-frequency small-signal parameters of each system, calculated from voice-coil impedance measurements [4], are presented in Table I. These parame-

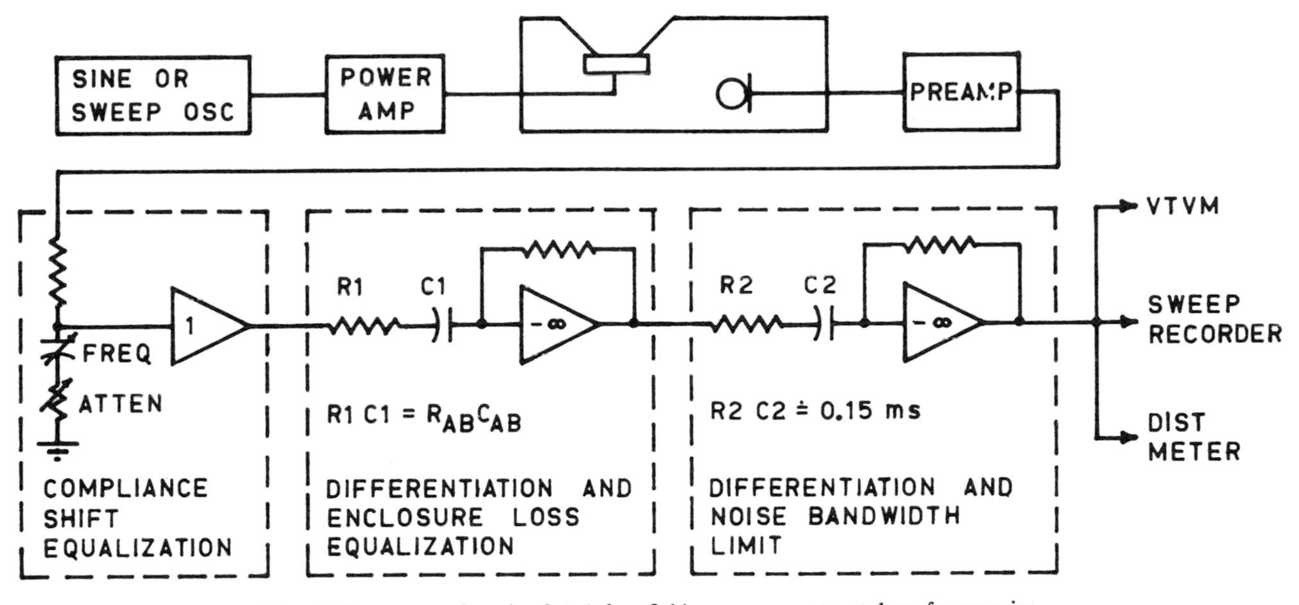

Fig. 4. Test setup for simulated free-field measurements at low frequencies.

ters were used to compute the expected system response and to determine the required enclosure-loss equalization (see Appendix).

Fig. 5 presents the computed response of the closed-box system, together with the response measured with a condenser microphone placed inside the enclosure at a location where pressure variations were least troublesome. The agreement between the two response curves is quite good up to about 180 Hz, in fact better than might be expected considering the assumptions and approximations involved in both methods. Distortion curves for the closed-box system, obtained using the same experimental setup, appear in Fig. 6. The distortion maxima just below the system resonant frequency reflect the large diaphragm displacement of this substantially underdamped system.

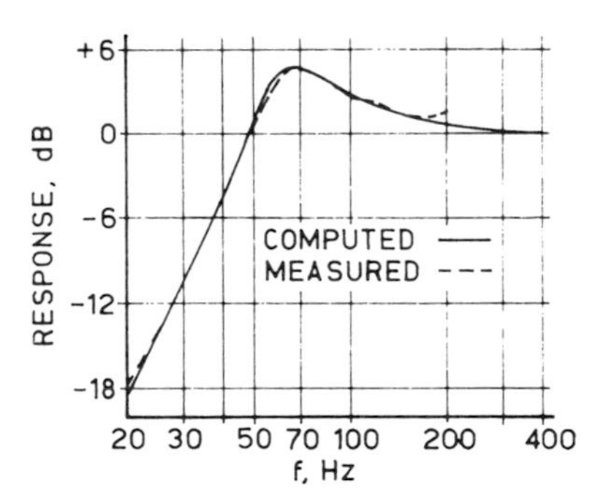

Fig. 5. Frequency response of closed-box system.

Fig. 7 presents the computed response of the vented-box system, together with the response obtained with the microphone in the enclosure. The agreement is again quite good, in this case up to about 250 Hz. Distortion curves for the vented-box system appear in Fig. 8. These are typical of a well-designed vented-box system, rising at frequencies below the vent-enclosure resonance.

The experimental results could not be checked in a true anechoic environment, but attempts to obtain the near-field response in a reverberant environment indicated that the response derived from enclosure pressure is in both cases likely to be more accurate than the response computed from the measured parameters.

Fig. 9 illustrates the application of the technique to final adjustment of a loudspeaker system. The frequency response of a vented-box system initially designed according to theory [4] is plotted for several conditions of enclosure tuning. The duct length for the vent which gives the flattest response (125 mm) is clearly indicated by these measurements which were made using a tweeter as a sensing transducer. The initial design value of the duct length was 150 mm. The sag in the response with this vent is attributable to a slightly excessive amount of damping in the driver compared to that theoretically required, and to the contribution of enclosure losses not taken into account in the initial design calculations.

VI. CONCLUSION

The measurement technique described is a useful means of obtaining the low-frequency response and distortion characteristics of small direct-radiator loudspeaker systems for design or evaluation purposes. It is simple and inexpensive compared with established free-field techniques.

The theoretical accuracy of the technique at *very* low frequencies is worth investigation as a means of testing and calibrating sound sources, anechoic chambers, and reverberant rooms.

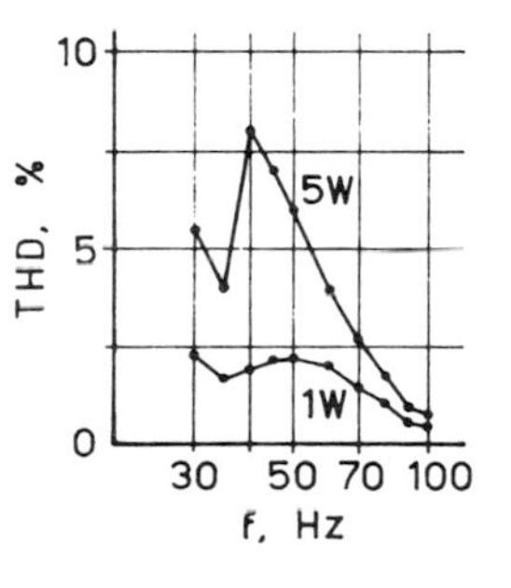

Fig. 6. Measured total harmonic distortion of closed-box system.

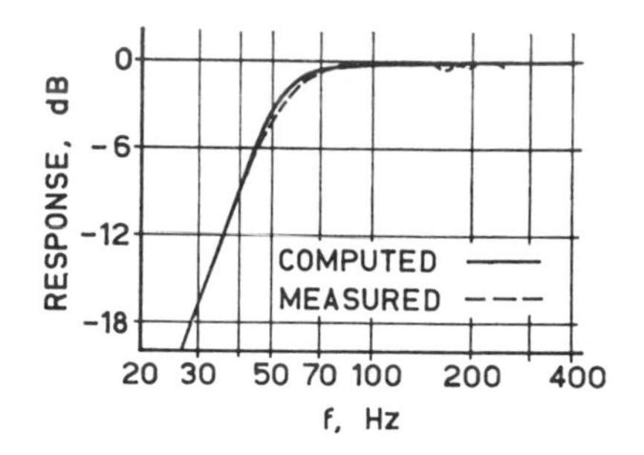

Fig. 7. Frequency response of vented-box system.

At higher frequencies, the equalization methods require further study, and accuracy of the technique should be checked by comparison with true free-field measurements.

APPENDIX—

APPROXIMATE MEASUREMENT OF ENCLOSURE ABSORPTION LOSSES

Absorption losses are only one type of loss that can occur in loudspeaker enclosures. It is difficult to separate the various kinds of losses but relatively easy to obtain an indication of total losses. In some cases, absorption losses are dominant and the measured total losses are then an adequate indication of absorption losses.

Absorption losses may be considered dominant in closed-box systems which are completely filled with damping materials and free of significant enclosure leaks. They are rarely dominant in vented-box systems unless the enclosure contains damping materials which either extend well out from the walls or are hung across the center of the enclosure as curtains. In these cases the total-loss measurement methods given below may be used to evaluate the absorption losses for equalization purposes. In all other cases, R_{AB} will probably be too small to require equalization, and the other losses present will be accurately represented in the response measurement by their direct effects on the total system volume velocity.

The loss measurements require the identification of frequencies at which the voice-coil impedance of the loudspeaker system has a maximum or minimum magnitude. In most cases, the impedance phase is zero at these frequencies and the frequencies may thus be identified more quickly and accurately by measurement of phase. However, if zero phase does not occur very close to the magnitude maxima or minima, then the frequencies of the latter should be measured as carefully as possible and used in the calculations.

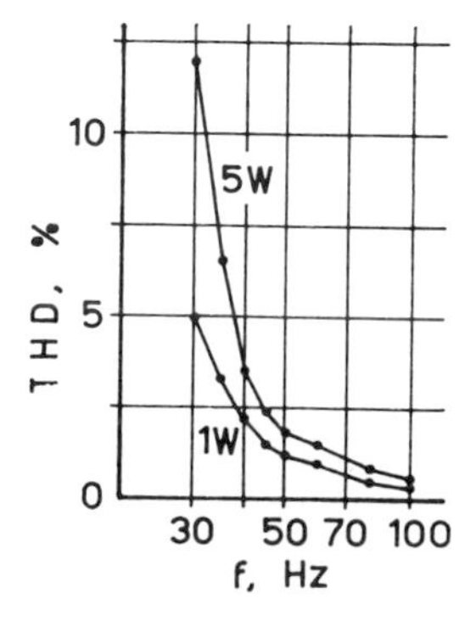

Fig. 8. Measured total harmonic distortion of vented-box system.

Closed-Box System

Measure carefully the dc resistance R_E of the driver voice coil and then the voice-coil impedance magnitude as a function of frequency; first with the driver in air, then with the driver in the enclosure. For the driver in air, find the frequency f_S for which the voice-coil impedance magnitude is a maximum. The ratio of this maximum impedance magnitude to the dc voice-coil resistance is defined as r_0. Next find the two frequencies $f_1<f_S$ and $f_2>f_S$ for which the impedance magnitude is $R_E\sqrt{r_0}$. Then calculate [4, eq. (97)]

$$Q_{MS} = \frac{f_S\sqrt{r_0}}{(f_2-f_1)} \tag{6}$$

and [4, eq. (95)]

$$Q_{ES} = \frac{Q_{MS}}{r_0-1}. \tag{7}$$

Similarly for the driver in the enclosure, find the frequency f_C for which the voice-coil impedance magnitude is a maximum, and let the ratio of maximum impedance magnitude to dc resistance be r_{0C}. Find the two frequencies f_{1C} and f_{2C} as above and calculate

$$Q_{MC} = \frac{f_C\sqrt{r_{0C}}}{(f_{2C}-f_{1C})} \tag{8}$$

and

$$Q_{EC} = \frac{Q_{MC}}{r_{0C}-1}. \tag{9}$$

If the driver mechanical resistance is independent of frequency, the contribution of this resistance to Q_{MC}, labeled $Q_{MC(S)}$, is simply

$$Q_{MC(S)} = Q_{MS}\frac{f_C}{f_S}. \tag{10}$$

This would be the value of Q_{MC} if there were no enclosure losses.

Now if Q_B is defined as the ratio of reactance to resistance for the enclosure at f_C, i.e.,

$$Q_B = 1/(2\pi f_C C_{AB} R_{AB}) \tag{11}$$

then the measured value of Q_{MC} will be such that

$$1/Q_{MC} = 1/Q_{MC(S)} + (1/Q_B)(C_{AT}/C_{AB}) \tag{12}$$

where C_{AT} is the total compliance of the system, i.e., enclosure and driver suspension acting together. If C_{AS} is the compliance of the driver suspension, then

$$1/C_{AT} = 1/C_{AS} + 1/C_{AB} \tag{13}$$

and it can be shown that [4, eq. (101)]

$$C_{AT}/C_{AB} = 1 - (f_S Q_{ES}/f_C Q_{EC}). \tag{14}$$

Combining Eqs. (10), (12), and (14),

$$Q_B = \left[1 - \frac{f_S Q_{ES}}{f_C Q_{EC}}\right]\frac{f_C Q_{MC} Q_{MS}}{f_C Q_{MS} - f_S Q_{MC}}. \tag{15}$$

The value of Q_B is thus calculated from the above measurements and used to determine the equalization circuit time constant from Eq. (11):

$$C_{AB}R_{AB} = 1/(2\pi f_C Q_B). \tag{16}$$

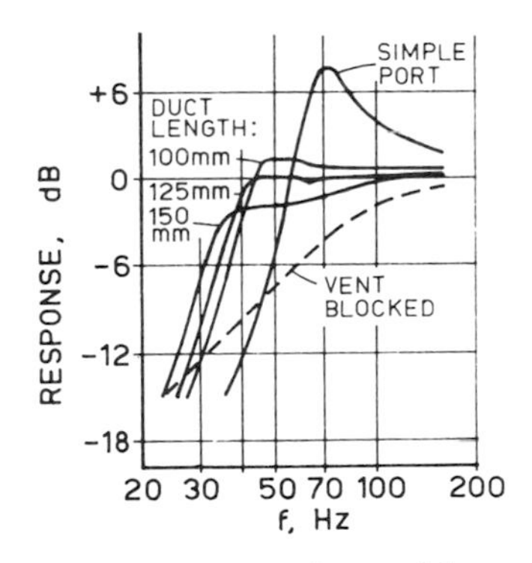

Fig. 9. Frequency response of vented-box system for various conditions of enclosure tuning.

Vented-Box System

Measure R_E and the driver voice-coil impedance magnitude as a function of frequency with the driver in air as above and find f_S, r_0, Q_{MS}, and Q_{ES}.

With the driver mounted in the vented enclosure, again measure the voice-coil impedance magnitude as a function of frequency. Find f_L, the lowest frequency for which the impedance magnitude is maximum, f_H, the next higher frequency of maximum impedance magnitude, and f_M, the frequency between f_L and f_H for which the impedance magnitude is a minimum. The ratio of the minimum impedance magnitude at f_M to the dc voice-coil resistance R_E is defined as r_M. Now calculate [4, eq. (106)]

$$\alpha = \frac{(f_H + f_M)(f_H - f_M)(f_M + f_L)(f_M - f_L)}{f_H{}^2 f_L{}^2}. \quad (17)$$

Then, to a sufficient approximation [4, eq. (107)],

$$Q_B = \frac{1}{\alpha Q_{ES}} \cdot \frac{f_M}{f_S} \cdot \frac{1}{r_M - 1} \quad (18)$$

where Q_B is the ratio of reactance to resistance for the enclosure at f_M. Then, as in the closed-box case, the required equalization time constant is

$$C_{AB} R_{AB} = 1/(2\pi f_M Q_B). \quad (19)$$

ACKNOWLEDGMENT

The basic idea for the measurement technique described here was suggested some years ago by A. N. Thiele, who also suggested the simple alternative of using a tweeter as the pressure transducer.

The experimental verification of the technique and study of equalization methods was carried out at the School of Electrical Engineering of the University of Sydney, as part of a program of postgraduate study into the low-frequency behavior of direct-radiator electrodynamic loudspeaker systems. Financial support for this program from the Australian Commonwealth Department of Education and Science is gratefully acknowledged.

The author wishes to thank Prof. J. R. Ashley for his generous cooperation in presenting this paper to the 41st Convention of the Audio Engineering Society and the Institution of Radio and Electronics Engineers Australia for granting permission for both representation and republication of this paper through the Audio Engineering Society.

REFERENCES

[1] I. H. Shearman, "Assessment of Loudspeaker Quality," *Proc. IREE (Australia),* vol. 31, p. 165 (June 1970).

[2] L. L. Beranek, *Acoustics* (McGraw-Hill, New York, 1954).

[3] J. E. Benson, "Theory and Design of Loudspeaker Enclosures," *Proc. IREE (Australia),* vol. 30, p. 261 (Sept. 1969).

[4] A. N. Thiele, "Loudspeakers in Vented Boxes," *Proc. IREE (Australia),* vol. 22, p. 487 (Aug. 1961); also *J. Audio Eng. Soc.,* vol. 19, pp. 382–392 (May 1971) and pp. 471–483 (June 1971).

THE AUTHOR

Richard H. Small was born in San Diego, California in 1935. He received a BS from California Institute of Technology in 1956, and an MSEE from Massachusetts Institute of Technology in 1958. Following this, for six years (1958 to 1964) he was engaged in electronic circuit design for high-resolution mass spectrometers and other analytical instruments at the Research Center of Consolidated Electrodynamics Corporation, a subsidiary of Bell & Howell Company.

During 1962, Mr. Small visited Norway as an OEEC Growing Points Fellow, and worked on the design of control circuits for semiautomatic machine tools at Norwegian Technical University. In 1964 he was employed in electronic and mechanical design for the Industrial Division of World Design Center, Tokyo.

Since moving to Australia in 1965, Mr. Small has worked as a Teaching Fellow in the School of Electrical Engineering, University of Sydney, and as a private consultant. He is presently a Commonwealth Postgraduate Research Student in the School of Electrical Engineering, University of Sydney, researching the field of direct-radiator electrodynamic loudspeaker systems.

Mr. Small is a member of the Audio Engineering Society, the Institute of Electrical and Electronics Engineers, and the Institution of Radio and Electronics Engineers, Australia.

The Sound Field in Home Listening Rooms*

ROY F. ALLISON AND ROBERT BERKOVITZ†

Acoustic Research, Inc., Cambridge, Mass.

Loudspeaker systems do not radiate uniformly at all angles because of cabinet diffraction, directivity effects, and driver interference near crossover frequencies. In order to assess the practical importance of these effects, and to determine the "frequency response" of typical room/loudspeaker combinations, measurements were made of the spectral balance at normal listener positions in 10 rooms used for music reproduction, using ⅓-octave pink noise. Results are compared with measured spectral balance in concert halls.

Even when the individual speakers in a high-fidelity speaker system radiate energy in a smooth and uniform manner at all forward angles, if each is measured by itself on a flat baffle, the system in which they are used does not do so. Interference between speakers in the crossover frequency regions causes reinforcement at some frequencies and cancellation at others. The frequencies at which these effects occur change with the angle from the speaker system axis at which the direct radiation is measured, because the speakers cannot occupy the same space on the mounting plate; therefore, as the microphone is moved around the cabinet, the differences in path lengths change.

Another source of similar perturbations in the system's radiation pattern is diffraction, which is really a form of self-interference. Mounting surface discontinuities, the grille cloth molding, and the dimensions of the cabinet itself all produce diffraction that affects the direct-wave radiation in a complex manner dependent on the angle of the cabinet with respect to the microphone.

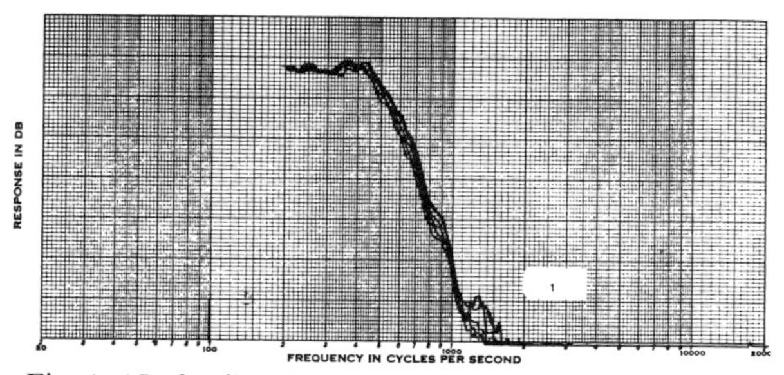

Fig. 1. 15° family of frequency response curves for woofer of three-way speaker system, measured in 2π anechoic chamber.

To illustrate how substantial these effects can be, we took an AR-3a system from stock and made several kinds of measurements on it. Our main anechoic chamber has nonreflective wedges on only five of the interior surfaces. The sixth is smooth concrete, with an opening in its center; speakers to be tested are placed at this opening with suitable adapter baffles so that they are flush with the inside chamber wall. In this manner a 2π radiation angle is obtained with minimum discontinuity.

* Presented October 12, 1970, at the 39th Convention of the Audio Engineering Society, New York.

† Mr. Berkovitz is currently with Dolby Laboratories, London, England.

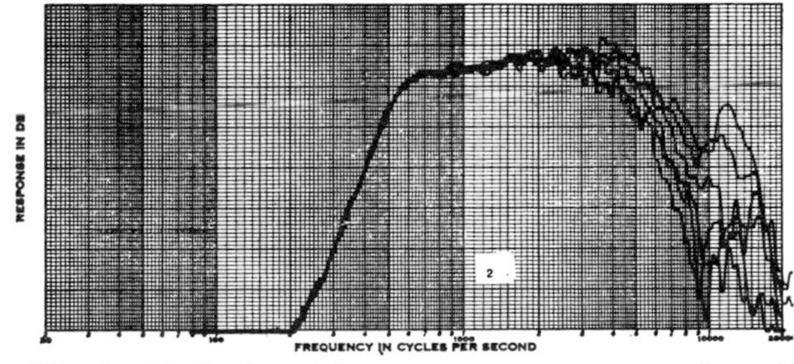

Fig. 2. 15° family of frequency response curves for mid-range unit of three-way speaker system, measured in 2π anechoic chamber.

Radiation into a hemisphere is typical of actual use conditions (whereas a 4π solid angle is not).

Fig. 1 shows the response (above 200 Hz) of the AR-3a woofer at six angles: 0°, 15°, 30°, 45°, 60°, and 75° from the axis, all superimposed. The woofer is in its cabinet but the grille cloth molding has been removed. Major vertical scale divisions are in increments of 5 dB.

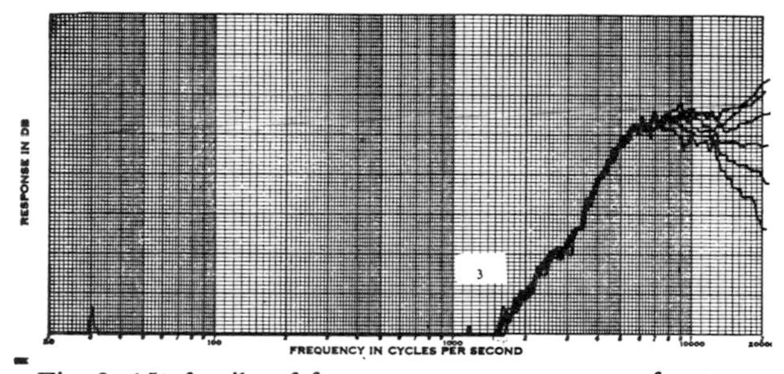

Fig. 3. 15° family of frequency response curves for tweeter of three-way speaker system, measured in 2π anechoic chamber.

Next (Fig. 2) is the mid-range speaker of the same AR-3a tested at the same six angles, 0° through 75°. The speaker was removed from the cabinet and installed on a flat baffle board, flush with the inside chamber wall. Its electrical input was supplied through the AR-3a crossover network. The level control is set at the maximum position. Note that the design crossover frequencies for the AR-3a are 575 Hz and 5 kHz.

Fig. 3 is a family of response curves of this system's tweeter, at maximum level control setting, with test conditions the same as for the mid-range unit.

The speakers were put back in the AR-3a cabinet and the complete system on-axis curve, with level controls at

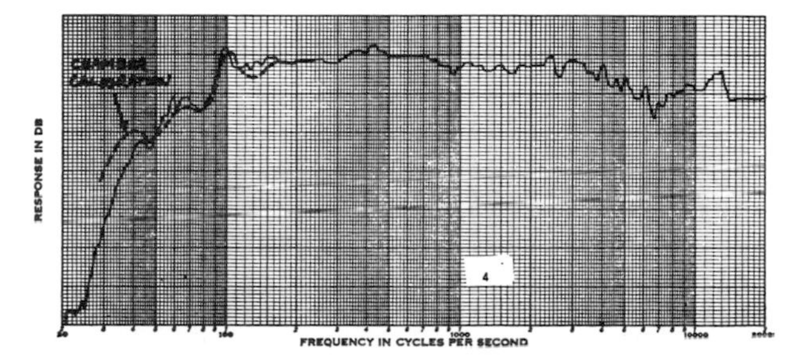

Fig. 4. Complete system's on-axis curve in same 2π chamber, showing effects of driver interference only. Speaker mounting plate of cabinet is flush with inside chamber wall.

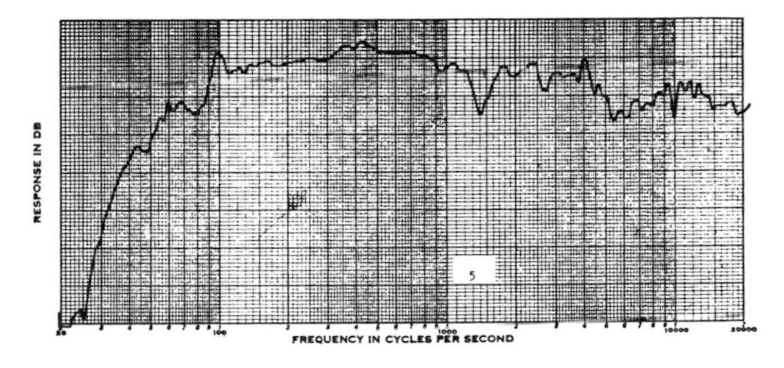

Fig. 5. Same test as Fig. 4, except that grille cloth molding has been added to cabinet, producing diffraction effects.

maximum settings, is shown in Fig. 4. The grille cloth molding is still not in place. Note the interference effect between mid-range and tweeter units in the crossover region. The low-frequency response follows the chamber calibration curve (the superimposed dash line) quite well to 45 Hz, and is 6 dB down at 30 Hz, exactly what an AR-3a woofer is supposed to do.

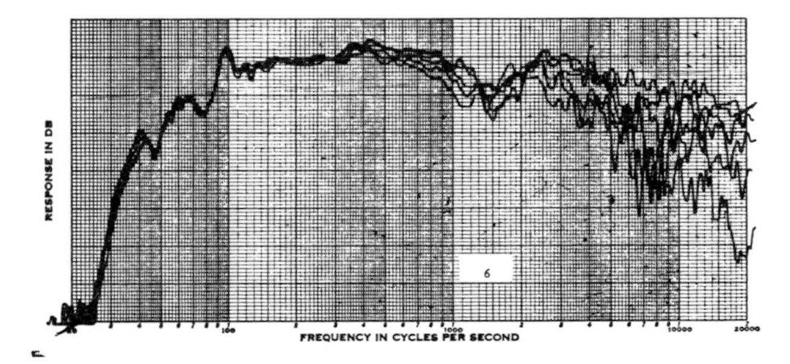

Fig. 6. 15° family of complete system curves with grille cloth molding, taken in 2π anechoic chamber.

Now we reinstall the grille cloth molding and make the front of the molding flush with the inside of the smooth chamber wall. Fig. 5 shows the on-axis response obtained with the level controls still set at maximum. The mere presence of the molding produces increased level (on axis) in the range from 300 to 1000 Hz, a 5- or 6-dB notch at 1400 Hz, and miscellaneous perturbations on up in frequency.

Figs. 6 and 7 are 15° families of the complete system, taken in a horizontal arc, first in one direction away from the system axis and then in the other. The grille molding is in place and the level controls are at maximum. It is difficult to assess performance because the

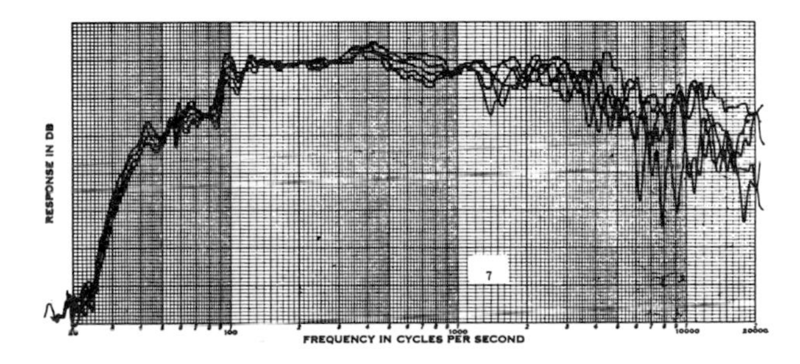

Fig. 7. 15° family of complete system curves with grille cloth molding, taken in 2π anechoic chamber.

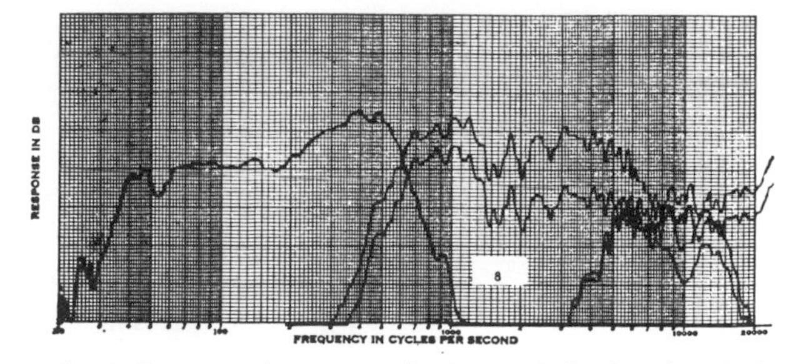

Fig. 8. Same speaker system in 4π anechoic chamber. Individual speakers measured separately, on axis, in cabinet with molding.

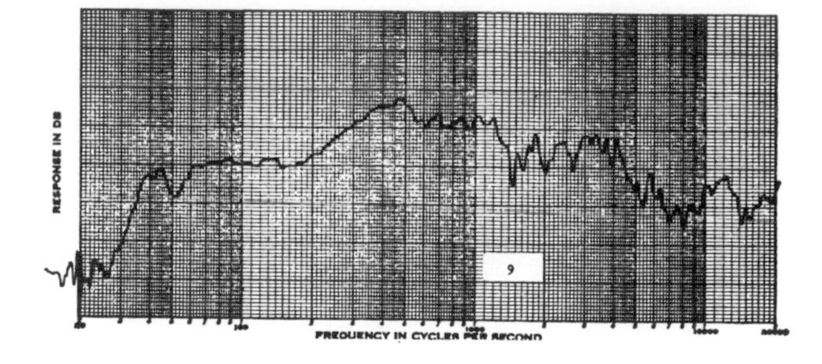

Fig. 9. 4π anechoic chamber frequency response curve for same speaker system on axis.

output level changes rapidly, not only with frequency but with small angular increments as well. And one must keep in mind that the output variation has been observed only in one plane around the system.

The picture becomes far more complex when the same system is measured in a 4π environment. We took this AR-3a to the large walk-in anechoic chamber at Harvard Acoustics Laboratory and repeated the measurements there. Fig. 8 shows on-axis response of the individual speakers of the system in the cabinet and with molding in place. Mid-range and tweeter curves are shown for both the suggested normal and maximum level control settings.

The most obvious feature of Fig. 8 is the woofer response. There is a continuous downhill slide from about 400 Hz, at which frequency the cabinet is a reasonably effective 2π baffle, to about 170 Hz, and then a flat response below that frequency. At 170 Hz and below the radiation angle is 4π steradians and the output, quite predictably, is lower than it was into a 2π angle.

Molding and cabinet-edge diffraction are clearly at work on the axial response curves of the mid-range unit. Fig. 9 is the on-axis system curve with molding, level controls at maximum. Some representative curves at other angles appear in Figs. 10 and 11.

It is commonly recognized that interference and diffraction do not change the total energy radiated by a speaker system; they merely redirect it, bunching it at favored angles for particular frequencies. The truth of this can be verified easily by diffuse-field measurements in a very reverberant environment. Fig. 12 is the response curve of this same AR-3a system taken in a reverberant chamber. Input to the system in this case is pink noise. The microphone (located behind the cabinet, so as to prevent any direct radiation from reaching it) is flat for random-incidence energy. Its output is fed to a General Radio swept 1/3-octave filter with coupled chart recorder. Superimposed on the response curve is the chamber calibration for flat energy input.

Clearly, the total energy output of this system is more easily predicted by the 2π anechoic measurements of the individual speakers than by the 4π measurements of the complete system with cabinet. But what do listeners hear from the system? Do they perceive the total energy output, or do they perceive as the "frequency response" of the system whatever the direct-radiation output may be at the angle of their location relative to the system?

We can provide intuitive answers for extreme cases. If listening is done in anechoic conditions (outdoors, for example), the only information reaching listeners is the direct wave, with some interference from a ground reflection. Its spectral balance is the only thing that can be perceived. Therefore, the quality of the individual speakers in the system is of significance but does not alone determine the system performance. Interference and diffraction play major roles in what is heard.

In a perfectly reverberant environment, on the other hand, it would not matter in the least what the frequency response might be for the radiation at any particular angle from the speaker system. It would not matter at what angle most of the energy were radiated at any particular frequency. So long as the *total* energy radiated from the system were constant at all frequencies of interest (and of course if there were no audible time differences in the radiation), the sound field in most of the room would have the same spectral balance as it would have if this energy were radiated in a perfectly omnidirectional manner.

But of course we all know that a typical listening room is not a perfect acoustic integrator. It is only necessary to walk around the room while some kinds of

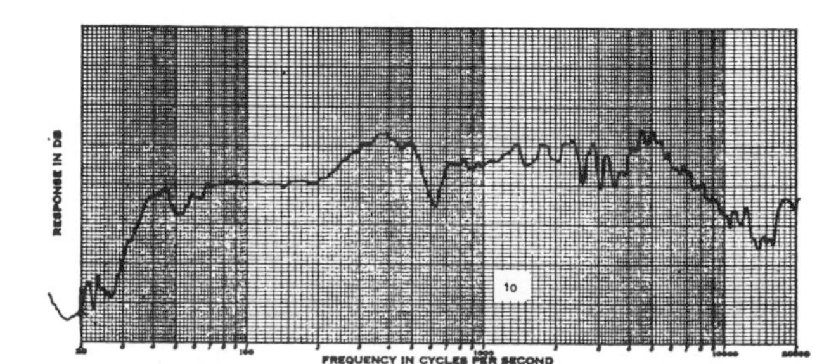

Fig. 10. 4π anechoic chamber frequency response curve for same speaker system $+30°$ off axis.

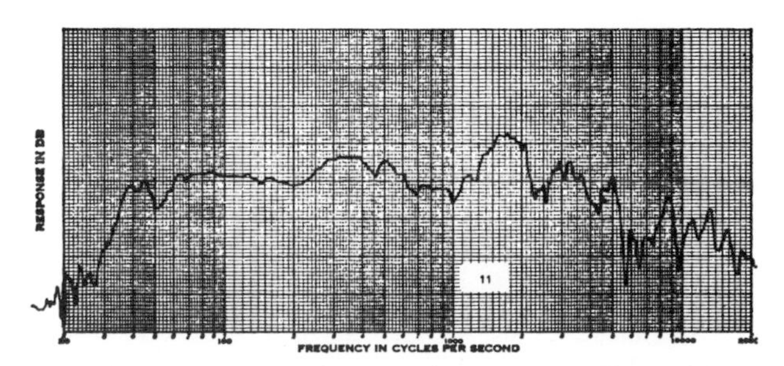

Fig. 11. 4π anechoic chamber frequency response curve for same speaker system $-60°$ off axis.

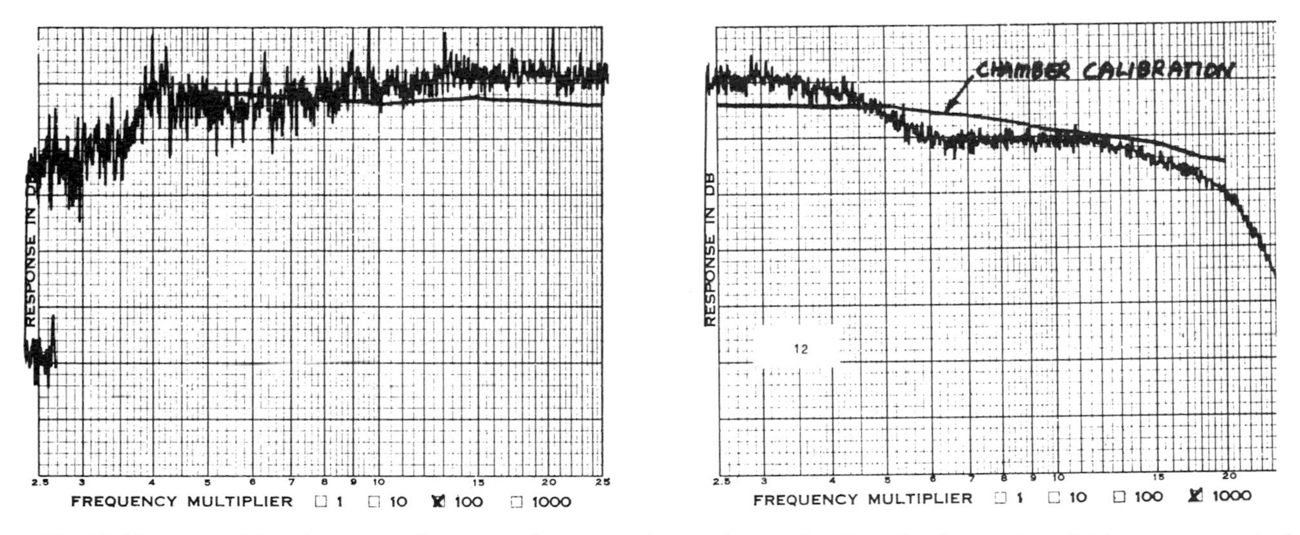

Fig. 12. ⅓-octave pink noise sweep of same speaker system in reverberant chamber, showing total available power output of system. Lower limit of chamber's diffuse-field accuracy is 500 Hz.

speakers are playing, and observe the constantly changing tonal balance, in order to realize that. Evidently, real rooms are neither completely anechoic nor completely reverberant, but fall at some semireverberant point between these extremes. It is important to know approximately where that point is if we are to understand why speaker systems that "measure" in a certain way sound as they do in use.

Beranek [1, ch. 10] has dealt with this question in a general theoretical way. As he points out, it is easier to understand what happens if we first consider the direct and reverberant sound fields separately.

The direct sound from the speaker decreases in sound pressure level in strict proportion to the distance from it, according to the so-called "square law." For each doubling of distance the direct-field sound pressure level decreases by 6 dB. If the source is highly directive, then of course the direct-field sound pressure level at a given distance varies in accordance with the directivity; it will be considerably higher on the axis of the lobe than it is off the axis. In other words, if the source is directive then a given direct-field sound pressure level amplitude will extend farther into the room, on the axis of a lobe, than it would for a nondirective source. Off the axis of the lobe it would not extend as far into the room.

The reverberant field, on the other hand, is by definition uniform in amplitude throughout the room except for the effect of room modes widely spaced at lower frequencies (standing waves). In a typical living room standing waves have little effect on the reverberant-field sound pressure level at a particular location above 1 kHz, and steadily increasing effect below that frequency.

Aside from the effects of standing waves, the reverberant-field sound pressure level is (theoretically) determined only by two factors, the power level of the source and the room constant R. R is a factor expressing the average energy absorption coefficient of the room surfaces and the total surface area. Thus the room can be thought of as an acoustic energy sink, with a drain stopper that leaks at a rate proportional to the amplitude of energy contained. The source of energy (the loudspeaker) pours energy into the sink at a given rate, and the steady-state amplitude of this energy is determined by the rate at which energy is absorbed by the room surfaces and furnishings. The steady-state energy, which is the reverberant field, is independent of the directivity of the source or the position it occupies in the room, at least above 1000 Hz. Below 1000 Hz the reverberant field in a living room is not dependent on the directivity of the source, but it is dependent to some extent on the position of the source, because position affects room mode excitation.

Fig. 13 brings together the direct- and reverberant-field sound pressure levels so that their relationship is apparent. The vertical scale on the left is total sound pressure level of the direct and reverberant fields combined, relative to the power level of the source, at the distances from the source shown on the horizontal scale at the bottom. Five sets of curves are given, corresponding to directivity factors Q of 1, 2, 5, 10, and 30. Each of these curves is shown for representative room constant values R of 50, 500, and 10 000.

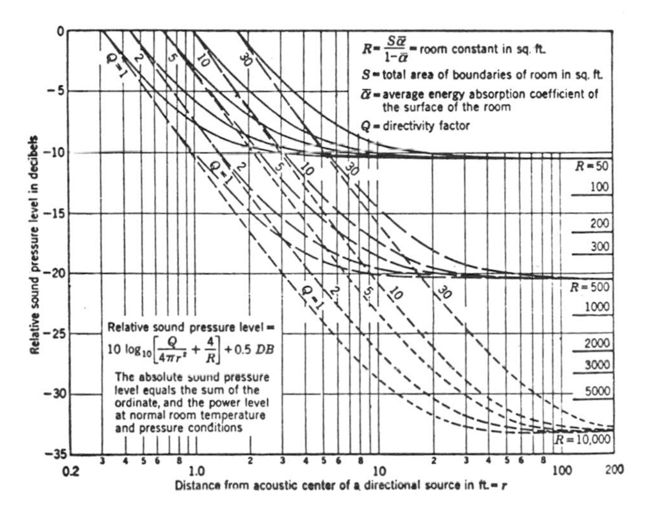

Fig. 13. Sound pressure levels in rooms as functions of distance from source, for various values of directivity and room absorption factors [1, p. 318].

As expected, the reverberant field's relative sound pressure level is entirely a function of R; the five Q curves converge to that value of sound pressure level representing the reverberant field only. The direct field predominates at distances close to the source and is submerged in the reverberant field farther away. For higher values of Q the direct field predominates at greater distances than for lower values. (Note that the chart assumes the measurement to be made *on* axis of the directivity lobe; if the measurement were made *off* axis, then of course the direct field would become insignificant very close to the source.)

What does the chart say about living rooms? Let us assume a living room of average size, say, 2500 cubic feet, which is a room 14 by 23 feet with average ceiling height. If this room is of "average" absorptivity, neither very live nor very dead, its room constant will be 200. Assuming that the loudspeaker is placed against one wall, its directivity factor will be 2 at low frequencies. If it is a high-quality unit, its directivity factor will be 2 also at middle frequencies. At high frequencies it will be at least 3 for even the highest quality systems, and 4 or 5 for merely very good speakers.

Following the horizontal line extension of $R = 200$, we see that it intersects the $Q = 2$ direct-field line at a distance of a little less than 3 feet. At 2¾ feet, then, the direct field is equal in level to the reverberant field for a nondirectional source placed against a wall in this average room. At 5½ feet the direct field is 6 dB down from the reverberant-field sound pressure level; the reverberant field is certainly predominant. This would apply at middle frequencies also for the best possible speaker systems.

For a Q value of 3, the direct and reverberant fields are of equal amplitude at about 3½ feet from the speaker. At 7 feet the direct field is 6 dB below the reverberant field. And for a Q of 5, the two fields are equal at 4½ feet; the reverberant field would not predominate by 6 dB for a listener on the axis of the speaker until he were at least 9 feet away from it.

Most typical listening positions are at least 6 feet away from the speakers. Probably it would be accurate to say also that 90% of the listeners are at least 9 feet away from the speakers when they are in their favorite chairs. If loudspeaker systems with very good high-frequency dispersion are used, therefore, Beranek's calculations would imply that listeners are almost always located in areas of the room in which the reverberant field is predominant for all frequencies being reproduced. But it should be noted that not all speaker systems, not even all quite costly ones, have very good dispersion at all frequencies. Q values of 10 or more are common, particularly at very high frequencies; that requires a distance of at least 12 feet to get well into the reverberant field.

Depressions or notches in the direct radiation at certain frequencies, due to interference, would not be heard by a listener because the sound pressure level at those frequencies would be maintained by the reverberant field. But what about direct-radiation *peaks* due to diffraction effects? An increase of 3 dB in the direct field, caused by diffraction, is equivalent to a doubling of the directivity index for that frequency at that angle. Here the situation is not so self-evident. In a practical sense there are other questions that might be raised about the

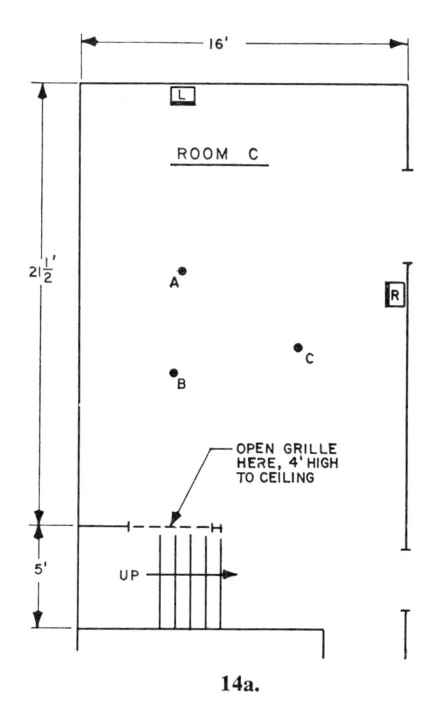

14a.

Fig. 14. A living room that might be considered typical, with ⅓-octave pink noise analyses of sound field at various listening locations.

importance of the direct and reverberant fields, in addition to the simple one of whether or not the relative amplitudes agree with Beranek's chart. There are three questions of fundamental importance.

1) In widely varying home listening situations, is the field at any practical listener location primarily direct rather than reverberant?

2) Even if the field is primarily reverberant on a random-incidence basis, do head and outer-ear shielding weight the field at the ear canal entrance toward the direct sound?

3) Whether or not the field at the ear canal is mostly reverberant, is there something in the ear/brain system that judges spectral balance only on the basis of the spectrum of first-arrival (direct) sound, much as it judges the *direction* of the source on the basis of first-arrival information?

To address ourselves directly to these questions, we measured the fields produced by loudspeakers in ten actual listening rooms that vary widely in type of fur-

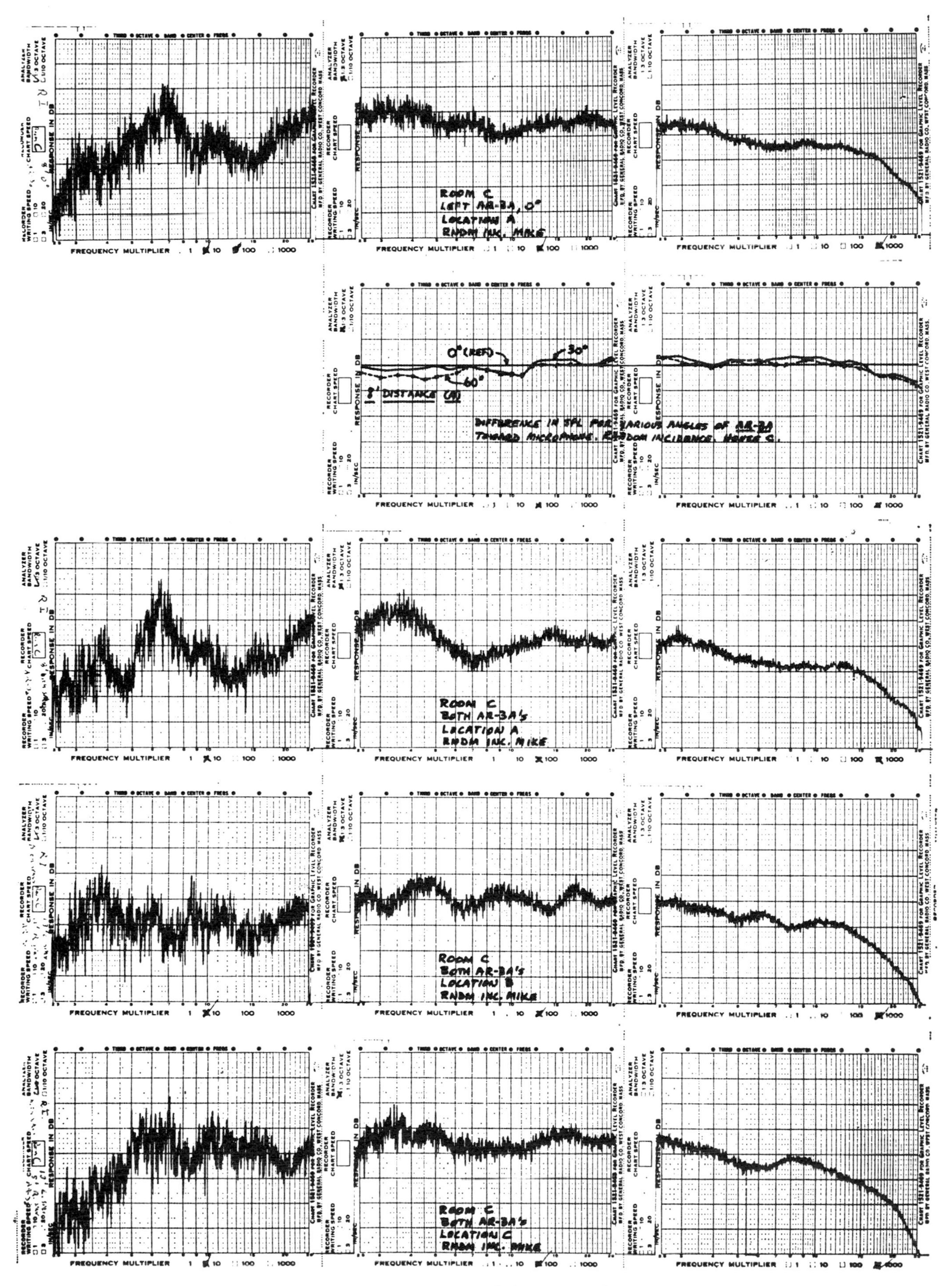

Fig. 14b. Random incidence recording.

nishing and size. Space does not permit showing the results of tests in all of the rooms,[1] but two of them are shown photographically and by scale drawings in Figs. 14 and 15, together with the data. Eight of the rooms are the living rooms or home music listening rooms of AR-3a owners who reside in the greater Boston area; two are office/listening rooms at the AR offices in Cambridge. None of the rooms was rearranged, nor the speaker systems moved, prior to the measurements. The speakers were not special in any way.

Most of the work involved the random-incidence field produced by AR-3a speakers in these rooms. We used pink noise, fed to one or both speakers, as the main source, and analyzed the microphone output by means of a General Radio ⅓-octave swept filter with coupled chart recorder. In order to avoid the possibility of bias in deciding on microphone positions we did not perform the analyses on the spot; we recorded the field samples on a Magnecord 1028 machine, with Scotch #203 tape, for the later filter analysis. Our random-incidence measurements were made with a ½-inch B&K microphone flat to 20 kHz for random-incidence fields, always placed at seated ear-level height.

Fig. 14**a** might be considered a normal or average living room. The AR-3a random-incidence field information for this room is shown in Fig. 14**b**. Individual charts are marked to identify the room, the microphone location (keyed in the scale drawing), and the fact that this is a random-incidence recording. There are basically two types of recordings here; those made with both speakers operating and facing as they normally do, and those made with a single speaker system facing directly at the microphone. For each single-speaker recording on the speaker axis, we made additional recordings with the speaker turned 30° and 60° away from the microphone, thereby changing significantly the frequency response of the direct-wave component arriving at the microphone. These additional recordings (not shown) are summarized as *differences* from the 0° recording. These differences give strong clues to the proportion of direct to reverberant sound at the microphone location. Turning the speaker, rather than moving the microphone, minimizes the influence of room modes on this aspect of the investigation. Measurements were made in other rooms at various distances ranging from very close (3 feet) to typical listening positions. Whenever possible we used the left-channel speaker for these angular measurements simply for consistency. Figs. 15**a** and 15**b** give data for a small listening room at the AR factory offices.

These (and all other recordings in this series of tests) were made with both the mid-range and tweeter level controls turned all the way up. We did this despite the fact that it produces unnatural balance on music recordings, because it is an adjustment easily made to achieve standard repeatable conditions, and because it shows the maximum output available from each of the three speakers in the system.

At typical listening positions the data indicate that the reverberant field is decidedly predominant. The curves show also that discernible room modes are almost nonex-

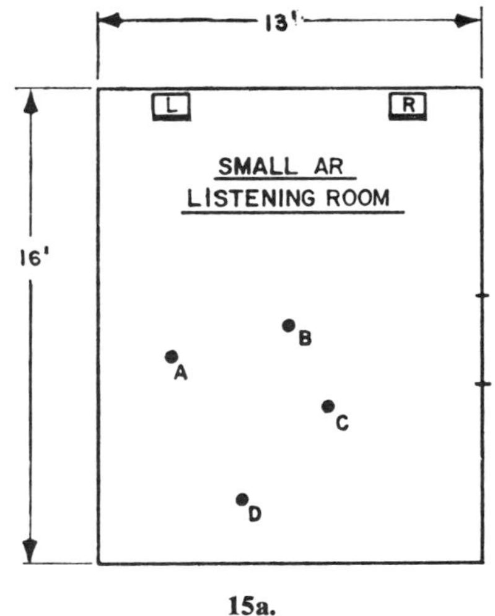

15a.

Fig. 15. A small listening room, with ⅓-octave pink noise analyses of sound field at various listening positions.

istent above 1 kHz. When modes are present at lower frequencies, their effect is different at different locations. It is difficult to see any justification for elaborate multifilter "room equalizers." If correction is needed, simple tone controls would do it better.

The second fundamental question was whether the physical shape of the head and pinnae change the ratio of direct to reverberant sound appreciably at the ear canal entrance from that which would exist at the same spot on a random-incidence basis. We placed a dummy head, with Altec type 21 microphones at the ear canal entrance, in the same locations as the random-incidence microphone locations, and repeated the angular measure-

[1] Full documentation is available on request to Acoustic Research, Inc., 24 Thorndike Street, Cambridge, Mass. 02141.

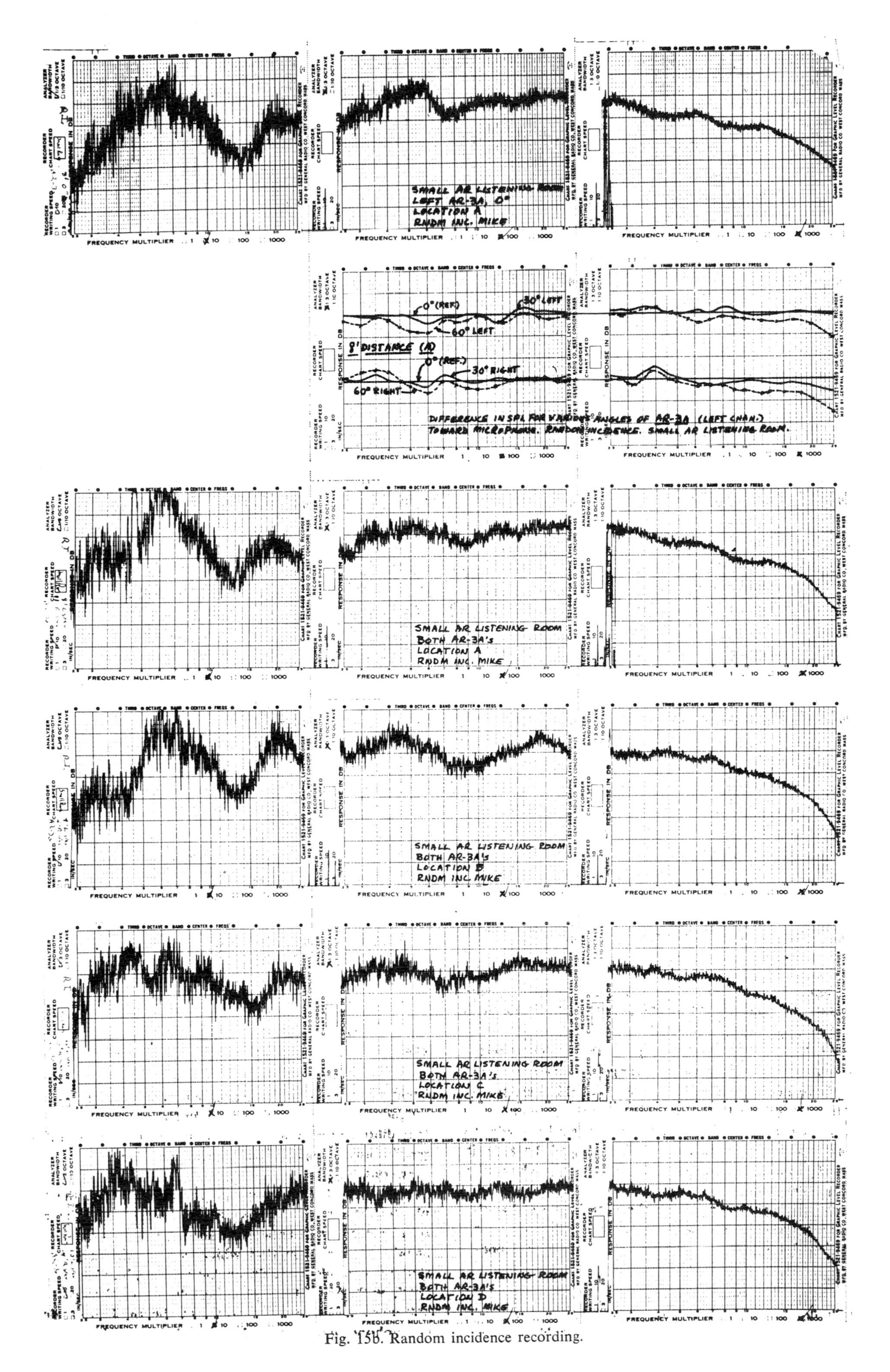

Fig. 15b. Random incidence recording.

ments. The dummy head faced the speaker directly in each case, of course. The difference curves are quite similar to those for the random incidence measurements. It is clear that the head does not affect the *ratio* of direct to reverberant energy significantly, although it does have a major effect on the spectral balance of the combined field at the ear canal entry.

We thought it advisable to obtain data on a quite different kind of speaker system, the AR-4x, to see how these same rooms treated relatively directional tweeter radiation. The AR-4x data were obtained in room *A* and in both AR listening rooms. As might be expected, since the AR-4x is a less complex system than the AR-3a, the reverberant field is predominant at room locations closer to the AR-4x (as compared with the AR-3a) for middle frequencies, and not nearly as close at high frequencies.

There remains still the third fundamental question to be answered. In an attempt to do so, we made binaural music recordings with the dummy head facing the speaker at various distances in rooms *A* and *B*. We turned the speaker at 10-second intervals during the course of each 1-minute recording. In each case the speaker faced the head directly (0°) for the first 10 seconds. Succeeding intervals were at speaker angles of 30°, 60°, 30°, 0°, and 30°. The spectral contribution of the direct component was thereby changed frequently. No changes could be detected in spectral balance beyond the 3-foot distance as the AR-3a was turned. Slight changes occurred in the AR-4x because of the high-frequency losses at wide angles, but only for the fairly close distances. Based on this evidence the answer to question 3 is also, "No." We believe that this is a subject warrranting a more thorough investigation.

These results can be summarized as follows.

1) We are convinced that home music listeners perceive the spectral balance of the *sum* of the direct and reverberant fields, and that the very small time differences between them have no effect on this perception of balance. In other words, directional perception based on precedence is carried on by a different mechanism than operates for the judgment of spectral balance.

2) When using loudspeaker systems that have low directivity factors at all frequencies, listeners at typical listening positions in virtually all living rooms are well within the area in which the reverberant field predominates. Predominance of the reverberant field becomes progressively less probable at typical listener locations as the directivity factor increases.

3) The reverberant field spectral balance is determined primarily by the acoustic *power* frequency response of the loudspeaker system. Thus the single most important factor in assessing the "frequency response" of a loudspeaker system is the *integrated output at all angles.* Moreover, because the output at low frequencies is influenced strongly by the solid angle into which the speaker radiates, either this measurement should be made with the speaker facing 2π steradians, or the difference should be taken into account.

For a realistic assessment of loudspeaker spectral performance both types of response curves are needed, reverberant energy response and anechoic curves to investigate directivity. Anechoic polar curves would do nicely for that.

It is necessary at this point to go into the matter of high-frequency balance relative to bass. Standing-wave modes in a single room make it virtually impossible to know with any assurance exactly what the *average* room effect on speaker performance may be. A more reliable indication would be obtained by averaging the relevant curves in all rooms, and we did that for Fig. 16. In preparing the composite we did the following.

1) We discarded data for the two AR listening rooms because they are not home living rooms.

2) We discarded the very close (3-foot) direct-field data taken where nobody listens.

3) We used only the data taken with both speakers of each stereo pair operating.

4) We plotted points for each of the remaining curves at the frequencies 30, 50, 70, 100, 150, 200, 250, 300, 400, 500, 600, 800, 1000, 1200, and 1500 Hz; 2, 3, 5, 7, 10, 15, and 20 kHz.

5) We averaged these levels for all the curves in each individual room.

6) We averaged the composite data for the eight rooms.

7) We subtracted the tape machine response error and plotted the resultant.

Fig. 16 shows the spectral distribution that will be obtained with the average of 16 AR-3a speakers at 22 locations in the average acoustical setting of 8 typical living rooms. Examination of this composite reveals several interesting characteristics.

1) The general trend in the range below 250 Hz demonstrates that the average real room does not give the low-frequency support that is commonly assumed. Since this falling response is not a property of the AR-3a when radiating into a hemisphere, and cannot be at-

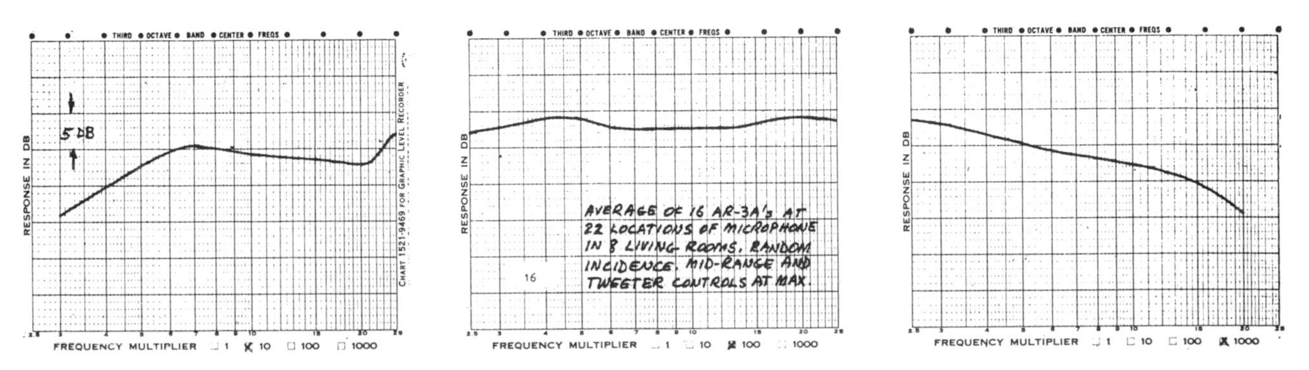

Fig. 16. Average ⅓-octave "frequency response" of combined loudspeaker system and room for normal listener locations in eight actual home installations.

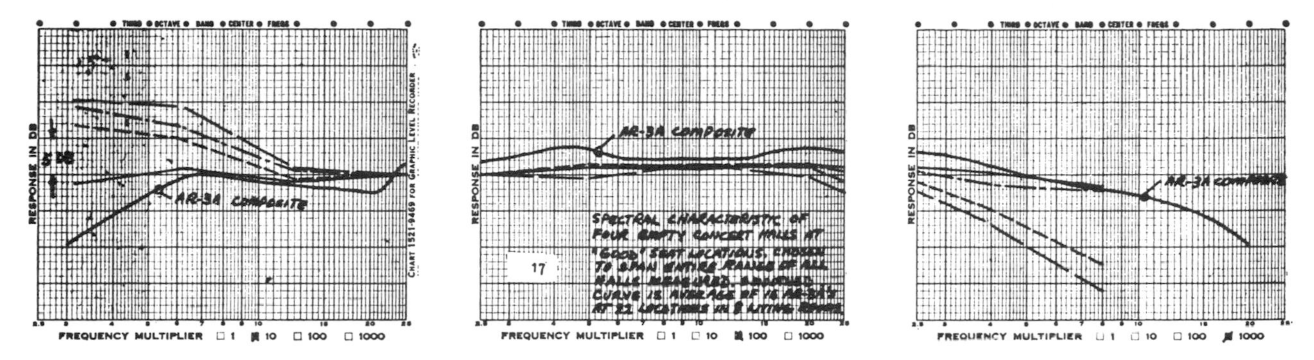

Fig. 17. Average loudspeaker and room response compared with "frequency response" of reverberant field of four empty concert halls. Hall measurements made at seated listener ear level, 1/3 to 1/2 distance from stage to rear of orchestra floor (by Bolt Beranek & Newman).

tributed to a large radiation angle (the average angle in these rooms is visually smaller, not larger, than 2π), it must clearly be the result of increasing energy absorption at low frequencies. Room furnishings do not absorb much at low frequencies (certainly not more than at middle frequencies). Evidently most of the loss is the result of inadequate boundary stiffness, flapping walls, floors, ceilings, and windows.

2) This low-frequency rolloff is interrupted by a 4-dB V-shaped notch centered just above 200 Hz. In addition, there is a smaller rise in output centered just above 400 Hz. These frequencies coincide precisely with quarter-wave and half-wave distances from the front of the cabinet to the wall behind the speaker system, which would produce reflections that alternately cancel and reinforce the forward radiation. These strong reflections significantly change the loading on the woofer,—which is not surprising since they occur at frequencies below that of ultimate radiation resistance. Furthermore, the more gradual slope for the V's lower-frequency leg is explained by the fact that the fronts of the speaker cabinets in these rooms can be (and some are) farther than 1.4 feet from the wall, but they cannot be much closer and most are approximately at that distance. Note that this effect is a function of the way speaker systems in general are used in homes. Nearly all systems made today are of about the same size and general low-frequency design. All should exhibit the same effect.

3) In the range from 250 to 2500 Hz, a decade of primary aural sensitivity, the response is within $\pm$ 1 dB. Keep in mind that this curve shows what *loudspeakers* are delivering to listeners' ears.

4) The average room absorption of high frequencies is not much greater than that of middle frequencies. This becomes apparent on comparing Figs. 16 and 12.

Microphones for both live broadcasts and recording sessions are invariably set up in the near field of the sound source, while concert-goers are in the reverberant field. In concert halls the reverberant field has a far more drastic high-frequency rolloff (relative to the bass) than is true of living rooms. Thus what is put into the speaker system is a near-field spectrum, usually made even "hotter" because the instruments are aimed at the microphones. To produce the same spectral balance at the ears of listeners in both concert halls and living rooms, the reproducing system must compensate for the difference between high-frequency rolloffs in concert halls and living rooms.

Fig. 17 shows the octave-band spectral distribution, at seated ear-level height, for four empty concert halls[2] with the composite AR-3a living room curve added. This information that has only recently come to our attention; it simply supports the qualitative and subjective judgements that have had to be made in the past on what seemed to be the proper "normal" settings for speaker level controls.

There is no way to get a close match to the average of the concert-hall curves below 250 Hz. The wall-reflection phenomenon in the living room AR-3a composite curve and the concert hall seat-dip phenomenon are so different in their effects on spectral distribution that a bass tone control could help only in a limited way. It is just as evident that the balance of bass to middle and high frequencies in these concert halls varies widely. The following surmises, however, seem to be reasonable.

1) With audiences in the halls, the level at middle and high frequencies relative to the bass range could be expected to decrease still further.

2) The broad sag in the concert-hall curves centered at 125–150 Hz is explained by Bolt, Beranek and Newman as the result of a "reactive acoustic impedance caused by the vertically compartmented seating geometry, significantly disturbing the sound field. . . . Near frequencies where the microphone-to-floor spacing is a quarter of one wavelength, the measured sound pressure is significantly lower than at a large distance from the floor."

With the audience in place, the seat dip probably is somewhat lessened in severity by damping. If that is true, the entire AR-3a curve should be raised to provide a better match at low frequencies, thus raising the middle- and high-frequency ranges still further above the concert-hall curve.

In the light of these findings we believe that typical operating settings for loudspeaker high-frequency balance controls should be well below the settings which produce flat acoustic energy output if the objective is a spectrum similar to that produced at a concert hall seat. In view of the variations found in both living room and concert

[2] The four halls for which information is shown here span the range from the brightest to the deadest of nine halls measured, with the average falling very close to the middle. All were measured without an audience. These data are from unpublished files of Bolt Beranek and Newman.

hall frequency balance, and the manner in which these variations occur, we think that home listeners should be encouraged to make more liberal use of amplifier tone controls.

Certainly, in view of current recording practice, flat electrical response in the playback system is more likely to be wrong than right, particularly if the loudspeaker systems used for playback are able to deliver nearly flat acoustical power output and are adjusted to do so.

ACKNOWLEDGMENT

We are grateful to Bolt Beranek and Newman, Cambridge, Mass., for the concert-hall reverberant field spectral data in Fig. 17.

REFERENCE

[1] L. L. Beranek, *Acoustics* (McGraw-Hill, New York, 1954), ch. 10.

THE AUTHORS

Roy F. Allison has been Editor of *Radio Communication, TV and Radio Engineering, Communication Engineering,* and *Audiocraft* magazines, as well as Audio Editor for *High Fidelity* magazine. Since 1959 he has been with Acoustic Research, Cambridge, Mass., first as Chief Engineer, then as Plant Manager. Since 1967 he has held the title of Vice President.

Robert Berkovitz came to the sound industry from Encyclopaedia Britannica in 1956 and had served since then in product development and marketing posts at Allied Radio Corporation, Dynaco, Jensen, and Acoustic Research. He has written frequently for consumer and technical publications on various aspects of music reproduction, and was responsible for the Acoustic Research Contemporary Music Project. He is now at Dolby Laboratories in London, England.

Modulation Distortion in Loudspeakers: Part III*

PAUL W. KLIPSCH

Klipsch and Associates, Inc., Hope, Ark. 71801

Distortion in loudspeakers is shown to be nearly proportional to power output. Typically a plot of log distortion versus dB output shows a 1:1 relation. In one sample loudspeaker the slope of the distortion versus output curve was in excess of 45 degrees. Comparison is shown between a direct radiator of 20-cm (8-in) diameter, one of 30-cm (12-in) diameter, and a high-efficiency horn of 0.45 m³ (16 ft³). At 95-dB sound pressure level output measured at 61 cm (2 ft) the 12-cm cone showed 18% (—15 dB ref 100%), the 30-cm cone showed 6% (—25 dB ref 100%), and the horn showed 0.8% (—42 dB ref 100%). Each curve of distortion versus output shows a slope of at least 45 degrees.

INTRODUCTION: In the popular "hi fi" press it has been stated that distortion in loudspeakers increases only slightly with power. Intuition or common sense dictate that this is a fallacy. Since intuition and especially common sense are rare in the "high fidelity" art, tests were conducted to support the intuitive logic that dictates distortion to be proportional to loudspeaker power output.

EXPERIMENTAL PROCEDURE

The spectrum analyzer was employed to determine harmonic distortion at different output levels and the modulation distortion resulting from a mixture of two frequencies. Three loudspeaker samples were used as tabulated in Table I.

Test frequencies of $f_1 = 41$ Hz and $f_2 = 350$ Hz were chosen, since in each case these frequencies would be radiated from the same bass diaphragm. The horn system crossover is 400 Hz. Of course, use of 41 and 1300 Hz would have resulted in substantially zero distortion for the horn, and very high first-order distortion for the direct radiators.

* Presented in part May 5, 1972, at the 42nd Convention of the Audio Engineering Society, Los Angeles. Parts I and II appeared in this *Journal,* vol. 17, pp. 194-206 (Apr. 1969) and vol. 18, pp. 29-33 (Feb. 1970).

In the case of the 30-cm speaker and the horn, equal sound pressure levels were used for the two frequencies. In the case of the 12-cm speaker, the amplitude of the higher frequency was 6 dB lower than the amplitude of the lower frequency.

In each case, harmonic distortion of f_1 varied only slightly with presence or absence of f_2, and in all cases the harmonics of f_1 were smaller than the sideband amplitudes of $f_2 \pm f_1$ and $f_2 \pm 2f_1$.

Since harmonic distortion contributed negligibly to the total distortion, and it was desired to plot a single value of distortion versus power, the total rms value of all significant sideband amplitudes was computed and plotted in dB.

Table I.

Sample Number	1 Direct Radiator	2 Direct Radiator	3 Large Horn
Basket diameter	30.5 cm (12 in)	20 cm (8 in)	
"Effective" cone diameter	23 cm (9 in)	16 cm (6.5 in)	
"Rigid" cone diameter	20 cm (8 in)	15 cm (6 in)	
Total bulk (approximately)	40 000 cm³ (1.5 ft³)	30 000 cm³ (1 ft³)	0.45 m³

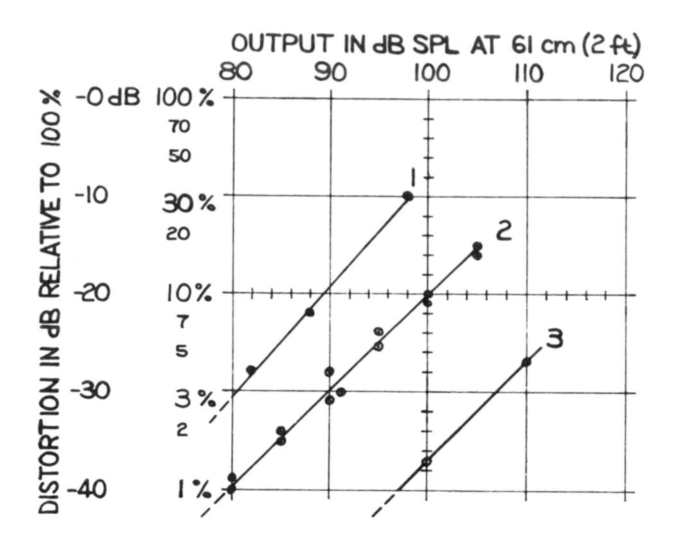

Fig. 1. Distortion versus output for 3 loudspeakers. Total distortion is mainly modulation (IM) resulting from mixture of $f_1 = 41$ Hz, $f_2 = 350$ Hz; harmonic distortion was from 7 to 10 dB lower than IM distortion in all cases. Curve 1—20-cm (8-in) direct-radiator loudspeaker in 30 000-cm^3 box (1 ft^3); peak power input at 98-dB output was 57 watts (limit of loudspeaker); curve 2—30-cm (12-in) direct-radiator loudspeaker in 40 000-cm^3 box (1.5 ft^3); peak power input at 105-dB output was 179 watts (limit of amplifier); curve 3—large-horn woofer, total bulk 0.45 m^3 (16 ft^3); peak power input at 110-dB output was 13 watts; no attempt was made to reach limits of either loudspeaker or amplifier.

Fig. 1 gives the rms distortion in dB (referred to 100% of the amplitude of the modulated frequency), plotted versus power output measured at 61 cm (2 ft).

RELATIVE IMPORTANCE OF AM, FM, AND HARMONIC DISTORTION

There are those who contend that Doppler (frequency modulation) distortion is inconsequential, the reasoning being based on the small frequency deviation which occurs. Using the example of a diaphragm excursion of 6 mm (¼ in) at 50 Hz, the displacement would be

$$x = \frac{1}{4} \sin (2\pi \times 50t)$$

and the velocity

$$v = \frac{1}{4} \times 2\pi \times 50 \cos (2\pi \times 50t)$$

$$v_{\text{peak}} = 200 \text{ cm/s (79 in/s)}.$$

Since the velocity of sound is $c = 344$ m/sec (13 500 in/s), the frequency deviation of a higher frequency being radiated from the same diaphragm would be only

$$\Delta v/c = 79/13\,500 = 0.0058$$

or a trifle over ½%. But the amplitudes of the sideband frequencies are known to be [1]

$$d = 0.033\, A_1 f_2 \quad (\%)$$

where A_1 is the amplitude of the motion at the lower frequency f_1 taken in the example as ¼ in, f_2 is the frequency of the modulated signal, and d is the rms sum of the sideband amplitudes expressed in percent of the amplitude of the higher frequency signal. Assuming $f_2 = 350$ Hz, then

$$d = 2.9\%$$

which may not be impressively large, but experiments show that it is plainly audible.

Then the critics of FM distortion fail to realize that AM distortion is frequently larger than FM distortion.

In the case of the 20-cm (8-in) direct-radiator cone the performance of which is depicted as curve 1 in Fig. 1, the AM component exceeded the FM component of total IM distortion. The maximum total IM distortion in the 20-cm cone was nearly 30%, of which only about 5% could be accounted for by the FM components.

Devotees of direct-radiator speakers view with alarm the high throat pressures in horns which allegedly produce high harmonic distortion [2], [3]. In the case of the horn (distortion depicted in curve 3, Fig. 1) harmonic distortion was 9 dB below the curve of total distortion.

DISCUSSION

Note that 80-dB output, and 1% distortion or 40 dB below 100% together represent a distortion output of 40-dB sound pressure level. The noise level in the test room, unweighted, was nearly 50 dB. If the analyzer had not been highly selective, measurements could not have been made down to 40 dB. As it was, determinations below −40 dB ref 100% entailed careful examination of the spectrograms to distinguish between noise and an almost vague glitch identifiably due to a sideband amplitude. It is submitted that the reviewers who felt that distortion increased only slightly with power were working at too low a level and were probably reading the output on a meter instead of a scope so that distortion and noise were indistinguishable. Obviously below the noise level the distortion plus noise will be constant and the ratio of distortion plus noise would first flatten and then assume a negative slope. While this is expressed as an opinion, it seems to be supportable.

CONCLUSION

The fact of the case is that distortion is closely proportional to power output. Also the distortion is closely proportional to diaphragm excursion. The 30-cm direct-radiator cone had to move about ⅓ as far as the 20-cm direct-radiator cone for the same output, and the distortion was close to 10 dB lower. The horn diaphragm motion was too small to be measured but could be estimated to be about ⅛ that of the 30-cm cone, so the 17-dB difference in distortion is the right order of magnitude.

REFERENCES

[1] G. L. Beers and H. Belar, "Frequency Modulation Distortion in Loudspeakers," *Proc. IRE*, vol. 31, pp. 132-138 (Apr. 1943).

[2] A. L. Thuras, R. T. Jenkins, and H. T. O'Neil, "Extraneous Frequencies Generated in an Air Carrying Intense Sound Pressure," *J. Acoust. Soc. Am.*, vol. 6, pp. 173-180 (Jan. 1935).

[3] S. Goldstein and N. W. McLachlan, "Sound Waves of Finite Amplitude in an Exponential Horn," *J. Acoust. Soc. Am.*, vol. 6, pp. 275-278 (Apr. 1935).

Note: Mr. Klipsch's biography appeared in the October 1972 issue.

Direct-Radiator Loudspeaker System Analysis*

RICHARD H. SMALL

School of Electrical Engineering, University of Sydney, Sydney, N. S. W., Australia

The low-frequency performance of direct-radiator loudspeaker systems can be accurately specified and is quantitatively related to the basic parameters of the system components. These systems function at low frequencies as low-efficiency electroacoustic high-pass filters; the frequency-dependent behavior is described by rational polynomial functions whose coefficients contain basic component parameters. These basic parameters, which are simple to evaluate, determine the system low-frequency response, efficiency, and power ratings.

Editor's Note:

This is the first of a series of papers by R. H. Small which will have a long-term impact on direct-radiator loudspeaker theory. This paper is mainly concerned with terminology, definitions, and setting a thorough background for the following papers on specific kinds of loudspeaker systems.

The work on efficiency, power considerations, and large-signal effects is the most accurate that I know of. The appendix contains the only derivation I know of in print for Thiele's methods of driver-parameter measurement.

J. R. Ashley

* Reprinted with permission from *IEEE Transections on Audio and Electroacoustics*, vol. AU-19, pp. 269-281 (Dec. 1971).

GLOSSARY OF SYMBOLS

B	magnetic flux density in driver air gap
c	velocity of sound in air ($=345$ m/s)
C_{AB}	acoustic compliance of air in enclosure
C_{AP}	acoustic compliance of passive radiator suspension
C_{AS}	acoustic compliance of driver suspension
C_{MS}	mechanical compliance of driver suspension ($=C_{AS}/S_D^2$)
C_{MES}	electrical capacitance due to driver mass ($=M_{AS}S_D^2/B^2l^2$)
e_g	open-circuit output voltage of source
f	natural frequency variable
f_{CT}	resonance frequency of driver in closed test box
f_S	resonance frequency of driver
$G(s)$	response function
k_x	system displacement constant
l	length of voice-coil conductor in magnetic field

L_{CES} electrical inductance due to driver compliance ($=C_{AS}B^2l^2/S_D^2$)

M_{ACT} acoustic mass of driver in closed test box including air load

M_{AP} acoustic mass of port or passive radiator including air load

M_{AS} acoustic mass of driver diaphragm assembly including air load

M_{MS} mechanical mass of driver diaphragm assembly including air load ($=M_{AS}S_D^2$)

P_A acoustic output power

P_{AR} displacement-limited acoustic power rating

P_E nominal electrical input power

P_{ER} displacement-limited electrical power rating

$P_{E(max)}$ thermally limited maximum input power

Q ratio of reactance to resistance (series circuit) or resistance to reactance (parallel circuit)

Q_E Q of driver at f_S considering system electrical resistance ($R_g + R_E$) only

Q_{ECT} Q of driver at f_{CT} considering electrical resistance R_E only

Q_{ES} Q of driver at f_S considering electrical resistance R_E only

Q_M Q of driver at f_S considering system nonelectrical resistances only

Q_{MCT} Q of driver at f_{CT} considering nonelectrical resistances only

Q_{MS} Q of driver at f_S considering driver nonelectrical resistances only

Q_T total Q of driver at f_S including all system resistances

R_{AB} acoustic resistance of enclosure losses due to internal energy absorption

R_{AL} acoustic resistance of enclosure losses due to leakage

R_{AP} acoustic resistance of port or passive radiator losses

R_{AS} acoustic resistance of driver suspension losses

R_{AT} acoustic resistance of total driver-circuit losses

R_E dc resistance of driver voice coil

R_{ES} electrical resistance due to driver suspension losses ($=B^2l^2/S_D^2R_{AS}$)

R_g output resistance of source or amplifier

R_{MS} mechanical resistance of driver suspension losses ($= R_{AS}S_D^2$)

$\mathcal{R}_{AR}$ acoustic radiation resistance

s complex frequency variable ($=\sigma + j\omega$)

S_D effective projected surface area of driver diaphragm

T time constant ($=1/2\pi f$)

u linear velocity

U volume velocity

V_{AS} volume of air having same acoustic compliance as driver suspension ($=\rho_0 c^2 C_{AS}$)

V_D peak displacement volume of driver diaphragm ($=S_D x_{max}$)

x linear displacement

x_{max} peak displacement limit of driver diaphragm

$X(s)$ driver diaphragm displacement function

$Z_{VC}(s)$ voice-coil impedance function

η efficiency

η_0 reference efficiency

ρ_0 density of air ($=1.18$ kg/m^3)

$\sigma_{x(P)}$ static displacement sensitivity of unenclosed driver expressed in meters per watt$^{1/2}$

ω radian frequency variable ($=2\pi f$)

INTRODUCTION: It is quite possible that the vagueness which infuses many discussions of loudspeakers has its roots in the chaotic terminology of the subject. The word "loudspeaker" itself long ago lost any specific meaning. Despite conflicting attempts by various nationalities to define it as a driver unit or as a complete system, the word retains value only as a general term and as an adjective. For the sake of clarity, this paper uses the common but more specific terms below.

A *source* is a device, usually an electronic power amplifier, which supplies electrical energy at a specified voltage or power level.

A loudspeaker *driver* is a transducer mechanism which converts electrical energy into mechanical and/or acoustical energy. The most common type of driver and the one dealt with in this paper is the moving-coil or electrodynamic driver consisting of a voice coil located in a permanently magnetized air gap and attached to a suspended diaphragm or "cone."

A *baffle* is a structure used to support a driver and to reduce or prevent cancellation of radiation from the front of the driver diaphragm by antiphase radiation from the rear.

An *enclosure* is a cabinet or box in which a driver is mounted for the purpose of radiating sound. The enclosure forms a closed geometrical surface except for the driver mounting aperture or other specified apertures.

A loudspeaker *system* is the combination of a driver (or drivers) with a structural radiation aid such as a horn, baffle, or enclosure which is used to convert electrical energy from a specified source into sound.

A *direct-radiator loudspeaker system* is a loudspeaker system which couples acoustical energy directly to the air from the driver diaphragm and/or simple enclosure apertures without the use of horns or other acoustical impedance-matching devices.

The *piston range* of a loudspeaker driver is that range of frequencies for which the wavelength of sound is longer than the driver diaphragm circumference. In this frequency range, a direct-radiator system using the driver in an enclosure will have an acoustic output which is essentially nondirectional.

Loudspeaker System Design

Direct-radiator loudspeaker systems have been in use for about half a century. During this time, much knowledge of the behavioral properties of various types of direct-radiator systems has been accumulated, but this knowledge is still uneven and incomplete. For example, closed-box systems are much better understood than vented-box systems, while quantitative design information for passive-radiator systems cannot be found in published form.

The design of a loudspeaker system is traditionally a trial-and-error process guided by experience: a likely driver is chosen and various enclosure designs are tried until the system performance is found to be satisfactory. In sharp contrast to this empirical design process is the synthesis of many other engineering systems. This begins with the desired system performance specifications and leads directly to specification of system components.

The latter approach requires the engineer to have precise knowledge of the relationships between system performance and component specifications. The method of analysis described in this paper is a means of obtaining this knowledge for the low-frequency performance of all types of direct-radiator loudspeaker systems; it is based on the high-pass-filter behavior of these systems.

Loudspeaker System Sensitivity and Efficiency

An ideal microphone converts sound pressure into voltage with equal sensitivity at all frequencies. Recording and reproducing systems are designed to process signal voltages representing sound pressure without distortion. To complete the sound reproduction process, an ideal loudspeaker system should convert voltage into sound pressure with equal sensitivity at all frequencies.

In practice, all loudspeaker systems have limited bandwidth. In the low-frequency region, they act as high-pass filters. The low-frequency design of a loudspeaker system may thus be regarded as the design of a high-pass filter [1], [2]. The principal difference is that the loudspeaker system designer has very limited control over the "circuit" configuration; his design freedom is limited to obtaining the best possible performance by manipulation of the system component values.

The frequency response of an electrical filter is normally described in terms of a dimensionless voltage or power ratio. Because a loudspeaker system is a transducer, its sensitivity versus frequency response is the ratio of two unlike quantities, sound pressure and voltage. However, the loudspeaker system response can also be defined in terms of a dimensionless power ratio which is proportional to the square of the above sensitivity ratio.

In the frequency range for which the system radiation is nondirectional, the free-field sound pressure at a fixed distance is proportional to the square root of the acoustic power radiated by the system [3, p. 189]. The electrical power delivered into a fixed resistance by the source is proportional to the square of the source output voltage. Thus the ratio of *the actual system acoustic output power* to *the electrical power delivered into a fixed resistance by the same source* represents exactly the square of the system sensitivity ratio (i.e., the system frequency response), except for a constant factor. If the fixed resistance is chosen to fairly represent the input impedance of the loudspeaker system, the value of the power ratio in the system passband is the nominal electroacoustic conversion efficiency of the system.

This method of defining loudspeaker efficiency is quite similar in principle to the power available efficiency definition used by Beranek [3, p. 190] in that both reveal the exact frequency response of the system. The principal advantage of the method used here is that the calculated passband efficiency of the system is independent of generator output resistance and realistically relates the acoustic power capability of the system to the electrical power rating of its source.

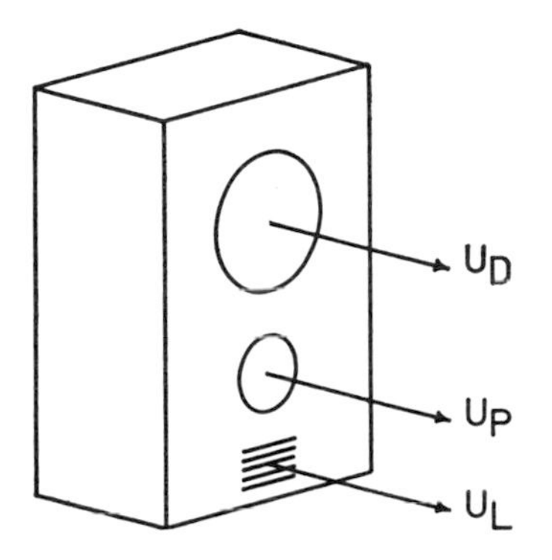

Fig. 1. Generalized direct-radiator loudspeaker system.

SMALL-SIGNAL PERFORMANCE RELATIONSHIPS

Acoustic Output Power

A generalized direct-radiator loudspeaker system [4, Fig. 1] is illustrated in Fig. 1. The system enclosure has apertures for a driver, a port (or passive radiator), and leakage. Electrical input to the driver produces air movement at the driver diaphragm, port, and leak; this air movement is shown in Fig. 1 as the acoustic volume velocities U_D, U_P, and U_L.

At very low frequencies, where the dimensions of and spacings between the enclosure apertures are much less than a wavelength, the system can be regarded as a combination of coincident simple sources [3, p. 93]. The acoustic output is thus nondirectional and is equivalent to that of a single simple source having a strength U_0 equal to the vector sum of the individual aperture volume velocities, i.e.,

$$U_0 = U_D + U_P + U_L. \qquad (1)$$

The acoustic power radiated by the system is then

$$P_A = |U_0|^2 \mathcal{R}_{AR} \qquad (2)$$

where

P_A acoustic output power
$\mathcal{R}_{AR}$ resistive part of radiation load on system.

Eq. (2) is generally valid to the upper limit of the driver piston range because the driver is normally the only significant radiator at frequencies high enough for the aperture spacings to become important.

In a recent paper [5], Allison and Berkovitz have demonstrated that the low-frequency load on a loudspeaker system in a typical listening room is essentially that for one side of a piston mounted in an infinite baffle. The resistive part of this radiation load [3, p. 216] is

$$\mathcal{R}_{AR} = \rho_0 \omega^2/(2\pi c) \qquad (3)$$

where

ρ_0 density of air
ω steady-state radian frequency
c velocity of sound in air.

Eq. (3) is valid only in the system piston range, but within this range the value of $\mathcal{R}_{AR}$ is independent of the size of the enclosure or its apertures.

Because mass cannot be created or stored at the en-

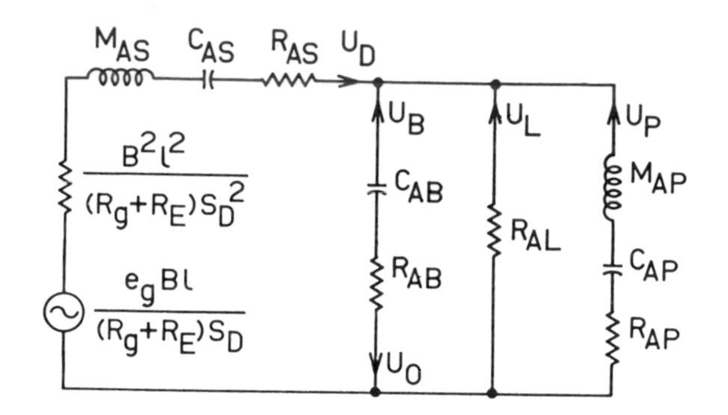

Fig. 2. Acoustical analogous circuit of generalized direct-radiator loudspeaker system.

closure boundaries, and because the sound pressure is normally much less than the atmosphere pressure, conservation of mass requires that

$$U_0 = -U_B \tag{4}$$

where U_B is the total volume velocity entering the enclosure. Eq. (4) holds even if the enclosure is internally divided. If the enclosure contains several cavities, then

$$U_B = U_{B1} + U_{B2} + U_{B3} + \cdots, \tag{5}$$

where each term on the right-hand side of Eq. (5) represents the net volume velocity entering each individual cavity.

Eqs. (1), (4), and (5) are general and hold for any number of cavities and apertures and any interconnection of these. They are vector equations which require that the relative phase of the various components be taken into account.

Although Eq. (4) is very simple, it is of key importance in the analysis of direct-radiator loudspeaker systems using an enclosure. In combination with Eq. (2), it reveals that the acoustic power radiated by the system is directly related to the volume velocity compressing and expanding air within the enclosure. This fact has been noted for bass-reflex enclosures by Beranek [3, p. 244], de Boer [1], and others; it is equally true for *all* direct-radiator system enclosures [4, eq. (72) ff].

Electrical Input Power

The nominal electrical input power to a loudspeaker system is defined here as the power delivered by the source into a resistor having the same value as the driver voice-coil resistance [2, eq. (10)]. Thus

$$P_E = \left[\frac{e_g}{R_g + R_E} \right]^2 R_E \tag{6}$$

where

P_E	nominal electrical input power
e_g	open-circuit output voltage of source
R_g	output resistance of source
R_E	dc resistance of driver voice coil.

The value of R_E is typically about 80% of the rated driver voice-coil impedance.

American [6], British [7], and international [8] standards make use of variously defined rating impedances in calculating the nominal input power to a loudspeaker driver. Because the calculated acoustic output power of the system depends on R_E and not on the fictitious rating impedance, the definition used here simplifies the expression for theoretical system efficiency derived below. This difference must be remembered if the computed piston-range reference efficiency of a system is to be compared with the efficiency measured according to the methods of one of the above standards.

EFFICIENCY

From Eqs. (2) and (6), the nominal power transfer ratio or efficiency η of a loudspeaker system is

$$\eta = \frac{P_A}{P_E} = |U_0|^2 \mathcal{R}_{AR} \frac{(R_g + R_E)^2}{e_g^2 R_E}. \tag{7}$$

The evaluation of this efficiency expression for a given system requires a knowledge of the relationship between U_0 and e_g. This relationship is found by examining the acoustical circuit of the system.

The development of acoustical circuits is described in excellent detail by Olson [9] and Beranek [3, ch. 3]. Fig. 2 is the impedance-type acoustical analogous circuit for the generalized loudspeaker system of Fig. 1 [4, Fig. 15]. In Fig. 2,

B	magnetic flux density in driver air gap
l	length of voice-coil conductor in magnetic field of air gap
S_D	effective projected surface area of driver diaphragm
M_{AS}	acoustic mass of driver diaphragm assembly including voice coil and air load
C_{AS}	acoustic compliance of driver suspension
R_{AS}	acoustic resistance of driver suspension losses
C_{AB}	acoustic compliance of air in enclosure
R_{AB}	acoustic resistance of enclosure losses due to internal energy absorption
R_{AL}	acoustic resistance of enclosure losses due to leakage
M_{AP}	acoustic mass of port or passive radiator including air load
C_{AP}	acoustic compliance of passive radiator suspension
R_{AP}	acoustic resistance of port or passive radiator losses.

Starting from the circuit of Fig. 2, the acoustical analogous circuits of most common direct-radiator systems can be obtained by removing or short-circuiting appropriate elements. Note that for the analogy used in this circuit, voltages represent acoustic pressures and currents

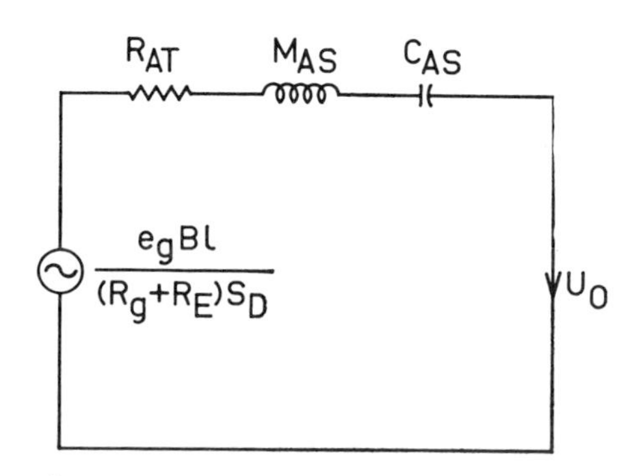

Fig. 3. Acoustical analogous circuit of infinite-baffle loudspeaker system.

represent volume velocities. The method of obtaining the system efficiency expression from analysis of the system acoustical circuit is illustrated below for the simple infinite-baffle system.

The acoustical analogous circuit of an infinite-baffle loudspeaker system is derived from the general circuit of Fig. 2 by removing the branches representing the passive radiator and enclosure leakage and short-circuiting the branch representing the interior of the enclosure to make the enclosure dissipation zero and the enclosure compliance infinite. The resulting circuit is shown in Fig. 3. A simplification has been made in this circuit by combining the remaining series resistances to form the total acoustic resistance

$$R_{AT} = R_{AS} + \frac{B^2 l^2}{(R_g + R_E) S_D^2}. \tag{8}$$

From circuit analysis of Fig. 3,

$$U_0 = \frac{e_g Bl}{(R_g + R_E) S_D s M_{AS}} \cdot G(s) \tag{9}$$

where

$$G(s) = \frac{s^2 C_{AS} M_{AS}}{s^2 C_{AS} M_{AS} + s C_{AS} R_{AT} + 1} \tag{10}$$

and s is the complex frequency variable.

For steady-state sinusoidal excitation $s = j\omega$, and Eqs. (5) and (9) may be combined with Eq. (7) to yield the infinite-baffle efficiency expression

$$\eta(j\omega) = \frac{\rho_0}{2\pi c} \frac{B^2 l^2}{R_E S_D^2 M_{AS}^2} |G(j\omega)|^2 \tag{11}$$

where $G(j\omega)$ is $G(s)$ from Eq. (10) with $s = j\omega$. Note that $G(j\omega)$ contains all the frequency-dependent terms of Eq. 11); the remainder of the expression contains only physical, numerical, and driver constants.

The last part of Eq. (11), i.e., the squared magnitude of $G(j\omega)$, is the infinite-baffle system frequency response expressed as a normalized power ratio. The normalized ratio of sound pressure to source voltage, i.e., the normalized sensitivity or sound pressure frequency response, is thus simply $|G(j\omega)|$; it can be seen from Eq. (10) that this is a second-order (12-dB per octave cutoff) high-pass filter function.

For any direct-radiator system using an enclosure, the expressions for total volume velocity and efficiency have the same form as Eqs. (9) and (11); only the function $G(s)$ is different for each system.

The system response function $G(s)$ contains complete information about the amplitude and phase versus frequency responses and the transient response of the system. $G(s)$ is always a high-pass filter function with a value of unity in the passband. Thus the constant part of Eq. (11) is the system passband efficiency.

ASSUMPTIONS AND APPROXIMATIONS

The acoustical analogous circuits of Figs. 2 and 3 are valid only for frequencies within the piston range of the driver; the circuit components are assumed to have values which are independent of frequency within this range.

Circuit elements which do not contribute enough impedance to affect the analysis are neglected. One of these elements is the radiation resistance. Although this resistance is responsible for the radiated power and is therefore included in Eq. (2), it is in fact quite small compared to the other impedances in the acoustical circuit [2, p. 489]. This is fortunate for purposes of analysis because the radiation resistance is not constant but varies with frequency squared. Also neglected is the driver voice-coil inductance which usually has negligible effects in the limited frequency range of this analysis.

The treatment of acoustical masses is simplified by adding together all masses appearing in series in the same branch of the analogous circuit. This means that physical and air-load masses are lumped together. While the resulting total mass is essentially constant with frequency, it may vary, in the case of the driver, with mounting location or mounting conditions. This must be remembered when dealing with the actual system and measuring its parameters.

SMALL-SIGNAL PARAMETERS

The response function and other describing equations of a loudspeaker system generally contain driver, enclosure, and source parameters. Knowledge of these relationships for a particular system is of practical use only if the parameter values are known or can be measured.

One key to the identification and measurement of the system parameters lies in the system electrical equivalent circuit. This is the dual of the system acoustical analogous circuit and may be derived from it; its formation is well explained in [9] and [3, ch. 3]. Once the circuit is determined, straightforward circuit analysis yields the relationship between the impedance measured at the voice-coil terminals of the actual system and the physical components which constitute the system. It is thus possible to determine the system parameters from measurement of the voice-coil circuit impedance.

Driver Parameters

The fundamental electromechanical driver parameters which control system small-signal performance are R_E, (Bl), S_D, C_{MS}, M_{MS}, and R_{MS}, where

- C_{MS} mechanical compliance of driver suspension $(= C_{AS}/S_D^2)$
- M_{MS} mechanical mass of driver diaphragm assembly including voice coil and air load $(= M_{AS} S_D^2)$
- R_{MS} mechanical resistance of driver suspension losses $(= R_{AS} S_D^2)$.

These parameters are fundamental because each can be set independently of the others, and each has some effect on the system small-signal performance.

For purposes of analysis and design, it is advantageous to describe the driver in terms of the four basic parameters used by Thiele [2] which are related to those above but are easier to measure and to work with. These are as follows.

- f_S resonance frequency of moving system of driver, defined by Eq. (12) and usually specified for driver in air with no baffle (f_{SA}) or on a specified baffle (f_{SB})

V_{AS} acoustic compliance of driver, expressed as an equivalent volume of air according to Eq. (15)

Q_{MS} ratio of driver electrical equivalent frictional resistance to reflected motional reactance at f_S, defined by Eq. (13).

Q_{ES} ratio of voice-coil dc resistance to reflected motional reactance at f_S, defined by Eq. (14).

The parameters Q_{MS} and Q_{ES} correspond to Thiele's Q_a and Q_e. They have been given the extra subscript S to make it clear that they apply to the driver alone and to prevent confusion with the *system* parameters Q_M and Q_E, corresponding to Thiele's Q_a and Q_e (total), defined at the end of this section.

Driver Electrical Equivalent Circuit

The electrical equivalent circuit of a driver in air or mounted on an infinite baffle is shown in Fig. 4. In this circuit,

C_{MES} electrical capacitance due to driver mass ($= M_{AS}S_D^2/B^2l^2$)

L_{CES} electrical inductance due to driver compliance ($= C_{AS}B^2l^2/S_D^2$)

R_{ES} electrical resistance due to driver suspension losses ($= B^2l^2/S_D^2R_{AS}$).

The circuit of Fig. 4 is the dual of Fig. 3. An important difference is that the real voice-coil terminals are available in Fig. 4.

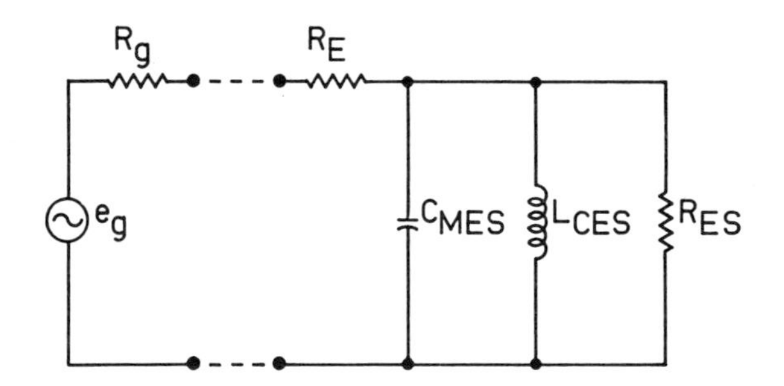

Fig. 4. Electrical equivalent circuit of moving-coil electrodynamic driver.

In Fig. 4, the driver reactances form a resonant circuit which has a resonance frequency $\omega_S = 2\pi f_S$, or a characteristic time constant T_S, given by

$$T_S^2 = 1/\omega_S^2 = C_{MES}L_{CES} = C_{AS}M_{AS}. \quad (12)$$

The Q of the driver resonant circuit with R_{ES} acting alone is

$$Q_{MS} = \omega_S C_{MES}R_{ES} = 1/(\omega_S C_{AS}R_{AS}). \quad (13)$$

Similarly, the Q with R_E acting alone, i.e., with $R_g = 0$, is

$$Q_{ES} = \omega_S C_{MES}R_E = \omega_S R_E M_{AS}S_D^2/(B^2l^2). \quad (14)$$

The parameter V_{AS} is a volume of air having the same acoustic compliance as the driver suspension. Thus [3, p. 129]

$$V_{AS} = \rho_0 c^2 C_{AS}. \quad (15)$$

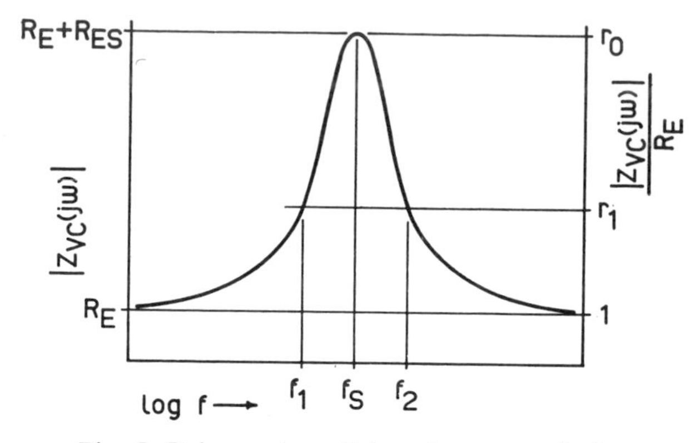

Fig. 5. Driver voice-coil impedance magnitude.

Driver Voice-Coil Impedance Function

The impedance of the circuit to the right of the voice-coil terminals in Fig. 4 is

$$Z_{VC}(s) = R_E + R_{ES}\left[\frac{sT_S/Q_{MS}}{s^2T_S^2 + sT_S/Q_{MS} + 1}\right]. \quad (16)$$

The steady-state magnitude $|Z_{VC}(j\omega)|$ of Eq. (16) is plotted in Fig. 5; this has the form of a resonance curve which is displaced upward by an amount R_E.

Measurement of Driver Parameters

If the voice-coil impedance of an actual driver is plotted against frequency with the driver in air or on a simple test baffle, the resulting plot will have the same shape as Fig. 5. The driver resonance frequency f_S is easily located where the measured impedance is a maximum. If the ratio of the maximum voice-coil impedance to the dc resistance R_E is defined as r_0, and the two frequencies $f_1 < f_S$ and $f_2 > f_S$ are found where the impedance magnitude is $\sqrt{r_0}R_E$, then as shown in the Appendix,

$$Q_{MS} = \frac{f_S\sqrt{r_0}}{f_2 - f_1} \quad (17)$$

and

$$Q_{ES} = \frac{Q_{MS}}{r_0 - 1}. \quad (18)$$

To obtain the value of V_{AS}, a known compliance is added to the moving system by mounting the driver in a small unlined test box which is closed except for the driver aperture. The above driver parameters are then remeasured and values obtained for the new resonance frequency f_{CT} and the electrical Q, Q_{ECT}. Then, as shown in the Appendix,

$$V_{AS} = V_T\left[\frac{f_{CT}Q_{ECT}}{f_SQ_{ES}} - 1\right] \quad (19)$$

where V_T is the net internal volume of the test box.

Source Parameters

The amplifier specifications that affect the small-signal performance of a loudspeaker system are frequency response and output resistance.

The frequency response of a good audio amplifier is usually wider and flatter than that of the loudspeaker system, and thus the frequency response function obtained from the system efficiency expression effectively describes the overall low-frequency response from the amplifier input terminals. The overall response may be modified or adjusted if desired by the addition to the amplifier of supplementary electrical filters [2].

The amplifier output resistance R_g is in series with the driver voice-coil resistance R_E and therefore affects the system behavior by influencing the total Q in the driver branch. Most modern amplifiers are designed to have a high damping factor, which means that R_g is made small compared to any expected value of R_E. This condition is usually assumed in the design of general-purpose loudspeaker systems, and the driver parameters are adjusted to give the required total Q.

If an amplifier and loudspeaker system are designed as a unit, extra design freedom may be gained by adjusting R_g to provide the desired total Q. Using suitable feedback techniques, R_g may be made positive, zero, or negative.

Measurement of Amplifier Source Resistance

The value of R_g may be found by driving the amplifier with a sinusoidal signal and measuring the amplifier output voltage under conditions of no load and rated load. If the no-load output voltage is e_0, the loaded output voltage is e_L, and the load resistance is R_L, then

$$R_g = R_L \frac{e_0 - e_L}{e_L}. \tag{20}$$

If there is no measurable difference between e_0 and e_L, R_g may be considered zero as far as its effect on total Q is concerned. Accurate measurement is not required in this case, as it is the *total* resistance $(R_g + R_E)$ that is important.

Amplifier specifications often give the value of R_g (or the damping factor for rated load) measured at 1 kHz. For purposes of calculating system Q at low frequencies, the value measured at 50 Hz is more meaningful.

Enclosure Parameters

The enclosure parameters vary in number according to the type of system. Referring to Fig. 2, all of the vertical branches on the right of the figure contain enclosure components.

The most important property of the enclosure is its physical volume V_B which determines the compliance C_{AB}. If the component M_{AP} is present in the system, with or without C_{AP}, the enclosure will exhibit a resonance frequency f_B (or time constant T_B). If C_{AP} is present, an additional resonance frequency f_P (or time constant T_P) is introduced. The enclosure or aperture losses may be accounted for by defining Q for the various branches at specified frequencies (f_B or f_P).

Measurement of Enclosure Parameters

In general, the change in the driver voice-coil impedance which occurs when the driver is placed in the enclosure permits identification of the enclosure parameters. Because the relationships are different for every type of enclosure, they are not presented here but will be included in later papers describing each type of system.

Composite System Parameters

In the analysis of direct-radiator loudspeaker systems, certain combinations of the component parameters occur naturally, and consistently, in the system-describing functions. One of these is the ratio of driver compliance to enclosure compliance C_{AS}/C_{AB}. This parameter, the *system compliance ratio*, is of fundamental importance to direct-radiator systems using an enclosure. It appears in the analyses published by Beranek [3, ch. 8] and Thiele [2], and in the equivalent stiffness ratio form S_B/S_S used by Novak [10]. The importance of this parameter to system performance justifies giving it a simplified symbol; in later papers the symbol α introduced by Benson [4, eq. (91)] will be used.

In tuned-enclosure systems, the frequency ratio f_B/f_S occurs naturally in the analysis. This is the *system tuning ratio*; Novak [10] has given it the symbol h.

In every type of system, the driver parameter Q_{ES} is altered by the presence of the source parameter R_g to form a system parameter

$$Q_E = Q_{ES} \frac{R_g + R_E}{R_E}. \tag{21}$$

The effective value of $(R_g + R_E)$ includes any significant resistance present in connecting leads and crossover inductors.

Similarly, the driver parameter Q_{MS} is modified if the system acoustical analogous circuit has an acoustic resistance in series with R_{AS}. The new system parameter Q_M is usually found by measurement.

The total Q of the driver branch of the system is then given by a composite system parameter

$$Q_T = \frac{Q_E Q_M}{Q_E + Q_M}. \tag{22}$$

FREQUENCY RESPONSE

Response Function

The response function $G(s)$ of a loudspeaker system may be obtained from the complete efficiency expression as illustrated earlier or by a simpler general method which provides only the response function. In Fig. 6 the acoustical analogous circuit of Fig. 2 is reduced to only four essential components:

p_g acoustic driving pressure given by

$$p_g = \frac{e_g Bl}{(R_g + R_E) S_D} \tag{23}$$

Z_{AS} impedance of driver branch, normally given by

$$Z_{AS}(s) = R_{AT} + sM_{AS} + \frac{1}{sC_{AS}} \tag{24}$$

Z_{AB} impedance of branch representing enclosure interior, normally given by

$$Z_{AB}(s) = R_{AB} + \frac{1}{sC_{AB}} \tag{25}$$

Z_{AA} impedance of all enclosure apertures (except that for the driver) which contribute to total output volume velocity. Note that U_A in Fig.

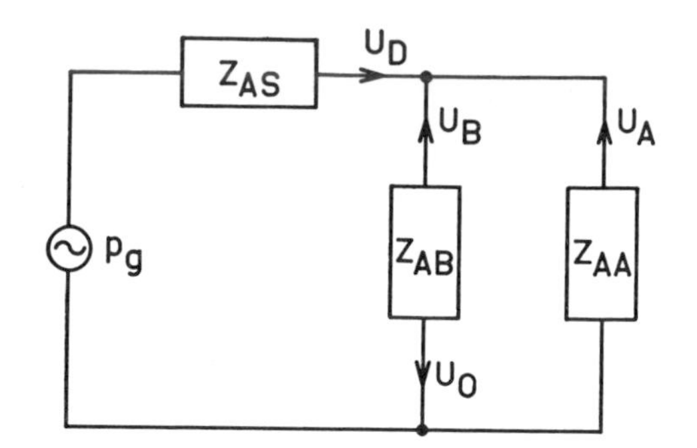

Fig. 6. Simplified acoustical analogous circuit corresponding to Fig. 2.

6 is equal to the sum of U_L and U_P in Fig. 2. Z_{AA} is determined by the specific enclosure design.

The response function is then in all cases

$$G(s) = sM_{AS}\frac{U_0}{p_g} = \frac{sM_{AS}}{Z_{AB}+Z_{AS}+Z_{AB}Z_{AS}/Z_{AA}}. \quad (26)$$

Simplifying the Response Function

The response function obtained from the system acoustical analogous circuit is always a normalized high-pass filter function which is in the form of the ratio of two polynomials in s. The polynomial coefficients contain various combinations of the acoustical masses, compliances, and resistances contained in the system.

The response function is easier to interpret if the acoustical quantities in the coefficients are replaced by the simpler system parameters described in the previous section. Because the coefficients must have dimensions of time only, it is always possible to redefine them in terms of system time constants (or resonance frequencies) together with such dimensionless quantities as Q, compliance ratios, mass ratios, and resistance ratios. These variables are easier for the electrical engineer to interpret than the unfamiliar acoustical quantities.

For the infinite-baffle system analyzed earlier, the response function $G(s)$ is given by Eq. (10). This expression is simplified by substituting

$$T_S{}^2 = C_{AS}M_{AS} \quad (12)$$

and

$$Q_T = 1/(\omega_S C_{AS} R_{AT}) \quad (27)$$

where Q_T is the total Q (at f_S) of the driver connected to the source. This is the same parameter defined for the general case in Eq. (22). Then

$$G(s) = \frac{s^2T_S{}^2}{s^2T_S{}^2 + sT_S/Q_T + 1}. \quad (28)$$

Using the Response Function

Once the system response function is known, the response of any specific system design can be determined if the system parameters are known or are measured so that the corresponding response function coefficients can be calculated. This process is useful in determining the response of existing or proposed systems but gives little insight into the means of improving such systems.

A more useful approach is to explore the behavior of the system response function to determine which coefficient values (i.e., parameter values) produce the most desirable response characteristics. This sounds like a formidable and time-consuming task suitable for computer application, but fortunately the response shapes of greatest interest to the loudspeaker system designer, e.g., those providing flat response in the passband, have already been studied extensively by filter designers.

Because loudspeaker systems have minimum-phase behavior at low frequencies, the amplitude, phase, delay, and transient responses are all related and cannot be specified independently. The most common criterion for optimum response in audio systems is flatness of the amplitude response over a maximum bandwidth, but there may be cases where the designer requires an optimized transient response or delay characteristic. Whatever criterion is used, it is translated into a set of optimum polynomial coefficients so that the system parameter values can be specified or adjusted accordingly.

The adjustment of loudspeaker system response is clearly analogous to the alignment of conventional types of filters. This is particularly apparent where the adjustment goal is the achievement of a predetermined response condition, rather than trial-and-error optimization.

Consider again the infinite-baffle system which has the response function given by Eq. (28). The general form of this class of response function as used by filter designers is

$$G(s) = \frac{s^2T_0{}^2}{s^2T_0{}^2 + a_1sT_0 + 1} \quad (29)$$

where

T_0 nominal filter time constant
a_1 damping, or shape, coefficient.

The behavior of Eq. (29) is well known and thus reveals the behavior of the infinite-baffle system when $T_S = T_0$ and $Q_T = 1/a_1$. Using standard curves for Eq. (29), the steady-state magnitude $|G(j\omega)|$ of Eq. (28) is plotted in Fig. 7 for several values of Q_T. The curve for $Q_T = 0.50$ corresponds to the condition for critical damping of the resonant circuit. The curve for $Q_T = 0.71$ is a maximally flat (Butterworth) alignment which has no amplitude peaking. The curves for $Q_T = 1.0$, 1.4, and 2.0 have amplitude peaks of approximately 1 dB, 3½ dB, and 6 dB, respectively, but provide extensions of half-power bandwidth as compared to the maximally flat alignment.

For this simple system, the design engineer can choose the response shape he desires and specify the system parameters accordingly; he can also see at a glance the effects of parameter tolerances.

REFERENCE EFFICIENCY

The first part of the efficiency expression (11) for a loudspeaker system contains only physical constants and driver parameters, while the last part, the system response function squared, is always unity for the portion of the piston range above system cutoff. Thus the first part of the expression is the passband or reference efficiency of the system. This reference efficiency, designated η_0, is given by

$$\eta_0 = \frac{\rho_0}{2\pi c}\cdot\frac{B^2l^2}{R_E S_D{}^2 M_{AS}{}^2}. \quad (30)$$

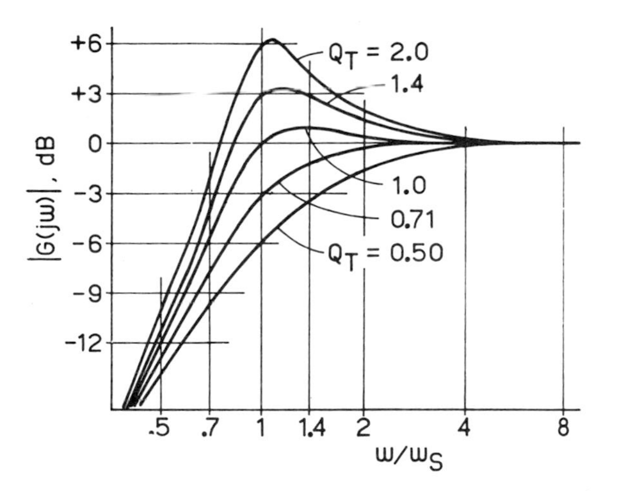

Fig. 7. Normalized frequency response of infinite baffle loudspeaker system.

In terms of the fundamental electromechanical driver parameters, this is

$$\eta_0 = \frac{\rho_0}{2\pi c} \cdot \frac{B^2 l^2}{R_E} \cdot \frac{S_D{}^2}{M_{MS}{}^2}. \quad (31)$$

It must be remembered that M_{AS} and M_{MS} include relevant air-load masses and any deliberate mass loading imposed by the enclosure.

Combining Eqs. (12), (14), and (15) with Eq. (30), the expression for reference efficiency becomes

$$\eta_0 = \frac{4\pi^2}{c^3} \cdot \frac{f_S{}^3 V_{AS}}{Q_{ES}}. \quad (32)$$

The reference efficiency of the system can thus be calculated from the basic driver parameters discussed in Section "Small-Signal Parameters." This result is surprising at first, because these parameters can be determined from simple electrical measurements. This means that the system piston-range electroacoustic efficiency can be found without any direct mechanical, magnetic, or acoustical measurements.

Note that Eq. (32) yields an efficiency twice as large as [2, eq. (76)]. This is because Thiele's expression is derived for the radiation load of a 4π-sr free field, while Eq. (32) assumes the radiation load of a 2π-sr free field. The latter is used here because it is more nearly representative of the radiation load presented to a loudspeaker system by a typical listening room [5].

The physical constants in Eq. (32) have a value of 9.6×10^{-7} in the International System, and this value may be used to compute efficiency if f_S is expressed in hertz and V_{AS} is expressed in cubic meters. However, the value of V_{AS} for most drivers is more conveniently expressed in liters (one liter $= 10^{-3}$ cubic meters). Thus for V_{AS} in liters,

$$\eta_0 = 9.6 \times 10^{-10} \frac{f_S{}^3 V_{AS}}{Q_{ES}}. \quad (33)$$

Alternatively, if V_{AS} is expressed in cubic feet,

$$\eta_0 = 2.7 \times 10^{-8} \frac{f_S{}^3 V_{AS}}{Q_{ES}}. \quad (34)$$

The calculated value of efficiency may be converted into decibels ($10 \log_{10} \eta_0$) or percent ($100\ \eta_0$). The reference efficiency of direct-radiator systems is quite low, typically of the order of one percent.

The resonance frequency of a loudspeaker driver is usually measured with the driver mounted on a standard test baffle having an area of a few square meters [7, sec. 3b], [8, sec. 4.4.1]. Alternatively, some manufacturers prefer to use an effectively infinite baffle, or no baffle at all. Because most drivers are ultimately used in enclosures, the system designer is most interested in the resonance frequency, Q and reference efficiency for an air-load mass equivalent to that of an enclosure; this condition is most nearly approached by a finite "standard" baffle.

If deliberate mass loading of the driver is employed in the system, e.g., placing a restricted aperture in front of the driver, the system reference efficiency will be less than the basic efficiency of the driver. The system efficiency can still be found from Eq. (32) if the values of f_S and Q_{ES} are measured under mass-loaded conditions. The efficiency reduction will be proportional to the square of the mass increase, as shown by Eq. (30).

LARGE-SIGNAL PERFORMANCE

Power Ratings and Large-Signal Parameters

Loudspeaker standards such as [6]–[8] provide only a general guide for the establishment of loudspeaker (driver) power ratings: the input power rating should be such that an amplifier of equivalent undistorted output power rating can be used with the loudspeaker without causing damage or excessive distortion.

At moderately high frequencies, where little diaphragm displacement is required of the driver, the power handling capability of a loudspeaker system is limited by the ability of the driver voice coil to dissipate heat. This leads to a thermally limited absolute maximum input power rating for the *driver*, regardless of the system design. This input power rating is designated $P_{E(max)}$.

At low frequencies much more diaphragm displacement is required of the driver, and it is necessary to establish an input power rating which ensures that the diaphragm is not driven beyond a specified displacement limit. This displacement-limited input power rating is often less than $P_{E(max)}$. Because diaphragm displacement is a function of enclosure design, the displacement-limited power rating is a property of the *system*, not the driver, although it depends on the driver displacement limit.

The displacement limit of a particular driver may be determined by any of a number of criteria. Among these are

1) prevention of suspension damage,
2) limitation of frequency-modulation distortion [11],
3) limitation of nonlinear (harmonic and amplitude-modulation) distortion [12].

For the purpose of this paper it is assumed that a peak displacement limit can be established; this limit is designated x_{max}.

The fundamental large-signal parameter of a driver at low frequencies is then

$$V_D = S_D x_{max}. \quad (35)$$

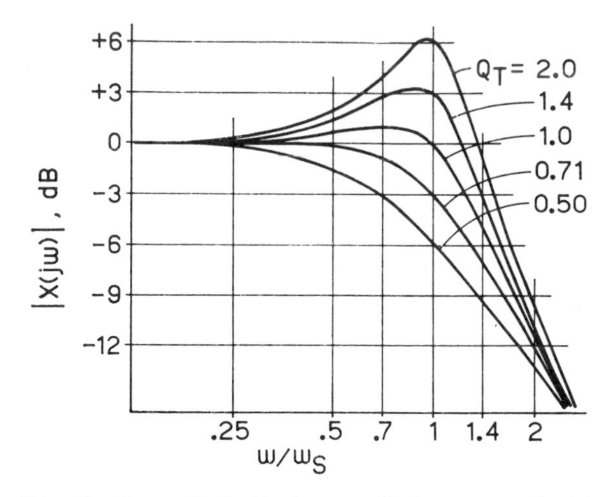

Fig. 8. Normalized diaphragm displacement of driver mounted on infinite baffle.

This parameter, the *diaphragm peak displacement volume,* is the volume of air displaced by the driver diaphragm in moving from rest to its peak displacement limit. It describes the volume displacement limitation and therefore the volume velocity versus frequency limitation of the driver. The practical usefulness of this parameter is illustrated in the following section.

Thus, in addition to the driver small-signal parameters discussed earlier, the system designer must know (or specify) the large-signal parameters $P_{E(\max)}$ and V_D.

Diaphragm Displacement

The small-signal diaphragm displacement of a loudspeaker system driver is determined from the system acoustical analogous circuit. The circuit is first analyzed to obtain the diaphragm volume velocity U_D. Division by S_D then gives the diaphragm velocity u_D, and a further division by s (i.e., integration) yields the diaphragm displacement x_D. The diaphragm displacement expression is always of the form

$$x_D = P_E^{1/2}\,\sigma_{x(P)}\,k_x\,X(s) \tag{36}$$

where

P_E nominal input power defined by Eq. (6)

$\sigma_{x(P)}$ static (dc) displacement sensitivity of unenclosed driver, expressed in meters per watt$^{1/2}$ and given by

$$\sigma_{x(P)} = \left[\frac{C_{MS}{}^2B^2l^2}{R_E}\right]^{1/2} = \left[\frac{V_{AS}}{2\pi\rho_0c^2f_SQ_{ES}S_D{}^2}\right]^{1/2} \tag{37}$$

k_x system displacement constant of unity or less

$X(s)$ normalized system displacement function.

$X(s)$ is always a *low-pass* filter function which has a value of unity at zero frequency.

For a particular system, the product of the displacement constant k_x and the displacement function $X(s)$ is evaluated by either of two methods. In the first method, the displacement expression (36) is established as described above and divided by $P_E^{1/2}\sigma_{x(P)}$ using Eqs. (6) and (37). In the second method, the acoustical analogous circuit is analyzed for the admittance seen by the generator, and this quantity is divided by sC_{AS}; referring to Fig. 6, this means that in all cases

$$k_xX(s) = \frac{1}{sC_{AS}}\cdot\frac{1+Z_{AB}/Z_{AA}}{Z_{AB}+Z_{AS}+Z_{AB}Z_{AS}/Z_{AA}}. \tag{38}$$

The resulting expression is then split into a constant factor k_x and a frequency-dependent factor $X(s)$ normalized to unity at zero frequency.

For the infinite-baffle system, circuit analysis of Fig. 3 reveals that the displacement constant is unity and the displacement function is

$$X(s) = \frac{1}{s^2T_S{}^2+sT_S/Q_T+1}. \tag{39}$$

The steady-state magnitude $|X(j\omega)|$ of this function is plotted against normalized frequency in Fig. 8. For this simple system, the curves are exact mirror images of those of Fig. 7.

DISPLACEMENT-LIMITED POWER RATINGS

Electrical Power Rating

A useful indication of the sinusoidal steady-state displacement-limited electrical input power capacity of a loudspeaker system is obtained by assuming linear diaphragm displacement for large input signals and limiting the peak value of x_D in Eq. (36) to $x_{\max}$. Thus

$$P_{ER} = \frac{1}{2}\left[\frac{x_{\max}}{\sigma_{x(P)}k_x|X(j\omega)|_{\max}}\right]^2 \tag{40}$$

where

P_{ER} displacement-limited electrical input power rating in watts

$|X(j\omega)|_{\max}$ maximum magnitude attained by system displacement function, i.e., its value at the frequency of maximum diaphragm displacement.

Substituting Eqs. (35) and (37) into Eq. (40),

$$P_{ER} = \pi\rho_0c^2\frac{f_SQ_{ES}V_D{}^2}{V_{AS}k_x{}^2|X(j\omega)|_{\max}{}^2}. \tag{41}$$

Acoustic Power Rating

The displacement-limited electrical power rating of a loudspeaker system places a limitation on the continuous power rating of the amplifier to be used with the system. This power rating, together with the reference efficiency of the system, then determines the maximum continuous acoustic power that can be radiated in the flat (upper) region of the system passband. Thus, using Eqs. (32) and (41), the steady-state displacement-limited acoustic power rating P_{AR} of the loudspeaker system is

$$P_{AR} = \frac{4\pi^3\rho_0}{c}\cdot\frac{f_S{}^4V_D{}^2}{k_x{}^2|X(j\omega)|_{\max}{}^2}. \tag{42}$$

This rating may easily be converted into a sound pressure level rating for standardized radiation and measurement conditions, e.g., [8, sec. 3.16]. The factor $4\pi^3\rho_0/c$ has the value 0.42 for SI units, i.e., for f_S in Hz and V_D in m^3.

Power Ratings of Infinite-Baffle System

The displacement-limited acoustic power rating of a driver mounted on an infinite baffle is found by setting $k_x = 1$ in Eq. (42). Thus,

$$P_{AR(IB)} = \frac{4\pi^3 \rho_0}{c} \cdot \frac{f_S{}^4 V_D{}^2}{|X(j\omega)|_{max}{}^2}. \quad (43)$$

For a given value of V_D, the acoustic power rating is a strong function of the driver resonance frequency. It is also sensitive to Q_T through $|X(j\omega)|_{max}$ (see Fig. 8), but is maximized for $Q_T \leq 0.71$.

As an example, consider an infinite-baffle system having a resonance frequency of 50 Hz and a second-order Butterworth response. If the driver is a 12-inch unit (effective radius 0.12 m) capable of $\pm$ 4 mm peak displacement, then $V_D = 0.18$ dm^3, and the acoustic power rating is $P_{AR} = 0.086$ watt. This is equivalent to a sound pressure level rating of 101.5 dB at a distance of 1 meter [3, p. 14].

Setting k_x equal to unity in Eq. (41), the displacement-limited electrical power rating of the infinite-baffle system is

$$P_{ER(IB)} = \pi \rho_0 c^2 \frac{f_S Q_{ES} V_D{}^2}{V_{AS} |X(j\omega)|_{max}{}^2}. \quad (44)$$

This equation demonstrates quantitatively the well-known fact that a woofer designed for acoustic-suspension use (i.e., with very low resonance and high compliance) has a low (input) power handling capacity, compared to that of a conventional woofer, if it is operated in air or on an infinite baffle.

The electrical power rating of the system in the above numerical example depends on the value of driver compliance. If the total moving mass of the driver has a typical value of 30 grams, the driver compliance, from Eq. (12), must be $V_{AS} = 0.1$ m^3. Ignoring mechanical losses and taking $Q_{ES} = Q_T = 0.71$, the electrical power rating from Eq. (44) is then $P_{ER} = 5$ watts. Comparing P_{AR} with P_{ER}, or using Eq. (33), the reference efficiency of the driver is $\eta_0 = 1.7\%$.

Note that the same ratings also apply to an infinite-baffle system using an 8-inch driver (effective radius 0.08 m) capable of $\pm$ 9-mm peak displacement (so that $V_D = 0.18$ dm^3) and having the same resonance frequency, acoustic compliance, and Q.

Assumptions and Corrections

The accuracy of the calculated displacement-limited power ratings depends on the assumptions that the diaphragm displacement is linear up to x_{max} and that the source power bandwidth extends down to the frequency of maximum displacement. Both assumptions may lead to conservative ratings.

For example, the infinite-baffle system described above reaches maximum displacement only at very low frequencies. This system might typically be driven by an amplifier with a low-frequency power bandwidth (−3 dB) of 30 Hz. If the plot of $|X(j\omega)|$ (with constant voltage drive) for $Q_T = 0.71$ in Fig. 8 is multiplied by the normalized power output curve of this amplifier, the resulting maximum value of $|X(j\omega)|$ falls from unity to about 0.7. A more realistic set of power ratings for this loudspeaker system would thus be $P_{ER} = 10$ watts and $P_{AR} = 0.17$ watt.

Similarly, if x_{max} is defined at a displacement beyond the linear range of the driver, then the actual input power required to reach this peak displacement will be higher than the calculated value. A correction factor can easily be computed from the actual displacement versus input characteristic of the driver.

CONCLUSION

The low-frequency response, efficiency, and power ratings of a direct-radiator loudspeaker system are determined by the parameters of the system components. These relationships are reciprocal; specification of the system performance places definite requirements on the component parameters. The most important system component is the driver, which is completely described only when a sufficient number of small-signal and large-signal parameters are specified.

An interesting result of the analysis in this paper is that the driver diaphragm area S_D does not appear explicitly in the small-signal response, small-signal efficiency, or displacement-limited power ratings of a loudspeaker system. This means that it is theoretically possible to design drivers of different diameter with identical values of the parameters f_S, Q_{MS}, Q_{ES}, V_{AS}, and V_D. Used in identical enclosures, these drivers must give identical small-signal performance and displacement-limited power capacity. The principal differences are that the larger driver will cost more but require less diaphragm displacement and thus produce less modulation distortion for a given acoustic output [11], [12].

Although the electrodynamic moving-coil driver has been manufactured throughout the world for decades, hardly a single manufacturer provides complete low-frequency parameter information with his products, or has ever been asked to do so. In the future, trial-and-error design of loudspeaker systems using available drivers will increasingly be replaced by system synthesis based on final performance specifications and resulting in specific driver parameter requirements. Driver manufacturers must be ready to meet demands of this kind and to provide complete parameter information with their products.

The parameters used to describe driver behavior in this paper are not the only consistent set that can be used. However, they do have the advantage of being easy to measure and to comprehend, and, as later papers will show, they are well suited for use in the analysis and design of complete systems.

APPENDIX

DRIVER PARAMETER MEASUREMENTS

Driver Q

From Eqs. (13) and (14),

$$\frac{Q_{MS}}{Q_{ES}} = \frac{R_{ES}}{R_E}. \quad (45)$$

The ratio of voice-coil maximum impedance to dc resistance, from Fig. 5, is therefore

$$r_0 = \frac{R_{ES}+R_E}{R_E} = 1+\frac{Q_{MS}}{Q_{ES}} \quad (46)$$

from which

$$Q_{ES} = \frac{Q_{MS}}{r_0-1}. \quad (18)$$

Also, the total driver Q with a zero-impedance source ($R_g = 0$) is given by

$$Q_{TS} = \frac{Q_{MS}Q_{ES}}{Q_{MS}+Q_{ES}} = \frac{Q_{MS}}{r_0}. \quad (47)$$

Eq. (16) now becomes

$$Z_{VC}(s) = R_E \frac{r_0+Q_{MS}(sT_S+1/sT_S)}{1+Q_{MS}(sT_S+1/sT_S)} \quad (48)$$

and

$$|Z_{VC}(j\omega)|^2 = R_E^2 \frac{r_0^2+Q_{MS}^2(\omega/\omega_S-\omega_S/\omega)^2}{1+Q_{MS}^2(\omega/\omega_S-\omega_S/\omega)^2}. \quad (49)$$

At any two frequencies $\omega_1 < \omega_2$ such that $\omega_1\omega_2 = \omega_S^2$, it can be shown using (49) that the impedance magnitudes will be equal. Let this magnitude be defined by

$$|Z_{VC}(j\omega_1)| = |Z_{VC}(j\omega_2)| = r_1R_E. \quad (50)$$

Then

$$|Z_{VC}(j\omega_{1,2})|^2 = r_1^2R_E^2$$

$$= R_E^2 \frac{r_0^2+Q_{MS}^2[(\omega_2-\omega_1)/\omega_S]^2}{1+Q_{MS}^2[(\omega_2-\omega_1)/\omega_S]^2} \quad (51)$$

and therefore

$$Q_{MS} = \frac{\omega_S}{\omega_2-\omega_1}\sqrt{\frac{r_0^2-r_1^2}{r_1^2-1}}. \quad (52)$$

If $r_1 = \sqrt{r_0}$, Eq. (52) reduces to

$$Q_{MS} = \frac{f_S\sqrt{r_0}}{f_2-f_1}. \quad (17)$$

Choosing $r_1 = \sqrt{r_0}$ not only makes the calculation simple but provides good measurement accuracy because f_1 and f_2 are reasonably well separated and are located in regions of high slope on the impedance curve.

As shown above, the frequencies f_1 and f_2 where the the measured voice-coil impedance magnitude is $\sqrt{r_0}R_E$ should satisfy the condition

$$\sqrt{f_1f_2} = f_S. \quad (53)$$

For most real drivers this is not precisely so because the fundamental driver parameters, particularly compliance and mechanical resistance, vary slightly with frequency or diaphragm excursion. Also, the voice-coil inductance, if large, will skew the curve slightly. However, for most well-designed drivers, the result computed from (53) is within about 1 Hz of the measured value. Eq. (53) is thus a useful check to catch measurement errors or to identify drivers which cannot be represented accurately by a set of constant-value parameters.

Driver Compliance

A simple unlined test enclosure at atmospheric pressure has an acoustic compliance C_{AB} related to its net internal volume V_T by [3, p. 129]

$$C_{AB} = V_T/\rho_0c^2. \quad (54)$$

A driver having total acoustical mass M_{AS} and compliance C_{AS} has a self-resonance defined by

$$T_S^2 = 1/\omega_S^2 = M_{AS}C_{AS}. \quad (12)$$

When this driver is mounted in the closed test box, a new resonance will be measured which is given by

$$T_{CT}^2 = 1/\omega_{CT}^2 = M_{ACT}\frac{C_{AB}C_{AS}}{C_{AB}+C_{AS}} \quad (55)$$

where M_{ACT} is the new total moving mass resulting from any change in the value of the diaphragm air load mass. Then

$$\frac{\omega_{CT}^2}{\omega_S^2} = \frac{M_{AS}}{M_{ACT}}\left[1+\frac{C_{AS}}{C_{AB}}\right]. \quad (56)$$

From Eq. (14),

$$Q_{ES} = \omega_S R_E M_{AS} S_D^2/(B^2l^2). \quad (57)$$

Similarly,

$$Q_{ECT} = \omega_{CT} R_E M_{ACT} S_D^2/(B^2l^2). \quad (58)$$

Therefore,

$$\frac{M_{AS}}{M_{ACT}} = \frac{\omega_{CT}Q_{ES}}{\omega_S Q_{ECT}} \quad (59)$$

and combining Eqs. (56) and (59),

$$1+\frac{C_{AS}}{C_{AB}} = \frac{\omega_{CT}Q_{ECT}}{\omega_S Q_{ES}}. \quad (60)$$

From Eqs. (15) and (54),

$$\frac{C_{AS}}{C_{AB}} = \frac{V_{AS}}{V_T} \quad (61)$$

and therefore

$$\frac{V_{AS}}{V_T} = \frac{\omega_{CT}Q_{ECT}}{\omega_S Q_{ES}} - 1 \quad (62)$$

or

$$V_{AS} = V_T\left[\frac{f_{CT}Q_{ECT}}{f_S Q_{ES}} - 1\right]. \quad (19)$$

The initial driver measurements (f_S and Q_{ES}) may be made with a baffle of any size or with no baffle. It is advisable, however, especially with low-resonance drivers, that the driver have its axis horizontal for both sets of measurements to avoid excessive static diaphragm displacement due to gravity.

Energy absorption in the test enclosure walls affects only the measured value of Q_{MCT} and thus has no effect on the compliance calculation. However, absorbing material placed inside the enclosure can affect the value of C_{AB} and should therefore not be used.

It is particularly important to avoid leaks in the test enclosure because these can also change the effective value of C_{AB} and seriously reduce the accuracy of the measurement. The test enclosure must be constructed carefully, and the driver under test must be checked for a tight seal at the mounting gasket. Some drivers have a built-in leakage path around the voice coil, others through a porous edge-suspension material. Measurements on these drivers must be used with caution. To test for leakage, apply an input signal of about 10 Hz at moderate level and listen carefully all around the enclosure and driver for "breathing" indicative of a leak.

Measurement Technique

Loudspeaker impedance measurements are commonly taken with either constant-voltage [3, p. 503] or constant-current [10, p. 13] drive. If the driver is perfectly linear or the measuring level is low enough, the two methods should give the same result. The constant-voltage method has the advantage of more nearly duplicating the usual operating conditions of the driver.

Accurate measurement of small-signal parameters requires a signal level that is small enough for all voltage and current waveforms to be undistorted sinusoids. Use an oscilloscope to observe waveforms and adjust the signal level accordingly. It is often necessary, particularly with unloaded high-compliance drivers, to measure parameters at an input level of 0.1 watt or less.

Measure the driver voice-coil resistance accurately with a dc bridge. A dummy resistance of the same value can then be made up and used as a calibrating load on the equipment for measuring impedance.

Do not trust the frequency scale of audio-sweep type beat frequency oscillators. For maximum accuracy, take frequency readings with a frequency or period counter or from the scale of a stable, accurately calibrated sine-wave generator.

ACKNOWLEDGMENT

This paper is part of the result of a program of postgraduate research into the low-frequency performance of direct-radiator electrodynamic loudspeaker systems. I am indebted to the School of Electrical Engineering of The University of Sydney for providing research facilities, supervision, and assistance, and to the Australian Commonwealth Department of Education and Science for financial support.

Numerous authors have contributed through their published works to the basic ideas which are developed here. I am particularly indebted to A. N. Thiele for having originated both the filter-oriented approach to analysis and the simple methods of parameter measurement which are described here, and to J. E. Benson for originating the simple generalized loudspeaker system concept, for contributing many hours to the discussion of terminology and symbols, and for carefully checking the equations and computations in the manuscript.

REFERENCES

[1] E. de Boer, "Acoustic Interaction in Vented Loudspeaker Enclosures," *J. Acoust. Soc. Am.*, vol. 31, p. 246 (Feb. 1959).

[2] A. N. Thiele, "Loudspeakers in Vented Boxes," *Proc. IREE (Australia)*, vol. 22, p. 487 (Aug. 1961); also, *J. Audio Eng. Soc.*, vol. 19, pp. 382-392 (May 1971), and pp. 471-483 (June 1971).

[3] L. L. Beranek, *Acoustics* (McGraw-Hill, New York, 1954).

[4] J. E. Benson, "Theory and Design of Loudspeaker Enclosures," *A.W.A. Tech. Rev.*, vol. 14, p. 1 (1968); also, *Proc. IREE (Australia)*, vol. 30, p. 261 (Sept. 1969).

[5] R. F. Allison and R. Berkovitz, "The Sound Field in Home Listening Rooms," presented at the 39th Convention of the Audio Engineering Society, October 1970, Preprint 779.

[6] American National Standards Institute, "American Standard Recommended Practices for Loudspeaker Measurements," Standard S1.5-1963 (1963).

[7] British Standards Institution, "British Standard Recommendations for Ascertaining and Expressing the Performance of Loudspeakers by Objective Measurements," B.S. 2498 (1954).

[8] International Electrotechnical Commission, "IEC Recommendation, Methods of Measurement for Loudspeakers," IEC Publ. 200 (1966).

[9] H. F. Olson, *Dynamical Analogies* (Van Nostrand, New York, 1943).

[10] J. F. Novak, "Performance of Enclosures for Low-Resonance High-Compliance Loudspeakers," *IRE Trans. Audio*, vol. AU-7, p. 5 (Jan.-Feb. 1959); also, *J. Audio Eng. Soc.*, vol. 7, p. 29 (Jan. 1959).

[11] P. W. Klipsch, "Modulation Distortion in Loudspeakers," *J. Audio Eng. Soc.*, vol. 17, p. 194 (Apr. 1969).

[12] P. W. Klipsch, "Modulation Distortion in Loudspeakers: Part II," *J. Audio Eng. Soc.*, vol. 18, p. 29 (Feb. 1970).

Note: Mr. Small's biography appeared in the January/February issue.

Closed-Box Loudspeaker Systems
Part I: Analysis

RICHARD H. SMALL

School of Electrical Engineering, The University of Sydney
Sydney, N.S.W. 2006, Australia

The closed-box loudspeaker system is effectively a second-order (12 dB/octave cutoff) high-pass filter. Its low-frequency response is controlled by two fundamental system parameters: resonance frequency and total damping. Further analysis reveals that the system electroacoustic reference efficiency is quantitatively related to system resonance frequency, the portion of total damping contributed by electromagnetic coupling, and total system compliance; for air-suspension systems, efficiency therefore effectively depends on frequency response and enclosure size. System acoustic power capacity is found to be fundamentally dependent on frequency response and the volume of air that can be displaced by the driver diaphragm; it may also be limited by enclosure size. Measurement of voice-coil impedance and other mechanical properties provides basic parameter data from which the important low-frequency performance capabilities of a system may be evaluated.

GLOSSARY OF SYMBOLS

B	magnetic flux density in driver air gap
c	velocity of sound in air ($=345$ m/s)
C_{AB}	acoustic compliance of air in enclosure
C_{AS}	acoustic compliance of driver suspension
C_{AT}	total acoustic compliance of driver and enclosure
C_{MEC}	electrical capacitance representing moving mass of system ($=M_{AC}S_D^2/B^2l^2$)
e_g	open-circuit output voltage of source (Thevenin's equivalent generator for amplifier output port)
f	natural frequency variable
f_C	resonance frequency of closed-box system
f_{CT}	resonance frequency of driver in closed, unfilled, unlined test enclosure
f_S	resonance frequency of unenclosed driver
$G(s)$	response function
k_x	displacement constant
k_P	power rating constant
k_η	efficiency constant
l	length of voice-coil conductor in magnetic gap
L_{CET}	electrical inductance representing total system compliance ($=C_{AT}B^2l^2/S_D^2$)
M_{AC}	acoustic mass of driver in enclosure including air load
M_{AS}	acoustic mass of driver diaphragm assembly including air load
P_{AR}	displacement-limited acoustic power rating
P_{ER}	displacement-limited electrical power rating
$P_{E(max)}$	thermally-limited maximum input power
Q	ratio of reactance to resistance (series circuit) or resistance to reactance (parallel circuit)
Q_{EC}	Q of system at f_C considering electrical resistance R_E only

Q_{ES}	Q of driver at f_S considering electrical resistance R_E only
Q_{MC}	Q of system at f_C considering system non-electrical resistances only
Q_{MS}	Q of driver at f_S considering driver non-electrical resistances only
Q_{TC}	total Q of system at f_C including all system resistances
Q_{TCO}	value of Q_{TC} with $R_g = 0$
Q_{TS}	total Q of driver at f_S considering all driver resistances
R_{AB}	acoustic resistance of enclosure losses caused by internal energy absorption
R_{AS}	acoustic resistance of driver suspension losses
R_E	dc resistance of driver voice coil
R_{ES}	electrical resistance representing driver suspension losses $(=B^2l^2/S_D{}^2R_{AS})$
R_g	output resistance of source (Thevenin's equivalent resistance for amplifier output port)
s	complex frequency variable $(=\sigma + j\omega)$
S_D	effective surface area of driver diaphragm
T	time constant $(=1/2\pi f)$
U_O	system output volume velocity
V_{AB}	volume of air having same acoustic compliance as air in enclosure $(=\rho_0 c^2 C_{AB})$
V_{AS}	volume of air having same acoustic compliance as driver suspension $(=\rho_0 c^2 C_{AS})$
V_{AT}	total system compliance expressed as equivalent volume of air $(=\rho_0 c^2 C_{AT})$
V_B	net internal volume of enclosure
V_D	peak displacement volume of driver diaphragm $(=S_D x_{max})$
x_{max}	peak linear displacement of driver diaphragm
$X(s)$	displacement function
$Z_{VC}(s)$	voice-coil impedance function
α	compliance ratio $(=C_{AS}/C_{AB})$
γ_B	ratio of specific heat at constant pressure to that at constant volume for air in enclosure
η_o	reference efficiency
ρ_o	density of air $(=1.18\ \text{kg/m}^3)$
ω	radian frequency variable $(=2\pi f)$

1. INTRODUCTION

Historical Background

The theoretical prototype of the closed-box loudspeaker system is a driver mounted in an enclosure large enough to act as an infinite baffle [1, Chap. 7]. This type of system was used quite commonly until the middle of this century.

The concept of the modern air-suspension loudspeaker system was established in a U.S. patent application of 1944 by Olson and Preston [2], [3], but the system was not widely introduced until high-fidelity sound reproduction became popular in the 1950's.

A compact air-suspension loudspeaker system for high-fidelity reproduction was described by Villchur [4] in 1954. Several more papers [5], [6], [7] set out the basic principle of operation but caused a spirited public controversy [8], [9], [10]. Unfortunately, some of the confusion established at the time still remains, particularly with regard to the purpose and effect of materials used to fill the enclosure interior. A recent attempt to dispell this confusion [11] seems to have reduced the level of controversy, and the fundamental validity of the air-suspension approach has been amply proved by its proliferation.

Technical Background

Closed-box loudspeaker systems are the simplest of all loudspeaker systems using an enclosure, both in construction and in analysis. In essence, they consist of an enclosure or box which is completely closed and air-tight except for a single aperture in which the driver is mounted.

The low-frequency output of a direct-radiator loudspeaker system is completely described by the acoustic volume velocity crossing the enclosure boundaries [12]. For the closed-box system, this volume velocity is entirely the result of motion of the driver cone, and the analysis is relatively simple.

Traditional closed-box systems are made large so that the acoustic compliance of the enclosed air is greater than that of the driver suspension. The resonance frequency of the driver in the enclosure, i.e., of the system, is thus determined essentially by the driver compliance and moving mass.

The air-suspension principle reverses the relative importance of the air and driver compliances. The driver compliance is made very large so that the resonance frequency of the system is controlled by the much smaller compliance of the air in the enclosure in combination with the driver moving mass. The significance of this difference goes beyond the smaller enclosure size or any related performance improvements; it demonstrates forcibly that the loudspeaker driver and its enclosure cannot be designed and manufactured independently of each other but must be treated as an inseparable *system*.

In this paper, closed-box systems are examined using the approach described in [12]. The analysis is limited to the low-frequency region where the driver acts as a piston (i.e., the wavelength of sound is longer than the driver diaphragm circumference) and the enclosure is active in controlling the system behavior.

The results of the analysis show that the important low-frequency performance characteristics of closed-box systems of both conventional and air-suspension type are directly related to a small number of basic and easily-measured system parameters.

The analytical relationships impose definite quantitative limits on both small-signal and large-signal performance of a system but, at the same time, show how these limits may be approached by careful system adjust-

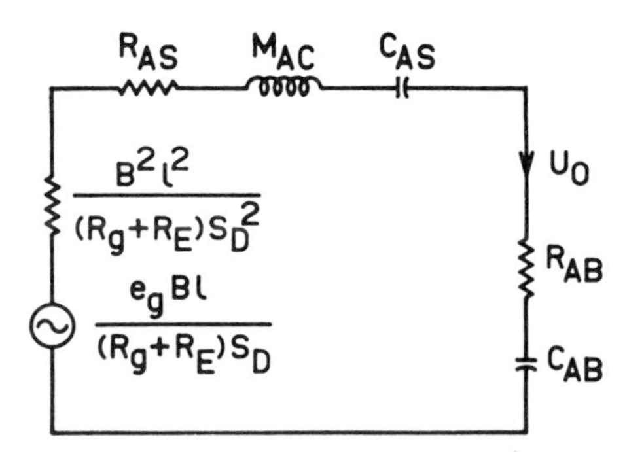

Fig. 1. Acoustical analogous circuit of closed-box loudspeaker system (impedance analogy).

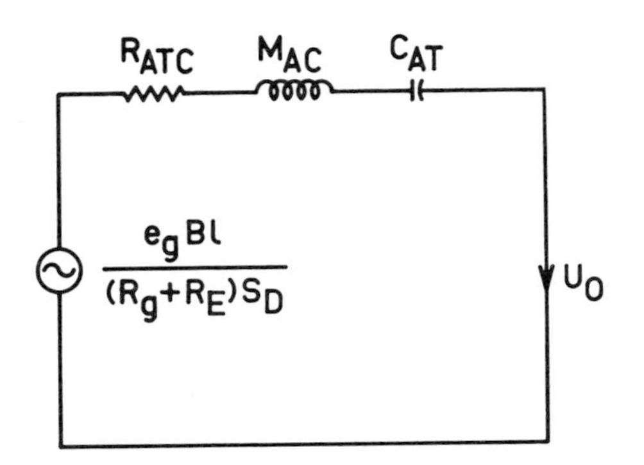

Fig. 2. Simplified acoustical analogous circuit of closed-box loudspeaker system.

ment. The same relationships lead directly to methods of synthesis (system design) which are free of trial-and-error procedures and to simple methods for evaluating and specifying system performance at low frequencies.

2. BASIC ANALYSIS

The impedance-type acoustical analogous circuit of the closed-box system is well known and is presented in Fig. 1. In this circuit, the symbols are defined as follows.

- B Magnetic flux density in driver air gap.
- l Length of voice-coil conductor in magnetic field of air gap.
- e_g Open-circuit output voltage of source.
- R_g Output resistance of source.
- R_E Dc resistance of driver voice coil.
- S_D Effective projected surface area of driver diaphragm.
- R_{AS} Acoustic resistance of driver suspension losses.
- M_{AC} Acoustic mass of driver diaphragm assembly including voice coil and air load.
- C_{AS} Acoustic compliance of driver suspension.
- R_{AB} Acoustic resistance of enclosure losses caused by internal energy absorption.
- C_{AB} Acoustic compliance of air in enclosure.
- U_0 Output volume velocity of system.

By combining series elements of like type, this circuit can be simplified to that of Fig. 2. The total system acoustic compliance C_{AT} is given by

$$C_{AT} = C_{AB}C_{AS}/(C_{AB} + C_{AS}), \tag{1}$$

and the total system resistance, R_{ATC}, is given by

$$R_{ATC} = R_{AB} + R_{AS} + \frac{B^2l^2}{(R_g + R_E)S_D{}^2}. \tag{2}$$

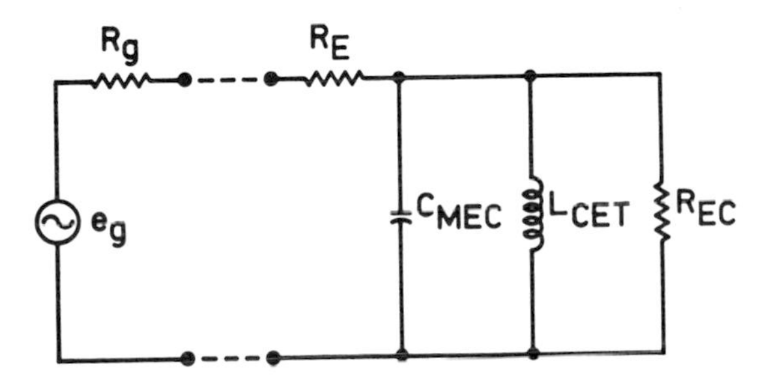

Fig. 3. Simplified electrical equivalent circuit of closed-box loudspeaker system.

The electrical equivalent circuit of the closed-box system is formed by taking the dual of the acoustic circuit of Fig. 1 and converting each element to its electrical equivalent [1, Chapter 3]. Simplification of this circuit by combining elements of like type results in the simplified electrical equivalent circuit of Fig. 3. This circuit is arranged so that the actual voice-coil terminals are available. In Fig. 3, the symbols are given by

$$C_{MEC} = M_{AC}S_D{}^2/B^2l^2, \tag{3}$$

$$L_{CET} = C_{AT}B^2l^2/S_D{}^2, \tag{4}$$

$$R_{EC} = \frac{B^2l^2}{(R_{AB} + R_{AS})S_D{}^2}. \tag{5}$$

The circuits presented above are valid only for frequencies within the driver piston range; the circuit elements are assumed to have values which are independent of frequency within this range. As discussed in [12], the effects of the voice-coil inductance and the resistance of the radiation load are neglected.

To simplify the analysis of the system and the interpretation of its describing functions, the following system parameters are defined.

ω_C ($=2\pi f_C$) Resonance frequency of system, given by

$$1/\omega_C{}^2 = T_C{}^2 = C_{AT}M_{AC} = C_{MEC}L_{CET}. \tag{6}$$

Q_{MC} Q of system at f_C considering non-electrical resistances only, given by

$$Q_{MC} = \omega_C C_{MEC} R_{EC}. \tag{7}$$

Q_{EC} Q of system at f_C considering electrical resistance R_E only, given by

$$Q_{EC} = \omega_C C_{MEC} R_E. \tag{8}$$

Q_{TCO} Total Q of system at f_C when driven by source resistance of $R_g = 0$, given by

$$Q_{TCO} = Q_{EC}Q_{MC}/(Q_{EC} + Q_{MC}). \tag{9}$$

Q_{TC} Total Q of system at f_C including all system resistances, given by

$$Q_{TC} = 1/(\omega_C C_{AT} R_{ATC}). \tag{10}$$

α System compliance ratio, given by

$$\alpha = C_{AS}/C_{AB}. \tag{11}$$

If the system driver is mounted on a baffle which provides the same total air-load mass as the system enclosure, the driver parameters defined in [12, eqs. (12), (13) and (14)] become

$$T_S{}^2 = 1/\omega_S{}^2 = C_{AS}M_{AC}, \tag{12}$$

$$Q_{MS} = \omega_S C_{MEC} R_{ES}, \tag{13}$$

$$Q_{ES} = \omega_S C_{MEC} R_E, \tag{14}$$

where $R_{ES} = B^2l^2/S_D{}^2R_{AS}$ is an electrical resistance representing the driver suspension losses. The driver compliance equivalent volume is unaffected by air-load masses and is in every case [12, eq. (15)]

$$V_{AS} = \rho_o c^2 C_{AS}, \tag{15}$$

where ρ_o is the density of air (1.18 kg/m³) and c is the

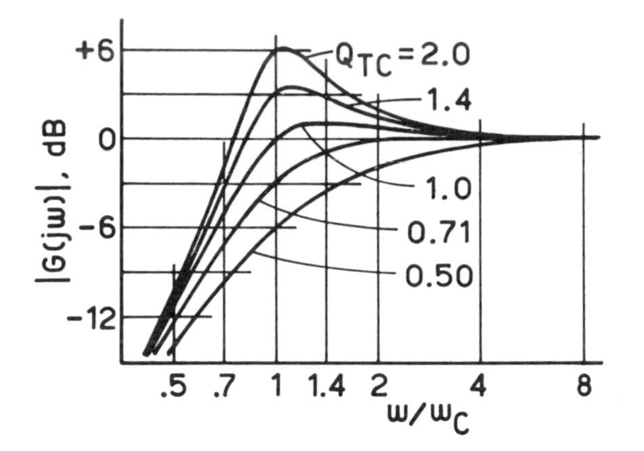

Fig. 4. Normalized amplitude vs normalized frequency response of closed-box loudspeaker system for several values of total system Q.

velocity of sound in air (345 m/s). In this paper, the general driver parameters f_S (or T_S), Q_{MS} and Q_{ES} will be understood to have the above values unless otherwise specified.

Comparing (1), (6), (8), (11), (12) and (14), the following important relationships between the system and driver parameters are evident:

$$C_{AS}/C_{AT} = \alpha + 1, \tag{16}$$

$$f_C/f_S = T_S/T_C = (\alpha+1)^{1/2}, \tag{17}$$

$$Q_{EC}/Q_{ES} = (\alpha+1)^{1/2}. \tag{18}$$

Following the method of [12], analysis of the circuits of Figs. 2 and 3 and substitution of the parameters defined above yields the system response function

$$G(s) = \frac{s^2T_C^2}{s^2T_C^2 + sT_C/Q_{TC} + 1}, \tag{19}$$

the diaphragm displacement function

$$X(s) = \frac{1}{s^2T_C^2 + sT_C/Q_{TC} + 1}, \tag{20}$$

the displacement constant

$$k_x = 1/(\alpha+1), \tag{21}$$

and the voice-coil impedance function

$$Z_{VC}(s) = R_E + R_{EC}\frac{sT_C/Q_{MC}}{s^2T_C^2 + sT_C/Q_{MC} + 1}, \tag{22}$$

where $s = \sigma + j\omega$ is the complex frequency variable.

3. RESPONSE

Frequency Response

The response function of the closed-box system is given by (19). This is a second-order (12 dB/octave cutoff) high-pass filter function; it contains information about the low-frequency amplitude, phase, delay and transient response characteristics of the closed-box system [13]. Because the system is minimum-phase, these characteristics are interrelated; adjustment of one determines the others. In audio systems, the flatness and extent of the steady-state amplitude-vs-frequency response—or simply frequency response—is usually considered to be of greatest importance.

The frequency response $|G(j\omega)|$ of the closed-box system is examined in the appendix. Several typical response curves are illustrated in Fig. 4 with the frequency scale normalized to ω_C. The curve for $Q_{TC} = 0.50$ is a second-order critically-damped alignment; that for $Q_{TC} = 0.71$ (i.e., $1/\sqrt{2}$) is a second-order Butterworth ($B2$) maximally-flat alignment. Higher values of Q_{TC} lead to a peak in the response, accompanied by a relative extension of bandwidth which initially is greater than the relative response peak. For large values of Q_{TC}, however, the response peak continues to increase without any significant extension of bandwidth. Technically, these responses for Q_{TC} greater than $1/\sqrt{2}$ are second-order Chebyshev ($C2$) equal-ripple alignments.

Whatever response shape may be considered optimum, Fig. 4 indicates the value of Q_{TC} required to achieve this alignment and the variation in response shape that will result if Q_{TC} is altered, i.e., misaligned, from the required value. For intermediate values of Q_{TC} not included in Fig. 4, Fig. 5 gives normalized values of the response peak magnitude $|G(j\omega)|_{max}$, the normalized frequency $f_{G\,max}/f_C$ at which this peak occurs, and the normalized cutoff (half-power) frequency f_3/f_C for which the response is 3 dB below passband level. The analytical expressions for the quantities plotted in Fig. 5 are given in the appendix.

Transient Response

The response of the closed-box system to a step input is plotted in Fig. 6 for several values of Q_{TC}; the time scale is normalized to the periodic time of the system resonance frequency. For values of Q_{TC} greater than 0.50, the response is oscillatory with increasing values of Q_{TC} contributing increasing amplitude and decay time [13].

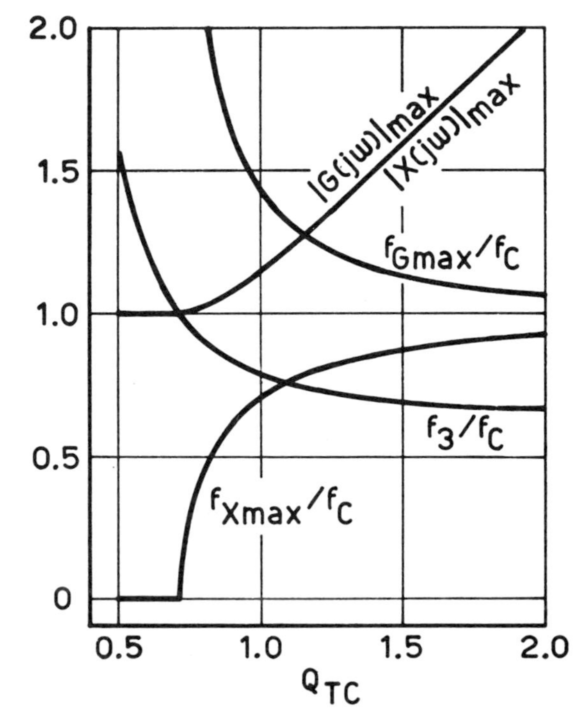

Fig. 5. Normalized cutoff frequency, and normalized frequency and magnitude of response and displacement peaks, as a function of total Q for the closed-box loudspeaker system.

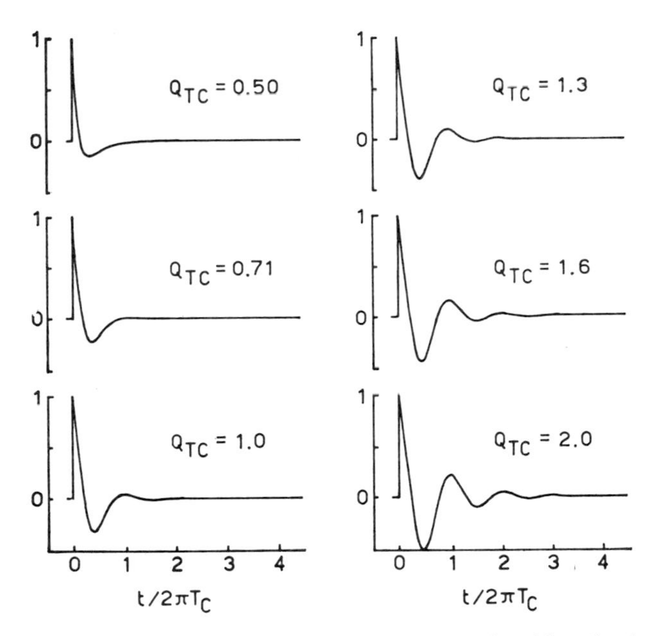

Fig. 6. Normalized step response of the closed-box loudspeaker system.

4. EFFICIENCY

Reference Efficiency

The closed-box system efficiency in the passband region, or system reference efficiency, is the reference efficiency of the driver operating with the particular value of air-load mass provided by the system enclosure. From [12, eq. (32)], this is

$$\eta_o = \frac{4\pi^2}{c^3} \cdot \frac{f_S{}^3 V_{AS}}{Q_{ES}}, \tag{23}$$

where f_S, Q_{ES} and V_{AS} have the values given in (12), (14) and (15). This expression may be rewritten in terms of the system parameters defined in section 2. Using (16), (17) and (18),

$$\eta_o = \frac{4\pi^2}{c^3} \cdot \frac{f_C{}^3 V_{AT}}{Q_{EC}}, \tag{24}$$

where

$$V_{AT} = \rho_o c^2 C_{AT} \tag{25}$$

is a volume of air having the same total acoustic compliance as the driver suspension and enclosure acting together. For SI units, the value of $4\pi^2/c^3$ is 9.64×10^{-7}.

Efficiency Factors

Equation (24) may be written

$$\eta_o = k_\eta f_3{}^3 V_B, \tag{26}$$

where

- f_3 is the cutoff (half-power or -3 dB) frequency of the system,
- V_B is the net internal volume of the system enclosure,
- k_η is an efficiency constant given by

$$k_\eta = \frac{4\pi^2}{c^3} \cdot \frac{f_C{}^3}{f_3{}^3} \cdot \frac{V_{AT}}{V_B} \cdot \frac{1}{Q_{EC}}. \tag{27}$$

The efficiency constant k_η may be separated into three factors: $k_{\eta(Q)}$ related to system losses, $k_{\eta(C)}$ related to system compliances, and $k_{\eta(G)}$ related to the system response. Thus

$$k_\eta = k_{\eta(Q)}\, k_{\eta(C)}\, k_{\eta(G)}, \tag{28}$$

where

$$k_{\eta(Q)} = Q_{TC}/Q_{EC}, \tag{29}$$

$$k_{\eta(C)} = V_{AT}/V_B, \tag{30}$$

$$k_{\eta(G)} = \frac{4\pi^2}{c^3} \cdot \frac{1}{(f_3/f_C)^3 Q_{TC}}. \tag{31}$$

Loss Factor

Modern amplifiers are designed to have a very low output-port (Thevenin) impedance so that, for practical purposes, $R_g = 0$. The value of Q_{TC} for any system used with such an amplifier is then equal to Q_{TCO} as given by (9). Equation (29) then reduces to

$$k_{\eta(Q)} = Q_{TCO}/Q_{EC} = 1 - (Q_{TCO}/Q_{MC}). \tag{32}$$

This expression has a limiting value of unity, but will approach this value only when mechanical losses in the system are negligible (Q_{MC} infinite) and all required damping is therefore provided by electromagnetic coupling ($Q_{EC} = Q_{TCO}$).

The value of $k_{\eta(Q)}$ for typical closed-box systems varies from about 0.5 to 0.9. Low values usually result from the deliberate use of mechanical or acoustical dissipation, either to ensure adequate damping of diaphragm or suspension resonances at higher frequencies, or to conserve magnetic material and therefore cost.

Compliance Factor

Equation (30) may be expanded to

$$k_{\eta(C)} = \frac{C_{AT}}{C_{AB}} \cdot \frac{V_{AB}}{V_B}, \tag{33}$$

where

$$V_{AB} = \rho_o c^2 C_{AB} \tag{34}$$

is a volume of air having an acoustic compliance equal to C_{AB}.

There is an important difference between V_B, the net internal volume of the enclosure, and V_{AB}, a volume of air which represents the acoustic compliance of the enclosure. If the enclosure contains only air under adiabatic conditions, i.e., no lining or filling materials, then V_{AB} is equal to V_B. But if the enclosure does contain such materials, V_{AB} is larger than V_B. The increase in V_{AB} is inversely proportional to the change in the value of γ, the ratio of specific heat at constant pressure to that at constant volume for the air in the enclosure. This has a value of 1.4 for the empty enclosure and decreases toward unity if the enclosure is filled with a low-density material of high specific heat [1, p. 220]. Equation (33) may then be simplified to

$$k_{\eta(C)} = \frac{\alpha}{\alpha + 1} \cdot \frac{1.4}{\gamma_B}, \tag{35}$$

where γ_B is the value of γ applicable to the enclosure.

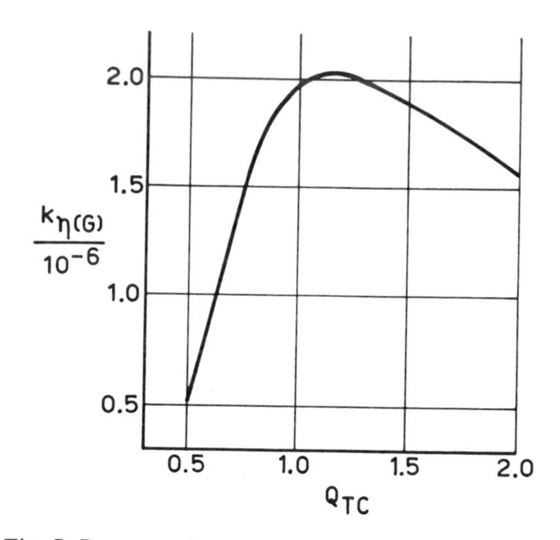

Fig. 7. Response factor $k_{\eta(G)}$ as a function of total Q for the closed-box loudspeaker system.

For "empty" enclosures, (35) has a limiting value of unity for $\alpha >> 1$. Air-suspension systems usually have α values between 3 and 10.

If the enclosure is filled, the $1.4/\gamma_B$ term exceeds unity, but two interactions occur. First, because the filling material increases C_{AB}, the value of α is lower than for the empty enclosure. Second, the addition of the material increases energy absorption within the enclosure, decreasing Q_{MC} and therefore reducing the value of $k_{\eta(Q)}$ in (32).

With proper selection of the amount, kind, and location of filling material, the net product of $k_{\eta(Q)}$ and $k_{\eta(C)}$ increases compared to the empty enclosure condition, but the increase is seldom more than about 15%. Haphazard addition of unselected materials may even reduce the product of these factors. Although theoretically possible, it is extremely unusual in practice for this product

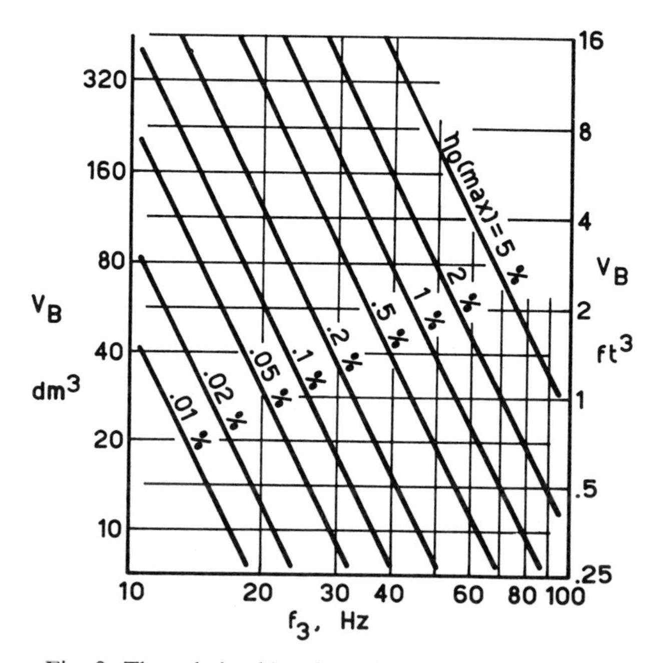

Fig. 8. The relationship of maximum reference efficiency to cutoff frequency and enclosure volume for the closed-box loudspeaker system.

to exceed unity. The effects of filling materials are discussed further in section 7.

Response Factor

The value of $k_{\eta(G)}$ in (31) depends only on Q_{TC} because (f_3/f_C) is a function of Q_{TC} as shown in Fig. 5 and (75) of the appendix. Fig. 7 is a plot of $k_{\eta(G)}$ *vs* Q_{TC}. Just above $Q_{TC} = 1.1$, $k_{\eta(G)}$ has a maximum value of 2.0×10^{-6}. This value of Q_{TC} corresponds to a $C2$ alignment with a ripple or passband peak of 1.9 dB. Compared to the $B2$ alignment having the same bandwidth, this alignment is 1.8 dB more efficient.

Maximum Reference Efficiency, Bandwidth, and Enclosure Volume

Selecting the value of $k_{\eta(G)}$ for the maximum-efficiency $C2$ alignment, and taking unity as the maximum attainable value of $k_{\eta(Q)}k_{\eta(C)}$, the maximum reference efficiency $\eta_{o(max)}$ that could be expected from an idealized closed-box system for specified values of f_3 and V_B is, from (26) and (28),

$$\eta_{o(max)} = 2.0 \times 10^{-6} f_3^3 V_B, \qquad (36)$$

where f_3 is in Hz and V_B is in m³. This relationship is illustrated in Fig. 8, with V_B (given here in cubic decimeters—1 dm³ = 1 liter = 10^{-3} m³) plotted against f_3 for various values of $\eta_{o(max)}$ expressed in percent.

Figure 8 represents the physical efficiency-bandwidth-volume limitation of closed-box system design. Any system having given values of f_3 and V_B must always have an actual reference efficiency lower than the value of $\eta_{o(max)}$ given by Fig. 8. Similarly, a system of specified efficiency and volume must have a cutoff frequency higher than that indicated by Fig. 8, etc. These basic relationships have been known on a qualitative basis for years (see, e.g., [11]). An independently derived presentation of the important quantitative limitation was given recently by Finegan [14].

There are two known methods of circumventing the physical limitation imposed by (36) or Fig. 8. One is the stabilized negative-spring principle [15] which enables V_{AT} to be made much larger than V_B but requires additional design complexity. The other is the use of amplifier assistance which extends response with the aid of equalizing networks or special feedback techniques [16]. The second method requires additional amplifier power in the region of extended response and a driver capable of dissipating the extra power.

The actual reference efficiency of any practical system may be evaluated directly from (24) if the values of f_C, Q_{EC} and V_{AT} are known or are measured. For air-suspension systems, especially those using filling materials, V_{AT} is often very nearly equal to V_B.

Efficiency-Bandwidth-Volume Exchange

The relationship between reference efficiency, bandwidth, and enclosure volume indicated by (26) and illustrated for maximum-efficiency conditions in Fig. 8 implies that these system specifications can be exchanged one for another if the factors determining k_η remain constant. Thus if the system is made larger, the parameters may be adjusted to give greater efficiency or extended bandwidth. Similarly, if the cutoff frequency is

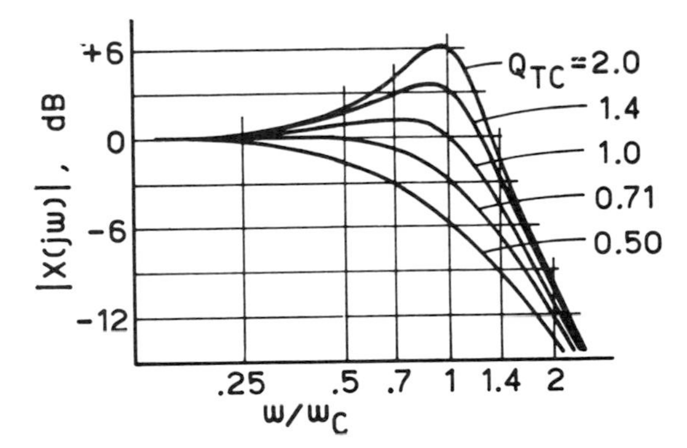

Fig. 9. Normalized diaphragm displacement of closed-box system driver as a function of normalized frequency for several values of total system Q.

raised, the parameters may be adjusted to give higher efficiency or a smaller enclosure.

If the value of k_η is increased, by reducing mechanical losses, by adding filling material, by increasing α, or by changing the response shape, the benefit may be taken in the form of smaller size, or higher efficiency, or extended bandwidth, or a combination of these. Each choice requires a specific adjustment of the enclosure or driver parameters.

5. DISPLACEMENT-LIMITED POWER RATINGS

Displacement Function

The closed-box system displacement function given by (20) is a second-order low-pass filter function. The properties of this function are examined in the appendix.

The normalized diaphragm displacement magnitude $|X(j\omega)|$ is plotted in Fig. 9 with frequency normalized to ω_C for several values of Q_{TC}. The curves are exact mirror images of those of Fig. 4. For intermediate values of Q_{TC}, Fig. 5 gives normalized values of the displacement peak magnitude $|X(j\omega)|$ and the normalized frequency $f_{X\max}/f_C$ at which this peak occurs. Analytical expressions for these quantities are given in the appendix.

Acoustic Power Rating

Assuming linear large-signal diaphragm displacement, the steady-state displacement-limited acoustic power rating P_{AR} of a loudspeaker system, from [12, eq. (42)], is

$$P_{AR} = \frac{4\pi^3\rho_o}{c} \cdot \frac{f_S{}^4 V_D{}^2}{k_x{}^2 |X(j\omega)|_{\max}{}^2}, \tag{37}$$

where V_D is the peak displacement volume of the driver diaphragm, given by

$$V_D = S_D x_{\max}, \tag{38}$$

and $x_{\max}$ is the peak linear displacement of the driver diaphragm, usually set by the amount of voice-coil overhang. Substituting (17) and (21) into (37), the steady-state displacement-limited acoustic power rating of the closed-box system becomes

$$P_{AR(CB)} = \frac{4\pi^3\rho_o}{c} \cdot \frac{f_C{}^4 V_D{}^2}{|X(j\omega)|_{\max}{}^2}. \tag{39}$$

For SI units, the constant $4\pi^3\rho_o/c$ is equal to 0.424.

Power Output, Bandwidth, and Displacement Volume

Equation (39) may be rewritten as

$$P_{AR(CB)} = k_P f_3{}^4 V_D{}^2, \tag{40}$$

where k_P is a power rating constant given by

$$k_P = \frac{4\pi^3\rho_o}{c} \cdot \frac{1}{(f_3/f_C)^4 |X(j\omega)|_{\max}{}^2}. \tag{41}$$

The acoustic power rating of a system having a specified cutoff frequency f_3 and a driver displacement volume V_D is thus a function of k_P; and k_P is solely a function of Q_{TC} as shown by (75) and (78) of the appendix.

The variation of k_P with Q_{TC} is plotted in Fig. 10. A maximum value occurs for Q_{TC} very close to 1.1. This is practically the same 1.9 dB ripple $C2$ alignment that gives maximum efficiency. For this condition, (40) becomes

$$P_{AR(CB)\max} = 0.85 f_3{}^4 V_D{}^2, \tag{42}$$

where P_{AR} is in watts for f_3 in Hz and V_D in m^3.

Equation (42) is illustrated in Fig. 11. P_{AR} is expressed in both watts (left scale) and equivalent SPL at one meter [1, p. 14] for 2π steradian free-field radiation conditions (right scale); this is plotted as a function of f_3 for various values of V_D. The SPL at one meter given on the right-hand scale is a rough indication of the level produced in the reverberant field of an average listening room for a radiated acoustic power given by the left-hand scale [1, p. 318].

Figure 11 represents the physical large-signal limitation of closed-box system design. It may be used to determine the optimum performance tradeoffs (P_{AR} *vs* f_3) for a given diaphragm and voice-coil design or to find the minimum value of V_D which is required to meet a given specification of f_3 and P_{AR}. The techniques noted earlier which may be used to overcome the small-signal limitation of Fig. 8 do not affect the large-signal limitation imposed by Fig. 11.

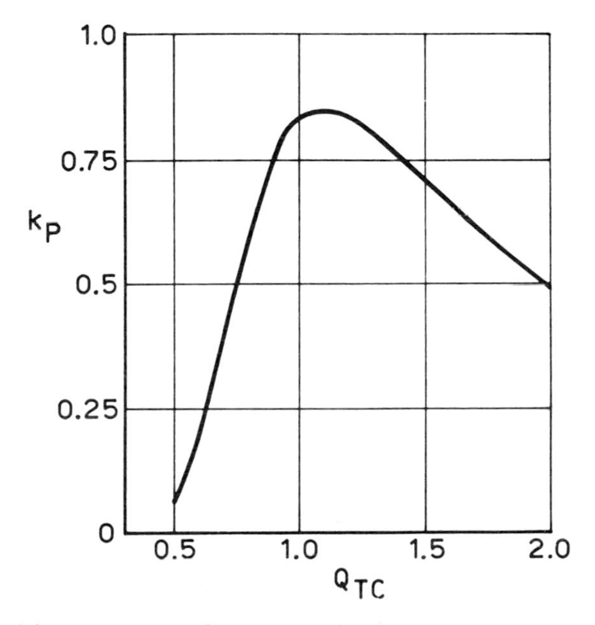

Fig. 10. Power rating constant k_P as a function of total Q for the closed-box loudspeaker system.

Power Output, Bandwidth, and Enclosure Volume

The displacement-limited power rating relationships given above exhibit no dependence on enclosure volume. For fixed response, it is the diaphragm displacement volume V_D that controls the system power rating. However, V_D cannot normally be made more that a few percent of V_B; beyond this point, increases in V_D result in unavoidable non-linear distortion, regardless of driver linearity, caused by non-linear compression of the air in the enclosure [3], [10]. If V_D is limited to a fixed fraction of V_B, the fraction depending on the amount of distortion considered acceptable, then Fig. 11 may be relabeled to show the minimum enclosure volume required to provide a given combination of f_3 and P_{AR} for the specified distortion level, as well as the required V_D.

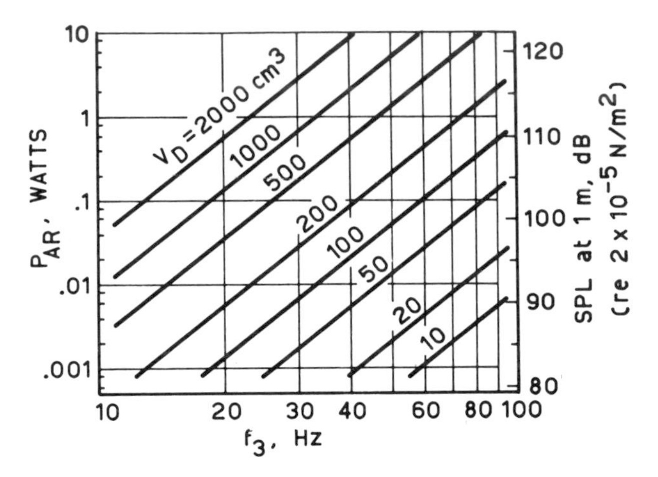

Fig. 11. The relationship of rated acoustic output power to cutoff frequency and driver displacement volume for a closed-box loudspeaker system aligned to obtain maximum rated power.

Program Bandwidth

Figure 10 indicates that k_P and hence the system steady-state acoustic power rating decreases for values of Q_{TC} below 1.1 if f_3 and V_D are held constant. However, it is clear from Fig. 5 that the frequency of maximum diaphragm displacement, $f_{X\max}$, is below f_3 for $Q_{TC} < 1.1$, and that as Q_{TC} decreases, $f_{X\max}$ moves further and further below f_3. This suggests that the steady-state rating becomes increasingly conservative, as Q_{TC} decreases, for loudspeaker systems operated with program material having little energy content below f_3. The effect of restricted power bandwidth in most amplifiers further reduces the likelihood of reaching rated displacement at $f_{X\max}$ for these alignments [12, section 7].

For closed-box loudspeaker systems used for high-fidelity music reproduction and having a cutoff frequency of about 40 Hz or less, or operated on speech only and having a cutoff frequency of about 100 Hz or less, an approximate *program* power rating is that given by (42) or Fig. 11 for any value of Q_{TC} up to 1.1. Above this value, $f_{X\max}$ is within the system passband and the program rating is effectively the same as the steady-state rating.

Electrical Power Rating

The displacement-limited electrical and acoustic power ratings of a loudspeaker system are related by the system reference efficiency [12, section 7]. Thus, if the acoustic power rating and reference efficiency of a system are known, the corresponding electrical rating may be calculated as the ratio of these.

For the closed-box system, (24) and (39) give the electrical power rating P_{ER} as

$$P_{ER(CB)} = \pi\rho_o c^2 \frac{f_C Q_{EC}}{V_{AT}} \cdot \frac{V_D^2}{|X(j\omega)|_{\max}^2}. \quad (43)$$

The dependence of this rating on the important system constants is more easily observed from the form obtained by dividing (40) by (26):

$$P_{ER} = \frac{k_P}{k_\eta} f_3 \frac{V_D^2}{V_B}. \quad (44)$$

It is particularly important to realize that for a given acoustic power capacity, the displacement-limited electrical power rating is inversely proportional to efficiency. Also, displacement non-linearity for large signals tends to increase P_{ER} over the theoretical linear value. Thus a high input power rating is not necessarily a virtue; it may only indicate a low value of k_η or a high distortion limit.

The overall electrical power rating which a manufacturer assigns to a loudspeaker system must take into account both the displacement-limited power capacity of the system, P_{ER}, and the thermally-limited power capacity of the driver, $P_{E(\max)}$, together with the spectral and statistical properties of the type of program material for which the rating will apply. The statistical properties of the signal are important in determining whether P_{ER} or $P_{E(\max)}$ will limit the overall power rating, because the overall rating sets the maximum safe continuous-power rating of the amplifier to be used. For reliability and low distortion, the overall rating must never exceed P_{ER}; but it may be allowed to exceed $P_{E(\max)}$ in proportion to the peak-to-average power ratio of the intended program material.

The resulting system rating is important when selecting a loudspeaker system to operate with a given amplifier and vice-versa. But it must be remembered that the electrical rating gives no clue to the acoustic power capacity unless the reference efficiency is known.

6. PARAMETER MEASUREMENT

It has been shown that the important small-signal and large-signal performance characteristics of a closed-box loudspeaker system depend on a few basic parameters. The ability to measure these basic parameters is thus a useful tool, both for evaluating the performance of an existing loudspeaker system and for checking the results of a new system design which is intended to meet specific performance criteria.

Small-Signal Parameters: f_C, Q_{MC}, Q_{EC}, Q_{TCO}, α, V_{AT}

The voice-coil impedance function of the closed-box system is given by (22). The steady-state magnitude $|Z_{VC}(j\omega)|$ of this function is plotted against normalized frequency in Fig. 12.

The measured impedance curve of a closed-box sys-

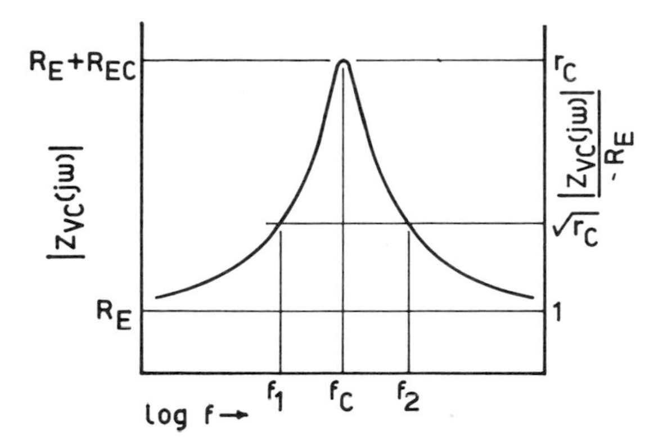

Fig. 12. Magnitude of closed-box loudspeaker system voice-coil impedance as a function of frequency.

tem conforms closely to the shape of Fig. 12. This impedance curve permits identification of the first four parameters as follows:

1) Measure the dc voice-coil resistance R_E.
2) Find the frequency f_C at which the impedance has maximum magnitude and zero phase, i.e., is resistive. Let the ratio of maximum impedance magnitude to R_E be defined as r_C.
3) Find the two frequencies $f_1 < f_C$ and $f_2 > f_C$ for which the impedance magnitude is equal to $R_E \sqrt{r_C}$.
4) Then, as in [12, appendix],

$$Q_{MC} = \frac{f_C \sqrt{r_C}}{f_2 - f_1}, \tag{45}$$

$$Q_{EC} = Q_{MC}/(r_C - 1), \tag{46}$$

$$Q_{TCO} = Q_{MC}/r_C. \tag{47}$$

To obtain the value of α for the system, remove the driver from the enclosure and measure the driver parameters f_S, Q_{MS} and Q_{ES} (with or without a baffle) as described in [12]; the method is the same as that given above for the system. The compliance ratio is then [12, appendix]

$$\alpha = \frac{f_C Q_{EC}}{f_S Q_{ES}} - 1. \tag{48}$$

Drivers with large voice-coil inductance or systems having a large crossover inductance may exhibit some difference between the frequency of maximum impedance magnitude and the frequency of zero phase. If the inductance cannot be bypassed or equalized for measurement purposes [17, section 14], it is better to take f_C as the frequency of maximum impedance magnitude, regardless of phase. It must be expected, however, that some measurement accuracy will be lost in these circumstances.

V_{AT} is evaluated with the help of (1), (11), (15), (25) and (34):

$$V_{AT} = V_{AB}V_{AS}/(V_{AB} + V_{AS}) = \frac{\alpha}{\alpha + 1} V_{AB}. \tag{49}$$

For unfilled enclosures, $V_{AB} = V_B$ and the value of V_{AT} may be computed directly using the measured value of α. If the system enclosure is normally filled, an extra set of measurements is required. The filling material is removed from the enclosure, or the driver is transferred to a similar but unfilled test enclosure. For this combination, the resonance frequency f_{CT} and the corresponding Q values Q_{MCT} and Q_{ECT} are measured by the above method. Then, as shown in [12, appendix],

$$V_{AS} = V_B \left[\frac{f_{CT} Q_{ECT}}{f_S Q_{ES}} - 1 \right], \tag{50}$$

where V_B is the net internal volume of the unfilled enclosure used (the system enclosure or test enclosure). Using (11), (15) and (34), V_{AB} for the filled system enclosure is then given by

$$V_{AB} = V_{AS}/\alpha. \tag{51}$$

This value of V_{AB} may now be used to evaluate V_{AT} using (49).

Large-Signal Parameters: $P_{E(max)}$ and V_D

The measurement of driver thermal power capacity is best left to manufacturers, who are familiar with the required techniques [18, section 5.7] and are usually quite happy to supply the information on request. Some estimate of thermal power capacity may often be obtained from knowledge of voice-coil diameter and length, the materials used, and the intended use of the driver [19].

The driver displacement volume V_D is the product of S_D and x_{max}. It is usually sufficient to evaluate S_D by estimating the effective diaphragm diameter. Some manufacturers specify the "throw" of a driver, which is usually the peak-to-peak linear displacement, i.e., $2x_{max}$. If this information is not available, the value of x_{max} may be estimated by observing the amount of voice-coil overhang outside the magnetic gap. For a more rigorous evaluation, where the necessary test equipment is available, operate the driver in air with sine-wave input at its resonance frequency and measure the peak displacement for which the radiated sound pressure attains about 10% total harmonic distortion.

7. ENCLOSURE FILLING

It is stated in section 4 that the addition of an appropriate filling material to the enclosure of an air-suspension system raises the value of the efficiency constant k_η. The use and value of such materials have been the subject of much controversy and study [4], [8], [9], [10], [11], [20].

There is no serious disagreement about the value of such materials for damping standing waves within the enclosure at frequencies in the upper piston range and higher. The controversy centers on the value of the materials at low frequencies. A more complete description of the effects of these materials will help to assess their value to various users.

Compliance Increase

If the filling material is chosen for low density but high specific heat, the conditions of air compression within the enclosure are altered from adiabatic to isothermal, or partly so [1, p. 220]. This increases the effective acoustic compliance of the enclosure, which is equivalent to increasing the size of the unfilled enclosure. The maximum theoretical increase in compliance is 40%, but using practical materials the actual increase is probably never more than about 25%.

Mass Loading

Often, the addition of filling material increases the total effective moving mass of the system. This has been carefully documented by Avedon [10]. The mechanism is not entirely clear and may involve either motion of the filling material itself or constriction of air passages near the rear of the diaphragm, thus "mass-loading" the driver. Depending on the initial diaphragm mass and the conditions of filling, the mass increase may vary from negligible proportions to as much as 20%.

Damping

Air moving inside a filled enclosure encounters frictional resistance and loses energy. Thus the component R_{AB} of Fig. 1 increases when the enclosure is filled. The resulting increase in the total system mechanical losses $(R_{AB} + R_{AS})$ can be substantial, especially if the filling material is relatively dense and is allowed to be quite close to the driver where the air particle velocity and displacement are highest. While unfilled systems have typical Q_{MC} values of about 5–10 (largely the result of driver suspension losses), filled systems generally have Q_{MC} values in the range of 2–5.

Value to the Designer

If a loudspeaker system is being designed from scratch, the effect of filling material on compliance is a definite advantage. It means that the enclosure size can be reduced or the efficiency improved or the response extended. Any mass increase which accompanies the compliance increase is simply taken into account in designing the driver so that the total moving mass is just the amount desired. The losses contributed by the material are a disadvantage in terms of their effect on $k_{\eta(Q)}$, but this is a small price to pay for the overall increase in k_η which results from the greater compliance. In fact, if efficiency is not a problem, the effect of increased frictional losses may be seen to relax the magnet requirements a little, thus saving cost.

Where a loudspeaker system is being designed around a given driver, the compliance increase contributed by the material is still an advantage because it permits the enclosure to be made smaller for a particular (achievable) response. The effect of increased mass is to reduce the driver reference efficiency by the square of the mass increase; this may or may not be desirable. The increased mass will also cause the value of Q_{EC} to be higher for a given value of f_C. This will be opposed by the effect of the material losses on Q_{MC}.

Often it is hoped that the addition of large amounts of filling material to a system will contribute enough additional damping to compensate for inadequate magnetic coupling in the driver. To the extent that the material increases compliance more than it does mass, Q_{EC} will indeed fall a little. And while Q_{MC} may be substantially decreased, the total reduction in Q_{TC} is seldom enough to rescue a badly underdamped driver as illustrated in [20]. If such a driver must be used, the application of acoustic damping directly to the driver as described in [21] is both more effective and more economical than attempting to overfill the enclosure.

Measuring the Effects of Filling Materials

The contribution of filling materials to a given system can be determined by careful measurement of the system parameters with and without the material in place. The added-weight measurement method used by Avedon [10] can be very accurate but is suited only to laboratory conditions. Alternatively, the type of measurements described in section 6 may be used:

1) With the driver in air or on a test baffle, measure f_S, Q_{MS}, Q_{ES}.
2) With the driver in the unfilled enclosure, measure f_{CT}, Q_{MCT}, Q_{ECT}.
3) With the driver in the filled enclosure, measure f_C, Q_{MC}, Q_{EC}.
4) Then, using the method of [12, appendix], the ratio of total moving mass with filling to that without filling is

$$M_{AC}/M_{ACT} = f_{CT}Q_{EC}/f_C Q_{ECT}, \qquad (52)$$

and the enclosure compliance increase caused by filling is

$$V_{AB}/V_B = \frac{(f_{CT}Q_{ECT}/f_S Q_{ES}) - 1}{(f_C Q_{EC}/f_S Q_{ES}) - 1}. \qquad (53)$$

5) The net effect of the material on total system damping may be found by computing Q_{TCO} for the filled system from (9) or (47) and comparing this to the corresponding $Q_{TCTO} = Q_{MCT}Q_{ECT}/(Q_{MCT} + Q_{ECT})$ for the unfilled system. These values represent the total Q (Q_{TC}) for each system when driven by an amplifier of negligible source resistance.

The usual result is that the filling material increases both compliance and mass but decreases total Q. The decrease in total Q may be a little or a lot, depending on the initial value and on the material chosen and its location in the enclosure.

REFERENCES

[1] L. L. Beranek, *Acoustics* (McGraw-Hill, New York, 1954).

[2] H. F. Olson and J. Preston, "Loudspeaker Diaphragm Support Comprising Plural Compliant Members," U.S. Patent 2,490,466. Application July 19, 1944; patented December 6, 1949.

[3] H. F. Olson, "Analysis of the Effects of Nonlinear Elements Upon the Performance of a Back-enclosed, Direct Radiator Loudspeaker Mechanism," *J. Audio Eng. Soc.*, vol. 10, no. 2, p. 156 (April 1962).

[4] E. M. Villchur, "Revolutionary Loudspeaker and Enclosure," *Audio*, vol. 38, no. 10, p. 25 (Oct. 1954).

[5] E. M. Villchur, "Commercial Acoustic Suspension Speaker," *Audio*, vol. 39, no. 7, p. 18 (July 1955).

[6] E. M. Villchur, "Problems of Bass Reproduction in Loudspeakers," *J. Audio Eng. Soc.*, vol. 5, no. 3, p. 122 (July 1957).

[7] E. M. Villchur, "Loudspeaker Damping," *Audio*, vol. 41, no. 10, p. 24 (Oct. 1957).

[8] R. C. Avedon, W. Kooy and J. E. Burchfield, "Design of the Wide-Range Ultra-Compact Regal Speaker System," *Audio*, vol. 43, no. 3, p. 22 (March 1959).

x_{max} being the peak linear displacement of the driver diaphragm, usually set by the amount of voice-coil overhang.

For the vented-box system, Eq. (15) gives $k_x = 1$. The displacement-limited acoustic power rating of the vented-box system then becomes

$$P_{AR(VB)} = \frac{4\pi^3 \rho_0}{c} \cdot \frac{f_S{}^4 V_D{}^2}{|X(j\omega)|_{max}{}^2}. \tag{38}$$

For SI units, the value of $4\pi^3\rho_0/c$ is 0.424.

Power-Rating Constant

Eq. (38) may be written in the form

$$P_{AR(VB)} = k_P f_3{}^4 V_D{}^2 \tag{39}$$

where k_P is a power-rating constant given by

$$k_P = \frac{4\pi^3 \rho_0}{c} \cdot \frac{1}{(f_3/f_S)^4 |X(j\omega)|_{max}{}^2}. \tag{40}$$

The value of f_3/f_S is already established for any alignment in the C4–B4–QB3 range. But from Fig. 17, $|X(j\omega)|$ has *two* maxima. The first occurs outside the system passband; this has a value of unity and is located at zero frequency for the QB3, B4, and moderate C4 alignments but slightly exceeds unity and is located below f_B for the extreme C4 alignments. The second maximum occurs within the system passband, above f_B, and is always smaller than the first.

There are thus two possible values for k_P, one if the system driving signal is allowed to have large-amplitude components at frequencies well below cutoff, and another, which is substantially larger, if the signal is restricted so that all significant spectral components are within the system passband.

Fig. 18 is a plot of the values of k_P for each of the above driving conditions as a function of the alignment parameters k and B for systems with lossless enclosures. The crosses in Fig. 18 indicate the values of k_P for a few selected alignments with $Q_L = 5$. The effect of this relatively severe amount of enclosure loss on k_P is negligible for the QB3 alignments but gradually increases as the extreme C4 alignments are approached. For these alignments, k_P is slightly reduced for the passband-drive case but slightly increased for the wideband-drive case.

Program Acoustic Power Rating

In most program applications, a portion of the driving signal spectrum lies below the system passband. The lower value of k_P given by Fig. 18 is then in general conservative, while the higher value is comparatively optimistic. A truly realistic value of k_P for program material can be evaluated only if the actual spectral power distribution of the particular driving signal is known. Thiele for example has obtained comparative power handling data for a number of system alignments (including amplifier-assisted alignments) based on a particular random-noise driving signal [20].

In most cases, provided that the program spectrum is principally within the system passband, a satisfactory program rating is obtained by setting k_P equal to 3.0, regardless of the alignment used. This is indicated by the broken line in Fig. 18. This compromise value for k_P is arrived at by considering, for the entire range of alignments, the passband and wideband values of k_P, the ratio of maximum displacements for passband- and wideband-drive conditions, and the degree to which the driving signal spectrum may extend below system cutoff before the displacement exceeds the passband maximum (see Fig. 17).

With this value of k_P, Eq. (39) becomes

$$P_{AR(VB)} = 3.0 f_3{}^4 V_D{}^2. \tag{41}$$

This relationship is generally applicable to all vented-box alignments for which the system passband includes the major components of the program signal spectrum. Whenever the signal and alignment properties are accurately known, a more exact relationship may be obtained with the help of Fig. 18 or by using Eq. (38) directly.

Power Output, Cutoff Frequency, and Displacement Volume

Eq. (41) is illustrated in Fig. 19. P_{AR} is expressed in both watts (left scale) and equivalent sound pressure

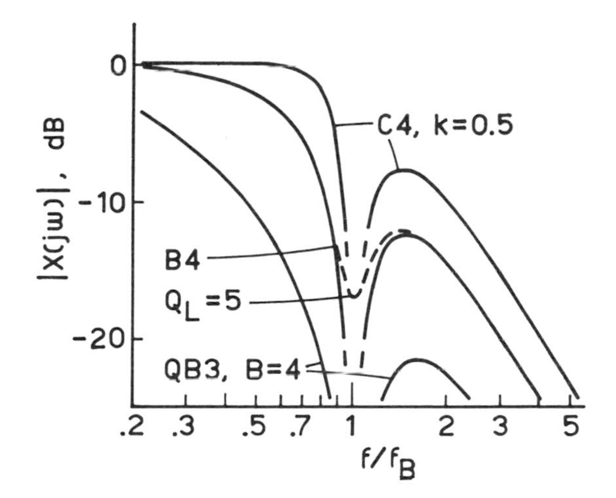

Fig. 17. Normalized diaphragm displacement of vented-box system driver as a function of normalized frequency for several typical alignments (from simulator).

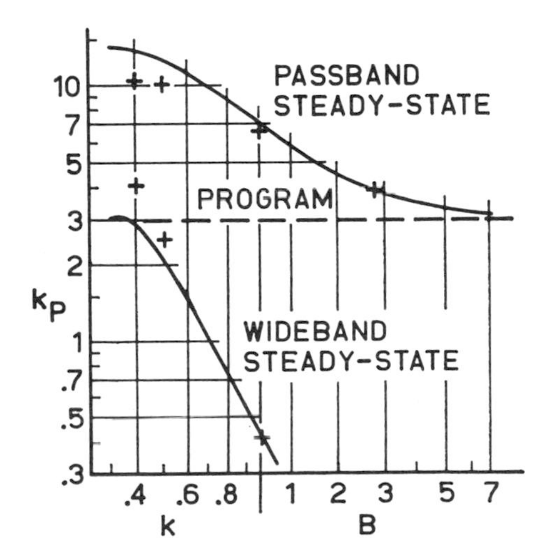

Fig. 18. Power rating constant k_P for vented-box loudspeaker system as a function of response shape. Solid lines are for lossless systems; crosses represent systems with $Q_L = 5$.

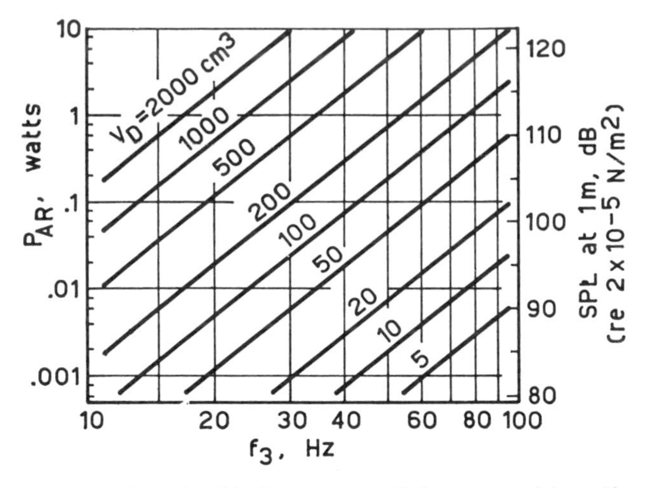

Fig. 19. Relationship between cutoff frequency, driver displacement volume, and rated acoustic power for a vented-box loudspeaker system operated on program material.

level (SPL) at 1 meter [3, p. 14] for 2π-steradian free-field radiation conditions (right scale). This is plotted as a function of f_3 for various values of V_D (note 1 cm^3 = 10^{-6} m^3). The SPL at 1 meter given on the right-hand scale is a rough indication of the SPL produced in the reverberant field of an average listening room for a radiated acoustic power given by the left-hand scale [3, p. 318]. For particular listening environments such as large halls, the reference just cited gives methods for computing the acoustic power required to obtain a specified SPL.

Fig. 19 represents the approximate physical large-signal limitation of vented-box system design. It may be used to determine the maximum performance tradeoffs (P_{AR} versus f_3) for a given voice-coil/suspension design or to find the minimum value of V_D which is required to meet a given specification of f_3 and P_{AR}.

Power ratings calculated from Eq. (41) or Fig. 19 apply only for "typical" program material which does not drive the system hard at frequencies below cutoff. For other circumstances the applicable rating may be higher or lower. Even where the condition of passband drive is met with regard to the intended program material, the vented-box system is clearly vulnerable to extraneous signals such as turntable rumble and subsonic control tones. These normally inaudible signals may produce audible harmonics or cause noticeable modulation distortion [21]. In cases where such signals are particularly troublesome and cannot otherwise be eliminated, the use of a closed-box design or one of the higher order amplifier-assisted vented-box alignments described by Thiele [10], [20] may provide relief.

Electrical Power Rating

The displacement-limited electrical power rating P_{ER} of the vented-box system is obtained by dividing the acoustic power rating Eq. (38) by the system reference efficiency Eq. (25). Thus,

$$P_{ER(VB)} = \frac{P_{AR(VB)}}{\eta_0} = \pi \rho_0 c^2 \frac{f_S Q_{ES}}{V_{AS}} \cdot \frac{V_D^2}{|X(j\omega)|_{\max}^2}. \quad (42)$$

This rating is subject to the same adjustments for program material as used above. Its dependence on the performance factors already discussed is easily observed from the form obtained by dividing Eq. (39) by Eq. (26):

$$P_{ER} = \frac{k_P}{k_\eta} f_3 \frac{V_D^2}{V_B}. \quad (43)$$

In practice, the values of P_{AR} and η_0 are much more important; these would normally be specified or calculated first. P_{ER} is then obtained directly from these numbers as indicated by Eq. (42). P_{ER} describes only the amount of nominal power which may be absorbed from an amplifier if thermal design of the voice-coil permits. It gives no indication of acoustic performance unless reference efficiency is known.

Enclosure and driver losses reduce η_0 without much effect on P_{AR} and thus lead to a higher value of P_{ER}. Driver displacement nonlinearity for large signals also has the effect of reducing efficiency at high levels, i.e., increasing the electrical input required to actually reach the driver displacement limit. In both cases, the extra input power is only dissipated as heat.

7. PARAMETER MEASUREMENT

The direct dependence of system performance characteristics on system parameters provides a simple means of assessing or predicting loudspeaker system performance from a knowledge of these parameters. The important small-signal parameters can be found with satisfactory accuracy from measurement of the voice-coil impedance of the system and its driver.

The voice-coil impedance function of the vented-box system is given by Eq. (16). A plot of the steady-state magnitude $|Z_{VC}(j\omega)|$ of this function against frequency has the shape illustrated in Fig. 20; the measured impedance curve of a practical vented-box system has this same characteristic shape.

The impedance magnitude plot of Fig. 20 has a minimum at a frequency near f_B (labeled f_M) where the impedance magnitude is somewhat greater than R_E. The additional resistance is contributed primarily by enclosure losses and is designated R_{BM} on the plot axis. There are two maxima in the impedance plot, located at frequencies below and above f_M. These are labeled f_L and f_H. At these frequencies, the magnitudes of the impedance maxima depend on both driver losses and enclosure circuit losses and are seldom equal.

Where only normal enclosure losses are present, the basic system parameters and the total enclosures loss Q_B may be found with satisfactory accuracy using the method developed by Thiele in [10]. The indicated value of Q_B may then be used to check the measurement approximations. Thiele's method is based on an initial assumption of negligible enclosure losses and may be summarized as follows. The relationships are derived in Appendix 2.

1) Measure the three frequencies f_L, f_M, and f_H where the impedance magnitude is maximum or minimum. The accurate identification of these frequencies may be aided by measuring the impedance phase; if this passes through zero at the appropriate maximum or minimum, the frequency of zero phase (which may be located with high precision) may be taken as the center of the maximum or minimum. However, if zero phase is not closely coincident with maximum or minimum magnitude, as may occur for moderate to high enclosure losses, the frequency of actual maximum or minimum impedance mag-

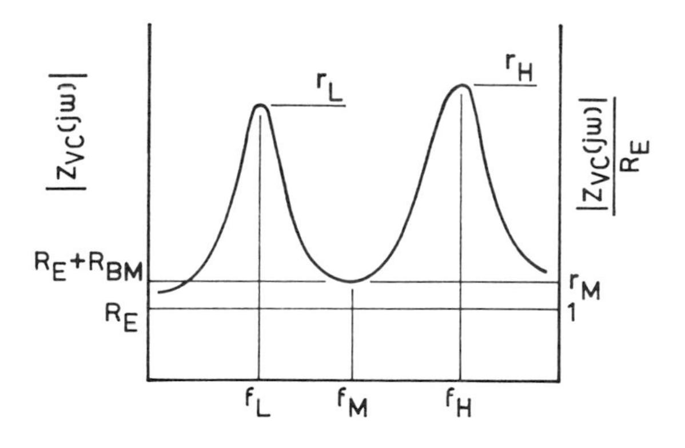

Fig. 20. Voice-coil impedance magnitude of vented-box loudspeaker system as a function of frequency.

nitude must be located as carefully as possible. Experience with many systems and experiments with the analog circuit simulator have shown that where the frequencies of zero phase and maximum or minimum magnitude do not coincide, the latter always provide more accurate values of the system parameters. Bypass any crossover networks for this measurement, and keep the measuring signal small enough so that both voltage and current signals are undistorted sinusoids. For the following calculations, assume that $f_B = f_M$.[2]

2) Calculate f_{SB}, the resonance frequency of the driver for the air-load mass presented by the enclosure, from the relationship

$$f_{SB} = \frac{f_L f_H}{f_B}. \tag{44}$$

3) Calculate the compliance ratio α from the relationship

$$\alpha = \frac{(f_H + f_B)(f_H - f_B)(f_B + f_L)(f_B - f_L)}{f_H^2 f_L^2}. \tag{45}$$

If the enclosure contains little or no lining material, the driver compliance equivalent volume V_{AS} may be calculated in terms of the enclosure net volume V_B. The relationship is, from Eqs. (9), (10), and (33),

$$V_{AS} = \alpha V_B. \tag{46}$$

4) Calculate the tuning ratio h from

$$h = f_B / f_{SB}. \tag{47}$$

5) Remove the driver from the enclosure, measure the driver parameters f_S, Q_{MS}, and Q_{ES} by the method of [12, Appendix],[3] and correct the driver Q values if necessary to correspond to the driver resonance frequency in the enclosure. This is done by multiplying the measured values of Q_{MS} and Q_{ES} by the ratio f_S/f_{SB}, where f_S is the resonance frequency for which Q_{MS} and Q_{ES} have been measured and f_{SB} is the resonance frequency in the enclosure found from Eq. (44). Usually if the driver parameters are measured on a test baffle of suitable size, the two resonance frequencies are almost identical and the correction is not required.

6) Calculate Q_{TS} from

$$Q_{TS} = \frac{Q_{ES} Q_{MS}}{Q_{ES} + Q_{MS}}. \tag{31}$$

7) Measure the minimum system impedance magnitude $R_E + R_{BM}$ at f_M and calculate

$$r_M = \frac{R_E + R_{BM}}{R_E}. \tag{48}$$

Then, using the corrected values of Q_{ES} and Q_{MS} obtained above, determine the total enclosure loss Q_B from the relationship

$$Q_B = \frac{h}{\alpha}\left[\frac{1}{Q_{ES}(r_M - 1)} - \frac{1}{Q_{MS}}\right]. \tag{49}$$

The term $1/Q_{MS}$ can usually be neglected.

8) The accuracy of the approximation $f_B \approx f_M$ on which the above method is based may be checked by calculating the approximate error introduced by the enclosure losses. Assuming that leakage losses are dominant in effect and that f_M is the measured frequency of zero phase, the error correction factor is

$$\frac{f_B}{f_M} = \sqrt{\frac{\alpha Q_B^2 - h^2}{\alpha Q_B^2 - 1}}. \tag{50}$$

This factor is usually quite close to unity. If it is significantly different from unity, it may be used to correct the value of f_B used in the above calculations to obtain better accuracy in the calculated parameter values.

The estimation or measurement of driver large-signal parameters is discussed in [22, Sec. 6].

With values determined for all important system parameters, system performance may be determined from the relationships given in earlier sections. The system frequency response may be calculated manually or using a digital computer but is most easily obtained by introducing the system parameters to an analog circuit simulator. The design of a simple simulator suitable for this purpose will be published in the future.

8. VENT REQUIREMENTS

The vent of a vented-box system must provide the necessary small-signal enclosure resonance frequency f_B; it must also provide the maximum required large-signal volume velocity without excessive losses or generation of spurious noises.

The second requirement can be satisfied by adjusting the vent area to a value which prevents the vent air velocity from exceeding a specified limit. An experimentally determined limit which avoids excessive noise generation is about 5% of the velocity of sound, provided that the inside of the vent is smooth and that the edges are rounded off with a reasonable radius. This velocity

[2] In [32, Appendix 4] Benson shows that if a large voice-coil inductance (or crossover inductance) is present, the measured value of f_M is lower than the true value of f_B, while f_L and f_H are negligibly affected. A much better approximation to f_B is obtained by carefully blocking the vent aperture and measuring the resonance frequency f_C of the resulting closed-box system [22]. Then, from [32, eq. (A4-6)], $f_B = (f_L^2 + f_H^2 - f_C^2)^{1/2}$. Because this relationship is true, f_C can be used directly in place of f_B in Eq. (45) to determine the system compliance ratio.

[3] Again, if the driver voice-coil inductance is large, Benson [32, Appendix 2] shows that the accuracy of determination of the Q values is improved if f_S in [12, eq. (17)] is replaced by the expression $\sqrt{f_1 f_2}$.

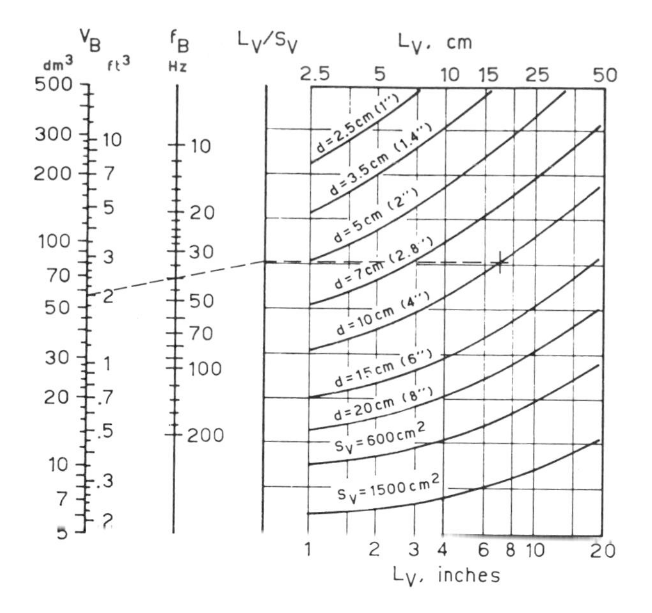

Fig. 21. Nomogram and chart for design of ducted vents.

limitation generally ensures acceptable losses as well, provided that the vent is not unduly obstructed.

The alignment, response, and power rating data of this paper combine to yield a relationship between vent area and maximum vent velocity for any given system. For program power ratings this relationship reduces to a simple approximate formula for vent area which limits the peak vent velocity, at maximum rated power input and at the frequency of maximum vent velocity, to 4½ % of the velocity of sound. This formula, which is accurate within ±10% for the entire C4–B4–QB3 range of alignments, is

$$S_V \geqq 0.8 f_B V_D \tag{51}$$

or

$$d_V \geqq (f_B V_D)^{1/2} \tag{52}$$

where S_V is the area of the vent in m² or d_V is the diameter of a circular vent in meters; V_D must be expressed in m³ and f_B in Hz. Because the noise generated depends on factors other than velocity (e.g., edge roughness), and because the annoyance caused by vent noise is subjective, this formula should be regarded as a general guide only, not as a rigid rule.

Once the area of the vent is determined, the length must be adjusted to satisfy the first requirement, i.e., correct enclosure tuning. There are many popular formulas and nomograms for doing this. Using Thiele's formulas [10, eqs. (60)–(65)], the nomogram and chart of Fig. 21 were constructed to simplify the calculation process for ducted vents.

To use Fig. 21, lay a straight-edge through the enclosure volume on the V_B line and the desired resonance frequency on the f_B line and find the intersection with the L_V/S_V line. This is illustrated on the figure with lightly dashed lines for V_B = 57 dm³ (2 ft³) and f_B = 40 Hz. Next, move horizontally to the right from this intersection point until a curve is reached on the chart which corresponds to the required minimum size determined from Eqs. (51) or (52). The intersection of the horizontal projection with this curve indicates on the horizontal scale the required duct length L_V for a vent of the prescribed size. For the example illustrated, if the minimum duct diameter is 100 mm (4 inches), the required length is about 175 mm (7 inches). End corrections for one open end and one flanged end are included in the construction of the chart. For intermediate vent areas the chart may be interpolated graphically.

For some proposed systems a satisfactory vent design cannot be found. This is particularly the case for small enclosures when a low value of f_B is desired. Also, tubular vents for which the length is much greater than the diameter tend to act as half-wave resonant pipes, and any noise generated at the edge is selectively amplified. In these cases it is better to use a drone cone or passive radiator in place of the vent [2], [23]. Systems of this type will be discussed in a later paper.

9. DIAPHRAGM–VENT MUTUAL COUPLING

Mutual Coupling Magnitude

The acoustical analogous circuit of a lossless vented-box system, modified to include mutual coupling [2], [6], is presented in Fig. 22. The mutual coupling components are inside the dashed lines. (The mutual coupling resistance [2] is equal to the radiation load resistance and is therefore neglected [4], [12].)

The acoustic mutual coupling mass M_{AM} has a maximum magnitude when the diaphragm–vent spacing is a minimum. A practical minimum spacing between the centers of diaphragm and vent is about $1.5a$, where a is the diaphragm radius. Using this value, and assuming radiation conditions of a 2π-steradian free field, the maximum value of M_{AM} is about $0.13/a$ [2]. This value is reduced for a 4π-steradian free-field load [6].

For a 12-inch driver with an effective diaphragm radius of 0.12 m, the mechanical equivalent M_{MM} of the acoustic mass M_{AM} has a maximum value of 2.2g. The mechanical diaphragm mass M_{MD} for 12-inch drivers varies from about 20g for older types used in large enclosures to more than 100g for newer types designed for use in compact enclosures. Thus the mutual coupling mass may have a magnitude of from 2 to 8% of the total moving mass of the driver when all of the diaphragm air-load mass is accounted for [3, pp. 216-217].

The effect of these values of mutual coupling mass was investigated using the analog circuit simulator. A "lossless" system aligned for a B4 response was compared to the same circuit with the driver and vent masses reduced by the amount of the mutual coupling

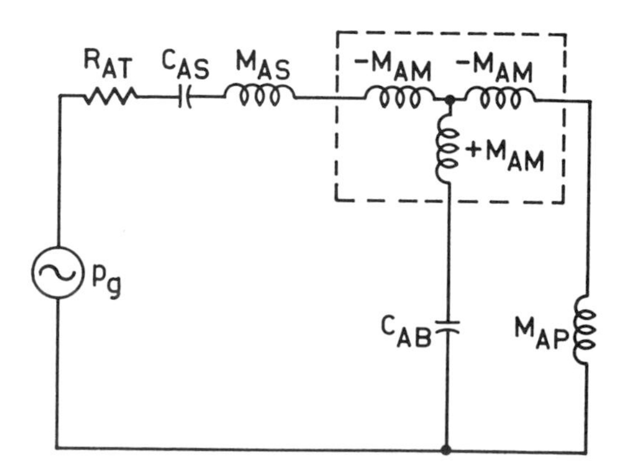

Fig. 22. Acoustical analogous circuit of lossless vented-box loudspeaker system modified to include effects of diaphragm–vent mutual coupling.

mass and the same amount of mass then introduced into the enclosure branch in agreement with Fig. 22.

Effect on Response

The effect of 2% mutual coupling mass on the frequency response could not be observed. The effect of 4% mutual coupling mass could be observed but was hardly worth taking into account. With 8% mutual coupling mass, the cutoff frequency was lowered by about 5% and the corner of the response curve became sharper as described by Locanthi. Similar effects were observed for other alignments.

It would appear that in most cases the effect of mutual coupling on system response is negligible. Only when a driver with a light diaphragm is mounted very close to the vent is the effect on response significant. It then amounts to a slight alignment shift with a very small decrease in cutoff frequency.

Effect on Measurement

Mutual coupling alters the location of the frequencies f_L and f_H of Fig. 20 but does not affect the location of f_M [2]. The shift in f_L and f_H toward each other upsets the calculation of the compliance ratio from Eq. (45), giving a value lower than the true value.

This suggests that if it is desired to measure the true compliance ratio of a system for which the magnitude of mutual coupling is very high, the vent should be blocked and the compliance ratio measured by the closed-box method described in [22]. However, if the parameters of a system are being measured only to evaluate the response of the system, the presence of mutual coupling may be ignored. Experiments on the analog circuit simulator show that the response of a system having the false calculated value of α and no mutual coupling is essentially identical to that of the actual system with its mutual coupling.

10. DISCUSSION

Features of Vented-Box Loudspeaker Systems

The vented-box loudspeaker system acts as a fourth-order high-pass filter. This basic fact determines the available range of amplitude, phase, and transient response characteristics. By suitable choice of parameters, the response may be varied from that of an extreme C4 alignment with passband ripple and very abrupt cutoff to that of an extreme QB3 alignment for which the response is effectively third order. The cost of the gentler cutoff slope and improved transient response of the QB3 alignment is a reduced value of the system efficiency factor $k_{\eta(G)}$, although this reduction is relatively small for real systems with typical enclosure losses. A further sacrifice in the value of this efficiency factor permits the use of SC4 alignments for which the transient response may approach that of a second-order system.

Perhaps the most important feature of the vented-box loudspeaker system is the very modest diaphragm excursion required at frequencies near the enclosure resonance frequency f_B. This feature is responsible for the relatively high displacement-limited power capacity of the system; it also helps to maintain low values of nonlinear distortion and modulation distortion [21].

The "misalignment" curves of Figs. 7 and 8 indicate the necessity for careful alignment of the vented-box system. The plurality of variables makes it very difficult to obtain optimum adjustment by trial-and-error methods, although simulators or computers may be used to speed up the process.

Comparison of Vented-Box and Closed-Box Systems

Most direct-radiator loudspeaker systems use or are based on either the closed-box or vented-box principle. It is therefore of interest to compare these two fundamental systems, and to observe the advantages and disadvantages of each.

One obvious difference is that the vented-box system is more complex, i.e., has more variables requiring adjustment, than the closed-box system. This difference means that satisfactory designs are relatively easier to obtain with the closed-box system and probably accounts for much of the popularity of this system.

The performance relationships derived in this paper for the vented-box system and in [22] for the closed-box system make possible a number of interesting quantitative comparisons which follow.

Response

The response of the vented-box system can typically be adjusted from fourth-order Chebyshev to quasi-third-order maximally flat; that of the closed-box system can be adjusted from second-order Chebyshev to an over-damped second-order condition approaching first-order behavior. This means the closed-box system is nominally capable of better transient response, but Thiele [10, Sec. 13] suggests the differences among correctly adjusted systems of both types are likely to be inaudible.

Efficiency

A comparison of Fig. 16 or Eq. (35) with [22, Fig. 7 or eq. (28)] reveals that the vented-box system has a maximum theoretical value of k_η which is 2.9 dB greater than that of the closed-box system. Both systems suffer to a similar degree from the combined effects of driver and enclosure losses, and both must sacrifice efficiency to make use of alignments which have better transient response than the maximum-efficiency alignment (see Fig. 15 and [22, Fig. 8]).

Typical values of k_η for practical designs still favor the vented-box system by about 3 dB. The larger efficiency constant may be used to obtain higher efficiency for the same size and cutoff frequency, a smaller enclosure size for the same efficiency and cutoff frequency, a lower cutoff frequency for the same size and efficiency, or any proportional combination of these [22, Sec. 4].

Power Capacity

The reduced diaphragm excursion of the vented-box system near the enclosure resonance frequency gives the vented-box system a higher power rating constant k_P than a comparable closed-box system. Comparing Eq. (41) with [22, eq. (35)], the advantage in favor of the vented-box system for average program material is a factor of 3.5, or 5½ dB; for particular applications it may be larger.

However, except for the extreme C4 alignments, this

advantage is limited to the passband; at frequencies well below cutoff, the vented-box system has a higher relative displacement sensitivity and is therefore more vulnerable to turntable rumble and other subsonic signals.

Driver Requirements

For a given specification of enclosure size and system cutoff frequency, the driver of a vented-box system requires a lighter diaphragm and greater electromagnetic coupling in the magnet-voice-coil assembly compared to the same size driver used in a closed-box system (cf. example of Section 12, Part III, with that of [22, Sec. 10]). These differences are physically consistent with the higher efficiency of the vented-box system. However, for equivalent acoustic power rating, the peak displacement volume V_D and therefore the peak diaphragm displacement x_{max} is substantially smaller for the vented-box driver. Because x_{max} determines required voice-coil overhang, total amount of magnetic material required for the vented-box driver is not necessarily greater.

The closed-box system driver must have high compliance relative to the enclosure if maximum efficiency is to be achieved. While high driver compliance may be beneficial to the vented-box design in terms of transient response, it is not necessary. In fact, a maximum efficiency constant is obtained for the vented-box system with a relatively low value of compliance ratio, and maximum displacement-limited power capacity is obtained with very low values.

Enclosure Size

It is stated above that the larger value of k_η for the vented-box system may be used to obtain a size advantage, i.e., the enclosure may be smaller than that of a closed-box system having the same efficiency and cutoff frequency. Then, despite the smaller enclosure size, if the drivers have equal peak displacement volume, the larger value of k_P for the vented-box system must give a higher acoustic power rating.

This is theoretically correct, but it is practically possible only so long as V_B remains very much larger than the maximum volume displacement required. The maximum air-volume displacement from the enclosure of a vented-box system is larger than V_D because of the contribution of the vent; if this *total* volume displacement exceeds a small percentage of V_B, the compression of air within the enclosure becomes nonlinear to such a degree that the system must produce distortion regardless of the driver linearity [3, p. 274].

In most practical loudspeaker system designs, V_D is indeed very much smaller than V_B, and power capacity is not limited by enclosure size. However, if extreme miniaturization is attempted or if a driver is specifically designed to obtain a very large value of V_D, this limitation may become relevant.

It is important to realize that two direct-radiator loudspeaker systems operated at the same frequency and *acoustic* power level have the same total output volume velocity and displacement regardless of the type of system [12, eq. (2)]. Thus for both closed-box and vented-box systems, adequate enclosure volume is essential to the production of high acoustic output power with low distortion at low frequencies. Some size reduction is possible for closed-box systems if motional feedback is used to control distortion [24], but this technique can be difficult to apply successfully [25].

Typical System Performance

A sampling of commercial vented-box loudspeaker systems was tested in late 1969 by measuring the system parameters as described in Section 7 and programming these into the analog simulator to obtain the system response. For a few systems, the response obtained in this way was checked by indirect measurement [26].

Most of the samples tested fitted into the same two categories previously described for closed-box systems [22, Sec. 8]: systems with a volume of 40 dm^3 (1.5 ft^3) or more, a cutoff frequency of 50 Hz or lower, and relatively flat response; and smaller systems with a cutoff frequency above 50 Hz and several decibels of peaking in the response above cutoff. There was, however, a greater tendency for these two categories to overlap.

While most of the systems were probably designed by traditional trial-and-error methods, the general objectives of system manufacturers appear remarkably consistent. The larger systems fulfill the traditional requirements for high-fidelity reproduction, while the smaller systems suit the apparent requirements of the mass marketplace.

REFERENCES

[2] B. N. Locanthi, "Application of Electric Circuit Analogies to Loudspeaker Design Problems," *IRE Trans. Audio,* vol. PGA-6, p. 15 (Mar. 1952); republished in *J. Audio Eng. Soc.,* vol. 19, p. 778 (Oct. 1971).

[3] L. L. Beranek, *Acoustics* (McGraw-Hill, New York, 1954).

[4] F. J. van Leeuwen, "De Basreflexstraler in de Akoestiek," *Tijdschrift Nederlands Radiogenootschap,* vol. 21, p. 195 (Sept. 1956).

[6] R. H. Lyon, "On the Low-Frequency Radiation Load of a Bass-Reflex Speaker," *J. Acoust. Soc. Amer.* (Letter), vol. 29, p. 654 (May 1957).

[10] A. N. Thiele, "Loudspeakers in Vented Boxes," *Proc. IREE (Australia),* vol. 22, p. 487 (Aug. 1961); republished in *J. Audio Eng. Soc.,* vol. 19, p. 382 (May 1971), and p. 471 (June 1971).

[12] R. H. Small, "Direct-Radiator Loudspeaker System Analysis," *IEEE Trans. Audio Electroacoust.,* vol. AU-19, p. 269 (Dec. 1971); republished in *J. Audio Eng. Soc.,* vol. 20, p. 383 (June 1972).

[20] A. N. Thiele, "Equalisers for Loudspeakers," presented at the 12th National Convention of the IREE (Australia), (May 1969).

[21] P. W. Klipsch, "Modulation Distortion in Loudspeakers," *J. Audio Eng. Soc.,* vol. 17, p. 194 (Apr. 1969), and vol. 18, p. 29 (Feb. 1970).

[22] R. H. Small, "Closed-Box Loudspeaker Systems," *J. Audio Eng. Soc.,* vol. 20, p. 798 (Dec. 1972), and vol. 21, p. 11 (Jan./Feb. 1973).

[23] H. F. Olson, J. Preston, and E. G. May, "Recent Developments in Direct-Radiator High-Fidelity Loudspeakers," *J. Audio Eng. Soc.,* vol. 2, p. 219 (Oct. 1954).

[24] E. deBoer, "Theory of Motional Feedback," *IRE Trans. Audio,* vol. AU-9, p. 15 (Jan./Feb. 1961).

[25] H. W. Holdaway, "Design of Velocity-Feedback Transducer Systems for Stable Low-Frequency Behavior," *IEEE Trans. Audio,* vol. AU-11, p. 155 (Sept./Oct. 1963).

[26] R. H. Small, "Simplified Loudspeaker Measurements at Low Frequencies," *Proc. IREE (Australia),* vol. 32, p. 299 (Aug. 1971); republished in *J. Audio Eng. Soc.,* vol. 20, p. 28 (Jan./Feb. 1972).

[32] J. E. Benson, "Theory and Design of Loudspeaker Enclosures, Part 3—Introduction to Synthesis of Vented Systems," *A.W.A. Tech. Rev.,* vol. 14, p. 369 (Nov. 1972).

Vented-Box Loudspeaker Systems Part III: Synthesis

RICHARD H. SMALL

School of Electrical Engineering, The University of Sydney, Sydney, N.S.W. 2006, Australia

The analytical relationships developed in Parts I and II which relate the performance characteristics of the vented-box loudspeaker system to the basic parameters of its components make possible the straightforward design of loudspeaker systems meeting specific performance goals. A set of desired system performance specifications may be checked for realizability and then used to determine the required physical properties of all the system components. The most suitable enclosure design for a particular driver may also be readily determined.

Editor's Note: Part I of Vented-Box Loudspeaker Systems appeared in the June issue and Part II in July/August.

11. SYSTEM SYNTHESIS

System-Component Relationships

The relationships between response and system parameter adjustment are given in Part I by Figs. 6 and 9–13 for the "flat" C4–B4–QB3 alignments. Enclosure losses cannot be known exactly in advance but can be predicted from experience. For example, for numerous commercial systems and laboratory enclosures in the range of 25–100 dm^3 (1–4 ft^3) measured in the course of this research, the most commonly measured values of Q_B are between 5 and 10 with a general tendency for Q_B to fall with increasing enclosure volume.

For enclosures of moderate size, the assumption of an equivalent Q_L value of 7 is a very satisfactory starting point for design purposes. In this case Fig. 11 is used to represent the basic relationships between driver parameters, system parameters, and system response. If a higher or lower value of Q_B is expected with some confidence, one of the other figures is used.

The appropriate alignment and response relationships (Fig. 11 or otherwise) and the efficiency, power capacity, and vent design relationships established in Parts I and II permit the design of vented-box systems in complete detail. Procedures are described and illustrated below for two important cases, design of an enclosure to suit a particular driver and design of a complete system starting from required performance specifications.

Design with a Given Driver

The design of an enclosure to suit a given driver

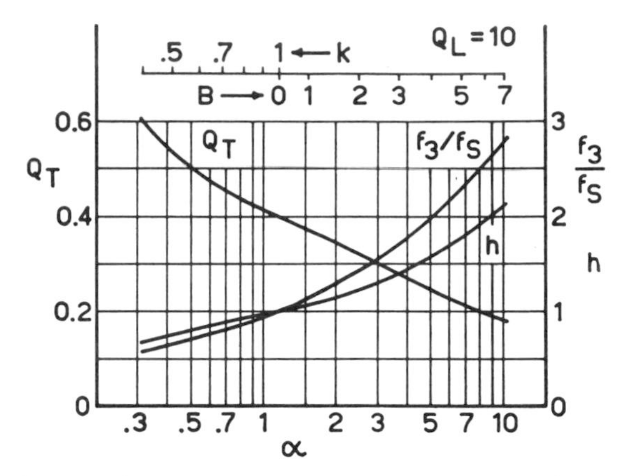

Fig. 10. Alignment chart for vented-box systems with $Q_B = Q_L = 10$.

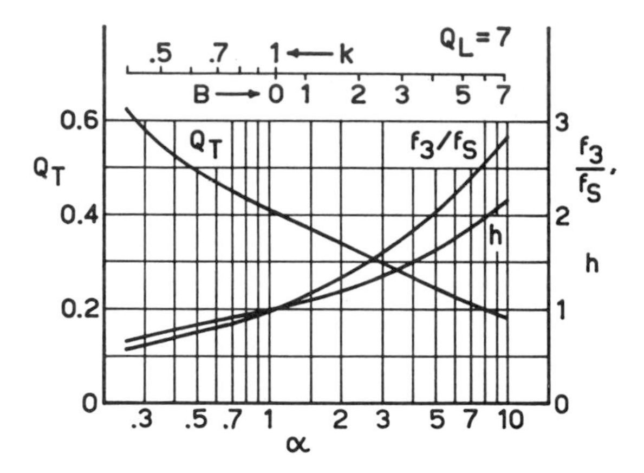

Fig. 11. Alignment chart for vented-box systems with $Q_B = Q_L = 7$.

starts with a knowledge of the driver small-signal parameters f_S, Q_{TS}, and V_{AS}; f_S and Q_{TS} must be adjusted if necessary to correspond to enclosure mounting conditions. If these parameters are not already known, they may be measured by the methods given in [10] or [12] using a standard baffle to provide air-mass loading as for an enclosure (see also Section 7 in Part II of the present paper, including Footnote 3).

The value of Q_{TS} is of primary importance. If the loudspeaker system is to be used with a modern amplifier having very low output (Thevenin) resistance, then Q_T for the system will be equal to Q_{TS} for the driver. From Figs. 6 and 9–13 it is clear that Q_T must be no larger than about 0.6 for successful application in a vented enclosure.

If Q_{TS} has a reasonable value, then the optimum value of α for a system using the driver is found from, say, Fig. 11 by locating the measured value of Q_{TS} on the Q_T curve in the figure and observing the corresponding value of α on the abscissa. This value of α then determines the optimum value of V_B using Eq. (46). It also determines the required value of h (and therefore f_B) and the corresponding value of f_3 for the system as indicated on the same figure. If the resulting system design is not acceptable (f_3 too high, V_B too large, etc.), then it is probable that the driver is not suitable for use in a vented-box system.

The design process may alternatively be begun by selecting an enclosure size V_B which suits aesthetic or architectural requirements. This determines α and hence the required enclosure tuning f_B, the required value of Q_T, and the resulting cutoff frequency f_3. If the value of f_3 is not satisfactory, then the driver and the enclosure size chosen are not compatible. If f_3 is satisfactory but the required Q_T is very different from Q_{TS}, it may be possible to use the driver as discussed below.

There are limited ways of salvaging a driver having unsatisfactory parameter values. If the value of Q_{TS} is too high to fit an alignment which is otherwise desirable in terms of enclosure size and bandwidth, an acoustically resistive material such as bonded acetate fiber may be stretched over the rear of the driver frame to reduce the effective value of Q_{MS}, thus lowering Q_{TS} [17], [27]. The correct amount of resistive material is determined experimentally by remeasurement of Q_{TS} as material is added. Q_T may also be reduced by using a negative value of amplifier output resistance R_g [10, Sec. 12], [28] to produce a low value of Q_E, where [12, eq. (21)]

$$Q_E = Q_{ES}\frac{R_g + R_E}{R_E} \tag{53}$$

because in this case [12, eq. (22)]

$$Q_T = Q_E Q_{MS}/(Q_E + Q_{MS}). \tag{54}$$

Both methods reduce Q_T without changing Q_{ES}; thus the value of $k_{\eta(Q)}$ from Eq. (29), and therefore η_0 for the system, will be lower than could be achieved by altering the magnet design to reduce Q_{ES} directly.

Sometimes the value of Q_{TS} is found to be undesirably low. This may be remedied by placing a resistor in series with the voice coil to increase R_E and therefore Q_{ES} or by using a positive value of R_g to increase Q_E.

If the driver proves satisfactory and an acceptable system design is found, the system reference efficiency is calculated from the basic driver parameters using Eq. (25). The approximate displacement-limited acoustic power rating of the system is computed from Eq. (41) if V_D is known. V_D usually can be evaluated as described in [22, Sec. 6]. The approximate displacement-limited input power rating is then found by dividing the acoustic power rating by the reference efficiency as indicated by Eq. (42). The vent design is carried out in accordance with Section 8 of Part II.

Example of Design with a Given Driver

The following small-signal parameters were measured for an 8-inch wide-range driver manufactured in the United States:

$$f_S = 33 \text{ Hz}$$

$$Q_{MS} = 2.0$$

$$Q_{ES} = 0.45$$

$$V_{AS} = 57 \text{ dm}^3 \text{ (2 ft}^3\text{)}.$$

The large-signal characteristics specified by the manufacturer are as follows.

1) "Total linear excursion of one-half inch." From this, $x_{max} = 6$ mm, and, assuming a typical effective diaphragm radius of 0.08 m,

$$V_D = 120 \text{ cm}^3.$$

2) "Power capacity 25 watts program material." From this it is assumed that for program material the thermal capacity of the driver is adequate for operation with amplifiers of up to 25-watt continuous rating.

By calculation from Eqs. (31) and (25).

$$Q_{TS} = 0.37$$
$$\eta_0 = 0.44\% .$$

Assuming that the amplifier to be used with the system has negligible Thevenin output resistance, Q_T for the system will be 0.37. Taking $Q_B = 7$ initially, Fig. 11 indicates that the enclosure volume will be relatively small; a more likely value of Q_B is thus about 10. Using Fig. 10 then, a QB3 response with $B = 1.0$ can be obtained for which the system parameters are

$$\alpha = 1.55$$
$$h = 1.07$$
$$f_3/f_S = 1.16.$$

Thus the required enclosure volume is

$$V_B = V_{AS}/\alpha = 37 \text{ dm}^3 \ (1.3 \text{ ft}^3).$$

The enclosure must be tuned to

$$f_B = hf_S = 35 \text{ Hz}$$

and the system cutoff frequency is

$$f_3 = 38 \text{ Hz.}$$

From Eq. (41) the displacement-limited program acoustic power rating of the system is

$$P_{AR} = 3.0 f_3{}^4 V_D{}^2 = 90 \text{ mW}.$$

The corresponding displacement-limited program input power rating is

$$P_{ER} = P_{AR}/\eta_0 = 20 \text{ W}.$$

Because this is less than the manufacturer's input power rating, it should be quite safe to operate the system with an amplifier having a continuous power rating of 20 watts.

From Eq. (52) the minimum diameter of a tubular vent is $(V_D f_B)^{1/2}$ or 65 mm (2.6 inches). From Fig. 21, the required vent length is 175 mm (7 inches) for a tubing of this diameter.

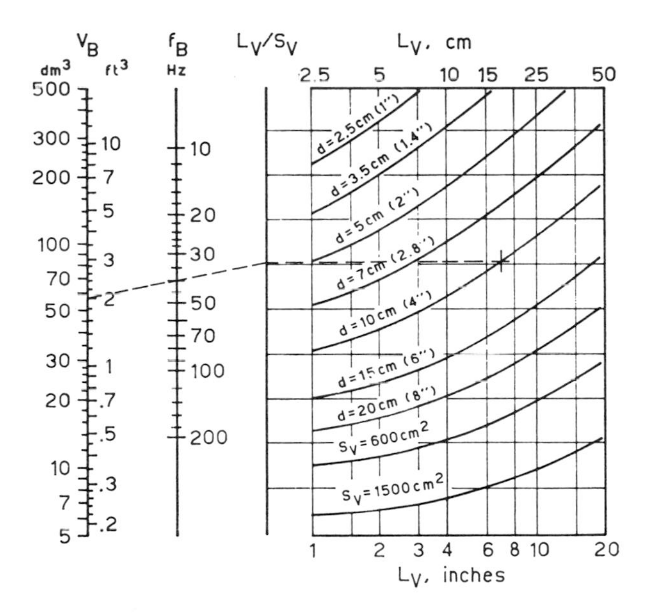

Fig. 21. Nomogram and chart for design of ducted vents.

Design from Specfications

The important performance specifications of a loudspeaker system include frequency response, efficiency, power capacity, and enclosure size. The complexity of the vented-box system makes control of all these specifications quite difficult when traditional trial-and-error design techniques are used. In contrast, the analytical relationships developed in this paper make possible the direct synthesis of a vented-box system to meet any physically realizable set of small-signal and large-signal specifications and even provide a check on realizability before design is begun.[4]

Specification of system frequency response basically amounts to specification of an alignment type and a cutoff frequency f_3. While the emphasis in this paper is on the "flat" C4–B4–QB3 alignments, any other desired alignment may be specified, e.g., the degenerated Chebyshev type 2 (DT2) alignment used by Nomura which provides passband peaking [11]. Appendix 1 shows how the required system alignment parameters may be calculated from the polynomial coefficients of any desired alignment based on the assumed or expected value of Q_B. For any alignment in the C4–B4–QB3 range, the necessary alignment data are provided in Figs. 9–13. The frequency response specification thus fixes the values of the parameters α, Q_T, f_S, and f_B.

For a specified frequency response, the designer may specify also the enclosure size or the reference efficiency; but he may not specify both unless the values satisfy the realizability requirements of Section 4. If the enclosure volume V_B is specified, the required driver compliance is then

$$V_{AS} = \alpha V_B. \qquad (46)$$

The required value of the driver parameter Q_{ES} is found from the required value of Q_T by allowing for reasonable values of R_g (typically zero) and Q_{MS} (typically 5, but varies greatly depending on the amount of mechanical damping deliberately added to the suspension to suppress higher frequency resonances). The system efficiency is then calculated from Eq. (25).

The power capacity of the system may be specified in terms of either P_{ER} or P_{AR}, but not both unless the values agree with the attainable system efficiency. It is possible to specify both independently only if neither V_B nor η_0 are separately specified; then the required value of η_0 is given by the ratio of P_{AR} to P_{ER}, and the required enclosure volume which will provide this efficiency for the specified frequency response is found from Eqs. (26) and (28) using values of $k_{\eta(Q)}$ and $k_{\eta(G)}$ obtained from Eq. (32) and Fig. 15 and based on the estimated or expected values of Q_{MS} and Q_B.

Assuming that V_B and P_{AR} are specified and that η_0 has been determined from Eq. (25), P_{ER} is given by

$$P_{ER} = P_{AR}/\eta_0. \qquad (42)$$

The required value of V_D for the driver is found from

[4] See [32, Sec. 5 and 6] for an extensive discussion of the principles of system small-signal response synthesis.

Eq. (41) using the given values of f_3 and P_{AR}. Check that $V_D << V_B$. The thermally limited maximum input power rating of the driver $P_{E(\max)}$ must be not less than the value of P_{ER} divided by the peak-to-average power ratio of the program material to be reproduced.

The vent is designed so that the area S_V satisfies Eq. (51) and the effective length-to-area ratio gives the required f_B in combination with the enclosure volume V_B as determined from Fig. 21.

The driver is completely specified by the parameters calculated above and may be designed by the method given in Section 12.

Example of System Design from Specifications

A loudspeaker system to be used with an amplifier having very low output resistance must meet the following specifications:

$$f_3 = 40 \text{ Hz}$$
$$\text{Response} = \text{B4}$$
$$V_B = 57 \text{ dm}^3 \text{ (2 ft}^3\text{)}$$
$$P_{AR} = 0.25 \text{ W program peaks; expected peak-to-average power ratio 5 dB.}$$

It is assumed that the enclosure losses will correspond to $Q_B = Q_L = 7$ and that the driver mechanical losses will correspond to $Q_{MS} = 5$.

Using Fig. 11, the B4 response is located at a compliance ratio of

$$\alpha = 1.06$$

for which the required system parameters are

$$h = 1.00$$
$$f_3/f_S = 1.00$$
$$Q_T = 0.40.$$

Therefore the required driver parameters are

$$V_{AS} = 60 \text{ dm}^3 \text{ (2.1 ft}^3\text{)}$$
$$f_S = 40 \text{ Hz}$$
$$Q_{TS} = 0.40$$

and the required enclosure tuning is

$$f_B = 40 \text{ Hz}.$$

Taking $Q_{MS} = 5$ and using Eq. (31),

$$Q_{ES} = 0.44.$$

From Eq. (25) the reference efficiency of the system is then

$$\eta_0 = 0.84\%$$

and from Eq. (42) the displacement-limited electrical power rating is

$$P_{ER} = 30 \text{ W}.$$

This requires that the system amplifier have a continuous power rating of at least 30 watts. For the 5-dB expected peak-to-average power ratio of the program material, the thermal rating $P_{E(\max)}$ of the driver must be at least 9.5 watts [22, Sec. 5].

From Eq. (41), the displacement volume of the driver must be

$$V_D = 180 \text{ cm}^3.$$

This is only about 0.3% of V_B. Then, from Eq. (52), a tubular vent should be at least 85 mm (3.4 inches) in diameter. From Fig. 21, the length should be 115 mm (4.5 inches) for a tubing of this diameter.

12. DRIVER DESIGN

Driver Specification

The process of system design leads to specification of the required driver in terms of the basic design parameters f_S, Q_{ES}, V_{AS}, V_D, and $P_{E(\max)}$. To complete the physical specification of the driver, the arbitrary physical parameters S_D and R_E must be selected and the resulting mechanical parameters calculated. This process is described in [22, Sec. 10] and is illustrated by the example below.

Example of Driver Design

The basic design parameters of the driver required for the system in the example of the previous section are

$$f_S = 40 \text{ Hz}$$
$$Q_{ES} = 0.44$$
$$V_{AS} = 60 \text{ dm}^3$$
$$V_D = 180 \text{ cm}^3$$
$$P_{E(\max)} = 9.5 \text{ W}.$$

These specifications could be met by drivers of 8–15-inch advertized diameter [15].

Choosing a 12-inch driver, the effective diaphragm radius a will be approximately 0.12 m, giving

$$S_D = 4.5 \times 10^{-2} \text{ m}^2$$

and

$$S_D^2 = 2.0 \times 10^{-3} \text{ m}^4.$$

The required mechanical compliance and mass of the driver are then [22, eqs. (61) and (62)]

$$C_{MS} = V_{AS}/(\rho_0 c^2 S_D^2) = 2.14 \times 10^{-4} \text{ m/N}$$
$$M_{MS} = 1/[(2\pi f_S)^2 C_{MS}] = 74 \text{ g}.$$

M_{MS} is the total moving mass including air loads. Assuming that the driver diaphragm occupies one third of the area of the front baffle of the enclosure and using [3, pp. 216-217] to evaluate the air loads, the mass of the voice coil and diaphragm alone is

$$M_{MD} = M_{MS} - (3.15a^3 + 0.65\pi\rho_0 a^3) = 64 \text{ g}.$$

The electromechanical damping resistance must be [22, eq. (64)]

$$B^2 l^2/R_E = 2\pi f_S M_{MS}/Q_{ES} = 42 \text{ N}\cdot\text{s/m}.$$

For the popular 8Ω rating impedance, R_E is usually about 6.5 Ω. The required Bl product for such a driver is then

$$Bl = 16.5 \text{ T}\cdot\text{m}.$$

For the required displacement volume of 180 cm³, the peak linear displacement of the driver must be

$$x_{\max} = V_D/S_D = 4.0 \text{ mm}.$$

This is approximately the amount of voice-coil overhang required at each end of the magnetic gap. The total "throw" of the driver is then 8.0 mm (0.32 inch). This requirement presents no great difficulty so far as the design of the suspension is concerned.

The choice of a smaller driver diameter results in a lighter diaphragm and a less costly magnetic structure, but a greater peak displacement is then required, e.g., 9 mm (18-mm total throw) for an 8-inch driver.

The voice coil must be able to dissipate 9.5 watts nominal input power without damage.

13. DESIGN VERIFICATION

The suitability of a prototype driver designed in accordance with the above method may be checked by measuring the driver parameters as described in [12].

One of the driver parameters which is difficult to control in production is the mechanical compliance C_{MS}. Any shift in this compliance changes the measured values of both f_S and Q_{ES} as well as V_{AS}. Fortunately, system response is not critically sensitive to the value of C_{MS} so long as M_{MS} and B^2l^2/R_E have the correct values. Thus if the measured value of V_{AS} is not too far off its specified value, the driver will be satisfactory provided the quantities $f_S{}^2V_{AS}$ and f_S/Q_{ES}, which together indicate the effective moving mass and magnetic coupling, correspond to the same combinations of the specified parameters.

The effect of variations in C_{MS} on the response of a vented-box system is shown in Fig. 23 for a B4 alignment. The ±50% variation illustrated is larger than that commonly encountered. The relative effects are smaller for higher compliance ratios (i.e., QB3 alignments) and larger for lower compliance ratios (C4 alignments).[5]

The completed system may be checked by measuring its parameters as described in Section 7 and comparing these to the initial specifications. The actual system performance may also be verified by measurement in an anechoic environment or by an indirect method [26].

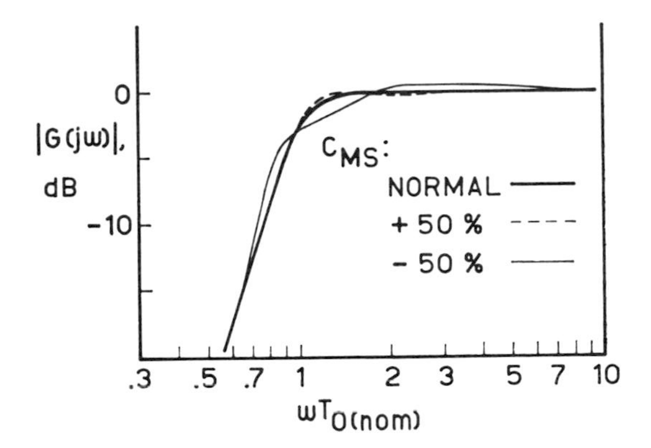

Fig. 23. Variation in frequency response of a B4-aligned vented-box system for changes in driver compliance C_{MS} of ±50% (from simulator).

14. SPECIFICATIONS AND RATINGS

Drivers

The moving-coil or electrodynamic driver has long been the workhorse of the loudspeaker industry. However, system designers have not been fully aware of the importance or usefulness of a knowledge of the important fundamental parameters of these drivers. They have instead used trial-and-error design techniques and relied on acoustical measurements of a completed system to determine the performance characteristics of the system.

The most important message of this paper and those that have preceded it is that trial-and-error design techniques are not only wasteful but unnecessary. Design may be carried out by direct synthesis provided the system designer either knows the parameters of a given driver or can obtain a desired driver by specifying its parameters.

It is essential for a driver manufacturer to specify all the important parameters of a driver so that system designers can completely evaluate the small-signal and large-signal performance obtainable from that driver. In addition to the specific physical properties of diaphragm size and voice-coil resistance (or rating impedance), the designer needs to know the values of the parameters f_S, Q_{ES}, Q_{MS}, V_{AS}, V_D, and $P_{E(max)}$. Conversely, where the designer needs a driver having particular values of these parameters, the driver manufacturer must be able to work from such specifications to produce the driver.

Because the basic design parameters above are directly related to the fundamental mechanical parameters such as M_{MD}, C_{MS}, B, and l, which the driver manufacturer has long used, there need be no difficulty in supplying these parameters. There is every likelihood that feedback from system designers will be helpful to driver manufacturers in improving their products, particularly in finding the best tradeoffs among response, efficiency, and power capacity requirements which can be obtained for a given cost.

Systems

Because the frequency response, reference efficiency, and displacement-limited power capacity of a vented-box loudspeaker system are all directly related to a relatively small number of easily measured system and driver parameters, there is every incentive for system manufacturers to provide complete data on these fundamental performance characteristics with the basic system specifications.

The theoretical relationships developed here refer to a standard radiation load of a 2π-steradian free field. This is only an approximation to average listening-room conditions [29], but ratings and specifications based on these relationships are of unquestionable value in comparing the expected performance of different systems in a particular application.

There is little doubt that buyers and users of loudspeaker systems would appreciate an increase in the amount of quantitative and directly comparable data supplied with such systems, especially in the categories of reference efficiency and acoustic power capacity.

15. CONCLUSION

The vented-box loudspeaker system has been popular for decades but has recently been shunned in favor of the more easily designed closed-box system.

The quantitative relationships presented in this paper make the design of vented-box systems a relatively simple task, despite the complexity of these systems.

[5] A very recent paper by Keele [33] contains exact calculations of the sensitivity factors of vented-box alignments to all important driver and system parameters. The sensitivity to driver compliance is shown to be extremely low compared to that for most other parameters over a wide range of alignments.

They also indicate that the vented-box system has substantial advantages over the closed-box system in terms of the attainable values of the efficiency and power-rating constants, although these advantages are gained at the expense of transient response and immunity to subsonic signals.

As the design of vented-box systems becomes better understood, interest in these systems may be expected to increase again. This does not mean that the popularity of well-designed closed-box systems will diminish. The choice of one or the other will depend on the requirements of a particular application.

The ease with which the low-frequency performance of a loudspeaker system may be specified in terms of simply measured system parameters should encourage more complete specification by manufacturers of the important frequency response, reference efficiency, and power capacity characteristics of their products.

16. ACKNOWLEDGMENT

This paper is part of the result of a program of post-graduate research into the low-frequency performance of direct-radiator electrodynamic loudspeaker systems. I am indebted to the School of Electrical Engineering of the University of Sydney for providing research facilities, supervision, and assistance, and to the Australian Commonwealth Department of Education and Science for financial support.

My indebtedness to A. N. Thiele for the inspiration behind the research program has already been acknowledged. We are also grateful for his considerable encouragement, helpful suggestions, and valuable criticisms of techniques and results.

I am further indebted to J. E. Benson for his generous assistance in discussing the subject matter of this paper and in examining and criticizing early manuscripts, and to Dr. R. H. Frater for his valuable contributions to the organization of this paper.

Finally, I acknowledge with gratitude the generous and considerable efforts of R. C. Pols in providing an English translation of the van Leeuwen paper.

REFERENCES

[3] L. L. Beranek, *Acoustics* (McGraw-Hill, New York, 1954).

[10] A. N. Thiele, "Loudspeakers in Vented Boxes," *Proc. IREE (Australia)*, vol. 22, p. 487 (Aug. 1961); republished in *J. Audio Eng. Soc.*, vol. 19, p. 382 (May 1971), and p. 471 (June 1971).

[11] Y. Nomura, "An Analysis of Design Conditions of a Bass-Reflex Loudspeaker Enclosure for Flat Response," *Electron. Commun. Japan*, vol. 52-A, no. 10, p. 1 (1969).

[12] R. H. Small, "Direct-Radiator Loudspeaker System Analysis," *IEEE Trans. Audio Electroacoust.*, vol. AU-19, p. 269 (Dec. 1971); republished in *J. Audio Eng. Soc.*, vol. 20, p. 383 (June 1972).

[15] J. R. Ashley and M. D. Swan, "Improved Measurement of Loudspeaker Driver Parameters," presented at the 40th Convention of the Audio Engineering Society, Los Angeles (Apr. 1971). Preprint 803.

[17] J. F. Novak, "Designing a Ducted-Port Bass-Reflex Enclosure," *Electron. World*, vol. 75, p. 25 (Jan. 1966).

[22] R. H. Small, "Closed-Box Loudspeaker Systems," *J. Audio Eng. Soc.*, vol. 20, p. 798 (Dec. 1972); vol. 21, p. 11 (Jan./Feb. 1973).

[26] R. H. Small, "Simplified Loudspeaker Measurements at Low Frequencies," *Proc. IREE (Australia)*, vol. 32, p. 299 (Aug. 1971); republished in *J. Audio Eng. Soc.*, vol. 20, p. 28 (Jan./Feb. 1972).

[27] J. L. Grauer, "Acoustic Resistance Damping for Loudspeakers," *Audio*, vol. 49, p. 22 (Mar. 1965).

[28] W. Steiger, "Transistor Power Amplifiers with Negative Output Impedance," *IRE Trans. Audio*, vol. AU-8, p. 195 (Nov./Dec. 1960).

[29] R. F. Allison and R. Berkovitz, "The Sound Field in Home Listening Rooms," *J. Audio Eng. Soc.*, vol. 20, p. 459 (July/Aug. 1972).

[32] J. E. Benson, "Theory and Design of Loudspeaker Enclosures, Part 3—Introduction to Synthesis of Vented Systems," *A.W.A. Tech. Rev.*, vol. 14, p. 369 (Nov. 1972).

[33] D. B. Keele, Jr., "Sensitivity of Thiele's Vented Loudspeaker Enclosure Alignments to Parameter Variations," *J. Audio Eng. Soc.*, vol. 21, p. 246 (May 1973).

Vented-Box Loudspeaker Systems Part IV: Appendices

RICHARD H. SMALL

School of Electrical Engineering, The University of Sydney, Sydney, N.S.W. 2006, Australia

The appendices present a method of calculating the system parameters required to obtain a desired alignment defined by transfer-function polynomial coefficients in the presence of enclosure losses together with diaphragm displacement data for that alignment, a derivation of the parameter-impedance relationships that permit parameter evaluation from voice-coil impedance measurements, and a method of evaluating the amounts of absorption, leakage, and vent losses present in a vented-box loudspeaker system.

Editor's Note: Part I of Vented-Box Loudspeaker Systems appeared in the June issue, Part II in July/August, and Part III in September.

APPENDIX 1 FOURTH-ORDER FILTER FUNCTIONS AND VENTED-BOX SYSTEM ALIGNMENT

General Expressions

The general form of a prototype low-pass fourth-order filter function $G_L(s)$ normalized to unity in the passband is

$$G_L(s) = \frac{1}{1 + a_1 s T_0 + a_2 s^2 T_0^2 + a_3 s^3 T_0^3 + s^4 T_0^4} \quad (55)$$

where T_0 is the nominal filter time constant and the coefficients a_1, a_2, and a_3 determine the actual filter characteristic.

Tables of filter functions normally give only the details of a low-pass prototype function; the high-pass and bandpass equivalents are obtained by suitable transformation. For the high-pass filter function $G_H(s)$, the transformation (retaining the same nominal time constant) is

$$G_H(sT_0) = G_L(1/sT_0). \quad (56)$$

This leads to the general high-pass form of Eq. (20):

$$G_H(s) = \frac{s^4 T_0^4}{s^4 T_0^4 + a_1 s^3 T_0^3 + a_2 s^2 T_0^2 + a_3 s T_0 + 1}. \quad (57)$$

Study of the magnitude-versus-frequency behavior of filter functions is facilitated by the use of the magnitude-squared form

$$|G_H(j\omega)|^2 = \frac{\omega^8 T_0^8}{\omega^8 T_0^8 + A_1 \omega^6 T_0^6 + A_2 \omega^4 T_0^4 + A_3 \omega^2 T_0^2 + 1} \quad (58)$$

where

$$A_1 = a_1^2 - 2a_2$$
$$A_2 = a_2^2 + 2 - 2a_1 a_3$$
$$A_3 = a_3^2 - 2a_2. \quad (59)$$

Using Eq. (58) it can be shown that the magnitude response of G_H is down 3 dB, i.e., $|G_H|^2 = ½$, at a frequency f_3 given by

$$f_3/f_0 = d^{½} \quad (60)$$

where

$$f_0 = 1/(2\pi T_0) \quad (61)$$

and d is the largest positive real root of the equation

$$d^4 - A_1 d^3 - A_2 d^2 - A_3 d - 1 = 0. \quad (62)$$

Coefficients of Some Useful Responses

Butterworth Maximally Flat Amplitude Response (B4)

This well-known response is characterized by [10], [18]

$$a_1 = (4+2\sqrt{2})^{1/2} = 2.6131$$
$$a_2 = 2+\sqrt{2} = 3.1412$$
$$a_3 = a_1 = 2.6131$$
$$A_1 = A_2 = A_3 = 0$$
$$f_3/f_0 = 1.0000$$

Bessel Maximally Flat Delay Response (BL4)

The normalized roots are given in [19]. They yield

$$a_1 = 3.20108 \qquad A_1 = 1.4638$$
$$a_2 = 4.39155 \qquad A_2 = 1.2857$$
$$a_3 = 3.12394 \qquad A_3 = 0.9759.$$
$$f_3/f_0 = 1.5143$$

Chebyshev Equal-Ripple (C4) and "Sub-Chebyshev" (SC4) Responses

These responses are both described in [14]; the $C4$ responses are further described in [32]. The pole locations may be derived from those of the Butterworth response by multiplying the real part of the Butterworth pole by a factor k which is less than unity for the $C4$ responses and greater than unity for the $SC4$ responses. The filter-function coefficients are then given by

$$a_3 = \frac{k(4+2\sqrt{2})^{1/2}}{D^{1/4}}$$
$$a_2 = \frac{1+k^2(1+\sqrt{2})}{D^{1/2}}$$
$$a_1 = \frac{a_3}{D^{1/2}}\left[1-\frac{1-k^2}{2\sqrt{2}}\right] \qquad (63)$$

where

$$D = \frac{k^4+6k^2+1}{8}.$$

For the $C4$ responses, the passband ripple is given by

$$\text{dB ripple} = 10\log_{10}[1+K^4/(64+28K+80K^2+16K^3)] \qquad (64)$$

where

$$K = 1/k^2 - 1.$$

Quasi-Third-Order Butterworth Responses (QB3)

This class of response is described in [10] and [32]. In this paper, the response is varied as a function of the parameter B given by

$$B = A_3^{1/2}. \qquad (65)$$

The other coefficients are given by

$$A_1 = A_2 = 0$$
$$a_2 > 2+\sqrt{2}$$
$$a_1 = (2a_2)^{1/2}$$
$$a_3 = (a_2^2+2)/(2a_1). \qquad (66)$$

Because the direct relationships between B and the a coefficients are very involved, the range of responses is computed by taking successive values of a_2 and then computing a_1, a_3, A_3, and B.

Other Possible Responses

Other fourth-order responses which can be obtained with the vented-box system include transitional Butterworth–Thompson [18], transitional Butterworth–Chebyshev [30], Thiele interorder [31], and degenerated Chebyshev [11].

The degenerated Chebyshev responses of the second kind ($DT2$) described by Nomura [11] look particularly appealing for cases where a smooth bass lift (similar to an underdamped second-order response, but with a steeper cutoff slope) is desired. Nomura's design parameters are readily convertible into those of this paper.

Computation of Basic Alignment Data

The basic alignment data are obtained by using the coefficient–parameter relationships given by Eqs. (21)–(24). The steps are as follows.

1) For a given response and value of Q_L calculate

$$c_1 = a_1 Q_L$$
$$c_2 = a_3 Q_L. \qquad (67)$$

2) Find the positive real root r of

$$r^4 - c_1 r^3 + c_2 r - 1 = 0. \qquad (68)$$

3) Then, using Eqs. 60–62 to obtain f_3/f_0, the alignment parameters are

$$h = r^2$$
$$f_3/f_S = h^{1/2}(f_3/f_0)$$
$$\alpha = a_2 h - h^2 - 1 - (1/Q_L^2)(a_3 h^{1/2} Q_L - 1)$$
$$Q_T = hQ_L/(a_3 h^{1/2} Q_L - 1). \qquad (69)$$

For infinite Q_L the above expressions reduce to Thiele's formulas:

$$h = a_3/a_1$$
$$f_3/f_S = h^{1/2}(f_3/f_0)$$
$$\alpha = a_2 h - h^2 - 1$$
$$Q_T = 1/(a_1 a_3)^{1/2}. \qquad (70)$$

Computation of Displacement Maxima

Eq. (14) may be written in the generalized form

$$X(s) = \frac{b_1 s^2 T_0^2 + b_2 s T_0 + 1}{s^4 T_0^4 + a_1 s^3 T_0^3 + a_2 s^2 T_0^2 + a_3 s T_0 + 1} \qquad (71)$$

where T_0, a_1, a_2, and a_3 are given by Eqs. (21)–(24) or by the alignment specification and

$$b_1 = 1/h$$
$$b_2 = 1/(h^{1/2} Q_L). \qquad (72)$$

The magnitude-squared form of this expression is

$$|X(j\omega)|^2 = \frac{B_1\omega^4 T_0^4 + B_2\omega^2 T_0^2 + 1}{\omega^8 T_0^8 + A_1\omega^6 T_0^6 + A_2\omega^4 T_0^4 + A_3\omega^2 T_0^2 + 1} \qquad (73)$$

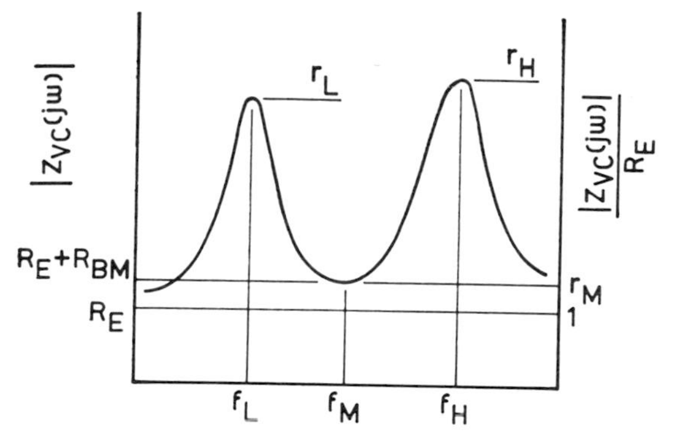

Fig. 20. Voice-coil impedance magnitude of vented-box loudspeaker system as a function of frequency.

where the A_i coefficients are given by Eq. (59) and

$$B_1 = b_1^2$$
$$B_2 = b_2^2 - 2b_1. \quad (74)$$

The value of $|X(j\omega)|_{max}^2$ for any alignment is found by differentiating Eq. (73), setting the result equal to zero, solving for the value of $\omega^2 T_0^2$, and then replacing this solution in Eq. (73) and evaluating the expression. There are always at least three frequencies of zero slope for Eq. (73): zero, near f_B, and above f_B. For the extreme C4 alignments, there is a fourth frequency, below f_B. The first of these frequencies gives unity displacement; the second is not of interest because it gives a displacement minimum. The third frequency gives the displacement needed to evaluate the displacement-limited power capacity for bandwidth-limited drive conditions. The procedure is as follows.

1) For a given alignment and value of Q_L, calculate

$$C_4 = (1/2B_1)(A_1B_1 + 3B_2)$$
$$C_3 = (1/B_1)(A_1B_2 + 2)$$
$$C_2 = (1/2B_1)(3A_1 + A_2B_2 - A_3B_1)$$
$$C_1 = (1/B_1)(A_2 - B_1)$$
$$C_0 = (1/2B_1)(A_3 - B_2). \quad (75)$$

2) Find the largest positive real root G of

$$G^5 + C_4G^4 + C_3G^3 + C_2G^2 + C_1G + C_0 = 0. \quad (76)$$

(The normalized frequency of maximum passband displacement is then $f_{X\,max}/f_0 = G^{1/2}$).

3) Calculate

$$|X(j\omega)|_{max}^2 = \frac{B_1G^2 + B_2G + 1}{G^4 + A_1G^3 + A_2G^2 + A_3G + 1}. \quad (77)$$

The same procedure is used to determine the frequency of maximum displacement below f_B for the extreme C4 alignments by finding the smallest nonzero positive real root in 2). The corresponding maximum value of the displacement function magnitude is then determined as in 3).

APPENDIX 2
PARAMETER-IMPEDANCE RELATIONSHIPS

Determination of f_{SB} and α

For infinite Q_L, the steady-state form of Eq. (16) becomes

$$Z_{VC}(j\omega) = R_E + R_{ES}\frac{j(\omega T_S/Q_{MS})(1-\omega^2T_B^2)}{\omega^4T_B^2T_S^2 + 1 + \omega^2[(\alpha+1)T_B^2 + T_S^2] + j(\omega T_S/Q_{MS})(1-\omega^2T_B^2)}. \quad (78)$$

This expression has minimum magnitude and zero phase when the numerator of the second term is zero, i.e., when $\omega = 1/T_B$. Thus for this case, the frequency f_M of Fig. 20 is equal to f_B. The expression also has zero phase, with maximum magnitude, when the real part of the denominator of the second term is zero, i.e., for

$$\omega^2 = \frac{T_S^2 + (\alpha+1)T_B^2 \pm \sqrt{T_S^4 + (\alpha+1)^2T_B^4 + (2\alpha-2)T_B^2T_S^2}}{2T_B^2T_S^2}. \quad (79)$$

Let the solution using the plus sign be ω_H^2 and the solution using the minus sign be ω_L^2. Then

$$\omega_H^2 + \omega_L^2 = \omega_B^2 + (\alpha+1)\omega_S^2 \quad (80)$$

and

$$(\omega_H^2 - \omega_L^2)^2 = \omega_B^4 + (\alpha+1)^2\omega_S^4 + (2\alpha-2)\omega_B^2\omega_S^2. \quad (81)$$

Combining Eqs. (80) and (81), it can be shown that

$$(\omega_H^2 - \omega_L^2)^2 = (\omega_H^2 + \omega_L^2)^2 - 4\omega_B^2\omega_S^2 \quad (82)$$

which simplifies to

$$\omega_H^2\omega_L^2 = \omega_S^2\omega_B^2$$

or [10, eq. (105)]

$$f_S = \frac{f_Hf_L}{f_B} \quad (83)$$

where $f_S = f_{SB}$ is the resonance frequency of the driver for the particular air-load mass presented by the enclosure.

With f_S known, α can be found by rearranging Eq. (80) into

$$\alpha = \frac{f_H^2 + f_L^2 - f_B^2}{f_S^2} - 1. \quad (84)$$

Alternatively, substituting Eq. (83) into Eq. (80), it is easily shown that [10, eq. (106)]

$$\alpha = \frac{(f_H^2 - f_B^2)(f_B^2 - f_L^2)}{f_H^2f_L^2}. \quad (85)$$

This expression factors into

$$\alpha = \frac{(f_H + f_B)(f_H - f_B)(f_B + f_L)(f_B - f_L)}{f_H^2f_L^2}. \quad (45)$$

Approximate Determination of Q_B

From Fig. 3, Z_{VC} will be resistive when the portion of the circuit to the right of R_{ES} is resistive. The steady-state impedance of this portion of the circuit is

$$Z(j\omega) = R_{EL}\frac{(\alpha T_BQ_L)[-\omega^2T_B/Q_L + j\omega(1-\omega^2T_B^2)]}{\omega^4T_B^2T_S^2 + 1 - \omega^2[(\alpha+1)T_B^2 + T_S^2] + j\omega(T_B/Q_L)(1-\omega^2T_S^2)} \quad (86)$$

At a frequency of zero phase, the magnitude of $Z(j\omega)$ may be evaluated by taking the ratio of either the real or the imaginary parts of the numerator and denominator, because these ratios must be equal. That is, for zero phase,

$$|Z(j\omega)| = R_{EL}(aT_BQ_L)\frac{-\omega^2 T_B/Q_L}{\omega^4 T_B^2 T_S^2 + 1 - \omega^2[(a+1)T_B^2 + T_S^2]} = R_{EL}(aT_BQ_L)\frac{1-\omega^2 T_B^2}{(T_B/Q_L)(1-\omega^2 T_S^2)}. \quad (87)$$

Setting the real and imaginary ratios equal in the normal way leads to a very complex set of solutions for the exact frequencies of zero phase. However, it can be seen that the first ratio varies relatively slowly with frequency near ω_B (as indeed does $|Z_{VC}(j\omega)|$) and hence can be expected to have about the same magnitude at the frequency of zero phase ω_M very near to ω_B as it has at ω_B. This gives

$$|Z(j\omega_M)| \approx |Z(j\omega_B)| = R_{EL}. \quad (88)$$

The resistive voice-coil impedance measured at f_M, defined as $R_E + R_{BM}$ in Fig. 20, is thus made up of R_E plus the parallel combination of R_{ES} and R_{EL}. Evaluating this resistance and using Eqs. (5), (7), (8), (10), and (11), it can be shown that

$$Q_L = \frac{h}{a}\left[\frac{1}{Q_{ES}(r_M-1)} - \frac{1}{Q_{MS}}\right] \quad (49)$$

where r_M is $(R_E + R_{BM})/R_E$ as defined in Eq. (48) and Fig. 20. In many cases the $1/Q_{MS}$ term can safely be neglected.

Now, if the two ratios in Eq. (87) are equal at ω_M, the second must give the same value as the first. This requires that

$$\omega_M^2 = \frac{1-aQ_L^2}{T_S^2 - aT_B^2 Q_L^2} \quad (89)$$

which may be rearranged to give Eq. (50). The approximation made earlier in Eq. (88) seems justified by Eq. (50) for Q_B values as low as 5, because the difference between f_M and f_B is then at most a few percent. For lower values of Q_B (which are unusual), substantial inaccuracy must be expected. Inaccuracy can also be contributed by a significant voice-coil inductance (see [32]).

APPENDIX 3
MEASUREMENT OF ENCLOSURE LOSSES

Measurement Principle

In this method of measurement the system driver is used as a coupling transducer between the enclosure impedances and the electrical measuring equipment. The driver losses are subtracted from the total measured losses to obtain the enclosure losses. Greatest accuracy is therefore obtained where the driver mechanical losses are small and stable.

The method assumes that R_E remains constant with frequency (i.e., voice-coil inductance losses are negligible), that the individual enclosure circuit losses correspond to Q values of about 5 or more (so that $Q^2 >> 1$), and that any variation with frequency of the actual losses present can still be represented effectively by a combination of the three fixed resistances R_{AB}, R_{AL}, and R_{AP} of Fig. 1.

System Loss Data

From the system impedance curve, Fig. 20, find the three frequencies f_L, f_M, and f_H, and the ratio of the corresponding maximum or minimum impedance to R_E, designated r_L, r_M, and r_H.

Using the methods of Section 7 (Part II) or [32], determine the system compliance ratio a. Measure independently the driver resonance frequency f_S and the corresponding value of Q_{ES} as described in [12] or [32]. The driver mounting conditions for the latter measurements do not matter, because the product f_SQ_{ES} which will be used is independent of the air-load mass present.

Driver Loss Data

Let the symbol ρ be used to define the ratio

$$\rho = (R_{ES} + R_E)/R_E. \quad (90)$$

Because R_{ES} is in fact a function of frequency for real drivers, so too is ρ. Typically the variation is of the order of 2 to 4 dB per octave increase with increasing frequency.

At the resonance frequency of the driver, ρ is the ratio of the maximum voice-coil impedance to R_E which is defined as r_0 in [12]. The value of ρ for frequencies down to f_L may be measured by weighting (mass loading) the driver diaphragm and measuring the maximum voice-coil impedance at resonance for a number of progressively lower frequencies as more and more mass is added. A convenient nondestructive method of weighting is to stick modeling clay or plasticene to the diaphragm near the voice coil.

Unfortunately, there is no comparable simple way to reduce mass or add stiffness which will raise the driver resonance frequency without affecting losses. For simplicity, it is necessary to extrapolate the low-frequency data upward to f_H. This is risky if f_H is more than an octave above f_S but gives quite reasonable results for many drivers.

Under laboratory conditions, it is possible to fabricate a low-mass driver which is "normally" operated with a fixed value of added mass. This mass is selected so that the unloaded driver resonance occurs at a frequency equal to or greater than the value of f_H for the loaded driver in a particular enclosure. In this case the value of ρ can be accurately determined for the entire required frequency range by adding and removing mass.

Measure and plot (extrapolating if necessary) the value of ρ over the frequency range f_L to f_H. Find the values at f_L, f_M, and f_H and designate these ρ_L, ρ_M, and ρ_H.

These measurements should be carried out at the same time and under the same conditions as those for the system loss data above. The signal level should be the same and should be within small-signal limits at all times.

Enclosure Loss Calculation

Define:

$$H = f_H/f_M$$
$$L = f_M/f_L$$
$$F = f_M/(af_SQ_{ES}). \quad (91)$$

Calculate:

$$k_L = \frac{1}{r_L - 1} - \frac{1}{\rho_L - 1}$$

$$k_M = \frac{1}{r_M - 1} - \frac{1}{\rho_M - 1}$$

$$k_H = \frac{1}{r_H - 1} - \frac{1}{\rho_H - 1} \tag{92}$$

$$C_L = Fk_L(L^2 - 1)\left(1 - \frac{1}{L^2}\right)$$

$$C_M = (Fk_M)^{-1}$$

$$C_H = Fk_H(H^2 - 1)\left(1 - \frac{1}{H^2}\right) \tag{93}$$

$$\Delta = \left(H^2L^2 - \frac{1}{H^2L^2}\right) - \left(H^2 - \frac{1}{L^2}\right) - \left(L^2 - \frac{1}{H^2}\right)$$

$$N_L = C_M\left(H^2L^2 - \frac{1}{H^2L^2}\right) - C_H\left(L^2 - \frac{1}{L^2}\right) - C_L\left(H^2 - \frac{1}{H^2}\right)$$

$$N_A = -C_M\left(L^2 - \frac{1}{H^2}\right) + C_H(L^2 - 1) + C_L\left(1 - \frac{1}{H^2}\right)$$

$$N_P = -C_M\left(H^2 - \frac{1}{L^2}\right) + C_H\left(1 - \frac{1}{L^2}\right) + C_L(H^2 - 1). \tag{94}$$

Then the values of Q_L, Q_A, and Q_P which apply at the frequency f_M are found from

$$Q_L = \Delta/N_L$$
$$Q_A = \Delta/N_A$$
$$Q_P = \Delta/N_P. \tag{95}$$

Using the same data, the total enclosure loss Q_B at the frequency f_M is

$$Q_B(f_M) = 1/C_M = Fk_M. \tag{96}$$

The approximate formula for $Q_B = Q_L$ given in Eq. (49) differs from Eq. (96) only in that R_{ES} is assumed constant, i.e., that $\rho_M = r_0$. However, because ρ_M is seldom very different from r_0, and particularly because $r_M - 1$ is usually much less than $\rho_M - 1$, Eq. (49) provides an adequately accurate measurement of total losses for normal evaluation purposes.

REFERENCES

[1] A. L. Thuras, "Sound Translating Device," U. S. Patent 1,869,178, application Aug. 15, 1930; patented July 26, 1932.

[2] B. N. Locanthi, "Application of Electric Circuit Analogies to Loudspeaker Design Problems," *IRE Trans. Audio,* vol. PGA-6, p. 15 (Mar. 1952); republished in *J. Audio Eng. Soc.*, vol. 19, p. 778 (Oct. 1971).

[3] L. L. Beranek, *Acoustics* (McGraw-Hill, New York, 1954).

[4] F. J. van Leeuwen, "De Basreflexstraler in de Akoestiek," *Tijdschrift Nederlands Radiogenootschap,* vol. 21, p. 195 (Sept. 1956).

[5] E. de Boer, "Acoustic Interaction in Vented Loudspeaker Enclosures," *J. Acoust. Soc. Amer.* (Letter), vol. 31, p. 246 (Feb. 1959).

[6] R. H. Lyon, "On the Low-Frequency Radiation Load of a Bass-Reflex Speaker," *J. Acoust. Soc. Amer.* (Letter), vol. 29, p. 654 (May 1957).

[7] J. F. Novak, "Performance of Enclosures for Low-Resonance High-Compliance Loudspeakers," *IRE Trans. Audio,* vol. AU-7, p. 5 (Jan./Feb. 1959); also *J. Audio Eng. Soc.*, vol. 7, p. 29 (Jan. 1959).

[8] L. Keibs, "The Physical Conditions for Optimum Bass Reflex Cabinets," *J. Audio Eng. Soc.*, vol. 8, p. 258 (Oct. 1960).

[9] E. de Boer, "Synthesis of Bass-Reflex Loudspeaker Enclosures," *Acustica,* vol. 11, p. 1 (1961).

[10] A. N. Thiele, "Loudspeakers in Vented Boxes," *Proc. IREE (Australia),* vol. 22, p. 487 (Aug. 1961); republished in *J. Audio Eng. Soc.*, vol. 19, p. 382 (May 1971), and p. 471 (June 1971).

[11] Y. Nomura, "An Analysis of Design Conditions of a Bass-Reflex Loudspeaker Enclosure for Flat Response," *Electron. Commun. Japan*, vol. 52-A, no. 10, p. 1 (1969).

[12] R. H. Small, "Direct-Radiator Loudspeaker System Analysis," *IEEE Trans. Audio Electroacoust.*, vol. AU-19, p. 269 (Dec. 1971); republished in *J. Audio Eng. Soc.*, vol. 20, p. 383 (June 1972).

[13] D. E. L. Shorter, "Loudspeaker Cabinet Design," *Wireless World,* vol. 56, p. 382 (Nov. 1950), p. 436 (Dec. 1950).

[14] A. N. Thiele, "Filters with Variable Cut-off Frequencies," *Proc. IREE (Australia),* vol. 26, p. 284 (Sept. 1965).

[15] J. R. Ashley and M. D. Swan, "Improved Measurement of Loudspeaker Driver Parameters," presented at the 40th Convention of the Audio Engineering Society, Los Angeles (Apr. 1971), Preprint 803.

[16] B. C. Reith, "Bass-Reflex Enclosures," *Wireless World* (Letter), vol. 73, p. 38 (Jan. 1967).

[17] J. F. Novak, "Designing a Ducted-Port Bass-Reflex Enclosure," *Electron. World,* vol. 75, p. 25 (Jan. 1966).

[18] L. Weinberg, *Network Analysis and Synthesis* (McGraw-Hill, New York, 1962), ch. 11.

[19] R. M. Golden and J. F. Kaiser, "Root and Delay Parameters for Normalized Bessel and Butterworth Low-Pass Transfer Functions," *IEEE Trans. Audio Electroacoust.*, vol. AU-19, p. 64 (Mar. 1971).

[20] A. N. Thiele, "Equalisers for Loudspeakers," presented at the 12th National Convention of the IREE (Australia), (May 1969).

[21] P. W. Klipsch, "Modulation Distortion in Loudspeakers," *J. Audio Eng. Soc.*, vol. 17, p. 194 (Apr. 1969), and vol. 18, p. 29 (Feb. 1970).

[22] R. H. Small, "Closed-Box Loudspeaker Systems," *J. Audio Eng. Soc.*, vol. 20, p. 798 (Dec. 1972), and vol. 21, p. 11 (Jan./Feb. 1973).

[23] H. F. Olson, J. Preston, and E. G. May, "Recent Developments in Direct-Radiator High-Fidelity Loudspeakers," *J. Audio Eng. Soc.*, vol. 2, p. 219 (Oct. 1954).

[24] E. de Boer, "Theory of Motional Feedback," *IRE Trans. Audio,* vol. AU-9, p. 15 (Jan./Feb. 1961).

[25] H. W. Holdaway, "Design of Velocity-Feedback Transducer Systems for Stable Low-Frequency Behavior," *IEEE Trans. Audio,* vol. AU-11, p. 155 (Sept./Oct. 1963).

[26] R. H. Small, "Simplified Loudspeaker Measurements at Low Frequencies," *Proc. IREE (Australia),* vol. 32, p. 299 (Aug. 1971); republished in *J. Audio Eng. Soc.*, vol. 20, p. 28 (Jan./Feb. 1972).

[27] J. L. Grauer, "Acoustic Resistance Damping for Loudspeakers," *Audio,* vol. 49, p. 22 (Mar. 1965).

[28] W. Steiger, "Transistor Power Amplifiers with Negative Output Impedance," *IRE Trans. Audio,* vol. AU-8, p. 195 (Nov./Dec. 1960).

[29] R. F. Allison and R. Berkovitz, "The Sound Field in Home Listening Rooms," *J. Audio Eng. Soc.*, vol. 20, p. 459 (July/Aug. 1972).

[30] A. Budak and P. Aronhime, "Transitional Butterworth–Chebyshev Filters," *IEEE Trans. Circuit Theory* (Correspondence), vol. CT-18, p. 413 (May 1971).

[31] A. N. Thiele, "Response Shapes for Simplified Active Filters," *Proc. IREE (Australia),* to be published.

[32] J. E. Benson, "Theory and Design of Loudspeaker Enclosures, Part 3—Introduction to Synthesis of Vented Systems," *A.W.A. Tech. Rev.*, vol. 14, p. 369 (Nov. 1972).

[33] D. B. Keele, "Sensitivity of Thiele's Vented Loudspeaker Enclosure Alignments to Parameter Variations," *J. Audio Eng. Soc.*, vol. 21, p. 246 (May 1973).

Low-Frequency Loudspeaker Assessment by Nearfield Sound-Pressure Measurement*

D. B. KEELE, JR.

Electro-Voice, Inc., Buchanan, Mich. 49107

A loudspeaker test technique is described which depends on nearfield pressure measurements made in a nonanechoic environment. The technique allows extremely simple measurements to be made of frequency response, power response, distortion, and electroacoustical efficiency.

GLOSSARY OF SYMBOLS

a radius of circular radiator
a_D radius of diaphragm, $= \sqrt{S_D/\pi}$
a_V radius of circular vent, $= \sqrt{S_V/\pi}$
c velocity of sound in air, = 343 m/s
e_{in} voltage applied to driver input
f frequency, in Hz
f_B Helmholtz resonance frequency of vented box
f_3 low-frequency cutoff (−3 dB) of speaker system
I_o acoustic intensity, in power per unit area, $= p^2/(2\rho_o c)$ for a plane wave
k wave number, $= 2\pi/\lambda = \omega/c$
p peak sound pressure
p_F peak sound pressure in farfield of acoustic radiator
p_N peak sound pressure in nearfield of acoustic radiator
$p_{N_{rms}}$ root mean square sound pressure in nearfield of radiator, $= p_N/\sqrt{2}$
p_R peak sound pressure on axis of piston at distance r
P_A acoustic output power
P_E nominal electrical input power
Q ratio of reactance to resistance (series circuit) or resistance to reactance (parallel circuit)
Q_B Q or cabinet at f_B considering all system losses
r distance from pressure sample point to center of piston
R_E dc resistance of driver voice coil
S surface area
S_D effective projected surface area of driver diaphragm
S_V cross-sectional area of vent
SPL sound pressure level, in dB re 20 μ N/m^2
U_o output volume velocity of acoustic radiator
λ wavelength of sound in air, $= c/f$
η nominal power transfer efficiency, $= P_A/P_E$
η_0 reference efficiency defined for radiation into a half-space free field
ρ_0 density of air, = 1.21 kg/m^3 at 20° C
ω radian frequency variable, $= 2\pi f$.

INTRODUCTION: The low-frequency evaluation of a loudspeaker system with respect to frequency response, distortion, and power output has traditionally required the use of a large and expensive anechoic chamber or a cumbersome and often equally costly open-field outdoor testing site. Recently, Small [1] pointed out that valid measurements could be made at very low frequencies in any reasonable environment by sampling the pressure inside the enclosure.[1]

* Presented May 15, 1973, at the 45th Convention of the Audio Engineering Society, Los Angeles.

[1] Even the large anechoic chamber at Electro-Voice is not much good for low-frequency measurements below 40 Hz in the farfield (beyond 10 ft (3 m) from the speaker system being tested). EV engineers have resorted to Small's technique numerous times to measure response below this frequency.

This paper describes a very simple measurement method which is based on measurements taken in the nearfield outside the enclosure and, like Small's method, may be used in any environment. However, this method does not require the frequency-dependent signal processing circuitry of Small's method and is accurate over a wider frequency range.

THEORY

Pressure on Axis

Consider a rigid flat circular piston mounted in an infinite flat baffle (half-space) generating peak sinusoidal acoustic volume velocity U_o (Fig. 1). The nearfield and

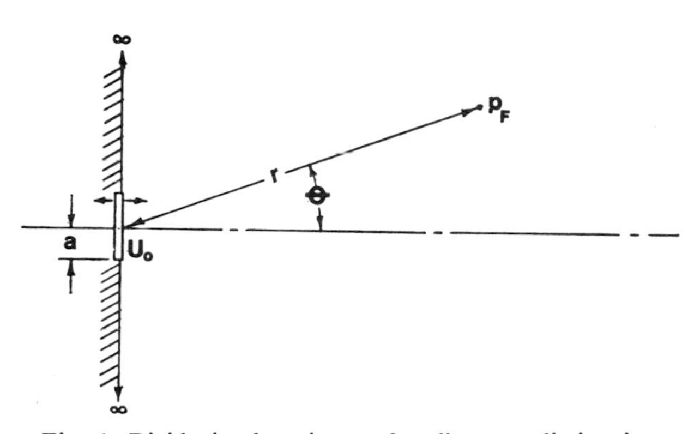

Fig. 1. Rigid circular piston of radius a radiating into a half-space freefield (2 π sr). The piston vibrates with peak volume velocity U_o and generates peak farfield pressure p_F at distance r away from center of piston.

farfield sound pressures for this case can be derived from the following equation, which gives the pressure magnitude along the piston axis for measurement distances r varying over the complete range of zero to infinity [2, p. 175]:

$$p_R = \frac{2\rho_o\, c\, U_o}{\pi\, a^2} \cdot \sin\left[\frac{k}{2}\left(\sqrt{r^2 + a^2} - r\right)\right] \tag{1}$$

where

- p_R peak pressure magnitude measured at distance r from piston
- a piston radius
- c velocity of sound in air, $=343$ m/s
- k wave number, $= 2\,\pi/\lambda = \omega/c$
- r distance from measuring point to center of piston
- U_o piston peak output volume velocity
- ρ_o density of air, $= 1.21$ kg/m^3 at 20° C.

Farfield Pressure

At points far from the piston where $r >> a$ and for low frequencies such that $ka < 1$, Eq. (1) can be shown to converge to

$$p_F = \frac{\rho_o\, c\, k\, U_o}{2\,\pi\, r} \tag{2}$$

where p_F is the peak axial pressure measured at distance r in the farfield of the piston. This relationship of course is the familiar equation that gives the farfield low-frequency sound pressure for any generalized simple sound source of strength U_o radiating from an infinite baffle [2, Eq. (7.40), p. 165]. Eq. (2) exhibits the well-known inverse relationship between pressure and distance.

Nearfield Pressure

At points very close to the center of the piston where $r << a$, Eq. (1) gives

$$p_N = p_R\,(r = 0) = \frac{2\,\rho_o\, c\, U_o}{\pi\, a^2} \cdot \sin\left(\frac{ka}{2}\right) \tag{3}$$

where p_N is the peak pressure in the nearfield at the center of the piston. If the frequency is low enough such that $ka < 1$, Eq. (3) reduces to

$$p_N = \frac{\rho_o\, c\, k\, U_o}{\pi\, a}\,. \tag{4}$$

Fig. 2 shows a plot of Eq. (3) divided by $\rho_o\ ckU_o/(\pi a)$ as a function of $ka/(2\pi) = a/\lambda$. This plot represents the normalized frequency dependence of the pressure in the nearfield of a rigid piston operating in the constant acceleration mode. The pressure is found to be constant up to the frequency where $a/\lambda = 0.26\,(ka = 1.6)$, the pressure fall being just 1 dB at this frequency. For frequencies such that the piston radius is a wavelength or multiple of a wavelength ($a = n\,\lambda$ for $n = 1, 2, 3, \ldots$), nulls are found to exist because of interference effects. For frequencies above $a/\lambda = 0.5$ ($ka > \pi$) the pressure envelope falls at 6 dB per octave.

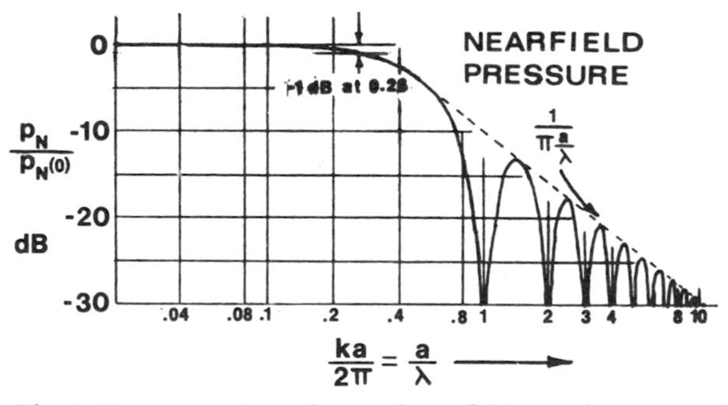

Fig. 2. Frequency dependence of nearfield sound pressure at points close to center of a rigid circular piston operating in a constant accelerating mode (mass-controlled region). Nearfield pressure nulls are found to exist whenever the piston's radius is equal to a wavelength or integral multiple thereof.

Near–Far Pressure Relationships

Dividing Eq. (4) by Eq. (2) and solving for p_N yields

$$p_N = \frac{2\,r}{a} \cdot p_F\,. \tag{5}$$

This surprising result shows that for low frequencies ($ka < 1$) the nearfield sound pressure is directly proportional to the farfield sound pressure. The relationship depends only on the ratio of the piston radius to the farfield sample distance and is independent of frequency. From a practical measurement standpoint, the nearfield sound pressure p_N and volume velocity U_o are essentially independent of the environment into which the piston is radiating [1, p. 29]. This means that valid inferences can be made about the low-frequency farfield anechoic operation of a particular speaker system from nonanechoic measurements of the nearfield sound pressure.

A parallel derivation for the case of a piston radiating into a full space at low frequencies yields

$$p_N = \frac{4r}{a} \cdot p_F . \qquad (6)$$

Measuring Distance

To investigate more fully the axial sound pressure dependence on measuring distance, Eq. (1) is examined in more detail. For distances from the piston less than 0.75 a^2/λ, plane waves are radiated which are contained essentially within a cylinder of diameter $2a$ [3, p. 187]. For distances beyond $2a^2/\lambda$ approximately spherical divergence is found to hold, where the pressure falls inversely as the distance. For frequencies equal to or higher than the frequency where $a = \lambda$ ($ka \geqq 2$), the pressure is found to go through a series of maxima with intervening nulls as the distance from the piston's surface is increased. For low frequencies such that $ka < 2\pi$ the only pressure null occurs at $r = \infty$. A plot of Eq. (1), normalized to the maximum axial pressure for several values of a/λ, is in Fig. 3.

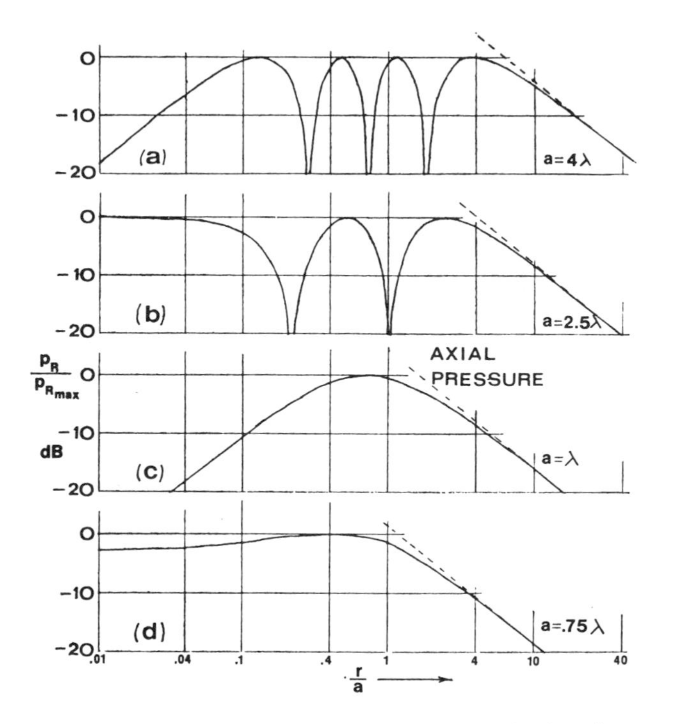

Fig. 3. Sound pressure along axis of a rigid circular piston radiating into a half-space freefield for several values of a/λ.

If the upper frequency of measurement is limited such that $ka < 1$, a division of Eq. (1) by Eq. (4) with the substitution $\sin X \approx X$ yields:

$$\frac{p_R}{p_N} = \frac{\sqrt{r^2 + a^2} - r}{a} = \sqrt{\left(\frac{r}{a}\right)^2 + 1} - \frac{r}{a}. \qquad (7)$$

Eq. (7) gives the low-frequency axial dependence of pressure on measuring distance normalized to the nearfield pressure occurring at $r = 0$. A plot of Eq. (7) on a dB versus log (r/a) scale is shown in Fig. 4. To be within 1 dB of the true nearfield pressure, the measuring pressure microphone must be no farther away from the center surface of the piston than $0.11a$. For low frequencies, farfield conditions exist for distances beyond $2a$.

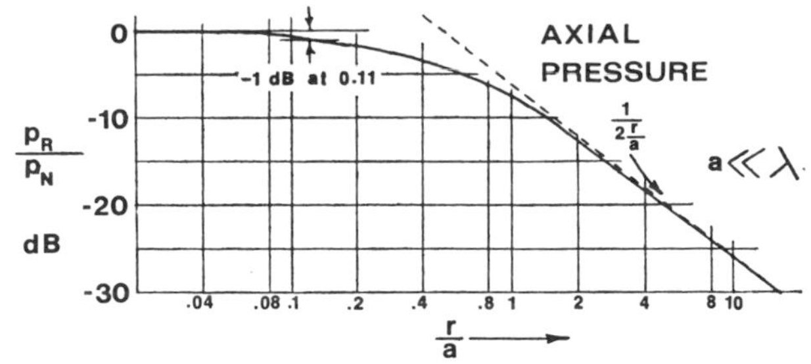

Fig. 4. Sound pressure along axis of a rigid circular piston radiating into a half-space freefield, for frequencies low enough such that $ka < 1$ (loudspeaker piston range).

Flat Piston Pressure Distribution

The analysis so far has considered only measurement points near the center and along the axis of a flat circular piston. In general, the nearfield sound pressure distribution over the surface of a piston is very complicated, especially for the higher frequencies ($ka > 2\pi$). Zemanek [3], in an excellent numerical analysis, presents the fine details of the nearfield pressure distribution for a circular piston operated in this higher frequency range.

Fortunately, in the low-frequency piston range of operation ($ka < 1$) the nearfield pressure is very well behaved and smoothly distributed. For $ka \leqq 2$, McLachlan [4, p. 49] has evaluated the exact expression for the pressure distribution at the surface of a rigid circular piston. Fig. 5, which shows the radial dependence of pressure magnitude for $ka = 0.5$ and 2, displays some of McLachlan's work. Examination of Fig. 5 reveals that the low-frequency nearfield pressure varies quite gradually as a function of surface position reaching a maximum at the piston center.

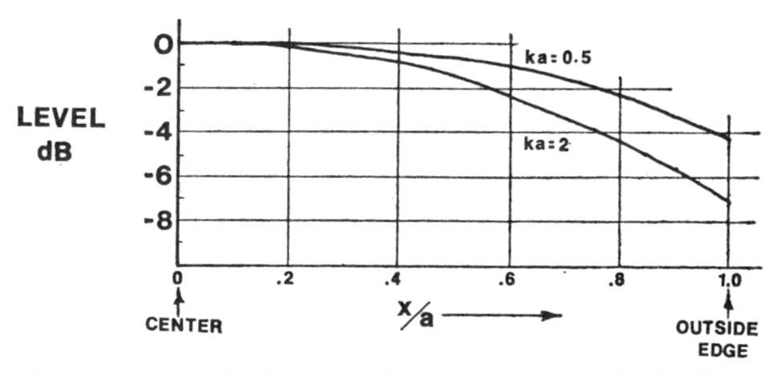

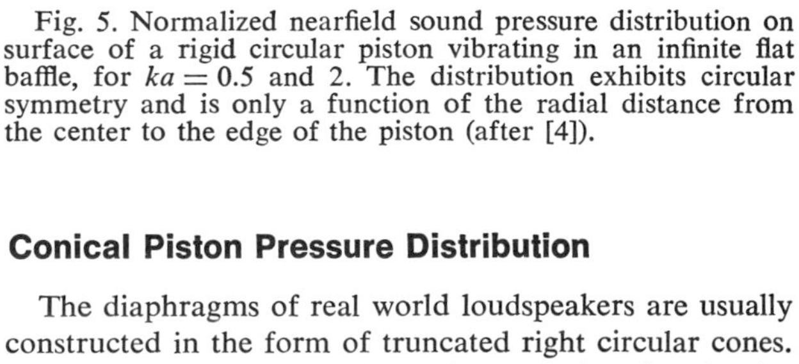

Fig. 5. Normalized nearfield sound pressure distribution on surface of a rigid circular piston vibrating in an infinite flat baffle, for $ka = 0.5$ and 2. The distribution exhibits circular symmetry and is only a function of the radial distance from the center to the edge of the piston (after [4]).

Conical Piston Pressure Distribution

The diaphragms of real world loudspeakers are usually constructed in the form of truncated right circular cones. The crucial question in this study is whether flat circular piston theory can be extended to measurements on conical pistons.

The author is unaware of any documented studies of the nearfield sound distribution of a vibrating cone and cannot give a definite answer to the question posed above. However, nearfield measurements made on a number of direct-radiator cone speaker systems have correlated extremely well with measurements made by other conventional means. In every case the nearfield sample was taken where the nearfield pressure was at a maximum, i.e., usually at a point near the cone's apex or speaker's dust dome.

Radiated Sound Power

The total radiated sound power output of an arbitrary acoustic source radiating into a half-space is found by integrating the intensity function over a hemisphere enclosing the source. If the radius of the hemisphere is large

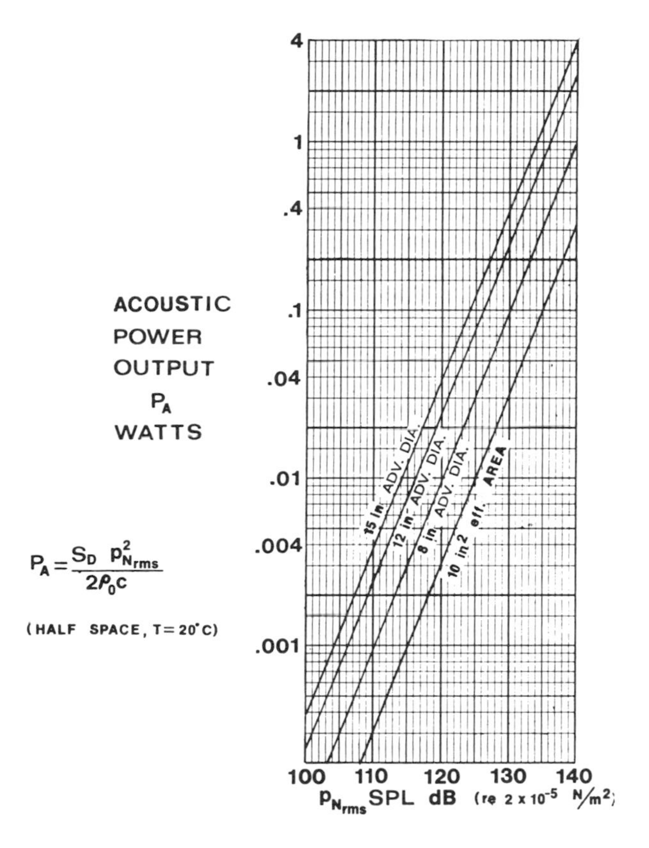

Fig. 6. Total radiated sound power P_A of a rigid circular piston radiating into a half-space to nearfield sound pressure level measured at points close to center of piston, for low frequencies such that $ka < 1$. The following piston sizes are plotted: 10-in² (64.5-cm²) effective (actual) area, 8-in (20.3-cm) advertised diameter (6.2-in (15.7-cm) effective diameter), 12-in (30.5-cm) advertised diameter (9.8-in (26.9-cm) effective diameter), and 15-in (38-cm) advertised diameter (12.6-in (32-cm) effective diameter).

enough so that all points on the hemisphere are in the farfield of the source, and if the source is radiating essentially omnidirectionally ($ka < 1$), the radiated acoustic power is given by

$$P_A = \int\int_{S_0} I_0 \, dS = \frac{\pi r^2}{\rho_0 c} \cdot p_F^2 . \tag{8}$$

Solving Eq. (5) for p_F and substitution into Eq. (8) yields

$$P_A = \frac{\pi a^2}{4 \rho_0 c} \cdot p_N^2 = \frac{S_D}{4 \rho_0 c} \cdot p_N^2 \tag{9}$$

where S_D is the effective area of the piston.

Eq. (9) may be rewritten for the case of rms pressure by substitution of $p_N = \sqrt{2}\, p_{N_{rms}}$ yielding

$$P_A = \frac{S_D}{2 \rho_0 c} \cdot p_{N_{rms}}{}^2 . \tag{10}$$

This equation indicates that for the low-frequency piston range operation of the radiator ($ka < 1$), the total radiated sound power may be assessed by a simple measurement of the nearfield sound pressure at the center of the piston. Fig. 6 plots this relationship for acoustic power output in watts versus $p_{N_{rms}}$ in dB re 20 μN/m² for several values of piston size.

Efficiency

The power conversion efficiency of the transducer is given by the ratio of the acoustic output power to nominal electrical input power for radiation into a specified environment (taken here as half space or 2 π sr). For the specific case of a loudspeaker driver with voice coil dc resistance R_E, the nominal electrical input power P_E is defined as the power available across R_E for applied source voltage e_{in} [5, p. 386]:

$$P_E = e_{in}{}^2 / R_E . \tag{11}$$

The efficiency may be computed in terms of the nearfield pressure and input voltage by dividing Eq. (10) by Eq. (11), giving

$$\eta = \frac{P_A}{P_E} = \frac{S_D R_E}{2 \rho_0 c} \cdot \frac{p_{N_{rms}}{}^2}{e_{in}{}^2} . \tag{12}$$

This relationship yields efficiencies that are within 1 dB of the true efficiency for $ka < 1.6$ (assuming the piston operates rigidly in this region). Fig. 7 plots this relationship for the specific situation of 1 volt rms applied to a driver whose R_E is 10 ohms, for several values of piston size. For other values of R_E, the values of η obtained from this figure can be scaled accordingly (if R_E is higher or lower than 10 ohms the efficiency is higher or lower in direct proportion). An efficiency curve has been included in Fig. 7 for a piston of 10 in² (64.5 cm²) true effective area to ease computations of efficiency for radiators of other sizes. Thus the efficiency of any driver is the value given by this curve multiplied by the ratio of actual piston area to 10 in² (64.5 cm²) and again by the ratio of actual voice-coil resistance to 10 ohms.

Frequency and Power Response

As stated earlier, Eq. (5) indicates that the relationship between near and far sound pressures depends only on two length constants and is independent of frequency (for $ka < 1$). Therefore, low-frequency response can be measured quite simply by plotting the nearfield pressure (in dB) versus frequency. Total acoustic power output versus frequency can then be derived using Eq. (10) or Fig. 6.

Distortion

Because of relation (5), completely valid measurements of low-frequency harmonic distortion can be made in the nearfield and these should correlate well with an identical set of measurements in the farfield if all distortion components are within the specified frequency limit. Somewhat lower nearfield distortion values are to be expected where distortion harmonics exceed this limit. The relatively high SPL found in the nearfield of a piston can actually aid distortion measurements because the acoustic signal-to-noise ratio is much improved. In most cases, meaningful distortion tests can be made even in a noisy laboratory environment.

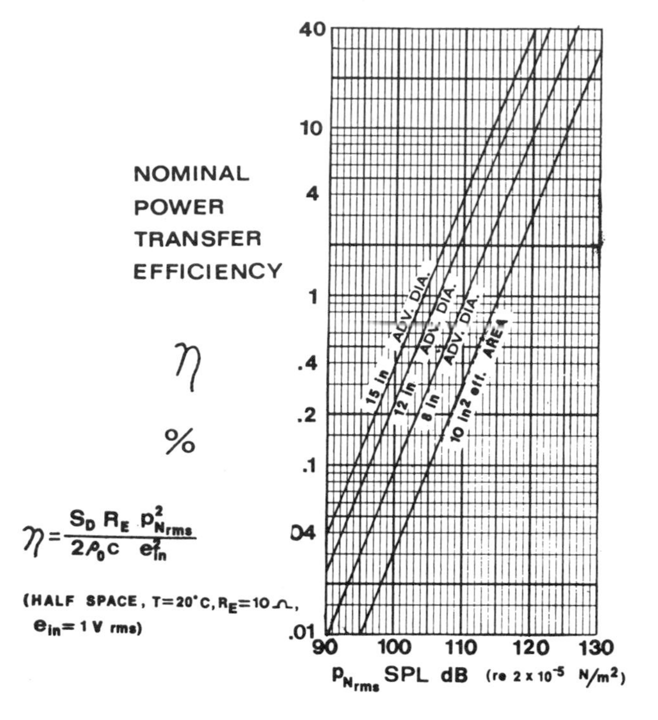

Fig. 7. Relationship between nominal efficiency of a loudspeaker driver operating as a rigid piston and radiating into a half-space and nearfield sound pressure level, for frequencies low enough such that $ka < 1$. The graph is normalized to unit input voltage ($e_{in} = 1$V rms) and voice coil resistance R_E of 10 ohms. Refer to Fig. 6 for description of piston sizes.

LOUDSPEAKER SYSTEM MEASUREMENTS

The nearfield pressure measurement technique is a very powerful tool for evaluating the performance of assembled loudspeaker systems. A nearfield pressure frequency response measurement of each driver in a system (both in and out of the system) can answer a whole host of questions concerning low-frequency bass response, overall system frequency response, system efficiency, relative efficiency, and levels between drivers, distortion, etc.

Closed Box

The woofer's nearfield pressure frequency response, measured with constant known drive voltage, is a direct analogue of the frequency response that would be measured in an anechoic chamber (half-space loading) for the piston range of operation. Figs. 6 and 7 can be used in this case to plot system acoustic power output and efficiency as a function of frequency (knowing e_{in}, R_E, and resultant nearfield SPL).

In-box measurements of nearfield SPL can be taken of all the drivers in a multiway system with crossover connected to provide data for computation of relative levels, approximate overall frequency response, efficiencies, and crossover frequencies. Eq. (5) can be used to compute each individual driver's contribution to the farfield pressure. Assuming roughly equal individual driver directional characteristics and equal farfield pressure contributions (equal efficiencies), the nearfield SPL is found to be inversely proportional to the linear dimensions of each driver (i.e., the tweeter, which is the smallest, has the highest nearfield SPL).

Vented Box

The nearfield pressure technique is found to work well for measurement of the low-frequency characteristics of the vented enclosure system. The complete system operation for a multiway vented-box system can be assessed in the same manner as the closed-box system by measuring the nearfield pressure of each driver individually. The following comments apply to the piston-range operation of the woofer mounted in the vented enclosure.

The vented-box system frequency response can be evaluated using the nearfield method. Benson [6, p. 47] displays the theoretical overall low-frequency response of a 4th-order Butterworth (Thiele's alignment no. 5 [7]) vented system, along with the individual contributions of the vent and driver. Fig. 8 is a reproduction of these data.

The driver diaphragm response is found to exhibit a null at the vented-box resonance frequency f_B. The depth of the null is found to be directly related to the total cabinet losses Q_B [8, p. 414]. A simple measurement of the driver nearfield SPL frequency response reveals the value of f_B by noting the frequency of the null. The driver reference efficiency η_0 can be derived (with the aid of Fig. 7) by noting the nearfield SPL in the level response region above 2 f_B with 1 volt rms applied.

The vent's contribution to the total system output can be likewise determined by a nearfield response measurement of the vent. For best results, the measurement microphone should be placed in the center of the vent, flush with the front surface of the cabinet. Practical measurements of the vent nearfield output in the frequency range above f_B reveal that the measured response is contaminated by crosstalk from the diaphragm. Valid nearfield SPL measurements of the vent can only be made for frequencies less than about $1.6 f_B$.

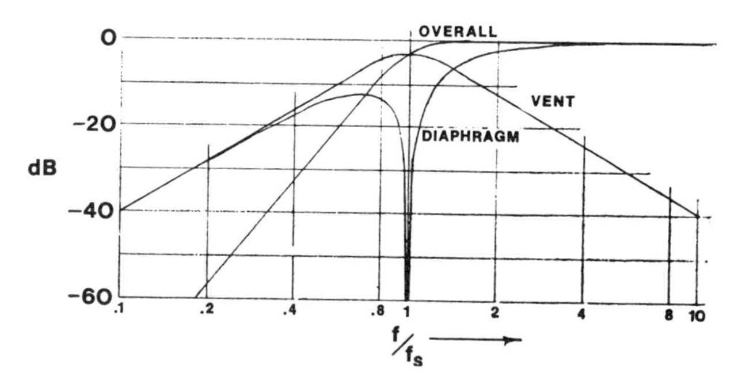

Fig. 8. Theoretical sound pressure frequency response of a vented undamped-enclosure loudspeaker system aligned so that the overall response conforms to a 4th-order Butterworth high-pass filter function (Thiele alignment no. 5 [7]). Individual farfield pressure responses are shown for the contributions of vent and diaphragm (after [6]).

The individually measured nearfield responses of the vent and driver may be used to construct an approximate farfield overall system frequency response. Eq. 5 must again be used to adjust the relative levels of diaphragm and vent, according to their respective diameters, before the responses can be summed. For example, if the vent diameter is one half the effective diameter of the driver diaphragm, the driver output must be increased by 6 dB before the outputs can be summed. The summation implied here is of course vectorial, where both magnitude and phase must be considered. It is noted, however, that the port and cone are roughly in phase above f_B and out of phase below f_B (for high cabinet Q). At f_B the system output is predominantly that of the vent. For situations where crosstalk is not much of a problem, one might even perform the indicated summation by using two microphones (one for the diaphragm and one for the vent) and then combining the microphone outputs by the use of a microphone mixer with input gains set appropriately.

EXPERIMENTAL MEASUREMENTS

Measurements were taken experimentally on several different types of systems to verify the theory and techniques put forth in this paper. A list of the measuring equipment used, along with a brief explanation of how Small's box-pressure measurement method [1] was implemented, is outlined in the Appendix.

SPL and Frequency Response Versus Distance

Eqs. (5), (7), and Fig. 4 were checked by making experimental measurements in the anechoic chamber on a 4½-in (11.4-cm) (1½-in (3.8-cm) effective piston radius) full-range driver in a closed box, flush mounted in the center of an 8- by 4-ft (2.4- by 1.2-m) baffle board (roughly a half-space for distances not far from the board). The 395-in³ (6473-cm³) closed test box was roughly cubical, with external dimensions of 7.75 by 8.25 by 8.5 in (19 by 21 by 21.7 cm). The driver was mounted from the outside, off center, on the 8.25- by 8.5-in (21- by 21.7-cm) face.

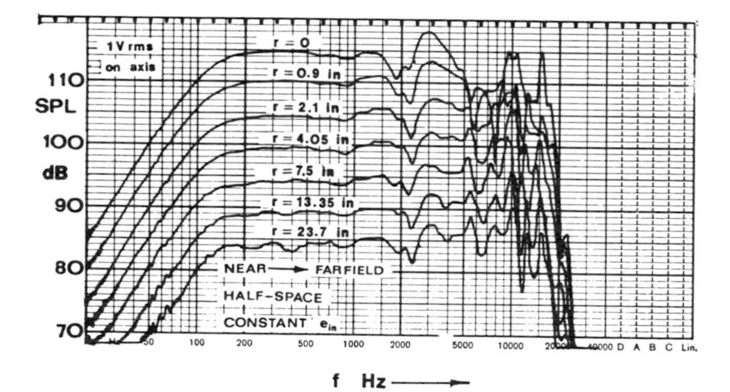

Fig. 9. Experimental measurements performed to check Eq. (7) and Fig. 4. The source is a 4.5-in (11.4-cm) wide-range driver, mounted in a 395-in³ (6473-cm³) closed box, flush mounted in the center of a 4- by 8-ft (1.2- by 2.4-m) sheet of ¾-in (1.9-cm) plywood. Seven anechoic axial frequency response measurements were made with the measurement microphone the indicated distance from the diaphragm. The distances chosen correspond to low-frequency axial attenuations of 0, −5, −10, −15, −20, −25, and −30 dB relative to the nearfield pressure at $r = 0$.

Several axial constant-voltage frequency responses were taken at different distances from the driver, extending from the nearfield ($r < 0.11a$) into the farfield ($r > 5a$ for low frequencies). Distances corresponding to low-frequency axial attenuations of 0, −5, −10, −15, −20, −25, and −30 dB (referred to nearfield pressure) were chosen ($r = 0$, $0.6a$, $1.4a$, $2.7a$, $5a$, $8.9a$, and $15.8a$, from Fig. 4). Fig. 9 shows the results of these measurements. The figure indicates close agreement with theory for all frequencies less than about 2 kHz ($ka \approx 1.4$). Note the large variation in signal-to-noise ratio between the responses in Fig. 9 and the improvement gained in the nearfield ($r = 0$).

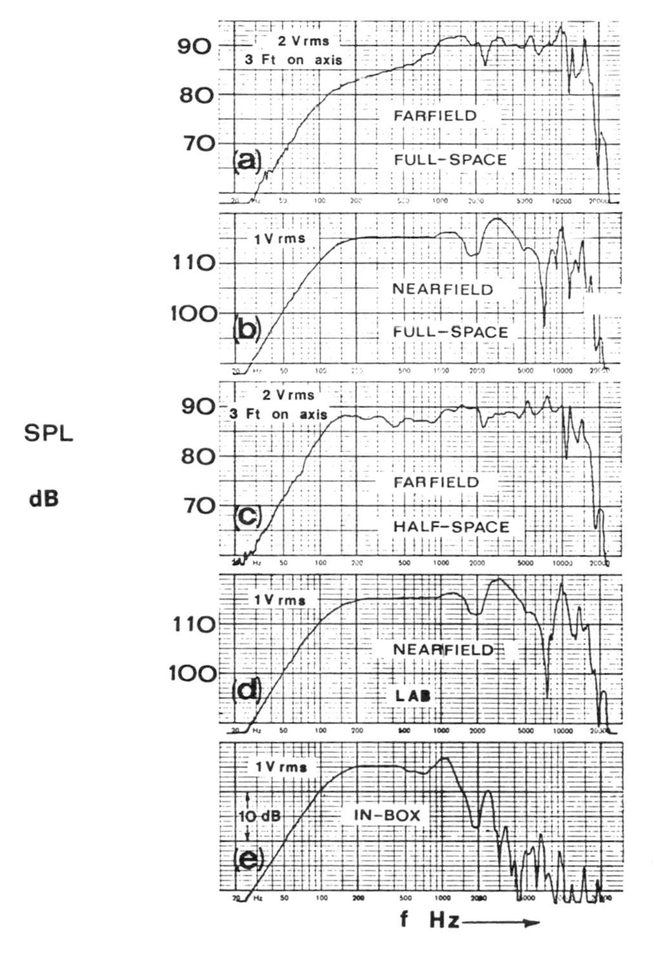

Fig. 10. Experimental frequency response measurements on the 4.5-in (11.4-cm) closed-box system of Fig. 9. The response was measured five different ways. **a.** In anechoic chamber in farfield (4 π sr). **b.** In anechoic chamber in driver's nearfield (4 π sr). **c.** On a 4- by 8-ft (1.2- by 2.4-m) baffle board, in chamber, in farfield (2 π sr). **d.** In lab on floor, in nearfield. **e.** In box using the method of Small [1].

Frequency Response Measured by Different Methods

The axial frequency response of the 4½-in (11.4-cm) closed-box system, described in the previous section, was measured using several different methods: 1) in the anechoic chamber in the driver's farfield (full space), 2) in the anechoic chamber in the driver's nearfield (full space), 3) in the anechoic chamber mounted on the 4- by 8-ft (1.2- by 2.4-m) baffle board in the driver's farfield (half-space), 4) in the laboratory sitting on the test bench in the driver's nearfield, and 5) inside the test box enclosure using Small's box-pressure measurement method [1]. These test results are displayed in Fig. 10.

Note the differences between the farfield responses of Fig. 10**a** and **c** that were measured in the 4 π and 2 π environments. Diffraction effects and increasing cabinet directivity with frequency causes a rising characteristic in the response from about 100 to 800 Hz in the 4 π space [9], [10].

Keeping in mind the expected differences between Fig. 10**a** and **c**, the frequency responses measured by the five methods show good agreement below 500 Hz. A comparison between the two indirect methods (Fig. 10**d**, **e**) reveals that the nearfield technique yields accurate response data about 1½ octaves higher than the box-pressure technique.

System Measurements

To illustrate system measurements with the nearfield technique, two loudspeaker systems were measured, an 8-in (20.3-cm) two-way closed-box acoustic suspension system and a 15-in (38.1-cm) three-way vented-box system.

Closed-Box

The closed-box direct-radiator system consisted of an 8-in (20.3-cm) diameter (6.2-in (15.7-cm) effective piston diameter) high-compliance woofer, and a 2½-in (6.4-cm) diameter (2-in (5-cm) effective diameter) closed-back tweeter.

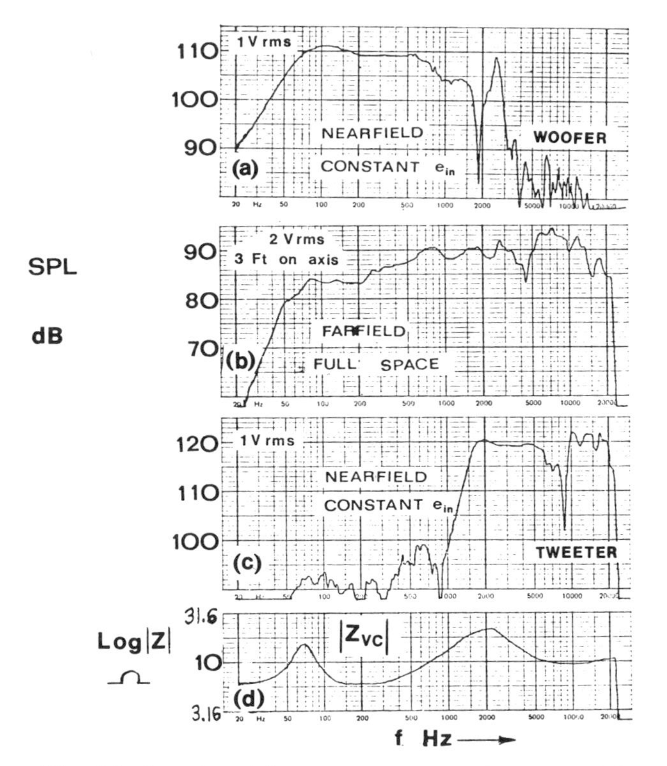

Fig. 11. Experimental measurements made on an 8-in (20.3-cm) woofer 2.5-in (6.3-cm) tweeter, two-way acoustic-suspension closed-box system. **a.** Nearfield frequency response of woofer (crossover connected for all these tests) with constant applied voltage. **b.** Frequency response in anechoic chamber in farfield (4 π sr). **c.** Nearfield response of tweeter with 1 volt rms applied. **d.** System driving-point impedance magnitude versus frequency.

Nearfield frequency responses were run on both drivers in this system with a constant system input voltage of 1 volt rms. The tests were run with the drivers mounted in the enclosure, in their correct positions, with the system crossover connected. An anechoic chamber free-field (full-space) response was measured for comparison. These responses are shown in Fig. 11.

The nearfield measurement of the tweeter (Fig. 11**c**) shows that its nearfield SPL is roughly 10 dB higher than that of the woofer. This level difference is expected because the tweeter is roughly one third the diameter of the woofer (assuming equal farfield SPL for each driver operating in the piston range). The measured voice-coil resistance R_E of the woofer is 4.8 ohms, and the calculated efficiency for the level portion of the system low-frequency piston range (200–500 Hz) is 0.35%.

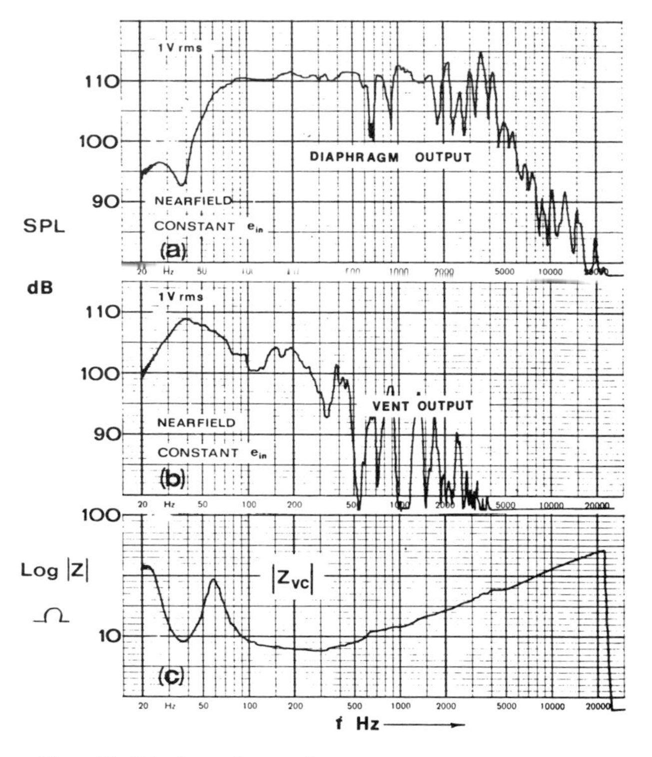

Fig. 12. Display of experimental measurements taken on 15-in (38.1-cm) vented-box system theoretically set up for a 4th-order Butterworth response with a corner (−3 dB) frequency of 40 Hz. **a.** Nearfield pressure frequency response at center of driver's diaphragm. **b.** At center of vent. **c.** Woofer's driving point impedance magnitude versus frequency.

Vented-Box

The measurements on the vented enclosure system were limited to the woofer section only. The three-way 15-in (38.1-cm) vented-box system consists of a direct-radiator vented-box low end with horn-loaded midrange and tweeter. The low end of this system is designed to have a 4th-order Butterworth high-pass response (Thiele alignment no. 5) with $f_B = f_3 = 40$ Hz. The driver's effective piston diameter is 13 in (33 cm) [$S_D = 133$ in^2 (858 cm^2)], the vent size is 7 by 10¾ in (17.8 by 27.3 cm) [$S_V = 75$ in^2 (484 cm^3)], and the net internal box volume V_B is 6.3 ft^3 (0.18 m^3). The voice-coil dc resistance R_E is 6.5 ohms.

The nearfield SPL measurements on this system are shown in Fig. 12 along with an impedance curve. The vent measurement was taken with the test microphone held in the center of the vent flush with the enclosure's outside surface (for valid vent measurements, the system drive voltage must be low enough to ensure sinusoidal air movement and low turbulence at the vent output). Fig. 13 displays photographs of the nearfield measurements being taken on this system.

The driver diaphragm output (Fig. 12**a**) shows good correspondence with the theoretical curve displayed in

Fig. 8. The vent output (Fig. 12**b**) shows the effects of diaphragm crosstalk above 80 Hz when compared to Fig. 8.

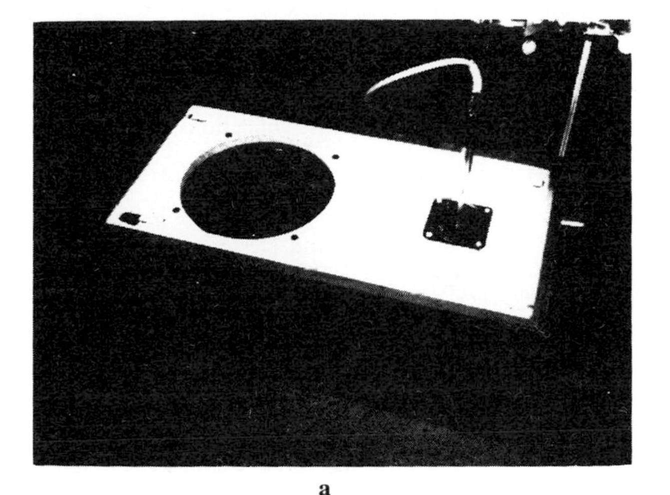

a

b

c

Fig. 13. Nearfield measurements on assorted direct radiators in nonanechoic environment. **a.** Tweeter in 8-in (20.3-cm) two-way closed-box system (¼-in (0.6-cm) microphone). **b.** Woofer in 15-in (38.1-cm) vented-box system. **c.** Vent in 15-in (38.1-cm) vented-box system.

An approximate overall low-frequency response was derived from these data by first computing the relative size ratio between vent and driver diaphragm:

$$\frac{a_D}{a_V} = \sqrt{\frac{S_D}{S_V}} = \sqrt{\frac{133}{75}} = 1.33.$$

This value corresponds to a farfield pressure level shift of about +2.5 dB in favor of the diaphragm (for equal nearfield SPL, the diaphragm would contribute 2.5 dB more level to the farfield pressure because of its larger size).

Examination of the nearfield responses for vent and cone (Fig. 12**a** and **b**) reveals that the vent output at box resonance (about 38 Hz) is down approximately 2 dB from the diaphragm's output in the level response region extending from 100 to 500 Hz. The total system output is therefore down about 4.5 dB at 38 Hz. This single-point output computation at f_B, coupled with the knowledge that the vented-box system rolls off at 24 dB per octave below f_B, was used with the measured cone output response (Fig. 12**a**) to derive the approximate low-frequency response in Fig. 14 ($f_3 \approx 41$ Hz). The efficiency in level portion of the piston-range response, from Fig. 7, is 3.1%.

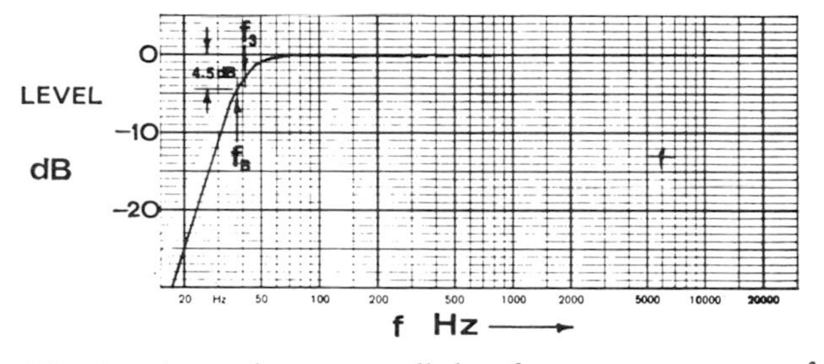

Fig. 14. Approximate overall low-frequency response of 15-in (38.1-cm) vented-box system derived from measurements made using nearfield pressure sampling technique (Fig. 12). The response indicates that system is slightly mistuned from a 4th-order Butterworth alignment at 40 Hz because the box resonance frequency f_B is somewhat low.

CONCLUSION

The theory presented, along with supporting experimental measurements, shows that loudspeaker system piston-range characteristics can easily be measured by sampling the nearfield pressure with a test microphone held close to the acoustic radiator. Valid nearfield measurements may be taken in any reasonable environment without the use of an anechoic chamber or large outdoor test site. Experimental measurements using the nearfield technique show excellent agreement with more traditional test methods.

APPENDIX

Experimental Measuring Equipment

The following equipment was used in making the measurements presented in this paper.

1) Beat frequency audio oscillator, Bruel and Kjaer (B&K) type 1014.

2) Power amplifier, 200 watt, McIntosh, model MI-200AB.

3) Capacitor microphone, ¼ in, B&K type 4135 with follower.

4) Capacitor microphone, ½ in, B&K type 4133 with follower.

5) Precision measurement amplifier, B&K type 2606.

6) Graphic level recorder, B&K type 2305.

Implementation of Box-Pressure Measurements

The frequency equalization network used to implement Small's box-pressure measurement method [1] was corrected only for the $1/\omega^2$ behavior [1, p. 29, eq. (2) and (3)] of the box pressure. Box compliance shift and enclosure loss effects were not compensated for. A second-order high-pass RC filter, with corner frequency of 1 kHz (−3 dB), was used to provide an approximate ω^2 response up to about 1 kHz for these measurements.

ACKNOWLEDGMENT

The author is indebted to Raymond J. Newman, Senior Engineer, Loudspeaker Systems, at Electro-Voice, for first making the observation that nearfield measurements correlated well with anechoic measurements. (When the author first joined Electro-Voice in June 1972, Ray had been making frequency response measurements using this method for about a year.)

The criticism and review of this manuscript by John Gilliom, Chief Product Engineer, Loudspeakers, at EV, and Ray Newman is gratefully acknowledged. The author is further indebted to Dr. Richard H. Small of the University of Sydney, Australia, for comments, suggested revisions, and constructive criticisms of this paper.

REFERENCES

[1] R. H. Small, "Simplified Loudspeaker Measurements at Low Frequencies," *J. Audio Eng. Soc.*, vol. 20, pp. 28–33 (Jan./Feb. 1972).

[2] L. E. Kinsler and A. R. Frey, *Fundamentals of Acoustics* (Wiley, New York, 1962).

[3] J. Zemanek, "Beam Behavior Within the Nearfield of a Vibrating Piston," *J. Acoust. Soc. Am.*, vol. 49, pp. 181–191 (1971).

[4] N. W. McLachlan, *Loudspeaker Theory, Performance, Testing and Design* (Publications, New York, 1960).

[5] R. H. Small, "Direct-Radiator Loudspeaker System Analysis," *J. Audio Eng. Soc.*, vol. 20, pp. 383–395 (June 1972).

[6] J. E. Benson, "Theory and Design of Loudspeaker Enclosures Part I: Electro-Acoustical Relations and Generalized Analysis," *Amalgamated Wireless (Australasia) Ltd. Tech. Rev.*, vol. 14, pp. 1–57 (Aug. 1968).

[7] A. N. Thiele, "Loudspeakers in Vented Boxes," *J. Audio Eng. Soc.*, vol. 19, pp. 382–392 (May 1971); pp. 471–483 (June 1971).

[8] J. E. Benson, "Theory and Design of Loudspeaker Enclosures Part III: Introduction to Synthesis of Vented Systems," *A.W.A. Tech. Rev.*, vol. 14, pp. 369–484 (Nov. 1972).

[9] H. F. Olson, "Direct Radiator Loudspeaker Enclosures," *J. Audio Eng. Soc.*, vol. 17, pp. 22–29 (Jan. 1969).

[10] R. F. Allison and R. Berkovitz, "The Sound Field in Home Listening Rooms," *J. Audio Eng. Soc.*, vol. 20, pp. 459–469 (July/Aug. 1972).

Note: Mr. Keele's biography appears in the January/February 1973 issue of the Journal.

The Influence of Room Boundaries on Loudspeaker Power Output*

ROY F. ALLISON

Allison Acoustics Inc.,
Natick, Mass. 01760

Although it is well known that nearby boundaries affect the radiation angle (and thereby the power output) of small acoustic sources, loudspeaker systems generally have not been designed with due regard for these effects. Conventional loudspeakers oriented in typical use positions in living rooms exhibit variations of the order of 5 to 12 dB in low-frequency power output. The problem is examined quantitatively and some practical measures for improvement are suggested.

INTRODUCTION: A source of acoustic energy is "small" when its physical dimensions are small in comparison with the wavelengths being radiated. Therefore, the diaphragms of direct-radiator loudspeaker systems are small acoustic sources at low frequencies.

The acoustic power output of such a source is a function not only of its volume velocity but also of the resistive component of its radiation load. Because the radiation resistance is so small in magnitude in relationship with the other impedances in the circuit, any change in its magnitude produces a proportional change in the magnitude of radiated power.

The resistive component of the radiation load, in turn, is inversely proportional to the solid angle of space into which the acoustic power radiation occurs. If radiation is into half-space, or 2π steradians, the power radiated is twice that which the same source would radiate into full space, or 4π steradians. If radiation is confined to π steradians by two intersecting boundaries, the power output of the source is again doubled. And if the radiation is further confined to $\pi/2$ steradians, by placing the source in a corner formed by three mutually perpendicular boundaries, its power output is doubled once more. Olson [1] depicts this graphically and these relationships are familiar ones. In the same reference, however, Olson warns that such results hold true only when the dimensions of the source and the distance to the boundaries are small compared with the wavelength. That qualification's import has not been generally appreciated.

Direct-radiator loudspeaker systems have been designed for, and tested in, environments of either 4π or 2π steradian radiation angle. The 2π option has been gaining acceptance in recent years; Small [2] used 2π in his definitive work on direct-radiator systems because it approximated reality in living rooms more closely than 4π. Allison and Berkovitz [3], however, found a substantial low-frequency notch (Fig. 1) in the average of 22

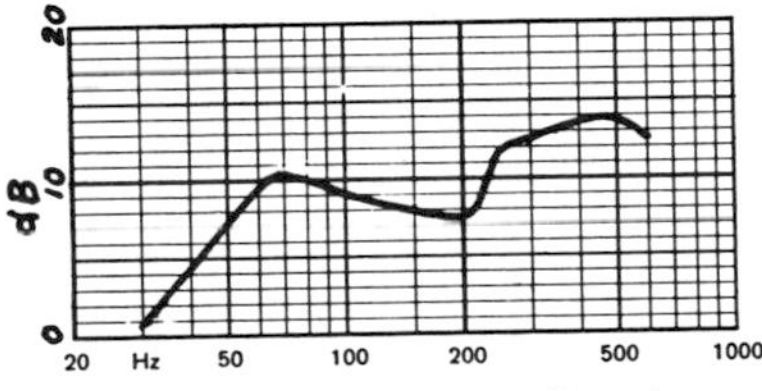

Fig. 1. Average spectral balance at 22 listening positions in 8 living rooms, produced by 16 closed-box speaker systems of moderate size fed one-third octave pink noise.

spectral balance curves obtained at actual listening positions in eight living rooms. The investigation that is the subject of this paper was prompted by that finding. More recently Long [4] showed reverberant response curves of loudspeakers placed at various locations in a room but

*Presented May 7, 1974, at the 48th Convention of the Audio Engineering Society, Los Angeles.

did not explain the pronounced dips at middle-bass frequencies in terms of power output. Rosenberg [5], in a 1973 paper on the problems of making meaningful measurements on a loudspeaker, pointed out the necessity of placing it in a typical use orientation with respect to room boundaries because its power output is dependent on such placement. He suggested a test room containing at least three reflecting boundaries.

The objects of this paper are to define quantitatively how a low-frequency loudspeaker's power output is related to its position in a room, to test the theory with actual measurements, to develop general rules for optimal placement, and to show how loudspeaker system cabinet design can facilitate such optimal placement.

TEST CONDITIONS AND EQUIPMENT

A single loudspeaker system, typical of the great majority now in use by serious listeners, was used for all tests. It is a three-way closed-box acoustic suspension system, with a nominal crossover from woofer to mid-range speaker at 575 Hz. The grille cloth molding was removed for the tests, and the mid-range and tweeter speakers were disconnected. Without molding the overall dimensions of the cabinet are 25 by 14 by 10¼ inches (63.5 by 35.5 by 26 cm). The woofer is nominally 12 inches (30.5 cm) in diameter. It is centered in the 14-inch (35.5 cm) dimension of the front panel and its center is located 7½ inches (19 cm) from one end of the 25-inch (63.5-cm) front-panel dimension.

Measurements were made outdoors, using sine wave signals. The boundaries were clay soil and poured concrete. Because the aim was to measure total power radiated, measurements of output were made so as to sample adequately the entire space into which the speaker radiated. Pressure levels obtained were converted to intensity, weighted according to the solid angle represented, summed for the entire radiation angle, and the sum converted to PWL (power level re 130 dB = 1 acoustic watt). As a check on accuracy of measurement equipment, the test system was checked for absolute output level versus frequency in a 4π environment by an independent acoustics laboratory. Agreement was within 1 dB.

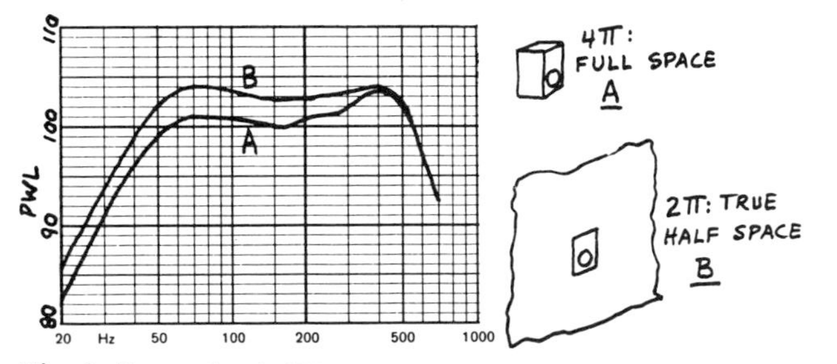

Fig. 2. Power level (PWL) versus frequency of test woofer with radiation angle loads of 4π steradians (curve A) and 2π steradians (curve B). At upper end of frequency range cabinet front panel reduces radiation angle toward 2π or half-space, with increase in power radiated (A). Power input to system is 1 watt at 3.5 ohms.

Where distances to boundaries are not shown in illustrations, the closest cabinet panel is 1 inch (2.5 cm) distant from a wall at ground level (to allow for baseboards in real rooms) or ½ inch (1.27 cm) from a wall if above ground level.

Test equipment consisted of the following Bruel & Kjaer units: type 1024 sine-random generator, type 4133 microphone and type 2619 preamplifier, type 4230 sound level calibrator, type 2113 spectrometer, and type 2305 level recorder. An AR power amplifier was used to drive the loudspeaker.

Fig. 2 shows PWL versus frequency for the test loudspeaker under two standard measurement conditions, 4π and 2π space. Note that the 4π curve rises to and meets the 2π curve at the upper end of the woofer's frequency range. This is explained by the fact that the minimum dimension of the cabinet front panel, 14 inches (35.5 cm), is ½ wavelength at 485 Hz. At this frequency and above, the panel is an effective 2π baffle for the woofer.

SINGLE BOUNDARY CASE

There are several possible methods for calculating the effect of a nearby boundary on the power output of a small source. A very simple way is shown in Fig. 3, considering the source and its image beyond the boundary to be a pair of small sources vibrating in phase and equal in strength. The pressure directivity pattern for such a pair of sources is given by Beranek [6]. For each assumed value of x/λ, the relative pressure is found at arbitrary distance for consecutive small increments of θ. Squaring these pressure values, multiplying by $\cos\theta$, and summing the values thus obtained yields the total relative power radiated for the assumed value of x/λ. Repeating this process for the range of values of x/λ of interest produces the curve shown in Fig. 4. A computer is most helpful in this task.

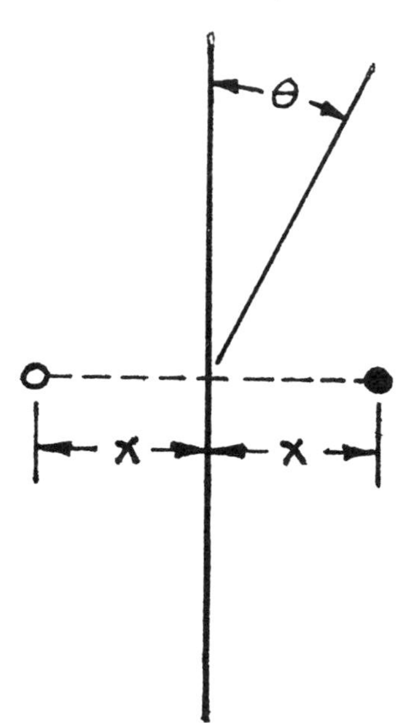

Fig. 3. Model of sound source close to a reflecting boundary. Directional pattern and power output in real half-space are the same as they would be if boundary were removed and the image source were present instead.

Pressure directivity pattern:

$$p = \frac{\sin[(4\pi\, x/\lambda)\sin\theta]}{2\sin[(2\pi\, x/\lambda)\sin\theta]}$$

Relative power radiated for a particular value of x/λ:

$$P = \sum_{\theta=0}^{\pi} p^2 \cos\theta$$

The predicted 3-dB augmentation of power output is obtained only when the source is a very small fraction of a wavelength from the boundary. At 0.1 wavelength the gain is about 2.5 dB. It falls to zero dB (the full-space power output magnitude) at $\lambda/4$. An interesting phenomenon is apparent in the region between $\lambda/4$ and $\lambda/2$: the radiated power is actually less than the 4π space value, reaching a minimum of about -1 dB. Above $\lambda/2$, the boundary has virtually no effect on radiated power. If the distance between source and boundary is 24 inches (61 cm), $\lambda/4$ occurs at 140 Hz.

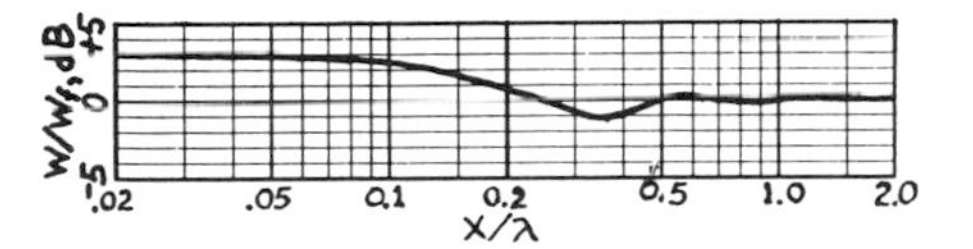

Fig. 4. Augmentation of power output versus free-field value for a single reflecting boundary. When distance x to the boundary is a small fraction of wavelength, the effective radiation angle is reduced to 2π steradians.

The test loudspeaker system (in common with others similar in size and configuration) is nearly always used with its back placed close to a wall, as in Fig. 5. When so placed the average path length from the center of the woofer to the wall is 21 inches (53.3 cm). Using this value for x in Fig. 4, and applying the boundary augmentation versus frequency magnitudes so obtained to the full-space power curve in Fig. 2 (curve A), the calculated power response, curve A, in Fig. 5 is predicted. This is in close agreement with the measured power versus frequency curve, curve B in Fig. 5.

It is clear that the saddle-shaped power curve is the result of changes in the radiation angle over the woofer's operating range. At low frequencies the boundary is effective in restricting the radiation angle to 2π steradians.

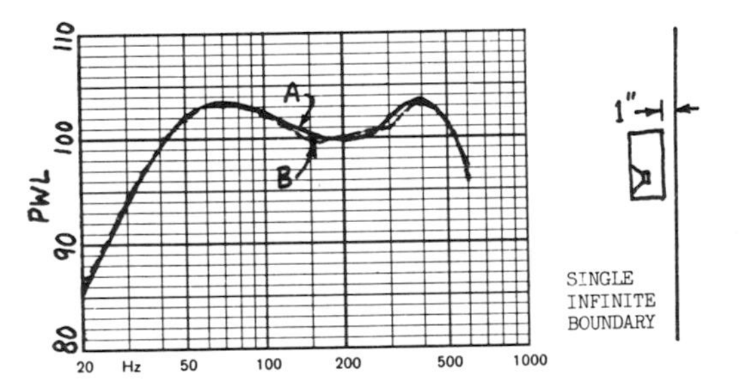

Fig. 5. Calculated (A) and measured (B) PWL versus frequency for test system with back of cabinet parallel with and 1 inch (2.5 cm) from single boundary. Saddle-shaped output indicates that distance from woofer to wall is too great for maintenance of boundary augmentation up to frequency at which front panel becomes effective 2π baffle.

In the middle frequency range the boundary is too far away to serve this purpose, and the cabinet front panel is not large enough to have any effect. Consequently in this frequency region the radiation angle is 4π steradians. At higher frequencies the cabinet front panel reduces the effective angle again to 2π.

Merely increasing the front panel dimensions would not eliminate this effect, because the path length from woofer to boundary would be correspondingly increased. In order to keep the radiation angle at or close to 2π over the full range of the woofer, it is necessary to place the woofer close enough to the boundary so that it remains effective in solid angle reduction up to the frequency at which the cabinet front panel becomes effective. In other words, x must not exceed one half the minimum dimension of the woofer mounting panel.

The most immediately obvious way in which to accomplish this is to mount the woofer in a panel facing the boundary, as shown in Fig. 6. But simple things are rarely

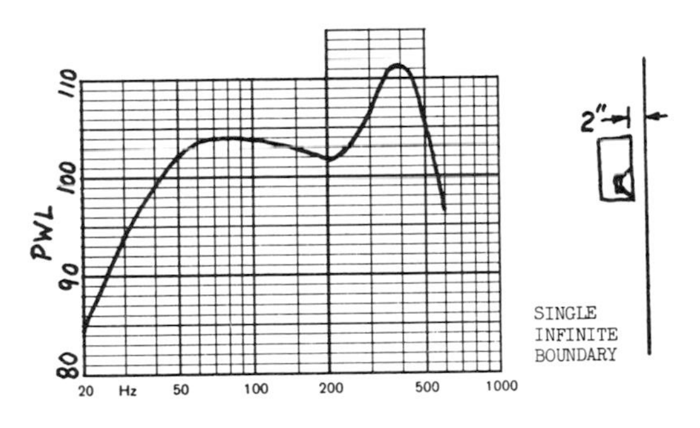

Fig. 6. Facing woofer panel of cabinet toward wall creates conical horn in space between, with new problem worse than old one.

simple, and a conical horn formed by the space between the boundary and the cabinet panel loads the woofer to produce a large peak in power output.

When the test cabinet is turned so that its side is close to the boundary (Fig. 7), a power versus frequency curve is obtained that is virtually identical with the true 2π response (Fig. 2, curve B). The only significant difference is an increase in cutoff slope above 450 Hz, where x/λ is in the 0.25 to 0.5 region.

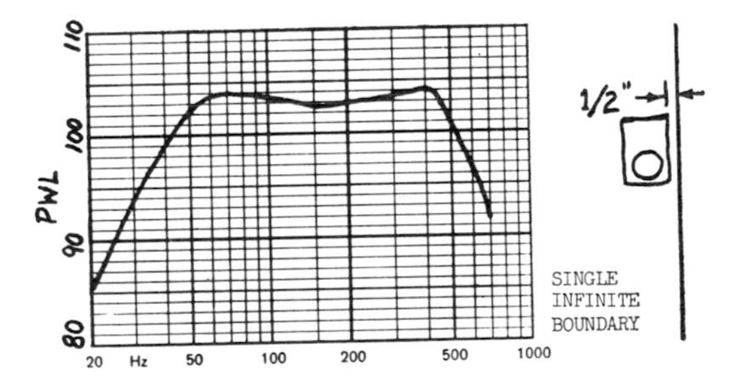

Fig. 7. Simply putting the side of the cabinet next to the wall, so that distance from center of woofer to wall is not more than half the minimum dimension of cabinet's woofer mounting panel, maintains 2π radiation angle throughout frequency range, avoids horn loading. But rooms have more than one wall.

TWO- AND THREE-BOUNDARY CASES

Real rooms have more than one wall which must be considered. Waterhouse [7, 8] and Waterhouse and Cook [9] have investigated extensively the matter of boundary influence on small sound sources. The formulas given by Waterhouse are:

for a single boundary,

$$W/W_f = 1 + j_0(4\pi x/\lambda);$$

for two boundaries intersecting at a right angle,

$$W/W_f = 1 + j_0(4\pi y/\lambda) + j_0(4\pi z/\lambda) + j_0[4\pi(y^2 + z^2)^{1/2}/\lambda]$$

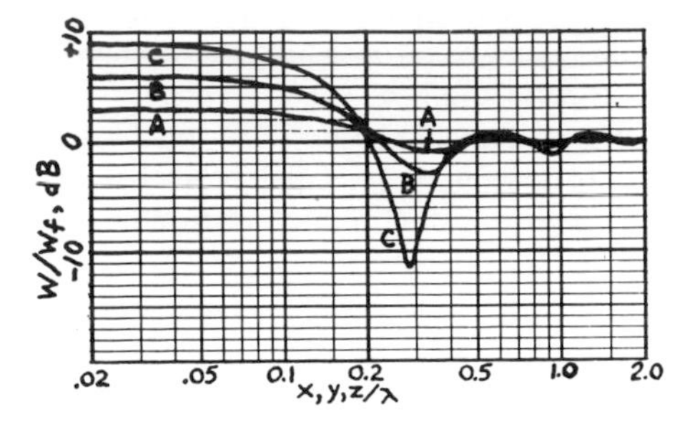

Fig. 8. Power output of a source relative to its free-field power output, when close to a single wall (A), two walls intersecting at a right angle (B), and three mutually perpendicular walls (C). Abscissa shows source location in terms of fractional wavelengths (x/λ, y/λ, and z/λ). For two- and three-boundary cases, curves apply only on lines of symmetry ($y=z$ or $x=y=z$).

and for three intersecting boundaries mutually perpendicular,

$$W/W_f = 1 + j_0(4\pi x/\lambda) + j_0(4\pi y/\lambda) + j_0(4\pi z/\lambda) + j_0[4\pi(x^2 + y^2)^{1/2}/\lambda] + j_0[4\pi(x^2 + z^2)^{1/2}/\lambda] + j_0[4\pi(y^2 + z^2)^{1/2}/\lambda] + j_0[4\pi(x^2 + y^2 + z^2)^{1/2}/\lambda]$$

where W is the power radiated by a source located at x/λ, y/λ, and z/λ with respect to reflecting boundaries. W_f is the power that would be radiated by the source in 4π steradian space, and $j_0(a) = \sin a/a$, the spherical Bessel function.

These expressions are plotted as curves A, B, and C, respectively, in Fig. 8 for a source located symmetrically

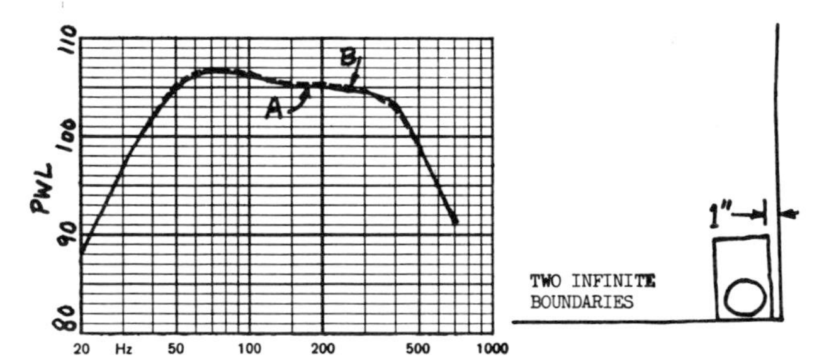

Fig. 9. Calculated (A) and measured (B) PWL versus frequency for test system with cabinet side and bottom adjoining two intersecting boundaries. 1-inch (2.5-cm) spacing from wall is for baseboard; actual distances to center of woofer from boundaries are 7½ and 8 inches (19 and 20 cm). Effective radiation angle of π steradians is well maintained. However, third boundary must be considered in practical rooms.

with respect to the boundaries. Curve A is identical with that in Fig. 4. A remarkable feature of both curves B and C is the very significant reduction in power output below the full-space magnitude which occurs for distances in the region of 0.3λ. For the two-boundary case, the radiated power reaches a minimum of -3 dB; for the three-boundary case, about -11.5 dB. Thus a source located on the line of symmetry from a corner intersection will experience, within the range of frequencies for which the spacing is less than 0.5λ, a variation in radiation resistance of 20 dB. For locations off the line of symmetry the variation is less than 20 dB but is likely to be of appreciable magnitude.

As the source is placed closer to the boundaries, the frequency at which the notch appears becomes higher. In the two-boundary case (Fig. 9) it is possible to get the test

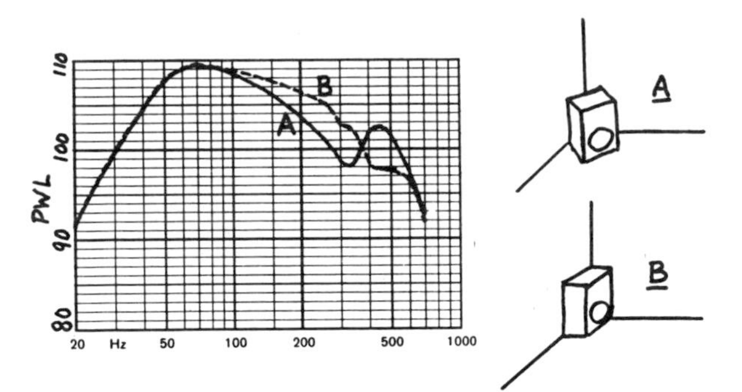

Fig. 10. A. PWL versus frequency for two orientations of test system in a room corner. Results of the unconventional placement (B) are clearly superior, but this cabinet design prevents getting the woofer close enough to corner apex to maintain $\pi/2$ radiation angle over full range.

system close enough to the intersection to yield a useful result. The only price paid for a smooth power output curve approximately 5 dB above the full-space value is a reduction in the upper cut-off frequency to about 400 Hz. Of course that is of no consolation if the crossover frequency of the system cannot be made that low, or in the case of a full-range speaker.

When this practice is attempted in a three-boundary corner, however, it is less successful. Fig. 10B shows a rather steeply sloped power output curve. The test system in this position would be usable only with a crossover frequency of 300 Hz or so, and a decrease in the system Q would also be desirable in order to decrease the slope. On the other hand, conventional orientation of the cabinet in this corner (Fig. 10A) probably would be needed for

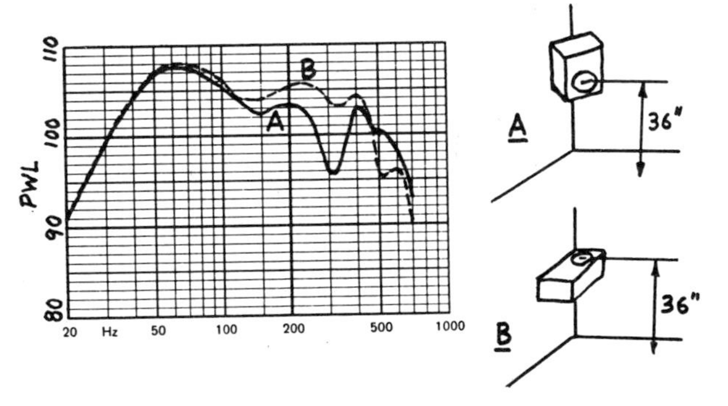

Fig. 11. How power output is affected by moving the cabinet up 3 feet (0.9 m) from the corner along the wall intersection. Here orientation B is very much better than A.

adequate room coverage from the middle- and high-frequency speakers. The low-frequency power response would be considerably worse with the cabinet in this attitude.

Moving the cabinet up off the floor along the wall intersection (Fig. 11) provides no improvement with conventional cabinet orientation. It is obvious that the notch just above 300 Hz in curves A of both Figs. 10 and 11 is produced primarily by reflections from the walls, not the floor. When these reflections are moved up in frequency

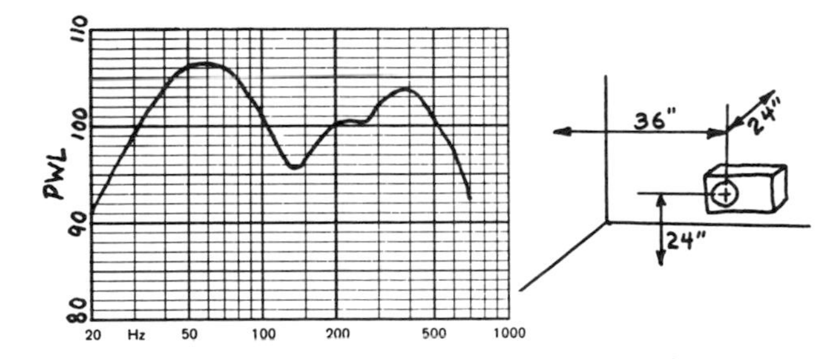

Fig. 12. Simulation of low-frequency results to be expected from an "omni" system placed well away from a corner into the room. Getting clear from all the boundaries is not the way to avoid the effect of the corner; it merely moves the hole down in frequency.

by means of the unconventional orientation (Fig. 11*B*), power output in the woofer range becomes considerably more uniform.

Some loudspeaker systems are meant to be used at locations a few feet from any boundary. Fig. 12 shows the power output of the test system when the woofer is

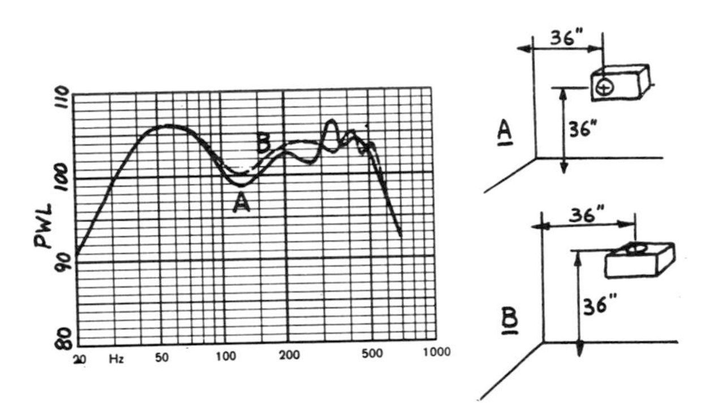

Fig. 13. Fairly typical location for a "bookshelf" speaker system, on a table or shelf close to one wall and 3 feet (0.9 m) from the intersection of another wall. Power output not as irregular as in Fig. 12, but not very much better. Getting woofer as close as possible to the nearest boundary (curve *B*) is, again, better than conventional orientation.

24 inches (61 cm) above the floor, 24 inches (61 cm) from one wall, and 36 inches (91.4 cm) from the other wall. It is apparent that the strong effects of the corner cannot be avoided by moving the source away from all the boundaries by any reasonable distance.

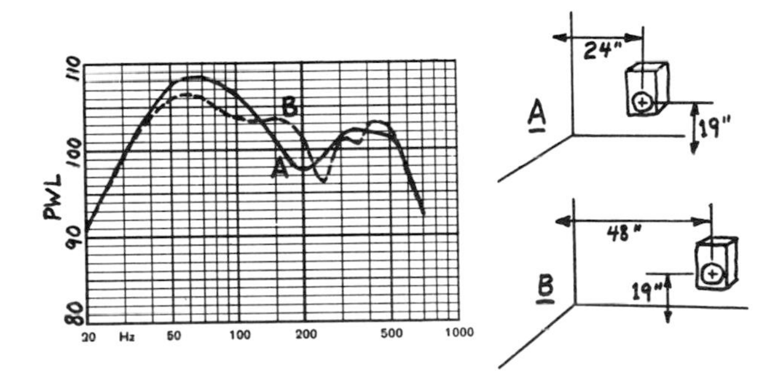

Fig. 14. PWL versus frequency for test system standing on base 11 inches (28 cm) high, with back of cabinet close to one wall and at two distances from other closest wall. 4-foot (1.2-m) curve *B* would be preferred to that for 2-foot (0.6-m) distance from third boundary *A*, but at neither distance does this widely used system on its base provide uniform power output, despite its potential capability to do so.

A more typical placement of a loudspeaker system such as the test unit is that shown in Fig. 13. With conventional orientation the variation in power output is about 7½ dB in the woofer's frequency range. Some improvement is secured by turning the side of the cabinet to the wall.

Probably the most common placement for systems of this kind is on a low base, stand, or table as in Fig. 14, with the woofer end of the cabinet down and the back close to one wall. Power level versus frequency curves are shown for two distances from the other wall.

The sequence in Fig. 15 reveals what may be the most practical way to obtain reasonably flat power output from the test system in an actual room. The woofer is kept as close as possible to two boundaries; as the system is moved gradually away from the third boundary, the power output versus frequency curve becomes progres-

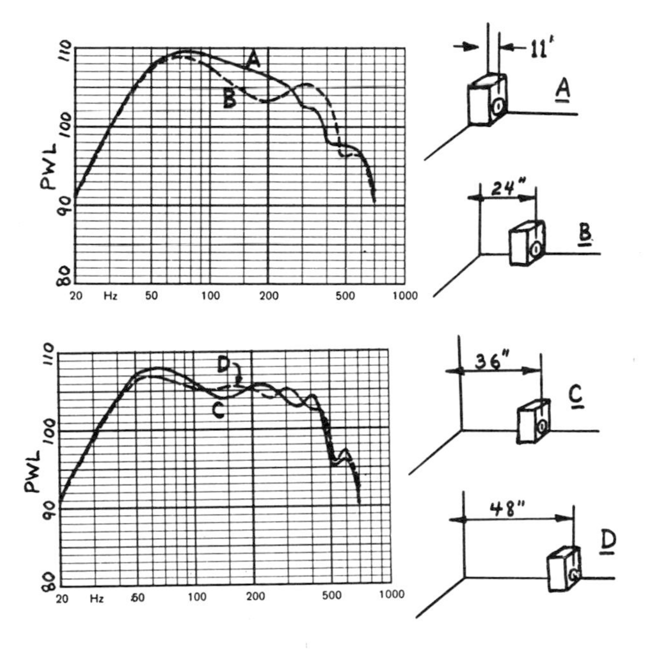

Fig. 15. Sequence showing the effect of positioning the bottom and side of the test system next to the floor and one wall, and moving the system away from the other wall in increments of 1 foot (0.3 m). For curve *A* the woofer center is at the minimum possible distance from the third boundary, 11 inches (28 cm); for *B*, 2 feet (0.6 m); for *C*, 3 feet (0.9 m); and for *D*, 4 feet (1.2 m).

sively more smooth and less tilted. At the 4-foot (1.2-m) distance (curve *D*), the power output variation is ±1½ dB up to 450 Hz.

OTHER CONSIDERATIONS

Calculations were made with the assumption that the boundaries were 100% reflecting, which implies infinite stiffness. The close agreement of the measurements with calculated values demonstrates that the actual boundaries used (packed clay soil and poured concrete) approached the ideal. Walls in real rooms are usually not so stiff; consequently, neither the reinforcement nor the destructive interference should be as fully effective as shown. On the other hand, even frame walls and floors are relatively stiff at their intersections, and it is the reflections from areas close to intersections that are of primary importance. Not much amelioration of the effects should be expected in practical room situations.

Other room boundaries in addition to the three nearest the source will of course generate standing waves at the room resonance modes, but will have little effect on power output. In most cases the nearest "other" boundary, for a system placed as in Fig. 15, will be the ceiling. A boundary has little effect beyond 0.75λ. If the ceiling is 7½ feet (2.3 m) above the woofer, it will be 0.75λ away at 113 Hz. Therefore the three nearest boundaries alone control the effective radiation angle above 113 Hz. Between 113 and 75 Hz, this hypothetical ceiling reflection would increase power output very slightly, reaching a maximum of less than 1 dB at about 92 Hz. Radiated power would be decreased between 75 and 37.5 Hz, with a minimum of about -1 dB at 53 Hz. Power output would be increased gradually below 37.5 Hz, reaching $+2$ dB at 20 Hz and increasing asymptotically toward $+3$ dB at still lower frequencies.

The woofer in the test system was designed originally for a relatively low crossover frequency, and only the woofer range is dealt with here. But the same boundary effects apply to mid-range units as to woofers. In order to minimize the effect of a boundary intersection on the mid-range unit, the distance between them must be at least 0.75λ at the crossover frequency. Therefore, while a very low crossover frequency may be helpful in keeping the woofer out of trouble, it will exacerbate the mid-range problem.

The shortcomings of presently used test facilities for loudspeaker systems now become insistently clear. Neither a 4π nor a 2π anechoic chamber can yield much information on how the system will behave at low frequencies in an actual use situation. Rosenberg's suggestion for a test room consisting of three mutually perpendicular hard boundaries, with the other three boundaries completely absorptive, deserves serious consideration. This is the only kind of test facility of reasonable size and cost that can be used to assess power output at low frequencies in a realistic manner. It is far better than a reverberant room of comparable size, because there are no nondiffuse standing waves present to interfere with accurate measurements. The measurements must be made at a sufficient number of points as to provide an accurate sampling of the total power output, of course.

CONCLUSIONS

It has been shown that the low-frequency power output of contemporary loudspeaker systems, when they are used in real rooms, is affected adversely and significantly by reflected impedance from the boundaries. These effects are unavoidable with loudspeaker systems designed in accordance with current practice.

The most severe effects are those which occur when the system is placed at a distance from all room boundaries; the worst case is that in which it is remote and equidistant from them. Some improvement within the normal woofer frequency range is obtained when the woofer is placed very close to one boundary only. Significant improvement is attainable if the woofer is placed very close to two intersecting boundaries and several feet from the other. With woofers of the usual size and enclosures of conventional design it is not possible to place the woofer close enough to three boundaries simultaneously so that a $\pi/2$ radiation angle can be maintained up to a convenient crossover frequency. Finally, care must be taken to place the mid-range unit beyond the adverse influence of boundary intersections at and above the crossover frequency; that is to say, at least 0.75λ from the intersection. One system designed in accordance with these findings is shown in Fig. 16.

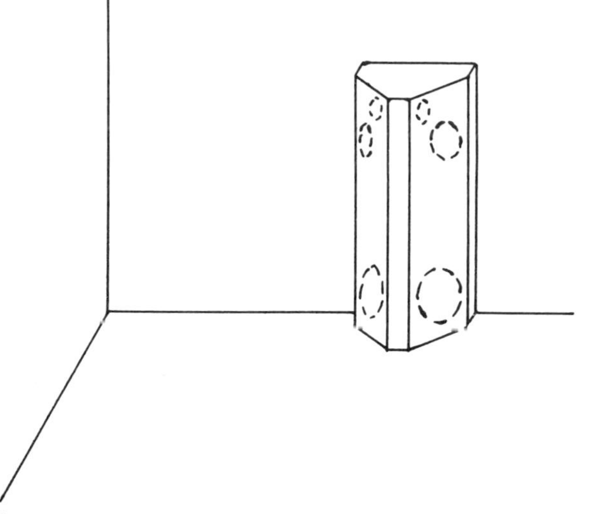

Fig. 16. A new loudspeaker system, designed to optimize boundary augmentation so that the radiation angle is controlled and the acoustic power input to the room is constant with frequency.

It remains true that the ultimate determinant of fidelity to an original source is the sound field at the listener's ears. Even if a loudspeaker system is made capable of delivering uniform power to a room, the energy is redistributed by the room's nondiffuse resonance modes, and the listener's location with respect to these standing waves is not knowable.

Nevertheless, if loudspeaker systems are designed with due regard for these boundary effects, another hitherto unpredictable variable, the loudspeaker's actual radiation load, can be brought under control. This will certainly reduce the average deviation from the ideal of the sound field in the room. The improvement that is possible is easily audible and appears to be worth the effort.

REFERENCES

[1] H. F. Olson, *Acoustical Engineering* (Van Nostrand, Princeton, N. J., 1957), p. 32.

[2] R. H. Small, "Direct-Radiator Loudspeaker System Analysis," *J. Audio Eng. Soc.*, vol. 20, (June 1972).

[3] R. F. Allison and R. Berkovitz, "The Sound Field in Home Listening Rooms," *J. Audio Eng. Soc.*, vol. 20, (July/Aug. 1972).

[4] E. M. Long, "Loudspeaker Instrumentation," preprint 864(B-4), 42nd Convention of the Audio Eng. Soc. (May 1972).

[5] U. Rosenberg, "Loudspeaker Measurement and Consumer Information," preprint F-4(R), 44th Convention of the Audio Eng. Soc. (Feb. 1973).

[6] L. Beranek, *Acoustics* (McGraw-Hill, New York, 1954), p. 94.

[7] R. V. Waterhouse, "Interference Patterns in Reverberant Sound Fields," *J. Acoust. Soc. Am.*, vol. 27, no. 2 (Mar. 1955).

[8] R. V. Waterhouse, "Output of a Sound Source in a Reverberation Chamber and Other Reflecting Environments," *J. Acoust. Soc. Am.*, vol. 30, no. 1 (Jan. 1958).

[9] R. V. Waterhouse and R. K. Cook, "Interference Patterns in Reverberant Sound Fields II," *J. Acoust. Soc. Am.*, vol. 37, no. 3 (Mar. 1965).

THE AUTHOR

Roy Allison went from a background as an editor of radio engineering and consumer audio magazines to Acoustic Research, Inc. in 1959. He became chief engineer in 1960, Plant Manager in 1964, and Vice President/Engineering and Manufacturing in 1967. He left Acoustic Research at the end of 1972 and is now President of Allison Acoustics Inc.

Mr. Allison is a Fellow of Audio Engineering Society and a Member of Institute of Electrical and Electronics Engineers.

Calculating the Directivity Factor γ of Transducers from Limited Polar Diagram Information[1]

MICHAEL A. GERZON

Mathematical Institute, University of Oxford, Oxford, England

The calculation of the directivity factor γ of loudspeakers and microphones (including gun microphones) from polar diagrams measured in two planes only is described. Tables of "weights" for measurements taken at intervals of 10°, 15°, 20°, 22½°, 30°, and 45° are given. Some of the theory is also outlined which uses numerical integration on the surface of the sphere using a product Fejér/Clenshaw–Curtis rule. Rule-of-thumb estimates are given for the maximum directivity factors that can be estimated by this procedure for various intervals.

INTRODUCTION: In a series of notes, Davis [1], [2] and Wilson [3], [4] gave methods of determining the directivity factor γ of loudspeakers from polar diagrams measured in two planes, vertical and horizontal, through the nominal axis of the loudspeaker. Their methods involved integrating the total energy response of the polar diagram over all directions by adding together the energy gain in various directions, each being multiplied by a suitable coefficient or "weight." Unfortunately, their weights were determined by the area of a "slice" of the surface of the sphere of directions. Thus their methods are analogs on the sphere of midpoint or trapezium rules for ordinary numerical integration, and these methods are well known to be of poor accuracy [5].

We give a theoretically optimal method of determining the directivity factor γ of a loudspeaker or microphone from the polar diagrams taken in the vertical and horizontal planes through the nominal axis of the transducer. Since the theory involves some mathematical difficulties, we divide this paper into 2 parts. The first consists of a description of the practical use of our method of determining γ, with tables for data measured at intervals of 10°, 15°, 20°, 22½°, 30°, and 45°, and some "rules of thumb" to indicate when the estimate for γ is likely to be unreliable. The second part consists of the theory which involves a method of numerical integration similar to that proposed by Fejér [6] in 1933, and essentially the same as the method of Clenshaw and Curtis [7], [5, ch. 2 pp. 83-87].

PRACTICAL DETERMINATION OF γ

Suppose that we are given as data two polar diagrams (polar energy responses) $f(\theta)$ and $g(\theta')$, where θ is the angle from the forward axis in the horizontal plane and θ' the angle from the forward axis in the vertical plane. (If these are given in decibels as $F(\theta)$ and $G(\theta')$, then $f(\theta) = 10^{0.1F(\theta)} = \text{anti-log}_{10}\, 0.1F(\theta)$, and similarly for $g(\theta')$).

[1] We use the notation γ rather than Q or R_θ (see [3]) since the latter two can be misleading (R_θ depends on a function of *two* angles, θ and ϕ). γ has been used for "directivity factor" on several previous occasions in this *Journal* (see [8], [12]).

Suppose further that we have measured $f(\theta)$ and $g(\theta')$ at intervals of $180°/n$. The problem is to estimate the directivity factor γ of the exact polar diagram $h(\theta,\phi)$, where θ is the angle from the axis, and ϕ the angle around the axis. The mathematical definition of γ is

$$\gamma = \frac{h(\theta,\phi)_{\max}}{\frac{1}{4\pi}\iint h(\theta,\phi) \sin\theta \, d\theta \, d\phi} \tag{1}$$

where the integration is over all directions (θ,ϕ). This is simply the ratio of maximum energy gain to the average of the energy gains over all directions.

We may compute γ from our data as follows. Writing $(1/4\pi) \iint h(\theta,\phi) \sin\theta \, d\theta \, d\phi$ as $I[h]$, then

$$I[h] \cong w_0 f(0) + \tfrac{1}{4} \sum_{i=1}^{n-1} w_i \left[f\left(\frac{180°}{n} i\right) + f\left(-\frac{180°}{n} i\right) + g\left(\frac{180°}{n} i\right) + g\left(-\frac{180°}{n} i\right) \right] + w_n f(180°) \tag{2}$$

where the weights w_i will be given shortly. Note that $f(0) = g(0)$ and $f(180°) = g(180°)$. Then we have that

$$\gamma = h(\theta,\phi)_{\max}/I[h]. \tag{3}$$

Thus, as long as we know $h(\theta,\phi)_{\max}$, this completes our determination of γ. $h(\theta,\phi)_{\max}$ is often equal to $f(0)$, but for asymmetric polar diagrams it may be determined by inspection of the polar diagrams.

The weights w_i are given in Table I for $n = 4, 6, 8, 9, 12$, and 18, i.e., for $180°/n = 45°, 30°, 22\frac{1}{2}°, 20°, 15°$, and $10°$. Theoretically, as indicated in the following section, they are given by the formulas

$$w_0 = w_n = (1/2n) \sum_{r=0,2,4,\ldots}^{n}{}'' \; -\frac{1}{r^2-1}$$

$$w_i = (1/n) \sum_{r=0,2,4,\ldots}^{n}{}'' \; -\frac{1}{r^2-1} \cos\left(\frac{180° \, ri}{n}\right) \quad \text{for } i \neq 0, n \tag{4}$$

where the sums are over all even r up to n, and where the double prime indicates that the terms with $r = 0$ and (in the case that n is even) $r = n$ are halved.

If polar diagrams in additional planes through the forward axis are available (e.g., four planes at 45° from one another), then formula (2) is modified only in that each term of the $\sum_{i=1}^{n=1}$ term becomes an average over the, say, eight half-planes involved, rather than over the four half-polar-diagrams in the case already described.

Accuracy

Theoretically a formula averaging over only two planes in the manner indicated is unreliable for polar energy responses containing spherical harmonic components of order greater than 3 (see next section). The maximum directivity factor that can be achieved with such third-order energy polar diagrams is $\gamma = 6$, and so any estimate of γ in excess of, or comparable to, 6 (say, $\gamma \geqslant 4$) obtained by this method must be regarded as unreliable.

However, in many cases, such as gun microphones or paraboloidal reflector microphones, we have reason to suppose that there is a reasonable degree of symmetry about the axis of the polar diagram, i.e., that there are no spherical harmonic components of the polar diagram of the form $Y_l^m(\theta,\phi)$ (where ϕ is measured around the axis and θ from it) with large "azimuthal" frequency m (say, no $m > 3$). (See any text on spherical harmonics, e.g., [11], for the definition of Y_l^m). In this case the limiting factor in the measurement of γ will be the number $2n$ of points around each plane polar diagram used in the determination. In these circumstances, it turns out (see next section) that polar energy responses of spherical harmonic order up to n can be measured, with a highest possible directivity factor of around $(\frac{1}{2}n+1)^2$. Thus for $180°/n = 10°$, and assuming good (but not necessarily perfect) axial symmetry, directivity factors up to about $(\frac{1}{2}\times 18+1)^2 = 100$ can be measured, using data spaced apart by 10° intervals.

The weights given by Table I for 10° intervals do not differ very greatly from those given in [1]–[4], certainly not enough to affect results significantly from a practical viewpoint. The reasons for using the values given here may be summarized as follows.

1) The tables given here are the optimal weights from a theoretical viewpoint. Even though errors in the tables of [1]–[4] may be small in comparison with other sources of

Table I.

	Angle (degrees)	Weights w_i
$n = 4$	0 or 180	0.03333 3333
	45 or 135	0.26666 6667
	90	0.40000 0000
$n = 6$	0 or 180	0.01428 5714
	30 or 150	0.12698 4127
	60 or 120	0.22857 1429
	90	0.26031 7460
$n = 8$	0 or 180	0.00793 6508
	22½ or 157½	0.07310 9325
	45 or 135	0.13968 2540
	67½ or 112½	0.18085 8929
	90	0.19682 5397
$n = 9$	0 or 180	0.00617 2840
	20 or 160	0.05828 3728
	40 or 140	0.11264 2162
	60 or 120	0.15097 0018
	80 or 100	0.17193 1253
$n = 12$	0 or 180	0.00349 6503
	15 or 165	0.03302 8712
	30 or 150	0.06577 1266
	45 or 135	0.09238 1692
	60 or 120	0.11348 6512
	75 or 105	0.12633 7847
	90	0.13099 4931
$n = 18$	0 or 180	0.00154 7988
	10 or 170	0.01478 5498
	20 or 160	0.02998 0282
	30 or 150	0.04356 3973
	40 or 140	0.05613 7598
	50 or 130	0.06681 8462
	60 or 120	0.07559 9942
	70 or 110	0.08198 2300
	80 or 100	0.08596 0196
	90	0.08724 7523

error, it is advisable to minimize those sources of error that we can control.

2) The method given in this paper includes (see next section) an analysis of when the result is exact, and describes the source of errors in other cases.

3) The justification of the tables of weights in [1]–[4] relied on the assumption that the successive sample values of the polar diagrams changed slowly with angle. The present method only demands that the angular frequency components of the polar energy diagram have frequencies that are less than half the sampling frequency. This means that useful calculations can be made either when the polar diagram consists of many lobes of comparable magnitude, or when the sampling interval is quite a bit larger than 10°.

It is known [13] that many different methods of estimating the directivity factor (varying from crude methods of estimating the beamwidth to a full sphere integration) give results that are adequately close to the correct value, provided that the polar diagram consists of one main lobe plus other lobes of much smaller magnitude. The present method does not depend on this assumption, and so is also suitable for cases such as bidirectional transducers and transducers with multiple interference nulls within the forward polar diagram.

The spherical harmonic theory of the next section can sometimes give a useful guide as to when the method of this paper will give adequate results. Consider the transducer as lying in a snug-fitting cylinder whose axis coincides with the nominal transducer axis. Let the length of the cylinder be l and its diameter d. Then, as a rule of thumb, the polar energy diagram measured with a sound of wavelength λ will include possibly significant spherical harmonic components whose Fourier frequency around the axis are of orders up to $2\pi d/\lambda$, and whose plane polar diagrams measured through the nominal axis include Fourier components of order up to $2\pi l/\lambda$. Thus ideally, to ensure reasonable accuracy we should have $2\pi d/\lambda \leq 3$ and $2\pi l/\lambda \leq n$, where $n+1$ is the number of sample points used in each half-plane polar diagram.

These rule-of-thumb inequalities often may be grossly violated in practice with little harm, even though one can construct mathematically polar diagrams that give inaccurate estimates for γ when these conditions are grossly violated. Cases where the first condition matters little include transducers with almost perfect axial symmetry (e.g., paraboloidal reflector microphones). A case where the second condition can often be ignored is when the polar diagram is so ragged that it may be regarded as largely random in nature. In other cases, the highest order spherical harmonic components may in fact be of low amplitude. In these latter cases, a visual examination of the polar diagram will often suggest the Fourier frequency n of the highest order significant components, and an interval size of less than $180°/n$ may safely be used. It is, on the other hand, not possible to determine from the data in only two orthogonal planes whether two planes are enough. Ideally, polar diagrams in four or more planes through the axis should be used, but the two-plane method has the advantage of using easily available data.

Two sources of error have not been discussed at all in this paper, but should be recognized. First, if the value $h(\theta,\phi)_{max}$ does not lie on one of the measured polar diagrams, then our estimate for γ has the same proportionate error due to this cause as the estimate used for h_{max}. We have not investigated the best way of estimating h_{max} from polar diagrams in two planes only. Second, if we measure transducers that are extended in space or that have large γ, then measurements made too close to the transducer (in the near field) will not give the same polar diagram as that measured at spatial infinity. For transducers not involving velocity transducer elements, the near field for a sound of wavelength λ consists roughly of points whose distance from the transducer is less than about $\frac{1}{4}\pi d^2/\lambda$, where d is the maximum spatial extent (say in meters) of the transducer. It will be seen that we are often forced to make measurements in the near field, and it is not easy to say whether this introduces significant errors in the estimation of γ. We expect this error to be worse for the case (e.g., loudspeakers, reflector microphones) where the maximum spatial extent is orthogonal to the nominal axis rather than along it.

THEORY

We wish to determine $I[h]$ over the surface of a sphere numerically. Numerical integration over the surface of the sphere is now well understood (see McLaren [9] and Stroud [10]), but numerical analysts are primarily concerned with choosing accurate numerical rules involving the smallest possible number of points on the sphere, rather than with choosing these points conveniently for experimental measurement. For example, ideally we should use the 72-point precision 14 (i.e., it is accurate for up to 14th-order spherical harmonics) rule described by McLaren [9] and Stroud [10, ch. 8 p. 302], but this involves using some experimentally very awkward directions in space around our transducer, and these data are somewhat unlikely to be available in published information.

Given information in just the two planes, and then only at equal angular intervals, we shall have to use a product rule [10, ch.2] for numerical integration on the sphere. Denote a direction by its direction cosines (x, y, z) with $x^2 + y^2 + z^2 = 1$. Note that $z = \cos\theta$, $x = \cos\phi \sin\theta$, and $y = \sin\theta \sin\phi$, where θ is the angle from the axis, and ϕ is that around it. Then

$$I[h] = \frac{1}{4\pi} \int_{-1}^{1} \int_{0}^{2\pi} h(\cos\phi \sqrt{(1-z^2)}, \sin\phi \sqrt{(1-z^2)}, z)\, d\phi\, dz \tag{5}$$

from Eq. (1) by the change of variable $z = \cos\theta$, where $h(x, y, z)$ denotes the polar diagram as a function of direction cosines.

Now consider, for a moment, integrals of functions in one of the variables ϕ and z only. Let $j(\phi)$ be a function of the angle ϕ. Then it is well known (and pretty obvious) that

$$\frac{1}{2\pi} \int_{0}^{2\pi} j(\phi)\, d\phi \cong \frac{1}{m} \sum_{i=1}^{m} j\left(\frac{360°}{m} i\right), \tag{6}$$

where the integration rule (6) is exact for functions $j(\phi)$ with no Fourier components above the $(m-1)$th harmonic.

Moreover, for a function $k(z)$ we may always put

$$\tfrac{1}{2}\int_{-1}^{1} k(z)\,dz \cong \sum_{i=0}^{n} w_i k(z_i)\,, \qquad (7)$$

where the weights w_i and points z_i may be chosen such that Eq. (7) is exact for all polynomials $k(z)$ of degree $\leqslant n$.

Now $h(\cos\phi\,\sqrt{(1-z^2)}, \sin\phi\,\sqrt{(1-z^2)}, z)$ as a function of ϕ certainly has no Fourier components above nth harmonic if $h(x, y, z)$ has no spherical harmonic component above nth spherical harmonic, and

$$\frac{1}{2\pi}\int_0^{2\pi} h(\cos\phi\,\sqrt{(1-z^2)}, \sin\phi\,\sqrt{(1-z^2)}, z)\,d\phi$$

is clearly a polynomial function of the nth degree in z, since $h(x, y, z)$ is also. Putting Eqs. (6) and (7) together, we thus have

$$I[h] \cong \sum_{i=0}^{n} w_i \left[\frac{1}{m}\sum_{j=1}^{m} h\left(\cos\left(\frac{360°}{m}j\right)\sqrt{(1-z_i^2)},\right.\right.$$
$$\left.\left.\sin\left(\frac{360°}{m}j\right)\sqrt{(1-z_i^2)}, z_i\right)\right]\,, \qquad (8)$$

which is exact provided that h has no spherical harmonic components of order exceeding n, and that h as a function of ϕ has no Fourier components of greater than $(m-1)$th harmonic. The formula (8) is termed a product rule for the surface of the sphere (see [10, ch. 2, pp. 40-43]).

In our case, we require $m = 4$, so as to use points in two perpendicular planes disposed around the nominal axis of the transducer. Thus our rule necessitates that h as a function of ϕ have no Fourier components of greater than third harmonic.

We also require in our case, because of our preassigned choice of measurement points at equal angles around a polar diagram, that

$$z_i = \cos\left(\frac{180°}{n}i\right). \qquad (9)$$

The choice of the w_i in Eq. (7) that leads to the most accurate integration rule (in the sense of integrating exactly polynomials $k(z)$ of as high a degree as possible) with the particular points (9) is known as the "interpolatory rule" for the points (9). This interpolatory rule is in fact that described by Clenshaw and Curtis [7], [5, ch. 2 pp. 83-87], although they do not give the w_i explicitly in the form (4). Formulas very similar to Eq. (4) are given by Fejér [6] for interpolatory rules for the points $z_i = \cos([180°/(n+1)]i)$ with $i = 1,2,\ldots,n$, and for $z_i = \cos((180°/n)(i-\tfrac{1}{2}))$ with $i = 1,2,\ldots,n$.

Since an explicit derivation for Eq. (4) does not seem to be published, we give a quick proof here, but see also [7], [5, pp. 83-87]. If Eq. (7) obeying Eq. (9) is to be accurate for all polynomials $k(z)$ of degree $\leqslant n$, then for all $0 \leqslant m \leqslant n$,

$$\tfrac{1}{2}\int_{-1}^{1} T_m(z)\,dz = \sum_{i=0}^{n} w_i\,T_m(\cos\theta_i) \qquad (10)$$

where $\theta_i = 180°\,i/n$ and $T_m(z)$ is the mth degree Chebyshev polynomial defined by

$$T_m(\cos\theta) = \cos m\theta.$$

Thus,

$$\tfrac{1}{2}\int_{-1}^{1} T_m(z)\,dz = \tfrac{1}{2}\int_0^{\pi}\cos m\theta\,\sin\theta\,d\theta$$
$$= \tfrac{1}{4}\int_0^{\pi}\sin(m+1)\theta - \sin(m-1)\theta\,d\theta$$
$$= 0 \quad \text{if } m \text{ odd}$$
$$= \frac{-1}{m^2-1} \text{ if } m \text{ even.}$$

Thus

$$\sum_{i=0}^{n} w_i\cos m\theta_i = 0 \quad \text{if } m \text{ odd} \qquad (11)$$
$$= \frac{-1}{m^2-1} \quad \text{if } m \text{ even.}$$

Note that the left-hand side of (11) is the Fourier cosine transform of w_i, and use the fact that

$$\frac{1}{n}\sum_{i=0}^{n}{}''\cos r\theta_i\cos m\theta_i = \begin{cases} 0 & \text{if } r \neq m \\ 1 & \text{if } r = m = 0 \text{ or } r = m = n \\ \tfrac{1}{2} & \text{if } r = m \text{ and } 0 < r < n \end{cases}$$

where the double prime indicates to halve the $i = 0$ and $i = n$ terms to get

$$w_0 = w_n = (1/2n)\sum_{r=0,2,4,\ldots}^{n}{}'' \frac{-1}{r^2-1}$$

$$w_i = (1/n)\sum_{r=0,2,4,\ldots}^{n}{}'' \frac{-1}{r^2-1}\cos r\theta_i \quad \text{when } 0 < i < n$$

which proves Eq. (4).

To summarize, we have shown that the method of determining $I[h]$ given in the preceding section is exact provided that h is not of order greater than n and has no Fourier component of order greater than 3 about the nominal axis at which the two planes of measurement meet. This is clearly the best we can do with the points at our disposal, since we cannot better Eq. (6) for m points on the circumference of a circle, and the w_i have been chosen to be the best possible.

Finally, we give some degree of justification for the rule of thumb for estimating the highest γ that can be reliably measured as follows. The "polar diagrams" that we have considered are all polar energy responses, and not polar amplitude responses. Since energy is the square of amplitude, an amplitude polar diagram of spherical harmonic order $\tfrac{1}{2}n$ will give an energy polar diagram of order n. By the directivity factor theorem of [8], the maximum γ that can be obtained from an amplitude polar diagram of order $\tfrac{1}{2}n$ is $\gamma = (\tfrac{1}{2}n+1)^2$. Thus the rule (2) with Eq. (4), which is reliable only for polar energy responses of order $\leqslant n$, is certainly unreliable for γ exceeding $(\tfrac{1}{2}n+1)^2$.

Strictly, the above argument only applies when n is even,

but in practice, it is a useful guide also for odd n. Take, for example, the case of energy polar diagrams of order $\leqslant 3$ (we have already shown that γ can be computed exactly in this case). An axially symmetric polar diagram of this type may be written $h(x, y, z) = az^3 + bz^2 + cz + d$. Because h is a polar energy response, it must be positive for $-1 \leqslant z \leqslant 1$, so that $\gamma = h_{max}/I[h]$ is maximized for a function of the form $h(x, y, z) = (z+1+\beta)(z+1-\alpha)^2$, where $\beta \geqslant 0$ and $0 \leqslant \alpha < 2$, if we put the maximum of h at $z = 1$. The usual methods of finding the maximum for γ shows that this is achieved for $\beta = 0$ and $\alpha = 1$, for which values $\gamma = 6$. Thus the highest γ for third/order polar energy responses is $\gamma = 6$.

ACKNOWLEDGMENT

We would like to thank the referee for acquainting us with the work of reference [13], and Dr. Peter Craven for introducing us to the mysteries of Clenshaw–Curtis integration.

REFERENCES

[1] D. Davis, ''On Standardizing the Measurement of Q,'' *J. Audio Eng. Soc.* (Forum), vol. 21, pp. 730-731 (Nov. 1973).

[2] D. Davis, ''Further Comments on Directivity Factor,'' *J. Audio Eng. Soc.* (Forum), vol. 21, pp. 827-828 (Dec. 1973).

[3] G. L. Wilson, ''Directivity Factor: Q or R_θ? Standard Terminology and Measurement Methods,'' *J. Audio Eng. Soc.* (Forum), vol. 21, pp. 828-833 (Dec. 1973).

[4] G. L. Wilson, ''More on the Measurement of the Directivity Factor,'' *J. Audio Eng. Soc.* (Forum), vol. 22, pp. 180-182 (Apr. 1974).

[5] P. J. Davis and P. Rabinowitz, *Numerical Integration* (Blaisdell Publ., Waltham, Mass., 1967).

[6] L. Fejér, ''Mechanische Quadraturen mit positiven Cotesschen Zahlen,'' *Math. Z.*, vol. 37, pp. 287-309 (1933).

[7] C. W. Clenshaw and A. R. Curtis, ''A Method for Numerical Integration on an Automatic Computer,'' *Num. Math.*, vol. 2, pp. 197-205 (1960).

[8] M. A. Gerzon, ''Periphony: With-Height Sound Reproduction,'' *J. Audio Eng. Soc.*, vol. 21, pp. 2-10 (Jan./Feb. 1973).

[9] A. D. McLaren, ''Optimal Numerical Integration on a Sphere,'' *Math. Comp.*, vol. 17, pp. 361-383 (1963).

[10] A. H. Stroud, *Approximate Calculation of Multiple Integrals* (Prentice Hall, Englewood Cliffs, N.J., 1971).

[11] I. M. Gel'fand, R. A. Minlos, and Z. Ya Shapiro, *Representations of the Rotation and Lorentz Groups and their Applications* (Pergamon Press, Oxford, 1963).

[12] B. Weingartner, ''Two-Way Cardioid Microphone *J. Audio Eng. Soc.*, vol. 14, pp. 244-251 (Jul. 1966).

[13] R. J. Bobber, ''Approximations to the Directivity Index,'' Naval Research Lab. Rep. 7750 (AD 778 660). May 1, 1974.

Dr. Gerzon's biography appeared in the March 1975 issue.

An Introduction to the Design of Filtered Loudspeaker Systems*

J. E. BENSON

Electroacoustical Consultant
Formerly of Amalgamated Wireless (Australasia) Limited, Sydney, Australia

An analysis is given of the overall response and input impedance of second-order loudspeaker systems when fed through first- and second-order electrical filters. Some useful relationships are established which are applicable to the design of crossover networks with loudspeaker terminations and which also lead to the synthesis of composite high-pass systems.

INTRODUCTION: The use of isolated auxiliary electrical filters as a means of modifying the response of loudspeaker systems has been known for a long time in the form of tone-control circuits in audio amplifiers. These have usually been designed by well-known methods independently of the loudspeaker systems with which they operate.

Techniques for synthesizing the overall response of the combination of particular loudspeaker systems with such isolated filters to desired prototype forms were first discussed by Thiele [1]. Thiele's work implied the use of high-pass filters of first and second order coupled to the loudspeaker systems by means of isolating amplifiers, and he showed that these composite systems could be synthesized to classical prototype forms (such as Butterworth and Chebyshev) of appropriately higher order than those applicable to the loudspeaker systems alone. An essential assumption for the synthesis procedure was that the effects of inevitable voice-coil inductance could be neglected. The effects of significant voice-coil inductance on the synthesized responses of conventional loudspeaker systems have been discussed in a recent paper by the present author [2, Appendix 9].

The use of auxiliary filters directly coupled to the loudspeaker terminals has also been known for many years in the form of crossover networks in multichannel

* An earlier version of this paper appeared in the *AWA Technical Review,* Vol. 15, No. 1, (1973).

loudspeaker systems. In the design of these networks it has often been considered adequate, for practical purposes, to calculate the cutoff frequency on the basis of a resistive termination whose value is equal to the magnitude of the "nominal" input impedance of the loudspeaker driver. (Some recent discussions of the problems of such systems have been given by Ashley [3], Small [4], and Ashley and Kaminsky [5].)

While this approach may be considered satisfactory in specific circumstances, it may be shown that, in general, quite serious deviations from the intended performance can occur when the filters are terminated by actual loudspeakers.[1] The factors responsible for this are the motional impedance and the voice-coil inductance. The effect of the motional impedance is to raise the input impedance to very high values at the frequency or frequencies of system resonance where the diaphragm velocity is greatest. The effects of voice-coil inductance are twofold. The first is that, by interacting with the motional impedance on the high-frequency side of the fundamental resonance, a series resonant condition (second resonance) occurs which reduces the input impedance to its minimum value of approximately that of the voice-coil resistance. (The nominal input impedance is usually chosen to be slightly above this value.) The other effect of voice-coil inductance is to increase the input impedance with frequency in the region above the second resonance. The significance of these characteristics of the input impedance is the effect they have on the transmission loss of the filter when terminated by the loudspeaker. The extent of this interaction may be examined in practice by comparing the voice-coil terminal voltage with that of the filter output when operating into its nominal terminating resistance.

As may be expected, the deviation from the intended performance depends on the relationship between the nominal filter cutoff frequency f_C and the frequency of the "second resonance" f_R. When $f_C \simeq f_R$ and the voice-coil inductance is moderately small, the filter termination in the cutoff region will be predominantly resistive and approximately equal to the nominal impedance. This will result in satisfactory cutoff characteristics, providing the attenuation rate of the filter is sufficient to avoid significant interaction with the rising driver impedance above and below f_R. If, however, the voice-coil inductance, the filter cutoff frequency, or both are increased, the effects on response shape and the measured cutoff frequency become significant.

It is proposed in this paper to examine these effects when simple electrical filters are coupled to simple second-order loudspeaker systems of the open-baffle or closed-box types. The filters will be of both first and second order, each comprising both low-pass and high-pass types.

This will serve as an introduction to some important practical applications which we hope to examine in later papers. Among these are the design of crossover networks working with loudspeaker terminations and the use of direct-coupled high-pass filters as a means of varying the cutoff frequency of the system in relation to that of the fundamental driver resonance.

FIRST-ORDER FILTERS

Low-Pass Filter

Fig. 1 shows the electrical equivalent circuit of a loudspeaker driver fed from a constant-voltage generator e_G through a pure inductance L_1, chosen to give a nominal cutoff frequency ω_1 when considered as part of a low-pass filter whose terminating resistance is R_{VC}. Then defining

$$Q_1 = R_{VC}/L_1\,\omega_1 \qquad (1)$$

it follows that for a filter loss of 3 dB at ω_1, $Q_1 = 1$ or

$$L_1\omega_1 = R_{VC}. \qquad (2)$$

Now let

$$h_1 = \omega_1/\omega_S \qquad (3)$$

where ω_S is the principal resonance frequency of the driver (or system, in the case of the closed-box system)[2] defined by

$$L_{CES}C_{MES}\,\omega_S{}^2 = 1 \qquad (4)$$

where L_{CES} and C_{MES} are the electrical circuit equivalents of the effective driver (or system) compliance and diaphragm mass, respectively, as given in [2, Eqs. (69) and (68)].

Input Impedance

If the voice-coil Q is defined by

$$Q_{VC} = L_{VC}\omega_S/R_{VC} \qquad (5)$$

the mechanical Q of the driver suspension system by

$$Q_M = R_{ES}/L_{CES}\omega_S = R_{ES}C_{MES}\,\omega_S \qquad (6)$$

and the electrical Q due to electromagnetic damping by

$$Q_E = R_{VC}/L_{CES}\omega_S = R_{VC}C_{MES}\omega_S \qquad (7)$$

then, using the relationship

$$1/Q_S = 1/Q_M + 1/Q_E \qquad (8)$$

where Q_S is the total system Q, it may be shown (see

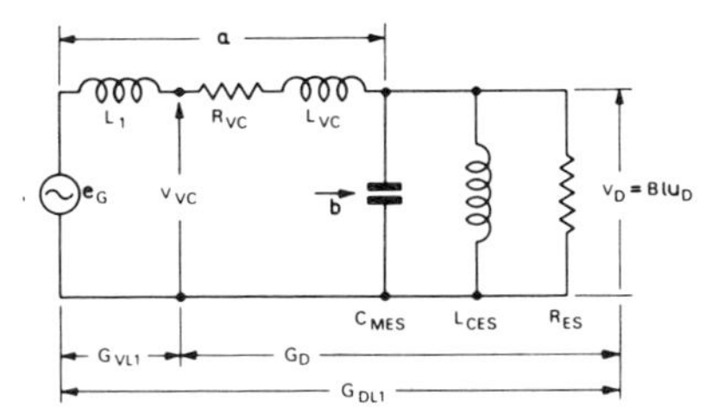

Fig. 1. Electrical equivalent circuit of a loudspeaker driver fed via a series inductance designed to operate in combination as a first-order low-pass filter.

[1] Indications of the effects on the overall acoustic output of a driver fed via a single inductor and alternatively via a single capacitor (first-order filter) were given by J. R. Ashley in "Correction of Crossover Confusion," presented at the 42nd Convention of the Audio Engineering Society, Los Angeles, May 1972.

[2] Note that, although the symbols for the driver alone are used in this analysis, these may be interpreted as applying to the corresponding closed-box parameters where this form of the second-order system is to be employed.

Appendix) from a direct analysis of Fig. 1 that the normalized input impedance Z_{EQN}/R_{VC} for the first-order low-pass system is given by

$$Z_{NL1}(s_N) = \frac{f_3(s_N)}{s_N^2 + (1/Q_M)\, s_N + 1} \tag{9}$$

where $s_N = s/\omega_S = j\omega/\omega_S = jg$ is the normalized complex frequency variable and

$$f_3(s_N) = (Q_{VC} + 1/h_1)\, s_N^3 + \left\{1 + (1/Q_M)\,(Q_{VC} + 1/h_1)\right\} s_N^2 + (1/Q_S + Q_{VC} + 1/h_1)\, s_N + 1. \tag{10}$$

It will be noted that Eq. (9) reduces, when $h_1 \to \infty$ (i.e., using Eqs. (2) and (3), when $L_1 \to 0$) to

$$Z_{NL1}(s_N) = \frac{N_3(s_N)}{s_N^2 + (1/Q_M) s_N + 1} = Z_{N(D)} \qquad (h_1 \to \infty) \tag{11}$$

where

$$N_3(s_N) = Q_{VC} s_N^3 + \left(1 + \frac{Q_{VC}}{Q_M}\right) s_N^2 + \left(\frac{1}{Q_S} + Q_{VC}\right) s_N + 1 \tag{12}$$

as given previously [6, Eq. A3-4] for the input impedance of the driver only when voice-coil inductance is included. (Note that for the driver alone, $g_0 = 1$ in [6, Eq. A3-4]).

Overall Response

To find the transfer function for sound pressure, or diaphragm acceleration, we first find[3]

$$v_D(s) = Bl\, u_D(s) \tag{13}$$

from Fig. 1, where Bl is the product of gap flux density and voice-coil winding length and $u_D(s)$ is the diaphragm velocity (or strictly the Laplace transform thereof). Thus it may be shown from Fig. 1 (see Appendix, Eqs. (47) and (48)) that

$$\frac{v_D(s)}{e_G(s)} = \frac{b}{a + b} = \frac{(1/Q_E)\, s_N}{f_3(s_N)} \tag{14}$$

where $f_3(s_N)$ is the expression already defined in Eq. (10). Using Eqs. (7), (13), and (14) and the relationship $C_{MES} = m_D/(Bl)^2$ [2, Eq. (68)], the diaphragm acceleration is then given by

$$a_D(s) = s u_D(s) = \frac{e_G(s)\, Bl}{R_{VC} m_D}\, G_{DL1}(s_N) \tag{15}$$

where

$$G_{DL1}(s_N) = \frac{s_N^2}{f_3(s_N)} \tag{16}$$

is the acceleration or sound-pressure response function for the overall system and m_D is the effective mechanical mass of the driver diaphragm.

[3] The symbol v is used here to designate circuit voltages resulting from injected electromotive forces which are designated by e as, for example, e_G.

The impedance function given in Eq. (9) together with its imaginary component jY_Z have been plotted in Fig. 2**a** for $Q_S = 0.7071$, $Q_M = 3$, $Q_{VC} = 0.1$, and $h_1 = 10$. Also shown is a set of response curves plotted from Eq. (16) for the same value of Q_S and various values of Q_{VC} and h_1 as indicated. Note that the condition $h_1 \to \infty$ makes $L_1 \to 0$, and this, together with $L_{VC} = 0$, yields the familiar second-order Butterworth (B2) response. Fig. 2**b** shows a set of curves corresponding to those of Fig. 2**a**, but for $Q_S = 1$.

Because L_1 and L_{VC} are in series, and because, from Eqs. (2), (3), and (5),

$$L_{VC}/L_1 = h_1 Q_{VC} \tag{17}$$

the system behaves like a simple driver having an increased voice-coil Q given by

$$Q_{VC}' = (L_{VC} + L_1)\, \omega_S/R_{VC} = Q_{VC} + 1/h_1. \tag{18}$$

This will be evident if Eq. (18) is combined with Eq. (10) and the result compared with Eq. (12). It follows that the curves in Fig. 2 labeled $h_1 = 10$, $Q_{VC} = 0.1$ will correspond to those of a simple driver with $Q_{VC} = 0.2$, as was given previously [2, Fig. A9-1] for $Q_1 = 0.7071$. Also the curves labeled $h_1 \to \infty$, $Q_{VC} = 0.1$ in Fig. 2 will be seen to be identical with those for $h_1 = 10$, $Q_{VC} = 0$. Both response curves shown fall off at 6 dB per octave for high values of g.

Voice-Coil Voltage

It is convenient when checking the practical performance of filtered loudspeaker systems to find the actual filter response by measuring the voltage across the voice-coil

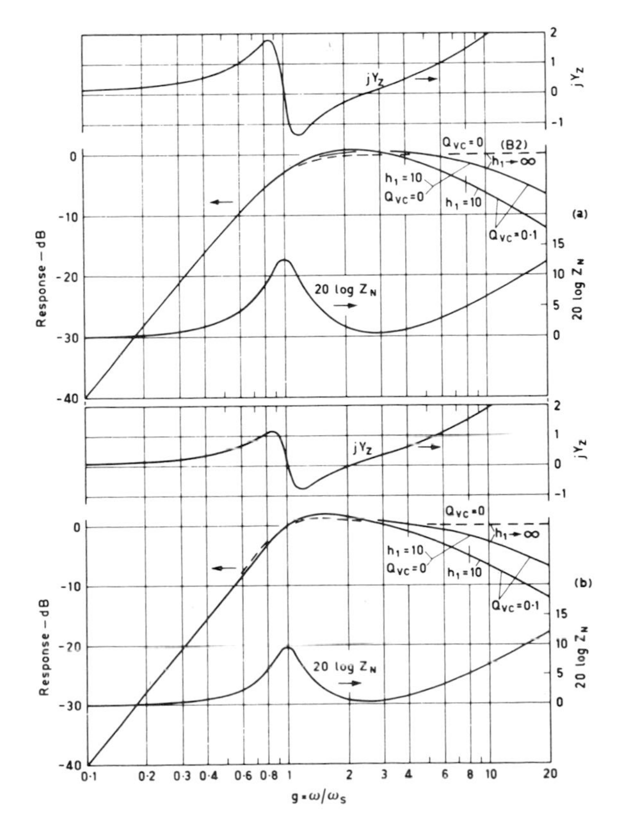

Fig. 2. Response curves for system of Fig. 1 for $Q_{VC} = 0.1$, $Q_M = 3$, $h_1 = 10$. **a.** $Q_S = 0.707$. **b.** $Q_S = 1$.

terminals, with constant input, as a function of frequency. Comparison of this with the response at this point computed from measured values of the system parameters provides a convenient check on their accuracy and hence on that of the computed overall sound-pressure response. The expression for the ratio of the voice-coil to input voltages may be shown from an analysis of Fig. 1 to be

$$\frac{v_{VC}}{e_G} = G_{VL1}(s_N) = \frac{N_3(s_N)}{f_3(s_N)} \tag{19}$$

where $N_3(s_N)$ was defined in Eq. (12) and $f_3(s_N)$ in Eq. (10). Note also that when $h_1 \to \infty$ these two expressions are equal so that $G_{VL_1}(s_N) = 1$, as expected, when $L_1 = 0$.

Driver Response

The sound-pressure response of the driver alone, as given previously (see [2, Eq. A9-6], noting that $g_0 = 1$ and $G_{H_2} = G_D$), is

$$G_D(s_N) = \frac{s_N^2}{N_3(s_N)}\,. \tag{20}$$

As would be expected from Fig. 1, the following relationships are seen to hold between the three transfer functions given in Eqs. (16), (19), and (20):

$$G_{DL1}(s_N) = G_{VL1}(s_N) \cdot G_D(s_N) \tag{21}$$

$$= \frac{N_3(s_N)}{f_3(s_N)} \cdot \frac{s_N^2}{N_3(s_N)} \tag{22}$$

$$= \frac{s_N^2}{f_3(s_N)}\,. \tag{16}$$

Nominal Filter Response

The nominal filter response corresponding to the nominal cutoff frequency defined by Eqs. (2) and (3) may be derived from $G_{VL1}(s_N)$ by putting $Q_{VC} = 0$ and making the motional impedance zero. This can be achieved mathematically by putting Q_M and therefore Q_S approximately equal to zero. Putting these values in Eq. (19) yields,

$$G_{VL1}(s_N) = \frac{1}{s_N/h_1 + 1} = G_{L1}(s_N)\,,\ \text{(say,)} \tag{23}$$

which is a first-order low-pass filter function normalized to $\omega_1 = h_1\,\omega_S$.

Fig. 3 shows curves for the responses G_{DL1}, G_D, and G_{VL1} for the conditions of Fig. 2**b**. Shown also (displaced by 10 dB) is the nominal filter response G_{L1} (broken curve) obtained by putting $Q_M = Q_S = 10^{-6}$ and $Q_{VC} = 0$ in the computation for G_{VL1}. The adjacent solid curve G_{L1}' is the corresponding filter response when terminated by R_{VC} and L_{VC} in series. This will be seen to track closely, particularly at high frequencies, with the voice-coil voltage G_{VL1} obtained across the input impedance of the driver. The overall normalized input impedance Z_N is shown in the lower set of curves together with that of the driver alone $Z_{N(D)}$ and the filter alone $Z_{N(F)}$ when terminated by R_{VC} and L_{VC} only.

High-Pass Filter

Fig. 4 shows the circuit corresponding to Fig. 1 for the case of a first-order high-pass filter comprising a capacitor C_1 feeding directly into the input impedance of the driver. Using the same notation and methods as previously, with the exception that the equivalent of Eq. (2) is now

$$R_{VC} C_1 \omega_1 = 1 \tag{24}$$

the input impedance and the sound-pressure and voice-coil transfer functions may be shown to be as follows.

Input Impedance

The normalized input impedance $Z_{E(IN)}/R_{VC}$ is given by

$$Z_{NH1} = \frac{f_4(s_N)}{s_N\{s_N^2 + (1/Q_M)s_N + 1\}} \tag{25}$$

where

$$f_4(s_N) = Q_{VC}s_N^4 + (1 + Q_{VC}/Q_M)\,s_N^3 + (h_1 + 1/Q_S + Q_{VC})\,s_N^2 + (1 + h_1/Q_M)\,s_N + h_1. \tag{26}$$

When $h_1 = 0$, i.e., $\omega_1 = 0$ and hence $C_1 = \infty$, Eq. (25) reduces to Eq. (11) for the driver alone.

Overall Response

The overall response function corresponding to Eq. (16) is now

$$G_{DH1}(s_N) = \frac{s_N^3}{f_4(s_N)} \tag{27}$$

where $f_4(s_N)$ has been defined in Eq. (26).

Voice-Coil Voltage

The voice-coil voltage transfer function $G_{VH1} = v_{VC}/e_G$ may be shown from Fig. 4 or the relationships correspond-

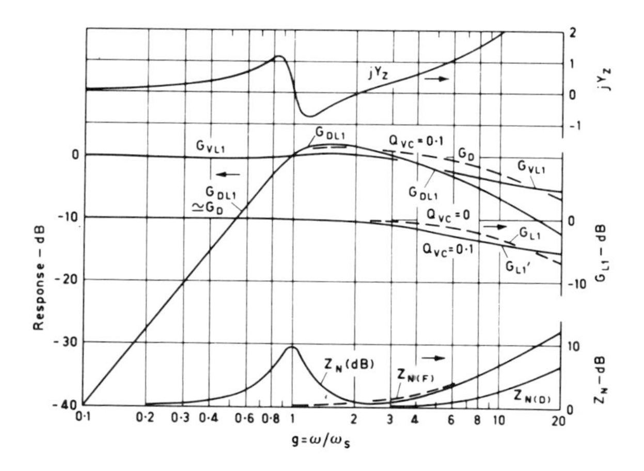

Fig. 3. Response curves for parameter values of Fig. 2**b** illustrating the relationship $G_{DL1} = G_{VL1}\,G_D$. Also shown are filter-response and impedance curves.

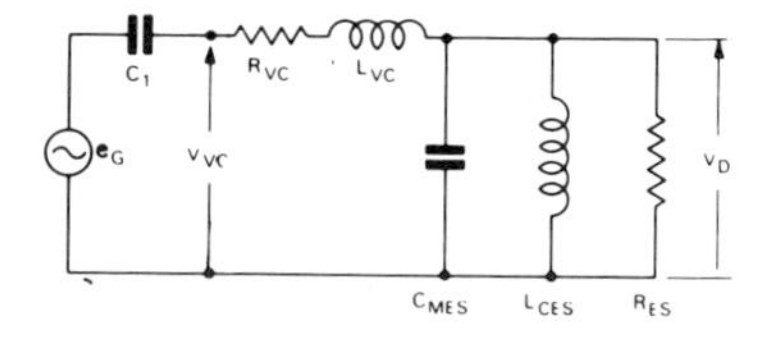

Fig. 4. Circuit of Fig. 1, but for high-pass filter.

ing to Eq. (21) to be

$$G_{VH1}(s_N) = \frac{s_N N_3(s_N)}{f_4(s_N)} \qquad (28)$$

where the terms are defined in Eq. (12) and (26).

It is possible, using the methods described earlier [2] in connection with reflex systems, to establish synthesis procedures to obtain specified prototype responses from the circuit of Fig. 4, providing the voice-coil inductance may be neglected. As it is not practicable in this introductory paper to give the details of this work, two examples of the results only will be given. These take the form of curves computed from the foregoing response equations using the parameters which have been obtained from the synthesis relationships.

The first example, presented in Fig. 5, is a third-order Butterworth (B3) maximally flat response shown as the solid curve marked G_{DH1} (B3) in the top set for which $Q_{VC} = 0$. The other parameters required for the synthesis are shown in the figure caption. It will be noted that the −3-dB cutoff frequency occurs at $g = 0.8$, which is the cube root of the frequency ratio h_1. Shown also in the top set of curves are those for the voice-coil voltage response G_{VH1} and the driver response alone G_D. The overall response G_{DH1} for $Q_{VC} = 0.1$ has been plotted below (displaced by 10 dB) for comparison. The deviation from the maximally flat form will be seen to be negligibly small up to $g \simeq 6$, above which rolloff due to voice-coil inductance becomes significant. Below this curve (also displaced 10 dB) is a set of three curves showing the nominal filter response G_{H1} $(Q_{VC} = 0)$, when terminated in R_{VC} only (broken curve), and close to it, the solid curve for G_{H1} $(Q_{VC} = 0.1)$ showing the effect on the filter response of including L_{VC}. The curve G_{VH1} in this group shows the effect on the filter response of including the motional impedance as well as the voice-coil inductance. The lower pair of curves shows the overall input impedance Z_N and that of the driver alone $Z_{N(D)}$ $(h_1 = 0)$, both with $Q_{VC} = 0.1$.

The second example is given in Fig. 6 in which the top three curves, taken for $Q_{VC} = 0$, show the synthesized third-order Chebyshev response for 1-dB ripple (upper solid curve G_{DH1}, also marked C3) together with the voice-coil response G_{VH1} and the response of the driver alone G_D. (Note that the ripple is negative, which is characteristic of odd-order high-pass Chebyshev responses when normalized to unity at high frequencies.) The next lower curve (displaced by 10 dB) shows the overall response G_{DH1} for $Q_{VC} = 0.1$. It will be seen that the voice-coil inductance has actually reduced the ripple below that of the synthesized C_3 response, giving a substantially flat response up to $g = 7$, above which the normal rolloff occurs. The next group of three curves, as in Fig. 5, shows the effects relative to the nominal filter response G_{H1} $(Q_{VC} = 0)$ of the voice-coil inductance, curve G_{H1} $(Q_{VC} = 0.1)$, and also the motional impedance shown by the curve G_{VH1} $(Q_{VC} = 0.1)$ for the voice-coil voltage. The lower set of curves shows the overall input impedance Z_N with and without voice-coil inductance, and also the input impedance $Z_{N(D)}$ for the driver alone with $Q_{VC} = 0$.

Fig. 7 shows a set of response and impedance curves for a commercial dome tweeter, the measured parameters of which are given in the caption. This tweeter was notable among a number of others tested in having a particularly high value of Q_M. The curves of Fig. 7 demonstrate the unsuitability of a simple first-order filter for use with tweeters of this type. It will be noted that, because of the high motional impedance at resonance, the voice-coil voltage and overall response rise to high values at $g \simeq 0.95$. These are of the same order as the maximum values achieved in the intended passband region, i.e., for $g > 8$. This example

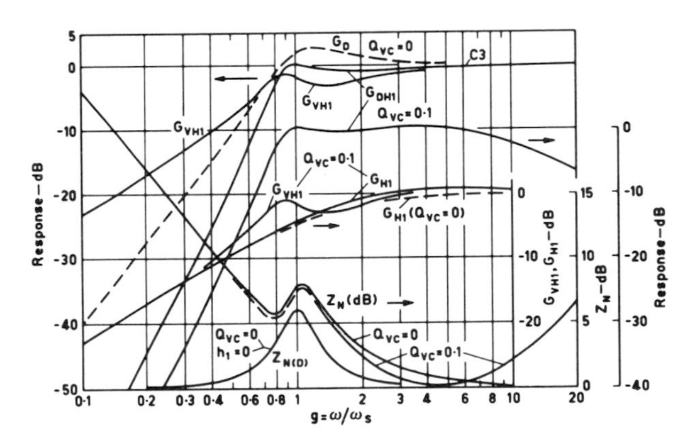

Fig. 6. Curves as for Fig. 5, but having parameters computed to synthesize a C3 alignment with a ripple excursion of 1 dB, i.e., $Q_S = 1.23$, $Q_{VC} = 0$, $Q_M = 2.45$, $h_1 = 1.42$.

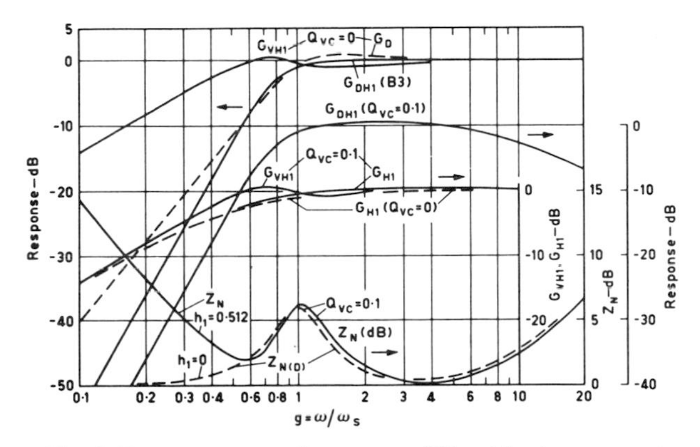

Fig. 5. Response curves for system of Fig. 4 having parameters computed to synthesize a B3 alignment, i.e., $Q_S = 0.92$, $Q_{VC} = 0$, $Q_M = 1.84$, $h_1 = 0.512$. Responses for $Q_{VC} = 0.1$ are also shown.

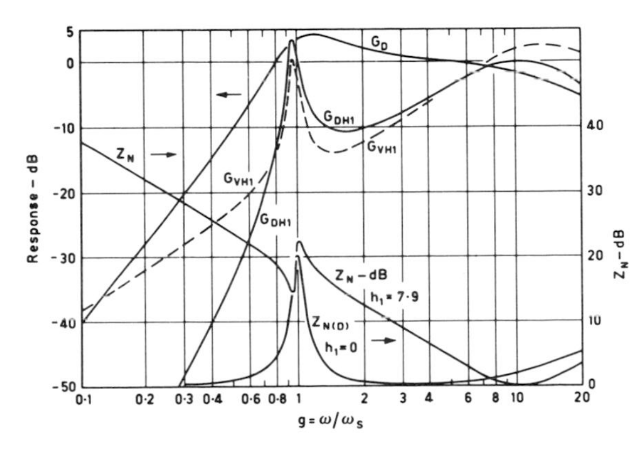

Fig. 7. Response curves computed for measured parameters of a commercial tweeter using circuit of Fig. 4 in which C_1 was chosen to give a nominal cutoff frequency of 7 kHz requiring $h_1 = 7.9$. Tweeter parameters $Q_S = 1.5$, $Q_{VC} = 0.078$, $Q_M = 15.8$.

will be discussed later when the tweeter is driven from a second-order filter having the same cutoff frequency ratio h_1 which was chosen to achieve a cutoff at 7 kHz with this particular tweeter.

Fig. 8 shows two measured sound-pressure response curves for the tweeter of Fig. 7, curve A having been taken without and curve B with the coupling capacitor C_1. The circled points, which were taken from the computed curves of Fig. 7 (after conversion of the frequency scale), show good agreement with the measured curves in the region of interest, i.e., in the low-frequency region up to approximately 4 kHz. For higher frequencies the measured curves show a rise in response indicating a broad resonance due to electroacoustic properties of the tweeter which are not accounted for by the measured parameters applicable to the simple equivalent circuit of Fig. 4.

SECOND-ORDER FILTERS

Impedance and Response Functions

As the analysis of the second-order systems reveals a number of interesting relationships and common functions between the low-pass and high-pass types, it is convenient to discuss these together. The equivalent electrical circuits of the two systems are shown in Fig. 9 for which the following terms are defined:

$$L_1C_1\omega_1^2 = 1 \tag{29}$$

$$Q_1 = \frac{R_{VC}}{L_1\omega_1} = R_{VC}C_1\omega_1. \tag{30}$$

Then retaining h_1 as defined in Eq. (3), it may be shown from an analysis of Fig. 9, using methods similar to those given in the Appendix for Fig. 1, that the normalized input impedance takes the form

$$Z_{N(i)} = \frac{f_{5(i)}(s_N)}{D_{4(i)}(s_N)} \tag{31}$$

where the subscript i stands for L or H, indicating the low-pass or high-pass case. The relevant functions are then as follows:

$$\begin{aligned} f_{5(H)}(s_N) = {} & Q_{VC}s_N^5 + \left(1 + \frac{Q_{VC}}{Q_M}\right)s_N^4 \\ & + \left(\frac{1}{Q_S} + Q_{VC} + \frac{h_1}{Q_1} + h_1^2Q_{VC}\right)s_N^3 \\ & + \left\{1 + \frac{h_1}{Q_1Q_M} + h_1^2\left(1 + \frac{Q_{VC}}{Q_M}\right)\right\}s_N^2 \\ & + \left\{h_1^2\left(\frac{1}{Q_S} + Q_{VC}\right) + \frac{h_1}{Q_1}\right\}s_N + h_1^2 \end{aligned} \tag{32}$$

$$f_{5(L)}(s_N) = \frac{f_{5(H)}(s_N)}{h_1^2} \tag{33}$$

$$\begin{aligned} D_{4(L)}(s_N) = {} & \frac{Q_{VC}Q_1}{h_1}s_N^4 + \frac{Q_1}{h_1}\left(1 + \frac{Q_{VC}}{Q_M}\right)s_N^3 \\ & + \left\{1 + \frac{Q_1}{h_1}\left(\frac{1}{Q_S} + Q_{VC}\right)\right\}s_N^2 \\ & + \left(\frac{1}{Q_M} + \frac{Q_1}{h_1}\right)s_N + 1 \end{aligned} \tag{34}$$

and

$$\begin{aligned} D_{4(H)}(s_N) = {} & (1 + h_1Q_{VC}Q_1)\, s_N^4 \\ & + \left\{\frac{1}{Q_M} + h_1Q_1\left(1 + \frac{Q_{VC}}{Q_M}\right)\right\}s_N^3 \\ & + \left\{1 + h_1Q_1\left(\frac{1}{Q_S} + Q_{VC}\right)\right\}s_N^2 + h_1Q_1s_N. \end{aligned} \tag{35}$$

The sound-pressure transfer functions are then

$$G_{DL2}(s_N) = \frac{s_N^2}{f_{5(L)}(s_N)} \tag{36}$$

and

$$G_{DH2}(s_N) = \frac{s_N^4}{f_{5(H)}(s_N)} \tag{37}$$

The voice-coil voltage functions are found using Eq. (20) for the driver response function and noting the relationship equivalent to Eq. (21),

$$G_{Di}(s_N) = G_{Vi}(s_N)\, G_D(s_N). \tag{38}$$

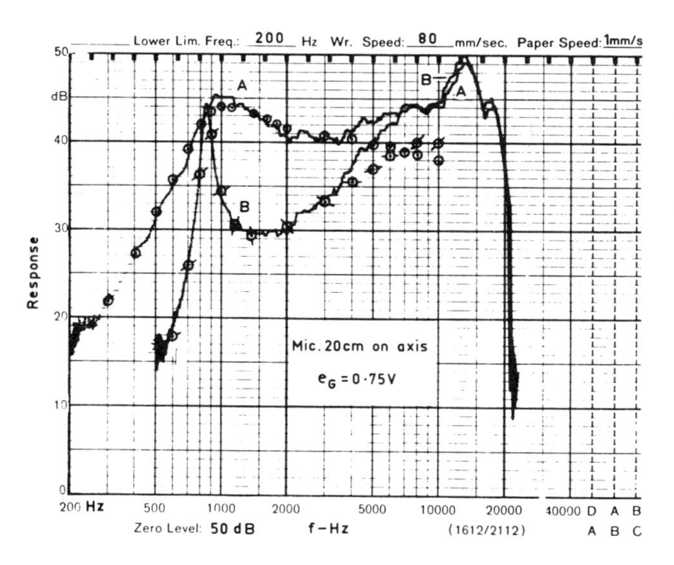

Fig. 8. Measured frequency response of tweeter of Fig. 7. Curve A—tweeter alone (C_1 removed): curve B—C_1 = 3.32 μF.

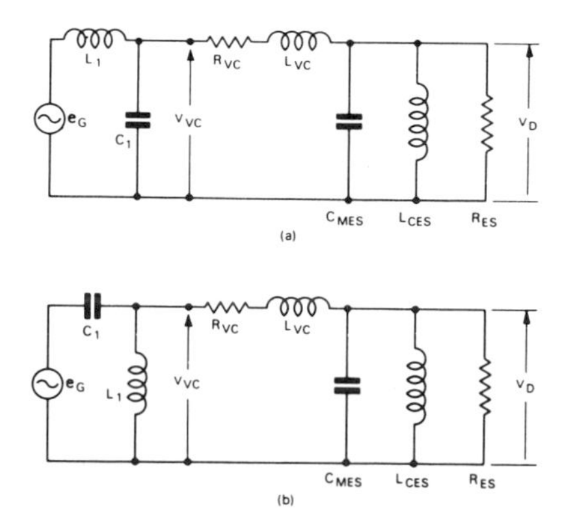

Fig. 9. Electrical equivalent circuits for loudspeaker driver fed via second-order filters. **a.** low-pass type. **b.** high-pass type.

Hence

$$G_{VL2}(s_N) = \frac{G_{DL2}(s_N)}{G_D(s_N)}$$

$$= \frac{N_3(s_N)}{f_{5(L)}(s_N)} \quad (39)$$

$$G_{VH2}(s_N) = \frac{G_{DH2}(s_N)}{G_D(s_N)}$$

$$= \frac{s_N^2 N_3(s_N)}{f_{5(H)}(s_N)}. \quad (40)$$

Low-Pass Filter Responses

Fig. 10 shows a set of response curves computed for the circuit of Fig. **9a** using the parameters given in the caption. The filter is a second-order Butterworth (B2) with a nominal cutoff frequency of $10\omega_S$, and the driver Q is also assumed to be that of a B2 alignment. The voice-coil Q is representative of large woofers. From the upper set of curves in Fig. 10 it will be seen that the overall response G_{DL2} near the driver cutoff ($g = 1$) does not deviate greatly from the ideal $B2_{(H)}$ response. The rise in the region of $g = 2$ is similar to, but rather greater than, that due to voice-coil inductance alone (see [2, Fig. A9-1]) because of the added series inductance of the filter. It is in the region of the filter cutoff frequency ($g \simeq h_1$) that the most severe deviations occur. These are due to the disturbance of the correct filter termination caused by the existence of the voice-coil inductance.

It will be noted from the lower curves that the input impedance Z_N passes through a broad maximum above the second resonance and then through a sharp minimum at $g = 13$. (The inverse effects will be seen in the upper response curves for G_{DL2} and G_{VL2}.) The broad maximum in Z_N is due to the damped antiresonance between C_1 and the predominantly inductive series circuit comprising L_{VC}, R_{VC}, and the low capacitive motional reactance. At the higher frequency ($g = 13$) this whole circuit becomes capacitive and series resonates with L_1 to give a low input impedance and a high voice-coil voltage.

By shunting the voice-coil terminals with a compensating network comprising a series combination $R_1 = k R_{VC}$, $C_2 = 1/kh_1 Q_2 R_{VC}\omega_S$, it is possible, with a suitable choice of parameters, to minimize these disturbing effects in both impedance and response. By way of example, curves for $G_{DL2(C)}$ and $G_{VL2(C)}$ for values of $k = Q_2 = 1$ are shown in the center of Fig. 10, displaced by 10 dB, and the corresponding impedance curve is shown below by the broken line $Z_{N(C)}$. (The analysis for the compensated system, being appreciably more extensive than that given above will be reserved for a later occasion.)

High-Pass Filter Responses

Fig. 11 shows a set of response curves for the circuit of Fig. **9b** with parameters computed from synthesis theory (to be presented subsequently) to achieve an overall response G_{DH2} conforming to a C4 alignment with a ripple excursion of 1 dB in the absence of voice-coil inductance, i.e., $Q_{VC} = 0$. The required parameter values are given in the caption. Increase of Q_{VC} to 0.1 was found to have a negligible effect (< 0.2 dB) on the voice-coil voltage response G_{VH2} but causes significant deviations to the overall response G_{DH2} and input impedance Z_N at high frequencies. The curves for these are shown as broken lines, that for G_{DH2} ($Q_{VC} = 0.1$) being displaced by 10 dB for clarity. The physical explanation of the synthesized response will be apparent from the curve for voice-coil voltage G_{VH2}. The system response which, for the speaker alone, would fall rapidly below $g = 1$, will be seen to be held up by the rise of voice-coil voltage caused by the resonance of the filter circuit at $g = h_1 = 0.516$. The driving power is relatively high at this frequency because of the sharp minimum of input impedance (22 dB below R_{VC}), or approximately 0.08 R_{VC}. It follows also that a very large diaphragm amplitude will be required at cutoff frequency by comparison with that of the corresponding reflex system [2]. The amplitude response is shown by the curve G_X which peaks along with G_{VH2} and the minimum of Z_N in the region of the filter resonance where the input phase expressed by the imaginary component jY_z passes through zero. The filter components L_1, C_1 may be found directly from Eq. (30) when Q_1, R_{VC}, and ω_1 have been specified.

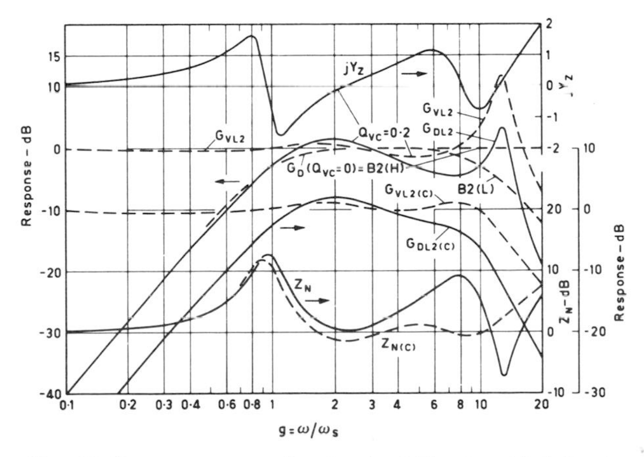

Fig. 10. Response curves for circuit of Fig. **9a** with following parameters: $Q_S = Q_1 = 0.707$, $Q_{VC} = 0.2$, $Q_M = 3$, $h_1 = 10$. Shown also are curves taken with a compensating network as described.

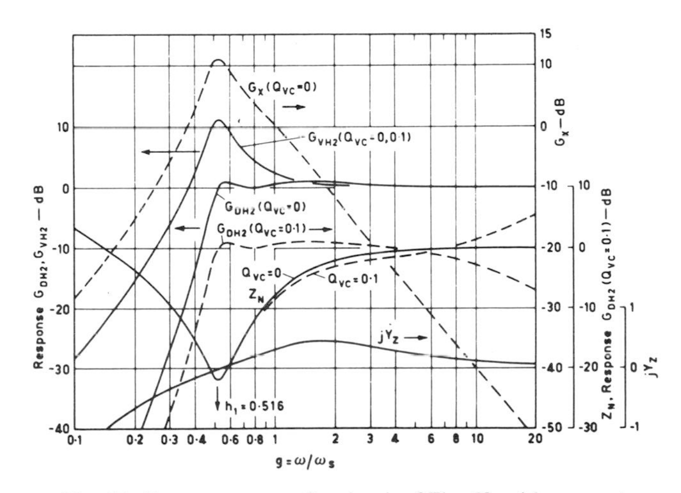

Fig. 11. Response curves for circuit of Fig. **9b** with parameters computed to synthesize a C4 alignment with a ripple excursion of 1 dB, i.e., $Q_S = 0.802$, $Q_1 = 3.320$, $Q_{VC} = 0$, $Q_M = 0.955$, $h_1 = 0.516$.

A second example of the application of the circuit of Fig. **9b** is given in Fig. 12. This has been plotted for the same tweeter employed for Fig. 7, which illustrated the effect of driving it from a first-order filter. The overall response G_{DH2} conforms substantially to the expected high-pass response, having its −3-dB cutoff at approximately $g = h_1 = 7.9$, and a hump in the region of $g = 1$, which is small by comparison with that observed in the response shown in Fig. 7. The rise of 3.5 dB at $g = 13$ accompanied by the minimum impedance of −6.7 dB relative to R_{VC} is due to the mistermination of the filter caused by the inclusion of L_{VC} in series with R_{VC}. Above this point, G_{DH2} falls and Z_N rises due to the continually increasing reactance of L_{VC} as the frequency increases. The voice-coil voltage response G_{VH2}, differing from it, in fact, by the driver response given as the curve D_D in Fig. 7.

The broken curves marked $Q_2 = 3$ in Fig. 12 show the effect of adding voice-coil inductance compensation as discussed in connection with Fig. 10. Note that while this prevents the overshoot of response and reduces the depth of the impedance minimum, it does not prevent the rolloff of sound-pressure response at high frequencies, which is due to the reduction of the net voltage appearing across the motional impedance.

SUMMARY AND CONCLUSIONS

This introductory study of the response and impedance characteristics of second-order loudspeaker systems driven by directly coupled passive filters has revealed some interesting effects which are of significance in the design of high-level crossover filters and in the use of auxiliary filters to modify the response of loudspeaker systems.

These effects are due to one or both of the characteristics of the input impedance of a simple loudspeaker by which it deviates from the nominal impedance, normally taken to be a pure resistance and having a value slightly above that of the voice-coil resistance. These characteristics are due to the voice-coil inductance and motional impedance.

In the case of low-pass filters of first order (series inductance only), the motional impedance has negligible effect and the voice-coil inductance can be considered as part of the effective filter inductance.

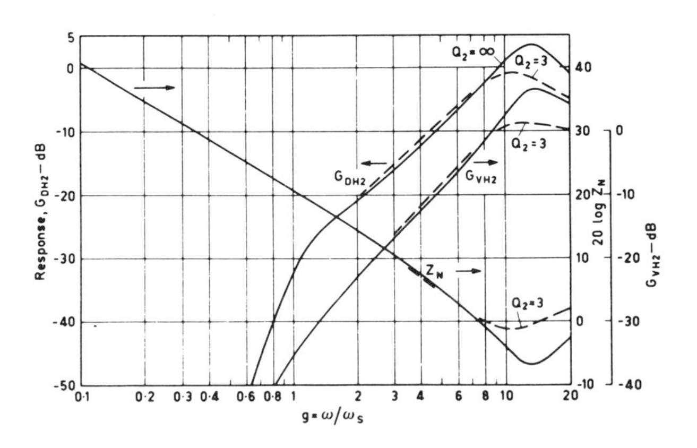

Fig. 12. Response curves for circuit of Fig. **9b** using tweeter whose measured parameters were given for Fig. 7. Additional circuit parameters are $Q_1 = 0.707$ and, for broken-line curves, $Q_2 = 3$.

For second-order low-pass filters having, as is common in crossover applications, a cutoff frequency of the order of ten times that of the driver resonance, the motional impedance at cutoff is capacitive and negligibly low. This allows L_{VC} and R_{VC} to appear in series across the filter capacitor, producing in the region of nominal cutoff a broad maximum of input impedance followed by a sharp minimum. The corresponding variations of output were indicated in Fig. 10 which showed also how these effects can be reduced by voice-coil inductance compensation.

In the case of high-pass filters of first order, having a cutoff frequency likewise well above the driver resonance, the response is very critical to the mechanical Q of the driver. When this is high, a high signal voltage appears across the voice-coil terminals at driver resonance resulting in a high peak of output with corresponding large and possibly damaging excursion. These effects are important for midrange drivers and tweeters coupled by a single capacitor. The only solution possible in such cases is to reduce the value of Q_M, which can be done with open-back cone-type drivers by means of acoustic damping applied to the housing [7]. This leads to the possibility (to be discussed in a later paper) of approximating a synthesized third-order response (such as a B3 or C3 alignment) having the desired relationship between cutoff frequency and driver resonance frequency.

If, as in the case of dome or horn tweeters, additional damping is impracticable, the only remaining solution is to use a higher-order filter which will reduce the voltage available to the driver at its fundamental resonance to a negligibly low value. This virtually eliminates the response peak in the attenuation band due to motional impedance, but leaves the problem of the pass-band peak which, as was shown in Fig. 12, is due to the effect of voice-coil inductance on the filter termination. This can be reduced by a compensating network, as previously, leaving only the inherent rolloff of response due to diminishing voice-coil current with increasing frequency.

If it is practicable to control all relevant driver parameters, it is possible to synthesize fourth-order responses of C4, B4, or QB3 [1] form according to the desired relationship between the system cutoff and the driver resonance frequencies. These responses are, of course, subject to modification by the presence of voice-coil inductance, part of which only can be offset by a simple *R-C* compensating network.

The present paper, which has been confined to second-order loudspeaker systems driven by first- or second-order filters, has opened up a number of areas for more detailed investigation. Some of these have been carried out and results presented briefly in the form of numerical examples. These include techniques for system synthesis and voice-coil inductance compensation. Other practical problems awaiting investigation are the effects of filters on reflex loudspeaker systems, the input impedance of parallel-input low-pass and high-pass systems, optimization of compensating networks, and the selection of cutoff frequencies required for smooth transition between elements in multi speaker systems. It is hoped to deal with these along with applications to practical systems in subsequent papers.

APPENDIX

DERIVATION OF INPUT IMPEDANCE AND OVERALL RESPONSE FUNCTION FOR A LOUDSPEAKER DRIVER FED VIA A SERIES INDUCTANCE

It will be seen from Fig. 1 that the series inductance L_1 operating into the input impedance of the loudspeaker driver constitutes a first-order low-pass filter with R_{VC} as its termination, provided that L_{VC} is negligible and the cutoff frequency is sufficiently high that the motional impedance indicated by the symbol b is also negligible. These assumptions are required only to establish a definition of the nominal cutoff frequency ω_1, as given by Eq. (2).

Input Impedance

Using the symbols a and b, respectively, for the series and parallel combinations of impedances shown in Fig. 1, the input impedance is

$$Z_{E(IN)}(s) = a + b \tag{41}$$

where

$$a = L_1 s + L_{VC} s + R_{VC} \tag{42}$$

and

$$b = \frac{1}{C_{MES} s + 1/L_{CES} s + 1/R_{ES}}$$

$$= \frac{L_{CES} s}{L_{CES} C_{MES} s^2 + L_{CES} s/R_{ES} + 1} \tag{43}$$

Normalizing to R_{VC}, and using the definitions given in Eqs. (2) to (8) we may write the normalized input impedance as

$$Z_N(s) = Z_{NL1}(s) = \frac{Z_{E(IN)}(s)}{R_{VC}} = \frac{a+b}{R_{VC}} \tag{44}$$

$$= \frac{L_1 s}{R_{VC}} + \frac{L_{VC} s}{R_{VC}} + 1 + \frac{L_{CES} s/R_{VC}}{s^2/\omega_S^2 + (1/Q_M)(s/\omega_S) + 1}$$

$$= \frac{s}{h_1 \omega_S} + \frac{Q_{VC} s}{\omega_S} + 1 + \frac{(1/Q_E)(s/\omega_S)}{(s^2/\omega_S^2) + (1/Q_M)(s/\omega_S) + 1} \tag{45}$$

Finally, using the normalized frequency variable $s_N = s/\omega_S$, we may write

$$Z_{NL1}(s_N) = \frac{s_N}{h_1} + Q_{VC} s_N + 1 + \frac{(1/Q_E) s_N}{s_N^2 + (1/Q_M) s_N + 1} \tag{46}$$

$$= \frac{f_3(s_N)}{s_N^2 + (1/Q_M) s_N + 1} \tag{9}$$

which is Eq. (9), $f_3(s_N)$ being given by Eq. (10).

Overall Response

To find the overall transfer function for diaphragm acceleration (which is proportional to sound pressure) we first find v_D, the voltage developed across the motional impedance as a result of the injected electromotive force e_G. Thus using Eqs. (41)–(46) and (9),

$$v_D(s) = \frac{b}{a+b} \cdot e_G(s) \tag{47}$$

$$= \frac{b/R_{VC}}{(a+b)/R_{VC}} e_G(s) = \frac{b/R_{VC}}{Z_{NL1}(s_N)} e_G(s)$$

$$= \frac{(1/Q_E) s_N e_G(s)}{s_N^2 + (1/Q_M) s_N + 1} \cdot \frac{s_N^2 + (1/Q_M) s_N + 1}{f_3(s_N)}$$

$$= \frac{(1/Q_E) s_N e_G(s)}{f_3(s_N)}. \tag{48}$$

We may now express the diaphragm acceleration in terms of v_D as follows. By definition,

$$a_D(s) = s u_D(s) \tag{49}$$

which, using Eq. (13), becomes

$$a_D(s) = \frac{s v_D(s)}{Bl}. \tag{50}$$

Noting that $s_N = s/\omega_S$ and using Eq. (48),

$$a_D(s) = \frac{e_G(s) s^2}{Q_E Bl\, \omega_S} \cdot \frac{1}{f_3(s_N)}. \tag{51}$$

Then using Eq. (7) and the relationship from [2, Eq. (68)], namely,

$$C_{MES} = m_D/(Bl)^2 \tag{52}$$

$$Q_E = R_{VC} C_{MES} \omega_S \tag{7}$$

$$= \frac{R_{VC} m_D \omega_S}{(Bl)^2}. \tag{53}$$

Hence, from Eq. (51), using Eq. (53),

$$a_D(s) = \frac{e_G(s)\, Bl}{R_{VC} m_D} \cdot \frac{s_N^2}{f_3(s_N)} \tag{54}$$

$$= \frac{e_G(s) Bl}{R_{VC} m_D} G_{DL1}(s_N) \tag{15}$$

where

$$G_{DL1}(s_N) = \frac{s_N^2}{f_3(s_N)}. \tag{16}$$

ACKNOWLEDGMENT

The author would like to thank Dr. R. H. Small of Sydney University for valuable discussions during the formative stages of this paper and particularly for confirming with his analog simulator the principal impedance and response curves of Fig. 10 and also for reviewing the final manuscript. Thanks are due also to Rowan K. Butler for recording the measured response curves of Fig. 8.

REFERENCES

[1] A. N. Thiele, "Loudspeakers in Vented Boxes," *Proc. I.R.E. (Aust.)*, vol. 22, p. 487, (Aug. 1961); also *J. Audio Eng. Soc.*, vol. 19, pp. 382-392 (May 1971), and pp. 471-483 (June 1971).

[2] J. E. Benson, "Theory and Design of Loudspeaker Enclosures, Part 3—Introductin to Synthesis of Vented Systems," *A.W.A. Tech. Rev.*, vol. 14, p. 369 (1972).

[3] J. R. Ashley, "On the Transient Response of Ideal Crossover Networks," *J. Audio Eng. Soc.*, vol. 10, p. 241 (July 1962).

[4] R. H. Small, "Constant-Voltage Crossover Network Design," *Proc. I.R.E.E. (Aust.)*, vol. 31, p. 66 (March 1970); also *J. Audio Eng. Soc.*, vol. 19, pp. 12-19 (Jan. 1971).

[5] J. R. Ashley and A. L. Kaminsky, "Active and Passive Filters as Loudspeaker Crossover Networks," *J. Audio Eng. Soc.*, vol. 19, pp. 494-502 (June 1971).

[6] J. E. Benson, "Theory and Design of Loudspeaker Enclosures, Part 2—Response Relationships for Infinite Baffle and Closed-Box Systems," *A.W.A. Tech. Rev.*, vol. 14, p. 225 (1971).

[7] J. L. Grauer, "Acoustic Resistance Damping for Loudspeakers," *Audio*, vol. 49, p. 22 (Mar. 1965).

THE AUTHOR

J. Ernest Benson was born in 1911 and educated at Sydney University, where he received the degrees of B.Sc. in 1932, B.E. (Hons. Cl.1, Elect. Eng.) in 1934 and Dip. Ed. in 1935. He joined the staff of the Research Laboratory of Amalgamated Wireless (Australasia) Ltd. in Dec. 1934, where he worked on the development and applications of piezoelectric quartz crystals. For published work in this field, he received the M.E. degree with Hons. Cl.1 and University Medal from Sydney University in 1946.

His work from the early 1950s became increasingly concerned with the applications of electroacoustics to sound reproduction and, in due course, provided the basis for the design of the loudspeaker systems installed by AWA in the Sydney Opera House. For this work he shared in the Prince Philip Prize for Australian Design, awarded to AWA in 1972.

In December 1974, he completed 40 years service with AWA, and was also awarded the D.Sc.Eng. degree by Sydney University, which was conferred on April 19, 1975. His thesis entitled "Collected Papers on Electro-Acoustics, Television and Piezo-Electricity," comprised 25 papers published from 1936 to 1972 in the AWA Technical Review, of which he has been Editor since 1948.

Dr. Benson retired in March 1975 and is continuing his active career with further publications and consulting work in electroacoustics and the design of high-quality sound systems. He has recently been appointed to the Publications Board of the IREE. He is currently a Fellow of the IREE and I.E.E. (London) and a Member of the I.E. Aust., the Australian Acoustical Society and the AES and is Chairman of the Technical Committee on Electro-Acoustics and Recording of the Standards Association of Australia.

The Sound Field in Home Listening Rooms, II*

ROY F. ALLISON

Allison Acoustics Inc., Natick, MA 01760

The average of sound pressure level versus frequency curves at listener locations in home listening rooms has been shown to have a substantial trough in the middle of the bass range. Reflected impedance from the room boundaries causes a reduction in woofer loading (and thereby a loss of acoustic power output to the room) in the same frequency region for conventional loudspeaker systems in normal positions in a room. Uniform power output versus frequency can be obtained by appropriate design of the loudspeaker system and its proper placement with respect to the room boundaries. The effect of these measures on the sound field as measured at typical listener locations in several listening rooms is reported.

INTRODUCTION: In 1972 Allison and Berkovitz [1] measured sound pressure versus frequency at listener locations in several living rooms, produced by the loudspeaker systems being used in those rooms. When 22 response curves were averaged, the composite curve was rather smooth except for a surprising low-frequency notch (Fig. 1). It was known that the loudspeaker systems did not show any such anomaly when tested in anechoic environments. In every room where these tests were made, however, the owner had placed the loudspeaker cabinets conventionally, that is, with the back close to a room wall. Therefore it was assumed that the strong reflection from this wall reduced the woofer's power output at the frequency for which the distance to the center of the woofer was a quarter wavelength.

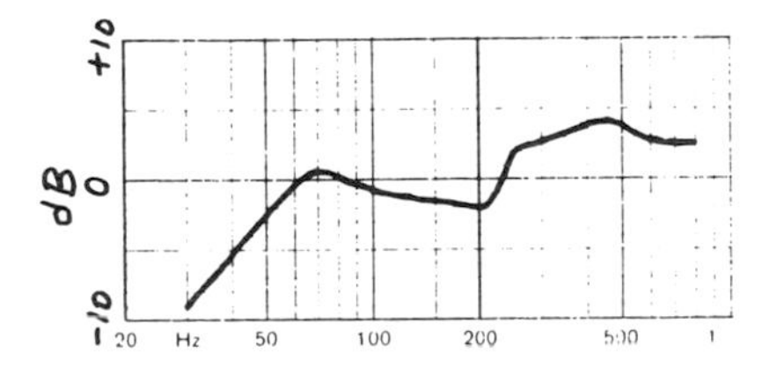

Fig. 1. Average sound pressure level versus frequency at 22 listening locations in eight living rooms. Pink noise input to loudspeaker systems, one-third octave analysis.

Allison investigated in detail in a 1974 paper [2] the effects of room boundaries on loudspeaker power output, confirming experimentally the results predicted by Waterhouse [3], [4] and Waterhouse and Cook [5] in a series of papers published from 1955 through 1965. Allison tested the acoustic power output of the woofer of a closed-box system with outside dimensions of 25 by 14 by 10¼ inches (635 by 355 by 260 mm), a design typical of contemporary high-quality loudspeaker systems, under a wide range of environmental conditions. This "test standard system" is capable of extraordinarily flat acoustic power output when operating into ideal 2π steradian space, but when oriented conventionally in real rooms its power output variation is typically 5–12 dB. The variation can be as much as 20 dB. Fig. 2 shows PWL (power level re 130 dB = 1 acoustic

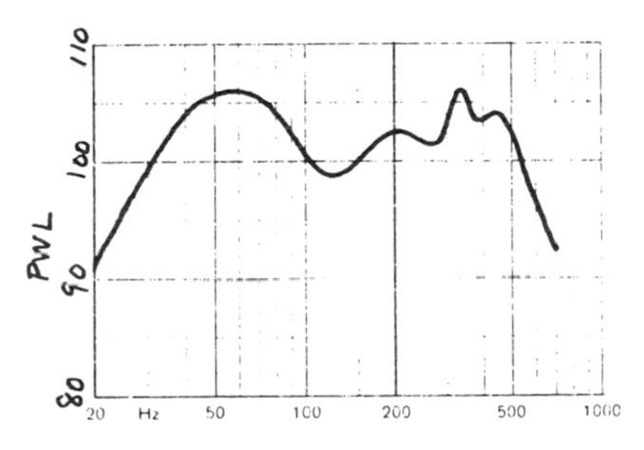

Fig. 2. Power level versus frequency for test standard loudspeaker system. Cabinet back close to wall, center of woofer 3 ft (0.9 m) from adjacent wall and same distance above floor.

* Presented November 3, 1975, at the 52nd Convention of the Audio Engineering Society, New York.

watt) versus frequency for this loudspeaker system when placed with respect to the three nearest room boundaries, as it might be on a bookshelf. Fig. 3 shows PWL versus frequency for the same loudspeaker system in another common orientation—on a low base or a small table.

It was found that a quite unconventional orientation of the test loudspeaker system was required in order to load it uniformly so that it could generate relatively flat power input to the room. The woofer must be brought as close as possible to two intersecting room boundaries and kept away from any other. As Fig. 4 shows, when the woofer end of the box is put against one room boundary (the floor, in this case), the side of the box is brought close to one wall, and the nearest other wall is at least a few feet distant, then the power output of the woofer is smooth and not excessively tilted. But a lower than normal crossover frequency is necessary for a woofer used in this way, and the mid-range loudspeaker must be kept far away from a boundary intersection or the power notch is simply transferred from the bass to the middle range. A sketch of a system designed to meet these requirements was shown in [2]. A production system modeled after it is shown in Fig. 5.

The room boundary paper concluded with a caveat: "It remains true that the ultimate determinant of fidelity to an original source is the sound field at the listener's ears. Even if a loudspeaker system is made capable of delivering uniform power to a room, the energy is redistributed by the room's nondiffuse resonance modes, and the listener's location with respect to these standing waves is not knowable.[1]

"Nevertheless, if loudspeaker systems are designed with due regard for these boundary effects ... (it) will certainly reduce the average deviation from the ideal of the sound field in the room ..."

It is the purpose of this present paper to show quantitatively how the sound fields at a significant number of listener locations are affected by loudspeaker orientation with respect to the room boundaries, so that the practical improvement to be expected from a flat bass power input to the room can be determined.

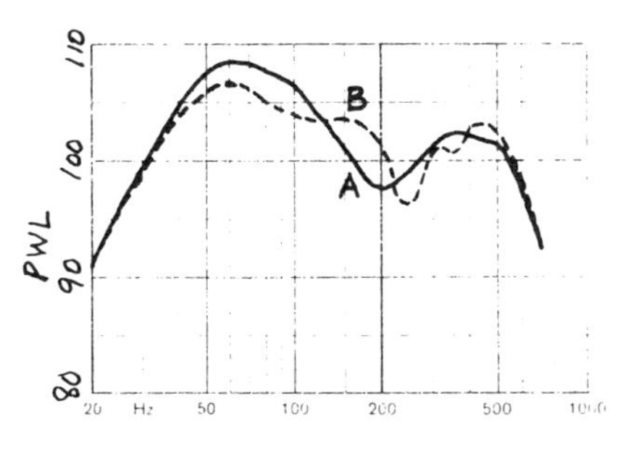

Fig. 3. Power level versus frequency for test standard system with cabinet back close to wall. Center of woofer 19 inches (480 mm) above floor, distance to adjacent wall 2 ft (0.6 m) for curve *A* and 4 ft (1.2 m) for curve *B*.

[1] After these words were written, Groh [6] described a method of "placement equalization." This involves determination of the standing waves in a listening room that are related to peaks and dips in the measured sound pressure versus frequency curves at a listener location, and moving the loudspeaker systems and/or listener position so as to smooth the room transmission curves. It is a useful technique but rather disruptive of conventional furniture arrangements.

TEST PROCEDURE AND EQUIPMENT

The aim was to measure how much, if any, improvement in uniformity of the sound field can be expected by real listeners in real rooms if the bass power input to the rooms is made flat. Put another way, is the difference worth while, or do the field aberrations introduced by standing waves in normal rooms completely swamp any power output variations of the source?

To answer these questions, the sound fields at actual listener locations in five rooms were measured. Stereo music systems had been installed in each of these five rooms for some time. Locations for the two loudspeaker systems, and seating arrangements for listeners, had been chosen without benefit of sound measurements. The residents had set up each room making the usual compromises between what seemed to be a reasonable loudspeaker placement on the one hand, and furnishings, comfort and appearance on the other.

No changes were made in any of the rooms for these tests. A series of measurements was made for every listener location in each room, a "listener location" being defined as a chair or sofa where people normally sat while listening to reproduced music seriously. Obviously not every seating location in every room met the requirement. In one room there were four listener locations; in three rooms, three listener locations each; and in the fifth room, only one. Thus there were 14 listener locations altogether. In each case the measuring microphone was placed as close as could be estimated to the center of the space where the listener's head would normally be, but the vertical position of the microphone diaphragm was always maintained at 1 meter (39⅜ inches) above the floor. This is an arbitrary dimension, but it certainly approximates the average distance of a seated listener's ears from the floor.

The location of both the left- and the right-channel loudspeaker systems as found in each room was marked on the

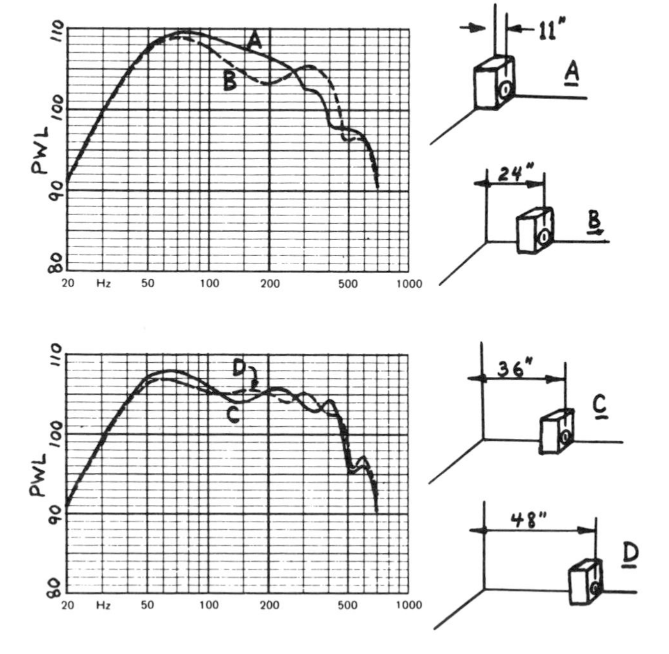

Fig. 4. Power level versus frequency for test standard loudspeaker system oriented as shown with respect to three nearest room boundaries.

floor with masking tape. Subsequently measurements were made at each listener location for loudspeaker systems placed at both marked locations; the height of the test system above the floor was varied in accordance with the test program, but the loudspeaker system location was maintained vertically over the original mark.

Four measurements were made at each listener location for each of the loudspeaker locations. The first three measurements in each group were made with the same test standard loudspeaker system as was used in Allison's 1974 room boundary paper [2], with only the woofer operative. The power output of this system in a wide variety of environments has been documented. The three orientations used for measurement were as follows.

1) Back of cabinet parallel with and close to the rear wall, center of woofer 48 inches (1.2 m) above the floor. The exact power output versus frequency curve will vary in accordance with the distance to the nearest side wall in each case, but it will always be similar to that shown in Fig. 2.

2) Back of cabinet parallel with and close to the rear wall, center of woofer 19 inches (483 mm) above the floor. The power output curve should be similar to those shown in Fig. 3.

3) Woofer end of cabinet on the floor, side of cabinet parallel with and close to the wall. In this orientation the power output versus frequency curve of the test system will be considerably smoother, and (depending on the distance in each case to the nearest adjacent wall) similar to one of the curves shown in Fig. 4.

The fourth measurement in each group was made with the loudspeaker system shown in Fig. 5. This is a direct-radiator loudspeaker system specifically designed for uniform power loading by the room. In each case it was located at the floor mark with its base on the floor and its back close to the rear wall. This system will be identified henceforth as system *D*.

In each room, therefore, eight response curves were taken at each listener position: a group of the four measurements described above for the left marked loudspeaker location, and another group of four for the right loudspeaker location. With a total of 14 listener positions among the five rooms, there are 28 loudspeaker-to-listener transmission curves for each of the four loudspeaker–room coupling combinations.

The test signal was pink noise from a General Radio type 1382 random-noise generator driving a Dyna power amplifier. Voltage at the amplifier output terminals was 3.5 volts rms.[2] The noise bandwidth of the GR 1382 is 20 Hz to 50 kHz. Consequently the power available to the loudspeaker within each one-third octave band was $(12/Z)$—15.3 dB, where Z is the nominal impedance. Z is 3.5 ohms for the test standard system and 8 ohms for system *D*.

The measuring microphone was a ¼-inch (6.4-mm) diameter B & K type 4135, used with B & K type 2619 preamplifier, type 4230 sound level calibrator, type 2113 spectrometer, and type 2305 level recorder. For the one-third octave bands centered at 200 Hz and lower, recorder chart paper speed was 0.1 mm/s, giving an averaging time of 50 s for each band. Pen writing speed was 4 mm/s. Above 200 Hz the paper speed was switched to 0.3 mm/s, and writing speed to 16 mm/s. One of the 28 groups of room transmission curves is shown in Fig. 6.

In the five rooms a broad spectrum of characteristics was

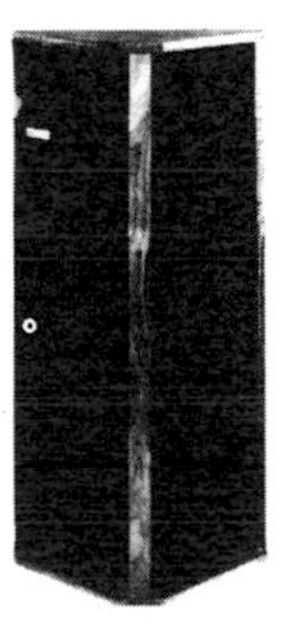

Fig. 5. Loudspeaker system *D* designed for uniform power output into a room. A woofer is mounted at the bottom of each of the two forward-facing panels in the prism-shaped cabinet. A mid-range unit and tweeter are mounted at the top of each of the same two panels.

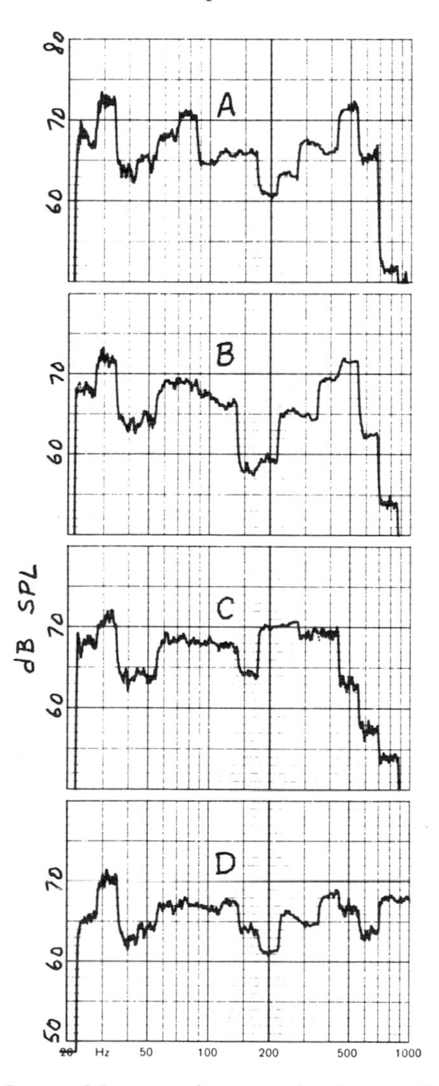

Fig. 6. Group of four sound pressure level versus frequency curves for room 1, listening location 3, left loudspeaker location. Pink noise signal, one-third octave analysis. Curves *A*–*D* are for loudspeaker systems and orientations as described in text.

[2] 3.1 volts as read on a Data Precision model 245 which, like most ac voltmeters, responds to an average rectified value but is calibrated to read rms values of a sine wave. The true rms value of Gaussian noise is 11.3% higher than the indicated reading on such a voltmeter.

found. The floor area varied from 175 ft² (16.3 m²) to 406 ft² (37.7 m²). One room was very nearly square; another room was almost twice as long as it was wide. The other rooms had intermediate proportions. Left and right loudspeaker systems were on a long wall in two rooms, a short wall in two rooms, and on intersecting walls in the other room. There did not seem to be any abnormality common to all the rooms that would bias the test results in any way.

ANALYSIS OF DATA

After reading one-third octave band sound pressure level values from the level recorder charts and tabulating them, the first step was to investigate the amplitude of band-to-band variations in sound pressure level for each individual curve.

Inspection of the data reveals that, within each group of four curves, the three curves for the test standard loudspeaker system in orientations *A*, *B*, and *C* are always very much alike in the one-third octave bands centered below 80 Hz. Moreover, the curve for loudspeaker system *D* always has the same relationship to the other three curves of the group in this frequency range. Consequently there is no reason to extend the analysis below the 80-Hz band.

At the upper end a functional limit is set by the useful range of the test standard system which, in orientation *C*, does not extend much above 400 Hz. For that reason the analysis is limited to the eight one-third octave bands with center frequencies at 80, 100, 125, 160, 200, 250, 315, and 400 Hz.

Three numbers were derived to characterize each of the 112 individual curves.

1) $\overline{X}$, the mean value of the eight one-third octave sound pressure level values. Calculation of $\overline{X}$ is necessary in order to derive σ, but it is of some importance in its own right also, because it is a rough indication of the system's efficiency in this frequency range.

2) σ, the standard deviation. This is obtained by subtracting each of the eight one-third octave sound pressure level values from the mean value, squaring each deviation, averaging the squared values, and extracting the square root of the average. In other words, it is the rms value of deviations from the mean; it is the best indication of response "roughness."

3) The magnitude of the difference between maximum and minimum values of sound pressure level within this frequency range, abbreviated max−min. This measure of the extreme deviations is also useful in evaluating response roughness.

Table I is a summary of the average values of $\overline{X}$, σ, and max−min in decibels for the curves taken at listener positions in each room, and also shows the average values for all rooms (with each room given equal weight). The average values for all rooms taken together are displayed graphically in Fig. 7.

It is clear that, on the average, flatness of the sound field at listener locations is well correlated with flatness of power

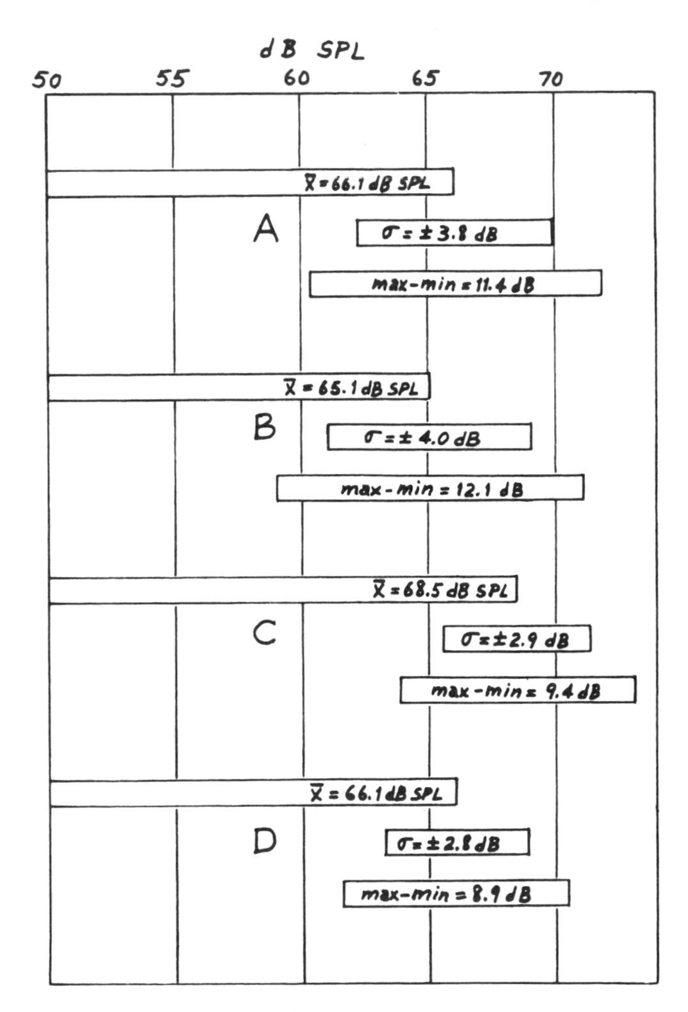

Fig. 7. Comparison of $\overline{X}$, σ, and max−min averages for five listening rooms, with loudspeaker systems oriented as described in text. See also Table I.

Table I. Average values of $\overline{X}$ (dB SPL), σ(dB), and max−min (dB) derived for each individual sound pressure level versus frequency curve at listener positions in each room, and the average values for all rooms with equal weight per room. Analysis is for 1/3-octave bands from 80 to 400 Hz inclusive.

	Standard, *A*			Standard, *B*			Standard, *C*			System *D*		
	$\overline{X}$	σ	max−min	$\overline{X}$	σ	max−min	$\overline{X}$	σ	max−min	$\overline{X}$	σ	max−min
Room 1	66.34	2.92	9.13	65.10	3.64	11.38	68.26	2.53	8.06	66.24	2.53	7.94
Room 2	64.13	3.14	8.83	64.01	4.27	12.08	67.95	2.79	8.83	64.21	2.90	9.17
Room 3	63.78	5.76	18.25	62.21	4.79	13.75	65.07	3.01	11.0	62.85	3.50	11.0
Room 4	67.57	3.64	11.33	67.01	3.64	12.25	70.22	3.05	9.33	69.07	2.57	8.0
Room 5	68.69	3.30	9.58	67.29	3.67	11.08	71.16	3.23	9.92	68.01	2.51	8.33
Average of rooms	66.1	3.8	11.4	65.1	4.0	12.1	68.5	2.9	9.4	66.1	2.8	8.9

input to the room from loudspeaker systems. How significant this amount of improvement is must be judged by the reader, but there is no doubt that it is distinctly audible.

There is another noteworthy aspect of these data. At frequencies below 80 Hz the sound pressure level values recorded for the test standard system are virtually constant regardless of the orientation. Between 80 and 400 Hz, however, the mean value of sound pressure level at listener locations is 2.4 dB higher for orientation *C* than for orientation *A*, and 3.4 dB higher than for orientation *B*. This is indicative of a real and useful increase in efficiency of the system in this 2⅔ octave frequency range.

At any listener location the sound pressure level versus frequency curve is determined by two variables that are virtually independent: the power output versus frequency of the loudspeaker system, and the distribution of standing wave patterns versus frequency in the room. It is to be expected that, among a large number of samples, there will be a few cases in which the two variables will tend to complement each other; that is to say, occasionally a nonflat loudspeaker power curve will result in a smoother sound pressure level curve at a listener location than would be obtained with a loudspeaker system having a flat power output. Here there are 28 samples for each orientation of the test standard system and for system *D*. Using σ as the criterion for smoothness, and ranking the curves within each group in order of increasing values of σ (1 would be the smoothest curve, 4 would be the roughest), the results are as shown in Table II.

In 22 cases of a possible 28, one of the systems generating relatively flat acoustic power *(C* or *D)* produced the smoothest sound pressure level versus frequency curve at the listener location. The roughest curve was produced by one of the nonflat systems in 25 cases.

It is instructive to examine the data in another way. If we average the sound pressure level values by frequency for all curves representing the same loudspeaker orientation one room at a time, and then average the room values giving equal weight to each room, the average response curves shown in Fig. 8 are obtained. Standing wave patterns have only a second-order effect; these curves are a fair approximation of the average sound energy flow in a plane 1 meter (39⅜ inches) above the floor.

The total power emitted by the test standard system in orientation *C* does not really have the mild dip shown at 125 Hz in Fig. 8, curve *C*. This dip is attributable to the fixed distance of the microphone to the floor plane and the nearly constant distance to the ceiling. It can be assumed that the other curves in Fig. 8 include a depression by a similar amount at that frequency.

Table II. Number of times each loudspeaker orientation ranked first, second, third, and fourth in smoothness of sound pressure level versus frequency curve at listener locations. There are 28 groups of four curves each.

Rank	Curve *A*	Curve *B*	Curve *C*	Curve *D*
1	5	1	10	12
2	5	3	10	10
3	9	8	5	6
4	9	16	3	0

Table III gives values of $\overline{X}$, σ, and max−min for the weighted average response curves of Fig. 8.

CONCLUSION

Loudspeaker systems which are designed and/or located with respect to room boundaries so as to produce uniform power output nearly always provide more uniform sound fields at listener locations than do conventionally designed and oriented systems. This is true despite the presence of nondiffuse normal resonance modes in home listening rooms.

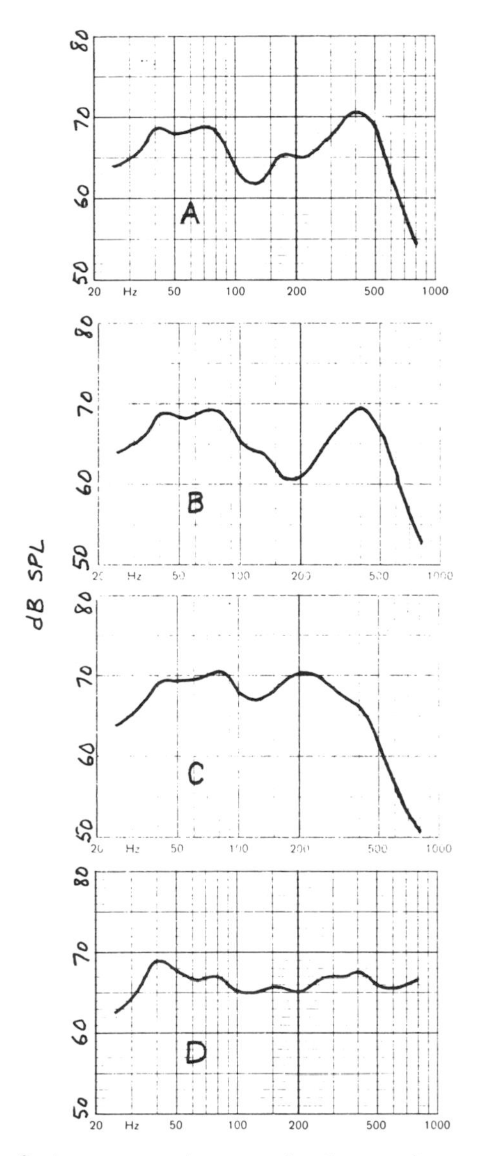

Fig. 8. Average sound pressure level versus frequency, with equal weight per room, of 28 curves at listener positions for each of the loudspeaker system orientations.

Table III. $\overline{X}$, σ, and max−min derived from the average values of 28 sound pressure level versus frequency curves, with equal weight per room, for the one-third octave bands from 80 through 400 Hz.

	A	B	C	D
$\overline{X}$, SPL	66.1	65.1	68.5	66.1
σ, dB	2.65	3.06	1.44	1.02
max−min, dB	8.7	8.4	4.2	2.7

REFERENCES

[1] R. F. Allison and R. Berkovitz, "The Sound Field in Home Listening Rooms," *J. Audio Eng. Soc.*, vol. 20, pp. 459-469 (July/Aug. 1972).

[2] R. F. Allison, "The Influence of Room Boundaries on Loudspeaker Power Output," *J. Audio Eng. Soc.*, vol. 22, pp. 314-320 (June 1974).

[3] R. V. Waterhouse, "Interference Patterns in Reverberant Sound Fields," *J. Acoust. Soc. Am.*, vol. 27, (Mar. 1955).

[4] R. V. Waterhouse, "Output of a Sound Source in a Reverberation Chamber and Other Reflecting Environments," *J. Acoust. Soc. Am.*, vol. 30, (Jan. 1958).

[5] R. V. Waterhouse and R. K. Cook, "Interference Patterns in Reverberant Sound Fields II," *J. Acoust. Soc. Am.*, vol. 37, (Mar. 1965).

[6] A. R. Groh, "High-Fidelity Sound System Equalization by Analysis of Standing Waves," *J. Audio Eng. Soc.*, vol. 22, pp. 795-799 (Dec. 1974).

THE AUTHOR

Roy Allison went from a background as an editor of radio engineering and consumer audio magazines to Acoustic Research, Inc. in 1959. He became chief engineer in 1960, Plant Manager in 1964, and Vice President/Engineering and Manufacturing in 1967. He left Acoustic Research at the end of 1972 and is now President of Allison Acoustics Inc.

Mr. Allison is a Fellow of Audio Engineering Society and a Member of Institute of Electrical and Electronics Engineers.

Active Crossover Networks for Noncoincident Drivers

SIEGFRIED H. LINKWITZ

Hewlett-Packard Company, Santa Rosa, Calif.

The spatial separation between drivers in a loudspeaker system affects the radiation pattern over the frequency range where more than one driver contributes to the total acoustic output. An analysis of conventional crossover networks shows that the main lobe of the radiation pattern shifts in direction and increases in amplitude. A new network transfer function, which can easily be realized with operational amplifiers, eliminates this problem. Additional active delay networks are used to compensate for offsets in the acoustical planes from which the individual drivers radiate. The audibility of phase distortion is investigated with the conclusion that it is undetectable for the proposed types of networks.

INTRODUCTION: The design of a frequency-dividing network to feed the individual drivers in a loudspeaker system is a difficult task if optimum results are desired. In the case of a passive dividing network between a single amplifier and several drivers, problems arise because the impedance of these drivers is frequency dependent. Most likely this impedance is not purely real over the frequency range where the transition in acoustic output from one driver to the other has to be made. Thus simple filter theory cannot be used. Furthermore the drivers are likely to have different efficiencies so that attenuation has to be incorporated into the dividing network. This increases the source impedance which the driver sees and reduces the damping of its mechanical resonance.

Because maximum damping is needed for the woofer to control its low-frequency behavior, no attenuation can be allowed in the low-pass filter which drives the woofer. This then means that the tweeter has to have efficiency equal to or higher than the woofer and restricts the choice of units that could be combined with a particular woofer or necessitates the use of matching transformers.

Finally there is the problem of designing the dividing network so that it presents a tolerable impedance to the power amplifier driving it. The active crossover network gets around all of these problems and offers some additional benefits. Each driver is driven directly from its own power amplifier whose gain may be adjusted to equalize differences in efficiencies between the drivers. This gives complete freedom in selecting drivers.

The output impedances of the power amplifiers directly control the damping of the drivers without intervening crossover networks, and each can be optimized for its particular driver if necessary.

The load presented to each amplifier is less frequency dependent. System distortion is reduced because the woofer channel may be driven into clipping without also affecting the midrange or tweeter channel.

Because the signal is divided into the separate frequency ranges at the input to the power amplifier where one deals with low-level signals and a well-defined interface between the electronics, it now becomes possible to choose from a wide variety of dividing networks which can be conveniently realized with operational amplifiers.

The difficulty now becomes to decide which network is optimum. This paper is an attempt to classify the different networks which have been used, to point out some of their properties which have not been considered before, and to propose a unique class of filters which appears to be the best engineering compromise. This compromise is based upon a consideration of the radiation patterns produced by different networks operating with noncoincident drivers as well as the transient responses of those networks.

THE PROBLEM

The design problem is illustrated in Fig. 1. Two sound sources H and L contribute to the sound pressure at point P_1 in space. This point is "on axis" of the cabinet C–C, but at unequal distances from the drivers because the effective plane of radiation for driver L is offset by the distance d_2 from that of driver H.

The objective is to apply such an input signal to H and L that the sound pressure at P_1 is independent of frequency. To simplify the analysis, the sound pressure at point P_0 will be considered first. This point has equal distance from H and L and is assumed to be located on the axis of both drivers.

The signal arriving at this point has the transfer function

$$F_0 = F_H + F_L. \quad (1)$$

F_H is the transfer function of the driver H and its associated high-pass filter, while F_L is the corresponding low-pass function. The driver axis can be made to coincide with the cabinet axis either by physically mounting driver H by a distance d_2 behind the plane C–C or by electrically delaying the signal which is applied to H by the time which it takes a signal to propagate the distance d_2 in air. A simple circuit for producing such electrical delay will be shown later.

The problem is thus reduced to that of Fig. 2. Of interest is the sound pressure not only on axis but also at angles α off axis. This is modified by the separation of the drivers d_1 which causes different path lengths to point P and thus changes the phase with which the sound pressures from H and L combine at P. It is also influenced by the relative phase of the electrical signals driving H and L.

First the sound pressure for the on-axis point P_0 will be considered. The combined acoustic output should be as frequency independent as possible. It will be described by the transfer function F_0. Later on the effect of the transfer function F_0 upon the radiation pattern will be investigated.

THREE FILTER TYPES

The transfer function

$$F_0 = F_H + F_L \quad (1)$$

will meet the requirement of frequency independence to varying degrees, depending on the crossover network design. F_0 can be classified to belong to one of the following three types of functions:

1) F_0 is frequency independent in amplitude and phase;

2) F_0 is frequency independent in amplitude only and exhibits a frequency-dependent phase shift;

3) F_0 is frequency dependent both in amplitude and phase.

The first type is the transfer function for the "constant-voltage" crossover network:

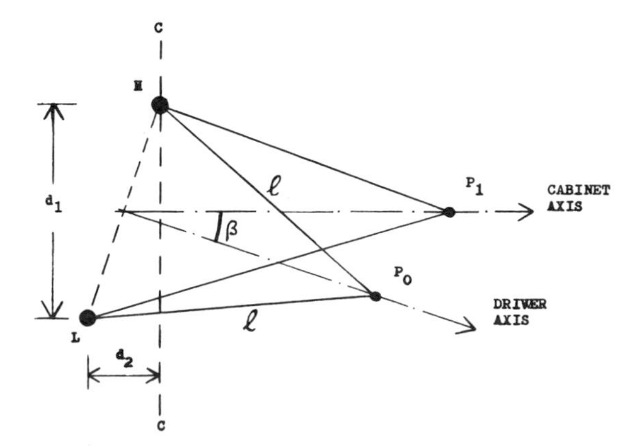

Fig. 1. Radiation from two sources H and L which are separated by a distance d_1 and offset by d_2 in their planes of radiation.

$$F_0 = F_H(s) + F_L(s) = 1 \quad (2)$$

where s denotes the complex frequency,

$$s = \sigma + j\omega \quad (3)$$

where

$$\omega = 2\pi f \quad (4)$$

the radian frequency. Eq. (2) would seem to give the ideal crossover network because it introduces no frequency response or transient distortion.

The second type of transfer function describes the "all-pass" crossover network:

$$F_0 = F_H(j\omega) + F_L(j\omega) = 1\, e^{j\varphi(\omega)}. \quad (5)$$

Its steady-state frequency response is unity, but it has a frequency-dependent phase shift $\varphi(\omega)$ which produces delay or transient distortion.

The third type of network is a "compromise" between the constant-voltage and the all-pass networks:

$$F_0 = F_H(j\omega) + F_L(j\omega) = [1 + r(\omega)]\, e^{j\varphi(\omega)}. \quad (6)$$

Some frequency response ripple $r(\omega)$ is traded for reduced delay distortion due to $\varphi(\omega)$.

EXAMPLES FOR THE THREE FILTER TYPES

The constant-voltage crossover network has been described in detail elsewhere [1]–[4]. The combination of a first-order Butterworth low-pass filter with a first-order Butterworth high-pass filter gives the simplest constant-voltage crossover:

$$F_L = \frac{1}{1 + s_n} \quad (7)$$

$$F_H = \frac{s_n}{1 + s_n} \quad (8)$$

$$F_H + F_L = 1. \quad (2)$$

Here s_n is the complex frequency normalized to the nominal crossover frequency f_c:

$$s_n = \frac{s}{2\pi f_c}. \quad (9)$$

This is not a very practical filter because of its slow cutoff behavior of 6 dB per octave. A more useful filter with 12-dB per octave slopes is synthesized from the following transfer functions [1]:

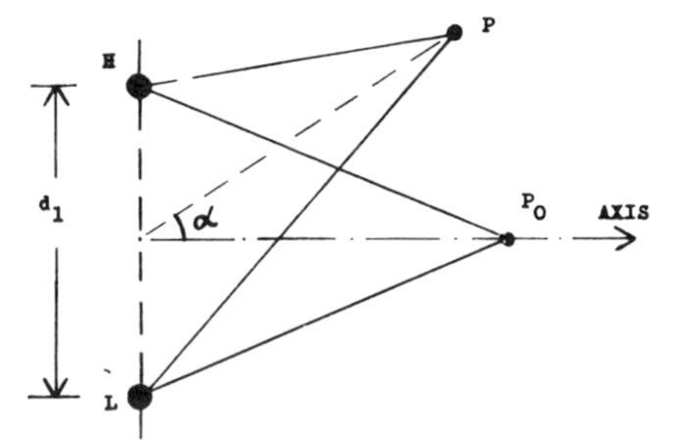

Fig. 2. Radiation from coplanar sources H and L.

$$F_L = \frac{1 + 3.7\, s_n}{1 + 3.7\, s_n + 3.7\, s_n^2 + s_n^3} \tag{10}$$

$$F_H = \frac{3.7\, s_n^2 + s_n^3}{1 + 3.7\, s_n + 3.7\, s_n^2 + s_n^3}. \tag{11}$$

It will be shown that the constant-voltage networks produce undesirable radiation patterns when the drivers are noncoincident.

The criterion for an all-pass crossover network is

$$F_0 = F_L(j\omega) + F_H(j\omega) = 1\, e^{i\varphi(\omega)}. \tag{5}$$

The third-order Butterworth low-pass and high-pass filters form such networks. The low-pass transfer function is

$$F_L = \frac{1}{1 + 2\, s_n + 2\, s_n^2 + s_n^3} \tag{12}$$

and the high-pass is

$$F_H = s_n^3\, F_L. \tag{13}$$

The combined transfer function is

$$F_0 = F_L \pm F_H = \frac{1 \pm s_n^3}{1 + 2\, s_n + 2\, s_n^2 + s_n^3}. \tag{14}$$

Note that either sign can be chosen simply by reversing the phase of one of the drivers.

After substituting $s_n = j\omega_n$, where $\omega_n = \omega/2\,\pi f_c$, the combined frequency response is then

$$|F_0(j\omega_n)| = \left| \frac{1 \mp j\omega_n^3}{1 + 2j\omega_n - 2\,\omega_n^2 - j\omega_n^3} \right|$$

$$= \sqrt{\frac{1 + \omega_n^6}{(1 - 2\omega_n^2)^2 + (2\omega_n - \omega_n^3)^2}} = 1. \tag{15}$$

The phasing of the drivers makes no difference to the steady-state amplitude response. This is so because the phase difference between F_L and F_H is 270° for the plus sign and 90° for the minus sign. The two outputs are always in phase quadrature.

This can be seen readily from the complex frequency plane of Fig. 3. The poles of F_L are the same as those of F_H. The high-pass filter has three additional zeros at the origin of the complex frequency plane. These zeros cause an additional phase shift of 3 × 90° relative to the low-pass filter for any frequency ω.

It can be shown that the group delay

$$t_g = -\frac{d\varphi}{d\omega} \tag{16}$$

is different for the two connections:

$$t_{g+} = 2\, \frac{1 + \omega_n^2}{1 - \omega_n^2 + \omega_n^4} \tag{17}$$

$$t_{g-} = 2\, \frac{1}{1 + \omega_n^2}. \tag{18}$$

The in-phase connection of the drivers results in four times as much delay at the crossover frequency $\omega_n = 1$ as the out-of-phase connection, which therefore should be chosen to minimize transient distortion.

The third-order Butterworth filter is particularly useful for passive crossover networks because of its steep 18-dB per octave cutoff slopes and low delay distortion, but it gives a radiation pattern which is not symmetrical with respect to the driver axis because the outputs from H and L are in phase quadrature.

The "compromise" network is characterized by

$$F_0 = F_L(j\omega) + F_H(j\omega) = [1 + r(\omega)]\, e^{j\varphi(\omega)} \tag{6}$$

and

$$t_g = -\frac{d\varphi}{d\omega} \tag{16}$$

optimized. The transfer functions F_L and F_H might be Gaussian or Butterworth/Thomson filters which would cause some ripple r in the frequency response of F_0 but reduce the frequency dependency of the group delay. The second-order Butterworth function which is often used for crossovers will be considered as part of this class. For the low-pass network,

$$F_L = \frac{1}{1 + \sqrt{2}\, s_n + s_n^2}. \tag{19}$$

The high-pass network is

$$F_H = s_n^2 F_L \tag{20}$$

and the combined output

$$F_0 = F_L \pm F_H = \frac{1 \pm s_n^2}{1 + \sqrt{2}\, s_n + s_n^2}. \tag{21}$$

The frequency response becomes

$$|F_0(j\omega_n)| = \left| \frac{1 \mp \omega_n^2}{1 + j\omega_n \sqrt{2} - \omega_n^2} \right| = \frac{1 \mp \omega_n^2}{\sqrt{1 + \omega_n^4}}. \tag{22}$$

If the drivers are connected in phase, the combined output will cancel at the crossover frequency $\omega_n = 1$. For the out-of-phase connection a 3-dB rise in frequency response results at the crossover frequency.

The group delay is the same for either connection:

$$t_g = \sqrt{2}\, \frac{1 + \omega_n^2}{1 + \omega_n^4}. \tag{23}$$

This group delay is 40% larger at the crossover frequency $\omega_n = 1$ than that of the third-order Butterworth derived network, Eq. (18). The 3-dB peak in frequency response and slower cutoff rate of 12 dB per octave would seem to make this network a poor choice except for cost.

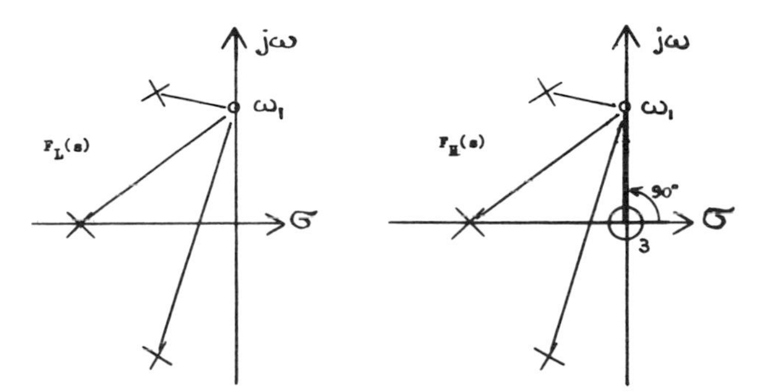

Fig. 3. Complex frequency plane representation of the third-order Butterworth low-pass and high-pass filters.

RADIATION PATTERN

It should be emphasized again that the discussion of crossover networks so far only considered the sound pressure at points P_0 which are equidistant from both drivers (Figs. 1 and 2). For this case the constant-voltage crossover network is clearly optimum because it introduces no phase shift or amplitude variation to the combined outputs from H and L. Now the frequency response at some arbitrary point P will be analyzed. For simplification this point is assumed to be far enough away from the drivers so that lines drawn from H and L to P are essentially parallel (Fig. 4). The difference in path length between P and the two drivers is

$$l = d_1 \sin \alpha. \tag{24}$$

This causes a phase shift difference between the output signals coming from H and L of

$$\varphi_l = 360^\circ \frac{l}{\lambda} = 360^\circ \frac{d_1}{\lambda} \sin \alpha. \tag{25}$$

Here λ is the wave length of the frequency radiated from H and L. The electrical networks driving H and L have their own phase shift φ_L and φ_H which depends on the type of filter used. The total phase difference $\Delta\varphi$ between the signals from H and L at point P then becomes

$$\Delta\varphi = \varphi_H - \varphi_L + 360^\circ \frac{d_1}{\lambda} \sin \alpha. \tag{26}$$

Signals will add in phase at point P in space whenever

$$\Delta\varphi = \pm\, n\, 360^\circ \tag{27}$$

and subtract when

$$\Delta\varphi = \pm\, (2n + 1)\, 180^\circ \tag{28}$$

where $n = 0,1,2,\cdots$. The strongest interaction between the drivers will occur at the crossover frequency where both contribute equal-amplitude signals. For frequencies which are much higher or lower than the crossover point the radiation pattern of the system is determined only by the radiation pattern of the driver which is active in that range.

RADIATION PATTERN FOR DIFFERENT FILTER TYPES

The previously discussed crossover functions will be analyzed for their radiation patterns at the crossover frequency. The constant-voltage network is represented by:

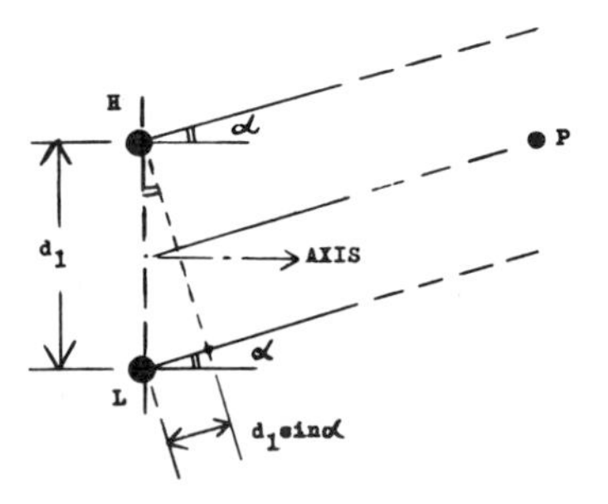

Fig. 4. Definitions for calculation of far-field radiation pattern.

$$F_L = \frac{1 + 3.7\, s_n}{1 + 3.7\, s_n + 3.7\, s_n^2 + s_n^3} \tag{10}$$

$$F_H = \frac{3.7\, s_n^2 + s_n^3}{1 + 3.7\, s_n + 3.7\, s_n^2 + s_n^3}. \tag{11}$$

The all-pass network consists of a third-order Butterworth low-pass and high-pass network connected out of phase:

$$F_L = \frac{1}{1 + 2\, s_n + 2\, s_n^2 + s_n^3} \tag{12}$$

$$F_H = -\, s_n^3 F_L. \tag{29}$$

The second-order Butterworth function is used for a compromise filter with 3-dB ripple:

$$F_L = \frac{1}{1 + \sqrt{2}\, s_n + s_n^2} \tag{19}$$

$$F_H = -\, s_n^2 F_L. \tag{30}$$

It will be assumed that the spacing d_1 between the drivers equals one wavelength at the crossover frequency, i.e.,

$$\frac{d_1}{\lambda} = 1. \tag{31}$$

This could be the case of a 10-inch (254-mm) frame for the woofer and a 4-inch (101-mm) frame for the tweeter mounted as close together as possible so that d_1 = 7-inches (177-mm) and considering a crossover frequency of 1.7 kHz.

For this case the phase difference at P becomes, from Eqs. (26) and (31),

$$\Delta\varphi = (\varphi_H - \varphi_L) + 360^\circ \sin \alpha. \tag{22}$$

Table I summarizes the characteristics of the networks.

The constant-voltage design exhibits a radiation pattern with a 6-dB peak 20° below the axis and signal cancellation

Table I. Characteristics at the crossover frequency for a relative driver spacing of $d_1/\lambda = 1$ and $d_2 = 0$.

	Constant Voltage	Allpass	Compromise
Magnitude of F_H or F_L	0 dB	−3 dB	−3 dB
Relative phase $\varphi_H - \varphi_L$	120°	90°	0°
Cutoff slope	12 dB/oct	18 dB/oct	12 dB/oct
Angle α for maximum amplitude	−20°	−15°	0°
Maximum amplitude	+6 dB	+3 dB	+3 dB
Angle α for signal cancellation	+10° −56°	+15° −49°	±30°
Schematic radiation pattern	+6dB	+3dB	+3dB

at 10° above the axis. The network has its desired properties only for points on axis which are on the skirt of the radiation pattern between signal cancellation and the 6-dB peak.

This is clearly not an ideal filter because the radiation pattern shifts with frequency. At low and high frequencies the maximum of radiation occurs along the driver axis. For frequencies in between the pattern tilts downward and increases 6 dB in amplitude.

The all-pass network as exemplified by the third-order Butterworth shows a slightly better behavior because it peaks by only 3 dB at 15° below the axis. Furthermore the frequency range over which it shows this directional shift in the pattern is narrower than for the constant-voltage filter because it has steeper cutoff slopes. This reduces the overlap and interaction between drivers.

The second-order Butterworth design as the "compromise" filter has a symmetrical radiation pattern. It is the only filter of the three which would result in a loudspeaker system with an acoustic axis that does not move as frequency changes. Unfortunately though it still has a 3-dB peak at the crossover frequency.

The narrowing in the beam width of the radiation pattern in these examples was caused by the distance d_1 between the drivers. Increasing d_1/λ will increase the number of peaks and cancellations and result in a multibeam radiation pattern. This may mask other faults in a crossover design. For best performance though the drivers must be as close together as possible, i.e., $d_1/\lambda < 1$.

The tilting in the pattern is controlled by the phase difference $\varphi_H - \varphi_L$ between the drive signals. In order to avoid the frequency-dependent tilt this phase difference has to be zero as in the example of the second-order Butterworth network, or the drivers have to be coaxially mounted.

OPTIMUM CROSSOVER FUNCTION

From the foregoing observations of the three different networks it is now possible to set down the requirements for the filter function which would give the optimum performance when the drivers are separated by a distance d_1, as is the case for most practical loudspeaker systems.

1) The phase difference $\varphi_H - \varphi_L$ between the drive signals at the crossover frequency has to be zero in order to avoid tilting in the radiation pattern.

2) The output amplitude from the high-pass and low-pass section has to be 6 dB down at the crossover frequency so that the sum of the two is unity and no peaking occurs.

3) The phase difference $\varphi_H - \varphi_L$ has to be the same for all frequencies so that the symmetry of the radiation pattern is preserved above and below the crossover frequency.

This last requirement is the same as saying that high-pass and low-pass filters must change their phase at the same rate with frequency, that is, they must have identical group delay. High-pass and low-pass filters with identical poles in the complex frequency plane and zeros at $s = 0$ for the high-pass filter will satisfy this criterion. For $\varphi_H - \varphi_L \equiv 0$ there has to be an even number of zeros, and for a −6-dB crossover amplitude the poles have to be double poles.

It has been pointed out by R. Riley that the cascade of two identical Butterworth filters will meet all the above requirements. Thus all the available design information for active Butterworth filters can be directly used for this type of crossover network.

The resulting network is an all-pass filter. For example, cascading two first-order Butterworth filters to obtain a second-order, 12-dB per octave slope crossover network:

$$F_L = \frac{1}{(1 + s_n)^2} \tag{33}$$

$$F_H = \left(\frac{s_n}{1 + s_n}\right)^2 \tag{34}$$

$$F_0 = F_L \pm F_H = \frac{1 \pm s_n^2}{(1 + s_n)^2} \tag{35}$$

$$|F_0(j\omega_n)| = \left|\frac{1 \mp \omega_n^2}{1 - \omega_n^2 + j^2\omega_n}\right| = \frac{1 \mp \omega_n^2}{1 + \omega_n^2}. \tag{36}$$

Again the drivers have to be connected out of phase, otherwise cancellation would occur.

Phase reversal of one of the drive signals can serve as an easy performance test. The amount of on-axis cancellation which can thus be obtained is a direct measure of how well the outputs from H and L are matched in amplitude and phase.

NETWORK REALIZATION

Of practical interest are the two- and four-pole crossover networks with 12- and 24-dB per octave cutoff slopes. Fig. 5 shows possible designs which give the amplitude and group delay responses shown in Fig. 6. It should be noted that the 24-dB per octave filter function is difficult to realize as a passive network because of the double complex poles.

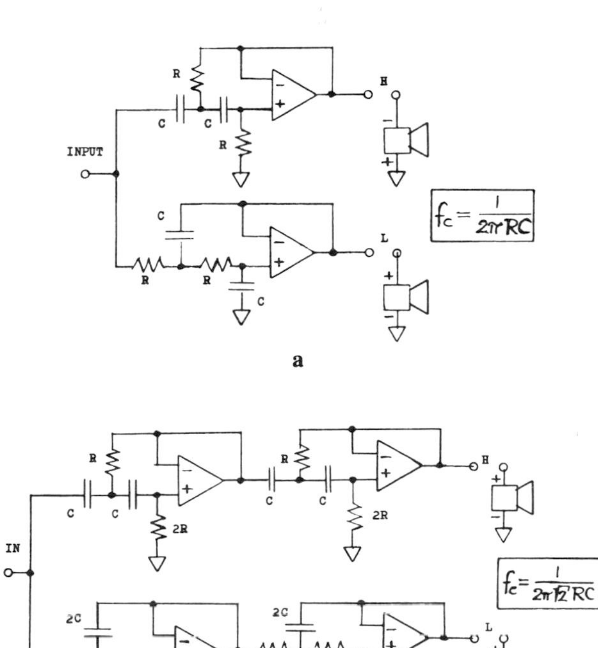

Fig. 5. Realization of optimum crossover function. **a.** 12-dB per octave filter. **b.** 24-dB per octave filter.

CORRECTING DRIVER OFFSET

In the analysis so far it has been assumed that both drivers radiate from the same acoustical plane and that the distance d_2 in Fig. 1 is zero. Going back to the earlier example of a 10-inch (254-mm) woofer and a 4-inch (101-mm) tweeter frame, the distance d_2 might be estimated to be the offset between voice coils when both drivers are mounted in the same cabinet panel C–C. Assuming $d_2 = 3$ inches (75 mm) and $d_1 = 7$ inches (177 mm), the radiation pattern will be tilted at the crossover frequency by the angle

$$\beta = \arctan \frac{d_2}{d_1} = 23°. \qquad (37)$$

In order to preserve the benefits of the new crossover design this frequency-dependent rotation of the radiation pattern has to be eliminated. Probably the easiest way to accomplish this is to delay the electrical signal to driver H by the time

$$t_g = \frac{d_2}{v} = \frac{3 \text{ inches} \cdot \text{seconds}}{12\,624 \text{ inches}} = 240\ \mu\text{s}. \qquad (38)$$

First-order all-pass networks of the configuration in Fig. 7 can be cascaded to give sufficient delay. The transfer function for this circuit is

$$F(s) = \frac{1 - sCR}{1 + sCR} \qquad (39)$$

and the delay is

$$t_g = -\frac{d\varphi}{d\omega} = \frac{2RC}{1 + (\omega RC)^2} \qquad (40)$$

$$t_g = \frac{1}{\pi f_0} \frac{1}{1 + (f/f_0)^2} \qquad (41)$$

with

$$f_0 = \frac{1}{2\pi RC}. \qquad (42)$$

Because this delay is frequency dependent except when $f << f_0$, care has to be taken that the frequency f_0 is sufficiently higher than the crossover frequency f_c. Requiring that $f_0 \geq 3 f_c$, the delay t_g' which can be obtained per stage becomes

$$t_g' \leq \frac{1}{10 f_c} \qquad (43)$$

For a 1.7-kHz crossover frequency $t_g' = 60\ \mu$s, and thus four stages have to be cascaded to obtain the 240-μs delay needed in the example.

It is obvious that a large amount of circuitry is required when the acoustical planes of the two drivers are very different. But without this correction the main lobe of the radiation pattern would shift away from the cabinet axis whenever both drivers contribute to the total acoustic output, namely, in the crossover region of the frequency spectrum.

For optimum crossover network design the drivers have to be made to radiate from the same acoustical plane which should be parallel to the cabinet front panel. Then the cascaded Butterworth sections of Fig. 5 will give a frequency-stable main axis of the radiation pattern and constant amplitude for the summed signals from H and L.

AUDIBILITY OF DELAY DISTORTION

The optimum network has all-pass characteristics. The amplitude response is unity, but the phase of the summed signal changes with frequency. The network has a frequency-dependent group delay

$$t_g = \frac{2}{1 + \omega_n^2} \qquad (44)$$

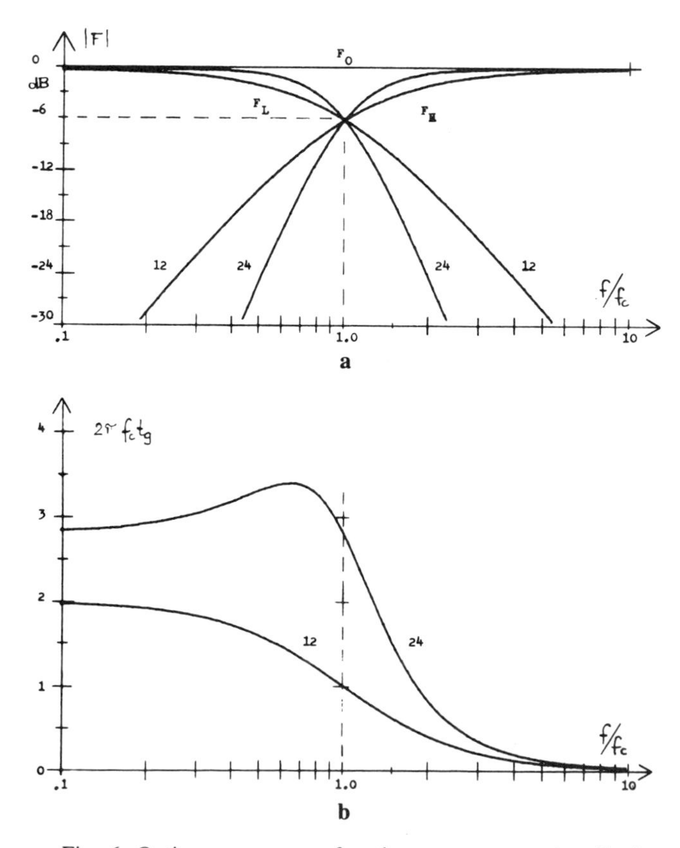

Fig. 6. Optimum crossover function response. **a.** Amplitude response. **b.** Group delay response.

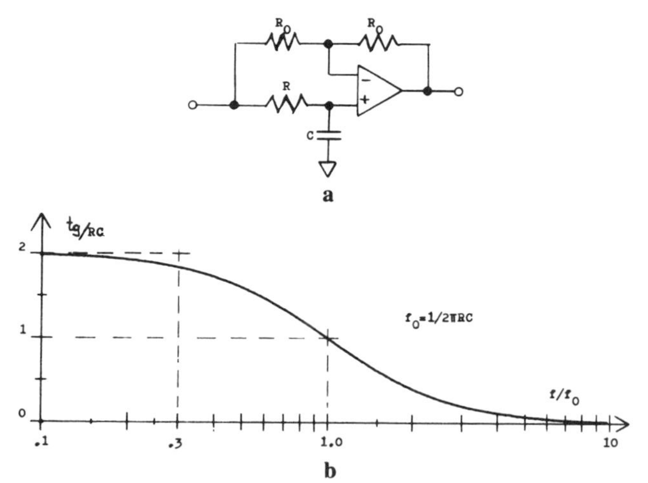

Fig. 7. **a.** First-order all-pass delay network. **b.** Its group delay response.

for the 12-dB per octave crossover and

$$t_g = 2\sqrt{2}\,\frac{1 + \omega_n^2}{1 + \omega_n^4} \tag{45}$$

for the 24-dB per octave networks.

Whenever a signal that is made up of more than one spectral component is subjected to a frequency-dependent delay, the relative phase between the spectral components is shifted and a phase-distorted time function of the signal results. The question arises, when does the delay distortion become audible? The circuit of Fig. 7 can be used to introduce varying amounts of delay distortion into a signal path. Fig. 8 gives a configuration for higher order all-pass networks where $F_1(s)$ might be a band-pass filter. Using headphones it has been found that delay distortion is generally not audible even when the waveforms observed on an oscilloscope look greatly distorted [5].

There are a few exceptions which have limited practical significance.

1) Some change can be noticed even with a first-order all-pass filter when listening to clicks of very low repetition rate (< 5Hz).

2) A second-order all-pass network can introduce a ringing sound on clicks and square waves if its Q is high enough.

3) A change in sound character can be detected with high sound level square waves and first-order all-pass networks. This may involve nonlinearities in the ear.

Because the optimum filters described have a gradually changing group delay characteristic, no ringing can be noticed and they introduce no audible delay distortion on program material.

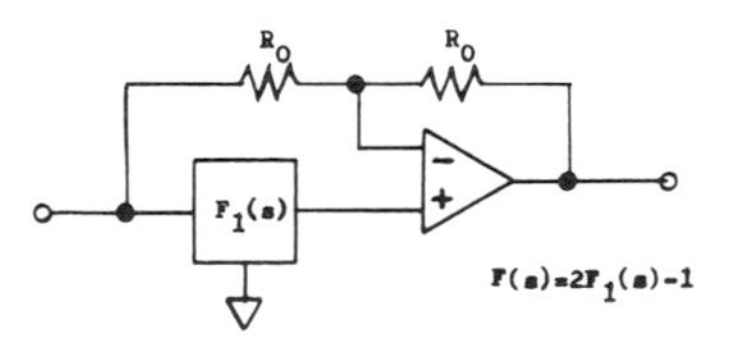

Fig. 8. General circuit for realizing all-pass transfer functions.

CONCLUSION

Active crossover design in the past has not considered the effects of mounting distances between drivers. The crossover networks based upon cascaded Butterworth sections have optimum radiation characteristics for systems where the distance between the drivers is not small compared to a wave length at the crossover frequency. This is the case for the majority of loudspeaker systems.

To utilize these networks it is necessary that both drivers radiate from the same acoustical plane. This can be achieved either mechanically by appropriate mounting or electrically by delay networks. Furthermore the drivers should be mounted one above the other and as close to each other as possible to obtain wide dispersion in the horizontal plane and a minimum number of radiation lobes in the vertical plane.

While the active-network approach may be costly and only applicable to top performance loudspeaker systems, it can result in a system with improved dispersion characteristics and thus a very firm stereo image.

On appropriate program material it will not only give a smooth lateral spread of the image but also a noticeable enhancement of depth perspective.

REFERENCES

[1] R. H. Small, "Constant-Voltage Crossover Network Design," *J. Audio Eng. Soc.*, vol. 19, pp. 12-19 (Jan. 1971).

[2] E. Baekgaard, "Loudspeakers—The Missing Link," presented at the 50th Convention of the Audio Engineering Society, London, 1975.

[3] P. K. Wall, "Active and Passive Loudspeaker Crossover Networks without Transient Distortion," presented at the 50th Convention of the Audio Engineering Society, London, 1975.

[4] J. R. Ashley and L. M. Henne, "Operational Amplifier Implementation of Ideal Electronic Crossover Networks," *J. Audio Eng. Soc.*, Vol. 19, pp. 7-11 (Jan. 1971).

[5] B. B. Bauer, "Audibility of Phaseshift," *Wireless World* (Apr. 1974).

THE AUTHOR

Siegfried H. Linkwitz was born in Bad Oeynhausen, Germany, in 1935. He received the Diplom-Ingenieur degree in electrical engineering from Darmstadt University in 1961. Upon graduation he joined Hewlett Packard Company in California as a research engineer for the design of microwave test equipment. He was involved with the development of signal generators, phase measuring RF voltmeters, and spectrum analyzers. At present Mr. Linkwitz is program manager in microwave spectrum analysis.

His interest in audio was stimulated by the gap between reproduced sound and life sound, and he focused on loudspeakers as the least developed component in the reproducing chain.

Mr. Linkwitz is a member of the IEEE.

A Technique for Observing Loudspeaker Wave-Front Propagation*

ISAMI NOMOTO, MAKOTO IWAHARA, AND HIDEO ONOYE

Victor Company of Japan, Ltd., Tokyo, Japan

For a shaped pulse excitation, responses at 3000 points in a plane through the major axis of a loudspeaker are measured and stored. The data are then processed and converted to visual representations at 10-μs intervals. The resulting display is photographed sequentially for observation of wave-front motion away from the loudspeaker.

INTRODUCTION: Conventionally the measurement of sound fields has been restricted to steady-state measurements with sine waves used as input. However, to understand the phenomena existing in the sound field such as the propagation, reflection, and diffraction of the sound waves, if measurements could be made with respect to time, it would be more effective.

This paper describes a method in which a microphone scans a given plane within a sound field, measuring the waveforms at each point, data from which measurements are recorded by a computer on magnetic tape. When this magnetic tape is run again, the patterns of sound pressure distribution at different instants of time are displayed on a cathode ray tube in perspective and filmed using a motion picture camera. When this film is projected at the correct speed, it makes it possible to understand how the sound field extends in space and changes in structure with time.

Using this method, measurements were carried out with different types of transducers. As a result, the sound propagation from these loudspeakers is better understood.

METHOD OF MEASUREMENT

The measuring method is as follows.

1) The many points at which measurements are to be carried out are located on the given plane in the sound field the structure of which is to be analyzed. The microphone is placed at one of these measuring points and an input signal is applied to the loudspeaker. The output wave from the microphone is then sampled and recorded taking into account the time at which it occurs with respect to the timing of the input signal. By scanning, this procedure is repeated at subsequent measuring points.

2) When the time-related waveforms from all measuring points have been recorded, the pattern of instantaneous values of sound pressures at the same instant in time after the input signal was applied to the loudspeaker can be drawn. This pattern represents the instantaneous structure of the sound field measured in the plane scanned by the microphone. This same procedure can be repeated for a different instant in time, at a given interval from the first instant.

3) The patterns of instantaneous sound pressure distribution are filmed with a motion picture camera in a single-frame exposure mode, and when projected at an appropriate speed the changes in the sound field with time can be easily observed.

BASIC CONSTRUCTION AND OPERATION OF TEST EQUIPMENT

Fig. 1 is a block diagram showing the basic construction of the trial measuring system.

Although the delta function contains components of all frequencies in equal amounts, and is one of the most suitable signals used for analysis in the time domain, it cannot be used in this case because of its intrinsic properties of infinitesimal width and infinite amplitude. In this method a raised-cosine pulse is used as the loudspeaker input signal. Of those signals which can be generated fairly easily, the raised-cosine pulse has a wider frequency range in which the level is constant and contains less components of unnecessary frequencies. The waveform and spectrum of the raised-cosine pulses used in these measurements are shown in Fig. 2. In fact there is no particular limitation on the waveform used; step functions or tone bursts could also be used, depending on the purpose of the measurement.

The microphone used is a ¼-inch (6 mm) microphone (B

* Presented November 3, 1975, at the 52nd Convention of the Audio Engineering Society, New York.

& K model 4135) with a frequency response flat up to about 100 kHz. This exceeds the upper limit of the spectrum of the raised-cosine pulse, and thus the microphone will have little influence on the measured waveform.

For the scanning mechanism moving the microphone, a modified $X-Y$ plane moving device from a reading microscope was used. It was designed to move in 2.5-mm steps in the longitudinal direction when pulses are applied to it, with the mechanism consisting of a combined motor gear cam and microswitch. The longitudinal scanning distance is about 200 mm, or 90 points. Movement in the transverse direction is done manually with a pitch of 5 mm and a total scanning distance of 160 mm, giving 33 rows.

At each measuring point, 100 data samples of the microphone output waveform are recorded at intervals of 10 μs. The total number of data samples is therefore 100 (samples per measuring point) $\times$ 90 (points per row) $\times$ 33 (rows) = 297 000. To handle this huge amount of data, an analog-to-digital converter, computer, and magnetic tape device are used for data collection and recording.

Our measurements are done in an anechoic chamber, but this is not a necessary condition. If there is no appreciable background noise, there is no reason why an ordinary room cannot be used. Measurements continue for only 1 ms after the pulse is applied to the loudspeaker; thus reflections from the walls cannot reach the microphone before the measurement is completed.

When the frequency divider circuit is actuated, one raised-cosine pulse is applied to the loudspeaker and the response waveform from the microphone at the corresponding measuring point is subject to analog-to-digital conversion at a sampling rate of 100 kHz and stored in the magnetic core memory of the computer. Then the microphone is moved by one step in the horizontal direction. As shown in Fig. 1, this operation is controlled on the basis of the 100-kHz rectangular wave oscillator by the combination of the frequency divider circuit and monostable multivibrators. The timing relationship between these components is shown in Fig. 3. After this measuring procedure has been repeated 90 times, the microphone reaches the end of one row. It is then set manually to scan the following row. In the meantime the data held in the magnetic core are transferred automatically to magnetic tape.

When the frequency divider is actuated again, at this point, the following row is measured. The measurement cycle is completed when this procedure has been repeated 33 times.

To display the sound pressure distribution patterns a cathode ray tube is used. Various formats of display were considered. For ease of understanding from both qualitative and quantitative viewpoints, a format similar to an oblique view of the surface of water along which a wave is traveling, as shown in Fig. 5, was adopted, where the height of the wave corresponds to the sound pressure level.

A movie camera is placed in front of the cathode ray tube, and its shutter is released automatically by a solenoid operated by a signal from the computer when one of the instantaneous patterns is fully displayed.

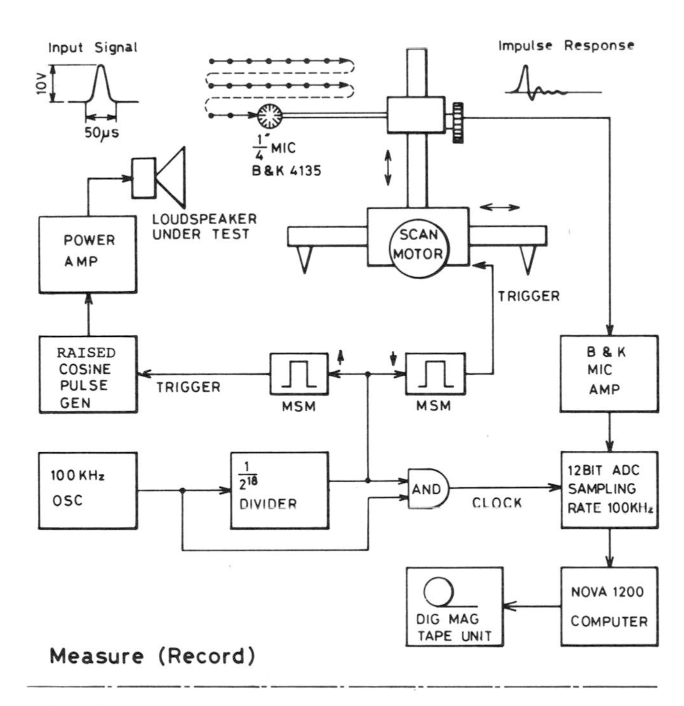

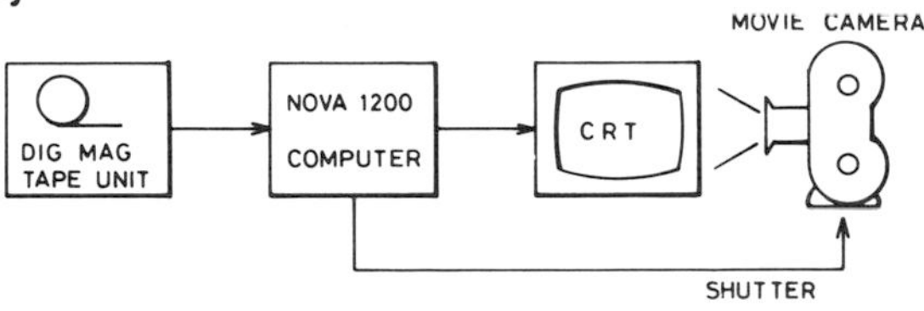

Fig. 1. Measurement system.

EXAMPLES OF MEASUREMENT

Fig. 5 shows six frames of these sound pressure distribution patterns obtained by measuring the response to raised cosine pulses of different tweeters.

As shown in Fig. 4, the measurement area is the plane containing the axis of the loudspeaker, one quarter of the

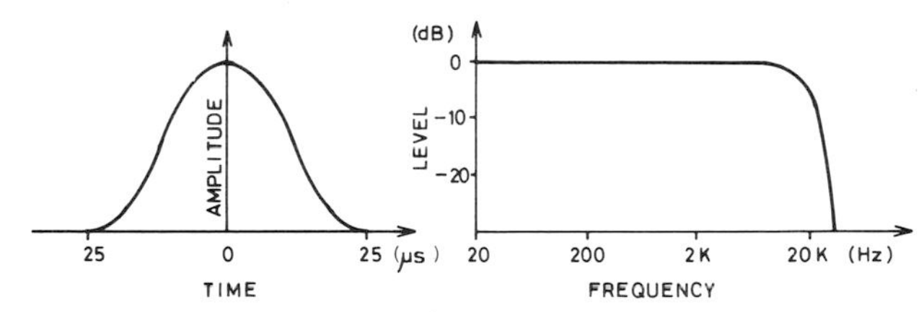

Fig. 2. Waveform and spectrum of input pulse.

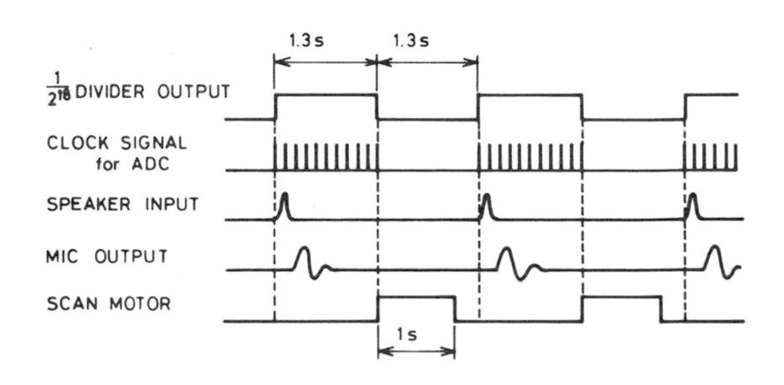

Fig. 3. Time chart.

plane's width away from the nearer edge. The loudspeaker axis is indicated by the straight line in Fig. 5. The loudspeaker is placed at the left of the measurement area. When the opening of the loudspeaker is not circular, the plane in the direction of the shorter axis is measured.

Regardless of the type of loudspeaker, input signals with a peak amplitude of 10 V are used.

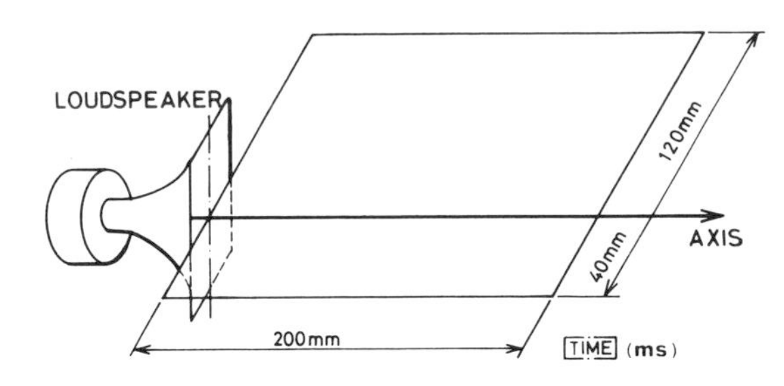

Fig. 4. Measurement area.

The tweeters used to obtain Fig. 5 were of the following types:

1) a horn tweeter with 80 mm by 19 mm rectangular opening;
2) a ribbon tweeter with a 50 mm by 8 mm rectangular ribbon and wide-angle short horn;
3) a tweeter with a 50 mm diameter paper cone;
4) an air-motion transformer with a 120 mm by 27 mm rectangular diaphragm;
5) a hard-dome tweeter with a 25 mm diameter dome;
6) a soft-dome tweeter with a 25 mm diameter dome.

Some of the speakers have horns of different lengths, and for this reason the frames shown are not taken at equivalent times but are frames in which the wave fronts are in about the same positions.

Fig. 6 shows examples of pulse response wave fronts propagated within a horn. The time at the right-hand lower corner of each frame is the time after the pulse was applied

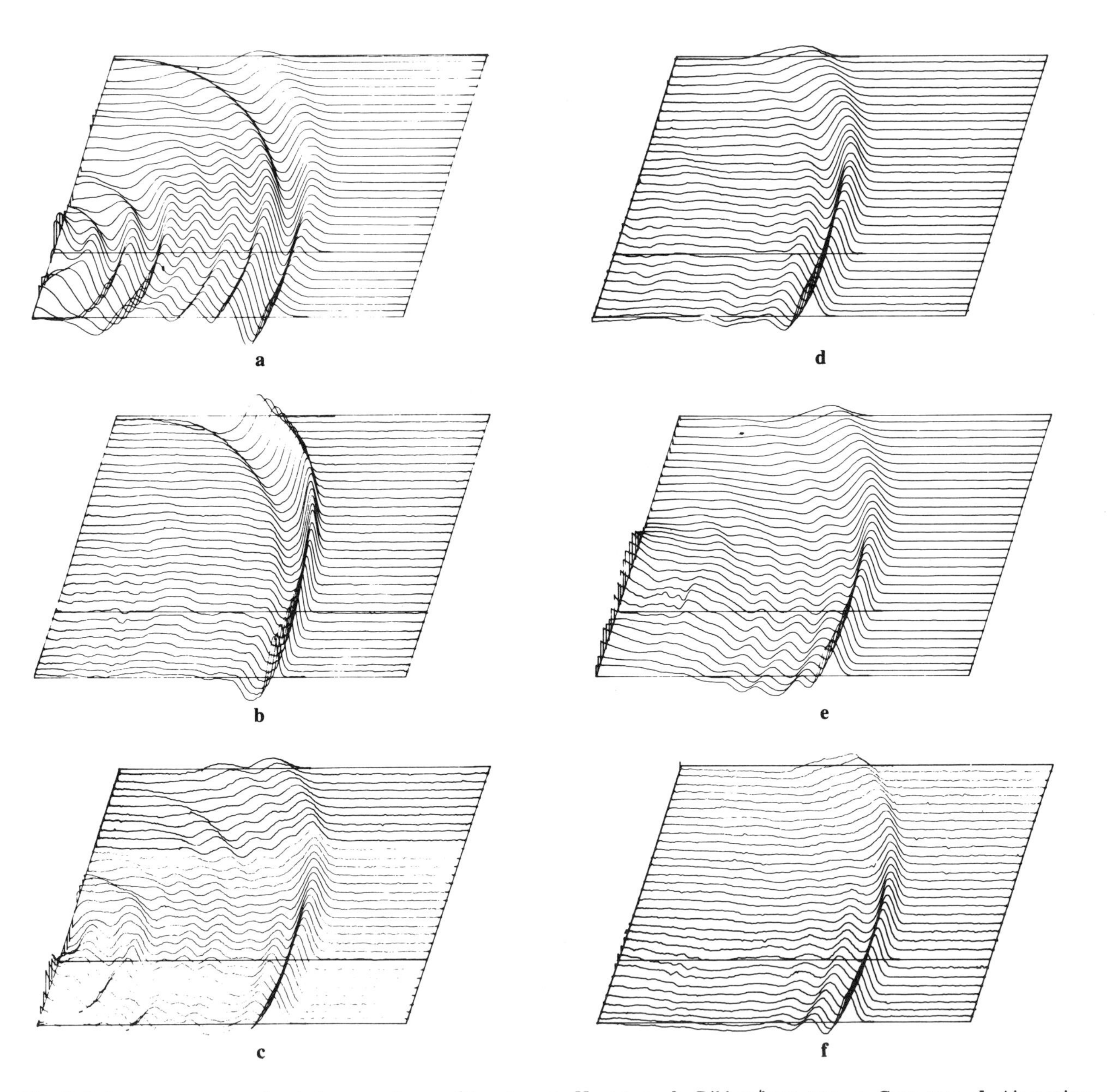

Fig. 5. Pulse response wave fronts for some types of tweeters. **a.** Horn type. **b.** Ribbon/horn type. **c.** Cone type. **d.** Air-motion transformer type. **e.** Hard-dome type. **f.** Soft-dome type.

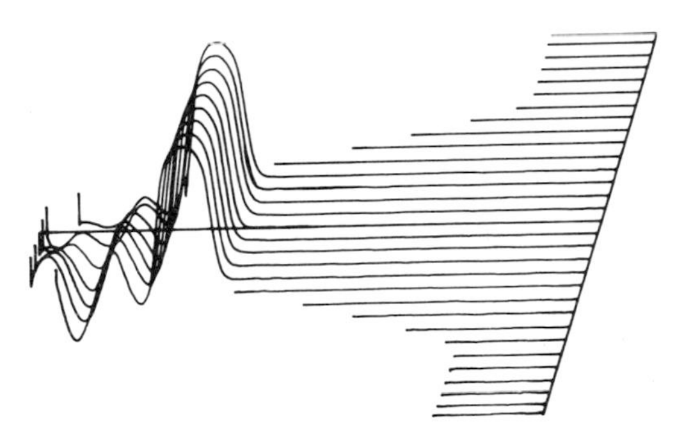

An arrow indicates waves reflected from the mouth.

1ms

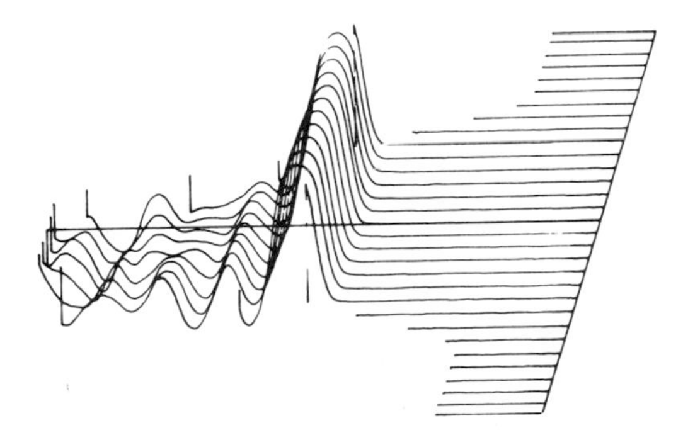

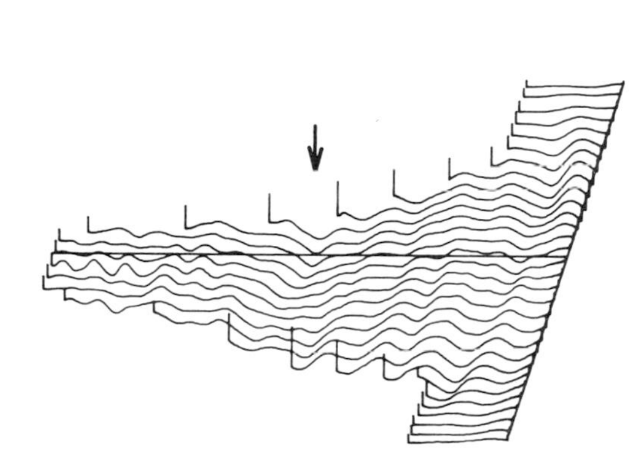

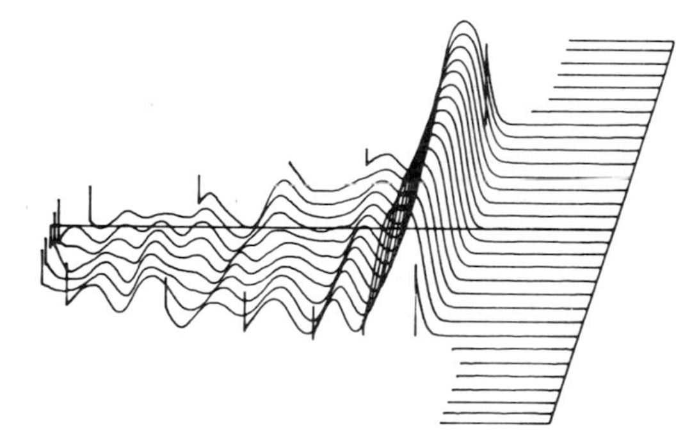

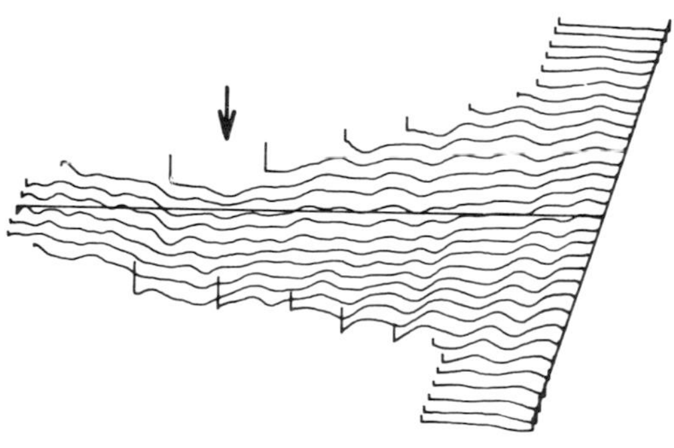

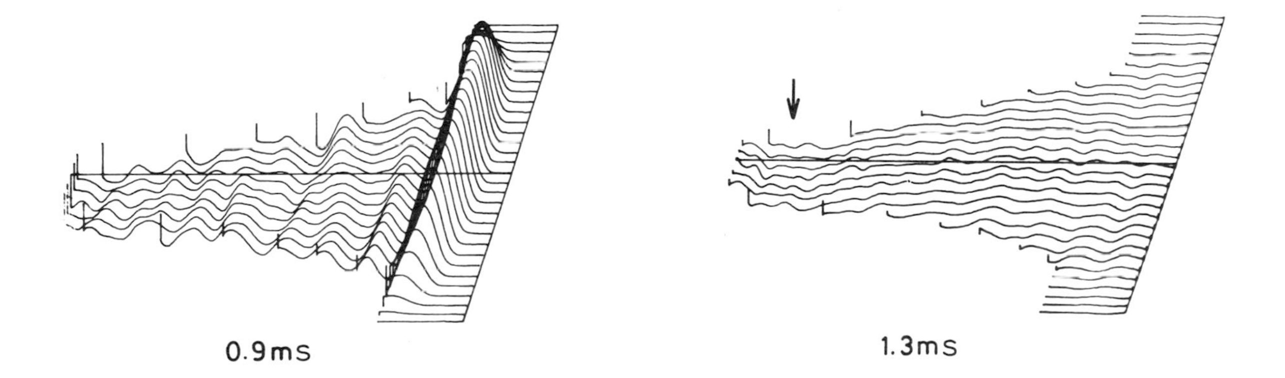

Fig. 6. Sound propagation in a horn.

to the driver. As shown by the arrows, the sound wave is reflected from the opening of the horn and propagated toward the inside of the horn with reverse polarity.

REFERENCES

[1] W. E. Kock and F. K. Harvey, *J. Acoust. Soc. Am.*, vol. 23, p. 149(A) (1951).

[2] W. E. Kock and F. K. Harvey, *Bell Syst. Tech. J.*, vol. 30, p. 564 (1951).

[3] J. T. Rainey and D. G. Neville, *Sound Vibration,* vol. 6, no. 12, p. 10 (1972).

[4] Y. Tannaka, Y. Kobayashi, and T. Miura, IEC Japan Rept. EA 74-13, 1974.

THE AUTHORS

I. Nomoto M. Iwahara H. Onoye

Isami Nomoto was born in Saitama, Japan. He studied electrical engineering at the Yokohama National University from which he graduated in 1955. That same year he joined Victor Company of Japan, Ltd., working in the area of loudspeaker design. Presently, he is engaged in loudspeaker development at the company's Audio Engineering Research Center.

•

Makoto Iwahara was born in 1948 in Hyogo, Japan. He completed the course of mechanical engineering at the Hiroshima University, where he also studied advanced photographic techniques. In 1971 he joined the Victor Company of Japan, Ltd., and is currently involved in loudspeaker research.

•

Hideo Onoye was born in Shimane, Japan. He graduated from the Tokyo University in 1970 where he studied electrical engineering, music and sound synthesis techniques. He then joined the Audio Engineering Research Center of the Victor Company of Japan, Ltd., where he is engaged in technical computation tasks, concentrating in the area of signal processing.

Some Aspects of the Self and Mutual Radiation Impedance Concept with Respect to Loudspeakers

OLUF JACOBSEN

Aarhus Teknikum, Aarhus, Denmark

The radiation impedance concept is employed to establish relations between the near-field sound pressure of a piston in a large wall, the radiated power, and the far-field sound pressure. Attention is drawn to the fact that at long wavelengths the relative pressure distribution across the piston tends to be constant, but not uniform.

A recapitulation is given of a simple theory of the mutual radiation impedance for two interacting pistons in a large wall, and expressions for the total radiated active and reactive power are derived. The interaction is strongly dependent on the phase difference between the piston velocities.

The influence of the mutual radiation impedance on the function of a vented loudspeaker cabinet has been investigated in detail, and is shown to be decisive below the port resonance frequency. The variations are large but unimportant, as they occur outside the active range of the radiator in question. The findings do not call for changes in design methods.

GLOSSARY OF SYMBOLS

a, a_1, a_2 (m)	Radius of piston
Bl (Tm)	Magnetic field intensity times wire length of voice coil
c (ms^{-1})	Velocity of sound in air
C_d, C_p (F)	Capacity analogous to mass of diaphragm + air, and of air in port
C_{mp} (N^{-1}m)	Compliance of air in loudspeaker box as seen from port
C_{md} (N^{-1}m)	Compliance of air in loudspeaker box as seen from diaphragm
d (m)	Distance between centers of two pistons
D, DI	Directivity factor, index
d_p	Dissipation factor for port
e_{in}, e_d, e_p (V)	Voltages in analog circuit at input, driver, and port
f, f_B (Hz)	Frequency, resonance frequency of port–box system
H_0, H_1, J_0, J_1	Struve and Bessel functions of zero and first order
I (Wm^{-2})	Intensity of sound
k (m^{-1})	Wavenumber
L_d, L_p (H)	Inductance analogous to compliance of driver and port
M_p (kg)	Mass of air in port
p, p_C, p_E, p_F, p_{FA}, p_N (Pa)	Sound pressure: C center, E edge of piston, F far-field, FA far-field axis, N near-field
$p_d = p_d'$, $p_p = p_p'$ (Pa)	Sound pressure in box at diaphragm *(d)* and at port *(p)*
P_r, P_{tot}, P_1, P_2, P_3 (W)	Active sound power, total (tot), from the driver (1), from port (2), and mutual power (3)
$q = q_1 = q_2$ (m^{3}s^{-1})	Volume velocity
Q_r (S)	Reactive sound power
r (m)	Distance from source
R_r, R_{r1}, R_{r11}, R_{r12} (Nm^{-1}s)	Radiation resistance *(r)*, total (r_1), self (r_{11}), mutual (r_{12})
R_e, R_d, R_p (Ω)	Voice coil resistance *(e)*, analogous resistance to mechanical resistance in driver *(d)* and in port *(p)*
S_r (VA)	Apparent sound power

S_d, S_p, S_t (m^2)	Area of diaphragm (d), port (p), and cross section of box (t)
v (ms^{-1})	Velocity
V (m^3)	Volume of box
X_r, X_{r1}, X_{r11}, X_{r12} ($Nm^{-1}s$)	Radiation reactance (r), total (r_1), self (r_{11}), mutual (r_{12})
x (m)	Distance from the center of piston (Fig. 1), frequency ratio f/f_B
Z_r, Z_{r1}, Z_{r11}, Z_{r12} ($Nm^{-1}s$)	Radiation impedance (r), total (r_1), self (r_{11}), mutual (r_{12})
Z_p, Z_{dp} ($Nm^{-1}s$)	Mechanical impedance of port (p) and of box (dp) as seem from driver (Z_p transferred to driver)
Z_p' Z_{dp}' ($Nm^{-3}s$)	Specific acoustic impedance
Z_{ep}, Z_{edp} (Ω)	Analogous electrical impedance of port circuit with lumped (ep) and with distributed (edp) impedances
φ	Phase angle difference
λ (m)	Wavelength
ρ (kg m^{-3})	Density of air
ω, ω_B (s^{-1})	Angular frequency, B of box circuit

INTRODUCTION: The radiation impedance concept is found useful—particularly at long wavelengths, where the expressions are simple and the reactive term predominates—to relate the near-field average pressure at a piston in a large wall to the far-field pressure, and to the pressure at the center and at the edge of the piston.

The importance of the interaction between the single radiators in a multispeaker system does not seem to have been investigated in detail so far, and the mutual radiation impedance concept in a simplified version is found useful to throw some light on this problem.

RADIATION IMPEDANCE, SINGLE PISTON

From a rigid circular piston, situated in a large wall and vibrating at a low frequency in air, energy is radiated in the far field as active power and in the near field as reactive power, the latter fluctuating between the source and the field.

At any moment the acoustic power is the product of the velocity v of the piston and the acoustic force f on the piston, caused by its vibration. For a periodic vibration, the mean value of the product over a period is the radiated active power. If the vibration is harmonic, the mechanical impedance loading the piston is

$$Z_{\text{mech}} = \frac{f}{v} \tag{1}$$

and it is by definition the radiation impedance $Z_r = R_r + jX_r$ of the piston. The apparent power is then

$$S_r = P_r + jQ_r = R_r\, v^2_{\text{rms}} + jX_r\, v^2_{\text{rms}} \tag{2}$$

P_r being the active, Q_r the reactive power.

It can be shown [1, p. 383] that

$$Z_r = R_r + jX_r = \rho c \pi a^2 \left[1 - \frac{J_1(2ka)}{ka} + j\frac{H_1(2ka)}{ka}\right] \tag{3}$$

where k is the wavenumber, $k = \omega/c = 2\pi/\lambda$, a is the radius of the piston, $J_1(2ka)$ is the Bessel and $H_1(2ka)$ the Struve function, both of the first order. The functions $1 - J_1(2ka)/ka$ and $M(2ka) = H_1(2ka)/ka$ are tabulated in [1, p. 901].

Series expansion ([1] or [2]) gives for $k^2a^2 << 1$,

$$Z_r = \rho c \pi a^2 [\tfrac{1}{2} k^2a^2 + j \frac{8}{3\pi} ka] \tag{4a}$$

$$\cong j\, \frac{8}{3} \rho c k a^3 = jX_r. \tag{4b}$$

SOUND PRESSURE AND POWER

From Eqs. (1) and (4b) we get the force f on a piston with velocity v,

$$F = Z_r\, v = j\, \frac{8}{3} \rho c k a^3 v, \qquad k^2a^2 << 1. \tag{5}$$

It is sometimes assumed (see, for example, [1, pp. 386–387]) that the pressure distribution across the piston is uniform at long wavelength, which would give the pressure p_N at the surface of the piston:

$$p_N = \frac{f}{\pi a^2} = \frac{8}{3\pi} \rho c k a v, \qquad k^2a^2 << 1. \tag{6}$$

The pressure distribution is, however, not quite uniform. The pressure at an arbitrary point cannot be expressed in closed form by known functions, but such expressions are available for the center (p_C) and for the edge (p_E) of the piston [3, pp. 78–79] in the form

$$p_C = j\, 2\rho c \sin(\tfrac{1}{2} ka)\, e^{-j(\frac{1}{2})ka}\, v \tag{7}$$

and

$$p_E = \tfrac{1}{2} \rho c\, [1 - J_0(2ka) + j\, H_0(2ka)]\, v \tag{8}$$

where $J_0(2ka)$ is the Bessel and $H_0(2ka)$ the Struve function, both of zero order. Series and tables are found in [2] or [4].

By series expansion of the functions we get

$$\frac{p_C}{p_E} = \frac{j\, 2 \sin(\tfrac{1}{2} ka)\, e^{-j(\frac{1}{2})ka}}{\tfrac{1}{2}(1 - J_0(2ka) + j\, H_0(2ka))} \tag{9a}$$

$$\cong \frac{\tfrac{1}{2} k^2a^2 + jka}{\tfrac{1}{2} k^2a^2 + j(2/\pi)\, ka} \tag{9b}$$

$$\cong \frac{\pi}{2} = 1.57 \ldots, \qquad k^2a^2 << 1. \tag{9c}$$

At long wavelengths the pressure at the edge of the piston is thus $2/\pi \sim -3.9$ dB of that at the center. Eq. (6) therefore gives an average value of the pressure across the piston.

The pressure distribution along a radius of the piston is shown in Fig. 1 for several values of ka (after [3]) and the ratio p_C/p_E in Fig. 2, calculated from Eq. (9a) and plotted against ka. The ratio varies less than 0.75 dB up to $ka = 1$, indicating (yet not proving) that the relative pressure distribution is essentially constant in this frequency range.

The power radiated into the far field is

$$P_r = R_r\, v^2_{\text{rms}} \tag{10a}$$

$$= \tfrac{1}{2}\, \rho c \pi k^2 a^2 v^2_{\text{rms}}, \qquad k^2a^2 << 1 \tag{10b}$$

uniformly distributed over the space angle 2π, which gives the intensity $I = P_r/2\pi r^2$ at a distance $r >> a$ from the center of the piston. But $I = p^2_{F\,\mathrm{rms}}/\rho c$, where p_F is the sound pressure in the far field. Hence

$$p_{F\,\mathrm{rms}} = \left[\frac{\rho c\, R_r}{2\pi r^2}\right]^{\frac{1}{2}} v_{\mathrm{rms}} \qquad (11a)$$

$$= \frac{\rho c k \pi a^2}{2\pi r} v_{\mathrm{rms}}, \qquad k^2a^2 << 1. \qquad (11b)$$

Taking the phase into account, we have [1], [3]

$$p_F = \frac{j\rho c k \pi a^2 v}{2\pi r} e^{-jkr}, \qquad k^2a^2 << 1 \qquad (12)$$

and from Eqs. (6) and (12) we get the ratio

$$\frac{p_F}{p_N} = \frac{3\pi}{16}\frac{a}{r}e^{-jkr}, \quad k^2a^2 << 1. \qquad (13)$$

From Eqs. (12) and (7) with $\sin(\frac{1}{2}ka) \cong \frac{1}{2}ka$,

$$\frac{p_F}{p_C} = \frac{a}{2r}e^{-jkr}, \qquad k^2a^2 << 1. \qquad (14)$$

This relation has recently been derived in [5, Eq. (5)], where its utility in loudspeaker test technique is demonstrated. For this purpose Eq. (14) is more useful than Eq. (13), as the pressure p_C is measured at a defined position, while p_N is an average value across the piston. This value is connected with p_C through Eqs. (13) and (14) as

$$p_N = \frac{8}{3\pi}p_C = 0.85 p_C, \qquad k^2a^2 << 1 \qquad (15)$$

independent of frequency at long wavelengths, which also indicates that the pressure distribution is constant.

It appears that in the low-frequency range concerned the near-field sound pressure p_E, p_N, and p_C for a given velocity v is determined mainly by X_r, the reactive (mass) term of the radiation impedance [see Eqs. (4)–(6)], while the far-field pressure p_F is determined by the radiation resistance R_r [see Eq. (11)].

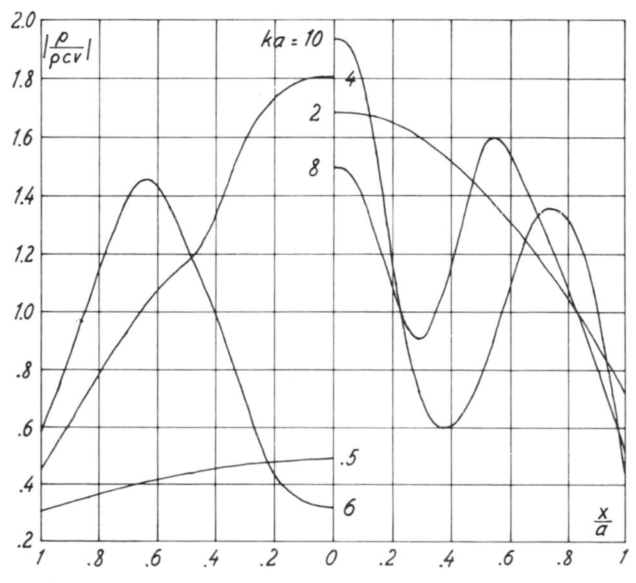

Fig. 1. Sound pressure distribution p along radius a of a circular piston in a large wall. The constant velocity is v, the distance from the center is x, and $k = \omega/c = 2\pi/\lambda$ (after Stenzel).

If we want to investigate the ratio (14) beyond the range $k^2a^2 << 1$, Eq. (7) can be used without frequency limitation, which also holds for Eq. (12) if $p_F = p_{FA}$ is the pressure at a point on the axis of the piston, and provided that $r >> a$ and $r > \frac{1}{2}ka^2$ [3], [5].

The function $(r/a)|p_{FA}/p_c|$ is plotted in Fig. 3 showing that Eq. (14) could be used up till about $ka = 5$ if the value ½ of the constant factor in Eq. (14) is replaced by a value taken from Fig. 3, in so far as the source behaves like a rigid piston in a large wall.

It might be even more useful to determine the radiated power P_r by measuring p_C, and for this purpose [5, Fig. 6] is suitable for $k^2a^2 << 1$.

Fig. 4 shows the relation between P_r and p_C also outside this range, given as

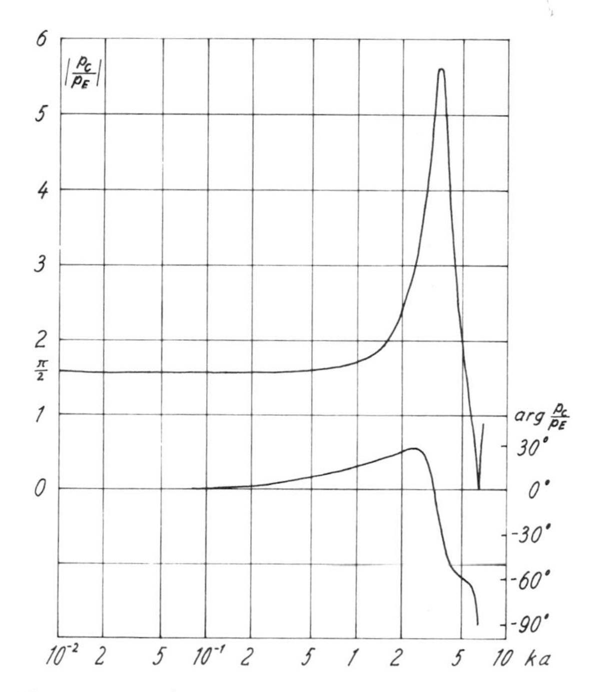

Fig. 2. Ratio p_C/p_E between sound pressure at the center and at the edge of a circular piston in a large wall. $ka = \omega a/c$ is a frequency variable for a given radius a.

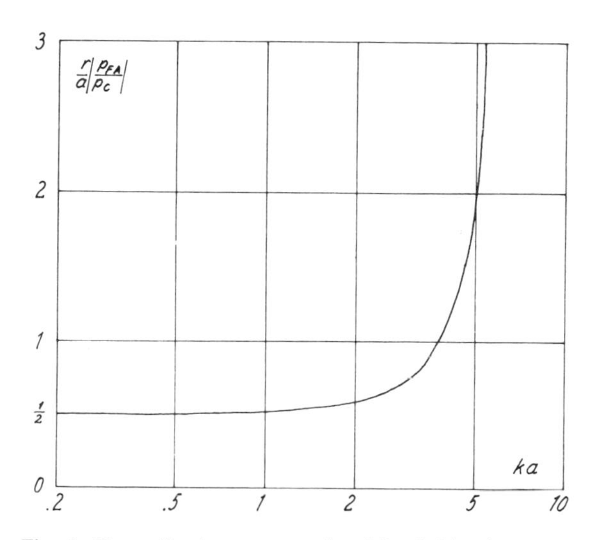

Fig. 3. Normalized pressure ratio of far-field axis pressure to near-field center pressure for a circular piston in a large wall. The piston radius is a and p_{FA} is measured at distance r from the center.

$$\frac{P_r}{a^2 p_{C\,\mathrm{rms}}^2} = \frac{\pi}{4\rho c} \frac{1 - J_1(2ka)/ka}{\sin^2(\frac{1}{2}ka)}$$

from Eqs. (3), (7), and (10a).

Finally the directivity factor of the piston can be expressed as

$$D = \frac{p^2_{FA\,\mathrm{rms}}}{p^2_{F\,\mathrm{rms}}} \tag{16}$$

where p_{FA} is the pressure at a point in the axis of the piston at a given distance, while p_F is what the pressure would be at the same distance if the power were radiated uniformly in all directions in the halfspace.

The directivity index DI = 10 log D can then be determined by Eqs. (3), (11a), (12), and (16) as

$$\mathrm{DI} = 10 \log \frac{k^2a^2}{2(1 - J_1(2ka)/ka)} \quad \mathrm{dB}.$$

DI $= f(ka)$ is plotted in Fig. 5, which shows that DI $\cong 0$ for $k^2a^2 << 1$ and DI $\cong 20 \log ka - 3$ dB for $k^2a^2 >> 1$.

TWO INTERACTING SOURCES—MUTUAL RADIATION IMPEDANCE

In order to increase the power-handling capacity, two or more similar loudspeakers are often used in parallel in the same box, their diaphragms having equal velocities. In the crossover region of multichannel systems more closely spaced speakers are working simultaneously, but with different velocities, and the same applies to a vented cabinet for the driver and the port. One of two interacting sources can be the image of the other in a reflecting wall.

It is possible to include the mutual influence between such sources in the impedance concept as shown in [6]–[9]. A rigorous treatment is complicated, but a simple yet useful derivation has been compiled from the literature and is recapitulated below.

Consider two circular pistons 1 and 2 in an infinite wall and with radii a_1 and a_2, velocities v_1 and v_2 of the same frequency, and with the distance d between the centers. The volume velocity of piston 2, $\pi a_2^2 v_2$, produces at piston 1 the (average) pressure [see Eq. (12)]

$$p_{12} = \frac{j\rho ck\ \pi a_2^2 v_2}{2\pi d} e^{-jkd}, \qquad d >> a_2 \tag{17}$$

where

$$je^{-jkd} = \sin kd + j \cos kd. \tag{18}$$

The velocity v_1 of piston 1 gives the self average pressure

$$p_{11} = \frac{Z_{r11}}{\pi a_1^2} v_1 \tag{19}$$

where the self radiation impedance is [see Eq. (4a)]

$$Z_{r11} = \frac{\rho c}{2\pi} k^2 (\pi a_1^2)^2 + j \frac{8}{3} \rho c k a_1^3, \qquad k^2 a_1^2 << 1. \tag{20}$$

The resulting radiation impedance of piston 1 is then

$$\begin{aligned} Z_{r1} &= \frac{p_{11} + p_{12}}{v_1} \pi a_1^2 = R_{r1} + j X_{r1} \\ &= \frac{\rho c}{2\pi} k^2 (\pi a_1^2)^2 \left[1 + \frac{a_2^2 |v_2|}{a_1^2 |v_1|} \frac{\sin(kd + \varphi)}{kd}\right] \\ &\quad + j \frac{8}{3} \rho c k a_1^3 \left[1 + \frac{3\pi}{16} \frac{a_2}{a_1} \frac{a_2}{d} \left|\frac{v_2}{v_1}\right| \cos(kd + \varphi)\right] \end{aligned} \tag{21}$$

where it is assumed that the phase of v_2 lags the angle φ behind that of v_1. φ then adds to the phase delay kd in the average transmission path length d from piston 2 to piston 1.

Exchanging subscripts 1 and 2 and sign of φ gives the expression for Z_{r2}.

The mutual radiation impedance Z_{r12} between piston 1 and piston 2 is for piston 1 the ratio f_{12}/v_2 of the partial force f_{12} on piston 1 due to the activity of piston 2, and the velocity v_2 of piston 2.

The total force on piston 1 from the activity of both pistons is $f_1 = f_{11} + f_{12}$ or $Z_{r1} v_1 = Z_{r11} v_1 + Z_{r12} v_2$ giving

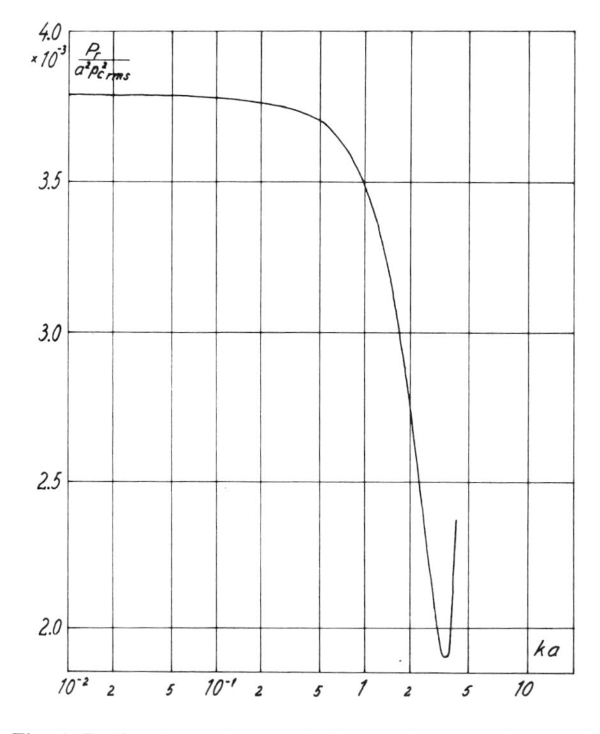

Fig. 4. Radiated sound power P_r from a piston in a large wall normalized against the square of its radius a and of the pressure $p_{C\mathrm{rms}}$ at its center. P_r is plotted against the frequency parameter $ka = \omega a/c$.

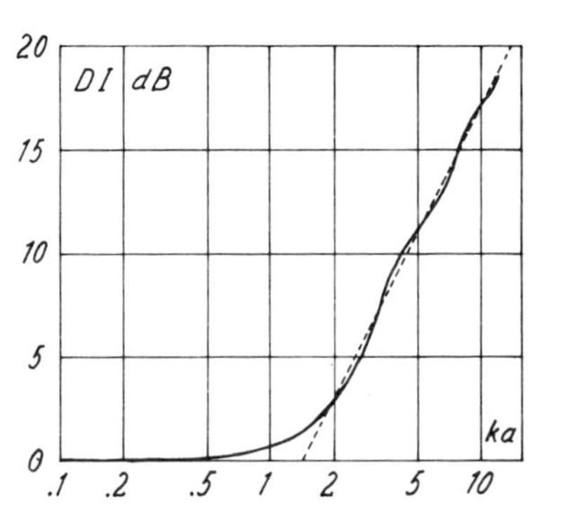

Fig. 5. Directivity index of a piston in a large wall versus frequency $(ka = \omega a/c)$. For $ka >> 1$, DI $\cong 20 \log ka - 3$ dB.

$$Z_{r1} = R_{r1} + j\,X_{r1} = Z_{r11} + Z_{r12}\,\frac{v_2}{v_1}. \tag{22}$$

R_{r12} and X_{r12} are then found by inspection of Eq. (21).

The total radiated apparent power from both pistons is then

$$S_r = P_r + j\,Q_r = Z_{r1}v_1^2 + Z_{r2}v_2^2 \qquad \text{(rms values).}$$

With Eq. (21) this gives

$$P_r = \frac{\rho c}{2\pi}\,k^2 \left\{(\pi a_1^2 v_1)^2 + (\pi a_2^2\, v_2)^2 + 2(\pi a_1^2 v_1)\,(\pi a_2^2 v_2)\,\cos\varphi\,\frac{\sin kd}{kd}\right\} \tag{23}$$

$$Q_r = \frac{8}{3}\rho\,\{a_1^3 v_1^2 + a_2^3 v_2^2 + \frac{3\pi}{8d}\,a_1^2\,a_2^2 v_1 v_2 \cos\varphi \cos kd\}. \tag{24}$$

The expressions for the total active power P_r and reactive power Q_r each comprises three terms, namely, the values for each piston in absence of the other plus one representing the interaction which disappears for a great distance d between them, and in that case the active powers are added as in an incoherent field.

At close spacing and low frequency where $\sin(kd)/kd \rightarrow 1$, the volume velocities in Eq. (23) are added as complex vectors as in a coherent field. The third term can be interpreted as the work (per second) the pistons are doing against each other's pressures.

By the derivation of the relations (17)–(24) it was assumed that $k^2a^2 << 1$ and $a << d$. It is, however, shown in [6] that the approximation is useful to $ka = 1$ and $kd = 2$ for two similar pistons (mutually tangent).

It is instructive to simplify things by putting $a_1 = a_2 = a$, $v_1 = v_2 = v$. Eq. (21) then becomes

$$Z_{r1} = R_{r1} + j\,X_{r1} = R_{r11}\left(1 + \frac{\sin kd}{kd}\right) + j\,X_{r11}\left(1 + \frac{3\pi}{16}\,\frac{a}{d}\cos kd\right) \tag{25a}$$

$$= R_{r11} f(kd) + j\,X_{r11} f\left(\frac{a}{d}, kd\right). \tag{25b}$$

The function $f(kd)$ is shown in Fig. 6 for $\varphi = 0$ and is the well-known weighting factor for the power output from two similar point sources separated by the distance d (compare, for example, [10]). For $kd \leqq 1$ the mutual resistance equals the self-resistance.

The function is usually derived by integrating the intensity produced by the pistons at a proper distance r over a hemisphere with radius r. Division of the resulting power by the mean square velocity of the pistons then yields $2R_{r1}$. For increasing d from $kd << 1$ the sound field becomes directive with dips in the directional pattern. If the pistons are moved apart on a circle centered at a point 0 in the plane of symmetry (Fig. 7), the pressure in 0 will remain constant, determined by the sum of the equal pressures p_1 and p_2 from the two sources, and hence by the sum of their volume velocities $q_1 = q_2$ as seen from Eq. (12) as

$$p = p_1 + p_2 = \frac{j\rho c k q_1}{2\pi r}\,e^{-jkr} + \frac{j\rho c k q_2}{2\pi r}\,e^{-jkr} = \frac{j\rho c k(q_1 + q_2)}{2\pi r}\,e^{-jkr} \tag{26}$$

independent of d. At all other points on the hemisphere p_1 and p_2 will differ in phase and magnitude resulting in a smaller pressure than in 0. Consequently the total emitted power decreases with d increasing.

It turns out that the directivity index is DI = 10 log $[2/(1 + \sin(kd)/kd)]$.

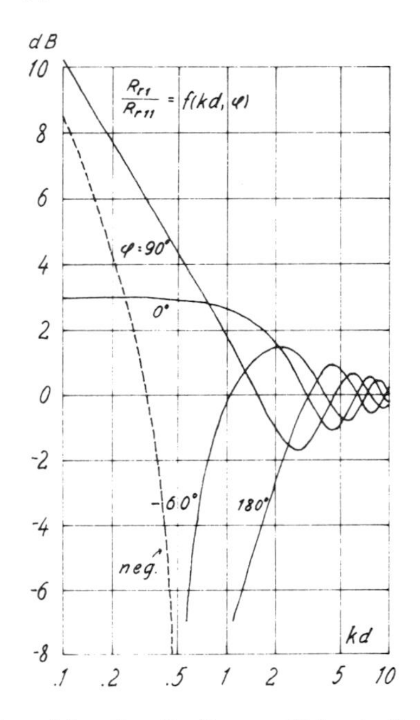

Fig. 6. Plot of function $R_{r1}/R_{r11} = f(kd, \varphi)$. R_{r1} is the total radiation resistance and R_{r11} the self-radiation resistance of one of two similar pistons in a large wall, separated by the center distance d and with the phase difference φ between their velocities of equal magnitude.

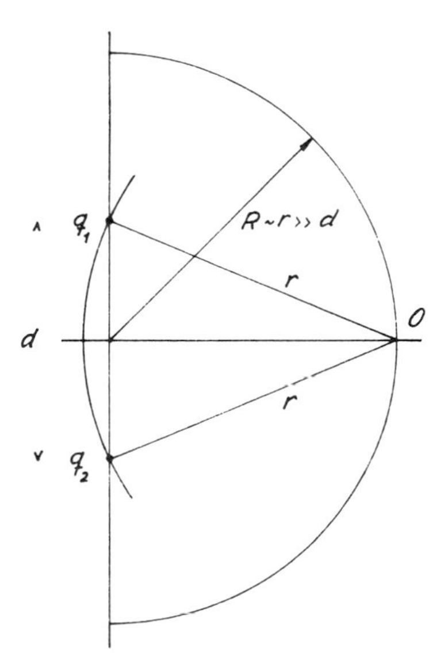

Fig. 7. At points 0 in the plane of symmetry of two pistons spaced d in a large wall, the sound pressure is determined by the equal volume velocities. They are in phase and added numerically in the expression for the sound pressure at the distance r from the pistons. At all other points on a sphere centered at the midpoint between the pistons and with radius $R \cong r >> d$, the velocities differ in phase and magnitude, giving a smaller pressure by complex addition.

In Fig. 6 is further plotted the function $f(kd, \varphi) = 1 + \sin(kd + \varphi)/kd$ for $\varphi = 90°$, $180°$, and $-60°$. It shows a strong dependence on φ. In Fig. 6 the ratio R_{r1}/R_{r11} exceeds 3 dB for $\varphi \neq 0$. This does not mean that the total radiated power is increased accordingly. The reason is that φ has opposite signs in the expressions for the two pistons, so that excessive power from one of them is absorbed by the other. The result is given by Eq. (23) as $P_r = 2 R_{r11} [1 + (\sin(kd)/kd) \cos \varphi] v^2_{rms}$ decreasing with increasing φ.

Removing $j\omega$ from the second term of Eq. (25a) gives the total mass load on a piston. The function $f(a/d, ka)$ is plotted in Fig. 8 for varying k (frequency) and constant d (spacing), and in Fig. 9 for varying d and constant k. It appears that in the close position of the pistons the total mass is about 130% of the self-mass at low frequencies (with the approximation implied in the method used). At higher frequencies and distances a decrease occurs. From Fig. 8 is seen that the mass term remains constant with frequency roughly to the limit $kd = 1$, as does the resistive term for $\varphi = 0$ (Fig. 6).

LOUDSPEAKER IN A VENTED BOX

As another example the interaction between the loudspeaker and the port in a box is investigated by means of a design according to Small [11] for a driver similar to that used in Small's design example of a closed-box system [12]. The electrical analog circuit used is shown in Fig. 10 with component values. As usual the radiation impedances are considered negligible in the electrical calculations, which will be checked afterwards. Radiation into 2π steradians is assumed.

For comparison the total pressure response curves calculated for $e_{in} = 1\ V_{rms}$, $r = 1$ m, without regard to changes in the mutual radiation impedances, is shown in Fig. 11 together with the contributions from the driver and the port per se. Further are shown the diaphragm amplitude and input impedance.

The velocity ratio of diaphragm to port, v_d/v_p, is determined from the circuit ($e = Blv$), remembering that the port is radiating from the backside as seen from the diaphragm, that is,

$$\frac{v_d}{v_p} = \left|\frac{v_d}{v_p}\right| e^{j\varphi} = x^2 - j\, d_p x - 1, \qquad x = f/f_B \tag{27}$$

where f_B is the box resonance frequency and d_p the dissipation factor for the port circuit. It is assumed that the radii a_d and a_p are equal and 0.125 m, that the center distance $d = 0.4$ m, and $f_B = 26$ Hz, $d_p = 0.1$.

Eq. (21) then gives for the driver with $\varphi = \arg(x^2 - 1 - jd_p x)$

$$\frac{R_{r1}}{R_{r11}} = 1 + \left|\frac{v_p}{v_d}\right| \frac{\sin(kd + \varphi)}{kd}$$

$$= 1 + \frac{\sin(kd + \varphi)}{kd\, |x^2 - 1 - j\, d_p x|} \tag{28}$$

which is plotted against frequency in Fig. 12. From Fig. 11 is seen that below resonance the port is in counterphase with the diaphragm and gives the larger output. The driver is therefore receiving power, rendering its radiation resistance negative with an extremum at 26 Hz, where the velocity ratio is large. This, on the other hand, reduces the significance of the driver radiation resistance with regard to the performance of the system.

Eq. (21) also gives for the driver

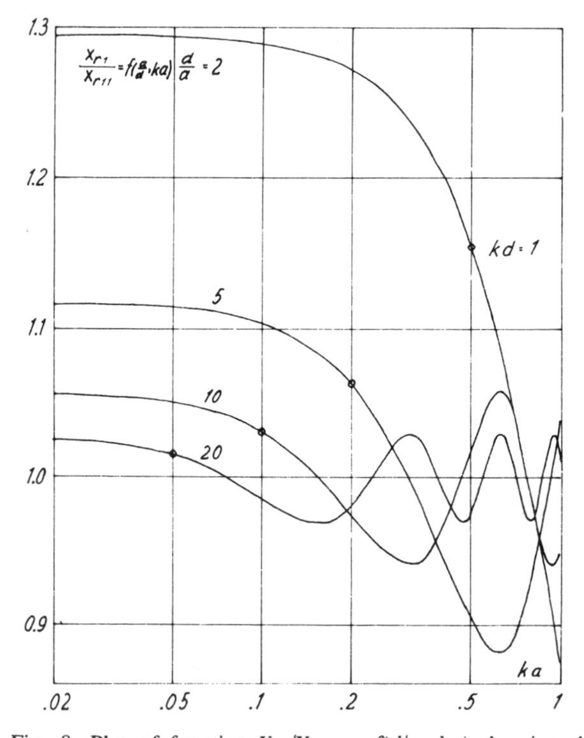

Fig. 8. Plot of function $X_{r1}/X_{r11} = f(d/a, ka)$ showing the frequency dependence ($ka = \omega a/c$) of the total mass load on one of two similar pistons with equal velocities in a large wall at different spacing-to-radius ratios d/a.

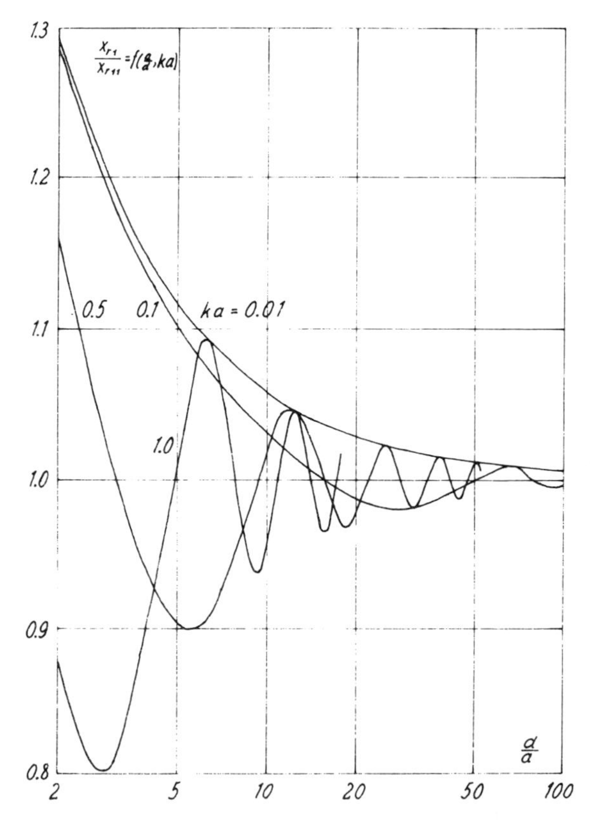

Fig. 9. Plot of function $X_{r1}/X_{r11} = f(d/a), ka)$ showing the spacing dependence of the total mass load on one of two similar pistons with equal velocities in a large wall at different frequencies ($ka = \omega a/c$).

$$\frac{X_{r1}}{X_{r11}} = 1 + \frac{3\pi}{16}\frac{a}{d}\left|\frac{v_p}{v_d}\right|\cos(kd + \varphi)$$

$$= 1 + \frac{3\pi}{16}\frac{a}{d}\frac{\cos(kd + \varphi)}{|x^2 - 1 - jd_p x|}. \quad (29)$$

This function is plotted in Fig. 13 and reminds one, not surprisingly, of coupled circuits.

The corresponding expressions for the port are

$$\frac{R_{r2}}{R_{r22}} = 1 + |x^2 - 1 - jd_p x| \frac{\sin(kd - \varphi)}{kd} \quad (30)$$

$$\frac{X_{r2}}{X_{r22}} = 1 + \frac{3\pi}{16}\frac{a}{d}|x^2 - 1 - jd_p x|\cos(kd - \varphi) \quad (31)$$

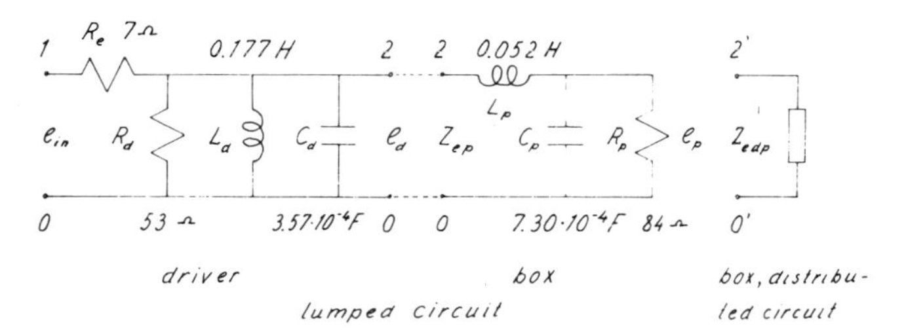

Fig. 10. Electrical analog circuit for a vented-box loudspeaker system. The driver magnet has a Bl product of 14 Tm, the effective radius of the membrane is 0.125 m, the mass 0.064 kg (+ air mass 0.006 kg), the compliance 9×10^{-4} N^{-1}m (f_d = 20 Hz), the dissipation factor $d_d = 1/Q_d = 2.38$, and the voice coil resistance 7 Ω. The box volume is 0.090 m³, the box resonance frequency f_B = 26 Hz, and the dissipation factor $d_p = 0.1$. The center spacing driver–port is 0.4 m.

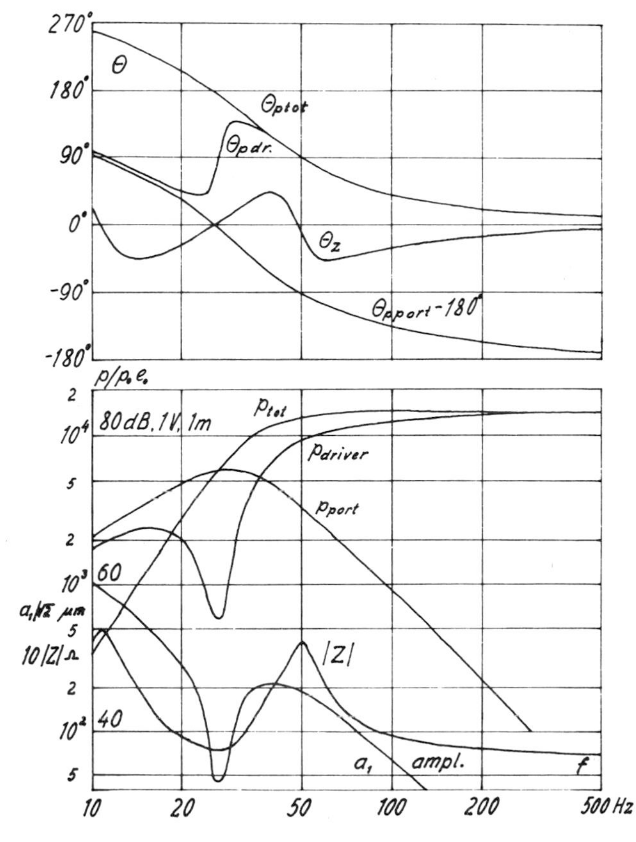

Fig. 11. Calculated response curves for the vented-box system described in Fig. 10, giving the total sound pressure level and the contributions from driver and port. The input impedance Z and the diaphragm amplitude a are also shown.

and they are plotted in Figs. 14 and 15. Here the salient points are found at higher frequencies, where the port contribution is small.

In this frequency range the internal phase shift in the box is of importance. In order to estimate the significance of a delay, a transmission line model of the box has been used. Well below the first normal mode of the box the pressure will be the same at all points inside it. Its function then depends only on its volume, and it can be thought of as a short transmission line of length d, cross section $S_t = V/d$ (V volume), with the driver as generator and the port as load (Fig. 18).

As shown in the Appendix [Eqs. (43)–(45)], this gives for the velocity ratio

$$\frac{v_d}{v_p} = x^2 \frac{\sin kd}{kd} - \cos kd - jd_p x \frac{\sin kd}{kd} \quad (45)$$

which takes the form of Eq. (27) for $k^2d^2 << 1$.

The impedance Z_{edp} of the distributed port network (Fig. 10) turns out to be

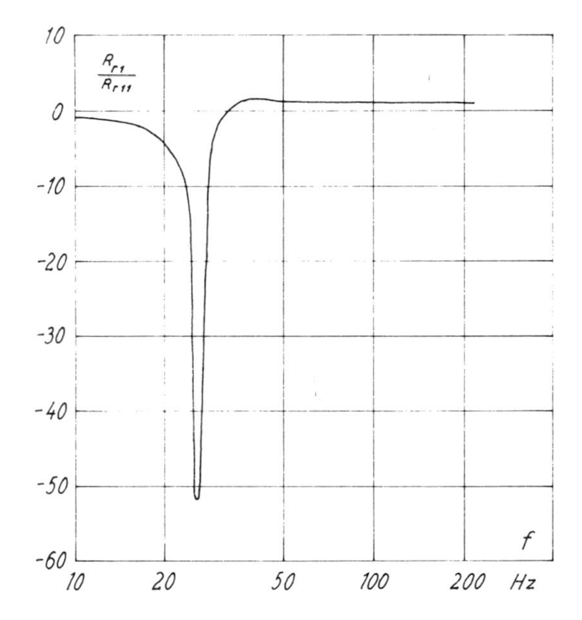

Fig. 12. Plot of R_{r1}/R_{r11} versus frequency f showing total to self-radiation resistance ratio for the driver in a vented box as described in Fig. 10.

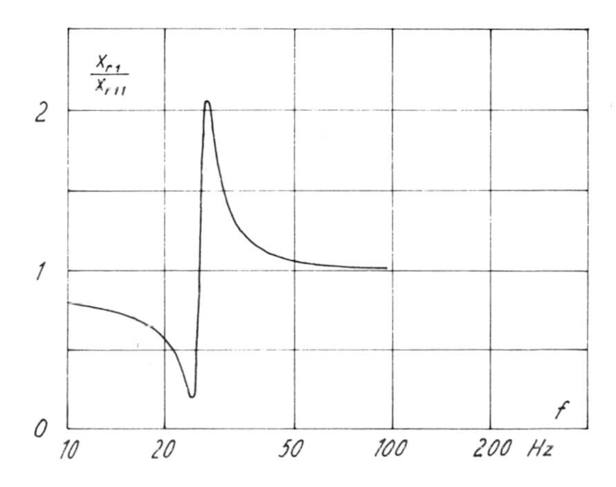

Fig. 13. Plot of X_{r1}/X_{r11} versus frequency f showing total to self-radiation reactance (mass) ratio for the driver in a vented box as described in Fig. 10.

$$Z_{\text{edp}} = \omega_p L_p \frac{1 - x^2 \dfrac{\tan kd}{kd} + j\, d_p\, x\, \dfrac{\tan kd}{kd}}{d_p + j(x + \dfrac{kd}{x} \tan kd)} \quad (43)$$

$$Z_{\text{ep}} = \omega_p L_p \frac{1 - x^2 + j\, d_p x}{d_p + j\, x}, \qquad k^2 d^2 << 1 \quad (44)$$

the latter expression being the impedance of the usual circuit.

Using Eq. (45) in Eqs. (28)–(31) gives the broken-line curves in the figures in question. The difference is significant at higher frequencies only.

The interaction can also be illustrated by Eq. (23). The first two terms in this expression are the powers which the driver and the port would radiate without interaction, while the third term represents the power radiation due to the interaction.

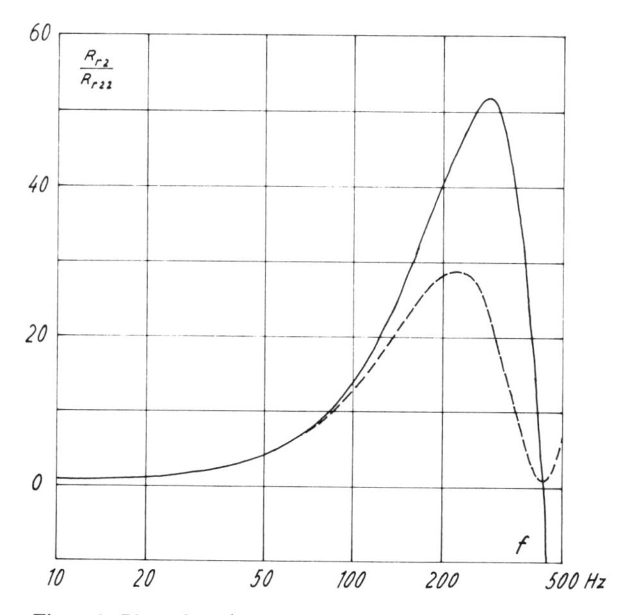

Fig. 14. Plot of R_{r2}/R_{r22} versus frequency f showing total to self-radiation resistance ratio for the port in a vented box as described in Fig. 10. The broken line refers to the transmission line model.

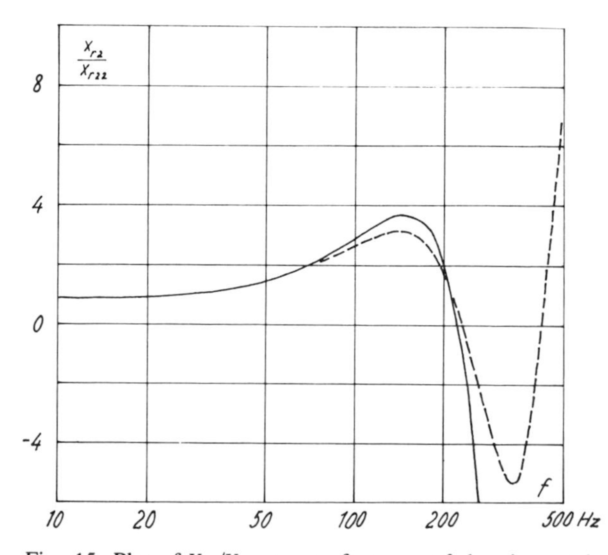

Fig. 15. Plot of X_{r2}/X_{r22} versus frequency f showing total to self-radiation reactance ratio for the port in a vented box as described in Fig. 10. The broken line refers to the transmission line model.

Each of the terms P_1, P_2, and P_3 is plotted together with the total power $\Sigma P = P_1 + P_2 + P_3$ in Fig. 16 for $d = 0.4$ m and in Fig. 17 without interaction. The broken lines represent negative (absorbed) power. The internal phase delay has not been taken into account, neither have the (small) changes in the mass loads in Figs. 16 and 17.

The figures demonstrate that the mutual radiation impedance has a decisive influence on the response below the port resonance.

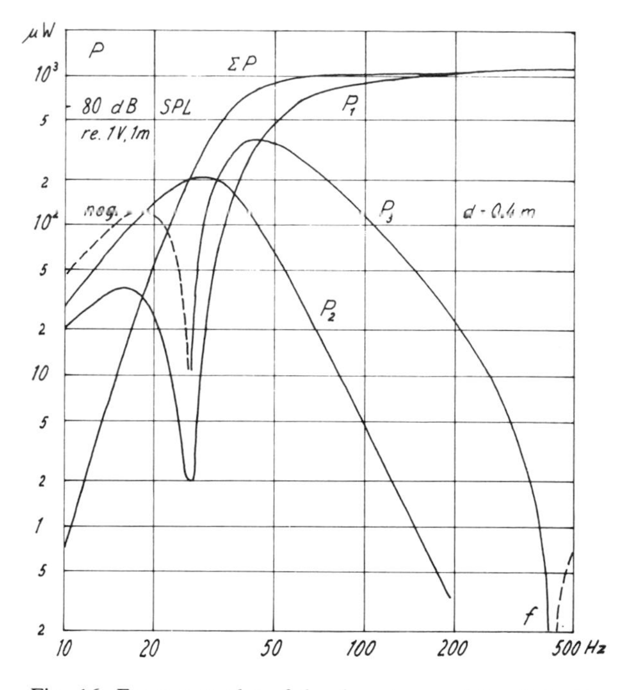

Fig. 16. Frequency plot of the three terms of Eq. (23). $P_1 = (\rho c/2\pi)\,(k\pi a_1^2 v_1)^2$ is the power which the driver would radiate if not loaded by the mutual impedance; $P_2 = (\rho c/2\pi)\,(k\pi a_2^2 v_2)^2$ is the power which the port would radiate without mutual impedance. $P_3 = 2(\rho c/2\pi)\,(\pi a_1^2 v_1 \pi a_2^2 v_2 \cos\varphi \sin(kd)/kd)$ is the power radiated due to the mutual impedance per se. $\Sigma P = P_r$ is the total radiated power with mutual impedance. The dotted curves represent power which is not radiated into the far field but exchanged between the radiators via the near field outside the box described in Fig. 10.

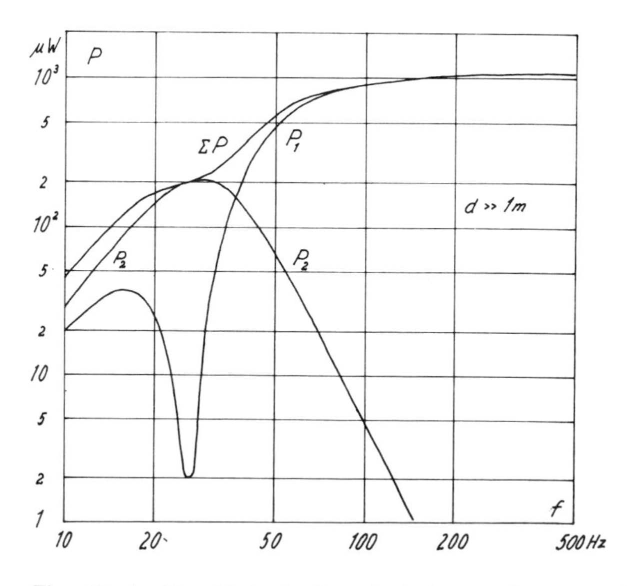

Fig. 17. As Fig. 16 in the hypothetical case of no mutual impedance.

DISCUSSION OF THE VENTED BOX SYSTEM

The calculations are based on the analog electrical circuit of Fig. 10 from which the radiation components are omitted. The voltages e_d and e_p are converted to volume velocities for the driver and the port $(e = Blv)$. The velocities are added as complex numbers to give the pressure at a point 1 m distant from both radiators for an input of 1 V. If it is arranged that the axis of both radiators are intersecting at the point of observation, this calculation holds good irrespective of spacing and frequency. The radiated power can then be calculated by means of the DI, which for $f = 40$ Hz, where the radiators have the same velocity and phase, amounts to 0.03 dB, indicating an almost hemispherical field. These calculations are not affected by the mutual radiation impedance, but it remains to be checked, whether it is of importance in the analog circuit. Regarding the internal phase delay in the box, the transmission-line model results coincide with those of the circuit in the active range of the port, and regarding magnitudes, the radiation resistance of the driver and the port $(a = 0.125$ m) is $R_{r11} = \pi/2\ \rho c k^2 a^4 = 3.56 \times 10^{-2}$ [Nsm^{-1}]. The corresponding shunt resistance to $R_d = 57\ \Omega$ in the circuit is $B^2 l^2/R_{r11} = 5.5$ kΩ $(Bl = 14$ Tm). At 26 Hz this value (Fig. 12) is -52 times smaller, or $-110\ \Omega$. The port network has a series resonance resistance of $\omega_B L_p d_p = 0.85\ \Omega$, making the influence of $-110\ \Omega$ negligible.

At 26 Hz the reactance of C_p (representing the port mass) is $d_p R_p = 8.4\Omega << 5.5$ kΩ. At 26 Hz X_{r1} varies from 20 to 200% of X_{r11}. The diaphragm mass is 64 g, the air mass $8/3\ \rho a^3 = 6$ g. The latter then varies from 1.2 to 12 g, the total mass from 65.2 to 76 g. The resonance frequency of the driver is $f_d = 20$ Hz, which moves from 20.7 to 19.2 by the variation of X_{r1}, which is unimportant and not included in the calculation of the response curves.

For the port the aberrations take place outside its active range. The conclusion is that despite the large variations in the mutual radiation impedance, the variations (but not the MRI itself) are of minor importance and need not be taken into account in the design. The reason is mainly that the variations take place outside the active frequency range of the radiator concerned.

NEAR-FIELD—FAR-FIELD RELATIONS

The relations can be investigated along the previously indicated lines. The self-pressure at the center of piston 1 is [see Eq. (7)]

$$p_{11C} = j\rho c k a_1 v_1, \qquad k^2 a_1^2 << 1 \tag{32}$$

and the pressure from piston 2 [see Eqs. (17) and (18)] for $\sin kd << \cos kd$

$$p_{12C} = j\rho c k a_2 \frac{a_2}{2d} \cos kd\ v_2. \tag{33}$$

Hence [see Eq. (21)]

$$p_{1C} = j\rho c k a_1 \left[1 + ½ \frac{a_2}{a_1} \frac{a_2}{d} \left|\frac{v_2}{v_1}\right| \cos (kd + \varphi)\right] v_1. \tag{34}$$

In the special case of similar pistons this gives for

$$p_{1C\ \mathrm{rms}} = \rho c k a \left[1 + \frac{a}{2d} \cos kd\right] v_{\mathrm{rms}}. \tag{35}$$

The radiated power is [see Eq. (23)]

$$P_r = \pi \rho c k^2 a^4 \left[1 + \frac{\sin kd}{kd}\right] v^2_{\mathrm{rms}}. \tag{36}$$

From Eqs. (33) and (34),

$$\frac{P_r}{p^2_{C\ \mathrm{rms}}\, a^2} = \frac{\pi}{\rho c} \frac{1 + \dfrac{\sin kd}{kd}}{1 + ½ \dfrac{a}{d} \cos kd} \cong \frac{2\pi}{\rho c} \frac{2d}{2d + a} \tag{37a}$$

and from Eqs. (11a) and (37a),

$$\frac{p_{F\ \mathrm{rms}}}{p_{C\ \mathrm{rms}}} \cong \frac{a}{r} \left[\frac{2d}{2d + a}\right]^{\frac{1}{2}} \tag{37b}$$

the approximation being within 0.5 dB up to $kd = 1$. The expressions for the general case imply a solution of Eq. (34) and the corresponding one for p_{2C} with respect to v_1 and v_2 for use in Eq. (23). Both magnitude and phase of the p_C must be known.

CONCLUSION

A relationship between near- and far-field sound pressure from a piston in a large wall has been established by means of the radiation impedance expression. The expression (13) differs slightly from a similar expression given in [5, Eq. (5)] relating the piston pressure at its center and the far-field pressure. The reason for this discrepancy can be traced to the fact that even at long wavelength the pressure is not uniform across the piston but assumes a constant distribution with the ratio $1{:}8/3\pi{:}2/\pi$ of center to average edge pressure.

How far this is useful for loudspeaker test measurement depends on the extent to which the results for a rigid piston can be applied to a loudspeaker diaphragm. Not only does it break up in modes at higher frequencies [14], but even at low frequencies the pressure distribution in the box may influence the velocity distribution of the diaphragm [13]. The results from the piston case should therefore be used *cum grano salis*.

The mutual impedance concept constitutes a more direct method of description of the interaction between two adjacent sources than the power integration method, which only gives the resistive part.

A rigorous treatment is cumbersome, but a simplified theory makes it possible to draw useful conclusions about the importance of the MRI in the case of a vented cabinet, where it appears that the total influence is great wherever the volume velocities are of comparable magnitude, but small if the velocity ratio is large. Even when the internal phase delay in the box is taken into consideration, there is no need for corrections in the analog electrical circuit within its general range of validity.

APPENDIX

VENTED LOUDSPEAKER BOX AS ACOUSTICAL TRANSMISSION LINE

Well below the frequency where the largest dimension of the box is half a wavelength, its function only depends on its volume V. The box might therefore be chosen with the length d, the center distance between driver and port, and the cross section area $S_t = V/d$. The driver at one end is the generator, the port at the other end is the load (Fig. 18).

Given the mechanical impedance $Z_{mp} = R_{mp} + j\omega M_p$ of the port, the mechanical impedance Z_{mdp} presented to the driver by the box can be expressed by transmission-line formulas for the specific acoustical impedances, the line velocities, and pressures (denoted by a prime) as follows:

$$Z'_{mdp} = Z_{mdp}\frac{S_t}{S_d^2} = \rho c\frac{\dfrac{Z'_{mp}}{\rho c} + j\tan kd}{1 + j\dfrac{Z'_{mp}}{\rho c}\tan kd}. \quad (38)$$

As the port radiates with its backside as seen from the driver, a minus sign must be added to the velocity ratio:

$$-\frac{v'_d}{v'_p} = -\frac{v_d S_d/S_t}{v_p S_p/S_t} = \cos kd + j\frac{Z'_{mp}}{\rho c}\sin kd \quad (39)$$

$$\frac{p'_d}{p'_p} = \frac{p_d}{p_p} = \cos kd + j\frac{\rho c}{Z'_{mp}}\sin kd. \quad (40)$$

Now

$$\frac{Z'_{mp}}{\rho c} = \frac{Z_{mp}}{\rho c}\frac{S_t}{S_p^2} = \frac{1}{kd}\left[\frac{R_{mp}S_t\omega d}{\rho c S_p^2 c} + j\frac{\omega M_p S_t \omega d}{\rho c S_p^2 c}\right], \quad k = \frac{\omega}{c}.$$

It is remembered that $V = S_t d$, and that $C_{mp} = V/(\rho c^2 S_p^2)$ is the box compliance for the port and $\omega_B^2 = 1/(C_{mp}M_p)$ is the square of the box resonance frequency. Then

$$\frac{Z'_{mp}}{\rho c} = \left[d_p\frac{\omega}{\omega_B} + j\left(\frac{\omega}{\omega_B}\right)^2\right]\frac{1}{kd}$$

$$= (d_p x + j x^2)\frac{1}{kd} \quad (41)$$

where $x = \omega/\omega_B$ and $d_p = \omega_B C_{mp} R_{mp}$ is the dissipation factor of the port. In the analog circuit the load impedance Z_{edp}, representing the port circuit, is

$$Z_{edp} = \frac{B^2l^2}{Z_{mdp}} = \frac{S_t B^2 l^2}{S_d^2 Z'_{mdp}}. \quad (42)$$

A combination of Eqs. (38), (41), and (42) gives

$$Z_{edp} = \omega_B C_{md} B^2l^2 \frac{1 - x^2\dfrac{\tan kd}{kd} + j x d_p\dfrac{\tan kd}{kd}}{d_p + j(x + \dfrac{kd}{x}\tan kd)} \quad (43)$$

where $C_{md}B^2l^2 = B^2l^2 S_t d/(\rho c^2 S_d^2) = L_p$ in the electrical circuit. This circuit gives for the impedance (Fig. 10)

$$Z_{ep} = \omega_B L_p\frac{1 - x^2 + j d_p x}{d_p + j x}, \qquad d_p = \frac{\omega_B L_p}{R_p}. \quad (44)$$

Eq. (43) is reduced to Eq. (44) for $kd << 1$. $|Z_{edp}|$ and $|Z_{ep}|$ are plotted against frequency in Fig. 19.

The port area can freely be chosen so that $S_p = S_d$. Eq. (39) then becomes

$$-\frac{v_d}{v_p} = \cos kd - x^2\frac{\sin kd}{kd} + j d_p x\frac{\sin kd}{kd} \quad (45)$$

which agrees with Eq. (27) for $kd << 1$. When substituted in Eqs. (28)–(31) they give the broken-line curves. Eqs. (27) and (45) are shown in Fig. 20. Damping material in the box would reduce the tops and dips of the curves.

If the box were made as the model used in the calculation, it would have a cross-sectional area of $V/d = 0.09/0.4 = 0.225 = 0.47 \times 0.47$ m², giving an upper limit of $f = c/2 \times 0.47 = 360$ Hz for the use of the model.

A more comprehensive analysis along this line requires the use of normal mode theory as outlined in [13] for a closed-box system.

ACKNOWLEDGMENT

The review, comments, constructive criticism, and suggested revisions of this paper by D. B. Keele, Jr. are gratefully acknowledged. The author is also indebted to Inger Skals Nielsen for an endless patience in the typing and for help with the translation together with Birgit Jacobsen.

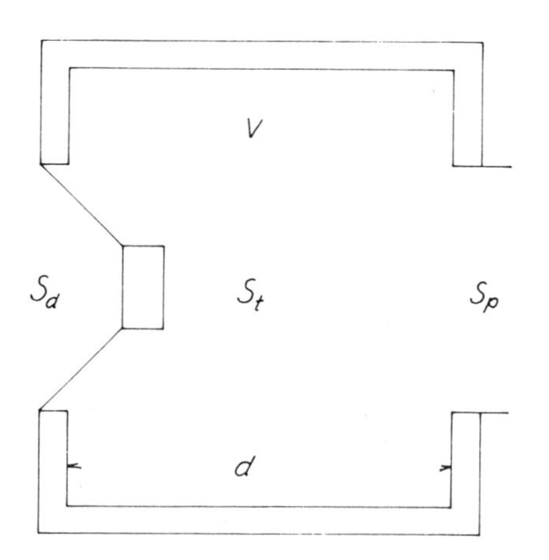

Fig. 18. Transmission-line model of a vented box as described in Fig. 10 with driver as generator and port as load.

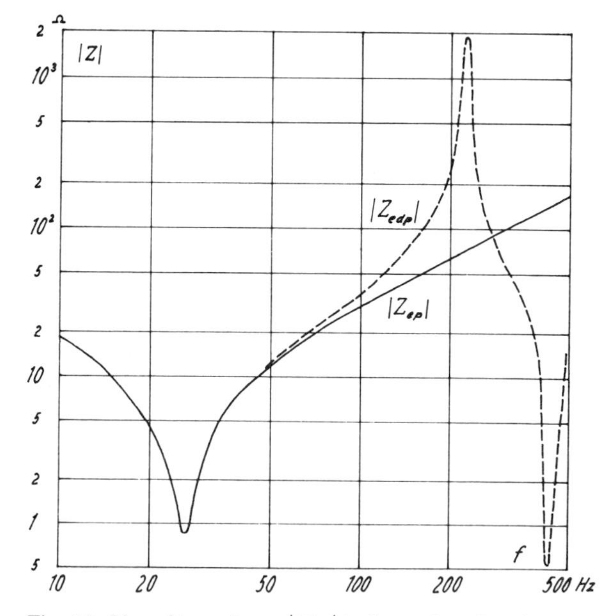

Fig. 19. Plot of impedance $|Z_{ep}|$ in the analog electrical circuit presented to the driver by the port circuit as described in Fig. 10. The broken line refers to the transmission-line model impedance $|Z_{edp}|$.

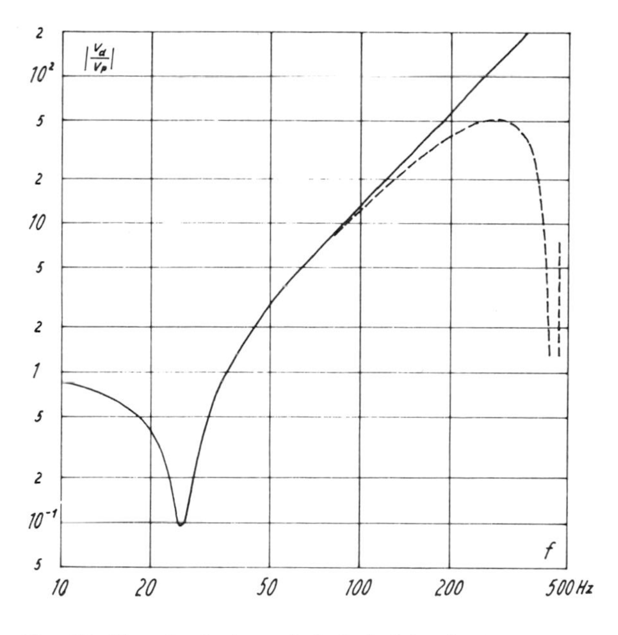

Fig. 20. Plot of velocity ratio $|v_d/v_p|$ of the diaphragm and the port velocities for a vented box as described in Fig. 10. The broken line refers to the transmission-line model.

REFERENCES

[1] P. M. Morse and K. U. Ingard, *Theoretical Acoustics* (McGraw-Hill, New York, 1968).

[2] N. W. McLachlan, *Bessel Functions for Engineers*, 2nd ed. (Oxford University Press, London, 1961).

[3] H. Stenzel and O. Brosze, *Leitfaden aur Berechnung von Schallvorgängen,* 2nd ed. (Springer Verlag, Berlin/Göttingen/Heidelberg, 1958).

[4] Jahnke and Emde, *Tables of Functions,* 4th ed. (Dover, New York, 1945).

[5] D. B. Keele, Jr., "Low-Frequency Loudspeaker Assessment by Nearfield Sound Pressure Measurement," *J. Audio Eng. Soc.,* vol. 22, pp. 154-162 (Apr. 1974).

[6] R. L. Pritchard, "Mutual Acoustic Impedance between Radiators in an Infinite Rigid Plane," *J. Acoust. Soc. Am.,* vol. 32, p. 730, (June 1960).

[7] T. V. Sathyanarayana, "Resonance and Efficiency of Column Speakers," *Acoustica,* vol. 28, p. 154, (Mar. 1973).

[8] E. de Boer, "Acoustic Interaction in Vented Loudspeaker Enclosures," *J. Acoust. Soc. Am.,* vol. 33, p. 246, (Feb. 1961).

[9] R. H. Lyon, "On the Low-Frequency Radiation Load of a Bass-Reflex Speaker," *J. Acoust. Soc. Am.,* vol. 29, p. 654, (May 1957).

[10] R. F. Allison, "The Influence of Room Boundaries on Loudspeaker Power Output," *J. Audio Eng. Soc.,* vol. 22, pp. 314-320, (June 1974).

[11] R. H. Small, "Vented-Box Loudspeaker Systems, II," *J. Audio Eng. Soc.,* vol. 21, pp. 438-444, (July/Aug. 1973).

[12] R. H. Small, "Closed-Box Loudspeaker Systems, II," *J. Audio Eng. Soc.,* vol. 21, pp. 13-18, (Jan./Feb. 1973).

[13] N. F. Meeker *et al.,* "The Acoustical Impedance of Closed Rectangular Loudspeaker Housings," *J. Acoust. Soc. Am.,* vol. 22, p. 206, (Mar. 1950).

[14] J. E. Goldberg *et al.,* "On the Calculation of the Axisymmetric Modes and Frequencies of Conical Shells," *J. Acoust. Soc. Am.,* vol. 32, p. 738, (June 1960).

THE AUTHOR

Oluf Jacobsen was born in Copenhagen, Denmark, on June 18, 1916. He graduated from the Technical University in Copenhagen as a M Sc EE in 1941 and worked with the State Railways, the Telephone Company, and in the acoustical department of a consultant firm.

In 1943 he became a Lecturer at the Engineering School Aarhus Teknikum and in 1953 head of the Electronics and Telecommunications Department. In 1970 he was elected Director and reelected 1972 and 1975. He has been a consultant in architectural acoustics, but now his occupation allows him to do only a little electroacoustics *con amore*. He is a Member of the Acoustical Society of America, of the Audio Engineering Society and of the Danish Acoustical Society.

The Use of Fibrous Materials in Loudspeaker Enclosures

L. J. S. BRADBURY

Department of Mechanical Engineering, University of Surrey, England

Fibrous tangles are frequently used in loudspeaker enclosures to damp acoustic resonances that might otherwise occur. However, in addition to their attenuating properties, fibrous tangles also reduce the propagation speed of the sound waves, and this could also be used to reduce the dimensions of labyrinth and horn-loaded enclosures. However, in order to use fibrous tangles in this way, it is necessary to be able to describe their effect on sound waves in a more precise way than is customary in designing loudspeaker enclosures. The present paper discusses a model of the interaction between sound waves and fibrous materials which seems to account for the main acoustic characteristics that are observed. The theory gives reasonable quantitative agreement with both the propagation speeds and attenuation rates obtained from experiments with a number of different fibrous materials, and an example is given of how the theory might be used in optimizing the use of tangles in a labyrinth type of enclosure. This is an example only, and the theory could also be used in designing other types of enclosures.

INTRODUCTION: When sound waves pass through a fibrous tangle such as fiber glass or wool, the speed with which they travel is different from the speed of sound in free air, and the waves are also strongly attenuated. In the design of loudspeaker enclosures, it is usually the attenuating properties which are made use of to absorb reflections inside the enclosure and prevent the occurrence of sharply tuned acoustic resonances. However, the effect of a fibrous tangle on the speed of sound could also be used to reduce the dimensions of labyrinth and horn-loaded loudspeakers, and this is perhaps a more interesting application of fibrous materials.

Although the use of fibrous materials in closed-box and Helmholtz-resonator cabinets has been the subject of many discussions (see, for example, [1], [2]), these have usually been of a general nature and have not included detailed arguments about the interaction between the sound waves and the fibrous material. In particular, an interesting but puzzling observation on the use of fibrous materials was described some years ago by Bailey [3], [4] in the design of a labyrinth type of enclosure. In this design Bailey examined the use of both fiber glass and several types of wool. He discovered that the behavior of long-haired wool was very different from that of the other materials and offered far superior acoustic properties for his particular labyrinth type of design. He found that at a packing density of about 0.5 lb/ft^3 (8 kg/m^3) the specific acoustic impedance of this material above 100 Hz was close to that of air, so that the effective stiffness of the cabinet was not greatly influenced by the presence of the tangle, and yet the wool still had a high attenuation rate so that the shorter wavelength resonances that might otherwise have occurred within the cabinet were well damped. On the other hand, at the low audio frequencies in the region of 30 Hz the wool appeared to reduce the speed of sound to about half its free-air value so that the half-wavelength labyrinth necessary to give an improved bass response was reduced in length from 30 ft (9 m) to 15 ft (4.5 m) for a 30-Hz wave. Although Bailey examined various fibrous tangles on an ad hoc basis, no attempt was made to study the influence of fibrous materials in a detailed way, and the purpose of the present paper is to examine more exactly the acoustic properties of fibrous tangles in the hope of encouraging their more precise use in the design of loudspeaker enclosures.

Although a considerable amount of work has been done on sound waves in porous materials (see, for example, Zwikker and Kosten [5]), this has usually been on materials in which the fibrous frame is very rigid, and this is not the case with the fibrous tangles that might be of use in loudspeaker enclosures. In any case, some aspects of the existing work are not altogether satisfactory so that the theory has been redeveloped along lines which are more closely similar to, say, the work of Dobbins and Temkin [6] on sound propagation in gas–particle mixtures. In its most complete form, the theory is fairly extensive, but it is sufficient for present purposes to present the results for the simplest form of the theory which accounts for the main acoustic features of fibrous tangles. It is not the aim of this paper to discuss the details of the analysis and, wherever possible, it is the physical significance of the results that has been stressed. However, for completeness, the relevant equations of motion and brief details of the analysis have been included in a compressed form in Appendix A.

FACTORS AFFECTING WAVES IN FIBROUS MATERIALS

For the fibrous materials used in loudspeaker enclosures, the volume occupied by the fibrous material is very small (5% of the volume at most), and the small space occupied by the fibers plays no direct role in the behavior of the sound waves.

The main effect which the fibrous material has on a sound wave passing through it arises from the aerodynamic drag on the fibers due to the sound waves. Now the fiber diameters are typically about 0.01 mm, which is much less than the wavelength of the sound waves. Under these circumstances and at the very low air velocities which arise from sound waves, it is possible to show that this aerodynamic drag is proportional to the velocity of the air flowing past the fibers.

In other words, the aerodynamic force per unit length and per unit cross-sectional area of the fibrous material is given as $\lambda(u_a - u_f)$, where u_a and u_f are the air and fiber velocities, respectively. λ is an aerodynamic drag parameter which is constant for a given fiber material at a particular packing density. Its significance and determination will be discussed later. If the mass of fiber per unit volume is P, then the equation of motion for the fibrous material is simply

$$P \frac{du_f}{dt} = \lambda (u_a - u_f) \tag{1}$$

where the left-hand side is mass × acceleration and the right-hand side represents the aerodynamic drag.

It should be noted that the fibrous material is assumed to have no mechanical stiffness of its own.[1] The significant factor in Eq. (1) is the parameter P/λ which arises in it. This parameter has the dimensions of time, and, in fact, it is representative of the time taken for the fibrous material to be set in motion by a sound wave passing through it. For simple harmonic waves, we can introduce a parameter $\omega P/\lambda$ which is essentially the ratio of the characteristic time required to set the fibers in motion to the period of the sound wave. ω is the angular frequency of the sound wave which is also $2\pi/T$, where T is the period. When the frequency is sufficiently high so that $\omega P/\lambda$ is much greater than 1, there is insufficient time during one cycle of a sound wave for the fibers to be set in motion, and under these circumstances, the sound waves pass through an essentially stationary fibrous frame. In this case the speed of sound is not greatly affected by the presence of the fibers, but, because of the high aerodynamic drag, the sound wave is strongly attenuated. By contrast, at low frequencies when $\omega P/\lambda$ is much less than 1, the fibers have sufficient time during one cycle of a wave to become virtually coupled with the air movements, and the air and fibers move as one. Under these circumstances the aerodynamic drag is very small and the sound waves are only weakly attenuated. However, the effective density of the air–fiber combination is $(P + \rho_a)$, where ρ_a is the density of the air, and if we assume for the moment that the pressure changes are still adiabatic, the speed of sound is reduced to $\sqrt{\gamma p_a/(P + \rho_a)}$, where p_a is the ambient air pressure and γ is the usual ratio of the specific heats.

In the above argument it was assumed that the pressure changes were adiabatic, and, in a more complete description of the propogation of sound waves through fibrous tangles, the influence of heat transfer to the fibers should be included. However, although it is perfectly possible to do this, it results in much more complex algebraic relationships, and since the maximum effect of changing from adiabatic to isothermal processes only results in a 20% reduction in the speed of sound, it is not worthwhile in the present context to include this factor.

PROPOGATION VELOCITY AND ATTENUATION RATE

The previous section attempted to briefly outline in general terms the influence of a fibrous tangle on a sound wave passing through it. In this section the detailed results of the theory outlined in Appendix A will be discussed. The theory shows that a simple harmonic sound wave of angular frequency ω propogates through a fibrous material like

$$\exp\left[-\beta \frac{\omega}{a_0} x\right] \exp\left[i \frac{\omega}{a_0} \alpha\left(x - \frac{a_0}{\alpha} t\right)\right]. \tag{2}$$

This expression represents a wave which travels with a velocity a_0/α, where a_0 is the normal adiabatic sound speed

[1] The neglect of the stiffness of the fibrous frame requires that $E/(Pa_0^2) << 1$, where E is the stiffness modulus of the fibrous tangle and a_0 is the ordinary speed of sound in free air. Even for densely packed fibers, $E/(Pa_0^2)$ has values only in the region of about 0.01.

for free air, i.e., $a_0 = \sqrt{\gamma p_a/\rho_a}$. The wave also decays exponentially with distance x with a power to the exponential of $\beta\ (\omega/a_o)\ x$. In more conventional terms, the attenuation in decibels per unit length is $20\beta\ (\omega/a_0)\ \log_{10} e = 8.69\beta\ \omega/a_0$. The parameters α and β are related to the packing density of the fibrous material P and the drag parameter λ by the expression

$$\alpha + i\beta = \sqrt{\frac{(1 + P/\rho_a) - i\omega P/\lambda}{1 + i\omega P/\lambda}}. \quad (3)$$

Separating the real and imaginary parts of this expression gives

$$\alpha = \left[\frac{(1 + P/\rho_a)^2 + (\omega P/\lambda)^2}{1 + (\omega P/\lambda)^2}\right]^{1/4} \cos\theta \quad (4a)$$

$$\beta = \left[\frac{(1 + P/\rho_a)^2 + (\omega P/\lambda)^2}{1 + (\omega P/\lambda)^2}\right]^{1/4} \sin\theta \quad (4b)$$

where

$$\theta = \tfrac{1}{2}\left[\tan^{-1}\frac{\omega P}{\lambda} - \tan^{-1}\frac{\omega P/\lambda}{1 + P/\rho_a}\right].$$

Before discussing these relationships further, the behavior of the results for high and low frequency should be noted. At low frequency when $\omega P/\lambda \to 0$, we have $\alpha \to \sqrt{1 + P/\rho_a}$ and $\beta \to 0$. In other words, the speed of sound is reduced to $\sqrt{\gamma p_a/(P + \rho_a)}$ in accordance with our earlier arguments, and there is no attenuation of the wave. At high frequencies when $\omega P/\lambda \to \infty$, the limiting cases are more difficult to obtain, but it can be shown that $\alpha \to 1$ and $\beta \to \tfrac{1}{2}\lambda/\rho_a\omega$. In other words, the speed of sound approaches the ordinary adiabatic speed of sound, but the wave is attenuated at a rate of $10\ (\lambda/\rho_a a_0)\ \log_{10} e$ decibels per unit length.

One further interesting result for the ratio of the fiber to air velocity should be noted. For simple harmonic waves, Eq. (1) gives

$$\left|\frac{u_f}{u_a}\right| = \frac{1}{\sqrt{1 + (\omega P/\lambda)^2}}. \quad (5)$$

The ratio of the sound speed in a fibrous tangle to the sound speed in free air is $1/\alpha$. This is shown in Fig. 1, calculated from Eq. (4a) for a variety of packing density ratios P/ρ_a and plotted against the nondimensional frequency parameter $\omega P/\lambda$. This figure also shows the ratio of the fiber to air velocities calculated from Eq. (5). The results shown clearly demonstrate in quantitative terms the effect that a fibrous tangle has on the speed of sound for various packing densities. It also shows how the fibers and air become coupled at low frequencies and decoupled at high frequencies.

As far as attenuation is concerned, it is convenient to divide the attenuation parameter $\beta\ \omega/a_0$ by the value it has at high frequencies, namely, $\tfrac{1}{2}\ \lambda/\rho_a a_0$. This gives a nondimensional attenuation parameter which is $2\beta\ (\omega P/\lambda)/(P/\rho_a)$. This parameter approaches zero at low frequencies and unity at high frequencies. Fig. 2 shows the variation of this parameter for different fiber packing densities.

RELATIONSHIP BETWEEN DRAG PARAMETER λ AND PACKING DENSITY P

The results obtained so far demonstrate the general effects of a fibrous tangle on sound waves, but in order to make practical use of the results, it is necessary to know the value of the aerodynamic drag parameter λ for a particular material and packing density. This parameter is usually obtained experimentally by passing a slow current of air through a sample of fibrous material and measuring the pressure drop across it. However, in order to discuss the acoustic behavior of fibrous materials in a general way, it would be preferable to have an explicit relationship for the drag parameter λ. Unfortunately, although there have been several investigations into the drag parameter, they have not been extensive enough to enable a general relationship to be convincingly obtained, but at least it is possible to suggest the form that such a relationship should take. This is based partly on previous experimental work, but also on the theory of the flow past small cylinders and spheres and the expression is that

$$\lambda = A\,\frac{\mu}{d^2}\left(\frac{P}{\rho_f}\right)^n$$

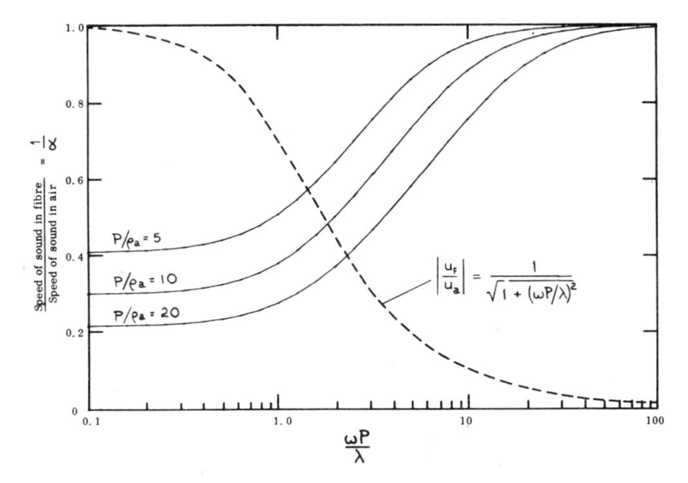

Fig. 1. Influence of a fibrous tangle on the speed of sound.

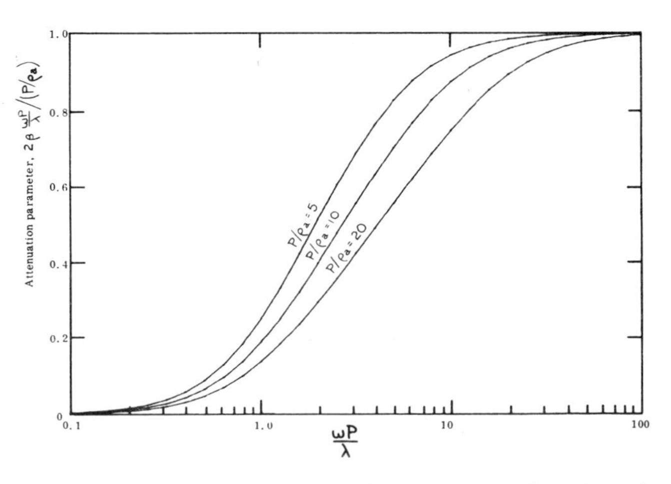

Fig. 2. Influence of a fibrous tangle on the attenuation of sound waves.

where A and n are constants, μ is the coefficient of viscosity of air, d is the fiber diameter, P is the packing density of the fibrous tangle, and ρ_f is the density of the fiber material. P/ρ_f is therefore the proportion of the volume taken up by the fibers. At normal temperatures, $\mu = 1.81 \times 10^{-5}$ kg/(m·sec) and if d is in meters, then λ is in kg/(m³·sec). Investigations carried out by both the author and others [7], [8] strongly suggest a value of n of about 1.4. However, there is little certainty about the precise value of the constant A. All the experimental results available on this topic are deficient in some way or other in the completeness of the information required to obtain values for the constant A. Results from different experiments give values of A ranging from 12 to about 50, depending on various assumptions that are made in analyzing the data. However, an average value of A is about 27. It is clear that this subject requires more investigation before full use can be made of the present results, but as a tentative expression, it will be assumed that the drag parameter is given by

$$\lambda = 27 \frac{\mu}{d^2} \left(\frac{P}{\rho_f}\right)^{1.4} \qquad (6)$$

EXPERIMENTAL RESULTS FOR THE SPEED OF SOUND AND ATTENUATION IN FIBROUS TANGLES

The only published experiments that the author has been able to find in which the speed of sound and attenuation have been directly measured in a fibrous tangle are due to Esmail–Begui and Naylor [9]. The measurements were made in fiber glass with two different packing densities. The details of the test conditions are given in Table I. One of the important details not available from their work is the diameter of the glass fibers. However, reference to other published work suggests that this was probably close to 0.0127 mm. The density of fiber glass would seem to be about four times that of water. The estimated values of the drag parameter λ obtained from Eq. (6) are about 70% of the values measured by Esmail–Begui and Naylor. However, for various reasons it is by no means obvious that the experimental values quoted by Esmail–Begui and Naylor are necessarily more accurate than our estimated values from Eq. (6). In consequence, calculations of the speed of sound and attenuation rate have been carried out from Eqs. (2), (3), and (4) for both the quoted and estimated values of the drag parameter. These results are compared with the experimental results in Figs. 3 and 4 for the speed of sound and attenuation rate, respectively. As far as the lower packing density is concerned, the experimental and theoretical results are in quite good agreement with one another. Using the measured value of the drag parameter λ gives rather better agreement with the experimental results for the speed of sound, but the attenuation results are in better agreement when the value of λ is estimated from Eq. (6). The same general comments apply to the results for the higher packing density, although in this case the calculated attenuation rates are both much higher than the experimental values. This difference possibly arises from the fact that the drag parameter λ is in reality frequency dependent with

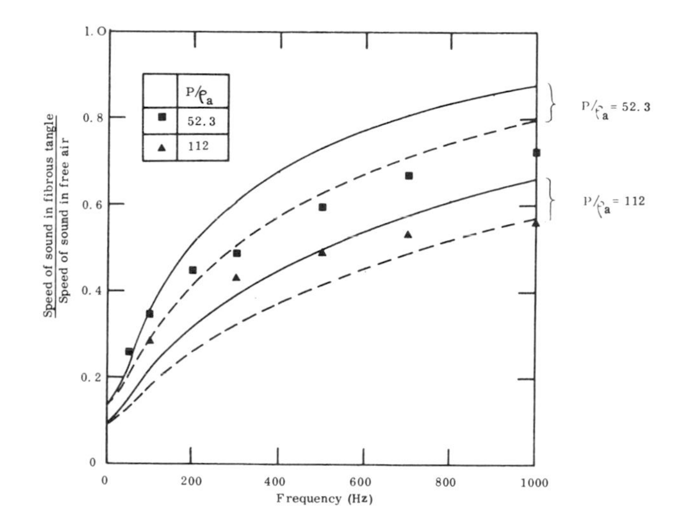

Fig. 3. Speed of sound in fiber glass (from [9]). Dashed lines—theoretical results using measured flow resistance; solid lines—theoretical results using calculated flow resistance.

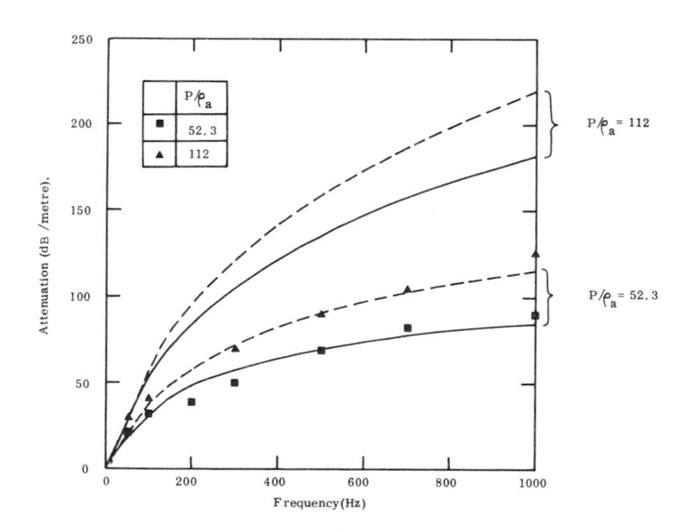

Fig. 4. Attenuation of sound waves in fiber glass (from [9]). Dashed lines—theoretical results using measured flow resistance; solid lines—theoretical results using calculated flow resistance.

Table I. Tests of Esmail-Begui and Naylor.

	PF Fiber glass	TWF Fiber glass
Packing density, P	135 kg/m³	63 kg/m³
Porosity, f	0.965	0.985
Density of fibers, $= P/(1-f)$	3860 kg/m³	4200 kg/m³
Measured flow resistance, λ	36 400 N·sec/m⁴	13 800 N·sec/m⁴
Estimated flow resistance, λ*	26 400 N·sec/m⁴	9100 N·sec/m⁴

* From Eq. (6) assuming a fiber diameter of 0.0127 mm.

this dependency itself being a function of the packing density. It would perhaps be possible to include such an effect into Eq. (6), but there is not really the evidence to make such an attempt worthwhile at the moment, and, from a practical standpoint, its effect would not be particularly significant at the fiber packing densities of interest to the loudspeaker designer.

In addition to the results above, some experiments were also carried out by the author using both fiber glass and wool. In addition to the sound measurements, estimates of the fiber diameters were made and the details of the tests are given in Table II, including the values of the drag parameter λ calculated from Eq. (6). Comparisons between the theoretical and experimental results are given in Figs. 5 and 6. The agreement between the calculated and experimental attenuation rates is quite good, although both sets of results for the speed of sound show the same tendency for the calculated values to lie below the experimental values at low frequencies and to lie somewhat above them at high frequencies. This tendency can also be observed in the comparisons with Esmail–Begui and Naylor's results. However, the general agreement between calculated and experimental results is certainly quite good enough to ensure that calculations of the acoustic behavior of loudspeaker cabinets would be a meaningful occupation. It is incidentally worth noting that the difference between the acoustic behavior of fiber glass and long-haired wool arises from the greater diameter of the wool fibers. Thus for the same packing density, the drag parameter of the wool is much less than that of the fiber glass.

The only remaining point about these results that should perhaps be noted is that the experiments are quite difficult to carry out with any accuracy. At low frequencies the speed of sound measurements involves the measurement of small phase angles, and a good deal of care has to be taken to ensure that the microphones used in the experiments do not pick up "short-circuit" waves traveling, for example, down the walls of the pipe in which the fibrous material is contained.

APPLICATION TO A FIBER-FILLED OPEN PIPE

It is not really the purpose of this paper to discuss in detail the acoustic behavior of loudspeaker enclosures because so many other factors properly need to be taken into account. However, it is perhaps worthwhile to show that meaningful calculations can be made of the influence of a fibrous material within an enclosure and, as an example, an examination will be made of a pipe of length L filled with a fibrous tangle. The pipe has a loudspeaker at one end and is open at the other end. This example, therefore, closely resembles the labyrinth type of loudspeaker discussed by Bailey [3], [4].

When there are waves going in both directions, we have the following results for the particle velocity and pressure due to the sound wave:

$$u(x,t) = \left[A \exp\left[i \frac{\omega}{a_0}(\alpha + i\beta)x\right] + B \exp -\left[i \frac{\omega}{a_0}(\alpha + i\beta)x\right]\right]\exp\left[-i\omega t\right] \quad (7a)$$

$$p(x,t) = \rho_a a_0 (\alpha + i\beta) \left[A \exp\left[i \frac{\omega}{a_0}(\alpha + i\beta)x\right] - B \exp\left[-i \frac{\omega}{a_0}(\alpha + i\beta)x\right]\right]\exp\left[-i\omega t\right] \quad (7b)$$

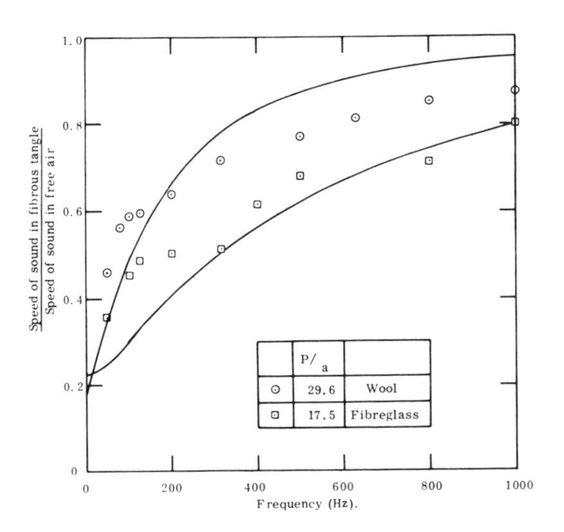

Fig. 5. Speed of sound in fiber glass and long-haired wool. Solid lines—theoretical results.

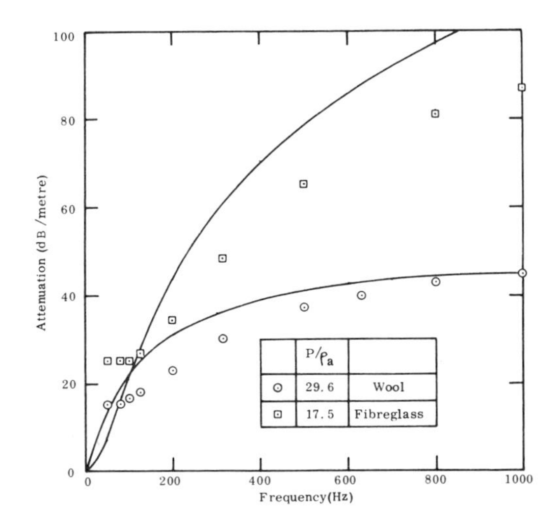

Fig. 6. Attenuation of sound waves in fiber glass and long-haired wool. Solid lines—theoretical results.

Table II. Present tests.

	Fiber glass	Long-Haired Wool
Packing density, P	21 kg/m³	35 kg/m³
Measured fiber diameter, d	0.005 mm	0.028 mm
Estimated flow resistance, λ*	12 600 N·sec/m⁴	5700 N·sec/m⁴

* From Eq. (6) assuming the specific gravities of fiber glass and wool are 4 and 1, respectively.

where $u(x,t)$ and $p(x,t)$ are the particle velocity and pressure, respectively, at any value of the distance x from the loudspeaker and time t. α and β are given by Eqs. (4a) and (4b), and A and B are constants which have to be determined from the details of the particular problem. For example, in the present case of a loudspeaker in a tube of length L which is open at the end $x = L$, we make use of the usual assumption that the pressure fluctuations are zero at this open end. From Eq. (7b) this gives

$$A \exp\left[i \frac{\omega}{a_0}(\alpha + i\beta)L\right] - B \exp\left[-i \frac{\omega}{a_0}(\alpha + i\beta)L\right] = 0.$$

At the other end of the pipe $x = 0$, the loudspeaker is vibrating periodically with a velocity given by $U_0 e^{-i\omega t}$ so that from Eq. (7a) we have

$$A + B = U_0.$$

These two expressions enable A and B to be determined.

The two results which are of particular interest in the context of loudspeaker design are (1) the impedance "seen" by the loudspeaker cone and (2) the ratio of the particle velocity at the end of the pipe to the velocity of the loudspeaker cone. The impedance Z "seen" by the loudspeaker cone is given by

$$\frac{Z}{\rho_a a_0} = \tfrac{1}{2} \left[\frac{\{\alpha \sinh(2\beta\omega L/a_0) + \beta \sin(2\alpha\omega L/a_0)\} + i\{\beta \sinh(2\beta\omega L/a_0) - \alpha \sin(2\alpha\omega L/a_0)\}}{\cos^2(\alpha\omega L/a_0) \cosh^2(\beta\omega L/a_0) + \sin^2(\alpha\omega L/a_0) \sinh^2(\beta\omega L/a_0)} \right]. \quad (8)$$

In the above form the real and imaginary components are easily identifiable. It should be noted that when the pipe is empty, $\alpha = 1$ and $\beta = 0$. Under these circumstances, the impedance is purely imaginary and is simply

$$\frac{Z}{\rho_a a_0} = -i \tan(\omega L/a_0).$$

If the particle velocity at the open end of the pipe is U_L and the loudspeaker velocity is U_0, then

$$\frac{U_L}{U_0} = \frac{\cos(\alpha\omega L/a_0) \cosh(\beta\omega L/a_0) + i \sin(\alpha\omega L/a_0) \sinh(\beta\omega L/a_0)}{\cos^2(\alpha\omega L/a_0) \cosh^2(\beta\omega L/a_0) + \sin^2(\alpha\omega L/a_0) \sinh^2(\beta\omega L/a_0)}. \quad (9)$$

The real and imaginary components are again easily identifiable.

Although these are rather cumbersome expressions, it is nevertheless comparatively straightforward to compute results for any particular practical example, and as a demonstration, calculations have been carried out for a 2-meter long pipe. This is roughly similar to the enclosure of Bailey and the calculations have been performed for fiber packing density ratios P/ρ_a of 9, 6, and 3. The calculations have been performed for fiber glass and long-haired wool using the measured values of their diameters of 0.005 mm and 0.028 mm, respectively. Eq. (6) has been used to calculate the drag parameter λ.

It is important to stress that the present results need careful interpretation, and only a very brief discussion of the results can be given here.

The main idea behind a labyrinth type of cabinet is that at high frequencies, the fibrous material should damp out all internal resonances and present a constant resistive impedance to the rear of the loudspeaker cone. At these higher frequencies the reactive impedance should be very small. However, at low frequencies bass lift is supposed to be achieved by producing sound from the open end of the labyrinth that is in phase with the sound radiating from the loudspeaker directly. This effect should occur when the wavelength of the sound in the pipe is in the region of twice the pipe length. In addition, bass lift can also arise from the quarter-wavelength resonances.

We will consider mainly the results of a wool-filled pipe. In order to first note the frequencies at which the quarter- and half-wavelength "resonances" occur, we will refer to Figs. 7 and 8 which show the real and imaginary components of the air velocity at the end of the wool-filled pipe. The frequencies corresponding to an odd number of quarter-wavelength resonances occur when the real component of the velocity shown in Fig. 7 is zero, i.e., when $\cos(\alpha\omega L/a_0)$ in Eq. (9) is zero. Thus the first quarter-wavelength resonances are at about 17 Hz, 25 Hz, and 37 Hz, respectively, for the packing density ratios of 9, 6, and 3. The frequencies corresponding to half-wavelength resonances occur when the imaginary component of the velocity in Fig. 8 is zero, i.e., when $\sin(\alpha\omega L/a_0)$ in Eq. (9) is zero. Thus these frequencies are about 55 Hz, 71 Hz, and 82 Hz, respectively, for wool packing density ratios of 9, 6, and 3.

It is interesting now to consider the "impedance" seen by the loudspeaker cone. As far as the real resistive part of the impedance is concerned, Fig. 9 shows that at a wool packing density ratio of 3, there is insufficient fiber to damp out the higher frequency resonances. However, at the two other packing density ratios of 6 and 9, there is only one really significant peak in the real impedance at frequencies slightly below the first quarter-wavelength frequencies. Above these frequencies, the resistive impedance approaches the specific acoustic impedance of air fairly rapidly, and it would appear that the optimum packing density ratio would lie between 6 and 9. This is equivalent to between 0.5 and 0.7 lb of wool per cubic foot (8 and 11 kg/m^3) and is exactly in the range suggested by Bailey.

If we examine the imaginary reactive impedances shown in Fig. 10, we find that these impedances at very low frequencies are negative. These negative imaginary impedances occur when the wavelengths are much longer than the pipe length and are simply the impedance due to the mass of air and fiber in the pipe. These are given simply by $Y = -i\omega(P + \rho_a)$. As the frequency increases, the imaginary impedances change sign and reach maxima at frequencies slightly above the first quarter-wavelength frequencies. Above these frequencies, the results for the packing density ratios of 6 and 9 fall away without very significant peaks and troughs, but the results for the packing density ratio of 3 again show that insufficient fiber is present to damp out the effect of the higher order pipe resonances.

Returning to the real and imaginary components of the velocity at the end of the pipe, Figs. 7 and 8, respectively, it is worth stressing that these results are not practically useful until calculations can be made in which the mechanical impedances of the loudspeaker driver unit are included. However, in general terms they show that the sound output from the open end of the pipe is only in phase with the direct loudspeaker output in the region of the half-wavelength resonances. But this in-phase component is not very large, and most of the bass lift would probably originate from the first quarter-wavelength resonance.

As a brief contrast with the wool results, Figs. 11 and 12 show the real and imaginary components of the impedance in the case of a pipe filled with fiber glass. These figures clearly demonstrate that fiber glass is a far less satisfactory material than wool because the real resistive impedance is much higher than that obtained from wool, and its value fluctuates markedly in the region of 50 Hz. Similarly, the imaginary reactive impedance does not approach zero as rapidly as in the case of a wool-filled pipe, and the values again fluctuate significantly in the frequency region below 50 Hz. One could not expect this type of impedance variation to produce a satisfactory low-frequency response from a loudspeaker cabinet.

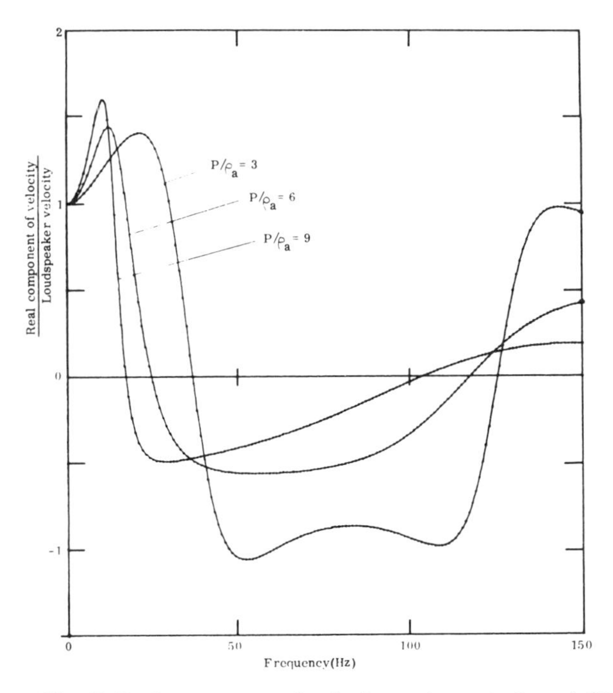

Fig. 7. Real component of velocity at the end of wool-filled pipe.

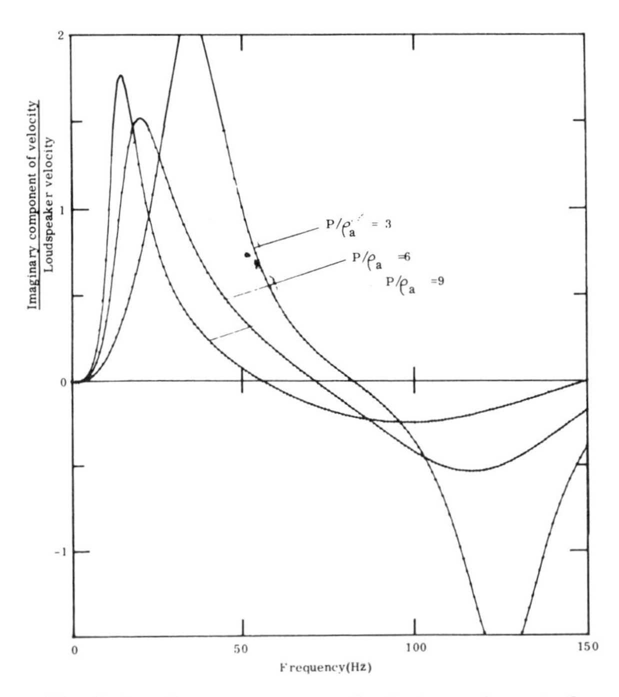

Fig. 8. Imaginary component of velocity at the end of wool-filled pipe.

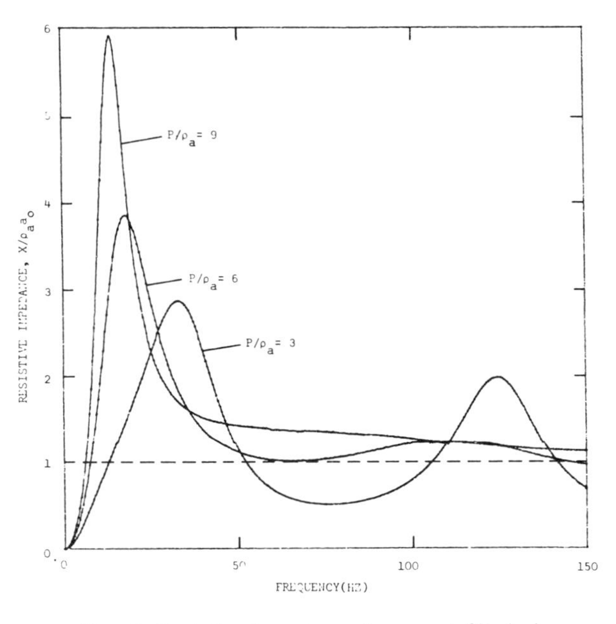

Fig. 9. Resistive impedance in a wool-filled pipe.

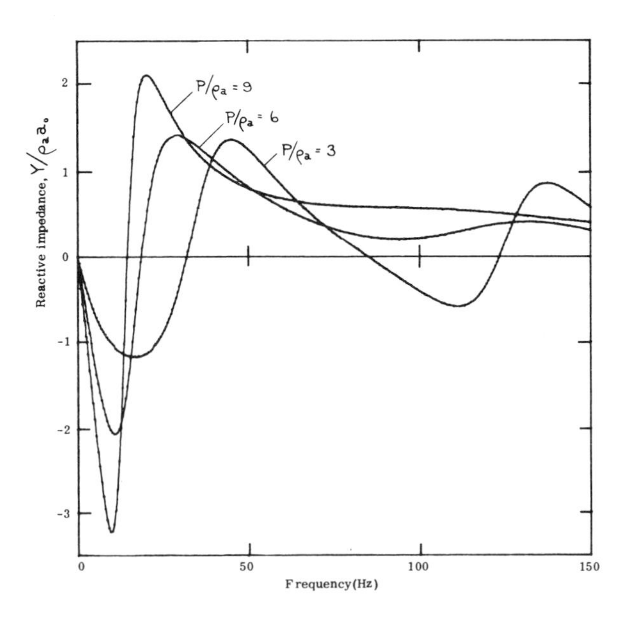

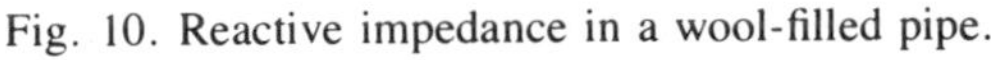

Fig. 10. Reactive impedance in a wool-filled pipe.

CONCLUDING REMARKS

The purpose of this paper has been to draw attention to the possibility of using fibrous materials in loudspeaker enclosures in a more precise way than is perhaps currently practiced.

There seems little doubt that the advantages and disadvantages of different fibrous materials could be examined theoretically once measurements of the fiber diameter and specific gravity were available. This approach would be a good deal cheaper than extensive experimental studies, and, furthermore, it is probable that the calculations for a particular type of enclosure could be extended to include the impedances of the driver units. The value of this type of approach is that it should enable the inevitable experimental work needed in loudspeaker development work to be concentrated more rapidly and directly onto the type of fibrous material and packing density ratios that are likely to give good results. No great difficulty should be experienced in examining, for example, the influence of fibrous materials on the behavior of either Helmholtz-resonator or horn-loaded enclosures.

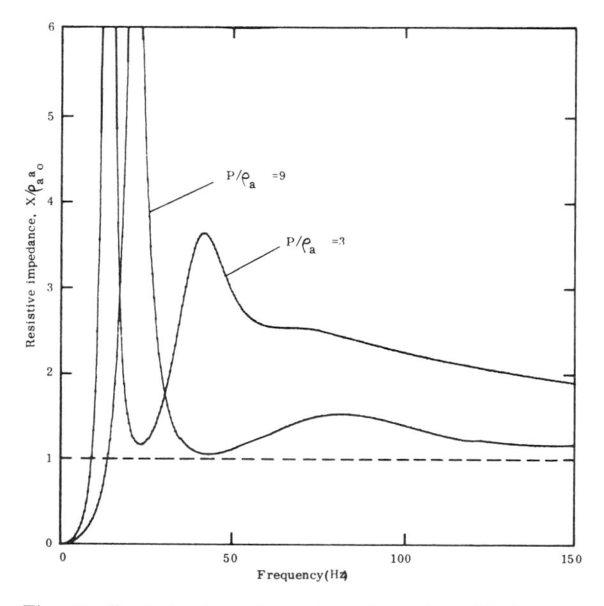

Fig. 11. Resistive impedance in a fiber-glass-filled pipe.

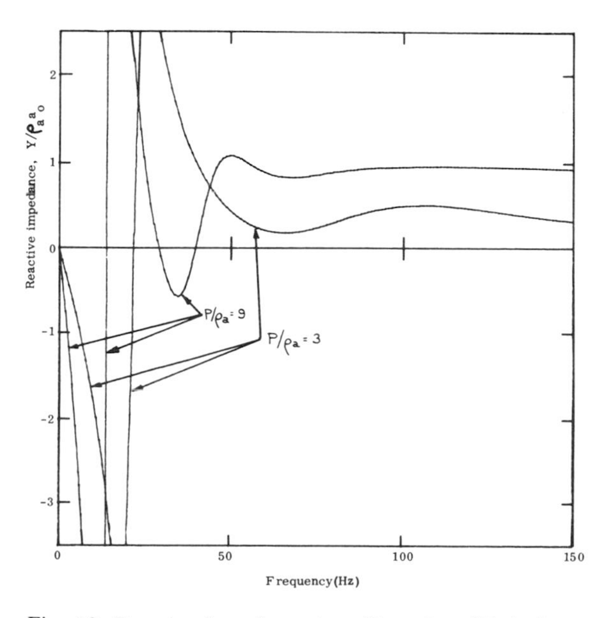

Fig. 12. Reactive impedance in a fiber-glass-filled pipe.

APPENDIX A

EQUATIONS OF MOTION FOR SOUND WAVES IN A FIBROUS TANGLE

The assumptions made are simply that the space occupied by the fibrous tangle is very small and also all the normal assumptions about the small amplitude of the sound waves. For the air we have the usual mass flow continuity equation, namely,

$$\rho_a \frac{\partial u'_a}{\partial x} + \frac{\partial \rho'_a}{\partial t} = 0 \tag{10}$$

where u'_a and ρ'_a are the velocity and density fluctuations of the air, respectively. ρ_a is the undisturbed density of air. The momentum equation for the air is

$$\rho_a \frac{\partial u'_a}{\partial t} = - \frac{\partial p'}{\partial x} - \lambda (u'_a - u'_f) \tag{11}$$

where p' is the fluctuation in air pressure, u'_f is the fiber velocity, and λ is the pressure drop caused by the aerodynamic drag on the fibers for a unit of air velocity. It will be assumed that pressure changes are adiabatic so that

$$\frac{p'}{\rho'_a} = a_0^2 \tag{12}$$

where a_0 is the adiabatic speed of sound.

The momentum equation for the fibers is simply

$$P \frac{\partial u'_f}{\partial t} = \lambda (u'_a - u'_f) \tag{13}$$

where P is the packing density of the fibrous material.

We are only interested in the propogation of simple harmonic waves in this paper, so that we can write

$$u'_a = U_a(s) e^{-i\omega t}$$

$$u'_f = U_f(x) e^{-i\omega t}$$

and so on for the pressure and density fluctuations. When these expressions are substituted into Eqs. (10)–(13), we can solve the equations to obtain the results given as Eqs. (2)–(5) in the main text.

REFERENCES

[1] J. R. Ashley and T. A. Saponas, "Wisdom and Witchcraft of Old Wives' Tales About Woofer Baffles," *J. Audio Eng. Soc.*, vol. 18, pp. 524-529 (Oct. 1970).

[2] R. H. Small, "Closed-Box Loudspeaker Systems, Pt. I: Analysis," *J. Audio Eng. Soc.*, vol. 20, pp. 798-808 (Dec. 1972).

[3] A. R. Bailey, "Non-resonant Loudspeaker Enclosure, *Wireless World* (Oct. 1965).

[4] A. R. Bailey, "The Transmission-Line Loudspeaker Enclosure," *Wireless World* (May 1972).

[5] C. Zwikker and C. W. Kosten, *Sound Absorbing Materials* (Elsevier, Amsterdam).

[6] R. A. Dobbins and S. Temkin, "Propagation of Sound in a Gas-Particle Mixture," *AIAA J.*, vol. 5, no. 12 (1967).

[7] R. H. Nichols, "Flow Resistance Characteristics of Fibrous Acoustical Materials," *J. Acoust. Soc. Am.*, vol. 19, no. 5 (1947).

[8] R. A. Taub, "Fibre-Tangle Interaction with an Airflow," *J. Fluid Mech.*, vol. 27, pt. 3 (1967).

[9] Z. Esmail-Begui and T. K. Naylor, "Measurements of the Propagation of Sound in Fibreglass," *J. Acoust. Soc. Am.*, vol. 25, no. 1 (1953).

THE AUTHOR

L. J. S. Bradbury received a degree in aeronautical engineering in 1958 and a Ph.D. in 1961 from Queen Mary College, University of London. From 1961 to 1965, he was a Senior Scientific Officer at the Royal Aircraft Establishment in Farnborough, working on the structure of turbulent jets and the aerodynamics of V/STOL aircraft.

From 1965 to 1970, Dr. Bradbury was a lecturer in the Aeronautics Department, Imperial College, and continued work on turbulent flows and on the development of instrumentation for studying them. During this time, he became interested in high fidelity and acoustics from which the present work developed. Since 1970, he has been a Reader in flow measurement at the New University of Surrey.

Radiation from a Dome*

JAMES M. KATES

Teledyne Acoustic Research, Norwood, MA 02062

The radiation characteristics of an axially vibrating rigid dome in an infinite baffle are calculated. The dome contour is found to have little effect up to $ka = 4$. Implications for loudspeaker design are discussed.

INTRODUCTION: Dome-shaped radiators are now commonly used for mid-range and high-frequency drivers. One reason for using a dome is the possibility that it has better dispersion than an equivalent flat piston over the nominal operating range of the driver. This assumption, however, has not been subjected to rigorous examination.

Because of the curved shape, a dome will have a null in its on-axis pressure response. A second assumption with regard to dome radiators is that this dip occurs when the height of the dome is exactly one-half wavelength [1]. This argument, however, ignores the difference in radiating area between the center of the dome and the rim and is therefore suspect.

The radiation behavior of an ideal dome was studied in order to test the above two assumptions. The dome is modeled as an infinitely rigid spherical cap, vibrating axially. Mechanical dome properties such as finite speed of wave propagation and normal modes of vibration are ignored. This enables the effects of shape alone to be isolated.

ANALYSIS

The analysis of the vibrating dome follows the procedure used by Kinsler and Frey [2] for a piston (see Fig. 1). The dome is assumed to be an aggregate of infinitesimal simple sources arrayed on a spherical cap, with all sources vibrating in phase. The incremental pressure dp produced by an infinitesimal area is then

$$dp = \frac{j\rho_0 ck}{2\pi r'} (u \; dS) \, e^{j(\omega t - kr')} \tag{1}$$

where

- j — $\sqrt{-1}$
- ρ_0 — density of air
- c — speed of sound in air
- k — wave number, $= \omega/c$
- ω — angular frequency, $= 2\pi f$
- r' — distance from the radiating surface element to the measurement position p
- u — axial velocity of the dome
- dS — infinitesimal surface area of the dome projected onto the x–y plane of Fig. 1.

From geometrical considerations the distance r' is given by

$$r' = [r^2 + \rho^2 - 2r\rho \cos\psi \sin\theta - 2rD(\rho) \cos\theta]^{\frac{1}{2}} \tag{2}$$

which can be approximated, for $\rho << r$, by a power series as

$$r' = r - \rho \cos\psi \sin\theta - D(\rho) \cos\theta \tag{3}$$

where the dome contour $D(\rho)$ is equal to

* Presented November 1, 1976, at the 55th Convention of the Audio Engineering Society, New York.

$$D(\rho) = (A^2 - \rho^2)^{\frac{1}{2}} - (A^2 - a^2)^{\frac{1}{2}}. \quad (4)$$

A is the dome radius of curvature and a is the equivalent piston radius (see Fig. 2). The distance term in the denominator of Eq. (1) can be approximated as $r' = r$ for distances far from the dome.

With these approximations, the pressure in the far field becomes

$$dp = \frac{j\rho_0 ck}{2\pi r} u e^{j(\omega t - kr)} e^{jk(\rho \cos\psi \sin\theta + D(\rho)\cos\theta)} \quad (5)$$

and

$$p = \frac{j\rho_0 ck}{2\pi r} u\, e^{j(\omega t - kr)} \int_0^a \rho d\rho$$

$$\int_0^{2\pi} e^{jk(\rho \cos\psi \sin\theta + D(\rho)\cos\theta)} d\psi. \quad (6)$$

Integrate over ψ to get

$$p = \frac{j\rho_0 ck}{r} u\, e^{j(\omega t - kr)}$$

$$\int_0^a e^{jkD(\rho)\cos\theta} \rho\, J_0(\rho k \sin\theta)\, d\rho. \quad (7)$$

Note that Eq. (7) can be used with $D(\rho)$ representing any surface of revolution.

We are primarily concerned with the directional characteristics of the radiator. The directivity term in the far-field radiation expression is

$$\frac{2}{a^2} \int_0^a e^{jkD(\rho)\cos\theta} \rho J_0(k\rho \sin\theta)\, d\rho \quad (8)$$

which depends on the observation angle θ and on the dimensionless product ka. If $D(\rho)$ is replaced by $-D(\rho)$, the magnitude of the directivity term remains unchanged, so an inverted dome has the same directional pattern as a noninverted dome. If $D(\rho) = 0$, this becomes the expression for a flat piston.

A closed-form solution of the integral is known only for $D(\rho) = 0$; therefore numerical integration of the directivity term was carried out. The zero-order Bessel function $J_0(x)$ was approximated by a power series [3], and the integration accomplished using a modification of a Romberg quadrature routine supplied by Hewlett-Packard [4]. The program output is a plot of the magnitude of the directivity term as a function of ka for a given observation angle θ.

RESULTS

Fig. 3 shows the on-axis ($\theta = 0$) response curves for dome contours ranging from a flat disk to a hemisphere. As the dome radius of curvature decreases, the zero in the response moves lower in frequency, but there is only a slight decrease in level for $ka < 4$. For a hemisphere the zero occurs at $ka \simeq 13$, while the dome height is one half wavelength at $ka = \pi$. Consider the implications for a 1-inch (254-mm) diameter dome tweeter. A typical unit covers from 4 to 16 kHz, or roughly the range $1 \leq ka \leq 4$. Over this operating range, variations of the dome contour have a maximum effect of less than 2 dB. The cancellation null occurs at $ka \simeq 13$, or about 56 kHz, for a hemisphere and at higher frequencies for flatter contours, well above the operating range of the driver. Thus varying the dome contour has no practical effects on the on-axis response of a typical unit.

Fig. 4 shows response curves for $\theta = 22½°$. Again, there is a maximum difference of 2 dB between the curves at $ka = 4$, and the first zero for the flat disk occurs at $ka \simeq 10.5$. The curves for the three domes are close to each other out to ka

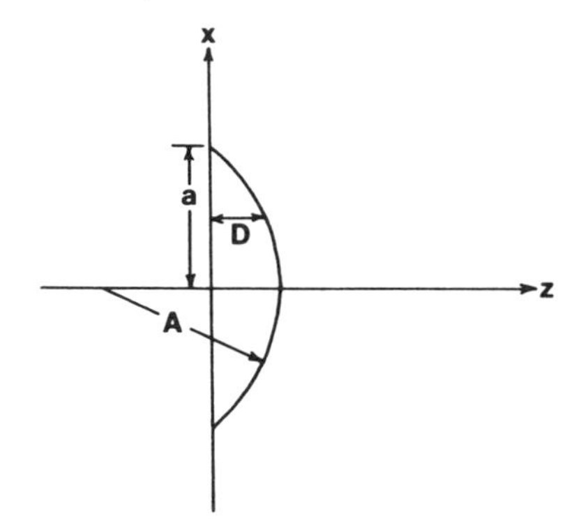

Fig. 2. Cross section of dome.

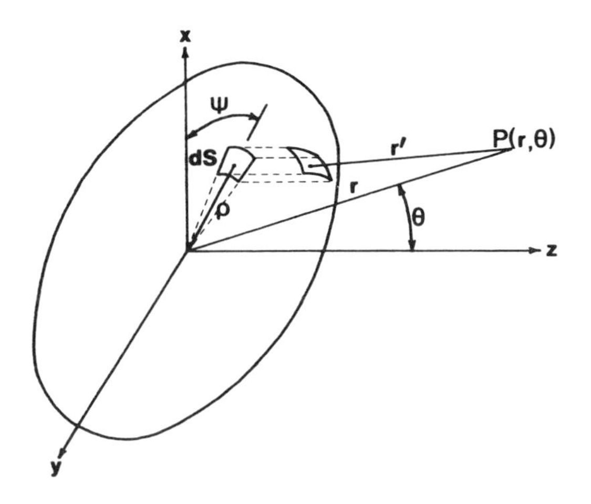

Fig. 1. Coordinate system and geometry used to derive the radiation characteristics of a dome.

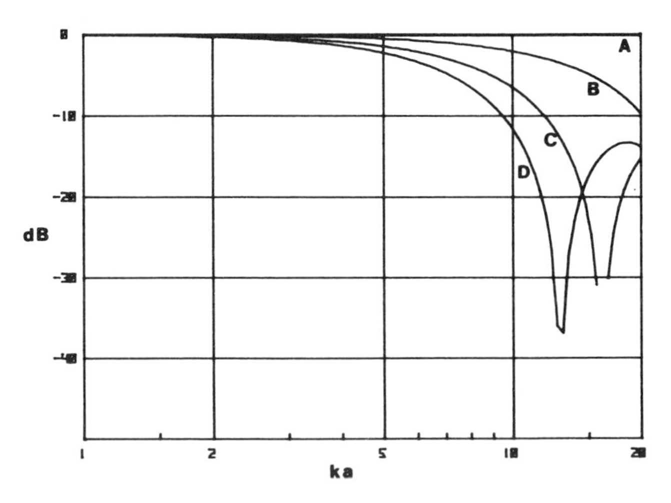

Fig. 3. On-axis response curves for different dome heights $D(0)$. A—0; B—$a/4$; C—$a/2$; D—a.

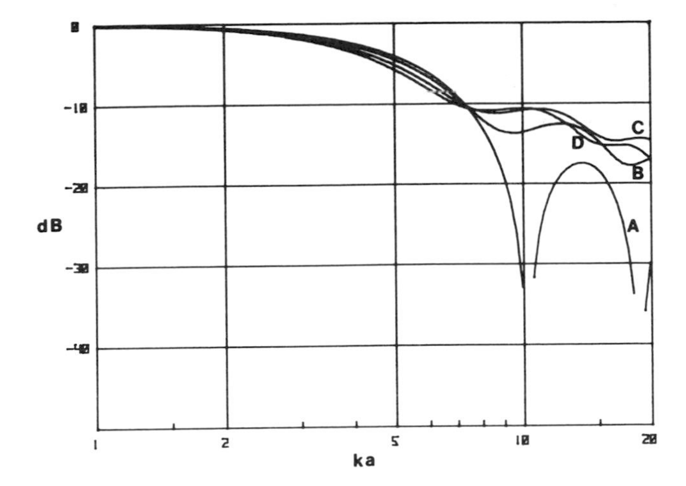

Fig. 4. Response curves for $\theta = 22\frac{1}{2}°$ and different dome heights $D(0)$. A—0; B—$a/4$; C—$a/2$; D—a.

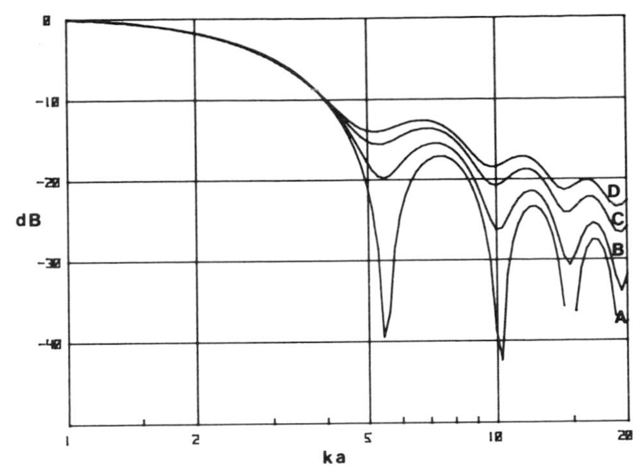

Fig. 5. Response curves for $\theta = 45°$ and different dome heights $D(0)$. A—0; B—$a/4$; C—$a/2$; D—a.

= 20, with the disk being worse only above $ka = 7$. Thus the directional term shows little variation for $ka \leq 4$, and the largest deviation lies well above the operating range of most drivers.

As one moves further off axis, the response curves become more and more similar to each other. In the limit of $\theta = 90°$ the dome contour becomes irrelevant since it shows up only in the $\exp(j\,k\,D(\rho)\cos\theta)$ term of the integrand, and $\cos(90°) = 0$. Thus all the $\theta = 90°$ curves would be identical. Fig. 5 shows that for $\theta = 45°$ the response dips are already starting to occur at identical frequencies, the major difference being that the smaller the dome radius of curvature, the smoother the curve and the higher the level above $ka = 4$. For $ka \leq 4$ the curves are virtually indistinguishable. Thus the dome contour makes essentially no difference in the response over the operating range of a typical driver for $\theta = 45°$, and the differences will decrease as the observation angle increases.

CONCLUSIONS

The assumption that a dome has markedly better dispersion than a flat disk is not valid. Most drivers are used in the range $ka < 4$, and within this range the greatest difference is less than 2 dB. In addition, an inverted dome will have directional characteristics identical with the noninverted dome studied here.

A dome does cause a zero in the on-axis response. This null occurs at $ka \simeq 13$ for a hemisphere, rather than at $ka = \pi$ as would be predicted by the half-wavelength assumption. Thus on-axis cancellation occurs at too high a frequency to be of practical concern.

The mechanical properties of the dome have been ignored in order to isolate the effect of the shape. In this way it was learned that the shape has little practical effect on the radiation pattern, and that a flat circular disk is an accurate approximation over the normal operating range of the driver. Drivers of this type should therefore be optimized on the basis of mechanical behavior as it is unlikely that this will cause any adverse effect on directional characteristics.

REFERENCES

[1] Y. Yuasa and S. Greenberg, "The Beryllium Dome Diaphragm—Its Use, Manufacture, and Importance in Loudspeaker Systems," Presented November 3, 1975, at the 52nd Convention of the Audio Engineering Society, New York, preprint 1087.

[2] L. E. Kinsler and A. R. Frey, *Fundamentals of Acoustics* (Wiley, New York, 1962), pp. 166-175.

[3] M. Abramowitz and I. A. Stegun, Eds., *Handbook of Mathematical Functions* (National Bureau of Standards, Appl. Math. Ser. 55, Washington, DC, 1968), p. 358 ff.

[4] *Hewlett-Packard Calculator 9820A Math Pac*, vol. 1 (Loveland, CO), pp. 99-103.

Mr. Kates's biography appeared in the May 1976, issue.

Analysis of Decoupled-Cone Loudspeakers

JAMES M. KATES

Teledyne Acoustic Research, Norwood, MA. 02062

The inclusion of a compliance ring in a cone can greatly affect the behavior of a loudspeaker. This behavior is studied through an analogous circuit model, and transfer functions are developed for the system behavior. Comparison with actual units shows that the analysis is accurate in predicting system response.

INTRODUCTION: A decoupled-cone loudspeaker is one in which the cone has been divided into two pieces and a compliant junction inserted between them. A common example is the use of a compliance ring molded into the cone, the ring providing a small amount of compliance and dividing the cone into an inner and an outer band. Other techniques include corrugations in the voice-coil former between the coil winding and the former-to-cone glue joint, which decouple the voice coil from the cone, and the use of a compliant former-to-cone glue joint that achieves the same purpose.

There are two reasons for using a decoupled cone. The first is to try to control the cone behavior in the frequency region where the cone goes into breakup. The decoupling action can provide a mechanical filter to roll off the response just before breakup, thus reducing response irregularities due to the modes in the cone. The second reason is to get more output in the upper region of the driver piston band. Here the decoupling action can reduce the moving mass at higher frequencies, resulting in an extended frequency range if the driver parameters are chosen properly.

A driver with a decoupled cone is a complicated mechanical system. An analysis of this system, with subsequent simplifications, can isolate the important parameters affecting the system. Knowledge of the effects of these parameters can then lead to more effective designs. The purpose of this paper is to present transfer functions that accurately describe the behavior of a decoupled-cone driver.

NOTATION

The following symbols are used in this paper.

- a_D effective driver radius
- a_V radius of inner cone section
- B_i coefficients of the polynomial $Q_D(s_N)$
- Bl driver Bl product, where B is the magnetic field strength and l the total length of wire in the field
- c speed of sound in air, 345 m/s
- C_{MB} mechanical compliance of enclosure volume
- C_{MS} mechanical compliance of driver suspension
- C_{MV} mechanical compliance of compliance ring
- E_g electromotive force
- F mechanical drive force
- f_C resonance frequency of outer-cone mass with ring compliance (and box compliance, where present)
- f_S resonance frequency of driver in free space
- G_C normalized transfer function for outer-cone acceleration or corresponding sound-pressure output versus input voltage
- G_T normalized transfer function for net driver sound-pressure output versus input voltage
- G_V normalized transfer function for inner-cone acceleration or corresponding sound-pressure output versus input voltage
- h ratio of outer-cone/compliance-ring to driver resonance frequencies, $\omega_C/\omega_S = f_C/f_S$
- M_{MC} mass of outer cone (includes radiation load)
- M_{MS} total moving mass, $M_{MC} + M_{MV}$
- M_{MV} mass of voice coil plus inner cone (includes radiation load)
- p_C sound pressure due to outer-cone motion
- p_T sound pressure due to sum of cone and voice-coil motions
- p_V sound pressure due to voice-coil and inner-cone motion
- Q_C Q of outer-cone/compliance-ring resonance due to mechanical damping in compliance ring
- Q_E Q of outer-cone/compliance-ring resonance due to electromagnetic damping
- Q_E' weighted Q, $Q_E' = Q_E(1 + \delta)$
- Q_S total driver Q at driver resonance frequency f_S
- Q_T total Q of simplified circuit

Manuscript received July 27, 1976; revised October 12, 1976.

Q_V Q of outer-cone/compliance-ring resonance due to mechanical damping in the surround
Q_D denominator of transfer functions G_i
R_E voice-coil electrical resistance
R_{ME} equivalent mechanical resistance of voice-coil/magnet system, $(Bl)^2/R_E$
R_{MS} mechanical resistance of spider
R_{MT} total mechanical resistance, $R_{MS} + R_{ME} + R_{MC}$
R_{MC} mechanical resistance of cone surround
R_{MV} mechanical resistance of compliance ring
S_C radiating area of outer cone
S_D total driver radiating area
S_V radiating area of voice-coil dust cap plus inner cone
s_N complex frequency normalized to ω_S
s_{N2} complex frequency normalized to ω_C
u_C velocity of outer cone
u_V velocity of voice coil and inner cone
Z_E electrical input impedance of driver
Z_M mechanical impedance of driver
α compliance ratio, C_{MS}/C_{MB}
β compliance ratio, C_{MS}/C_{MV}
γ mass ratio, M_{MV}/M_{MS}
δ mass ratio, M_{MV}/M_{MC}
η_{LF} nominal efficiency in driver passband
η_{HF} limiting efficiency at high frequencies
μ_{LF} nominal sound-pressure sensitivity in driver passband
μ_{HF} limiting sound-pressure sensitivity at high frequencies
ρ_0 density of air, 1.18 kg/m^3
ω_C angular resonance frequency of outer cone–compliance ring–box compliance assembly, $2\pi f_C$
ω_S angular resonance frequency of driver in free space, $2\pi f_S$.

EQUIVALENT CIRCUIT

The idea of a decoupled cone is not new. Olson built and analyzed such a system in 1934 [1], and texts by both Olson [2] and Beranek [3] include mechanical analogous circuits. The circuit used here is based on this previous work, with modifications to include the effect of a sealed enclosure.

Fig. 1 presents the impedance-type mechanical analogous circuit for a decoupled-cone loudspeaker in a sealed enclosure. The total system mass M_{MS} is usually shown as one element. In this circuit it is divided into two parts, the voice-coil/inner-cone mass M_{MV} and the outer-cone mass M_{MC}, with the joint between them having both compliance and damping resistance, these being C_{MV} and R_{MV}, respectively. The mechanical resistance term R_{MT} is also divided to allow allocation of damping resistance to the surround as R_{MC}, to the spider as R_{MS}, and to the voice-coil winding as R_{ME}. The surround is assumed to have a very large compliance, being used mainly to center the cone, and the outer cone is assumed to have much more area than the inner cone section. Therefore, the suspension compliance C_{MS} exists primarily in the spider, and the box compliance C_{MB} (which may include any contribution from the surround) acts primarily on the outer cone.

The major benefits of a decoupled cone are realized only if the decoupling action takes place in the nominal piston band of the driver, at frequencies low enough to avoid cone breakup. Thus for purposes of the mechanical circuit, the radiation impedance is assumed to be a pure mass load on the driver, and the voice-coil inductance is ignored as having only a secondary effect in the frequency range of interest.

The behavior of the analogous circuit at the extremes of the frequency range is simple. At very low frequencies the ring compliance C_{MV} appears as an open circuit, so $u_V = u_C$. The inner and outer masses M_{MV} and M_{MC} can then be combined, as can the resistances $R_{ME} + R_{MS} + R_{MC}$. Similarly, the total compliance is the spider compliance C_{MS} in series with the enclosure compliance C_{MB}. The result is a simple driver, with no decoupling, in a closed box. At very high frequencies the outer mass M_{MC} becomes an open circuit. As a result the total mass is now the inner mass M_{MV}, the total damping resistance is $R_{ME} + R_{MS} + R_{MV}$, and the total compliance is the spider compliance C_{MS} in series with the ring compliance C_{MV}. Most importantly, the outer-cone velocity u_C goes to zero, so the radiation is from the dust cap and inner cone alone.

SENSITIVITY AND EFFICIENCY

The low-frequency and high-frequency behavior of the analogous circuit can be used to establish limiting values for the system output. If the decoupling action is blocked ($C_{MV} = 0$), then the high-frequency behavior is that of a conventional driver in its piston band, and this can be used to establish reference levels for the output at frequencies below those where the decoupling action becomes important. At frequencies above the region of decoupling behavior, the limiting value of the voice-coil velocity can be used to establish high-frequency reference levels.

The desired reference levels involve the system velocities and the relationship between velocity and far-field pressure. The on-axis pressure for radiation into half-space by a piston of area S moving with axial velocity u is [4]

$$p = \frac{j\rho_0 f}{r} uS. \tag{1}$$

This gives the on-axis pressure radiated by the inner cone and dust cap as

$$p_V = \frac{j\rho_0 f}{r} u_V S_V \tag{2}$$

and the on-axis pressure radiated by the outer cone as

$$p_C = \frac{j\rho_0 f}{r} u_C S_C. \tag{3}$$

The net on-axis pressure radiated from both surfaces is then

$$p_T = p_C + p_V = \frac{j\rho_0 f}{r}(u_V S_V + u_C S_C). \tag{4}$$

With no decoupling the ring compliance $C_{MV} = 0$, and the limiting velocity value of u_C can be used to compute the low-frequency sound-pressure sensitivity μ_{LF}, which is defined as the ratio of the on-axis pressure at 1 meter to the input voltage. This is then given by

$$\mu_{LF} = \frac{\rho_0 Bl S_D}{2\pi R_E M_{MS}} \tag{5}$$

for radiation into half-space. When decoupling is allowed to occur, the limiting value of u_V can be used to compute the high-frequency sound-pressure sensitivity

$$\mu_{HF} = \frac{\rho_0 Bl S_V}{2\pi R_E M_{MV}}. \tag{6}$$

The ratio of acoustic power output to nominal electrical power input can be computed [5], [6] for the same limiting cases to yield the low-frequency and high-frequency reference efficiencies

$$\eta_{LF} = \frac{\rho_0}{2\pi c} \frac{(Bl)^2 S_D^2}{R_E M_{MS}^2} \tag{7}$$

and

$$\eta_{HF} = \frac{\rho_0}{2\pi c} \frac{(Bl)^2 S_V^2}{R_E M_{MV}^2}. \tag{8}$$

Since the pressure output is proportional to the radiating area times acceleration, the limiting sound-pressure sensitivities can also be used to obtain limiting acceleration sensitivities (acceleration per volt input). Thus μ_{LF} corresponds to an acceleration sensitivity of $2\pi\mu_{LF} / \rho_0 S_D$ and μ_{HF} to an acceleration sensitivity of $2\pi\mu_{HF} / \rho_0 S_V$.

In the case of a totally acoustically transparent dust cap and compliant former or former-to-cone glue joint, $S_V = 0$. This gives $\mu_{HF} = 0 = \eta_{HF}$, and radiation is from the cone alone. If a single wide-range unit is desired with uniform output, a necessary condition is that $\mu_{LF} = \mu_{HF}$. This means that $S_D M_{MV} = S_V M_{MS}$, which also gives $\eta_{LF} = \eta_{HF}$.

ANALYSIS

The analogous circuit for the decoupled-cone system is topologically identical with that for a passive-radiator loudspeaker system. This permits the use of the extensive analyses of passive-radiator systems [7]–[9]. It should be noted, however, that in the decoupled-cone system the parameters take on much different values than in the passive-radiator system, and that the direction of the velocity u_C is opposite to that used for the passive-radiator analysis. The analysis presented here for the decoupled-cone system is based on the general approach and systematic notation of Benson [7], [10].

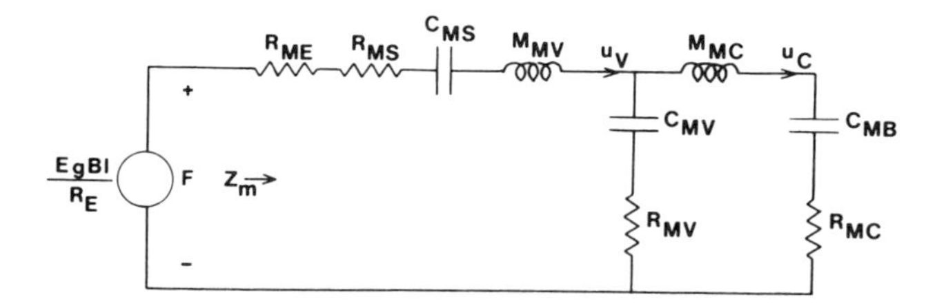

Fig. 1. Mechanical analogous circuit (impedance type) for decoupled-cone driver in a sealed enclosure.

First, the system parameters can be defined in terms of the equivalent circuit elements:

$$h = \omega_C / \omega_S \tag{9}$$

$$\alpha = C_{MS} / C_{MB} \tag{10}$$

$$\beta = C_{MS} / C_{MV} \tag{11}$$

$$\omega_C = \left[M_{MC} \left(\frac{C_{MV} C_{MB}}{C_{MV} + C_{MB}} \right) \right]^{-\frac{1}{2}} \tag{12}$$

$$\omega_S = (M_{MS} C_{MS})^{-\frac{1}{2}} \tag{13}$$

$$Q_C = M_{MC} \omega_C / R_{MC} \tag{14}$$

$$Q_S = M_{MS} \omega_S / R_{MT} \tag{15}$$

$$Q_V = (C_{MV} \omega_C R_{MV})^{-1}. \tag{16}$$

The circuit elements can now be expressed in terms of the system parameters:

$$C_{MS} = 1/M_{MS}\omega_S^2 \tag{17}$$

$$C_{MB} = C_{MS} / \alpha \tag{18}$$

$$C_{MV} = C_{MS} / \beta \tag{19}$$

$$M_{MV} = \frac{1}{C_{MS}\omega_S^2} \left(\frac{h^2 - \alpha - \beta}{h^2} \right) \tag{20}$$

$$M_{MC} = \frac{1}{C_{MS}\omega_S^2} \frac{\alpha + \beta}{h^2} \tag{21}$$

$$R_{MT} = \frac{1}{C_{MS} \omega_S Q_S} \tag{22}$$

$$R_{MV} = \frac{\beta}{h} \frac{1}{C_{MS} \omega_S Q_V} \tag{23}$$

$$R_{MC} = \frac{\alpha + \beta}{h} \frac{1}{C_{MS} \omega_S Q_C}. \tag{24}$$

There are three transfer functions of interest. $G_C(s_N)$ represents the outer-cone acceleration sensitivity normalized to the low-frequency limiting value of $2\pi\mu_{LF}/\rho_0 S_D$, where s_N is the complex frequency normalized to ω_S giving $s_N = s/\omega_S$. Thus for the ring compliance $C_{MV} = 0$, $\lim_{s_N\to\infty} G_C(s_N) = 1$. $G_V(s_N)$ represents the voice-coil/inner-cone acceleration sensitivity normalized to the same value. This gives

$$\lim_{s_N\to\infty} G_V(s_N) = \frac{S_D \mu_{HF}}{S_V \mu_{LF}} = \frac{h^2}{h^2 - \alpha - \beta}.$$

In addition $G_T(s_N)$ represents the normalized total sound-pressure output, which makes it a weighted sum (by area) of the acceleration transfer functions.

The denominator of the transfer functions is defined as $Q_D(s_N)$. $Q_D(s_N)$ is a polynomial in s_N, and it can be represented as

$$Q_D(s_N) = \sum_{k=0}^{4} B_k s_N^k \tag{25a}$$

where the coefficients are given by

$$B_4 = \frac{h^2 - \alpha - \beta}{h^2} \tag{25b}$$

$$B_3 = \frac{h^2-\alpha-\beta}{h}\left[\frac{1}{Q_C} + \frac{h}{h^2-\alpha-\beta}\frac{1}{Q_S} + \frac{\beta}{\alpha+\beta}\frac{1}{Q_V} + \frac{\beta}{h^2-\alpha-\beta}\frac{1}{Q_V}\right] \quad (25c)$$

$$B_2 = \left[1 + \beta + (h^2-\alpha-\beta) + \frac{h}{Q_C Q_S} + \frac{\beta}{\alpha+\beta}\frac{h}{Q_V Q_S} + \frac{\beta}{Q_V Q_C}\right] \quad (25d)$$

$$B_1 = h\left[\frac{h}{Q_S} + \frac{1}{Q_C} + \frac{\beta}{\alpha+\beta}\frac{1}{Q_V} + \frac{\alpha\beta}{\alpha+\beta}\frac{1}{Q_V} + \frac{\beta}{Q_C}\right] \quad (25e)$$

$$B_0 = h^2\left[\frac{\alpha+\beta+\alpha\beta}{\alpha+\beta}\right]. \quad (25f)$$

The transfer functions are then given by

$$G_V(s_N) = \frac{1}{Q_D(s_N)}\left[s_N^4 + h\left(\frac{1}{Q_C} + \frac{\beta}{\alpha+\beta}\frac{1}{Q_V}\right)s_N^3 + h^2 s_N^2\right] \quad (26)$$

$$G_C(s_N) = \frac{1}{Q_D(s_N)}\left[h\left(\frac{\beta}{\alpha+\beta}\frac{1}{Q_V}\right)s_N^3 + h^2 s_N^2\right] \quad (27)$$

$$G_T(s_N) = \frac{S_C}{S_D}G_C(s_N) + \frac{S_V}{S_D}G_V(s_N). \quad (28)$$

The electrical input impedance is given by

$$Z_E = R_E + \frac{(Bl)^2}{\dfrac{s_N\,\omega_S\,M_{MS}}{G_V(s_N)} - \dfrac{(Bl)^2}{R_E}}. \quad (29)$$

SIMPLIFIED ANALYSIS

It is useful to look at the system behavior in the frequency region around f_C alone. In order to simplify the circuit to show this behavior only, the following assumptions are made:

1) $h >> 1$
2) $\beta >> \alpha$
3) $Q_C >> 1$.

These assumptions safely separate the loudspeaker behavior into low-frequency and high-frequency ranges that can be treated separately. In terms of the analogous circuit, these assumptions translate into 1) the suspension impedance $1/sC_{MS} = 0$ as a result of the high-frequency range, 2) the box impedance $1/sC_{MB} = 0$ since the compliance ring is much stiffer than the air trapped in the box, and 3) $R_{MC} << \omega M_{MC}$ as a result of the high-frequency range. The assumption that f_C falls within the nominal passband of the driver is retained, so the voice-coil inductance is ignored and the radiation impedance is assumed to be an equivalent mass load. The simplified analogous circuit is given in Fig. 2.

The system parameters for the simplified circuit can be defined in terms of the following circuit elements:

$$\omega_C^2 = \frac{1}{M_{MC}C_{MV}} \quad (30)$$

$$Q_V = M_{MC}\omega_C/R_{MV} \quad (31)$$

$$Q_E = M_{MC}\omega_C/R_{MT} \quad (32)$$

$$\delta = M_{MV}/M_{MC} \quad (33)$$

$$\gamma = M_{MV}/M_{MS} = \delta/(1+\delta) \quad (34)$$

$$Q_E' = Q_E(1+\delta). \quad (35)$$

The transfer functions can now be simplified and expressed in terms of $s_{N2} = s/\omega_C = s_N \dfrac{\omega_S}{\omega_C}$ to yield:

$$Q_D(s_{N2}) = \gamma s_{N2}^3 + \left(\frac{1}{Q_V} + \frac{1}{Q_E'}\right)s_{N2}^2 + \left(1 + \frac{1}{Q_V Q_E'}\right)s_{N2} + \frac{1}{Q_E'} \quad (36)$$

with

$$G_V(s_{N2}) = \frac{1}{Q_D(s_{N2})}\left[s_{N2}^3 + \frac{1}{Q_V}s_{N2}^2 + s_{N2}\right] \quad (37)$$

$$G_C(s_{N2}) = \frac{1}{Q_D(s_{N2})}\left[\frac{1}{Q_V}s_{N2}^2 + s_{N2}\right] \quad (38)$$

$$G_T(s_{N2}) = \frac{S_C}{S_D}G_C(s_{N2}) + \frac{S_V}{S_D}G_V(s_{N2}). \quad (39)$$

The electrical input impedance is given by

$$Z_E = R_E + \frac{(Bl)^2}{\dfrac{s_{N2}\,\omega_C\,M_{MS}}{G_V(s_{N2})} - \dfrac{(Bl)^2}{R_E}}. \quad (40)$$

These equations are related to those derived from the complete circuit of Fig. 1 by the following identities:

$$s_N = h s_{N2} \quad (41)$$

$$\gamma = \frac{h^2-\alpha-\beta}{h^2} \quad (42)$$

$$\alpha + \beta = h^2/(1+\delta) \quad (43)$$

$$Q_E' = hQ_S. \quad (44)$$

RESONANCE BEHAVIOR

$Q_D(s_{N2})$, the denominator of the simplified transfer functions, is a third-order polynomial in s_{N2} having one real root and one complex pair of roots. In Eq. (36) assume that $\gamma \simeq 1$, $Q_E' >> 1$, and $Q_V Q_E' >> 1$. Then the real root occurs at approximately $s_{N2} = -1/Q_E'$, while the complex roots yield a resonance frequency of

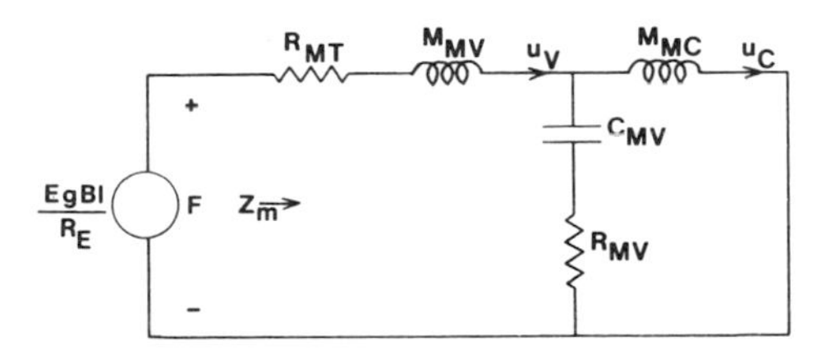

Fig. 2. Simplified analogous circuit (impedance type) for use in the frequency region near f_C.

$$\omega \simeq \omega_C/\sqrt{\gamma} = \left(\frac{M_{MS}}{M_{MC}\, M_{MV}\, C_{MV}}\right)^{\frac{1}{2}} \tag{45}$$

and a Q of

$$Q_T \simeq \sqrt{\gamma}\left(\frac{Q_V Q_E{}'}{Q_V + Q_E{}'}\right) < \sqrt{\gamma}\, \min\, (Q_V, Q_E{}'). \tag{46}$$

The normalized outer cone acceleration $G_C(s_{N2})$ has zeroes at $s_{N2} = 0$ and $s_{N2} = -Q_V$. These, combined with the poles of the denominator, yield a system that behaves like a simple resonance near $\omega = \omega_C/\sqrt{\gamma}$ and then has an asymptotic slope of -6 dB per octave above that frequency. The response maximum has an approximate value of

$$\max \simeq Q_T \sqrt{1 + \frac{1}{\gamma Q_V{}^2}}\,. \tag{47}$$

For $\gamma << 1$ this becomes $Q_E{}'/(Q_V + Q_E{}') \leq 1$, and for $\gamma \approx 1$ this is approximately Q_T.

The normalized voice-coil/inner-cone acceleration $G_V(s_{N2})$ has a zero at $s_{N2} = 0$, and a complex pair of zeroes giving a notch at $\omega = \omega_C$ with $Q = Q_V$. Because this zero at ω_C is close to the pole at $\omega = \omega_C/\sqrt{\gamma}$ in the denominator, the presence of each resonance will reduce the magnitude of the other. The zero will have the higher Q since $\sqrt{\gamma} \leq 1$, $Q_V Q_E{}'/(Q_V + Q_E{}') \leq Q_V$, and Q_T is approximately equal to the product of the two terms. For $\gamma << 1$, the two resonances will behave almost independently with the notch depth being $20 \log Q_V$ dB re 1 and the peak height $20 \log Q_T$ dB re $1/\gamma$, where $1/\gamma$ is the level of $G_V(s_{N2})$ as s_{N2} approaches infinity. As γ moves closer to 1, the dip and peak move closer to each other, which decreases the peak height and reduces the notch depth. For γ approaching 1, the notch depth can be approximated as

$$\min = 20 \log\, [Q_V \sqrt{(1-\gamma)^2 + 1/Q_V{}^2}]\ \text{dB re 1} \tag{48}$$

and the peak height as

$$\max = 20 \log\, [Q_T \sqrt{(1-\gamma)^2 + \gamma/Q_V{}^2}]\ \text{dB re level at}\ s_{N2} = \infty. \tag{49}$$

The net pressure output $G_T(s_{N2})$ is a weighted sum of $G_V(s_{N2})$ and $G_C(s_{N2})$. Since for most drivers the outer-cone area will be larger than the inner-cone plus dust-cap area, $G_T(s_{N2})$ behaves essentially like $G_C(s_{N2})$ in the region near $\omega = \omega_C/\sqrt{\gamma}$. At higher frequencies $G_T(s_{N2})$ behaves like $G_V(s_{N2})$ since the $G_C(s_{N2})$ term goes to zero.

DISCUSSION

In order to gain some insight into the behavior of a decoupled-cone driver, the simplified analysis equations (36)–(39) were programmed on a digital computer. Figs. 3–9 present the calculated behavior as various parameters are changed. The driver is assumed to have half its mass in the outer cone and half in the voice coil and inner cone, giving $\delta = 1$ and $\gamma = \frac{1}{2}$. Damping is assumed to yield $Q_V = 3$ and $Q_E = 3$. These three parameters—Q_V, Q_E, and δ—completely determine $G_C(s_{N2})$ and $G_V(s_{N2})$; each parameter is varied in turn to determine its effects on the transfer functions.

Fig. 3 presents curves for $G_C(s_{N2})$ as Q_V is varied. As the Q of the compliance ring is raised, the height of the resonance increases. Thus the damping in the compliance ring is critical in controlling the cone behavior at resonance. The height of the resonance varies from 1.5 dB for $Q_V = 1$ to 12 dB for $Q_V = 10$, while Eq. (47), based on the simplified resonance behavior approximation, predicts a range of 0.4 dB to 8.6 dB for the same values. So while Eq. (47) does not predict the exact level, it does accurately predict the trend of the curves, and the level estimate is close enough to be useful. All the curves approach the same asymptote of -6 dB per octave, although specifics of the cone behavior will dominate in this range. Compliance-ring damping is therefore very important to the system behavior.

Fig. 4 presents curves for $G_V(s_{N2})$ as Q_V is varied. Once again there is a very strong dependence on Q_V in determining the resonance Q. The notch depth ranges from 2 to 14 dB over the range of Q_V considered, and the peak height from -5.2 to $+6$ dB. Eq. (48) predicts a notch range of 1 to 14 dB, which agrees quite closely with the observed values, and Eq. (49)

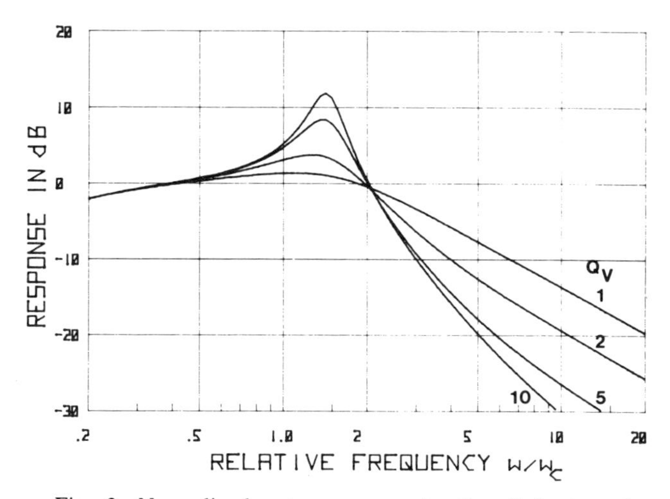

Fig. 3. Normalized outer cone acceleration $G_C(s_{N2})$ as the compliance-ring damping Q_V is varied from 1 to 10; electrical damping Q_E is fixed at 3 and the mass ratio δ at 1. The curves in Figs. 3–9 are based on the simplified analysis.

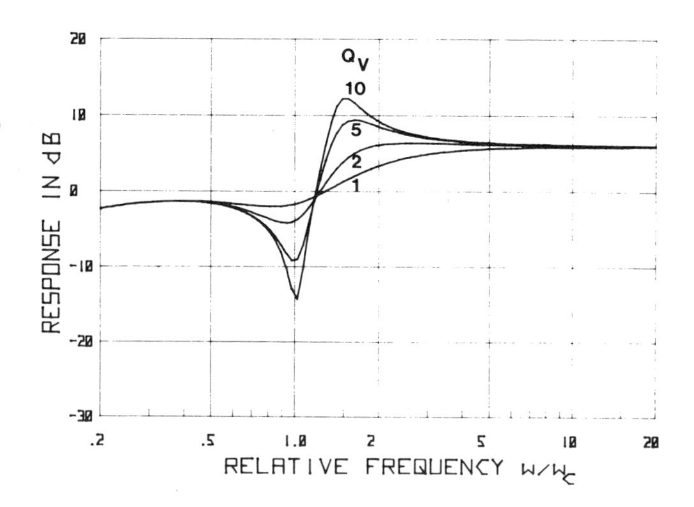

Fig. 4. Normalized voice-coil/inner-cone acceleration $G_V(s_{N2})$ as Q_V is varied from 1 to 10; $Q_E = 3$ and $\delta = 1$.

predicts peak levels of −5.6 to +2.5 dB, so here the disagreement is for large values of Q_V only. Thus these equations are sufficiently accurate to be useful approximations. The behavior of the voice-coil acceleration is thus a dip followed by a rise, with both levels strongly dependent on the compliance-ring damping.

Fig. 5 presents curves for $G_C(s_{N2})$ as Q_E is varied. It is immediately apparent that the electrical damping has a much weaker effect than Q_V. For large values of Q_E, and hence Q_E', the approximation becomes more precise, so for Q_E = 10 the measured value of 7 dB is close to the 6.2 dB predicted by Eq. (47), but the disagreement grows as Q_E decreases. Because the numerator of $G_C(s_{N2})$ does not depend on Q_E, all the curves approach the same asymptote. Thus varying Q_E affects the resonance behavior only slightly, and has no effect on the asymptotic behavior.

The curves for $G_V(s_{N2})$ as Q_E is varied are shown in Fig. 6. Here too Q_E has a much smaller effect than Q_V in controlling system behavior. The depth of the resonance notch at $s_{N2} = j$ is almost independent of Q_E, and the value of 5.1 dB predicted by Eq. (48) for Q_E = 10 agrees closely with the measured value of 5.5 dB. Because $\delta = 1$, Eq. (49) predicts a response value of 0.2 dB at $s_{N2} = j\sqrt{2}$ for $Q_E = 10$, which is essentially as calculated, and the resonance peak of 2.5 dB occurs at a slightly higher frequency. The larger the value of Q_E', the more accurate the approximations, and the smaller the effect of perturbations in Q_E. But even over a large range, Q_E has much less effect than Q_V.

In Fig. 7 Q_V and Q_E are kept constant while the mass ratio δ is varied, and the curves for $G_C(s_{N2})$ show three strong areas of dependence on δ. The resonance frequency is $s_{N2} = j/\sqrt{\gamma}$, so as δ goes from 5 to 0.2, the resonance goes from 1.10 to 2.45 times ω_C. The resonance peak height has a $\sqrt{\gamma}$ dependence in Q_T, as well as a dependence on δ in Q_E', so it goes from 9 dB to −0.5 dB over the same range of δ when measured at $\omega = \omega_C/\sqrt{\gamma}$. The third dependence is the coefficient of the asymptotic decay, $1/\gamma Q_V$, so the level increases as δ decreases, even though the slope stays the same. Thus reducing δ, which means reducing the ratio of the voice-coil mass to the outer-cone mass, extends the frequency response of the cone acceleration and reduces the Q of the resonance.

Fig. 8 presents curves for $G_V(s_{N2})$ as δ is varied. Again the strong dependence on δ is noted. Decreasing δ increases the depth of the notch at $\omega = \omega_C$, but decreases the Q of the resonance at $\omega = \omega_C/\sqrt{\gamma}$. Because the limiting value of the voice-coil acceleration goes as $1/\gamma$, reducing δ increases the acceleration and thus the sound output of the dust cap and

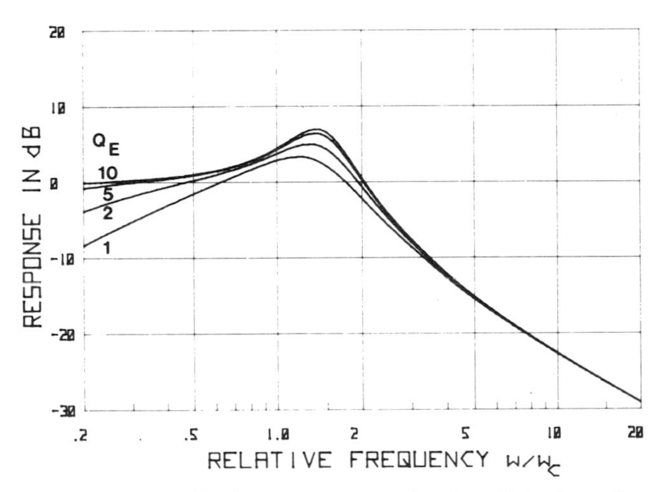

Fig. 5. Normalized outer-cone acceleration $G_C(s_{N2})$ as the electrical damping Q_E is varied from 1 to 10; Q_V = 3 and δ = 1.

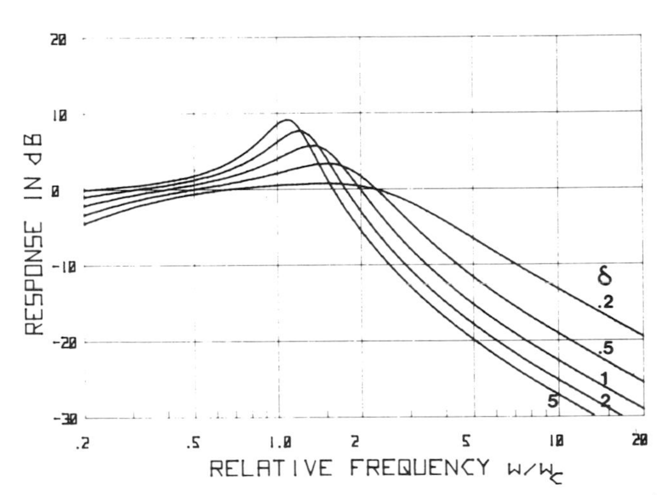

Fig. 7. Normalized outer-cone acceleration $G_C(s_{N2})$ as the mass ratio δ is varied from 0.2 to 5.0; Q_E = 3 and Q_V = 3.

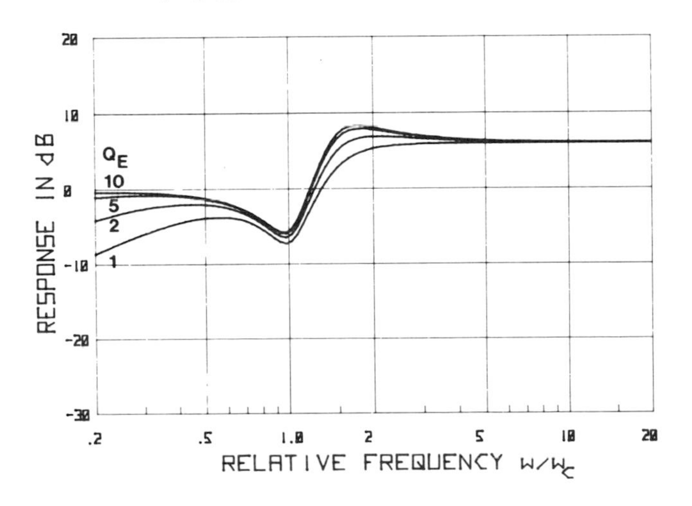

Fig. 6. Normalized voice-coil acceleration $G_V(s_{N2})$ as Q_E is varied from 1 to 10; Q_V = 3 and δ = 1.

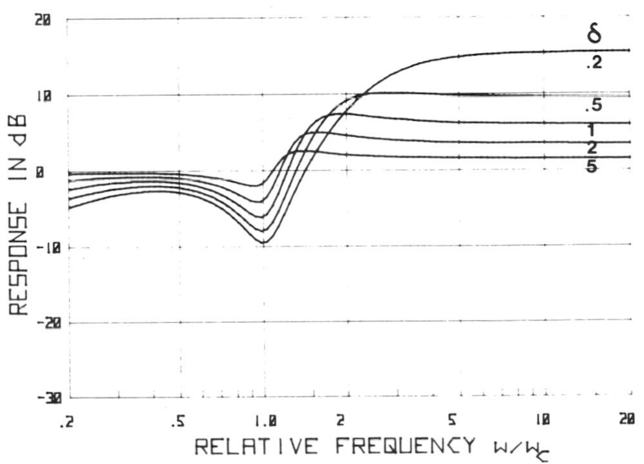

Fig. 8. Normalized voice-coil acceleration $G_V(s_{N2})$ as δ is varied from 0.2 to 5.0; Q_E = 3 and Q_V = 3.

inner cone at high frequencies. Thus δ affects both the resonance Q and the limiting value of $G_V(s_{N2})$, making the mass distribution of the system a very important factor.

The effect of δ on $G_T(s_{N2})$ is shown in Fig. 9. These curves correspond to the total acoustic output of a decoupled-cone driver as the compliance ring is moved from the apex to the rim of the cone. The damping factors Q_V and Q_E are held at 3, and the mass is assigned half to the voice coil and half to the cone. Since the inner- and outer-cone masses are assumed to be proportional to the surface area, moving the compliance ring toward the rim increases δ as well as reducing the outer-cone radiating area S_C and increasing the dust-cap plus inner-cone radiating area S_V. Both the redistribution of mass and the redistribution of the radiating area affect $G_T(s_{N2})$. For the compliance ring radius $a_V = 0$, only the outer cone radiates sound, and $G_T(s_{N2}) = G_C(s_{N2})$ with $\delta = 1$. As a_V increases, the inner cone contributes more and more to $G_T(s_{N2})$, and the final level moves closer to 0 dB. Since δ is also increasing, the resonance frequency moves closer to ω_C and the Q decreases. In the limit of $a_V = a_D$, there is no decoupling action and the result is a straight line because the driver is assumed to be operating in its piston band. Thus in terms of this lumped-parameter analysis, the location of the compliance ring strongly affects the total acoustic output of a unit.

Consideration of Fig. 9 also gives some physical insight into the decoupled-cone behavior. The voice-coil acceleration has its notch at $\omega = \omega_C$, and above this frequency its motion is 180° out of phase with the outer cone. As a result, the net output falls below the cone output above $\omega = \omega_C$, and the larger the inner-cone area, the greater the disparity between the outer-cone output and the net output in the region near $\omega = \omega_C/\sqrt{\gamma}$. At frequencies below $\omega = \omega_C$ the inner and outer cones behave as a single unit, which means that for h large enough the low-frequency design can be accomplished ignoring the decoupling action. Thus normal design procedures can be used for the low-frequency response, and the results of the above approximate analysis can be used for the decoupling-behavior design for a complete unit.

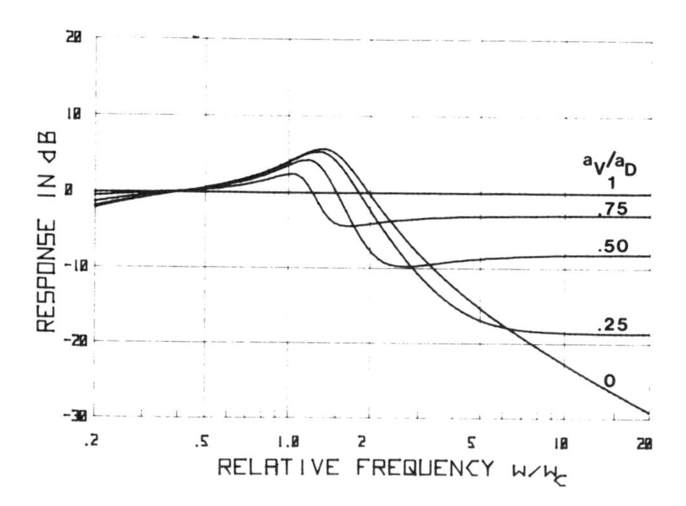

Fig. 9. Normalized sound-pressure output $G_T(s_{N2})$ as the compliance-ring radius to driver radius ratio a_V/a_D is varied from 0 to 1; $Q_E = 3$ and $Q_V = 3$.

EXAMPLE

Several woofers with decoupled cones were built in order to check the accuracy of the analysis. The response of one of one of these units is shown in Fig. 10, where the net acoustic output measured on-axis at 1 meter in an anechoic chamber is shown for an rms input of 2.83 V, along with the electrical input impedance. This driver has a compliant coupling between the cone and voice coil, but is otherwise a normal unit. Parameter values can be estimated from physical measurements of the driver and from the curves in Fig. 10; these values can then be used in the transfer functions and the results compared with the measured curves.

Physical measurements on this unit give a voice-coil radius $a_V = 22$ mm and an estimated outer-cone effective radius of $a_D = 80$ mm. Electrical measurements give $R_E = 6.0\ \Omega$ and $Bl = 7.0$ W/m. The voice-coil mass $M_{MV} = 9.4$ g, and the cone mass without any air load is $M_{MD} = 7.6$ g. Approximating the air load on two sides of the diaphragm in a cabinet yields $M_{MD} = 10.6$ g for a total moving mass of $M_{MS} = 20.0$ g. The total mechanical resistance $R_{MT} = R_{MS} + (Bl)^2/R_E$ is estimated to be 10 MKS mechanical ohms. From this the system Q is calculated to be $Q_S = M_{MS}\omega_S/R_{MT} = 0.534$. Further measurements yield a free-air resonance frequency of $f_S = 42.5$ Hz, and the enclosure volume used for the tests gives a value of $\alpha = 2.82$.

The decoupled-cone parameters can be estimated now that all the standard driver parameters have been calculated. The system mass distribution yields $\delta = M_{MV}/M_{MC} = 0.887$, giving $\gamma = \delta / (1 + \delta) = 0.470$. Fig. 10 shows an impedance peak at 620 Hz, and from Eq. (45) this occurs at $f = f_C / \sqrt{\gamma}$. This gives $f_C = 425$ Hz for a value of $h = f_C / f_S = 10$. Eq. (43) then yields $\beta = h^2/(1 + \delta) - \alpha = 50.2$. Combining Eq. (44) with Eq. (35) gives $Q_E = hQ_S / (1 + \delta) = 2.83$.

The final damping factors have to be estimated in a looser fashion. Surround damping is assumed not to be a serious effect, so $Q_C = 50$ is used. Eq. (46) can be used to estimate Q_V, since the peak on the graph is about 4.5 dB. Actually, it is easier to guess a value of Q_V and plug it into the maximum-value equation (47), iterating until a reasonable maximum value is reached. Doing this yields $Q_V = 4$, which gives $Q_T = \sqrt{\gamma}[Q_V Q_E'/(Q_V + Q_E')] = 1.57$ since $Q_E' = hQ_S = 5.34$. The peak level is then $Q_T \sqrt{1 + 1/\gamma Q_V^2} = 4.4$ dB.

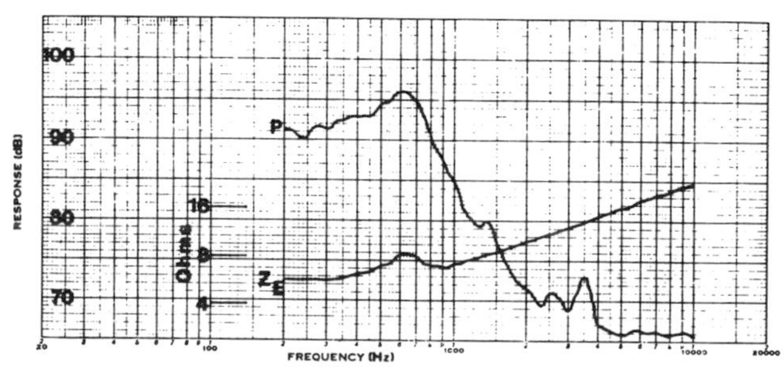

Fig. 10. Measured sound-pressure output p and electrical input impedance Z_E for 8-inch (0.2 m) driver with decoupled cone as described in text.

The values of $Q_C, Q_S, Q_V, \alpha, \beta, h$ are then used to compute $G_V(s_N)$ from Eq. (26) and $G_C(s_N)$ from Eq. (27). Including a_V and a_D allows the computation of $G_T(s_N)$ from Eq. (28) with all three transfer functions including the effects of the sealed enclosure. Curves for the three transfer functions are presented in Fig. 11, and the curve for $G_T(s_N)$ agrees quite closely with the measured net acoustic output. This reinforces the assumption that the decoupling action occurs in the nominal driver piston band, since the only disagreement is in the asymptotic behavior; the difference may be attributed in part to the voice-coil inductance, which is evident in the impedance curve of Fig. 10. Thus the transfer functions are accurate within the piston range, and the decoupling behavior can be considered to be superimposed on the normal high-frequency rolloff.

In this example, the low-frequency and high-frequency ranges can be separated, and the simplified analysis equations can be used. These require the values of δ, Q_V, and Q_E to compute $G_V(s_{N2})$ and $G_C(s_{N2})$, with a_V and a_D needed to compute $G_T(s_{N2})$. Note that the values of Bl, R_E, ω_C, and M_{MS} are needed to compute Z_E via Eq. (40). The results of using Eqs. (37) through (40) are presented in Fig. 12. These curves are identical with those of Fig. 11 above f_C, but begin to deviate below f_C because the enclosure effects are not included. The impedance curve ignores the voice-coil inductance, but predicts the 2.5-dB rise at resonance that occurs in Fig. 10 at 620 Hz. Thus when the necessary assumptions are met, the simplified analysis gives an accurate picture of the decoupling behavior.

CONCLUSIONS

A decoupled-cone loudspeaker is a resonant system. The interaction of the outer cone and the compliance ring causes a notch in the voice-coil acceleration, and the interaction of the two mass sections and the compliance ring causes resonance peaks in both the voice-coil and the outer-cone accelerations. This behavior is inherent in a decoupled-cone driver.

By choosing the ring compliance, damping, and position, the designer gains control over the system behavior. The total mass and its allocation plus the ring compliance determine the resonance peak frequency, and the damping in the compliance ring is critical in determining the height of the resonance peak. Increasing the damping reduces the peak level, but increases the cone output above resonance. The ring position determines the relative contributions of the inner and outer cones to the net acoustical output, which becomes especially important if extended high-frequency response is desired.

If a low resonance frequency f_C is desired, Eqs. (25) through (29) must be used to predict the total system response, including effects from the sealed enclosure. More typically f_C will be high enough to permit the use of the simplified analysis yielding Eqs. (36) through (40) and the subsequent formulas for the resonance behavior. For this case the low-frequency and high-frequency ranges can be designed separately, simplifying the procedure involved.

ACKNOWLEDGMENT

The author wishes to thank G. W. Benedetti for initiating this study and carrying out important preliminary experimental work, and Moses Gabbay for his careful and precise construction and measurement of the units used for this paper.

REFERENCES

[1] H. F. Olson, "A New Cone Loudspeaker for High Fidelity Sound Reproduction," *Proc. IRE*, vol. 22, pp. 33-46 (1934).

[2] H. F. Olson, *Acoustical Engineering* (Van Nostrand, New York, 1957), pp. 124-149.

[3] L. L. Beranek, *Acoustics* (McGraw-Hill, New York, 1954), pp. 183-207.

[4] L. E. Kinsler and A. R. Frey, *Fundamentals of Acoustics* (Wiley, New York, 1962), pp. 153-183.

[5] A. N. Thiele, "Loudspeakers in Vented Boxes, Parts I and II," *J. Audio Eng. Soc.*, vol. 19, pp. 382-392 (May 1971) and pp. 471-483 (June 1971).

[6] R. H. Small, "Direct-Radiator Loudspeaker System Analysis," *J. Audio Eng. Soc.*, vol. 20, pp. 383-395 (June 1972).

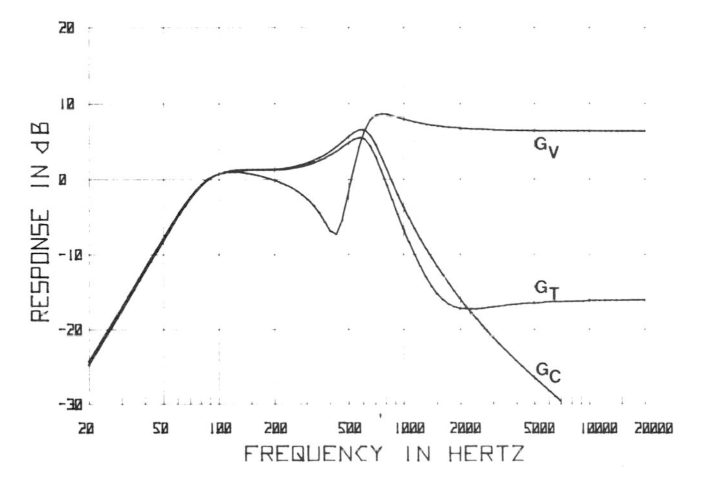

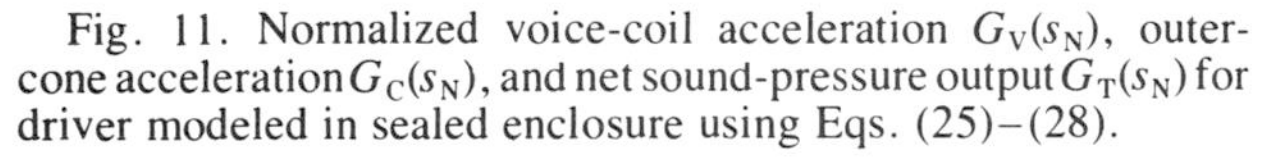
Fig. 11. Normalized voice-coil acceleration $G_V(s_N)$, outer-cone acceleration $G_C(s_N)$, and net sound-pressure output $G_T(s_N)$ for driver modeled in sealed enclosure using Eqs. (25)–(28).

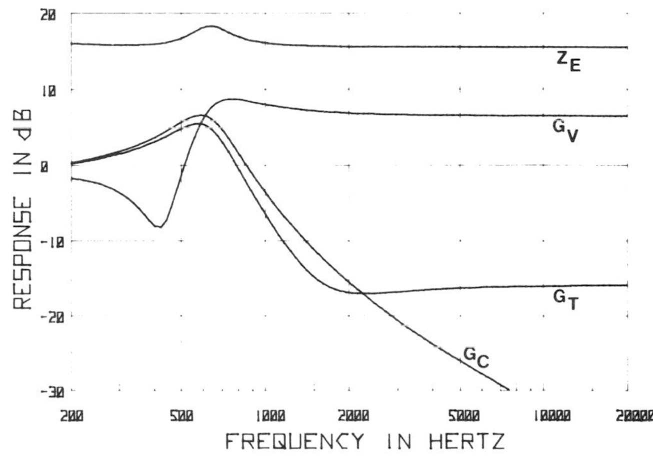

Fig. 12. Normalized voice-coil acceleration $G_V(s_{N2})$, outer-cone acceleration $G_C(s_{N2})$, net sound-pressure output $G_T(s_{N2})$, and electrical impedance Z_E for simplified circuit model of same driver using Eqs. (36)–(40). 0 dB corresponds to 1 ohm for Z_E.

[7] J. E. Benson, "Theory and Design of Loudspeaker Enclosures, Part I—Electro-Acoustical Relations and Generalized Analysis," *AWA Tech. Rev.*, vol. 14, p. 1 (Aug. 1968).

[8] Y. Nomura and Z. Kitamura, "An Analysis of Design Conditions for a Phase-Inverter Speaker System with a Drone Cone," *IEEE Trans. Audio Electroacoust.*, vol. AU-21, pp. 397-407 (Oct. 1973).

[9] R. H. Small, "Passive-Radiator Loudspeaker Systems, Part I: Analysis," *J. Audio Eng. Soc.*, vol. 22, pp. 592-601 (Oct. 1974).

[10] J. E. Benson, "Theory and Design of Loudspeaker Enclosures, Part 3—Introduction to Synthesis of Vented Systems," *AWA Tech. Rev.*, vol. 14, p. 369 (1972).

Mr. Kates's biography appeared in the May 1976 issue.

PROJECT NOTES/ENGINEERING BRIEFS

A NOVEL APPROACH TO LINEAR PHASE LOUDSPEAKERS USING PASSIVE CROSSOVER NETWORKS

ERIK BÆKGAARD

Bang & Olufsen A/S, Struer, Denmark

Assuming equal electroacoustic transducer efficiencies in a multiway loudspeaker system, the vector sum of the voltages to the individual drivers must be equal to the input voltage for the accurate transfer of amplitude and phase characteristics of the signal. It has been shown that this is achievable using 6-dB per octave passive filters or higher slope active filters at a low signal stage to avoid unacceptable loss of power. Passive filters of 6-dB per octave slope require transducers with a power bandwidth not achievable with today's technology, while active filters requiring multiple amplifier systems are still too expensive to be provided commercially, especially in multichannel sound systems.

Passive filters are described using one or more auxiliary loudspeakers, "the missing link," in 12-dB per octave and higher degree crossover networks, which at the same time fulfill the requirement that the vector sum of the part voltages be equal to the input, theoretically without loss of power in the crossover network. Linearity of phase and amplitude are thus assured in the electrical circuit. Other requirements for linear phase loudspeakers are also described. Comparisons between computer calculated transfer functions and results from a practical high-performance low-distortion loudspeaker are shown.

INTRODUCTION: Over the last few years, dictated by increasing knowledge of the physiology of hearing and the recognition of sound signals by the human ear, development of high-fidelity loudspeakers and loudspeaker systems with good transient response has had increasing interest for researchers. Further, one of the goals of audio products must be to reproduce sound signals as correctly and accurately as possible, at least to the extent that all forms of audible distortion are removed.

Hansen and Madsen [1], [2] have shown that one form of distortion that is audible is phase distortion, and that this affects transient performance. Thus it is not sufficient, as was previously believed, to be content with a flat amplitude–frequency characteristic and low harmonic and intermodulation distortion, which is achieved by the better designs with steep cut crossover networks, but also low phase distortion. All these qualities can be included in a common test specification, which will be called "voltage transfer error function."

This paper describes multiway loudspeaker systems, the drivers of which will, for theoretical analysis, be assumed to be perfect within the frequency range in which they are used. Thus the description will mainly cover crossover networks and, to limit its length, two-way systems consisting of bass and treble drivers only. The theory can obviously be extended to multiway systems, with each crossover point being regarded as a two-way combination of high- and low-pass filter.

STATEMENT OF ASSUMPTIONS AND DEFINITIONS

To permit the comparison of the amplitude, phase, and impulse characteristics of loudspeakers with various crossover networks, it is useful to record the following assumptions made in the development of the argument.

1) Each driver is assumed to be perfect, that is, it gives a sound pressure level proportional to the input voltage at the voice coil terminals throughout the frequency range in which it is used.

2) All drivers used in a particular loudspeaker system give the same sound pressure level for the same input voltage, independent of its impedance.

3) All drivers have a pure resistive load characteristic.

4) All drivers are mounted so that there is no difference in the path length of sound signals from any driver to the listener.

Only when these requirements are met, can one assume that the voltage received at the voice coil terminals of a driver is also an expression for the sound pressure output from that driver.

We now define a new function, the voltage transfer error function VTE(s):

$$\mathrm{VTE}(s) = \frac{V_{\mathrm{in}}(s) - V_0(s)}{V_{\mathrm{in}}(s)} = 1 - \frac{V_0(s)}{V_{\mathrm{in}}(s)}$$

$$= 1 - \sum_{i=1}^{n} F_i(s) \tag{1}$$

where $V_{\mathrm{in}}(s)$ is the voltage delivered to the terminals of the loudspeaker system, $F_i(s)$ the transfer function of each driver's crossover filter, and $V_0(s)$ the vector-sum of voltages to the individual drivers and thus an expression for the total sound pressure generated. In the case where there is constant total voltage transfer, this function becomes a constant.

For a two-way loudspeaker system consisting of bass and treble drivers which are driven from the crossover with transfer functions $F_l(s)$ and $F_h(s)$, respectively, Eq. (1) can be simplified to

$$VTE(s) = 1 - F_l(s)\, F_h(s) \tag{2}$$

where l and h represent the low- and high-pass sections, respectively. If the crossover network consists solely of loss-free passive LC filters, one can put down the condition for constant total voltage transfer, which is

$$\mathrm{VTE}(s) = 0. \tag{3}$$

In a practical case the preceding assumptions will not be valid, and this will be discussed later.

Transfer functions are denoted as functions in the complex frequency domain operating normalized, for example, $s_n = s/\omega_0$ where $\omega_0 = 2\pi f_0, f_0$ being the nominal crossover frequency. Butterworth filters are used in all examples, as they give maximally flat amplitude characteristic for each driver.

SECOND ORDER CROSSOVER (12 dB PER OCTAVE) IN PHASE

A typical circuit diagram for a second-order crossover network is shown in Fig. 1*a*.

$$F_l(s) = \frac{V_{ol}(s)}{V_{\mathrm{in}}(s)} = \frac{1}{s_n^2 + \sqrt{2}\, s_n + 1} \tag{4}$$

$$F_h(s) = \frac{V_{oh}(s)}{V_{\mathrm{in}}(s)} = \frac{s_n^2}{s_n^2 + \sqrt{2}\, s_n + 1} \tag{5}$$

$$R_l = R_h = R \tag{6}$$

$$C = \frac{1}{\sqrt{2}\, R\omega_0} \tag{7}$$

$$L = \frac{\sqrt{2}\, R}{\omega_0} \tag{8}$$

$$VTE(s) = 1 - F_l(s) - F_h(s)$$

$$= 1 - \frac{1}{s_n^2 + \sqrt{2}\, s_n + 1} - \frac{s_n^2}{s_n^2 + \sqrt{2}\, s_n + 1}$$

$$= \frac{\sqrt{2}\, s_n}{s_n^2 + \sqrt{2}\, s_n + 1}. \tag{9}$$

The analysis shows that a loudspeaker with two drivers operating in phase, fed from a second crossover network, does not fulfill the condition for constant voltage transfer.

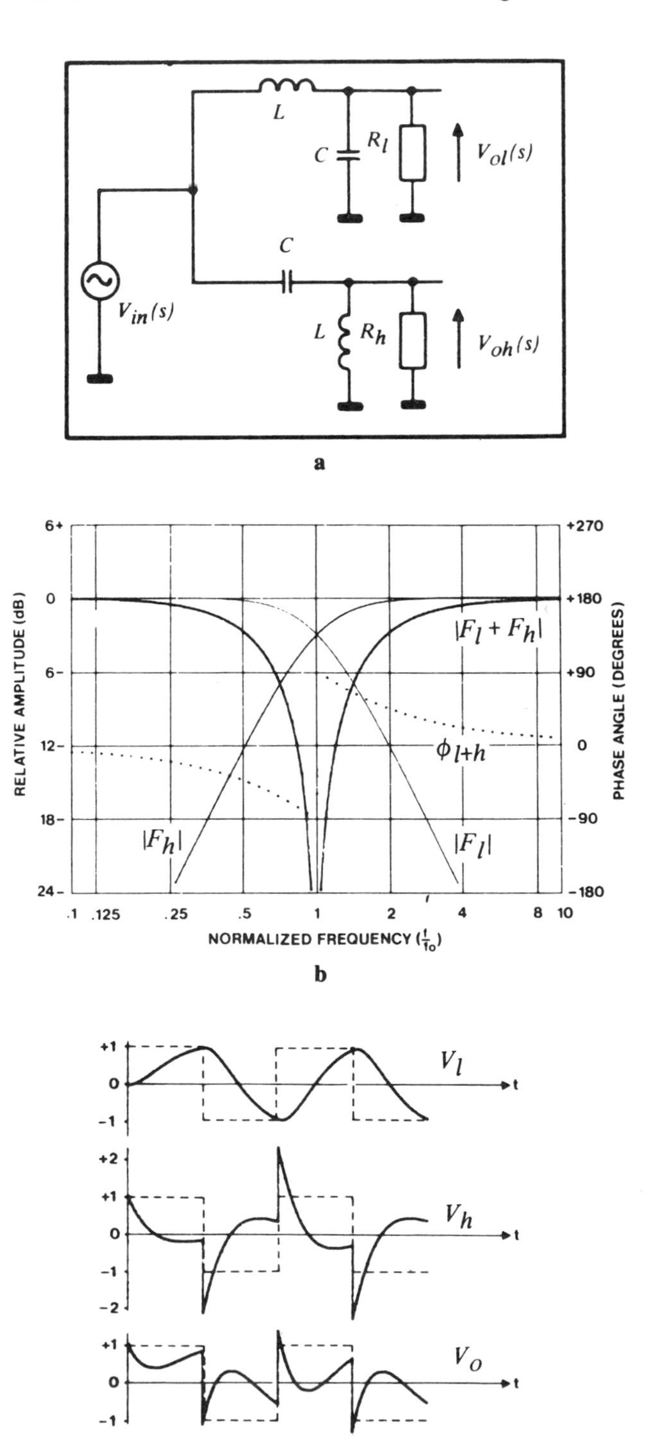

Fig. 1. Typical circuit diagram for second-order crossover network.

This can easily be seen in its amplitude, phase, and square-wave characteristics (Fig. 1*b* and *c*). The amplitude response has a null at the crossover frequency f_0, which can also be seen from the total transfer function in the frequency plane:

$$\frac{V_0(j\omega)}{V_{in}(j\omega)} = F_l(j\omega) + F_h(j\omega) = \frac{1-\omega_n^2}{1-\omega_n^2 + j\sqrt{2}\,\omega_n} \quad (10)$$

where

$$\omega_n = \frac{\omega}{\omega_0}. \quad (11)$$

SECOND-ORDER CROSSOVER (12 dB PER OCTAVE) REVERSED PHASE

The circuit diagram for this case is the same as that of Fig. 1*a*, but with one of the drivers connected with reserved polarity:

$$VTE(s) = 1 - F_l(s) - (-F_h(s)) = \frac{2\,s_n^2 + \sqrt{2}\,s_n}{s_n^2 + \sqrt{2}\,s_{n+1}}. \quad (12)$$

Thus a loudspeaker with two drivers operating out of phase also does not fulfill 'the condition for constant voltage transfer, as can be seen from the amplitude, phase, and square-wave characteristics (Fig. 2*a* and *b*). In this case there is a 3-dB peak at the crossover point, besides the phase shift in the region of the crossover frequency.

ADDING THE MISSING LINK

We can now look at an alternative method for achieving constant voltage transfer. The theory is based on the principle[1] that instead of attempting to correct the electrical transfer function in the crossover networks for one or both existing drivers, the error from the ideal transfer characteristic can be corrected by adding a compensating electroacoustic signal with a transfer characteristic such that the total transfer characteristic is a constant.

In practice a straightforward method of achieving this goal is to add one, or more, filler drivers to the normal bass and treble drivers. These, when fed from an altered crossover network to reproduce the transfer characteristic, $F_c(s)$ = VTE (s), will together with the transfer functions for the bass and treble drivers, $F_l(s)$ and $F_h(s)$, give the required constant total transfer function.

SECOND-ORDER CROSSOVER WITH FILLER DRIVER IN PHASE

For this crossover network with Butterworth response, as shown earlier,

$$F_c(s) = VTE(s) = \frac{\sqrt{2}\,s_n}{s_n^2 + \sqrt{2}\,s_{n+1}}. \quad (13)$$

[1] Patented

In this case the required transfer characteristic is easily achieved by a single filler driver R_c connected in series through a series LC circuit. The complete crossover network is shown in Fig. 3*a*, with amplitude and phase characteristics shown in Fig. 3**b**. Fig. 3**c** shows that the amplitude, phase, and transient characerisitics are correct, as expected.

$$R_l = R_h = R \quad (14)$$

$$L = \frac{\sqrt{2}\,R}{\omega_0} \quad (15)$$

$$L_c = \frac{R_c}{\sqrt{2}\,\omega_0} \quad (16)$$

$$C = \frac{1}{\sqrt{2}\,R\,\omega_0} \quad (17)$$

$$C_c = \frac{\sqrt{2}}{R_c\,\omega_0}. \quad (18)$$

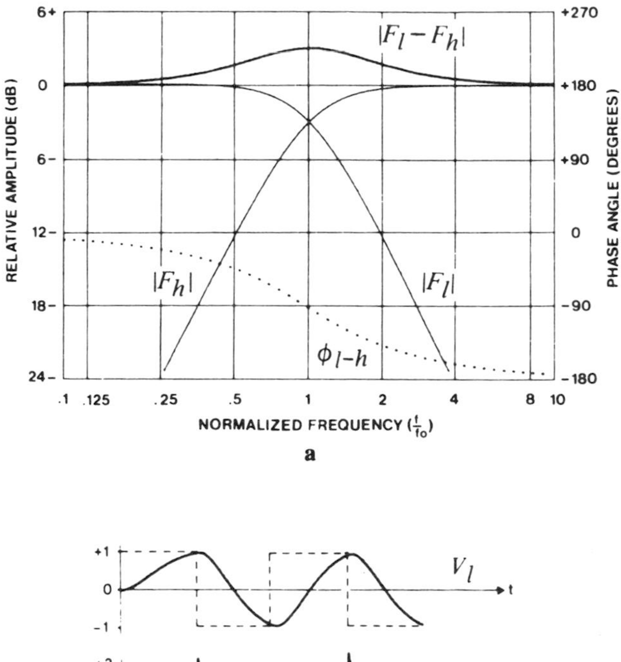

a

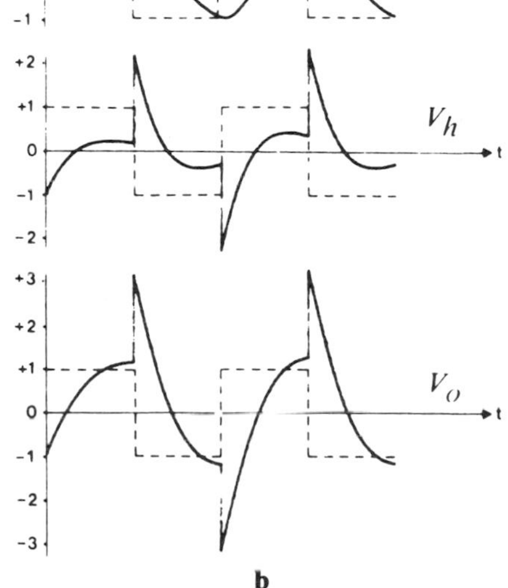

b

Fig. 2. Same as Fig. 1, but with one driver connected with reverse polarity.

$F_c(s)$ is a first-order bandpass function for a second-order crossover network, with a slope of 6 dB per octave and a −3-dB bandwidth of two octaves, that is, the signal is attenuated to both sides of a single peak frequency, to a −12-dB bandwidth of five octaves. Because of this, the design of a filler driver, with the required bandwidth, is within easily achievable limits.

The preceding loudspeaker system would be near perfect but for the fact that the total input impedance is no longer constant. It will vary from

$$R_{in} = R \quad \text{for } f >> f_0 \text{ and } f << f_0 \qquad \text{to}$$
$$R_{in} = R \| R_c \quad \text{for } f = f_0. \tag{19}$$

Conditions for constant input impedance are shown in Appendix A.

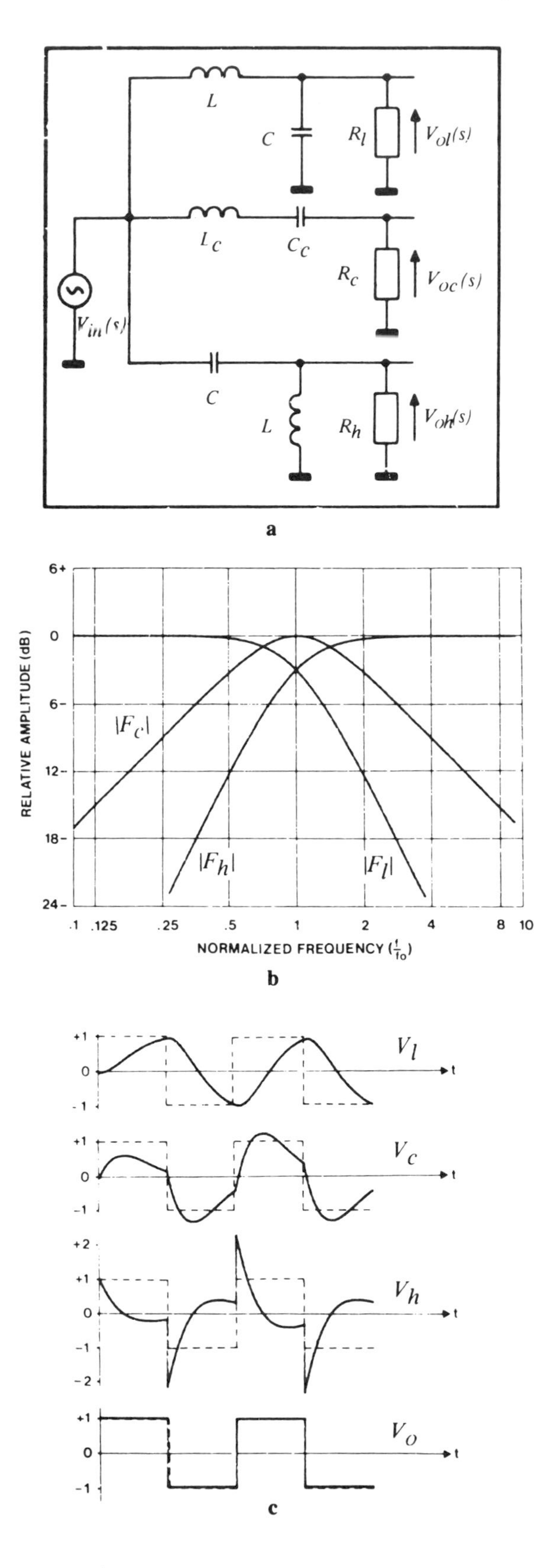

Fig. 3. Second-order crossover with filler drivers.

A PRACTICAL LOUDSPEAKER SYSTEM

A loudspeaker was constructed to verify the theoretical analysis presented in the preceding and to see the extent to which a practical loudspeaker could be made to reproduce square waves in an anechoic room. The setup consisted of a cabinet fitted with the necessary drivers, and external second-order crossover networks operating at a crossover frequency of 500 Hz. The crossovers could be switched to reproduce either with bass and treble drivers only, in phase or opposed phase, or with bass, treble, and filler drivers.

The response to a square-wave input, and the theoretical responses in all three cases, are shown in Figs. 4, 5, and 6. The close resemblance of the theoretical and actual curves leaves no doubt that practical loudspeaker systems can be made which reduce phase distortion to levels below audibility, using the methods explained.

The input level in all cases was 8 volts into 4 ohms, that is, 16 watts, at the crossover frequency.

PRACTICAL CONSIDERATIONS

It may be useful to note some of the deviations between theory and practice, and to point out some of the practical problems that must be solved in the design of a loudspeaker system. As far as drivers are concerned, these are seldom as perfect as assumed for the theoretical analysis, even within their nominal frequency limits. They tend to show limitations in their power-handling ability, amplitude response, and dispersion characteristic, but these, to some extent, may be compensated or corrected in the crossover network. These limitations have been described in various papers [3], [4], and we will not discuss them here any further.

Another problem is to ensure the same acoustic path length [5] from the acoustic axis of each driver to the listener. Differences in this respect will destroy otherwise correct transient response, even though it must be stressed that phase errors of this kind are small compared to those generated in incorrect crossovers. Drivers should be mounted as close to each other as possible, but differences in depth of the individual drivers make this insufficient by itself. One method of compensating for differences in depth is to position the loudspeakers on an angled mounting panel, as shown in Fig. 7. One can take advantage of the fact that a bass driver has a comparatively large dispersion angle, so that angling its axis has no effect on the sound received by the listener. The loudspeakers are thus effectively staggered a distance A, and the path length from the acoustic axis of each driver to the listener is the same. It should be noted, that this method is a satisfactory solution for the horizontal plane, but is ineffective in the vertical.

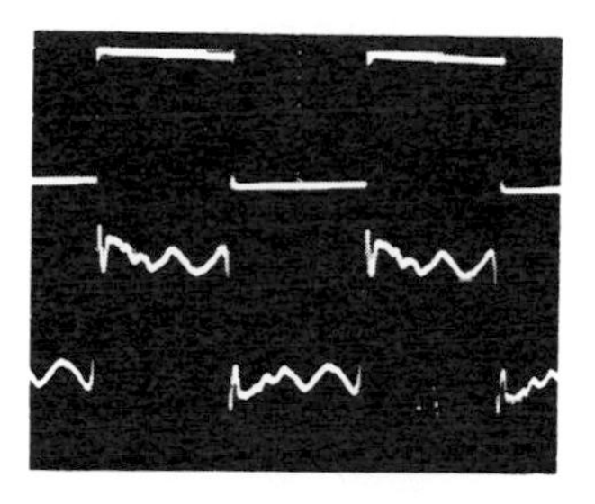

Fig. 4. With filler driver.

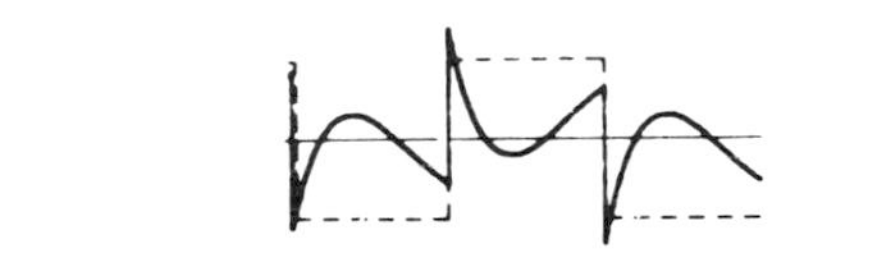

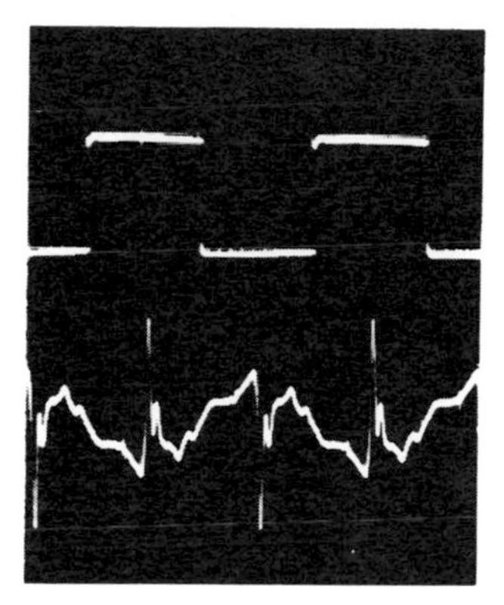

Fig. 5. In phase.

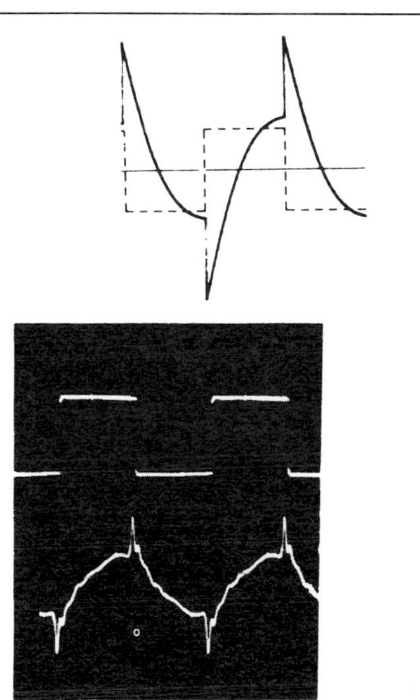

Fig. 6. Out of phase.

Fig. 8 shows the on-axis response and the effect of moving 15 and 30 degrees, respectively, on a horizontal plane in front of a prototype loudspeaker system built on the proposed principles. The input in all the examples is a square wave at the crossover frequency. It can be seen that there is almost no effect on transient performance.

Fig. 9*a* shows the calculated and actual responses, which are altered due to the time delay introduced, as would be the case if all the drivers were mounted on a flat panel. The delay introduced is 200μs (6.8 cm) for the bass driver and 100 μs (3.4 cm) for the filler driver.

For the purpose of this test, the microphone is positioned 15 degrees above the intended listening height to give the same results. There is now an effect on the performance, but this is still better than a conventional second-order crossover. It will be noticed that the loudspeaker system accurately follows the theoretically calculated response.

The effect of moving below the intended listening height is shown in Fig. 9*b*. Again the similarity between the predicted and actual responses is seen.

CONCLUSION

This paper has shown a way to design a multiway loudspeaker system free from amplitude and phase distortion, using inexpensive passive LC filters with crossover slopes of more than 6 dB per octave. Examples shown use the best known types of crossover, but the principles can obviously be used in conjunction with any other type of crossover. It has also been shown that loudspeaker systems do, in practice, closely follow theoretically predictable responses.

APPENDIX A

Input Impedance for Second-Order Crossover with Filler Driver

The conditions necessary for constant input impedance, for this crossover, can be calculated as follows. The general transfer functions for VTE(s) = 0 are

$$F_1(s) = \frac{1}{s_n^2 + as_n + 1} \tag{20}$$

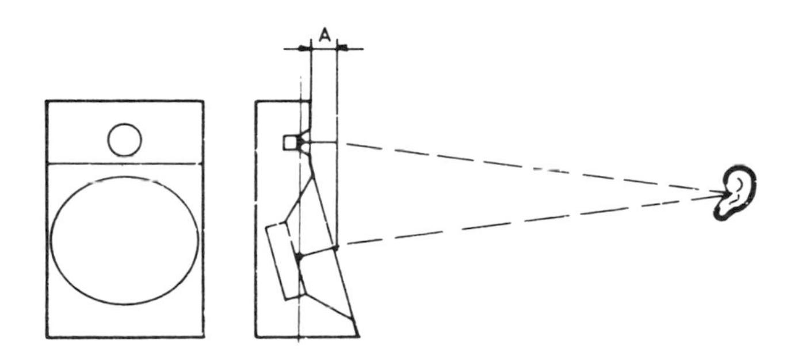

Fig. 7. Loudspeakers on angled mounting panel.

$$F_c(s) = \frac{as_n}{s_n^2 + as_n + 1} \quad (21)$$

$$F_h(s) = \frac{s_n^2}{s_n^2 + as_n + 1} . \quad (22)$$

The input impedances will be

$$Z_l(s) = R \frac{s_n^2 + as_n + 1}{1 + (1/a)\, s_n} \quad (23)$$

$$Z_c(s) = \frac{s_n^2 + as_n + 1}{(a/R_c)\, s_n} \quad (24)$$

$$Z_h(s) = R \frac{s_n^2 + as_n + 1}{s_n^2 + (1/a)\, s_n} \quad (25)$$

$$\Sigma\, Y_{in}(s) = \frac{s_n^2 + (2/a + a \cdot R/R_c)\, s_n + 1}{R(s_n^2 + as_n + 1)} \quad (26)$$

$$Z_{in}(s) = R \frac{s_n^2 + as_n + 1}{s_n^2 + (2/a + a \cdot R/R_c)\, s_n + 1} \quad (27)$$

If the input impedance may be allowed to vary between limits, say R and $X \cdot R$, one gets the following conditions:

$$X = \frac{a}{2/a + a \cdot R/R_c} \quad \text{or} \quad a = \sqrt{\frac{2X}{1 - (R/R_c)\, X}} . \quad (28)$$

For constant input impedance, $X = 1$. It should be noted that when $R_c 7R$, the efficiency of the filler driver must be higher than that of the basic drivers. Component values for

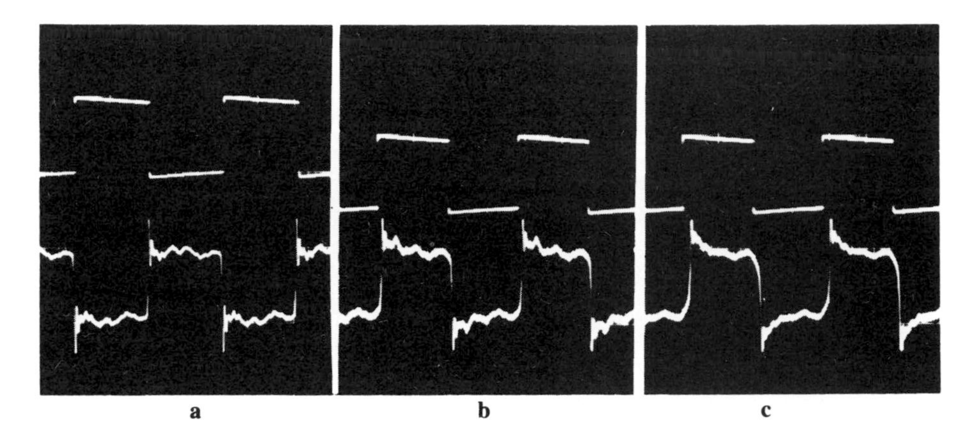

a b c

Fig. 8. Square-wave response. *a*. On axis. *b*. 15 degrees off axis. *c*. 30 degrees off axis.

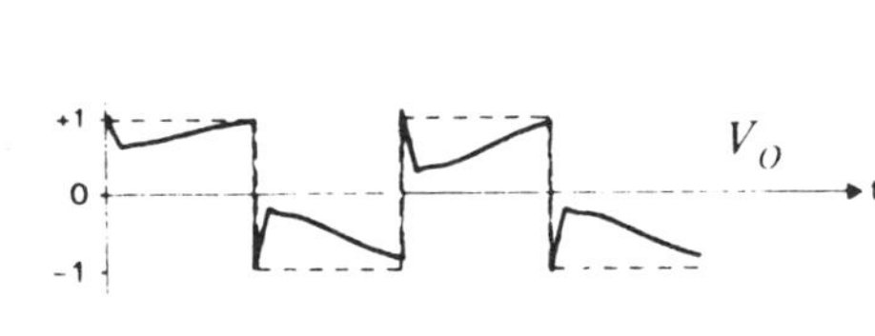

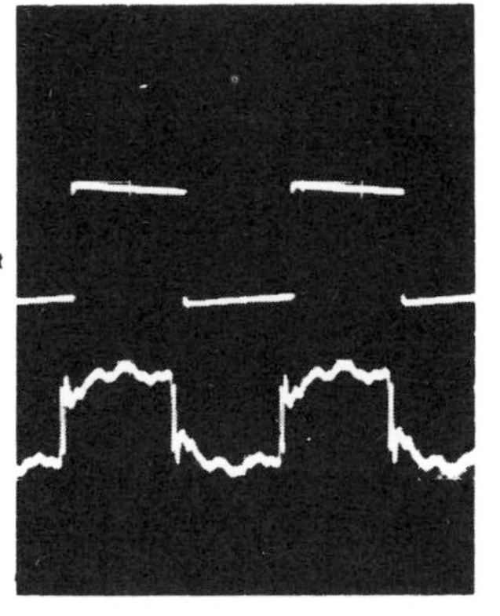

a

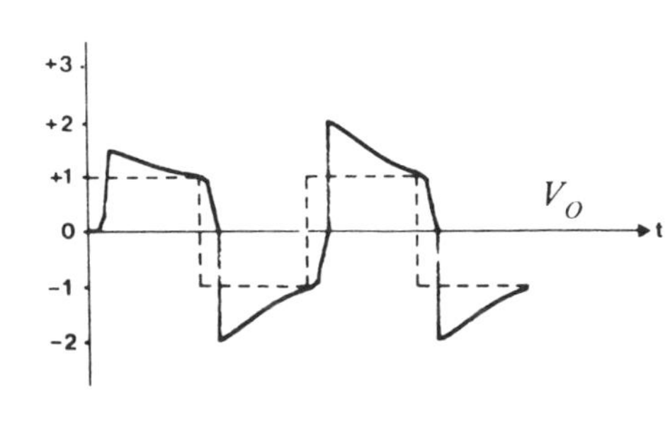

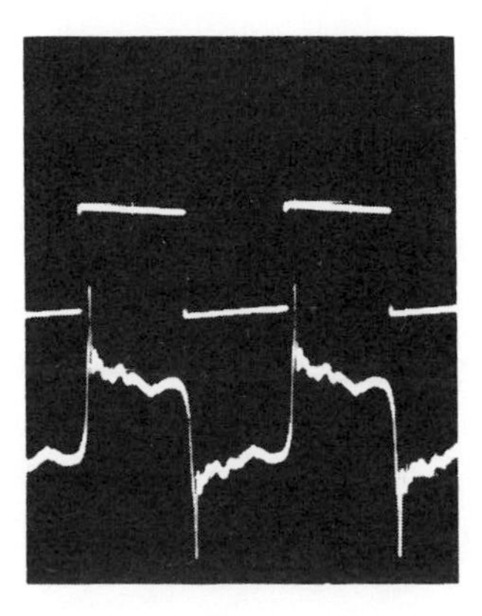

b

Fig. 9. Calculated and actual responses. *a*. Effect of time delay. *b*. Effect of moving below intended listening height.

this filter will then be

$$L = \frac{aR}{\omega_0} \tag{29}$$

$$L_c = \frac{R_c}{a\omega_0} \tag{30}$$

$$C = \frac{1}{aR\,\omega_0} \tag{31}$$

$$C_c = \frac{a}{R_c\,\omega_0}\,. \tag{32}$$

Fig. 10 shows the resultant amplitude characteristics for various values of a. Choice of any particular value in a particular application will depend on the bandwidth characteristics of the drivers available and the input impedance requirements for the loudspeaker system.

APPENDIX B

Third-Order Crossover with Two Filler Drivers

For a third-order crossover network, as shown earlier,

$$F_c(s) = VTE(s) = \frac{2\,s_n^2 + 2\,s_n}{s_n^3 + 2\,s_n^2 + 2\,s_n + 1}\,. \tag{33}$$

This function is easily achieved directly with the help of two filler drivers with the following transfer characteristics:

$$F_{c1}(s) = \frac{2\,s_n^2}{s_n^3 + 2\,s_n^2 + 2\,s_n + 1} \tag{34}$$

$$F_{c2}(s) = \frac{2\,s_n}{s_n^3 + 2\,s_n^2 + 2\,s_n + 1}\,. \tag{35}$$

Third-Order Crossover with Single Filler Driver

The third-order transfer function derived in the preceding belongs to a type that can be achieved easily with a single filler driver. Reducing the expression for $F_c(s)$ we find

$$F_c(s) = \frac{2\,s_n^2 + 2\,s_n}{s_n^3 + 2\,s_n^2 + 2\,s_n + 1} = \frac{2\,s_n\,(s_n + 1)}{(s_n + 1)\,(s_n^2 + s_n + 1)} = \frac{2\,s_n}{s_n^2 + s_n + 1} \tag{36}$$

$$R_l = R_c = R_h = R \tag{37}$$

$$\frac{\eta_c}{\eta_l} = \frac{\eta_c}{\eta_h} = 2 \tag{38}$$

$$L_{1l} = \frac{3R}{2\omega_0} \tag{39}$$

$$L_{2l} = \frac{R}{2\omega_0} \tag{40}$$

$$L_c = \frac{R}{\omega_0} \tag{41}$$

$$L_h = \frac{3R}{4\omega_0} \tag{42}$$

$$C_l = \frac{4}{3R\omega_0} \tag{43}$$

$$C_c = \frac{1}{R\omega_0} \tag{44}$$

$$C_{1h} = \frac{2}{3R\omega_0} \tag{45}$$

$$C_{2h} = \frac{2}{R\omega_0}\,. \tag{46}$$

This function can be achieved with a series LC network connected in series to the driver, provided the efficiency of the filler driver η_c is twice that of the basic drivers η. The complete crossover network is shown in Fig. 11a.

Higher Order Crossovers

In general it may be said that for a crossover network with filters of higher order where

$$F_l(s) = \frac{a_0}{N(s)} \tag{47}$$

$$F_h(s) = \frac{a_n s^n}{N(s)} \tag{48}$$

where

$$N(s) = a_0 + a_1 s + a_2 s^2 + \cdots + a_n s^n \tag{49}$$

the sum of signals to the basic loudspeakers will be

$$\frac{a_0 + a_n s^n}{N(s)}\,. \tag{50}$$

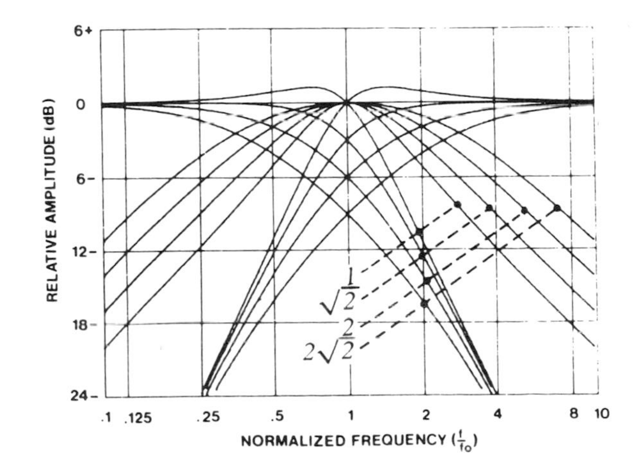

Fig. 10. Resultant amplitude characteristics for various values of a.

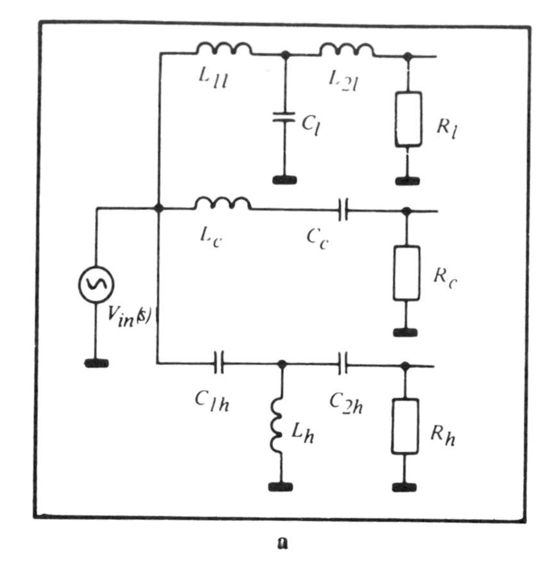

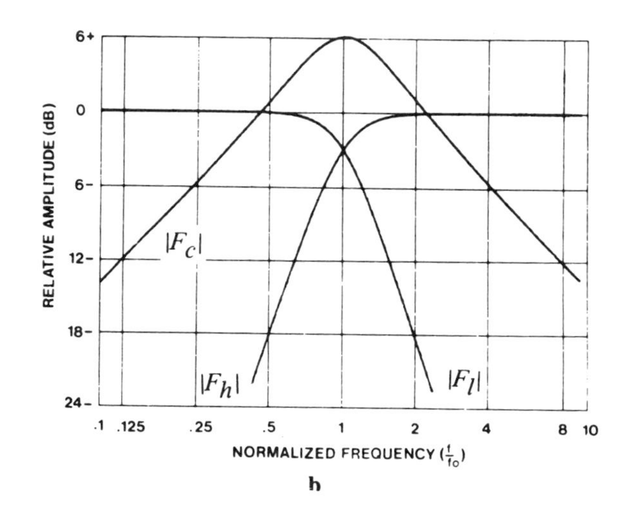

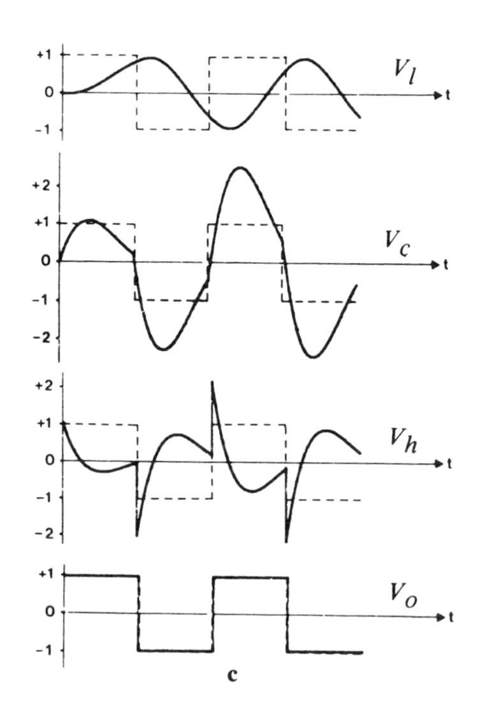

Fig. 11. Third-order crossover with single filler driver.

To achieve $\mathrm{VTE}(s) = 0$, it will be necessary to add an electroacoustic signal with a transfer characteristic

$$F_c(s) = \frac{a_1 s + a_2 s^2 + \cdots + a_{n-1} s^{n-1}}{N(s)} . \quad (51)$$

This signal can be obtained with $(n - 1)$ filler drivers with their respective transfer characteristics,

$$\frac{a_1 s}{N(s)}, \frac{a_2 s^2}{N(s)}, \ldots, \quad \frac{a_{n-1} s^{n-1}}{N(s)} . \quad (52)$$

APPENDIX C

ANALYSIS OF CONVENTIONAL CROSSOVERS

First-Order Crossover (6 dB per octave), (Fig.12)

$$F_l(s) = \frac{V_{ol}(s)}{V_{in}(s)} = \frac{1}{s_n + 1} \quad (53)$$

$$F_h(s) = \frac{V_{oh}(s)}{V_{in}(s)} = \frac{s_n}{s_n + 1} \quad (54)$$

$$L = \frac{R_l}{\omega_0} \quad (55)$$

$$C = \frac{1}{\omega_0 R_h} \quad (56)$$

$$\mathrm{VTE}(s) = 1 - \sum_{i=1}^{n} F_i(s) = 1 - F_l(s) - F_h(s)$$

$$= 1 - \frac{1}{s_n + 1} - \frac{s_n}{s_{n+1}} = 0. \quad (57)$$

Quasi Second-Order Crossover (6 dB per octave), (Fig. 13)

$$F_l(s) = \frac{V_{ol}(s)}{V_{in}(s)} = \frac{a s_n + 1}{s_n^2 + 2 a s_n + 1} \quad (58)$$

$$F_h(s) = \frac{V_{oh}(s)}{V_{in}(s)} = \frac{s_n^2 + a s_n}{s_n^2 + 2 a s_n + 1} \quad (59)$$

$$R_l = R_h = R \quad (60)$$

$$C = \frac{a}{R\omega_0} \quad (61)$$

$$L = \frac{R}{a\omega_0} \quad (62)$$

$$\mathrm{VTE}(s) = 1 - F_l(s) - F_h(s)$$

$$= 1 - \frac{a s_n + 1}{s_n^2 + 2 a s_n + 1} - \frac{s_n^2 + a s_n}{s_n^2 + 2 a s_n + 1}$$

$$= 0. \quad (63)$$

The value of a selected will depend on the limitations imposed in a practical application. If one requires maximum flat response for each driver, it can be shown [6] that this occurs at $a = \sqrt{2/3}$. Amplitude and square-wave characteristics are shown in Figs. 13**b** and **c**. Curves for other values of a are shown in Ashley and Kaminsky [7]. The crossover network will have constant input impedance at $a = 1$.

Third-Order Crossover (18 dB per octave) (Fig. 14)

$$F_l(s) = \frac{V_{ol}(s)}{V_{in}(s)} = \frac{1}{s_n^3 + s_n^2 + 2\,s_n + 1} \tag{64}$$

$$F_h(s) = \frac{V_{oh}(s)}{V_{in}(s)} = \frac{s_n^3}{s_n^3 + 2s_n^2 + 2s_n + 1} \tag{65}$$

$$L_{1l} = \frac{3R_l}{2\omega_0} \tag{66}$$

$$L_{2l} = \frac{R_l}{2\omega_0} \tag{67}$$

$$L_h = \frac{3R_l}{4\omega_0} \tag{68}$$

$$C_{1h} = \frac{2}{3R_h\,\omega_0} \tag{69}$$

$$C_{2h} = \frac{2}{R_h\,\omega_0} \tag{70}$$

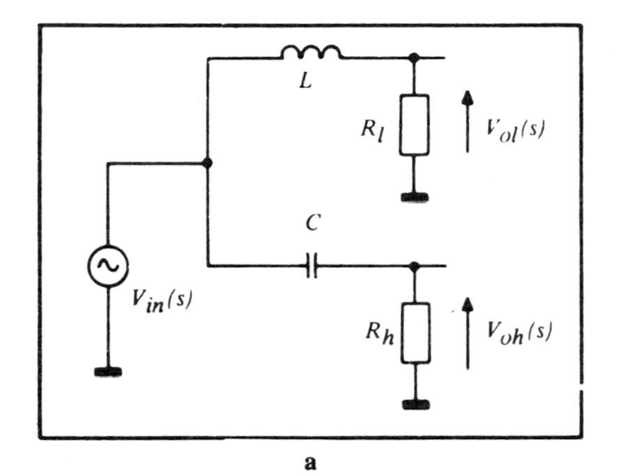

a

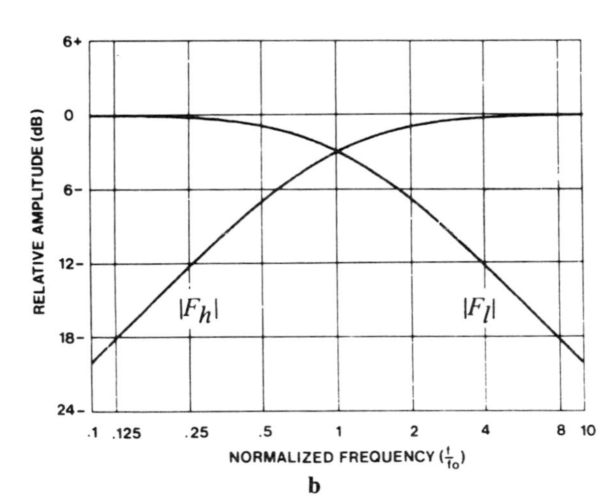

b

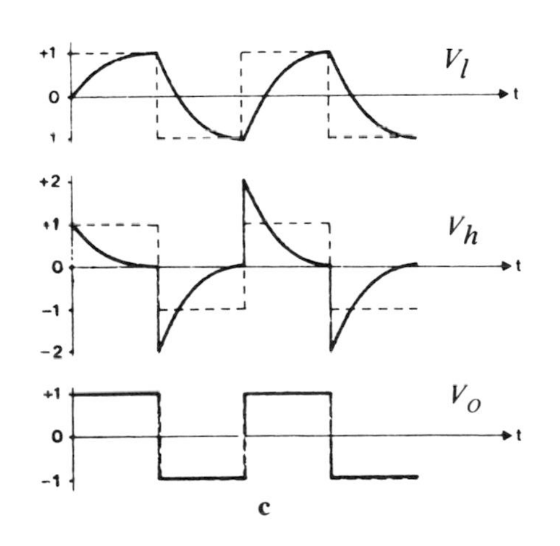

c

Fig. 12. First-order crossover.

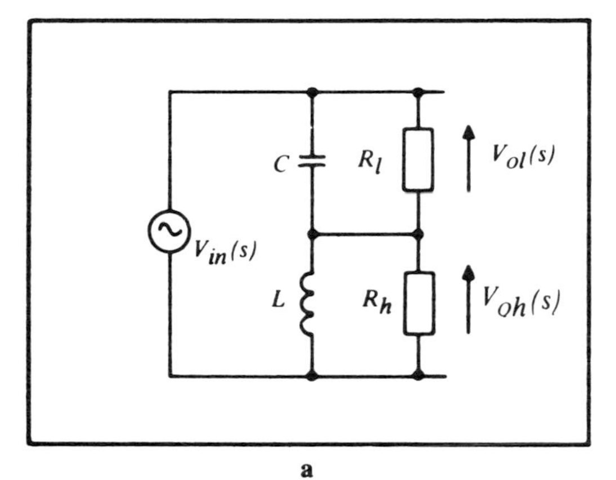

a

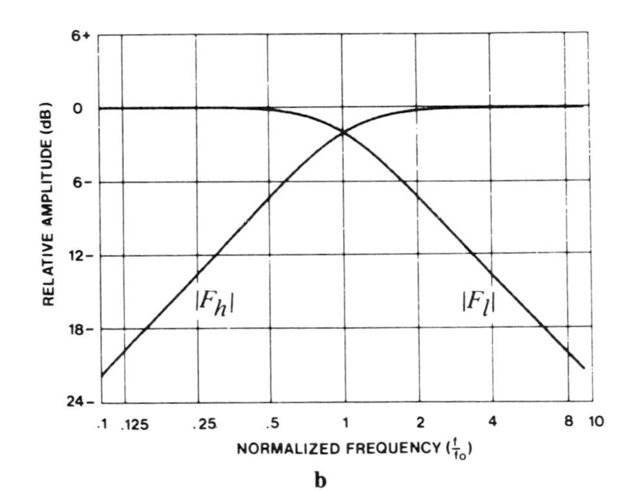

b

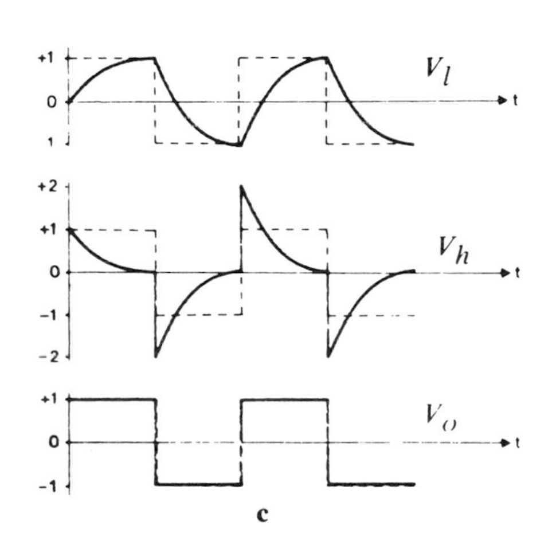

c

Fig. 13. Quasi second-order crossover.

$$C_l = \frac{4}{3R_l\,\omega_0} \tag{71}$$

$$\mathrm{VTE}(s) = 1 - F_l(s) - F_h(s) = \frac{2s_n^2 + 2s_n}{s_n^3 + 2s_n^2 + 2s_n + 1}. \tag{72}$$

Other Types of Crossover Networks

We have now analyzed the best known crossover networks. Their widespread use is no doubt due to their straightforward design principles and suitability for realization with passive LC components.

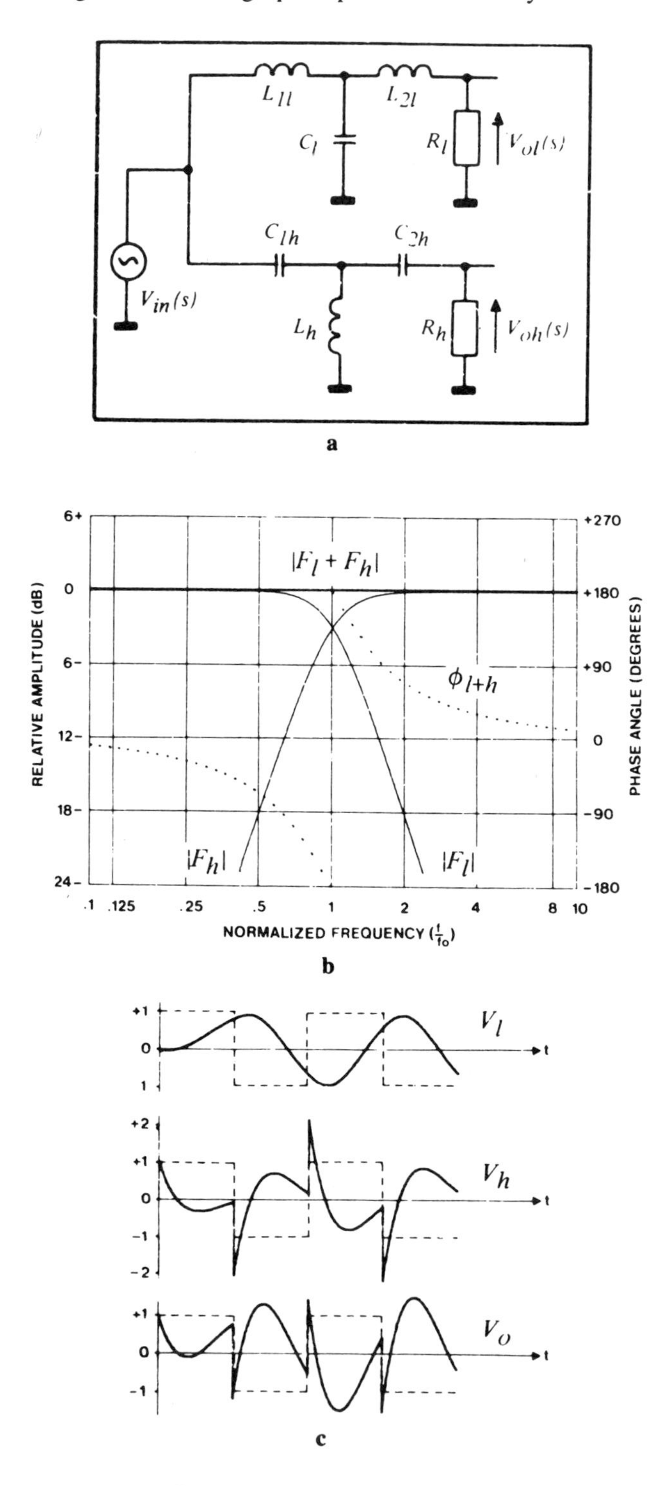

Fig. 14. Third-order crossover.

Some work has been done on the design of more complicated crossover networks [3], [7], [8] in order to achieve constant total voltage transfer, and at the same time have steep attenuation outside the driver's bandwidth. All of these have the drawback that they are based on active filters with individual amplifiers for each driver in order to avoid a large amplifier power loss. Further, attenuation in the crossover region is relatively gradual, and therefore they still require drivers with good performance over a large bandwidth. For example, in the case of one network giving slopes of 18 dB per octave, the overlap for 12-dB attenuation is over four octaves, which is not better than that for a first-order network, and considerably worse than that for second-order networks which have an overlap of two octaves.

This may account for the disappointing results with so-called phase linear loudspeakers observed by some researchers in listening tests, when compared with conventional loudspeakers.

ACKNOWLEDGMENT

The author wishes to thank all at Bang & Olufsen for the help he received at all stages of this project. He wants to thank particularly Esben Kokholm who proved the theories proposed in this paper by building and testing a prototype. His thanks also go to S. K. Pramanik who helped in translating and writing this manuscript, and to Jytte Tarlev whose patience was unending while typing it.

REFERENCES

[1] E. R. Madsen and V. Hansen, "Threshold of Phase Detection by Hearing," presented at the 44th Convention of the Audio Engineering Society, Rotterdam, The Netherlands, Feb. 20, 1973.

[2] V. Hansen and E. R. Madsen, "On Aural Phase work Design," *J. Audio Eng. Soc.*, vol. 19, pp. 12-19 (Jan. 1971)

[3] R. H. Small, "Constant-Voltage Crossover Network Design," *J. Audio Eng. Soc.*, vol. 19, pp. 12-19 (Jan. 1971)

[4] A. Schaumberger, "Impulse Measurement Techniques for Quality Determination in Hi-Fi Equipment, with Special Emphasis on Loudspeakers," *J. Audio Eng. Soc.*, vol. 19, pp.101-107 (Feb. 1971).

[5] R. C. Heyser, "Determination of Loudspeaker Signal Arrival Times parts I and III," *J. Audio Eng. Soc.*, vol. 19, pp. 734-743, 829-834, 902-905, (Oct., Nov., Dec. 1971).

[6] A. Budak and P. Aronlime, "Maximally Flat Low-Pass Filter," *IEEE Trans. Audio Electroscoust. (Mar. 1970).*

[7] J. R. Ashley and A. L. Kaminsky, "Active and Passive Filters as Loudspeaker Crossover Networks," *J. Audio Eng. Soc.*, vol. 19, pp.494-502 (June 1971).

[8] A. P. Smith, "Electronic Crossover Networks and their Contribution to Improved Loudspeaker Transient Response," *J. Audio Eng. Soc.*, vol. 19, pp.674-679 (Sept. 1971).

[9] J. R. Ashley, "On the Transient Response of Ideal Crossover Networks," *J. Audio Eng. Soc.*, vol. 10, p.241

(July 1962).
[10] J. R. Ashley and L. M. Henne, ''Operational Amplifier Implementation of Ideal Electronic Crossover Networks,'' *J. Audio Eng. Soc.*, vol. 19, pp.7-11 (Jan. 1971).

About the Author:

Erik Bækgaard was born in Mors in Northwest Jutland, Denmark, in 1939. After an apprenticeship as a radio technician, he studied at the Aarhus Technical College from 1960 to 1963, from which he received a degree in electronic engineering.

He served with the Royal Danish Air Force for sixteen months, before joining a hospital in Copenhagen, where he worked with medical electronic equipment. In 1966, he joined Bang & Olufsen A/S, at first as a product development engineer working with transistor radios, and later with advanced instrumentation.

At the present time, he is manager, electronic engineering of Bang & Olufsen's R & D Section. Mr. Bækgaard is a member of the Audio Engineering Society.

The Application of Digital Techniques to the Measurement of Loudspeakers

J. M. BERMAN AND L. R. FINCHAM

KEF Electronics Ltd., Tovil, Maidstone, Kent, England

A new approach to the problem of the measurement of loudspeaker characteristics is presented. A digital processor is used to obtain the loudspeaker's transfer function from a direct measurement of the impulse response. The measuring method is discussed in detail along with the forms of display which have so far been used. Some applications are discussed briefly. Finally, the method is shown to be suited to a system approach to the study and development of loudspeakers.

INTRODUCTION: A scientific approach to loudspeaker design and evaluation can only be based on the successful correlation of objective and subjective observations. While we can all too readily gather subjective information on loudspeakers, we have at our disposal only a very limited range of measurements which do not adequately account for the subtle subjective effects found in loudspeakers. Improvements in loudspeakers have not been matched by equivalent improvements in measuring techniques; relatively speaking the subject seems to grow less rather than more scientific, and design still proceeds by a mixture of science, art, and intuition.

An indication of how little loudspeaker measurements have progressed is to be found in the fact that the so-called "frequency-response" curve, which was first used over 50 years ago, is still regarded as the primary means of assessing loudspeaker performance, although it has long been recognized that many important aspects of subjective response cannot be related to the visual appearance of the frequency-response curve.

Many experimenters, observing that speech and music are primarily transient in nature, have turned to transient measurements in the form of tone bursts, step, and pulse responses, but these have always been hampered by signal-to-noise problems and the difficulties of interpretation. Others have recognized that amplitude response is but one part of the frequency response, and there has been considerable interest in the measurement of phase response.

The most significant advance has surely been made by Heyser [1, 2] who, using analog equipment, devised an elegant method of measuring loudspeaker response which overcame many of the previous difficulties. It was the publication of his method in 1969 which provided the inspiration for the digital measuring approach which is described in this paper. Both methods fall into the category of what might be described as the system approach to loudspeaker measurement, in which complete identification of the transfer function is attempted.

Work on the digital testing method was begun in 1971, and interim reports were given in 1973 [3] and 1975 [4]. The method has now been refined and verified over a large number of measurements, and this up-to-date account is based on first-hand knowledge of its use under day-to-day conditions.

THE LINEAR SYSTEM AND ITS MEASUREMENT

The input and output of a linear time-invariant system are always related unambiguously, and this relationship can be expressed as a function of either time or frequency. The time-domain representation takes the form of the response to an ideal impulse, known as the impulse response $h(t)$; the frequency domain counterpart takes the form of the familiar frequency response or transfer function $H(\omega)$, expressed as the real and imaginary parts of a complex function or as the corresponding amplitude and phase characteristics.

The impulse response and frequency response are related mathematically through the Fourier transform, and once either of these is known, the output may be predicted for any arbitrary input. This is calculated in the frequency domain by multiplication of the transfer function with the input expressed as a function of frequency and in the time domain by convolution of the input waveform with the impulse response [5]. These relationships are summarized in Fig. 1.

The advent of the fast Fourier transform (FFT) in the late sixties provided a fast convenient numerical method of transforming from one domain to the other and opened the door to a number of now well-established techniques for obtaining a system transfer function [6, 7]. The ability to measure, digitize, and subsequently manipulate the result numerically permits a wide range of excitation signals to be used, so that one can be chosen to suit the particular system under test.

The great advantage of this approach, which employs a numerical processor, such as a computer, is that once obtained, the system response completely defines the system behavior for *all* possible signals, both transient and steady state alike, and output waveforms can be obtained subsequently through calculation alone.

A loudspeaker, unlike an electrical network, does not have clearly defined output terminals. It creates an acoustic disturbance which radiates into space in a particularly complicated way. Though we would ultimately hope to characterize its behavior entirely, we concern ourselves here with the problem of identifying the behavior for one specific microphone position, and it is this that we refer to in identifying the transfer function of a loudspeaker. It is assumed throughout that the loudspeaker so defined is a linear time-invariant device.

The particular method which has been adopted for identifying system behavior involves a direct measurement of the impulse response. This is not a common approach, but it will be shown that it has significant advantages for the measurement of loudspeakers. In particular, because an impulse is the shortest possible exciting signal for a transfer function determination, the size of the room necessary to perform this measurement is minimized.

DIRECT MEASUREMENT OF LOUDSPEAKER IMPULSE RESPONSE

An impulse response can be obtained by exciting a loudspeaker with a sufficiently narrow pulse. This in itself requires no sophisticated techniques; indeed impulse responses were obtained by McLachlan as long ago as 1930 [8]. Others have since attempted to use the impulse response [9, 10], attracted to the feature that in exciting a system with an impulsive signal, we are effectively investigating its response to all frequencies. Such a narrow pulse, however, cannot always convey sufficient energy to the loudspeaker to give a signal-to-noise ratio that is adequate, if the impulse response is later to be used as a basis for computing the frequency response. Fortunately, the limitations of the signal-to-noise ratio can now be overcome by employing a technique known as signal averaging, which is easily implemented when a digital processor is used.

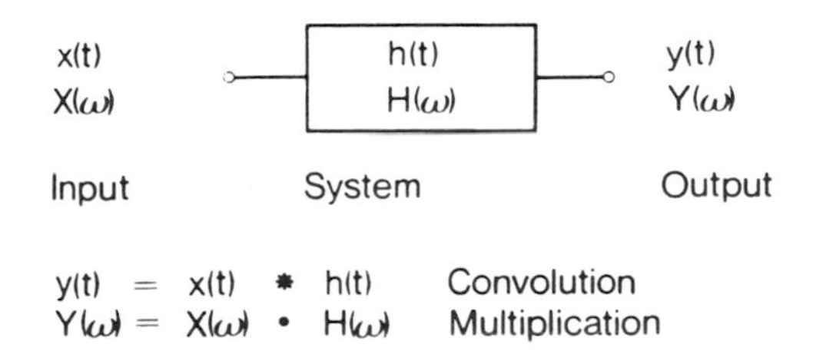

Fig. 1. Symbolic representation of linear system response, expressed in both time and frequency domains.

Measuring Method

The measuring chain is shown diagrammatically in Fig. 2. A repetitive short pulse, a single example of which is shown in detail in Fig. 3**a**, is amplified and fed to the loudspeaker, which is positioned close to the center of the measuring room, away from all reflecting surfaces. A microphone is used to detect the consequent acoustic disturbance which is amplified and digitized by the analog-to-digital converter and stored in the computer memory. After each pulse, sound propagates from the loudspeaker and arrives at the microphone after a time delay t_d; it continues out to the walls of the room where it is reflected, and after time t_r the first room reflection returns to the microphone (Fig. 3**b**). The interval between the input pulses is of the order of the room reverberation time, and as each response is captured it is added to a cumulative total of all previous results. The signal is thereby enhanced relative to the background noise, and when the required number of responses have been captured, the cumulative total is divided by the number of responses taken to provide the final result (Fig. 3**c**). This is known as signal averaging. Because the room response is of no interest in this context, all sampled values beyond t_r are set to zero (Fig. 3**d**). The loudspeaker-microphone time delay can also be removed by redefining the time origin (Fig. 3**e**). The loudspeaker impulse response can then be stored permanently on magnetic tape or disc.

Choice of Test Pulse

The primary consideration in selecting a pulse for impulse response measurements is that its spectrum should be flat over the range of frequencies which it is of interest to investigate. It would be convenient to use a pulse of extremely short duration in order to benefit from a spectrum having a greater bandwidth than required and consequently to have no worries about the detailed nature of the waveform. There is so little energy in a short pulse, however, that even with averaging to enhance the signal it is advisable to take a pulse whose energy content is as great as possible, and so a consideration of pulse shape cannot be avoided.

A rectangular pulse is chosen, first because of its close relationship to the ideal impulse, and second because it is so well defined and convenient to obtain in practice. The spectrum of the rectangular pulse has the familiar $(\sin x)/x$ shape shown in Fig. 4. A 10-μs pulse which has its first spectral zero at 100 kHz (Fig. 5) was chosen as a practical compromise between energy and spectral content, while at the same time contributing to the antialiasing function described in the section which follows. This shape of pulse has the additional benefit that it modifies the phase response of the final result only by introducing a small amount of linear phase shift equivalent to the pulse half-width. The practical pulse, of course, begins at $t = 0$,

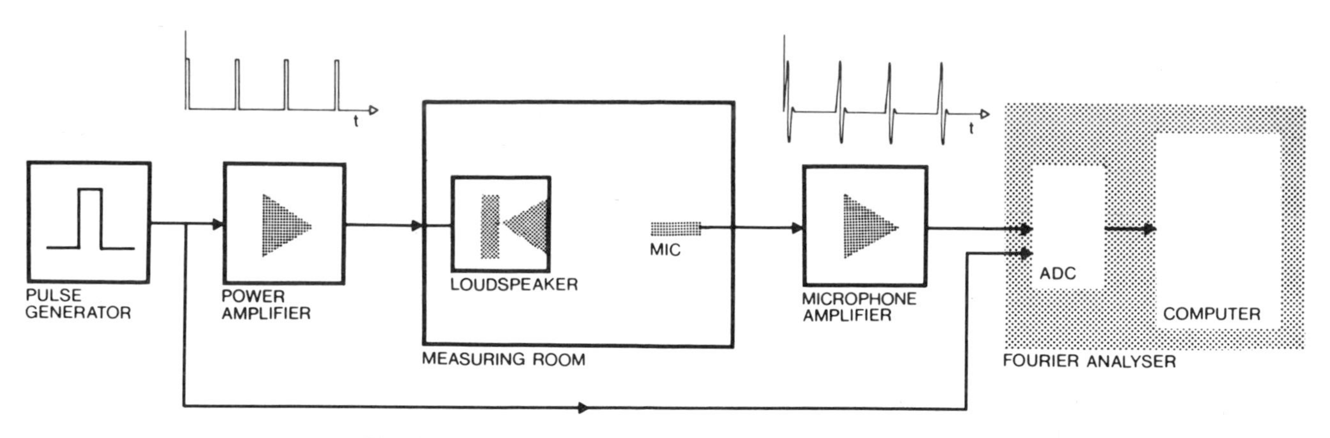

Fig. 2. Block diagram of impulse response measuring chain.

and it is of interest to note that the consequent linear phase shift shown in Fig. 5 appears curved only because of the logarithmic frequency display.

In attempting to provide the loudspeaker with as much energy as possible, the pulse height needs to be maximized, and the demands made of the power amplifier are therefore considerable. The single-sided pulse requires an amplifier with a voltage swing which in audio terms is quite out of proportion to the actual power in the signal. The 60-volt pulse used in practice requires a power amplifier which typically has a continuous rating of 200 watts into 8 ohms.

Sampling Rate and Antialiasing Precautions

In the analog-to-digital conversion process, the analog signal is sampled at equal intervals of time, and the resulting voltage levels are subsequently converted to digital values. If no frequency components greater than half the sampling frequency f_s are present, then the waveform is completely defined by these samples; if not then the components above f_s will "alias" or "fold" back into the frequency range below f_s [11]. This is one of the hazards of analog-to-digital conversion and is commonly safeguarded by employing an antialiasing filter which attenuates the signal sharply above the highest frequency of interest and reduces it to the level of the system noise by half the sampling frequency.

With a suitable choice of sampling rate, however, the antialiasing function for loudspeaker measurements can conveniently be performed by components which are already part of the measuring chain. In the measuring arrangement described in this paper, a half-inch microphone which has a natural cutoff above 40 kHz was chosen. This, along with the rolloff to the first zero of the pulse spectrum, in addition to that of the loudspeaker itself, is generally sufficient to provide adequate antialiasing when a sampling rate of 100 kHz is used. In the rare cases where it is not, the effects can readily be recognized.

Dynamic Range and Signal Averaging

The problem of dynamic range in the impulse measuring system is highlighted by considering the spectral equivalent of the short pulse, shown in Fig. 5. Because the energy is spread equally among all in-band spectral components, the effective amplitude of each individual component is very much less than that of the testing pulse. It can be shown that, because gain settings of all the equipment are determined by the pulse height, an immediate loss of more than 50 dB of the available dynamic range is inevitable for most loudspeaker measurements.

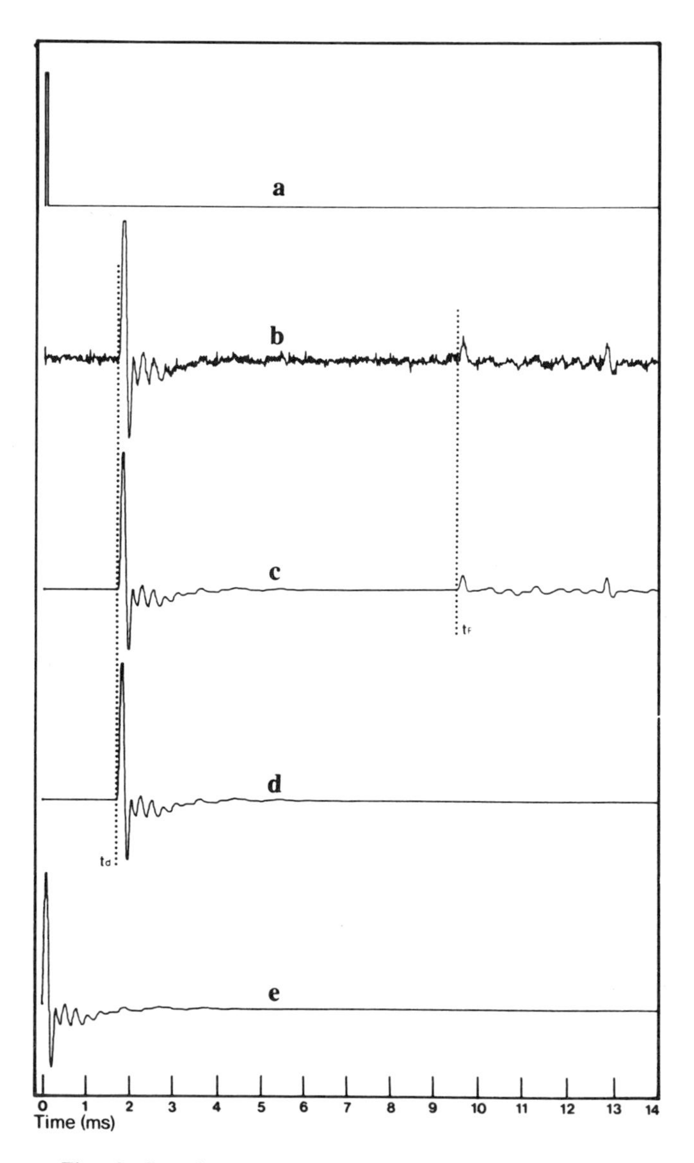

Fig. 3. Impulse response measuring sequence. **a**. Test pulse; **b**. Single-shot response; **c**. Signal-averaged response; **d**. Response after removal of room reflections; **e**. Impulse response, corrected for loudspeaker–microphone time delay.

In order to increase the signal-to-noise ratio, the input pulse is made to be repetitive, and the resulting microphone responses are stored and averaged by the computer. The pulse repetition rate is made to be as high as possible, consistent with residual sound from one impulse response making a negligible contribution to the next. The impulse response is successively reinforced, whereas random noise is not, and this gives a theoretical improvement in the signal-to-noise ratio of a factor of $\sqrt{N}$, where N is the number of averages. Signal averaging, however, is not the universal panacea which it appears to be at first sight. The theoretical improvement is only approached if the noise is entirely random. If periodic or impulsive components are present, the improvement is very much less, and because the $\sqrt{N}$ relationship is a law of diminishing returns, a quiet room is required if high-quality results are to be obtained (acoustic noise is rarely random in nature). For this reason it is essential to minimize any form of mains (line-frequency) hum or interference throughout the measuring equipment. A particularly severe effect occurs if there are periodic components coherent with the pulse repetition rate, for the noise is then reinforced in exactly the same way as the signal. It must also be remembered that signal averaging relies on the repeated coincidence of the measured signal. Variations in the time of arrival of the acoustic signal, which result from wind or thermal air currents, generally preclude outdoor measurements unless weather conditions are exceptionally calm and stable.

Finally, care should be taken over the manner in which the averaging is realized computationally. Loss of precision from, for instance, a simple integer realization with insufficient word length, can result in severe distortion of the averaged waveform.

The amount of averaging required depends entirely on the particular situation. In the limit, averaging can be continued to give a signal-to-noise ratio as great as the precision of the analog-to-digital converter will allow. The results for the present paper were obtained with 64 averages, which represents an 18-dB improvement in the signal-to-noise ratio.

Measuring Environment

The room in which measurements are made must be large enough so that the response of the loudspeaker dies down to a negligible level before the first room reflection arrives at the microphone. A room having a minimum dimension of 3 meters, for example, permits the capture of impulse responses up to 6 ms long for a measuring distance of 1 meter. This has been found adequate for the reliable characterization of loudspeakers down to a frequency of 200 Hz. For measurements extending to lower frequencies, a correspondingly larger room is required.

The total measurement time for a given number of averages depends on the pulse repetition rate, which in turn depends upon the reverberation time of the room at the frequencies of interest. While the environment need not be anechoic, a low reverberation time is advisable if the measurement time is to be kept reasonably short. The 64 averages needed for the results given in this paper take less than 30 seconds.

To obtain accurate impulse responses, the measuring conditions need far more consideration than would normally be given for steady-state measurements. Reflections from quite small objects can cause disturbances which are readily identified in the impulse response. Microphone stands, loudspeaker stands which are larger than the base of the loudspeaker under test, and other reflecting surfaces should be avoided. Even the microphone cable should be well covered with acoustic absorbent. Such reflections have only a small effect on the frequency response, but complicate the interpretation of the impulse response considerably. An example of the extremely high resolution inherent in this technique is given in Fig. 6. The pulse at 1.7 ms is a result of the reflection of the tweeter pulse in the 0.5-inch (12-mm) microphone capsule which is reflected again in the loudspeaker baffle; for such measurements the microphone needs to be angled at some 10° to avoid the effect. It is clear from these results that transient measurements are rarely taken with sufficient precautions to ensure meaningful results. It is tacitly assumed that

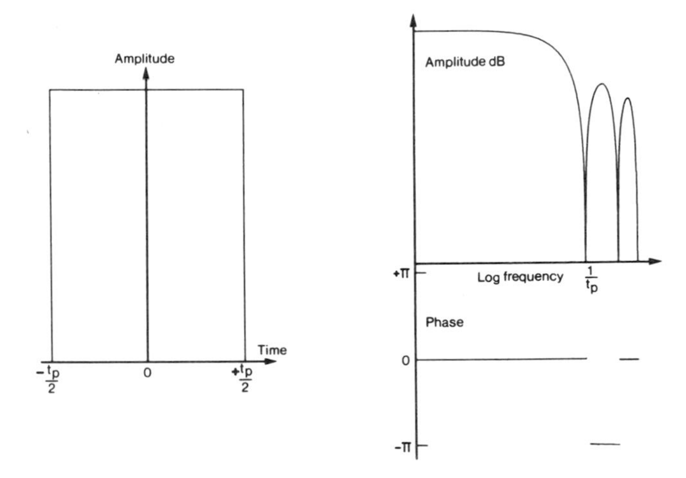

Fig. 4. Rectangular pulse (left) and its frequency spectrum.

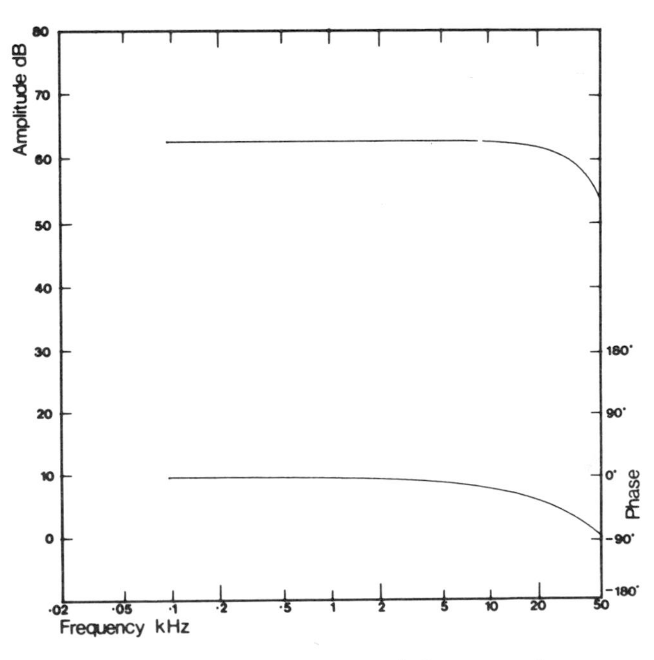

Fig. 5. Frequency spectrum of 10-μs test pulse.

conditions which are sufficient for a good steady-state measurement are sufficient for a transient one, but this is certainly not the case. As a corollary, it will be appreciated that reflections of this order are to be found in so-called "anechoic" chambers from metal parts such as floor supports and even from the absorbing material itself. So an anechoic chamber, while providing an excellent environment in terms of reverberation time, is extremely wasteful for impulse response measurements, in that only the internal chamber volume can be used.

Computation and Analog-to-Digital Conversion

A detailed discussion of computational techniques is not appropriate here, but consideration must be given to computational accuracy. A fast Fourier transform implemented in 16-bit arithmetic has been used, which has the ability continually to optimize its dynamic range. The computational errors are arranged to be equally distributed throughout the transform to give an effective accuracy of 12 bits. To take the maximum advantage of this FFT algorithm a 12-bit analog-to-digital converter is used which provides a peak-to-peak signal-to-noise ratio of 72 dB and a corresponding dynamic range in the frequency domain of over 80 dB.

EXPERIMENTAL VERIFICATION

The assumption of linearity raises the most serious potential objection to the impulse testing technique; most people feel intuitively that such a violent excitation must send the transducer into its nonlinear operating region. A pulse of 10 μs, however, is by its very nature so short that, even with an amplitude of 100 volts, the mechanical parts of the loudspeaker hardly move at all. Comparison of impulse and frequency responses, obtained with pulses of very different amplitudes, have shown no evidence of differences which could be attributed to nonlinear effects. Similarly, the polarity of the pulse used has been found to be of no consequence.

A comparison with traditional analog measurements may be made with results taken outdoors, because these are truly anechoic if the loudspeaker is sufficiently far from the ground. Fig. 7 compares results taken outdoors at a height of 10 meters above the ground with an equivalent digital measurement. For convenience of comparison, the digital result has been plotted on recorder paper with a grid identical to that used for the analog result. The impulse response was also used to calculate a tone burst and square wave response, and these are shown in Fig. 8 along with the equivalent analog measurements. The experience of intensive use of this measuring system alongside traditional analog measuring equipment has given complete confidence in the method.

SIGNAL PROCESSING AND PRESENTATION OF RESULTS

One of the great advantages of this digital approach to measurement is the ability to calculate, from one single measurement, the response of the loudspeaker to any possible excitation and to alter the form of display at will. It is interesting to note that whereas the analog results of

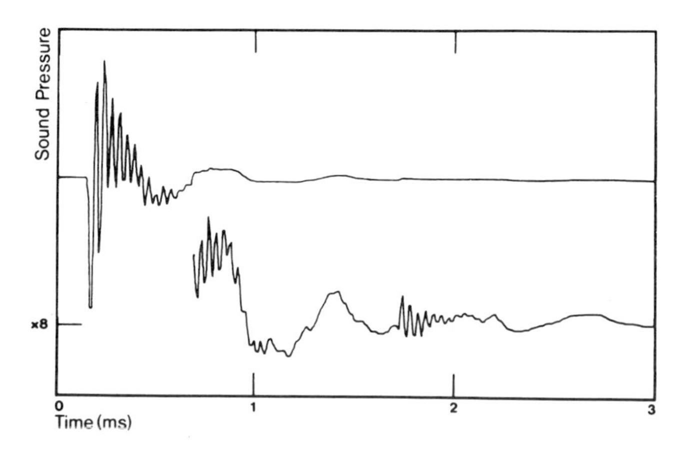

Fig. 6. Impulse response of high-frequency unit showing reflection from microphone capsule.

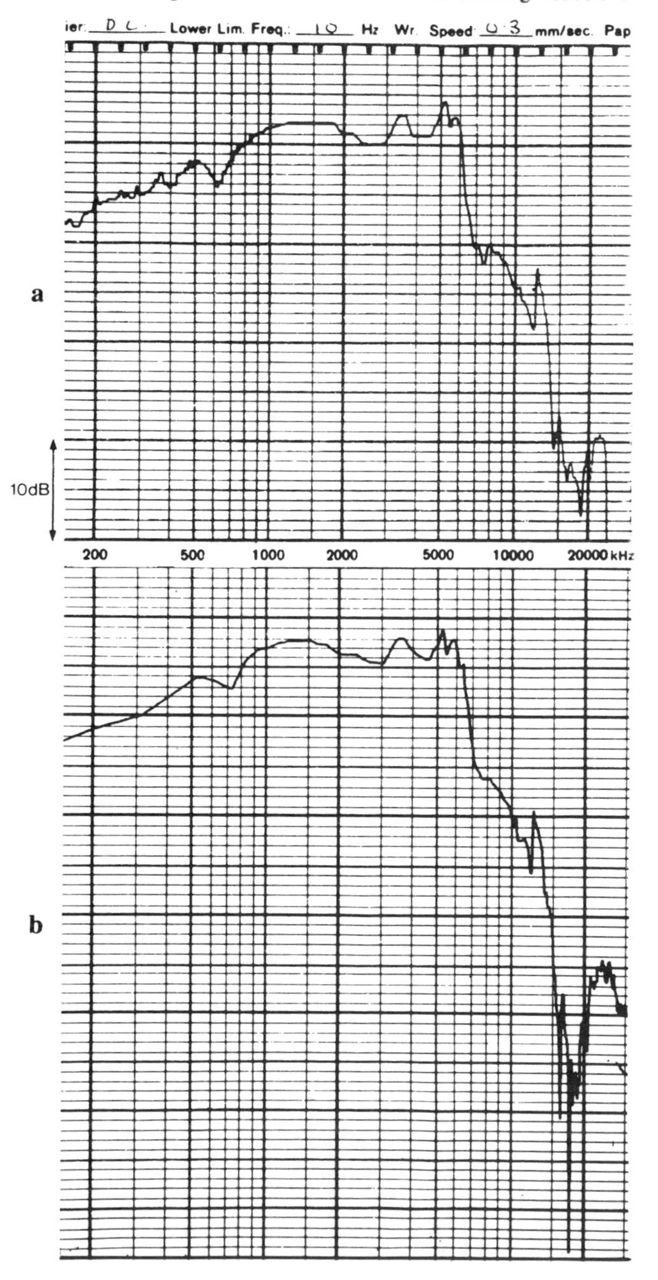

Fig. 7. Comparative amplitude responses of 200-mm drive unit in 45-liter enclosure. **a**. With swept sine-wave measurement outdoors; **b**. Equivalent digital measurement.

the previous section exist only as curves on recorder paper, the digital measurement, which is stored on magnetic disc and paper tape in impulse response form, can readily be recalled. Even now, many months after the measurement, we can continue to answer questions about different aspects of the performance.

The particular manner in which the impulse response data is processed and displayed, has been arrived at in the course of a search for optimum presentations of the information, but it in no way precludes alternatives.

Impulse Response

A surprising amount of information can be obtained from the impulse response alone. The increased dynamic range provided by signal averaging permits a detailed study of the response which was not previously possible with single-shot methods.

A threefold form of display has therefore been adopted in which the tail of the impulse response is magnified, first 8 times and then 64 times. This happens to be convenient for computation, since these magnifications are powers of 2. It gives, in three displays, an optimum view of most loudspeaker impulse responses and offers a visual dynamic range of over 50 dB. The information in the tail is entirely repeatable and can give considerable insight into a loudspeaker's behavior. Whereas loudspeakers of different types produce widely different results, impulse responses of units of the same type bear a close family resemblance. The results from two nominally identical units are shown in Fig. 9, demonstrating family likeness throughout the decay.

Frequency Response

The frequency response embodies both the amplitude-frequency and the associated phase-frequency response and is obtained from the impulse response by numeric transformation using the FFT.

The loudspeaker impulse response may be completely isolated from that of the room in which it is measured by setting to zero all values in the sampled waveform which occur from the start of the first room reflection. The Fourier transform of the resulting response is then a truly anechoic frequency response of the loudspeaker, even though the measurement is made in a semireverberant room.

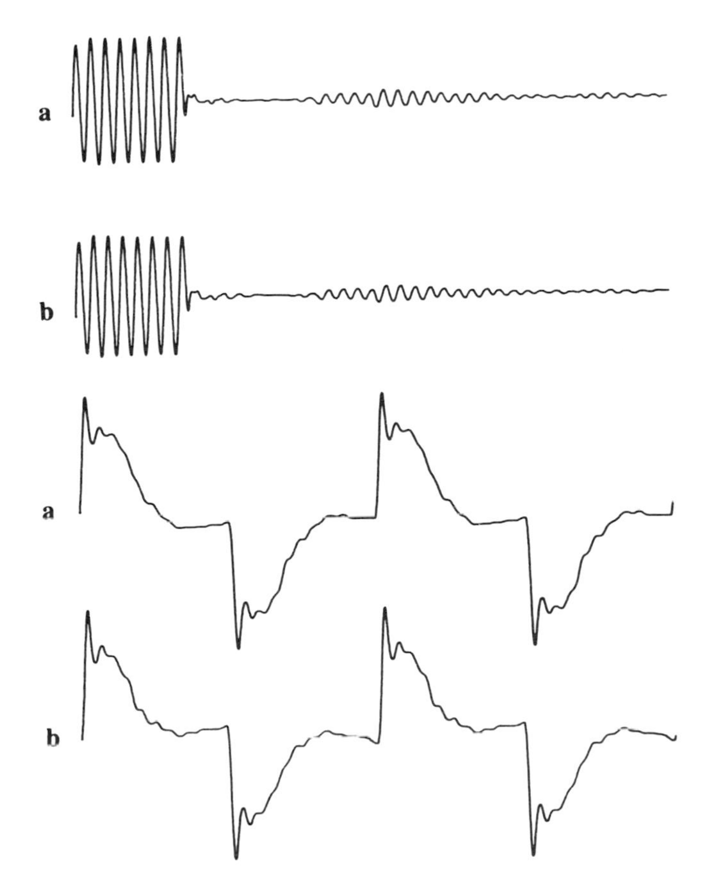

Fig. 8. Comparison of 4-kHz tone burst (above) and 1-kHz square-wave responses for the loudspeaker of Fig. 7. **a**. Measured directly; **b**. Computed from the impulse response.

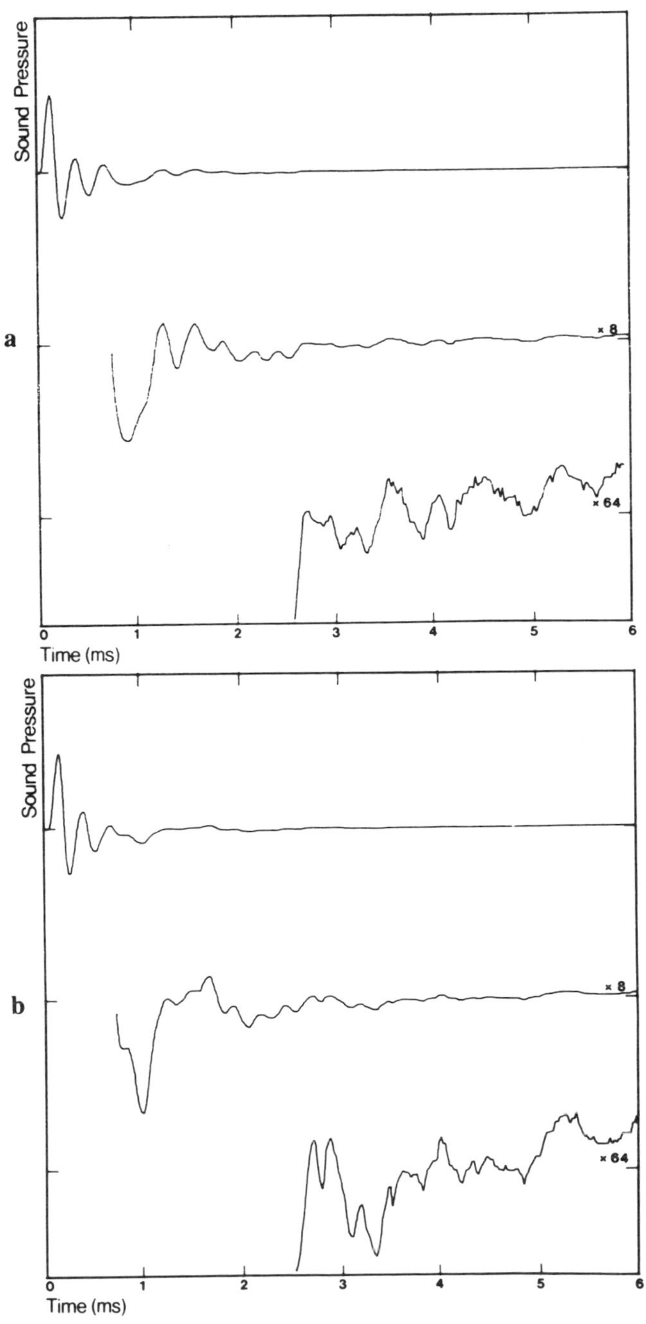

Fig. 9. Measured impulse responses of two nominally identical 110-mm drive units in a 7-liter closed box.

In the same way that the impulse response is represented by a set of samples, the frequency response, after operation of the FFT, is similarly represented by a set of discrete values. Appendix I deals with the relationship between these two domains. The number of samples required in the first instance is determined by the sampling rate, which has already been discussed, and the size of the room used for measurement, along with the additional consideration that the FFT algorithm requires samples which are a power of two in number (see Appendix I). All results given in this paper were obtained with a sampling rate of 100 kHz and a 10-ms length of signal capture resulting in 1024 samples. The 512 frequency components which result are consequently spaced approximately 100 Hz apart (see Appendix I).

If the impulse response has died away sufficiently before the first room reflection, then the frequency response of the device may be completely characterized; if not, some information will be lost resulting in a smoothed frequency response. In either case, the discrete values produced by the FFT do completely define the available knowledge about the response shape in the same way that samples of a time waveform define the continuous signal, so we need only interpolate correctly to construct a continuous curve. In practice, straight line interpolation is found to be adequate, although frequency response curves obtained in this way sometimes appear angular at low frequencies. If straight-line interpolation is used and the visual resolution is thought to be insufficient, more points can be obtained by adding zero values to the tail of the impulse response and thereby increasing the length of the data transformed. In the present case, for example, 4096 points would give a point spacing of 25 Hz. This procedure was adopted for the result shown in Fig. 7 **b**. It should be noted, however, that such a procedure only improves the visual presentation; it does not increase the information content.

In order to display the phase response in a meaningful way, the linear phase shift associated with the time taken for the sound to travel between loudspeaker and microphone (as evidenced by multiple phase rotations in Fig. 10**a**) has to be removed. It is not sufficient simply to calculate the time delay from a measurement of the physical distance between microphone and baffle. The effective acoustic center of a drive unit lies closer to the plane of the voice coil than to that of the baffle on which it is mounted. With analog phase measurements this represents a real difficulty, whereas with the impulse response method the time at which the response begins can be identified within one or two sampling points, and the necessary shifting of the time origin can easily be made. The compensated phase response is shown in Fig. 10 **b**.

Hilbert Transform

It has become common practice to refer to the amplitude response alone as the frequency response of a loudspeaker, whereas strictly speaking the frequency response, as already discussed, embodies both an amplitude and a phase characteristic. In certain cases the amplitude response is sufficient for complete characterization, so that the behavior can be deduced without recourse to the phase response. It happens that most system functions in linear network theory fall into this classification, known as minimum-phase functions, and the tradition which arose of reglecting phase response was subsequently carried over into the field of acoustics. It is of more than academic interest to know if a loudspeaker falls into the minimum-phase category. If it does, then the transient response may be improved by equalization of the amplitude response without regard for the phase response; if not, the same procedure may have quite the reverse effect and degrade the transient performance [2, p. 32].

The mathematical operation which relates the amplitude and phase of a minimum-phase device is known as the Hilbert transform. This is implemented in computational form so that the "minimum-phase" phase response can be

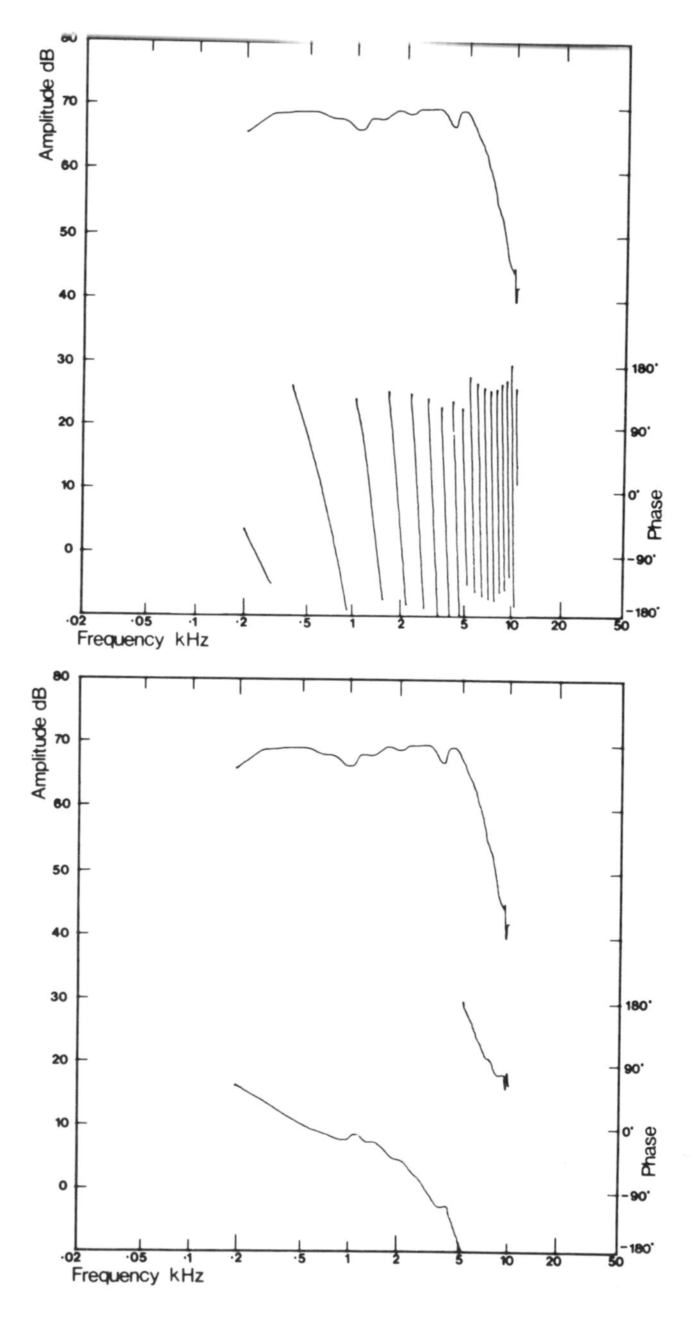

Fig. 10. Frequency response of 110-mm drive unit in 150-liter enclosure measured on axis at a distance of 25 cm. **a**. Before time-delay compensation. **b**. After time-delay compensation.

computed from the measured amplitude response and compared with the actual phase response. Fig. 11 shows the measured response of a twin-cone loudspeaker along with the calculated Hilbert transform, in which non-minimum phase shift behavior is clearly exhibited.

The Hilbert transform has been found to be of use in another important way. The exact acoustic position of a drive unit in a multiway system may be determined by finding how much delay must be removed to make the phase response coincide with the "minimum-phase" phase response; by definition, the minimum-phase response must have no linear phase shift in excess of that inherent in the system itself.

Cumulative Spectra

Impulse response and frequency response are statements of system behavior in the two mutually exclusive domains of time and frequency. In both of these the entire system behavior is visually presented but not, it seems, in an optimum form. Because speech and music are perceived as pitch varying with time, there is good reason to look for alternative methods of displaying the system information in a form which may correlate more closely with subjective response.

In 1948, Shorter pointed out that transient effects in loudspeakers, which were subjectively significant, often contributed so little to the steady-state response that objective identification of the faults was impossible [12]. He introduced the notion of delayed response curves for looking into this matter, and developed an experimental technique based on tone-burst responses to obtain such curves. Although this technique was shown to be of value, the difficulties of instrumentation prevented its coming into general use.

It is now possible, by simple computation and use of the FFT, to produce delayed response curves directly from the

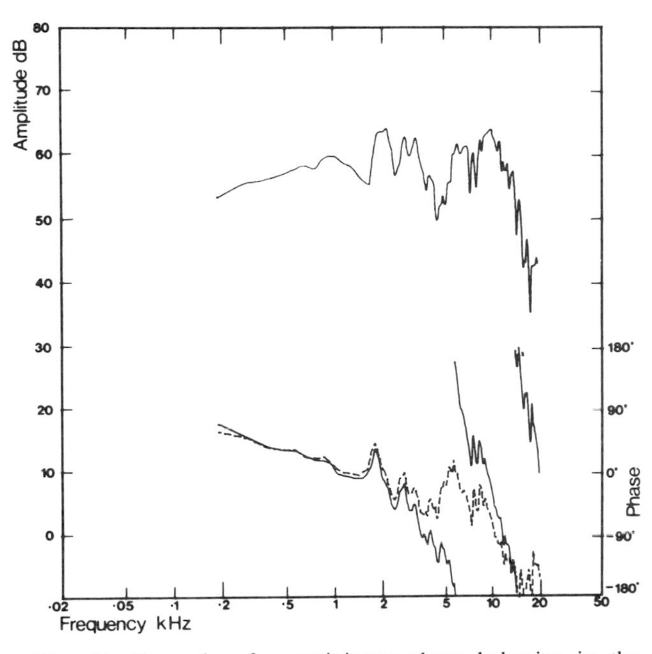

Fig. 11. Example of nonminimum-phase behavior in the frequency response of 200 mm twin-cone drive unit in 150-liter closed box. Dashed line indicates the Hilbert transform of the amplitude response.

impulse response. The three-dimensional perspective display of these multiple curves is given the term "cumulative spectra." Appendix II explains the method of calculation and confirms the relationship of this form of display to the tone-burst response. It is as though we were able simultaneously to excite the loudspeaker with all possible tone-bursts and to record the amplitude of each decaying frequency as a function of time.

The examples shown in Figs. 12–15 demonstrate two of the forms that this display can take. A linear amplitude scale is found to be useful for assessing the early part of the decay and a logarithmic amplitude scale for a more searching analysis of low-level information. A logarithmic frequency scale has been found to cause confusion of the display in the high-frequency region and a linear frequency representation has consequently been adopted.

APPLICATION OF THE METHOD

Specific applications of these digital techniques deserve detailed reports. For the present, this paper is concerned first with indicating in general terms how these techniques can usefully be applied to the development of loudspeakers, and second with demonstrating some practical results which have not previously appeared in the literature.

Drive Units

It is in the area of individual drive units that the forms of display discussed in this paper are used together to the greatest advantage. It is, of course, a most important area, because drive units are the fundamental building blocks of any loudspeaker system.

In contrast to the impulse responses of Fig. 9, which demonstrate nominally identical units, Figs. 12 and 13 show the results from two very different units. A linear amplitude cumulative-spectra display suffices to view the gross differences in the initial decay of these two loudspeakers, and to perceive that the faults in the unit with an irregular steady-state response are largely resonant in nature.

Figs. 14 and 15, on the other hand, demonstrate that small changes to a unit, while making only a small difference to the frequency response, can make dramatic changes to both the impulse response and the cumulative spectra. The two units are different only in respect of their voice-coil mass. The impulse response of Fig. 15 shows clear evidence of ringing, but even with this and the frequency response together, it is difficult to ascertain the exact frequency of this oscillation. In fact it becomes clear from the cumulative spectra that this ringing, which is evident as a ridge in the later spectra, emanates from a dip in the steady-state response and early spectra; not at all what might have been expected. These drive units were mounted in the same enclosure for the purpose of measurement, and the elevation at 1 ms which extends over the whole frequency range is confirmed to be a reflection from the rear of the enclosure. This could not have been identified from either time or frequency responses alone.

The Hilbert transform has been used to determine whether units are minimum-phase devices, and has led to

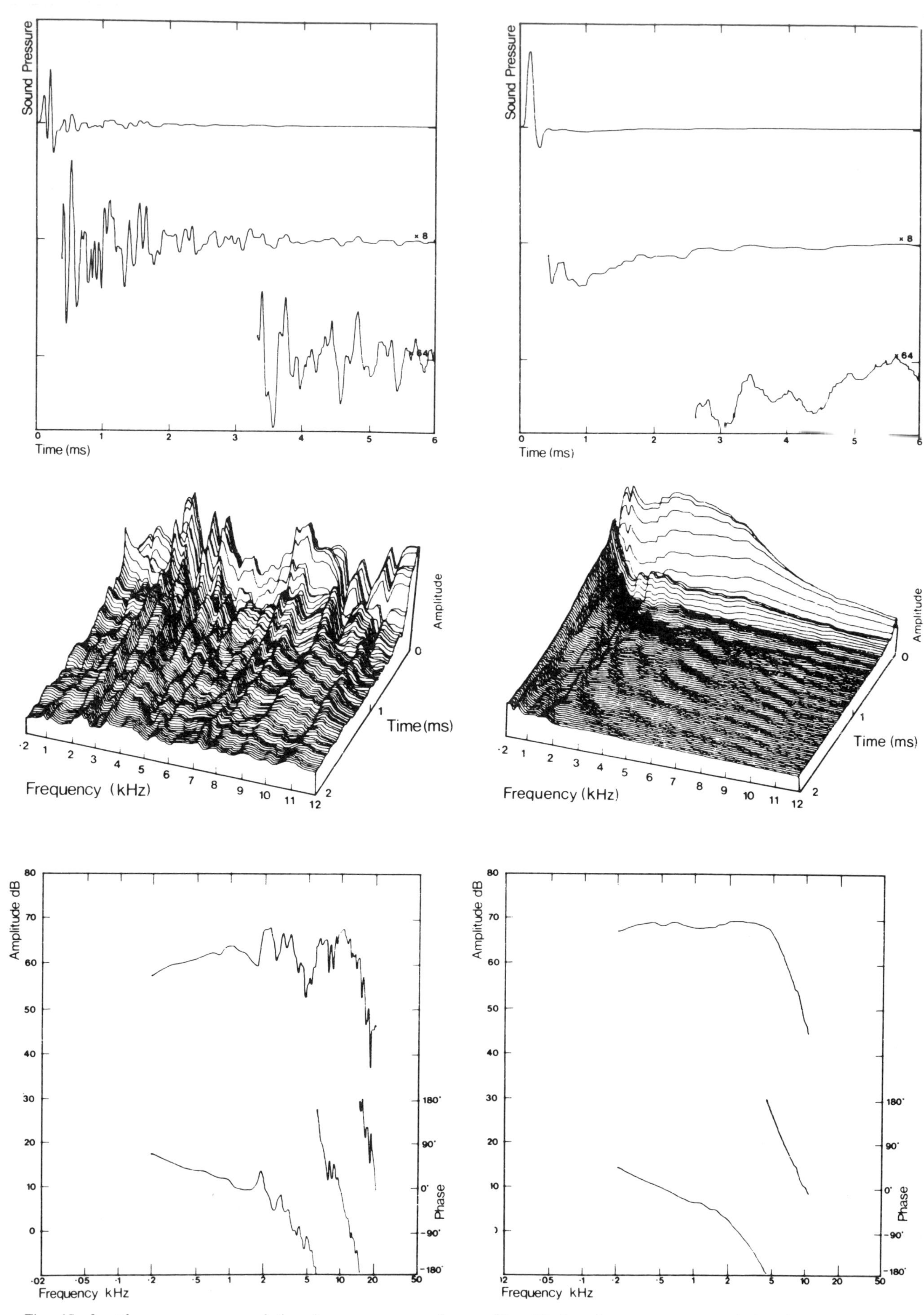

Fig. 12. Impulse response, cumulative decay spectra, and frequency response of 200-mm twin-cone drive unit in 150-liter closed box.

Fig. 13. Impulse response, cumulative decay spectra, and frequency response of 110-mm development drive unit in 150-liter closed box.

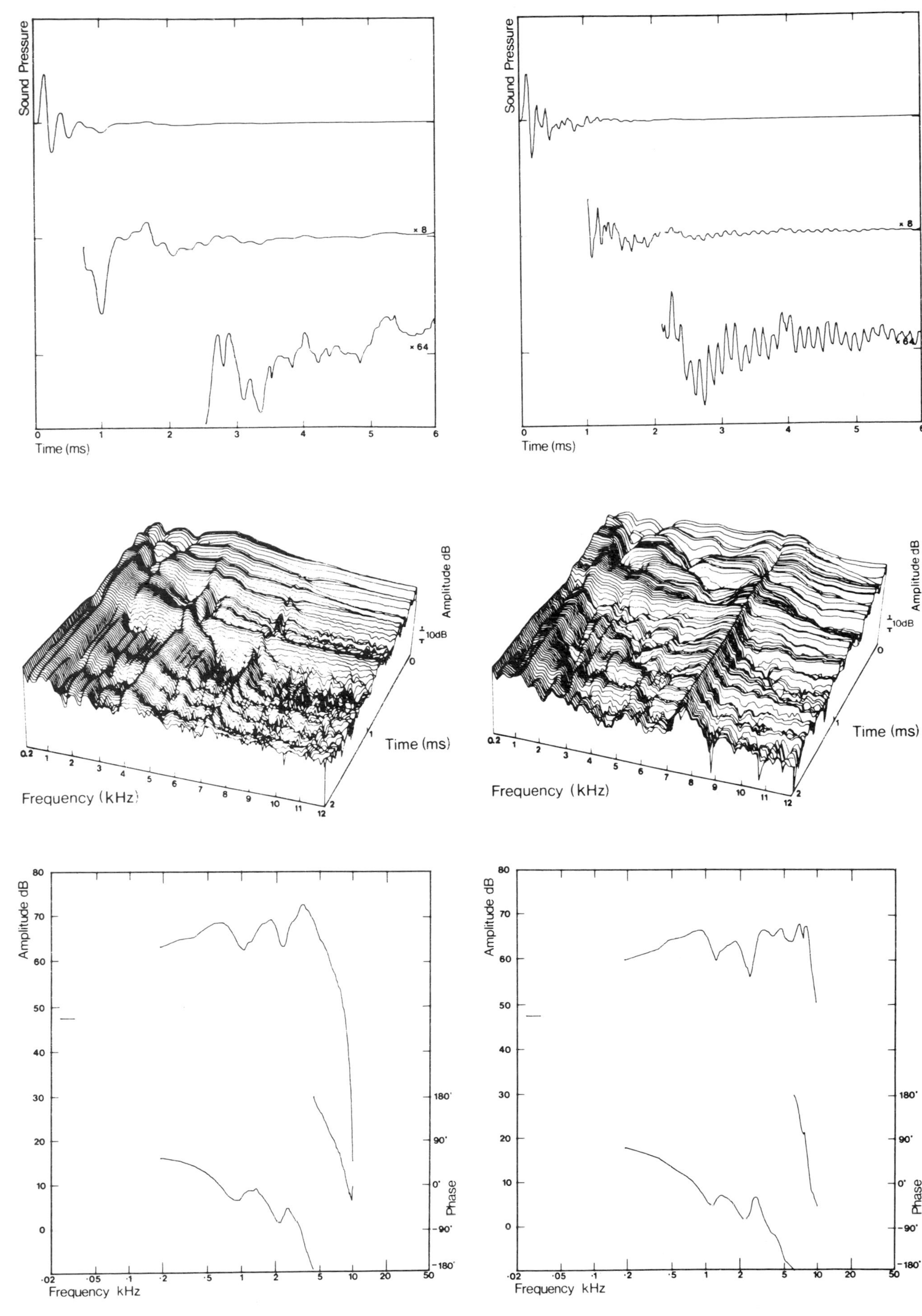

Fig. 14. Impulse response, cumulative decay spectra, and frequency response of 110-mm drive unit in 7-liter closed box.

Fig. 15. Impulse response, cumulative decay spectra, and frequency response of 110-mm drive unit with lightweight voice coil in 7-liter closed box.

the surprising result that the nonminimum-phase loudspeaker shown in Fig. 11 demonstrates a rare exception to the general rule. Almost every unit that has been measured has turned out to be of the minimum-phase variety, and a typical example of the agreement obtained is shown in Fig. 16.

Enclosures

The impulse response alone provides a useful way of separating the effect of a loudspeaker drive unit from the enclosure in which it is housed.

While the early part of the impulse response is related predominantly to the drive unit, the latter part is dominated by sound radiated from the enclosure walls and retransmitted through the loudspeaker cone after reflection within the enclosure. Each enclosure exhibits its own characteristic "signature" waveform, which is substantially independent of the drive unit. Fig. 17 shows one application of this, in which the effect of panel damping is demonstrated. The technique can, of course, equally be applied to the investigation of cabinet construction and lining materials.

Loudspeaker Systems

It is interesting to look at the manner in which individual drive units and crossovers combine to make a loudspeaker system. Fig. 18 shows the usual two-way arrangement in which a tweeter is mounted in the enclosure above the low-frequency unit and the measurement taken on the high-frequency unit axis. The effective acoustic position of the bass unit is further from the microphone than that of the high-frequency unit, and the measurements of curves A and B in Fig. 19, in which the impulse responses have been shifted to the time origin of the tweeter, show this clearly. When added together they produce the impulse response of Fig. 19**c** in which the disturbance after the first doublet, often interpreted as "ringing," is simply the delayed doublet generated by the bass unit. The frequency response of the complete system is shown in Fig. 20 along with the corresponding Hilbert transform. It will be seen that this is far from being a minimum-phase system, yet it is entirely typical of the response produced by multiway loudspeaker systems which have their units mounted in the same plane.

DISCUSSION

The paper has described a method for obtaining the transfer function of a loudspeaker by direct measurement of its impulse response. This is a complete description of

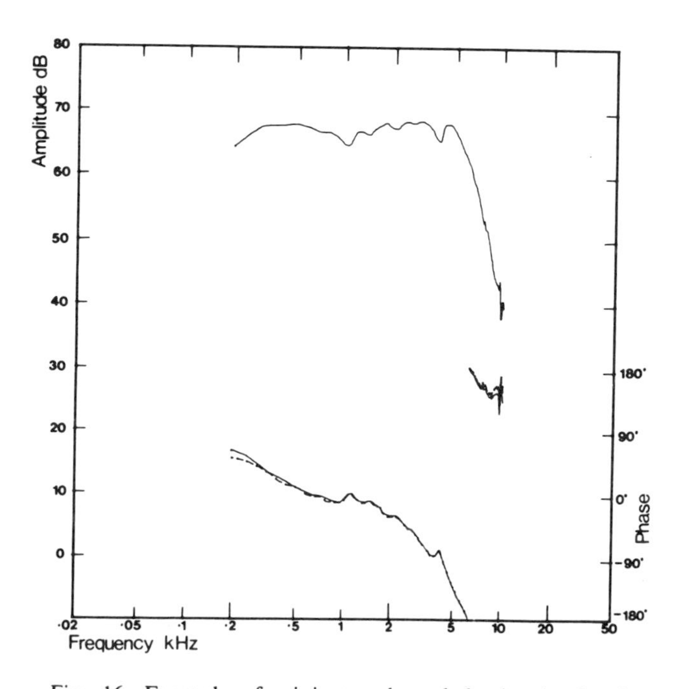

Fig. 16. Example of minimum-phase behavior in the frequency response of 110-mm drive unit in 150-liter closed box. Dashed line shows Hilbert transform of amplitude response.

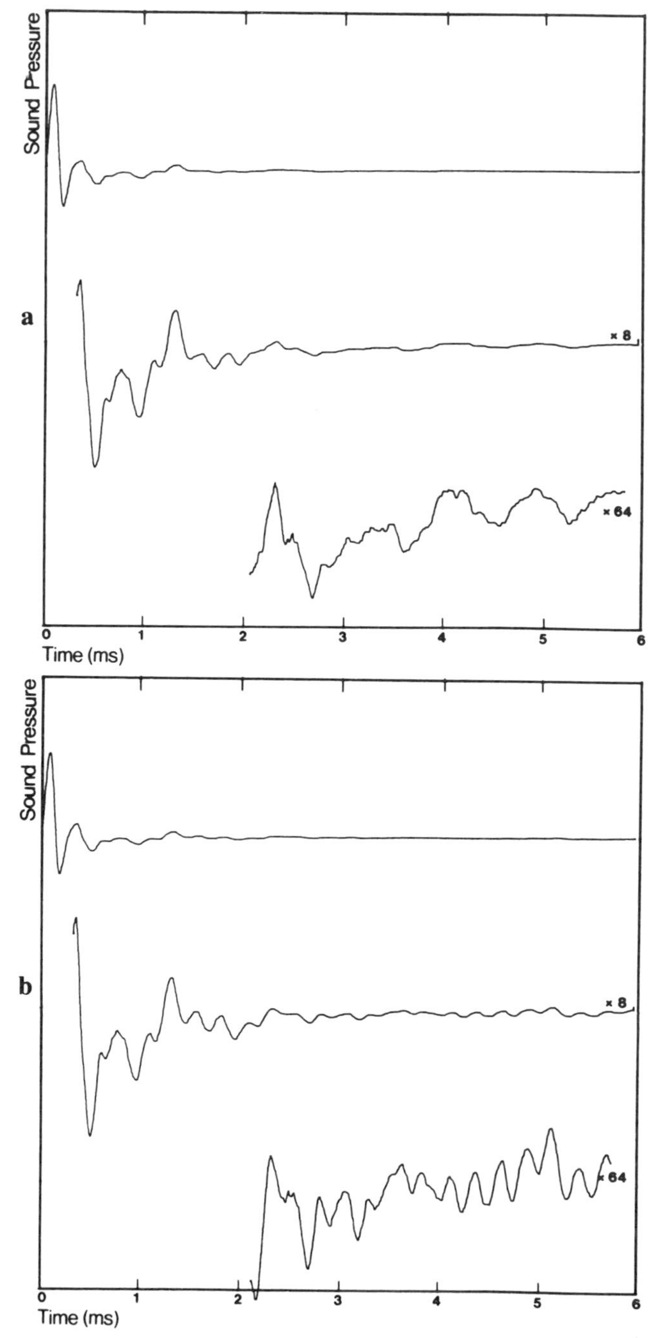

Fig. 17. Impulse responses of 110-mm drive unit in 7-liter, 12-mm chipboard closed box. **a**. Without panel damping. **b**. With panel damping.

the loudspeaker's behavior in its particular relation to the measuring microphone. Once the impulse response has been captured, the response of any steady-state or transient signal can be calculated and no further measurements are necessary. The method has been completely verified against equivalent analog measurements where such measurements have been possible. Some applications have been mentioned briefly to indicate how the particular displays of impulse and frequency response, Hilbert transform, and cumulative spectra can usefully be employed. However, these do not preclude other forms of display; indeed it is the flexibility of display which offers the future possibility of presenting the information in a form more closely related to subjective experience.

There is, without doubt, room for further improvement and modification of the measuring technique. No mention has been made of linear distortion introduced by parts of the measuring chain, but clearly the amplitude and phase response of the microphone, amplifiers, etc., will be superimposed on those of the loudspeaker under test. It is fortunate that so many measurements have been found to be minimum phase in nature because this in turn has confirmed that the measuring chain itself must be a minimum-phase system. Consequently, inaccuracies in the measuring chain can easily be compensated for by numeric manipulation, having consideration for the amplitude response alone, after the loudspeaker has been measured. Following from this, the pulse could be pre-

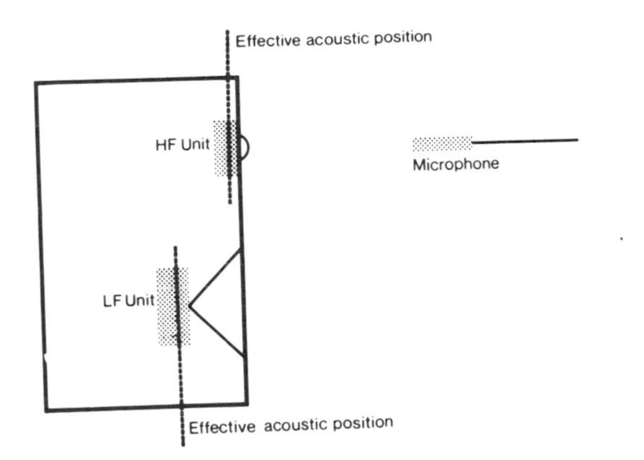

Fig. 18. Two-way loudspeaker system showing effective acoustic position of units relative to customary measuring microphone position.

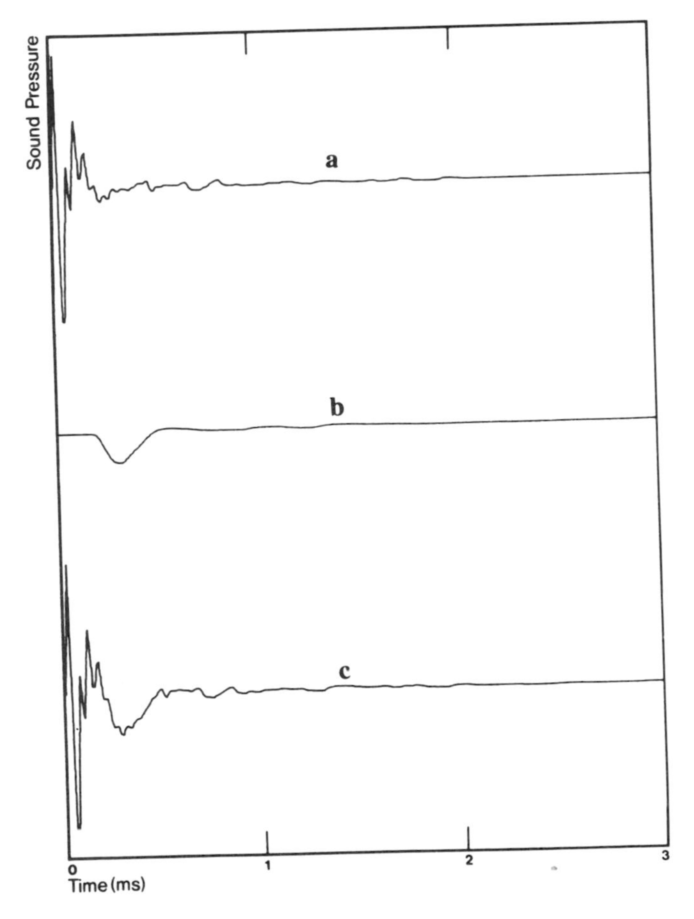

Fig. 19. Impulse responses of a two-way loudspeaker system measured on the tweeter axis at 1-meter distance. **a**. High-frequency unit and crossover; **b**. Low-frequency unit and crossover; **c**. Complete system.

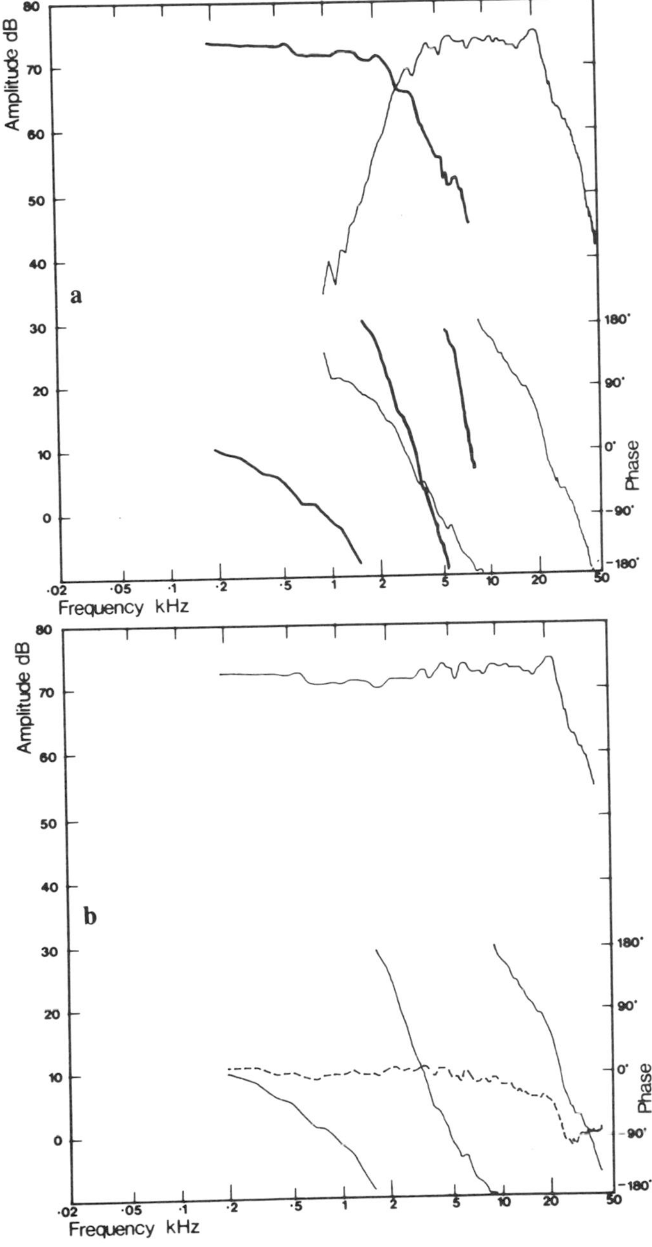

Fig. 20. Frequency responses of a two-way loudspeaker system. **a**. Low- and high-frequency units separately. **b**. Complete system. Dashed line shows Hilbert transform of amplitude response.

shaped and the measured result modified accordingly; such a technique would allow the signal to be optimized to take account of, for example, a less than ideal measuring environment.

Details of the equipment used for the results presented in this paper are given in Appendix III. The computer-based Fourier analyser may appear overspecified for the measuring technique inasmuch as the impulse response capture and subsequent Fourier transformation can now be performed with much more modest equipment. The measuring method, however, is just one part of a complete philosophy, rooted in linear system theory, which treats the component parts of a multiway loudspeaker as subsystems of a complete linear system. The impulse response provides a means of identifying each component part, and the associated ability to store each result, and to recall it for computation when required, facilitates the construction of the system response from the component parts alone. Once the drive units have been measured, for instance, loudspeaker system development can proceed by computer-aided design of crossovers without recourse to physical construction. Such manipulation requires elaborate facilities for handling the results after measurement, so a versatile processor is essential if this digital approach to loudspeaker measurement is to be used to full advantage.

APPENDIX I

The Fast Fourier Transform (FFT)

The FFT provides a highly efficient means of computing the reversible discrete Fourier transform (DFT) of a time series [13]–[15]. The coefficients of the DFT are calculated iteratively, which reduces the total number of arithmetic operations from N^2 to $2N \log_2 N$, so that the computation time of most signal analysis transforms is reduced from minutes to fractions of a second. It is, however, a condition of the iterative algorithm that the number of samples in the time series be exactly a power of 2.

N time-domain values give rise to an identical number in the frequency domain, which can be written in place of the time values during computation. The frequency domain is arranged in the form of $N/2 + 1$ real values from direct current to half the sampling frequency and $N/2 - 1$ related imaginary values. This takes advantage of the fact that the imaginary part is an odd function of frequency and consequently must always have a value of zero at direct current and at half the sampling frequency. Conversion from real and imaginary to amplitude and phase involves only a change of coordinates, which is of course reversible. Whereas time samples are separated by the sampling period $\Delta t = 1/f_s$, frequency values are $\Delta f = 1/t$ apart, where t is the total length of the initial time series. These relationships are summarized in Fig. 21, which shows a 16-point transform.

APPENDIX II

Cumulative Spectra

Consider the system, whose impulse response is $h(t)$, subjected to the sudden onset of a generalized sinusoidal oscillation $e^{j\omega t}$; the input excitation is then $U(t)\, e^{j\omega t}$, where $U(t)$ is a step function. The system output $y(t)$ at any instant t_1 can then be found by evaluating the convolution integral:

$$y(t) = \int_{-\infty}^{+\infty} U(t-\tau)\, e^{jw(t-\tau)}\, h(\tau)\, d\tau, \text{ at}$$
$$t = t_1. \tag{1}$$

This may be expressed as

$$y(t_1) = C \int_{-\infty}^{+\infty} H(\tau)\, e^{-jw\tau}\, d\tau \tag{2}$$

where $C = e^{jwt_1}$ and is constant and

$$H(\tau) = U(t_1 - \tau)\, h(\tau). \tag{3}$$

Eq. (2) may be recognized simply as the Fourier integral evaluation of $H(\tau)$ for the frequency ω. However, $H(\tau)$ is the product of the system impulse response $h(\tau)$, illustrated in Fig. 22**a**, and the delayed step function $U(\tau - t_1)$ reversed in time to become $U(t_2 - \tau)$, as shown in Fig. 22**b**.

It follows from this that at any given time t_1 after the onset of the sinusoidal oscillation, the instantaneous amplitude and phase of the response to all possible frequency excitations may be obtained by evaluating the Fourier transform of the step-function-windowed impulse response. By successively evaluating the Fourier transform for different values of t_1, we can build up a three-dimensional picture of the tone-burst response. Similarly, the decay of the output when a sinusoidal excitation abruptly ceases is calculated by multiplying the impulse response by the delayed step function $U(\tau - t_1)$ shown in Fig. 22**c**, and again performing successive Fourier transformation.

APPENDIX III

EQUIPMENT DETAILS

Lyons bipolar pulse generator: PG 71N
SAE power amplifier: Mark IIICM

Bruel & Kjaer half-inch microphone type 4133
Bruel & Kjaer microphone amplifier type 2606

Hewlett-Packard Fourier analyzer type 5451B (see Fig. 23).

ACKNOWLEDGMENT

The authors would like to acknowledge all those who have contributed to this project, in particular Mr. R. V. Leedham, Senior Lecturer in Electrical Engineering at the University of Bradford.

REFERENCES

[1] R. C. Heyser, "Acoustical Measurements by Time Delay Spectrometry," *J. Audio Eng. Soc.*, vol. 15, p. 370 (1967).

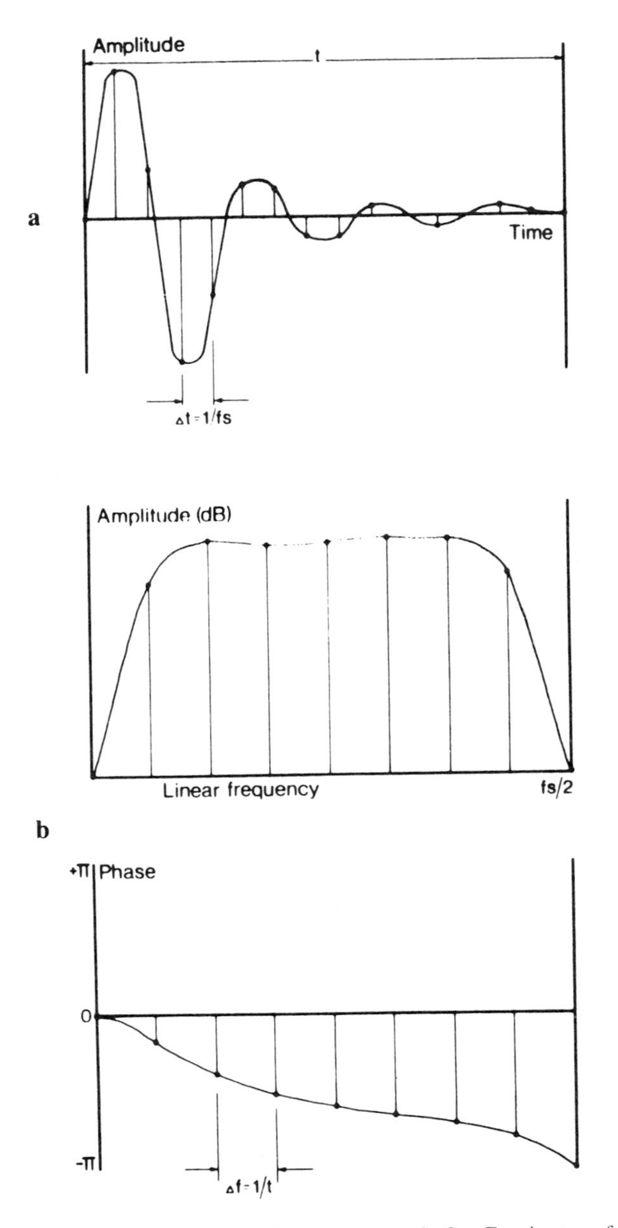

Fig. 21. Illustration of data structure in fast Fourier transform computations. **a**. Time-domain signal and its representation by discrete samples. **b**. Frequency-domain spectrum, presented as amplitude and phase, showing discrete frequency sample points and corresponding continuous transform.

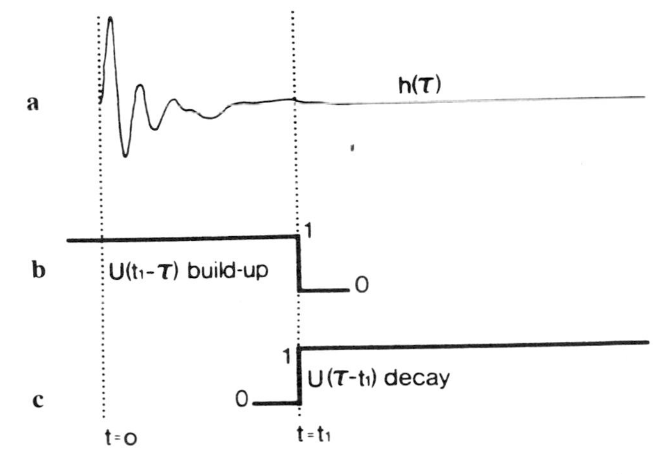

Fig. 22. Window functions used in cumulative-spectra calculations. **a**. Loudspeaker impulse response; **b**. Reversed delayed unit step; **c**. Delayed unit step.

Fig. 23. Hewlett-Packard Fourier analyzer type 5451B used for measuring impulse response of loudspeakers.

[2] R. C. Heyser, "Loudspeaker Phase Characteristics and Time Delay Distortion, Pts. I and II," *J. Audio Eng. Soc.*, vol. 17, p. 30 (1969); p. 130 (1969).

[3] L. R. Fincham and R. V. Leedham, "Loudspeaker Evaluation Using Digital Fourier Analysis," presented to British Section of the Audio Engineering Society at the IEE, London, England, Feb. 1973.

[4] J. M. Berman, "Loudspeaker Evaluation Using Digital Techniques," presented March 4, 1975, at the 50th Convention of the Audio Engineering Society, London, England.

[5] A. Papoulis, *The Fourier Integral and Its Applications* (McGraw-Hill Electronic Series, New York, 1962).

[6] P. R. Roth, "Effective Measurements Using Digital Signal Analysis," *IEEE Spectrum*, vol. 8 (Apr. 1971).

[7] R. G. White, "Evaluation of the Dynamic Characteristics of Structures by Transient Testing," *J. Sound Vib.*, vol. 15, no. 2, pp. 147-161 (1971).

[8] N. W. McLachlan, *Loudspeakers. Theory Performance, Testing and Design* (Dover, New York, 1960), pp. 332-336.

[9] P. Chapelle, "Les Essais Impulsionnels de Hautparleurs," *Electroacoust.*, vol. 17, p. 35 (1970).

[10] A. Schaumberger, "Impulse Measurement Techniques for Quality Determination in Hi-Fi Equipment, with Special Emphasis on Loudspeakers," *J. Audio Eng. Soc.*, vol. 19, p. 101 (1971).

[11] R. Bracewell, *The Fourier Transform and Its Applications* (McGraw Hill, New York, 1965), p. 189.

[12] D. E. L. Shorter, "Loudspeaker Transient Response—Its Measurement and Graphical Representation," *B. B. C. Quart.*, vol. 1, p. 121 (1946).

[13] W. T. Cochran *et al.*, "What Is the Fast Fourier Transform?" *IEEE Trans. Audio Electroacoust.*, vol. AU-15, p. 45 (1967).

[14] A. V. Oppenheim and R. W. Schafer, "Digital Signal Processing," (Wiley, New York, 1975).

[15] G. D. Bergland, "A Guided Tour of the Fast Fourier Transform," *IEEE Spectrum*, vol. 6, p. 41 (July 1969).

THE AUTHORS

M. Berman

L. Fincham

Michael Berman graduated in electrical engineering from Leeds University. In 1971 he received the Ph.D. degree from Bradford University for research in the field of room acoustics; he continued this work for a further two years under a fellowship from the Science Research Council of Great Britain.

From 1973 to 1975 Dr. Berman assumed responsibility for the investigation into digital methods of loudspeaker evaluation at Bradford University under a fellowship funded by KEF Electronics. He then joined KEF where he is currently in charge of the digital analysis installation.

Dr. Berman is a member of the Audio Engineering Society and the British Acoustical Society.

•

Laurie Fincham received the B.Sc. degree in electrical engineering from the University of Bristol in 1958.

From 1960 to 1964 he was a Loudspeaker Development Engineer with Goodman Loudspeakers, where he specialized in the design and development of high-fidelity loudspeaker systems and moving-coil drive units for electronic musical instruments.

After spending the next four years at Celestion, where he was Chief Engineer and responsible for high-fidelity loudspeaker development, he joined KEF Electronics in 1968. He is now Technical Director there.

Mr. Fincham is a member of the Audio Engineering Society and a member of two committees of the British Standards Institute (BSI) concerned with high fidelity, TLE/24 and TLE/26. He is also the UK representative for Working Groups 1 (Loudspeakers) and 9 (Listening Tests) of IEC Committee SC29B.

related reading

B.G. Belkin, "The Need for Transient Distortion Measurements in Loudspeakers," *Sov. Phys.-Acoust.* vol. 18, no. 2 (Oct.-Dec. 1972)

L.L. Beranek, *Acoustics* (McGraw-Hill Inc., New York, 1954).

E. de Boer, "Theory of Motional Feedback," *IRE Trans. on Audio* vol. AU-9, no. 1 (Jan.-Feb. 1961).

F.H. Brittain, "Metal Cone Loudspeaker," *Wireless World* (Nov. 1952).

A.D. Broadhurst, "Loudspeaker Enclosure to Simulate an Infinite Battle," *Acustica* vol. 39 (1978).

C.D. Capetanopoulos, "Measurement of the Directivity Characteristics of Loudspeakers and Microphones in a Reverberant Enclosure," *Trans. on Audio and Electroacoust.* vol. AU-20, no. 2 (June 1972).

M. Collems, *High Performance Loudspeakers* (Halsted, div. of John Wiley & Sons, Inc., New York, 1978).

C.A. Ewaskio and O.K. Mawardi, "Electroacoustic Phase Shift in Loudspeakers," *J. Acoust. Soc. Am.* vol. 22, no. 4 (July 1950).

F.J.M. Frankort, "Vibration Patterns and Radiation Behaviour of Loudspeaker Cones," *Philips Technical Review* vol. 36, no. 1 (1976).

C.L. Gilford, "The Acoustic Design of Talk Studios and Listening Rooms," *Proc. IEE* vol. 106, Part B. no. 27 (May 1959).

C.R. Hanna and J. Slepian, "The Function and Design of Horns for Loudspeakers—Reprint," *J. Audio Eng. Soc.* vol. 25, no. 9 (Sept. 1977).

"Discussion: The Function and Design of Horns for Loudspeakers—Reprinted from *Trans. AIEE*, Feb. 1924," *J. Audio Eng. Soc.* vol. 26, no. 3 (March 1978).

H.D. Harwood, "New BBC Monitoring Loudspeaker: Design of the Low-Frequency Unit," *Wireless World* (March 1968).

H.D. Harwood, "Loudspeaker Developments," *Brit. Acoust. Soc. Electroacoust. in Air and Water* (Jan. 1970).

H.D. Harwood, "Testing High-Quality Loudspeakers, Part II," *Audio* (Sept. 1971).

H.D. Harwood, "Some Factors in Loudspeaker Quality," *Wireless World* (May 1976).

R.C. Heyser, "Acoustical Measurements by Time Delay Spectrometry," *J. Audio Eng. Soc.* vol. 15, no. 4 (Oct. 1967).

H.W. Holdaway, "Design of Velocity-Feedback Transducer Systems for Stable Low-Frequency Behaviour," *IEEE Trans. on Audio* vol. AU-11, no. 5 (Sept.-Oct. 1963).

F.V. Hunt, *Electroacoustics* (John Wiley & Sons, Inc., New York, 1954).

J.A. Klaassen and S.H. de Koning, "Motional Feedback with Loudspeakers," *Philips Technical Review* vol. 29, no. 5 (1968).

S. Klein, "The Ionophone," *Onde Electrique* vol. 32 (1952).

P.W. Klipsch, "A Low-Frequency Horn of Small Dimensions," *J. Acoust. Soc. Am.* vol. 13 (Oct. 1941).

S.H. Linkwitz, "Loudspeaker System Design," *Wireless World* (May and June 1978).

N.W. McLachlan, *Loudspeakers* (Oxford University Press, England, 1934, reprinted Dover Publications, New York, 1960).

G. Rajkai, "Investigation of the Distortion of Dynamic Loudspeakers at Low Frequencies," *Seventh International Congress on Acoustics, Acoustical Commission of Hungarian Academy of Sciences, Budapest* (1971).

H.F. Olson, *Elements of Acoustical Engineering* (D. van Nostrand, New York, 1940).

H.F. Olson, *Acoustical Engineering* (Van Nostrand, Princeton, 1957).

C.W. Rice and E.W. Kellogg, "Notes on the Development of a New Type of Hornless Loudspeaker," *J. Am. Inst. Elec. Engrs.* vol. 44, no. 9 (Sept. 1925).

D.E.L. Shorter, "Loudspeaker Transient Response—Its Measurement and Graphical Representation," *BBC Quarterly* no. 1 (1946).

D.E.L. Shorter, "A Survey of Performance Criteria and Design Considerations for High-Quality Monitoring Loudspeakers," *IEE* Paper No. 2604 (April 1958).

R.H. Small, "Efficiency of Direct-Radiator Loudspeaker Systems," *J. Audio Eng. Soc.* vol. 19, no. 10 (Nov. 1971).

R.H. Small, "Performance Limitations and Synthesis of Direct-Radiator Loudspeaker Systems," *Proc. IREE* vol. 34, no. 8 (Aug. 1973).

W.R. Stroh, "Phase Shift in Electroacoustic Transducers," *Acoust. Res. Lab., Harvard Univ., Tech. Mem.* no. 42 (18 March 1958).

A.N. Thiele, "Loudspeakers, Enclosures and Equalisers," *Proc. IREE* vol. 34, no. 11 (Nov. 1973)

P.J. Walker, "Wide Range Electrostatic Loudspeakers," *Wireless World* (May, June and Aug. 1955).

R.E. Werner, "Loudspeakers and Negative Impedances," *IRE Trans. on Audio* vol. AU-6, no. 4 (Jul.-Aug. 1958).